MONOSACCHARIDE SUGARS

Chemical Synthesis by Chain Elongation, Degradation, and Epimerization

MONOSACCHARIDE SUGARS

Chemical Synthesis by Chain Elongation, Degradation, and Epimerization

Zoltán Györgydeák

Department of Organic Chemistry
Lajos Kossuth University
Debrecen, Hungary

István F. Pelyvás

Research Group of Antibiotics of the Hungarian Academy of Sciences
Lajos Kossuth University
Debrecen, Hungary

ACADEMIC PRESS

San Diego   London   Boston   New York   Sydney   Tokyo   Toronto

This book is printed on acid-free paper. ∞

Academic Press
a division of Harcourt Brace & Company
525 B Street, Suite 1900, San Diego, California 92101-4495, USA
http://www.apnet.com

Academic Press Limited
24-28 Oval Road, London NW1 7DX, UK
http://www.hbuk.co.uk/ap/

Library of Congress Cataloging-in-Publication Data

Györgydeák, Zoltán.
    Monosaccharide sugars : chemical synthesis by chain elongation, degradation, and epimerization / by Zoltán Györgydeák, István F. Pelyvás.
            p.   cm.
    Includes bibliographical references (p.   -   ) and index.
    ISBN 0-12-550360-1 (alk. paper)
    1. Monosaccharides--Synthesis.   I. Pelyvás, I. F. (István F.), date. II. Title.
    QD321.G97   1997
    547'.781304595--dc21   97-23437
                                                         CIP

PRINTED IN THE UNITED STATES OF AMERICA
97   98   99   00   01   02   QW   9   8   7   6   5   4   3   2   1

Dedicated to our Master, the late Professor Rezsö Bognár,
on the occasion of his 85th birth anniversary

CONTENTS

3 Preparation of Sugars with Isomerization   471

FOREWORD

Carbohydrate chemistry has been an important part of organic chemistry for well over a century. In the hands of Emil Fischer it played a major role in the historical evolution of stereochemistry. Then came the protracted disagreement between Hudson and Haworth about the size of the sugar rings. Another important advance was the recognition of the importance of ascorbic acid and Reichstein's beautiful synthesis thereof. Many other natural products were recognized to be carbohydrates. Even polymers such as starch and cellulose are carbohydrates. Indeed, nature has the habit of attaching sugars to all kinds of molecules, even triterpenoids and steroids. The aminoglycoside antibiotics again played an important role in stimulating the further growth of carbohydrate chemistry.

However, this is not the end of the story. Carbohydrates play an almost infinite role in the immune system and in cell recognition. Also, we cannot forget that DNA, RNA, and a host of modified nucleosides are all based on a carbohydrate component. Thus, carbohydrate chemistry will remain a major interest of organic chemists, biochemists, molecular biologists, and synthetic chemists for an indefinite period into the future.

This book by Drs. Zoltán Györgydeák and István F. Pelyvás is entitled *Monosaccharide Sugars: Synthesis by Chain Extension, Degradation, and*

Epimerization. It provides the chemist with a very useful summary of the synthetic manipulation of monosaccharides, which are the simplest kind of carbohydrate. Nevertheless, you cannot build up complex carbohydrates, such as are needed in cell regulation, without beginning with something simpler and more readily available.

This book presents a critical appreciation of synthetic methods for monosaccharides. It also deals with the use of monosaccharides for the production of "chirons" as defined by Stephen Hanessian. The synthesis of isotopically labeled carbohydrates is also covered. There are suitable experimental procedures included in each chapter.

This book will be of benefit to anyone who has to deal with carbohydrate chemistry. It is concerned with the fundamental building blocks—the mono-saccharides. In a world sinking under an avalanche of published journals, the struggle with the retrieval of important facts can be avoided by simply reading this book. Those who do will be grateful.

D. H. R. Barton

PREFACE

The synthesis of new chiral organic compounds, and the improved synthesis of known substances, will always be a major task for the professional chemist. The stereoisomerism which can arise even when two appropriately substituted sp^3-hybridized carbons are contained in a molecule makes it inevitable that the synthesis of such a molecule will call for the exercise of stereocontrol.

For constructing a target molecule with multiple chirality centers, either total synthesis or assembly from smaller chiral blocks may be considered. The present book intends to help in recognizing such chiral units as have been employed, or can be used as readily available chiral starting materials for buildup of complex organic structures.

Saccharides represent a unique family of polyfunctional compounds which can be chemically manipulated in a multitude of ways. This book presents, with the aid of illustrations and about 1700 references, previously applied and potentially useful strategies for the *synthesis* and *degradation* of monosaccharides. The result is a general overview and comparison of the construction of hardly available higher-carbon sugars, as well as smaller chiral synthons.

When describing the individual methods in each chapter, unique supplementary collections of the prepared sugar derivatives are provided in the form of Tables, while representative, well-established experimental procedures illustrate the practical potential of the discussed synthetic transformation. We hope that these features will save tedious literature searching by the reader engaged in research and education on the chemistry and biochemistry of saccharides and many other natural products.

We are indebted to our colleagues who helped us by making copies of some early papers available, and to Mr. Miklós Hornyák for his invaluable technical assistance in editing the artwork of the book. We thank the Alexander von Humboldt Foundation (Bonn, Germany) and the Hungarian Science Foundation (Budapest, Hungary; Grants OTKA 19327 and 23138) for financial support in various stages of our research and in the preparation of this manuscript.

Zoltán Györgydeák
István F. Pelyvás

ABBREVIATIONS AND ACRONYMS

Ac	acetyl
AIBN	2,2′-azobisisobutyronitrile
All	allyl
Ar	aryl
Bn	benzyl
BOC	*tert*-butoxycarbonyl
Bu	butyl
Bz	benzoyl
chxn	diisobutylcyclohexenediamine
CpFe(CO)	cyclopentadienyl-dicarbonyliron
DAST	diethylaminosulfur trifluoride
DBU	1,5-diazabicyclo[5.4.0]undec-5-ene
DCC	dicyclohexylcarbodiimide
DCHA	dicyclohexylamine
DIPEA	diisopropyl ethylamine
DMAP	4-dimethylaminopyridine
DMF	*N*,*N*-dimethylformamide
DMSO	dimethyl sulfoxide
DOPSA	[dimethyl(oxy)propyl](dimethylsilyl)acetylene

DQQ	2,3-dichloro-5,6-dicyano-1,4-benzoquinone
ee	enantiomeric excess
HMPA	hexamethylphosphoric triamide
HPLC	high performance liquid chromatography
KDO	3-deoxy-D-*manno*-2-octulosonic acid
LDA	lithium diisopropylamide
MCPBA	3-chloroperoxybenzoic acid
MEM	2-methoxy-ethoxymethyl
MOM	methoxymethyl
Ms	methanesulfonyl, mesyl
NMR	nuclear magnetic resonance
Ph	phenyl
Phth	phthaloyl
Piv	pivaloyl
p.p.m.	parts per million
Py	pyridine
TBDMS	*tert*-butyldimethylsilyl
TBDPS	*tert*-butyldiphenylsilyl
TBSOP	2-*tert*-butyldimethylsilyloxypyrrole
tetmen	*N,N,N',N'*-tetramethylene diamine
Tf	trifluoromethanesulfonyl
THF	tetrahydrofuran
THP	tetrahydropyranyl
TLC	thin layer chromatography
TMS	trimethylsilyl
Tr	trityl (triphenylmethyl)
Ts	*p*-toluenesulfonyl (tosyl)
Z	carbobenzyloxy

INTRODUCTION

Knowledge of carbohydrate chemistry continues to move ahead on many fronts. The field has become a rather complex discipline, as shown by the huge number of publications cited *Chemical Abstracts* under the term "Carbohydrates," and by the new journals addressing the field in the last few years.

Interest in the chemistry of carbohydrates has grown rapidly from the discovery of simple sugars in the nineteenth century to recognition of the biological roles of polyhydroxyalkyl aldehydes (aldoses) and polyhydroxyalkyl ketones (ketoses) in naturally occurring glycosides, nucleosides, oligo- and polysaccharides, and certain antibiotics. Following the pioneering research on sugars (*Tollens, Ledderhose, Dubrunfaut,* etc.), the studies of *Emil Fischer* are considered milestones, which have since been successfully utilized by researchers to this day.

The present book is aimed at treating carbohydrate chemistry through the eyes of a synthetic chemist who is using carbohydrates as naturally occurring, inexpensive starting materials in organic syntheses. A particularly attractive feature of carbohydrates is their chiral structure, permitting their use in synthetic research and in the chemical industry as "chiral pools." Numerous procedures have been known for the *chain extension* of appropriate sugars for synthesizing the target chiral compound (such as *N*-acetylneuraminic acid), or for the *degradation* of readily available sugars to chiral synthons with shorter carbon chains (such as D- or L-glyceraldehyde).

This book presents and discusses the literature to date on methods for carbon–carbon bond formation and degradation in the field of sugars, offering the production of higher-carbon sugars and related compounds, or smaller chiral synthons, respectively, from simple carbohydrate derivatives. Procedures reported for the epimerization of sugars, which are of great practical importance for the stereochemical interconversion of carbohydrate derivatives, are also discussed.

For the sake of simplicity, examples of these methodologies are taken from the field of *nonbranched sugars exclusively,* and discussion of neither the functional-group transformations involved and executed in the methods presented, nor the enzyme-mediated reactions, are within the scope of the book. Special emphasis was given to explaining and including results and experimental details from the early published literature, mostly in non-English-speaking countries. Our intention was to generalize the experimental procedures, and to use the recently established International Union of Pure and Applied Chemistry (IUPAC) Nomenclature for Carbohydrates. However, in many cases, this new nomenclature may cause difficulties when searching for older (but still extremely useful and reliable) data in the literature.

As mentioned above, the book is compiled into three major chapters; the first describes the reactions applicable to the *chain extension* of carbohydrates, the second summarizes the methods reported for *chain shortening* (degradation) of sugars, and the final chapter deals with the *epimerization reactions* of carbohydrate derivatives.

To avoid the use of four-digit reference numbers, the references are placed at the end of each subchapter (section). For technical reasons the literature is covered to the beginning of 1996. However, important, more recent references are briefly discussed in the "Note Added in Proof" section.

1

ASCENDING SYNTHESIS OF MONOSACCHARIDES

1.1. BUILDUP WITH TOTAL SYNTHESIS

1.1.1. The Formose Reaction

When the most simple aldehyde, formaldehyde, is treated with alkali, a sugar-like syrup is produced.[1] This reaction, discovered in the late nineteenth century, has been thoroughly investigated[2] with the goal of obtaining carbohydrates with total synthesis in the food industry and astronautics.

These complex mixtures of sugars and branched-chain sugars, produced from formaldehyde with self-condensation, are called *formose*. There are many well-known procedures for obtaining various product mixtures and, sometimes, for selective isolation of single substances; these procedures involve variation of the reaction conditions—specifically, the solvent [water, short-chain alcohols, N,N-dimethylformamide (DMF)], the catalyst, and added materials, as well as the temperature and the pressure. Contrary to the thermally induced polymerization reactions[3] of formaldehyde or the action of acids, the base-catalyzed process is an aldol reaction for the production of glycolaldehyde

$$2 \ CH_2O \rightarrow HOCH_2CHO$$

which can be detected in formose mixtures obtained under various conditions. Glycolaldehyde exerts an autocatalytic effect[4] on the process; similar reactions of other hydroxyaldehydes and endiol compounds have also been reported.[5] In certain cases addition of fructose or glucose to the reaction medium results in the formation[6] of formose mixtures with specific composition. Selective formation of C-hydroxymethylglycerol can be achieved by the addition of 2-diethylaminoethanol catalyst and a hexose, and the rate of conversion is strongly influenced[7] by the configuration of the added aldose and deoxyaldose. The catalysts commonly used in the formose reaction are shown in Table 1.1.

A basically simple reaction scheme of the formose reaction, as described by Pfeil and Ruckert,[8] is illustrated in Figure 1.1.

The formose reaction leads to the possible formation of stereoisomeric sugars, and yields of the isolation of individual substances are essentially dependent on the specific reaction conditions.

> *Standardized procedure for the preparation of the formose mixture*[8]   To a 30% aqueous formaldehyde solution (45 ml) water (225 ml) is added; the mixture is warmed up to 60°C in a thermostat and $Ca(OH)_2$ (5.0 g) is added when the alkaline content of the mixture reaches 0.22 M. Then samples are taken from the solution: first (because of the low conversion rate) 10 ml and then 4 ml. The samples are quenched with dilute formic acid and rendered salt-free by passing through an ion-exchange column. Freeze drying of the 10 to 15-ml eluants gives mixtures consisting of the condensation products and paraformaldehyde, which are separated by extraction with cold water. The extract is chromatographed by applying the upper phase of a 4:5:1 mixture of n-butanol–glacial acetic acid–water as the developing system, with anilinephthalate as the visualizing agent.

The primary product of the formose reaction is glycolaldehyde (**1.1**), which is further transformed in essentially two ways, depending on the reaction conditions[9]:

1. Under practically neutral conditions (e.g., $CaCO_3$) the glycolaldehyde produced in the formose reaction does not undergo dimerization into tetroses (**1.2**); instead, addition of a

TABLE 1.1   Catalysts for the Formose Reaction

Mineral compounds	Organic bases
$Ba(OH)_2$, $Ca(OH)_2$, $Mg(OH)_2$, $Pb(OH)_2$, $Sr(OH)_2$, LiOH, NaOH, KOH, TlOH, rare-earth hydroxides, $BaCO_3$, $CaCO_3$, $MgCO_3$, $MgSO_4$, CrO_3, MgO, PbO, TiO_2, V_2O_5, Ag_2O, MoO_3, ThO_2, Al_2O_3, ZnO, WO_3, kaolinite	Pyridine, picolins, collidine, 2-dimethylamino-ethanol, triethanolamine, tetraethylammonium hydroxide, thiamine, (benz)thiazolium salts, N-methylmorpholine, ion-exchange resins of strong basic character, N-methylpiperidine

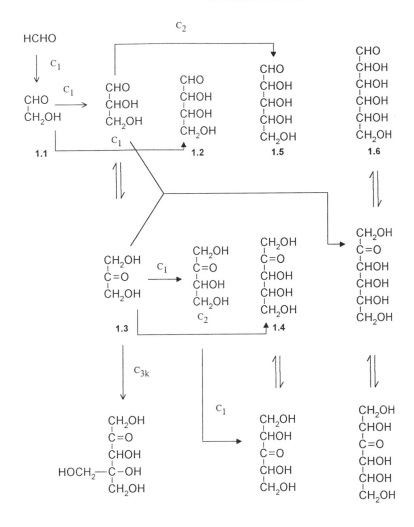

C_1 = formaldehyde
C_2 = glycolaldehyde
C_{3k} = dihydroxyacetone

FIGURE I.I

third formaldehyde molecule results in dihydroxyacetone (**1.3**). The reaction of this latter compound with glycolaldehyde gives ribulose (**1.4**), which is the final product when $CaCO_3$ is added, and it undergoes further transformation into ketopentoses or aldopentoses only after an elongated reaction time.

2. Under more alkaline conditions (e.g., addition of CaO) glycolaldehyde is converted into a mixture of tetroses, which are rather unstable under the given conditions and are transformed into triose (**1.3**)–pentose (**1.5**) mixtures.

Hexoses (**1.6**) are produced by the dimerization of dihydroxyacetone, which is possible only under more alkaline conditions, since, in the presence of $CaCO_3$, dihydroxyacetone gives tetrulose with glycolaldehyde. Further transformations by aldol-type condensation are inhibited by quick ring closure into furanoses or pyranoses—starting with the pentoses produced in the reaction. Except for the first step (the formation of glycolaldehyde), each step of the formose reaction is an aldol condensation, which is a reversible process. The condensation reactions leading to open-chain products are more favorable than those giving rise to branched-chain substances.

The conversion of formaldehyde into sugars is promoted by alcohols, and this is explained by the reduced base dissociation, and thus the inhibition of the Cannizzaro reaction.

Formose reaction in aqueous methanol[9]   To a stirred mixture of 30% aqueous formaldehyde (200 ml) and methanol (200 ml) CaO (3 g) is added. When the vigorous reaction has subsided, the mixture is kept at 40°C for 40 min, until the conversion of formaldehyde is complete. The pale-yellow solution is filtered through a glass filter, and the filtrate is acidified with dilute sulfuric acid and quickly neutralized with $BaCO_3$. The precipitate is filtered, the filtrate is concentrated at 4 torr pressure, and the sweet syrupy residue is chromatographed with a 5:3:1:3 *n*-butanol–pyridine–benzene–water developing system, with anilinephthalate as the visualizing agent.

For the preparation of larger quantities of formose, preliminary investigations have been carried out to ensure the application of the formose mixture as a sugar source. Figure 1.2 summarizes the methods reported[10] for the production of larger quantities of formose.

According to experience gained from the hydroformylation reaction[11] of formaldehyde (when the intermediate is also glycolaldehyde), this process also involves the formose reaction, with the production of nonbranched sugars. However, this reaction is essentially different from the transformations discussed above—the addition of the "synthesis gas" ($CO+H_2$) on formaldehyde is executed in pyridine in the presence of bis(triphenylphosphine)carbonyl rhodium(I) catalyst.[12] The consecutive reactions proceed as shown in Figure 1.3:

Depending on the selected route of transformation, various organic bases are used as catalysts for the conversion.

General procedure[12] *for the preparation of simple sugars from formaldehyde and "synthesis gas"* A solution of paraformaldehyde (622 mg, 20 mmol), bis(triphenylphosphine)carbonyl rhodium(I) chloride (69 mg, 0.1 mmol), and the tertiary amine (see Table 1.1) in pyridine (10 ml) is placed to a 54-ml stainless-steel autoclave and a pressure of 120 at of the "synthesis gas" ($H_2/CO = 2$) is applied. The reaction

500 g of 37% formaline ($d = 1.1141$)

21 liters of water

200 ml of methanol

50–60°C

30 g of $Ca(OH)_2$, stirring for 20 min

(the solution turns yellow)

Add 160 ml of 20% H_2SO_4 until the reaction

mixture becomes slightly acidic

Residue   Filtrate

Neutralize with powdered $CaCO_3$, heating at 80°C

for 30 min, clarifying with activated-carbon

Residue   Filtrate

Concentrate $\frac{1}{6}-\frac{1}{10}$ of its original volume in

vacuo. Apply a column of IR-120B (H^+)-resin

(2-liter column, washing 3 times with water)

Apply a column of IR-400 (OH^-)-resin

(2-liter column, washing 3 times with water)

Elution

116 g of formose syrup (80%)

FIGURE 1.2

is complete in 30 min at 120°C, when the cooled autoclave is opened and the reaction mixture is examined by thin-layer chromatography (TLC). The results are summarized in Table 1.2.

In studies of the various factors influencing the formose reaction, the influence of temperature was found to be very important and interesting. By conducting the $Ca(OH)_2$-catalyzed process at 98°C, investigators found that the reaction was no longer autocatalytic and the product distribution was more simple. Detailed studies have shown[13] that at 18% conversion C_6

$CH_2O + CO + H_2$	$\rightarrow$	$HOCH_2CHO$	$CH_2O + H_2$	$\rightarrow$	CH_3OH
$2\,CH_2O + CO + H_2$	$\rightarrow$	$C_3H_6O_3$	$2\,CH_2O + 2CO + 2H_2$	$\rightarrow$	$C_4H_8O_4$
$2\,CH_2O + 2CO + 2H_2$	$\rightarrow$	$C_5H_{10}O_5$	$3\,CH_2O + 3CO + 3H_2$	$\rightarrow$	$C_6H_{12}O_6$

FIGURE 1.3

TABLE I.2 Preparation of Simple Carbohydrates by Reaction of Formaldehyde with "Synthesis Gas" in Presence of Bis[Triphenylphosphinecarbonyl Rhodium(I)] Catalyst[12]

Cocatalyst (amine, mol/l)	Overall yields, (%)[a]	Yield (%)						
		CH_3OH	C_2^b	C_3	C_4	C_5	C_6	$\sum_{n=3}^{6} c_n$
Triethylamine (0.04)	97	7	53	14	16	6	1	37
Triethylamine (0.1)	98	9	34	20	25	8	2	65
Triethylamine (0.2)	94	9	18	21	27	14	5	67
Triethylamine (0.2)[c]	87	10	9	16	28	17	7	68
Triethylamine (0.2)[d]	79	15	5	17	20	16	6	59
Triethylamine (0.4)	89	11	9	19	22	20	9	69
Quinuclidine (0.2)	64	10	3	8	15	18	10	51
N,N-Dimethylbenzylamine (0.2)	99	9	61	12	13	3	1	28
N-Methybenzylamine (0.2)	88	5	75	5	2	1	0	8

[a] $CH_3OH + \sum_{n=3}^{6} c_n$
[b] Sum of glycolaldehyde plus ethylene glycol
[c] 1 h.
[d] At 140°C

monosaccharides are produced with excellent selectivity, glucose is the predominant product, and no branched-chain sugars are present. If the reaction is not quenched at this stage, saccharinic acids are produced, the formation of the products of the Lobry de Bruyn–Alberda van Ekenstein rearrangement is observed, and branched-chain sugars and sugar alcohols are also formed in Cannizzaro and crossed Cannizzaro reactions.[14]

Further selectivity can be achieved by application of nonaqueous solvents. Previous works (see Chapter 1, Ref. 15) have demonstrated that alcohols inhibit the Cannizzaro reaction. Thus, the formose reaction can be executed as low as at 0.05 CaO : HCHO composition, and contrary to that observed for water, the increase of the concentration of formaldehyde results in the growth of the yield of the sugar, which is 57% when the reaction is conducted at 60°C for 1 h with 0.15 M/liter of CaO and 5 M of formaldehyde.[16]

Preparation of methanolic formaldehyde solution[16]   After 200 g of paraformaldehyde is dissolved in 400 ml of dry methanol, the solution is boiled for 7 h. The formaldehyde content of the filtered solution is 12 M.

If the formose reaction is performed in an aqueous solution, production of large quantities of sugars can be achieved by keeping the concentration of formaldehyde low (<1 M), the pH should be 11.2, and to prevent the degradation of the sugars thus produced, the reaction should be quenched when it reaches the maximum value of the oxidation–reduction (oxidoreduction) potential. This point can be visually recognized; the reaction must be stopped immediately when the color turns yellow.[17]

Gas chromatography combined with mass spectrometry (GC–MS) allows deeper insight into the product mixture of the formose reaction. This methodology involves reduction of the produced sugars into alditols and subsequent derivatization into the corresponding trimethylsilyl ethers or O-trifluoroacetates. GC–MS analysis of the processed mixtures is then quite suitable for the detection of higher-carbon and branched-chain sugars as well.[18] Related examinations made it possible to select reaction conditions under which the formose mixture produced contains[19] 2-hydroxymethylglycerol (**4.1**), 2,4-(bis-hydroxymethyl)-1,2,3,4,5-pentanepentol (**4.2**), and 3-hydroxymethyl-1,2,3,4,5-pentanepentol (**4.3**). The product distribution and the routes of formation of these substances are summarized in Figure 1.4.

According to the results of Shigemasa *et al.*,[18] the process described in the preceding paragraphs consists of three steps:

1. Induction period (formation of C_2 and C_3 units, which then catalyze the process via the formation of a Ca complex).
2. The formose reaction, whose endpoint can be determined by measuring the oxidoreduction potential (the color turns yellow).

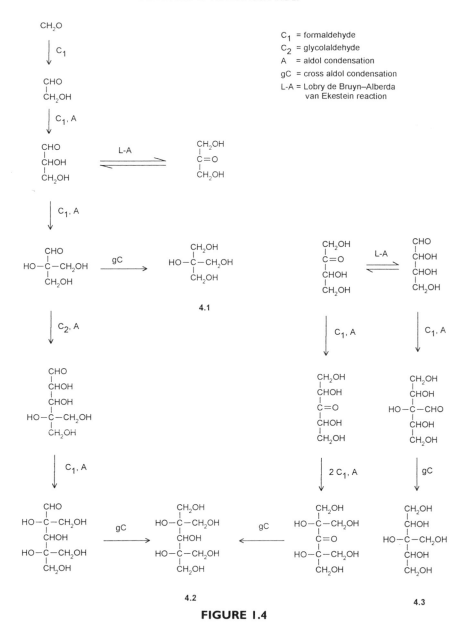

FIGURE 1.4

3. Degradation of the carbohydrate products of the formose reaction under the actual reaction conditions.

The reaction is suitable for the preparation of branched-chain sugars, as mentioned above, if D-fructose is added to the reaction mixture[20] in small concentrations.

The conversion of formaldehyde in aqueous media and in the presence of inorganic bases into monosaccharides is known to proceed in competition with the Cannizzaro reaction. Indeed, when tertiary amines are added, no Cannizzaro reaction takes place, and even concentrated formaldehyde solutions are readily transformed into formoses.[21] In addition, since the formaldehyde concentration can be more easily adjusted in the absence of inorganic bases, tertiary amines are more easily removable and recoverable than inorganic bases, and also, since crude formose can be purified so simply, this procedure might be of technical importance.

In the next procedure the induction period is avoided by addition of accelerators (e.g., formose itself, or glycerol).

Preparation of formose mixture with 2-dimethylaminoethanol as the base and glyceraldehyde as the accelerator[22] A mixture of 10% aqueous formaldehyde (10 ml), pyridine (52 g) and glyceraldehyde (1 g) is boiled for 3 h. The reaction mixture is concentrated, and the residue is treated with anion- and cation-exchange resins. The yield of the colorless and odorless formose is 9.67 g.

A selective formose reaction can also be achieved when the combination of 2-dimethylaminoethanol and a hexose, as the additive, is employed. In such a case 2-hydroxymethylglycerol is the major product.[7]

A branched-chain ketose, 2,4-(bis-hydroxymethyl)-3-pentulose was isolated when the reaction was catalyzed with $BaCl_2$ and KOH, and the same effect was observed with thiamine or $CaCl_2$/methanol.[23]

A surprising effect of boric acid on the formose reaction was observed; the major product was D,L-arabinitol, isolated in the form of crystalline pentaacetate.[24]

As mentioned above, thiazolium salts, generally useful in acyloin and benzoin condensations, can be employed very efficiently as catalysts in the formose reaction.[25] In DMF a multicomponent reaction mixture, consisting mainly of hexoses, is produced when the conversion of paraformaldehyde into formose is catalyzed[26] with 3-benzyl-5-(2-hydroxyethyl)-4-methylthiazolium chloride.

Preparation of formose with the aid of thiazolium salt catalysis[26] To a stirred solution of 3-benzyl-5-(2-hydroxyethyl)-4-methylthiazolium chloride (12.5 g, 185 mM) and triethyl amine (18.8 g, 186 mmol) in DMF (250 ml), 40 g of paraformaldehyde (133 mmol) is added, and then in 30 min periods further (33-mmol) portions (weighing 10 g each) of the starting aldehyde were added. The reaction is monitored by gas chromatography following trimethylsilylation, with samples taken occasionally. After completion of the reaction the mixture is neutralized with concentrated hydrochloric acid, and DMF is removed by evaporation under diminished pressure. The residue is diluted with water and extracted exhaustively with ether for 12 h. The aqueous solution is decolorized with carbon and poured onto the top of a 30 × 30-cm column filled with anion- and cation-exchange resins, and this treatment is repeated three times. The eluates are concentrated to obtain a yellowish or red residue weighing 15 g.

In DMF, combined catalysis of the formaldehyde condensation with vitamin B_1 and 2-dimethylaminoethanol results in the selective formation of dihydroxyacetone as the major product.[27] This latter substance is, again, the main product when 3-ethylbenzothiazolium bromide and triethylamine are used as the catalysts, and under such conditions no formation of glycolaldehyde was detected.[28]

An uronolactone, 3,3-bis-(C-hydroxymethyl)-3-deoxyfuranurono-1,4-lactone (**5.1**), is obtained in 33% yield when the formose reaction is catalyzed with sodium hydroxide and fructose in methanol[29] (Fig. 1.5). The major product (38%) of the formose reaction carried out under UV irradiation[18] is pentaerythritol (**5.2**) (Fig. 1.5). The reaction of paraformaldehyde with the "synthesis gas" (discussed previously) in the presence of a tertiary amine and 3-ethylbenzothiazolium bromide catalysts can, by changing the pressure, directed so that either trioses or tetroses are the major products.[12] The product distribution is shown in Table 1.3, and the reaction conditions were those indicated in Table 1.2.

A product mixture very similar to that of the formose reaction is obtained by the transformation of 2,3-dibromopropionaldehyde with dilute bases, preferably with barium hydroxide. In this case a sugar-like mixture is produced according to the following equation:

$$2\ BrCH_2-CHBr-CHO + 2\ Ba(OH)_2 \rightarrow C_6H_{12}O_6 + 2\ BaBr_2$$

However, the sugar-like character of the product was only supposed[30] by comparison of the osazone—obtained in moderate yield from the product—with that of formose, and no report on the identification and determination of the exact composition of this syrupy mixture has been published subsequently. According to Fischer,[31] the syrup can be obtained as follows.

Preparation of a sugar mixture from 2,3-dibromopropionaldehyde A solution of $Ba(OH)_2 \times 8\ H_2O$ (75 g) in water (1.25 liters) is cooled on an ice bath and under vigorous stirring 51 g of freshly distilled 2,3-dibromopropionaldehyde is added dropwise over a period of 45–60 min. Apart from a small resin-like residue, the bromo compound has completely reacted. The reaction mixture is first acidified slightly with sulfuric acid and concentrated sodium sulfate solution until $BaSO_4$ precipitation, which is usually complete in about 12 h. The precipitate is then filtered off, and the filtrate is *carefully* neutralized with NaOH and evaporated under diminished pressure. Treatment of the resulting syrup with phenylhydrazine gives an osazone (yield 13%) identical to that obtained from formose.

From this sugar mixture, termed *acrose* by Fischer, the optically active components were isolated in a long, tedious procedure involving the combi-

5.1   **5.2**

FIGURE 1.5

TABLE 1.3 Selective Synthesis of Trioses and Tetroses from Formaldehyde and "Synthesis Gas"[12]

Amine and additive	Pressure kPa	Overall yield (%)[a]	Methanol	Yield						Selectivity	
				C_2^b	C_3	C_4	C_5	C_6	C_n	C_3^c	C_4^d
Triethylamine	3,040	69	18	14	21	10	5	1	37	57	27
Triethylamine	6,080	93	16	20	26	17	11	3	57	46	30
Triethylamine	12,160	94	9	18	21	27	14	5	67	31	40
Triethylamine[e]	12,160	95	7	15	12	37	16	8	73	16	51
Dimethylbenzylamine[f]	12,160	92	4	26	6	41	7	8	62	10	66
Triethylamine-EB[g]	12,160	86	0	22	31	19	11	3	64	48	30
Triethylamine-EB[g]	6,080	53	0	1	40	7	4	1	52	77	13
Triethylamine-EB[g]	12,160	48	0	1	41	4	2	0	47	87	9

Note: The reactions were carried out at 120°C for 30 min with 0.2-mol/liter of amine concentrations.

[a]Methanol + C_4;

[b]Sum of ethylene glycol plus glycolaldehyde

[c]C_3/C_4

[d]C_4/C_n

[e]100°C, 2 h

[f]1 h at 100°C and then 1 h at 130°C

[g]0.05 mol/liter 3-ethylbenzothiazolium bromide

TABLE 1.4   **Conversion of Acrose into Optically Active Monosaccharides**

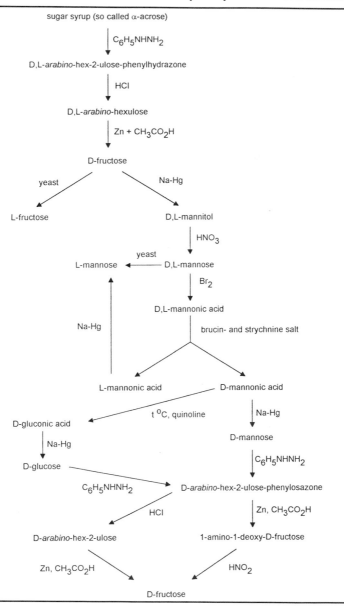

nation of chemical and enzymatic steps of separation. Thus, Emil Fischer succeeded in the isolation of L- and D-glucose, D- and L-mannose, and D- and L-fructose. These pioneering investigations have led to the discovery

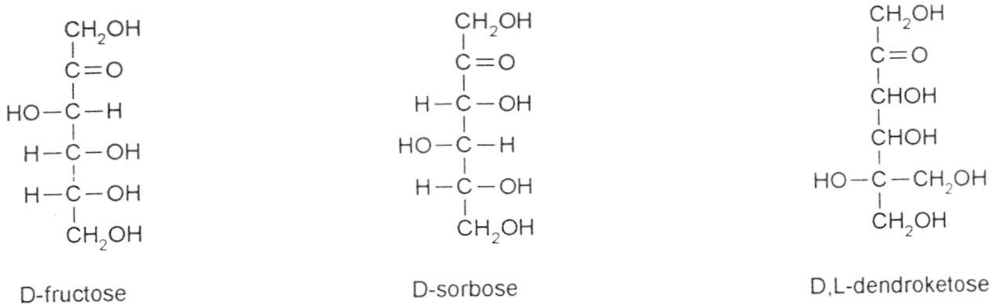

FIGURE 1.6

of the genetic relationship between hexoses.[32] These studies, aimed at obtaining optically active monosaccharides from *acrose*, are summarized in Table 1.4.

1.1.2. Syntheses from Glyceraldehyde

Condensation of two C_3 units (such as glyceraldehyde and dihydroxyacetone, which are easily interconverted in the Lobry de Bruyn–Alberda van Ekenstein oxidoreduction process), would formally lead to the formation of hexoses. Indeed, aldolization of D,L-glyceraldehyde gives D,L-fructose and D,L-sorbose,[31,33] and detailed studies[34] have revealed that dilute alkalies convert D-glyceraldehyde into a mixture containing 50% D-fructose and 44% D-sorbose. Changing the reaction conditions and applying enzymatic, dilatometric, polarimetric, and sugar-analytic methods allowed deeper insight[35] into the mechanism of this general, base-catalyzed process. These studies showed the formation of three materials: D-fructose, D-sorbose, and D,L-dentroketose (Fig 1.6).

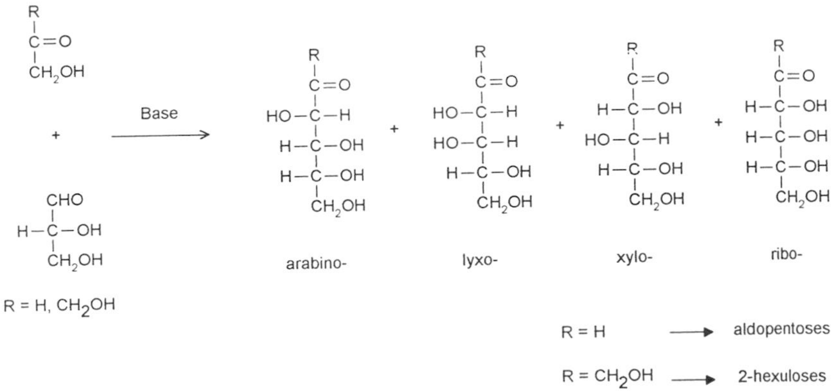

FIGURE 1.7

The overall yield and the D-fructose : D-sorbose : D,L-dentroketose ratio can be influenced by changing the nature and concentration of the catalyst (alkali hydroxides, alkaline-earth metal hydroxides, pyridine and alkyl-pyridines, imidazole) of the aldol condensation. Physicochemical studies aimed at the investigation of the aldolization of trioses have shown[36] that the reaction is first-order with respect to glyceraldehyde, and the rate-determining step is the formation of a carbanion from dihydroxyacetone. Aldolization of dihydroxyacetone is a second-order process. As in the case of trioses, aldol condensation is a complicated system of first- and second-order competitive-consecutive reactions, the type of the base-catalyzed reaction is determined by the initial concentration of the triose. Larger and smaller triose concentrations favor the aldolization process and isomerization (dehydration), respectively. At higher temperatures by-products are formed at the expense of the less stable D,L-dendroketose. The influence of pH can be controlled[37] by a pH-stat.

The combination of modern analytic methods allows deeper insight into the mechanism of the aldol condensation between glyceraldehyde and glycolaldehyde, which results in the products shown in Figure 1.7.

In the various product mixtures arising from aldolization, the diastereo-isomer ratios are very similar (see Table 1.5) and the observed stereoselec-tivity reflects a pericyclic intermediary state[38] formed on the attack of *cis*-endiolate on the aldehyde. Given this explanation, the preceding obser-vation, that the primary products of the condensation are D-fructose and D-sorbose, is easily understandable. The product ratio decreases in the following order: *arabino* > *xylo* > *ribo* > *lyxo*.

> *Aldolization of trioses*[38] A solution of D,L-glyceraldehyde (6 mg) or glycolalde-hyde (14 mg) and D,L-glyceraldehyde (6 mg) and the catalyst (see Table 1.5) in 4 ml of water is kept at room temperature for 45–60 min. The mixture is then neutralized with Dowex 50 W (H⁺) cation-exchange resin and filtered, and the

TABLE 1.5 Diastereomeric Ratio Observed in Aldol Condensation of Trioses and in Condensation of Glycolaldehyde and D,L-Glyceraldehyde

Concentration of catalyst	Diastereomeric ratio (%)							
	2-Hexuloses				Aldopentoses			
	ara	*xylo*	*ribo*	*lyxo*	*ara*	*xylo*	*ribo*	*lyxo*
LiOH 0.01 M	55	29	11	5	58	29	10	<3
NaOH 0.01 M	54	34	10	2	60	28	9	<3
Ca(OH)₂ 0.01 M	50	30	14	6	54	28	15	<3
Sr(OH)₂ 0.01 M	57	29	11	3	61	28	8	<3
Ba(OH)₂ 0.01 M	50	33	13	4	65	23	9	<3

filtrate is concentrated *in vacuo*. For gas chromatographic analysis, the product mixture is converted into O-isopropylidene derivatives.

REFERENCES TO SECTIONS 1.1.1 AND 1.1.2

1. A. Butlerow, *C. R. Hebd. Seances Acad. Sci.* **53**, 145 (1861); *Justus Liebigs Ann. Chem.* **120**, 295(1861).
2. T. Mizuno and A. H. Weiss, *Adv. Carbohydr. Chem. Biochem.* **29**, 173 (1974).
3. *Houben-Weyl, Methoden der Organischen Chemie*, Vol. E/20, p. 1390 (1987).
4. H. Schmalfuss and M. Congehl, *Biochem. Z.* **185**, 70 (1927); H. W. Maurer, J. N. BeMiller, and G. V. Smith, *J. Catal.* **103**, 239, 474 (1987); W. P. Huskey and I. R. Epstein, *J. Am. Chem. Soc.* **111**, 3157 (1989).
5. W. Langebeck, W Sander, F. Kühn, S. Hünig, and E. Katzschmann, *Angew. Chem.* **61**, 186 (1949).
6. Y. Shigemasa, K. Ookagi, N. Ueda, R. Nakashima, K. Harada, N. Takeda, M. Suzuki, and S. Saito, *J. Carbohydr. Chem.* **1**, 325 (1982/1983).
7. T. Matsumoto and S. Inoue, *J. Chem. Soc., Perkin Trans. 1*, p. 1975 (1982).
8. E. Pfeil and H. Ruckert, *Justus Liebigs Ann. Chem.* **641**, 121 (1961).
9. R. Mayer and L. Jäschke, *Justus Liebigs Ann. Chem.* **635**, 145 (1960).
10. T. Mizuno, M. Asai, A. Misaki, Y. Fujihara, K. Kawai, K. Muramatsu, and K. Banba, *Nippon Nogei Kagaku Kaishi* **45**, 344 (1971); **46**, 73 (1972).
11. T. Okano, M. Makino, H. Konishi, and F. Kiji, *Chem. Lett.* p. 1793 (1985).
12. T. Okano, H. Ito, H. Konishi, and J. Kiji, *Chem. Lett.* p. 1731 (1986).
13. V. A. Likhobolov, A. H. Weiss, and M. M. Sakharov, *React. Kinet. Catal. Lett.* **8**, 155 (1988).
14. J. M. de Bruijn, A. P. G. Kieboom, and H. van Bekkum, *J. Carbohydr. Chem.* **5**, 561 (1986).
15. R. Mayer, K. Runge, and H. Drechsel, *Z. Chem.* **3**, 134 (1963); T. I. Khomenko, M. M. Sakharov, and O. A. Golovina, *Usp. Khim.* **49**, 1079 (1980); *Chem. Abstr.* **93**, 150504h (1980).
16. Y. Shigemasa, Y. Matsuda, C. Sakazawa, R. Nakashima, and T. Matsuura, *Bull. Chem. Soc. Jpn.* **52**, 1091 (1979).
17. Y. Shigemasa, M. Shimao, C. Sakazawa, and T. Matsuura, *Bull. Chem. Soc. Jpn.* **48**, 2099 (1975); Y. Shigemasa, T. Fujitani, C. Sakazawa, and T. Matsuura, *ibid.* **50**, 1527 (1977).
18. R. D. Partridge, R. H. Weiss, and D. Todd, *Carbohydr. Res.* **24**, 29 (1972); Y. Shigemasa, Y. Matsuda, C. Sakazawa, and T. Matsuura, *Bull. Chem. Soc. Jpn.* **50**, 222 (1977).
19. Y. Shigemasa, O. Nagae, C. Sakazawa, R. Nakashima, and T. Matsuura, *J. Am. Chem. Soc.* **100**, 1309 (1978).
20. Y. Shigemasa, T. Taji, E. Waki, and R. Nakashima, *Bull. Chem. Soc. Jpn.* **54**, 1403 (1981).
21. K. Runge and R. Mayer, *Justus Liebigs Ann. Chem.* **707**, 161 (1967).
22. K. Runge and R. Mayer, DD. Pat. 44094 (1964/1965); *Chem. Abstr.* **64**, 17426h (1966).
23. Y. Shigemasa, S. Akagi, R. Nakashima, and S. Saito, *Carbohydr. Res.* **80**, C1 (1980); Y. Shigemasa, T. Ueda, and H. Saimoto, *Bull. Chem. Soc. Jpn.* **63**, 389 (1990); H. Saimoto, S. Yatani, H. Sashiwa, and Y. Shigemasa, *Tetrahedron Lett.* **36**, 937 (1995).
24. Y. Shigemasa, A. Matsuda, N. Ueda, R. Nakashima, K. Harada, N. Takeda, M. Suzuki, and S. Saito, *Carbohydr. Res.* **134**, C4 (1984).
25. D. Breslow, *J. Am. Chem. Soc.* **80**, 3719 (1958); T. Matsumoto, M.Ohishi, and S. Inoue, *J. Org. Chem.* **50**, 603 (1985); H. Stetter, R. Y. Rämsch, and H. Kuhlmann, *Synthesis*, p. 733 (1976).
26. J. Castells, F. Geijo, and F. López-Calahorra, *Tetrahedron Lett.* **21**, 4517 (1990).
27. Y. Shigemasa, H. Matsumoto, Y. Sasaki, K. Harada, N. Takeda, M. Suzuki, and S. Saito, *J. Carbohydr. Chem.* **2**, 343 (1983); Y. Shigemasa, Y. Sasaki, N. Ueda, and R. Nakashima, *Bull. Chem. Soc. Jpn.* **57**, 2761 (1984).

28. T. Matsumoto, H. Yamamoto, and S. Inoue, *J. Am. Chem. Soc.* **106**, 4829 (1984).
29. Y. Shigemasa, K. Oogaki, N. Ueda, R. Nakashima, K. Harada, N. Takeda, M. Suzuki, and S. Saito, *J. Carbohydr. Chem.* **1**, 325 (1982/1983).
30. E. Fischer and J. Tafel, *Ber. Dtsch. Chem. Ges.* **20**, 1088 (1887).
31. E. Fischer and J. Tafel, *Ber. Dtsch. Chem. Ges.* **20**, 2566 (1887); E. Fischer, *ibid.* **23**, 370 (1890).
32. E. Fischer, *Ber. Dtsch. Chem. Ges.* **23**, 370, 2114 (1890).
33. E. Schmitz, *Ber. Dtsch. Chem. Ges.* **46**, 2327 (1913).
34. H. O. L. Fischer and E. Baer, *Helv. Chim. Acta* **19**, 519 (1936).
35. C. D. Gutsche, D. Redmore, R. S. Buriks, K. Nowotny, H. Grassner, and C. W. Armbruster, *J. Am. Chem. Soc.* **89**, 1235 (1967).
36. J. Königstein and M. Fedoronko, *Collect. Czech. Chem. Commun.* **40**, 1183 (1975).
37. J. Königstein, D. Anderle, and F. Janacek, *Chem. Zvesti* **28**, 201 (1974).
38. S. Morgenlie, *J. Carbohydr. Chem.* **6**, 661 (1987).

1.2. BUILDUP OF SUGARS WITH ASCENDING SYNTHESIS

1.2.1. The Cyanohydrin Synthesis (Kiliani–Fischer synthesis)

A common way for the synthesis of rare, nonnatural, or longer-chain mono-saccharides and their [13]C- and ^{14}C-labeled derivatives is based on the elonga-tion of the carbon chain by *one* carbon atom. This method is essentially an asymmetric synthesis in which hydrogen cyanide is added to the carbonyl group of an aldose and the resulting epimeric hydroxycarboxylic acid nitriles ("cyanohydrins") are hydrolyzed into the corresponding aldonic acids via an intermediary imide. Then reduction of the lactone of the aldonic acid gives rise[1] to an aldose that carries *one more* carbon atom than the start-ing educt.

This well-elaborated and reliable procedure has been applied in many cases for obtaining extended-chain, modified monosaccharides. The forma-tion of the epimeric cyanohydrins is a fast reaction, and because of the chiral nature of the starting hydroxyaldehyde (educt), the final monosaccha-rides are never produced in the same quantities. Formally, cyanohydrin synthesis can be regarded as the conversion of an aldose (exisiting in cyclic form in solution) into epimeric hydroxynitriles via the open-chain form, in which the latter products are hydrolytically transformed—through an imine stage—into their respective lactones. Reduction of the lactone under mild acid conditions then furnishes the aldose with a chain that is longer by one carbon atom. The addition of the cyanide and the subsequent steps in cyanohydrin synthesis are illustrated in Figure 1.8 by the example of the chain extension of D-arabinose (**8.1**).

The existence and structure of the intermediary products shown in Figure 1.8 were justified by means of detailed ^{13}C-NMR studies.[2]

To obtain the product with the required configuration, a series of investigations was necessary. As an experimental rule, addition of HCN proceeds so that, in the presence of a small amount of ammonia, the

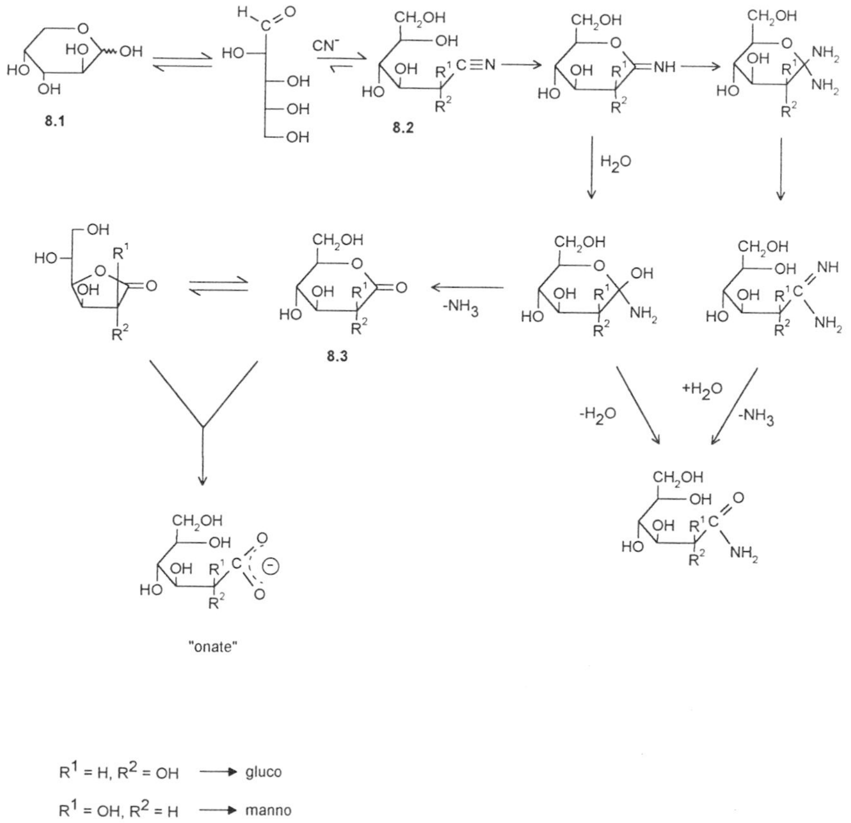

R^1 = H, R^2 = OH ⟶ gluco

R^1 = OH, R^2 = H ⟶ manno

FIGURE 1.8

2,4-*threo*-isomer (mannose in the preceding example) is the predominant product.[3] However, when the reaction is executed under more alkaline conditions the 70:30 *threo*:*erythro* ratio changes[4] to 27:73. No effect of complex-forming ions (Ca^{2+} or Cd^{2+}) has been observed under constant pH values. At the same time, the ratio of the epimeric chain-extended nitriles is strongly dependent[5] on the pH and the constitution of the educts used; significant differences have been observed[6] in the reactivity of α-D-glucose, α-D-galactose, and α- and β-disaccharides toward hydrogen cyanide.

Several procedures have been developed for the separation of the C-2 epimeric lactones (**8.3**), the main products of the cyanohydrin synthesis. Fractional crystallization, an obvious technique for this purpose, failed in many cases, but more easily crystallizable derivatives, such as the alkaloid salts or phenylhydrazones, could be readily separated, and the individual lactones were recovered.[1]

A quite useful example of this method is the preparation of gulose from xylose (in the case of both stereoisomers). Figure 1.9 shows this convenient cyanohydrin synthesis[7] to afford D-gulono-δ-lactone (**9.2**) from D-xylose (**9.1**).

> *D-Gulono-1,4-lactone (**9.2**)*[7]   A solution of potassium cyanide (0.14 g) and so-
> dium acetate (0.205 g) in water (15 ml) is cooled on an ice bath, and an ice-cold
> solution of D-xylose (0.3 g) in water (15 ml) is added. The mixture is kept at 0°C
> for 3 h and then at 5°C for 5 days. Aqueous sodium hydroxide (2 N; 5 ml) is added
> dropwise, the solution is warmed to 65°C, and air is bubbled through the reaction
> mixture for 12 h. After cooling it is passed through a column filled with Amberlite
> IR-120 ion-exchange resin, and a small trace of hydrochloric acid is added to the
> eluate, which is then evaporated and dissolved in 20 ml of methanol. Following
> treatment with charcoal, the solution is concentrated to 2 ml, a few drops of ethyl
> acetate are added, and after refrigeration, the product (43% calculated for KCN)
> is crystallized, m.p. 181–182°C, $[\alpha]_D$ −53 (c = 2.7 in water).

A wide range of procedures have been described for the preparation of epimeric cyanohydrins. Recent studies claim that application of anhydrous hydrogen cyanide is not essential[8] and an excess of potassium cyanide is suitable for a quick and complete conversion. As no comparison between the traditional, well-elaborated, and novel procedures has been published, certain sugars are still prepared according to the conventional methodology. Larger quantities of L-glucose and L-mannose are synthesized, in excellent yield, with anhydrous hydrogen cyanide in pyridine, and this preparation method offers advantages over that based on nitromethane condensation (see Section 1.2.3).

> *Reaction of hydrogen cyanide with L-arabinose: preparation of* L-glucose *and* L-
> mannose[9]   (*Caution:* The reaction should be carried out under a well-ventilated
> hood!) To a flask fitted with a glass stopper, dry pyridine (350 ml), L-arabinose
> (50 g, 0.33 mol), and anhydrous hydrogen cyanide (28–30 ml, 0.75 mol) are added
> and for dissolution, the flask is frequently shaken at room temperature. After
> complete dissolution (2–3 days) an additional volume (10 ml, 0.26 mol) of hydrogen
> cyanide is added and the mixture is kept at room temperature for 15 days (1–3 days
> if the reaction is conducted at higher temperature). Then 1–4 ml of triethylamine is
> added, which slightly changes the L-gluconitrile : L-mannononitrile ratio, and the
> solvent and the excess HCN are removed by evaporation under diminished pressure
> (bath temperature 40°C). The residual syrup is dissolved in dry ethanol (30 ml)
> and concentrated again, and this operation is repeated three times to remove traces

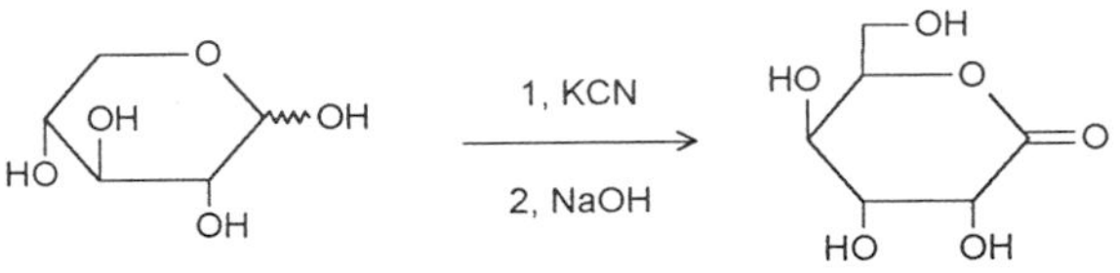

9.1   9.2

FIGURE I.9

of pyridine. On addition of the third portion of ethanol, crystallization begins. At this point ethyl acetate (30 ml) is added cautiously and then ether, up to a total volume of 1 liter. After remaining for 2 h at room temperature, the crystalline material is filtered off, washed with ether, and dried *in vacuo*. The yield of the product, which forms colorless resins, is 56.5 g (96%), m.p. 101–107°C (dec.), $[\alpha]_D$ +18.8 (c = 5 in pyridine; constant for 1 day).

L-*Mannose* A mixture of PdO/BaSO$_4$ catalyst (15 g) and water (100 ml) is prehydrogenated for 4 h, and a solution of 50 g (0.282 mol) of the cyanohydrin (mentioned earlier) in water (100 ml) and 2 N hydrochloric acid (170 ml, 0.34 mol) is added. After 5 h the hydrogen consumption is 5.8 liters, and after 8 h, 6.47 liters (theoretical: 6.35 liters). The catalyst is removed by centrifugation and washed with water. The combined solution is neutralized with 2 N sodium hydroxide solution (550 ml), and a solution of phenylhydrazine (80 ml) in 25% acetic acid (160 ml) is added. Precipitation of L-mannose phenylhydrazone begins in a few minutes and is complete in about 2 h. The product is filtered, washed with water, acetone, and ether and then dried *in vacuo* to obtain pale-yellow plates (44.4 g, 58% and 56%–calculated for the cyanohydrin and L-arabinose, respectively), m.p. 181–183°C. The L-mannose phenylhydrazone (44 g) thus obtained is decomposed with benzaldehyde, and on subsequent reduction with sodium borohydride, L-mannitol (24–26 g, 81–88%; overall yield 46–50% calculated for L-arabinose) is obtained.

L-*Glucose* The mother liquor of L-mannose phenylhydrazone is kept at 5°C for 1 day, filtered, and mixed with 100 ml of benzaldehyde. After remaining for a few hours at 4°C, the precipitated benzaldehyde phenylhydrazone is filtered off, and the filtrate is shaken with an additional 20 ml volume of benzaldehyde. The aqueous phase (~1 liter) is washed with chloroform (4 × 300 ml), concentrated to ~750, ml and passed through a column filled with Amberlite IR-120 cation-exchange resin. The resin is washed thoroughly with water (until negative Fehling probe is obtained), and the pH is adjusted to 3 with 400 ml of Amberlite IR-45 anion-exchange resin to remove chloride ions from the solution. The ~2-liter volume solution is evaporated after decolorization with charcoal (bath temperature 60–65°C) to a thick syrup (19 g), which is dissolved in hot water and mixed with dry, warm ethanol (200 ml). On seeding, L-glucose crystallizes (13.7 g, 26% calculated for L-arabinose), m.p. 144–147°C, $[\alpha]_D^{20}$ −51.4 (c = 4 in water plus a small trace of NH$_3$). After repeated recrystallization the specific optical rotation value is −52. A second crop of L-glucose can be isolated in form of a syrup by addition of water to the mother liquor. This is dissolved in a small volume of ethanol and allowed to slowly evaporate in a cup kept over concentrated sulfuric acid. After seeding, a mash of crystals is developed in 10 days, which can be isolated by filtration following rubbing with 96% ethanol in a mortar. Yield 2.6 g, m.p. 116–122°C, $[\alpha]_D^{20}$ −46 (in water plus traces of NH$_3$). Recrystallization from water–ethanol gives 1.3 g of crystalline L-glucose, m.p. 142–144°C, $[\alpha]_D^{20}$ −50.3.

The addition of hydrogen cyanide to a ketose is also a quick process, resulting in the formation of a single epimer. 2-*C*-Hydroxymethyl-D-glucose **(10.4)** can be prepared by the catalytic hydrogenation of 2-*C*-hydroxymethyl-D-glucononitrile **(10.2)** as shown in Figure 1.10.

Preparation of 2-C-hydroxymethyl-D-glucose **(10.4)** *from D-fructose* **(10.1)**[10] D-Fructose (10 g) is dissolved in pure *N,N*-dimethylformamide (30 ml) at 50°C and after cooling to 10°C, 1 ml of triethylamine and 50 ml of anhydrous hydrogen cyanide are added. The mixture becomes slightly warmer during this operation,

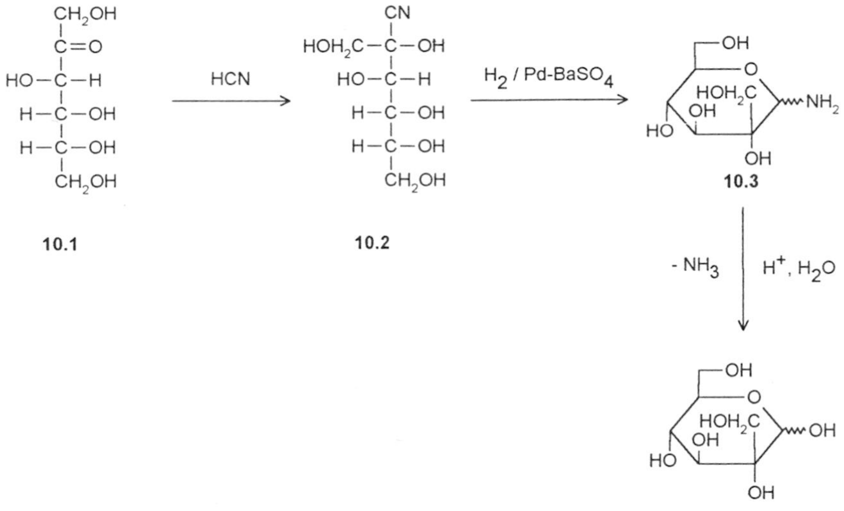

FIGURE 1.10

but no change in the color occurs. Upon storing at $-6°C$ for 5 h, the reaction mixture hardens to a colorless mass of crystals that is filtered, washed with cold ethanol and ether, and *dried at $-6°C$* in a desiccator over concentrated sulfuric acid and sodium hydroxide to furnish 8.7–10.5 g of colorless needles (76–91%), m.p. 105–110°C (dec.), $[\alpha]_D^{21}$ -3.3 ($c = 2.9$ in water. D-Fructose cyanohydrin can be stored for a longer period of time in a desiccator at $-6°C$. A mixture of PdO/ BaSO$_4$ catalyst[11] (30 g) and water (50 ml) is prehydrogenated, a solution of D-fructose cyanohydrin (10.5 g, 0.05 mol) in 0.5 N hydrochloric acid (100 ml) is added, and hydrogenation is continued at 1.32×10^{-3} torr for 25 min when the uptake of hydrogen has finished (1050 ml, ~0.047 mol). There is no HCN odor in the hydrogenated mixture. The catalyst is separated, and the colorless solution is diluted to 200 ml and poured onto a 3×40 cm column filled with Amberlite IR-120 (H$^+$) resin to bind ammonium ions and 1-deoxy-1-amino-2-C-hydroxymethyl-D-glucose. The column is washed with water until a sample of the eluate does not show positive Fehling reaction (eluate A). By elution with 1 N hydrochloric acid, 1-deoxy-1-amino-2-C-hydroxymethyl-D-glucose (**10.3**) is squeezed from the resin and the eluate is examined for ammonium chloride with the Nessler reagent; the ammonium salt is present in the eluate only after all of the produced sugar has been eluted (eluate B). Ammonium chloride is then eluted from the column with 4 N hydrochloric acid (eluate C). Evaporation of *eluate A* gives a colorless syrup (1.55 g) with $[\alpha]_D^{22}$ -92 ($c = 0.5$ in water), and on the basis of the specific optical rotation values of pure β-D-fructose ($[\alpha]_D^{22}$ -92) and α-2-C-hydroxymethyl-D-glucose ($[\alpha]_D^{22}$ $+42$) in water, the 2-C-hydroxymethyl-D-glucose content of the syrup is 92.5%, and the related value is 88.2% according to the Macleod method for the determination of aldoses. If the 2-C-hydroxymethyl-D-glucose content of eluate A is determined to be 90%, as an average, in the syrup, then eluate A provides 1.4 g of 2-C-hydroxymethyl-D-glucose (13.5%—calculated for 10.5 g of the starting D-fructose cyanohydrin) and 0.15 g (1.7%) of β-D-fructose. *Eluate B*, containing 1-amino-1-deoxy-2-C-hydroxymethyl-D-glucose, is concentrated to a 30-ml volume, and for a complete hydrolysis, it is boiled for 10 min. After dilution to 250 ml, ammonium chloride is separated by the application, again, a cation-exchange column (Amberlite IR-120, H$^+$). The column is washed with water until the eluate no longer reduces the Fehling solution (eluate D) and is then concentrated to a syrup. Ammonium chloride is washed down from the column with 4 N hydrochloric acid (eluate E). Evaporation of eluates C and E give 90% and 72%, respectively, of ammonium chloride.

Syrupy 2-*C*-hydroxymethyl-D-glucose (**10.4**) can be transformed into the easily crystallizable isopropylidene derivative whose hydrolysis readily gives the α anomer of 2-*C*-hydroxymethyl-D-glucose (m.p. 174–175°C).

Figure 1.11 shows the chain extension of 2-deoxy-D-ribose (**11.1**) and the details of the sequence of transformation of the individual, epimeric cyanohydrins, as well as the lactonization and reduction leading to aldoses— including the high-yield separation of the epimers by a simple crystallization and optimum conditions for the subsequent reduction (with sodium borohydride or sodium amalgam).[12]

Cyanohydrin synthesis from 2-deoxy-D-ribose[12] *3-Deoxy-D-ribono-1,4-lactone (11.2) and 3-deoxy-D-arabino-hexonic acid calcium salt (11.3):* In a 1-liter round-bottomed flask, 2.01 g of 97% NaCN and 1.49 g of NaOH are dissolved in water (186 ml) and the mixture is cooled down until freezing begins. A solution of 2-deoxy-D-ribose (5.0 g) in 0.2 M sodium hydrogen carbonate (186 ml) is added with stirring, and stirring is continued until complete dissolution occurs. (*Caution.* The operation should be carried out under a well-ventilated hood because of the evolution of ammonia.) This solution (which does not give a positive Fehling reaction) is passed through, in four portions, a (6.8 × 45 cm) column filled with Amberlite IR-120 (H$^+$) cation-exchange resin. The combined eluates and washings are concentrated under diminished pressure (bath temperature 60°C) to a pale-yellow syrup, which is then treated with dry ethanol (50 ml). Ethanol is distilled off *in vacuo,* and this operation is repeated with 50 and 25 ml of ethanol. The resulting syrup is diluted with acetone (25 ml) when 3-deoxy-D-*ribo*-hexono-1,4-lactone (**11.2**) is separated in the form of well-shaped octahedrons (yield 6.87 g), $[\alpha]_D^{20}$ +23.1 (in water). The mother liquor is concentrated *in vacuo,* and for complete removal of acetone, it is codistilled with a small volume of water. The syrupy residue is dissolved in water (60 ml), and calcium oxide is added until steady pink-colored reaction with phenolphthalein occurs. The excess calcium oxide is neutralized with a stream of carbon dioxide, and the solution is warmed to boil, filtered through a pad of Celite, and concentrated to a ~20-ml volume. The calcium salt (**11.3**) of 3-deoxy-D-*arabino*-hexonic acid {7.64 g, 24%, $[\alpha]_D^{20}$ −24 (c = 0.96 in water)} separates on standing at room temperature. The mother liquor of the first recrystallization is poured onto the top of a 3.4 × 37 cm column filled with Amberlite IR-120 (H$^+$) resin, and the eluate is concentrated to a syrup that is then codistilled with ethanol. The residue is dissolved in a small volume of acetone to effect separation of a second crop (6.7 g) of 3-deoxy-D-*ribo*-hexono-1,4-lactone. The combined crude lactone mixture is recrystallized from 17 parts of acetone and then from 0.5 part of water. The melting point of the pure lactone is 108–109°C, $[\alpha]_D^{20}$ +27 (c = 0.7 in water).

3-Deoxy-D-arabino-hexono-1,4-lactone (11.4) from the calcium salt of 3-deoxy-D-arabino-hexonic acid dihydrate (11.3) After 43 g of the calcium salt is dissolved in a sufficient volume of water, the solution is passed through a column filled with Amberlite IR-120 (H$^+$) cation-exchange resin. The eluate is concentrated to a syrup

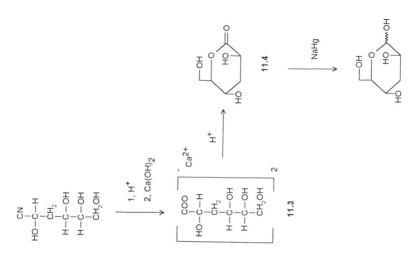

FIGURE 1.11

in vacuo, and traces of water are removed by codistillation with benzene (2 × 25 ml) and 1,4-dioxane (25 ml). Treatment of the residue with 1,4-dioxane (25 ml) gives 16.6 g (54%) of 3-deoxy-D-*arabino*-hexono-1,4-lactone, which is recrystallized from dry ethanol by the addition of pentane, m.p. 92–93°C, $[\alpha]_D^{20}$ +6.4 (*c* = 0.8 in water).

3-Deoxy-D-ribo-hexose (11.5)   First, 1.1 g of 3-deoxy-D-*ribo*-hexono-1,4-lactone (**11.2**) is dissolved in water (50 ml), sodium hydrogen oxalate (2 g) is added, then the solution is cooled to 0–5°C and a solution of sodium borohydride (0.5 g) in water (10 ml) is added under stirring while the pH is kept at 4.5–5 with oxalic acid. By further addition of oxalic acid the pH is decreased, thus degrading the excess of NaBH₄ at pH 3. The reaction mixture is concentrated to 15 ml, and for precipitation of the inorganic salts, it is diluted with methanol (50 ml). After filtration and concentration, the filtrate is passed through a 3 × 30-cm column filled with Amberlite IR-120 (H⁺) resin and the deionized eluate is freed from water by codistillation with benzene (50 ml). Then the residue is codistilled several times with a mixture of benzene (15 ml) and methanol (25 ml) until the flame probe is negative for boron. The material thus obtained is dissolved in 50 ml of water and deionized by passing through a 3 × 30-cm Duolite A-4 column, the eluate is concentrated, and 1 ml of dry ethanol is added. From the solution maintained at 5°C for a few days, crystals of the target sugar are separated (0.42 g, 38%, m.p. 102–104°C), these crystals are recrystallized from ethanol to obtain the pure, chromatographically homogeneous target compound (**11.5**) with m.p. 105–106°C and $[\alpha]_D^{20}$ +32 (*c* = 1 in water).

Several works report the application of sodium cyanide for the preparation of cyanohydrins. Two papers[13,14] deal with the synthesis of D-glucose and D-mannose starting from 2,3 : 4,5-di-*O*-isopropylidene-*aldehydo*-D-arabinose. For chain extension of 2,3 : 5,6-di-*O*-isopropylidene-D-mannofuranose, Fleet[15] applied 90°C reaction temperature.

If necessary, the reversible nitrile formation can be made irreversible with further, *in situ* reactions. An example of such a methodology is hydration with hydrogen peroxide,[16,17] as shown in Figure 1.12.

An additional methodology is based on the mesylation of the hydroxyl group ("cyano-mesylation"), which has been studied independently by two groups[18,19] for 1,2 : 3,4-di-*O*-isopropylidene-*α*-D-galactopyranos-6-ulose.

The cyanohydrin syntheses reported so far in the literature are summarized—in order of increasing length—in Table 1.6.

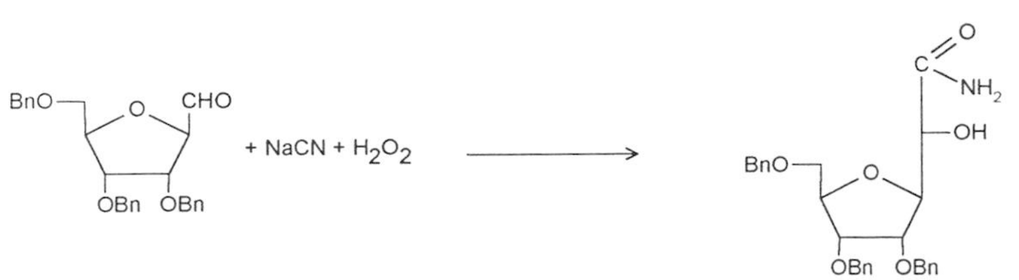

3,6-anhydro-4,5,7-tri-O-benzyl-D-*glycero*-D-*allo*-heptonamide

FIGURE I.12

TABLE 1.6 Previously Reported Cyanohydrin Syntheses

Starting saccharide	Product(s)	Ref(s).
D,L-Glyceraldehyde	A mixture of tetroses	20
D-Glyceraldehyde	D-Threose and D-erythrose	8,21–22
2,3-O-Isopropylidene-D,L-glyceraldehyde	A 3,4-O-isopropylidene-2-O-benzoyl derivative	23
D,L-Glyceraldehyde-3-phosphate	D,L-Erythrose-4-phosphate	24
D-Erythrose	D-Arabinose and D-ribose	25–27
D,L-Erythrose	1-^{14}C-D,L-Arabinose and 1-^{14}C-D,L-ribose	24
D-Threose	1-^{14}C-D-Xylose and 1-^{14}C-D-lyxose	26–29
D-Ribose	D-Allose and D-altrose	30–32
L-Ribose	L-Allose and D-altrose	33,34
L-Arabinose	L-Glucose and L-mannose	9,35,36
D-Arabinose	D-Glucose and D-mannose	9,36–43
	1-^{13}C-D-Glucose and 1-^{13}C-D-mannose	44
1-^{14}C-D-Arabinose	2-^{14}C-D-Glucose and 2-^{14}C-D-mannose	45
D-Xylose	D-Gulose and D-idose	7,46–47
1,2-O-Isopropylidene-D-xylo-pentodialdo-1,4-furanose	6-^{14}C-D-Glucose, 1,2-O-isopropylidene-β-L-*ido*-furanuronic acid, 1,2-O-isopropylidene-α-D-*gluco*-furanuronic acid, 6-^{13}C-D-glucose and 1,6-anhydro-6-^{13}C-β-L-*ido*-pyranose	53
D-Lyxose	1-^{14}C-D-Galactose and 1-^{14}C-D-talose	54,55
1-^{14}C-D-Lyxose	2-^{14}C-D-Galactose	45
D-Allose	D-*glycero*-D-*allo*-Heptose and D-*glycero*-D-*altro*-heptose	56
D-Altrose	D-*glycero*-D-*manno*-Heptose and D-*glycero*-D-*gluco*-heptose	57
D-Glucose	D-*glycero*-D-*gulo*-Heptose and D-*glycero*-D-*ido*-heptose	58–63
D-Galactose	D-*glycero*-L-*manno*-Heptose and D-*glycero*-L-*gluco*-heptose	64–68
D-Mannose	D-*glycero*-D-*galacto*-Heptose and D-*glycero*-D-*talo*-heptose	69–76

27

REFERENCES TO SECTION 1.2.1

1. *Houben-Weyl, Methoden der Organischen Chemie,* Vol. 8, p. 274 (1952); Vol. 7/2b, p. 1983 (1976); Vol. E 5, p. 1413 (1985); H. Krauch and W. Kunz, *Namenreaktionen der Organischen Chemie—Ein Beitrag zur Terminologie der Organischen Chemie, Biochemie und Theoretischen Organischen Chemie,* 2nd rev. ed. p. 253, 476, 477. A. Hüthig Verl., 1962; C. S. Hudson, *Adv. Carbohydr. Chem.* **1,** 1 (1945); J. D. Morrison and H. S. Mosher, *Asymmetric Organic Reactions,* Chapter 4. Prentice Hall, Englewood Cliffs, NJ., 1971; J. Stanek, J. Kocourek, M. Černy, and J. Pacák, *The Monosaccharides,* p. 144. Publ. House Czech. Acad. Sci., Prague, 1963; Z. Pakulski and A. Zamojski, *Pol. J. Chem.* **69,** 509 (1995).
2. R. Varma and D. French, *Carbohydr. Res.* **25,** 71 (1972); A. S. Serianni, H. A. Nunez, and R. Barker, *J. Org. Chem.* **45,** 3329 (1980); R. M. Blazer and T. W. Whaley, *J. Am. Chem. Soc.* **102,** 5082 (1980).
3. J. G. Maltby, *J. Chem. Soc.,* p. 2769 (1929)
4. H. S. Isbell, J. V. Karabinos, H. L. Frush, N. B. Holt, A. Schwebel, and T. T. Galkowski, *J. Res. Natl. Bur. Stand.* **48,** 163 (1952).
5. F. Micheel, *Chemie der Zucker und Polysaccharide,* p. 170. Geest & Portig, Leipzig, 1956.
6. W. Militzer, *Arch. Biochem.* **21,** 143 (1949).
7. R. K. Hulyalkar and J. K. N. Jones, *Can. J. Chem.* **41,** 1898 (1963).
8. A. S. Serianni, H. A. Nunn, and R. Barker, *Carbohydr. Res.* **72,** 71 (1979); A. S. Serianni, H. A. Nunez, M. L. Hayes, and R. Barker in *Methods in Enzymology,* (W. A. Wood, ed.), Vol. 89, Part D, p. 64. Academic Press, New York, 1982.
9. R. Kuhn and P. Klesse, *Chem. Ber.* **91,** 1989 (1958).
10. R. Kuhn and H. Grassner, *Justus Liebigs Ann. Chem.* **612,** 55 (1958).
11. R. Kuhn and H. J. Haas, *Angew. Chem.* **67,** 785 (1955).
12. H. B. Wood, Jr. and H. G. Fletcher, Jr., *J. Org. Chem.* **26,** 1969 (1961).
13. M. Watanabe and N. Tada, Takeda Chem. Ind., Jpn. Kokai Tokkyo Koho, JP 01,139,593 (1989); *Chem. Abstr.* **112,** 36371c (1990).
14. S. Nishimura and N. Hayashi, *Chem. Lett.,* p. 1815 (1991).
15. I. Bruce, G. W. J. Fleet, A. Girdhar, M. Haraldsson, J. M. Peach, and D. J. Watkin, *Tetrahedron* **46,** 19 (1990); A. R. Beecham, I. Bruce, S. Choi, O. Doherty, A. J. Fairbanks, G. W. J. Fleet, B. M. Skead, J. M. Peach, J. Sanders, and D. J. Watkin, *Tetrahedron: Asymmetry* **2,** 883 (1991); C. J. F. Bichard, A. J. Fairbanks, G. W. J. Fleet, N. G. Ramsden, K. Vogt, O. Doherty, L. Pearrce, and D. J. Watkin, *Tetrahedron: Asymmetry* **2,** 901 (1991).
16. G. Trummlitz and J. G. Moffatt, *J. Org. Chem.* **38,** 1841 (1973).
17. M. J. Robins and J. M. R. Parker, *Can. J. Chem.* **61,** 312 (1983).
18. H. Hashimoto, K. Asano, F. Fujii, and J. Yoshimura, *Carbohydr. Res.* **104,** 87 (1982).
19. S. Czernecki and J.-M. Valéry, *J. Carbohydr. Chem.* **5,** 235 (1986).
20. H. Kiliani, *Ber. Dtsch. Chem. Ges.* **21,** 915 (1888).
21. A. S. Serianni and R. Barker, *Can. J. Chem.* **57,** 3166 (1979).
22. A. S. Serianni, E. L. Clark, and R. Barker, *Carbohydr. Res.* **72,** 79 (1979).
23. R. Chenevert, R. Plante, and N. Voyer, *Synth. Commun.* **13,** 403 (1983).
24. A. S. Serianni, J. Pierce, and R. Barker, *Biochemistry* **18,** 1192 (1979).
25. S. David and J. Renaut, *Bull. Soc. Chim. Fr.,* p. 61 (1954).
26. P. C. Kline and S. Serianni, *J. Am. Chem. Soc.* **112,** 7373 (1990).
27. H. L. Frush and H. S. Isbell, *J. Res. Natl. Bur. Stand.* **51,** 307 (1953).
28. A. C. Neish, *Can. J. Chem.* **32,** 334 (1954).
29. H. S. Isbell, H. L. Frush, and N. B. Holt, *J. Res. Natl. Bur. Stand.* **53,** 325 (1954).
30. P. A. Levene and W. A. Jacobs, *Ber. Dtsch. Chem. Ges.* **43,** 3141 (1910).
31. F. P. Phelps and F. Bates, *J. Am. Chem. Soc.* **56,** 1250 (1934).

32. M. Steiger and T. Reichstein, *Helv. Chim. Acta* **19**, 184 (1936).
33. W. C. Austin and F. L. Humoller, *J. Am. Chem. Soc.* **55**, 2167 (1933).
34. W. C. Austin and F. L. Humoller, *J. Am. Chem. Soc.* **56**, 1153 (1933).
35. E. Fischer, *Ber. Dtsch. Chem. Ges.* **23**, 2611 (1890).
36. M. L. Wolfrom and H. B. Wood, *J. Am. Chem. Soc.* **73**, 730 (1951).
37. C. S. Hudson, *J. Am. Chem. Soc.*. **73**, 4489 (1951).
38. H. Kiliani, *Ber. Dtsch. Chem. Ges.* **19**, 3029 (1886).
39. H. Kiliani, *Ber. Dtsch. Chem. Ges.* **20**, 282 (1877).
40. H. Kiliani, *Ber. Dtsch. Chem. Ges.* **20**, 339 (1887).
41. H. G. Hers, J. Edelman, and V. Ginsburg, *J. Am. Chem. Soc.* **76**, 5160 (1954).
42. U. Drehmann and K. Uhlig, *J. Prakt. Chem.* **8**, 33 (1959).
43. D.E. Koshland and F. H. Westheimer, *J. Am. Chem. Soc.* **72**, 3383 (1950).
44. T. E. Walker, C. J. Unkefer, and D. S. Ehler, *J. Carbohydr. Chem.* **7**, 115 (1988).
45. H. S. Isbell, H. L. Frush, and R. Schaffer, *J. Res. Natl. Bur. Stand.* **54**, 201 (1955).
46. E. Fischer and I. W. Fay, *Ber. Dtsch. Chem. Ges.* **28**, 1975 (1895).
47. E. Fischer and R. Stahel, *Ber. Dtsch. Chem. Ges.* **24**, 528 (1891).
48. J. C. Sowden, *J. Am. Chem. Soc.* **74**, 4377 (1952).
49. R. Schaffer and H. S. Isbell, *J. Am. Chem. Soc.* **79**, 3867 (1957).
50. M. J. King-Morris, P. B. Bondo, R. A. Mrowca, and A. S. Serianni, *Carbohydr. Res.* **175**, 49 (1988).
51. M. Taniguchi, R. F. Nystrom, and K. L. Rinehart, Jr., *Carbohydr. Res.* **109**, 161 (1987).
52. R. Schaffer and H. S. Isbell, *J. Res. Natl. Bur. Stand.* **56**, 191 (1956).
53. D. L. Williams and T. M. Whaley, *J. Labelled Compd. Radiopharm.* **19**, 669 (1982).
54. H. S. Isbell, H. L. Frush, and N. B. Holt, *J. Res. Natl. Bur. Stand.* **53**, 217 (1954).
55. J. J. Topper and D. Stetten, *J. Biol. Chem.* **193**, 149 (1951).
56. J. W. Pratt and N. K. Richtmyer, *J. Am. Chem. Soc.* **77**, 6326 (1955).
57. D. A. Rosenfeld, N. K. Richtmyer, and C. S. Hudson, *J. Am. Chem. Soc.* **73**, 4907 (1951).
58. M. L. Wolfrom and H. B. Wood, *J. Am. Chem. Soc.* **73**, 2933 (1951).
59. E. Fischer, *Justus Liebigs Ann. Chem.* **270**, 64 (1892).
60. H. S. Isbell, *J. Am. Chem. Soc.* **56**, 2789 (1934).
61. C. S. Hudson, O. Hartley, and C. B. Purves, *J. Am. Chem. Soc.* **56**, 1248 (1934).
62. H. Kiliani, *Ber. Dtsch. Chem. Ges.* **20**, 339 (1887).
63. N. K. Richtmyer, *Methods Carbohydr. Chem.* **1**, 160 (1962).
64. E. Fischer, *Justus Liebigs Ann. Chem.* **288**, 139 (1895).
65. R. M. Hann, A. T. Merill, and C. S. Hudson, *J. Am. Chem. Soc.* **57**, 2100 (1935).
66. R. M. Hann and C. S. Hudson, *J. Am. Chem. Soc.* **59**, 548 (1937).
67. H. Kiliani, *Ber. Dtsch. Chem. Ges.* **21**, 915 (1888).
68. H. Kiliani, *Ber. Dtsch. Chem. Ges.* **22**, 521 (1889).
69. E. M. Montgomery and C. S. Hudson, *J. Am. Chem. Soc.* **64**, 247 (1942).
70. J. V. Karabinos, R. M. Hann, and C. S. Hudson, *J. Am. Chem. Soc.* **75**, 4320 (1953).
71. Z. J. Allan, *Collect. Czech. Chem. Commun.* **19**, 1242 (1954); *Chem. Listy* **48**, 873 (1954).
72. E. Fischer and J. Hirschberger, *Ber. Dtsch. Chem. Ges.* **22**, 365 (1889).
73. G. Pierce, *J. Biol. Chem.* **23**, 327 (1915).
74. V. Ettel, *Collect. Czech. Chem. Commun.* **4**, 504 (1932).
75. E. Fischer and F. Passmore, *Ber. Dtsch. Chem. Ges.* **23**, 2226 (1890).
76. H. S. Isbell, *J. Res. Natl. Bur. Stand.* **20**, 97 (1938).
77. F. B. La Forge, *J. Biol. Chem.* **41**, 251 (1920).
78. H. S. Isbell, *J. Res. Natl. Bur. Stand.* **19**, 639 (1937).
79. E. Zissis, N. K. Richtmyer, and C. S. Hudson, *J. Am. Chem., Soc.* **72**, 3882 (1950).
80. W. Mayer and B. Tollens, *Ber. Dtsch. Chem. Ges.* **40**, 2434 (1907).
81. E. Votocek, *Collect. Czech. Chem. Commun.* **6**, 528 (1934).
82. E. Fischer and O. Piloty, *Ber. Dtsch. Chem. Ges.* **23**, 3102 (1890).

83. E. Fischer and R. S. Morrell, *Ber. Dtsch. Chem. Ges.* **27**, 382 (1894).
84. J. R. Snyder and A. S. Serianni, *Carbohydr. Res.* **163**, 169 (1987).
85. P. A. Levene and J. Compton, *J. Biol. Chem.* **111**, 325, 335 (1935).
86. P. A. Levene and A. L. Raymond, *J. Biol. Chem.* **102**, 317 (1933).
87. R. M. Hann, A. T. Merrill, and C. S. Hudson, *J. Am. Chem. Soc.* **66**, 1912 (1944).
88. W. D. Maclay, R. M. Hann, and C. S. Hudson, *J. Am. Chem. Soc.* **60**, 1035 (1938).
89. R. M. Hann, W. D. Maclay, A. E. Knauf, and C. S. Hudson, *J. Am. Chem. Soc.* **61**, 1268 (1939).
90. R. M. Hann, A. T. Merrill, and C. S. Hudson, *J. Am. Chem. Soc.* **66**, 1912 (1944).
91. I. Dyong, *Carbohydr. Res.* **11**, 428 (1969).
92. K. Dziewiszek and A. Zamojski, *Carbohydr. Res.* **150**, 163 (1986).
93. A. S. Serianni and R. Barker, in *Isotopes in the Physical and Biochemical Sciences,* (B. Buncel and J. Jones, eds.), p. 211. Elsevier, Amsterdam, 1987.
94. L. H. Philippe, *Ann. Chim. Phys.* [8] **26**, 289 (1912).
95. H. Kiliani, *Ber. Dtsch. Chem. Ges.* **19**, 221 (1886).
96. R. Kuhn and H. Grassner, *Justus Liebigs Ann. Chem.* **612**, 55 (1958).
97. A. J. Fairbanks and G. W. J. Fleet, *Tetrahedron* **51**, 3881 (1995); A. J. Bell, R. J. Nash, and G. W. J. Fleet, *Tetrahedron: Asymmetry* **7**, 595 (1996).
98. L. Zervas and P. Sessler, *Ber. Dtsch. Chem. Ges.* **66**, 1698 (1933).
99. O. T. Schmidt and C. C. Weber-Molster, *Justus Liebigs Ann. Chem.* **515**, 43 (1934).
100. H. Kiliani, *Ber. Dtsch. Chem. Ges.* **18**, 3066 (1885).
101. H. Kiliani, *Ber. Dtsch. Chem. Ges.* **55**, 2817 (1922).
102. H. Kiliani, *Ber. Dtsch. Chem. Ges.* **61**, 1155 (1928).
103. H. Kiliani and G. Düll, *Ber. Dtsch. Chem. Ges.* **23**, 449 (1890).
104. R. J. Woods and A. C. Neish, *Can. J. Chem.* **31**, 471 (1953).
105. P. A. J. Gorin and A. S. Perlin, *Can. J. Chem.* **36**, 480 (1958).
106. I. Dijong and U. Wittkötter, *Chem. Ber.* **104**, 2090 (1971).
107. H. Fritz, J. Lehmann, and P. Schlesselmann, *Carbohydr. Res.* **74**, 309 (1979).
108. R. G. Ault, D. K. Baird, H. C. Carrington, W. N. Haworth, R. Herbert, E. L. Hirst, E. G. V. Percival, F. Smith, and M. Stacey, *J. Chem. Soc.*, p. 1419 (1933).
109. D. K. Baird, W. N. Haworth, R. W. Herbert, E. L. Hirst, F. Smith, and M. Stacey, *J. Chem. Soc.*, p. 62 (1934).
110. T. Reichstein, A. Grüssner, and R. Oppenauer, *Helv. Chim. Acta* **16**, 1019 (1933).
111. K. J. Hamilton and F. Smith, *J. Am. Chem. Soc.* **74**, 5162 (1952).
112. T. Reichstein, A. Grüssner, and R. Oppenauer, *Helv. Chim. Acta* **17**, 510 (1934).
113. L. Salomon, J. J. Burns, and C. G. King, *J. Am. Chem. Soc.* **74**, 5161 (1952).
114. W. N. Haworth, E. L. Hirst, J. K. N. Jones, and F. Smith, *J. Chem. Soc.*, p. 1192 (1934).
115. W. N. Haworth, E. L. Hirst, and J. K. N. Jones, *J. Chem. Soc.* p. 549 (1937).
116. T. Reichstein, L. Schwarz, and A. Grüssner, *Helv. Chim. Acta* **18**, 353 (1935).
117. M. Steiger, *Helv. Chim. Acta* **18**, 1252 (1935).
118. E. Votocek and S. Malachta, *Collect. Czech. Chem. Commun.* **3**, 265 (1931).
119. M. B. Perry and A. C. Webb, *Can. J. Chem.* **47**, 2893 (1969).

1.2.2. Synthesis of Acid Derivatives by Means of Nucleophilic Substitution

The reaction involving conversion of glycosyl halides with reagents such as mercuric cyanide or trimethylsilyl cyanide is used quite often and is unambiguously regarded as a chain elongation procedure since the resulting anhydroaldononitriles, as well as monosubstituted alditol derivatives susceptible to nucleophilic substitution, afford the respective 2-deoxy-

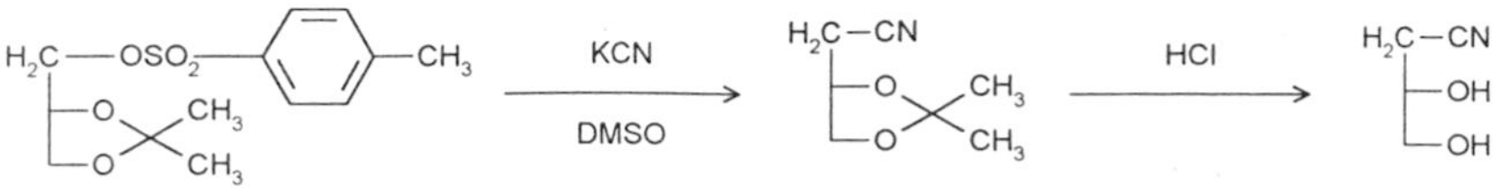

FIGURE 1.13

aldononitriles extended by one carbon atom in the chain. The most simple representative of this group, 2-deoxy-3,4-O-isopropylidene-D-*glycero*-tetrononitrile (**13.2**), was prepared[1] from 2,3-O-isopropylidene-1-O-(p-tolylsulfonyl)-D-glycerol (**13.1**) with excess of the reagents potassium cyanide, sodium iodide, and sodium hydrogen carbonate. Then the resulting syrupy, distillable product (**13.2**) was subjected to deprotection with hydrogen chloride in methanol, furnishing 2-deoxy-D-*glycero*-tetrononitrile (**13.3**) (Fig. 1.13):

> *Preparation of 2-deoxy-*D-glycero-*tetrononitrile (13.3) from 2,3-O-isopropylidene-1-O-(p-tolylsulfonyl)-*D-glycerol *(13.1)*[1] A suspension of **13.1** (1.69 g, 5.9 mmol), dry KCN (1.92 g, 29.5 mmol), NaI (4.43 g, 29.5 mmol) and NaHCO₃ (4.96 g, 5.9 mmol) in dry dimethylsulfoxide (Me₂SO) (distilled from CaH₂) is stirred at 80°C for 2 h in the absence of moisture. After cooling, the reaction mixture is poured into water (230 ml) and extracted with ether (4 × 50 ml). The combined organic extract is washed with aqueous NaHCO₃ (2 × 30 ml), dried (MgSO₄), and evaporated under reduced pressure. The crude product (0.636 g) is purified by column chromatography (eluant CHCl₃) on Kieselgel (30 g). Evaporation of the olive-green eluate gives 0.543 g of **13.2**, b.p. 60°C (133 Pa), $[\alpha]_D^{25}$ −5.44 (c = 9.4 in CHCl₃). A solution of nitrile **13.2** (0.54 g, 3.83 mmol) in dry methanol (105 ml) is cooled to 0°C, 1.87 M HCl in methanol (2.15 ml) is added with stirring, and the mixture is refrigerated (7°C) for 20–24 h. It is cooled to 0°C, dry ammonia gas is passed through the solution until alkaline (for litmus paper), and the solvent is evaporated. The residue is dissolved in acetone (7 ml), NH₄Cl is filtered off and washed with acetone (4 ml), and the combined filtrate is evaporated under diminished pressure. The residual syrupy **13.3** {(0.348 g, 90%), $[\alpha]_D^{24}$ +20.58 (c = 6.5 in EtOH)} is not further purified.

A similar result was obtained[2] with 2,4-di-O-ethylidene-1-iodo-D-erythritol (**14.1**) in which treatment with an equimolar quantity of sodium cyanide (Fig. 1.14) gave rise to 2-deoxy-3,5-O-ethylidene-D-ribononitrile (**14.2**), whose catalytic hydrogenation afforded 2-deoxy-D-ribose (**14.3**).

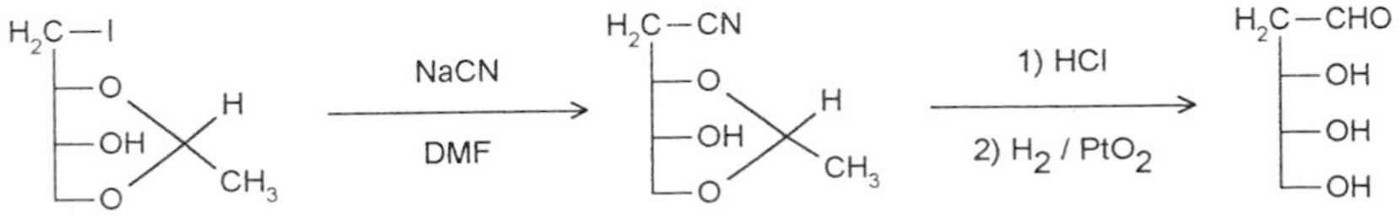

FIGURE 1.14

This procedure was found suitable for preparation of 1-^{14}C-labeled 2-deoxy-D-ribose, as well.[2]

An analogous procedure, involving the reaction of 2,3:4,5-di-*O*-isopropylidene-1-*O*-(*p*-tolylsulfonyl)-D-arabinitol (**15.1**) with sodium cyanide, followed by reduction of the resulting 2-deoxy-3,4:5,6-di-*O*-isopropylidene-D-*arabino*-hexononitrile (**15.2**) with diisobutyl aluminium hydride (Fig. 1.15), allowed the preparation[3] of 3,4:5,6-di-*O*-isopropylidene-2-deoxy-D-*arabino*-hexose (**15.3**), thus offering a convenient route to 2-deoxy-D-*arabino*-hexose. Functionalized derivatives of this latter sugar have served as key intermediates in syntheses of the aminodeoxyhexose components of various antibiotics.[4]

A similar extension can also be executed at the other, nonreducing end of the carbon chain of partially protected aldose derivatives. Thus, primary sulfonates and terminal anhydro derivatives have been converted with alkali cyanides into the corresponding deoxyurononitriles extended with one carbon atom in the chain. In the case of the anhydro sugar **16.1** (Fig. 1.16), water was found the best solvent to prepare[5] the heptofuranurononitrile **16.2**.

> *Preparation of 1,2-O-isopropylidene-6-deoxy-α-D-gluco-heptofuranurononitrile* (**16.2**)[5]   A mixture of 1,2-*O*-isopropylidene-5,6-anhydro-α-D-glucofuranose (**16.1**)

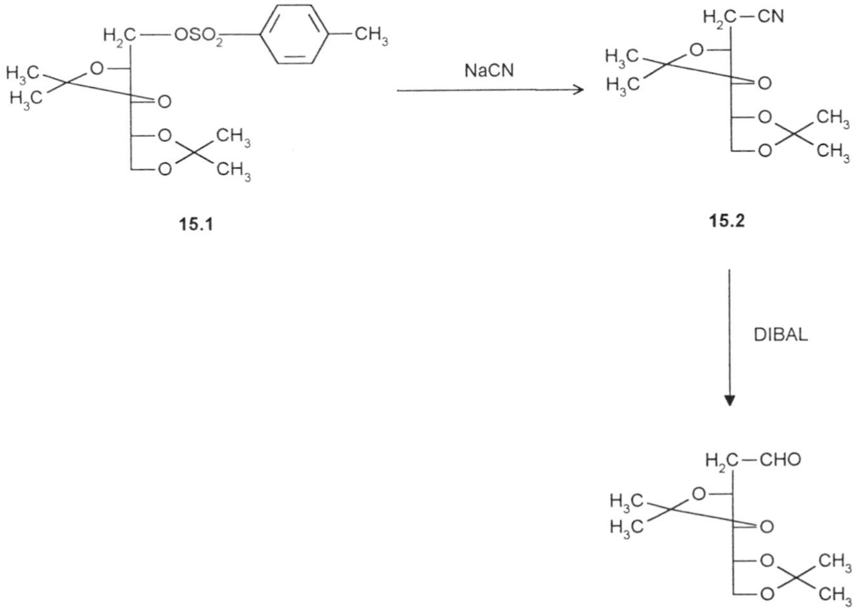

FIGURE 1.15

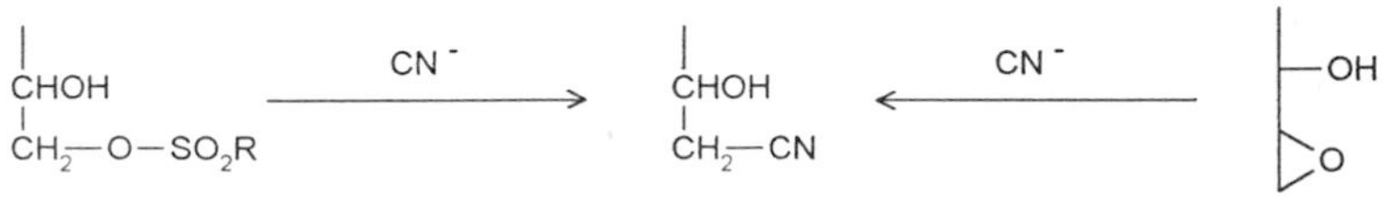

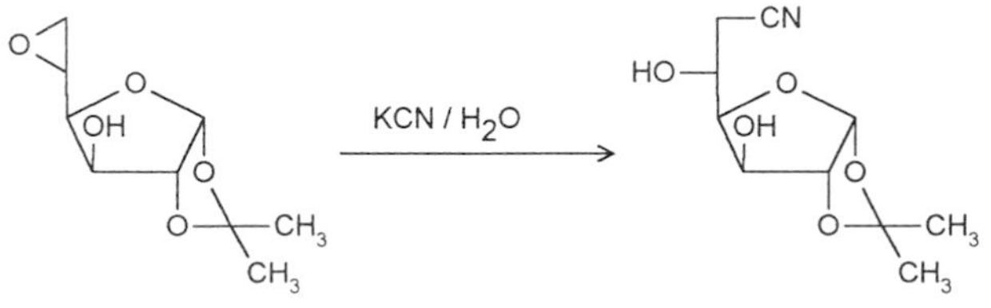

16.1   16.2

FIGURE 1.16

(6.6 g, 0.033 mol), KCN (3 g) and $MgSO_4 \times 6H_2O$ (6 g) in water (15 ml) is stirred at room temperature for 24 h. It is then filtered, the filtrate is evaporated, and the residue is taken up with $CHCl_3$. Following filtration, the organic solution is dried, decolorized with carbon, and concentrated. Addition of cyclohexane resulted in the crystallization of **16.2** (5.4 g, 72%), m.p. 111°C.

For the conversion of primary tosylates into the respective nitriles, again an excess of potassium cyanide should be used. When preparing 4,6-O-benzylidene-2-deoxy-L-galactononitrile (**17.3**) from 1,3-O-benzylidene-5-O-(p-tolylsulfonyl)-L-arabinitol (**17.1**), investigators first observed[6] the formation of an anhydro compound (**17.2**) (Fig. 1.17), whose reaction with potassium cyanide gives rise to the nitrile **17.3** with excellent yield.

Preparation of 4,6-O-benzylidene-2-deoxy-L-galactononitrile (17.3) from 17.1[6]   A solution of 1,3-O-benzylidene-5-O-(p-tolylsulfonyl)-L-arabinitol (**17.1**) (50 g) and KCN (16.5 g, 2 mol) in methanol (300 ml) is kept at room temperature

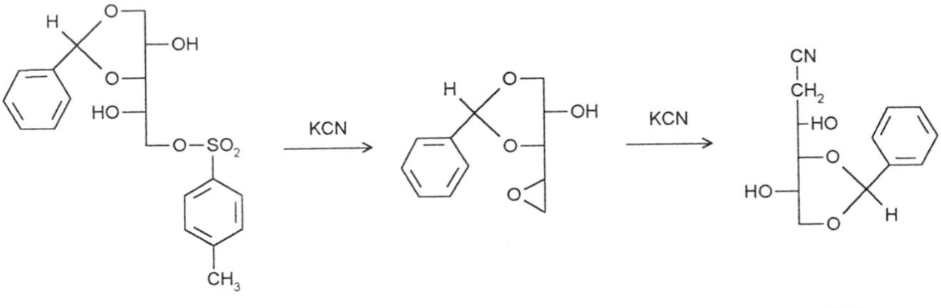

17.1   17.2   17.3

FIGURE 1.17

for 2 days and then equilibrated with ~7.5 ml of acetic acid. Potassium tosylate is filtered off and washed with methanol (100 ml), the combined filtrate is evaporated to dryness, and the residue is recrystallized from water (70 ml), to obtain **17.3** (29.4 g, 93%), m.p. 129°C. After repeated recrystallization, the pure product has m.p. 133°C, $[\alpha]_D^{20}$ +25.5 (c = 2.2 in pyridine).

Functionalization of the terminal hydroxyl group and chain extension with alkali cyanide can be conveniently executed in a one-pot operation. For example, methyl 2,3,4-tri-*O*-acetyl-6-deoxy-α-D-*gluco*-heptopyranuronononitrile (**18.2**) was readily obtained[7] from the corresponding C-6 hydroxy compound: methyl 2,3,4-tri-*O*-acetyl-α-D-glucopyranoside (**18.1**) according to a simple procedure shown in Figure 1.18.

> *Preparation of methyl 2,3,4-tri-O-acetyl-6-deoxy-α-D-*gluco-*heptopyranurononitrile (**18.2**) from (**18.1**)*[7] A solution of methyl 2,3,4-tri-*O*-acetyl-α-D-glucopyranoside (**18.1**) (9.6 g, 0.03 mol) and triphenylphosphine (7.9 g, 0.03 mol) in CCl₄ is refluxed for 15 min and diluted with Me₂SO (100 ml). The volatile components are then removed by distillation from a steam bath, so that the volume of the distillate is ~45 ml in the collector flask. Then, NaCN (2.5 g) is added to the residual mixture and the solution is warmed for 1.5 h. It is then poured into water (~800 ml) and kept at 25°C. The precipitated solid is filtered off, washed with cold water several times, and dissolved in hot methanol. The solution is filtered while hot and concentrated, and the residue is recrystallized from methanol. The crude product (4.5 g) is dissolved in CHCl₃, and petroleum ether is added until separation of crystals is observed. The product **18.2** has m.p. 132–133°C, $[\alpha]_D^{18}$ +147 (c = 0.7 in CHCl₃).

The 2-deoxyaldononitrile derivatives prepared from suitably functionalized monosaccharides with potassium cyanide are listed in Table 1.7.[8-18]

An alternative, but less frequently utilized route to related extended-chain 2-deoxyaldononitriles is based on the raction of aldose diethyl dithioacetals with a 2.5 molar excess of *in situ*–generated ICN to afford[19] a diastereoisomeric mixture of 2-ethylthio-2-deoxyaldononitriles elongated by one carbon atom (Fig. 1.19). Then chemoselective reduction of the ethylthio group over Raney nickel catalyst allowed the isolation of the target 2-deoxyaldononitriles.

Finally, the products obtained on chain extension with nitromethane (see Section 1.2.3) are also suitable for preparation of aldonoritriles elongated by one carbon atom in the sugar chain, when the saccharide carrying the introduced β-nitroethanol unit is subjected to the reaction sequence

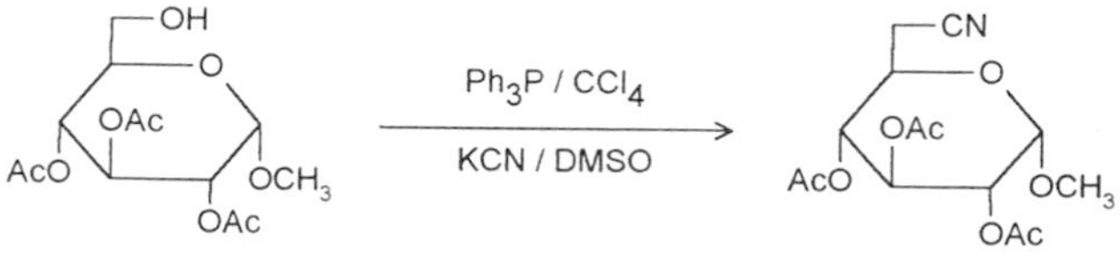

FIGURE 1.18

TABLE 1.7 2-Deoxycarbononitriles Derived from Monosaccharides by Treatment with Potassium Cyanide

Educt	Product	Yield (%)	M.p. (°C)	$[\alpha]_D$	Ref(s).
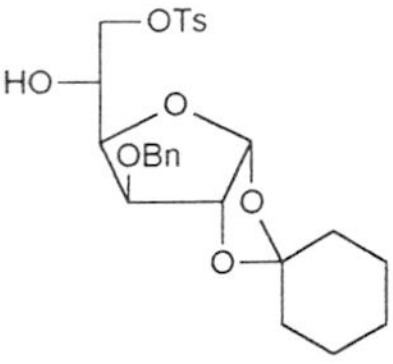	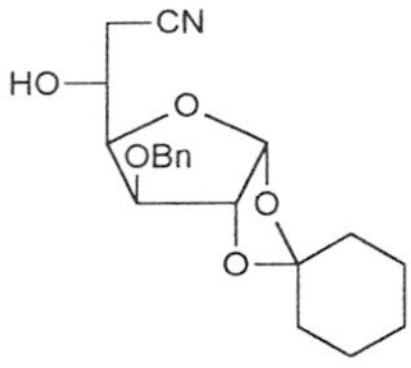	45	syrup	—	8
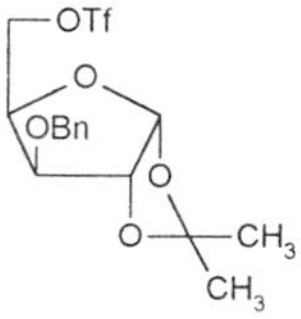	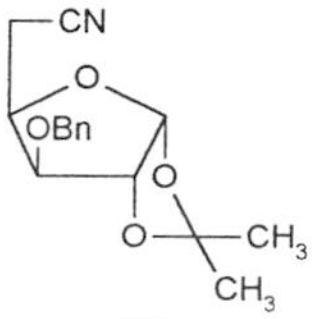	96	—	—	9
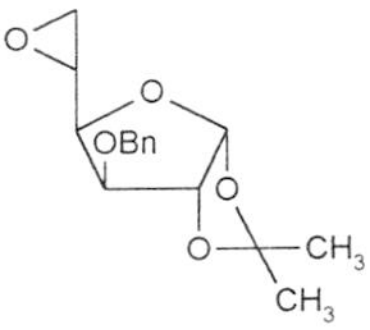	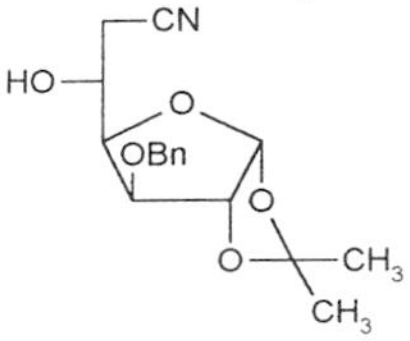	90	syrup	−62.4 (c = 0.75, CHCl₃)	5
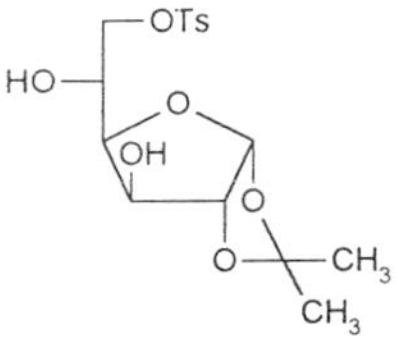	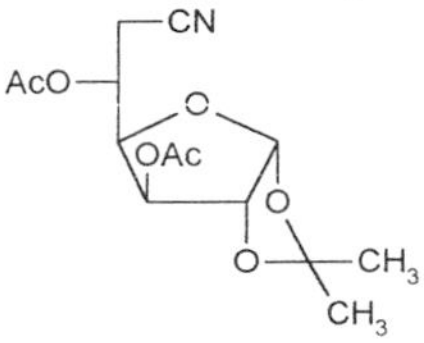	76	129	+4.3 (c = 3, pyridine)	10
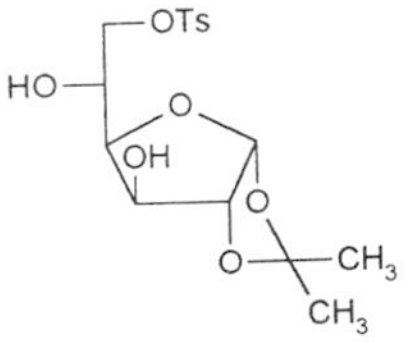	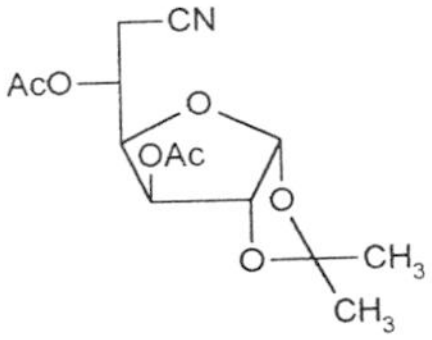	—	152	+12.9 (c = 2, pyridine)	10
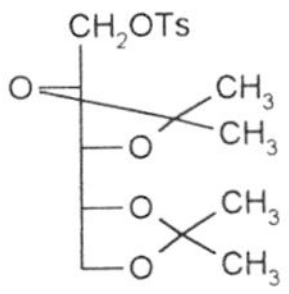	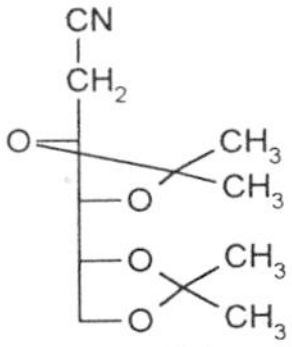	21	syrup	—	3
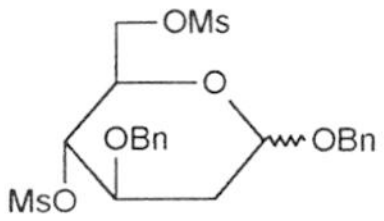	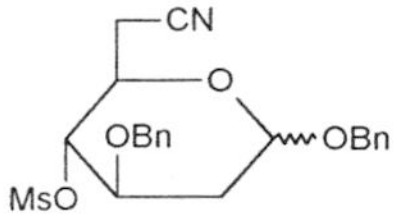	—	—	—	11
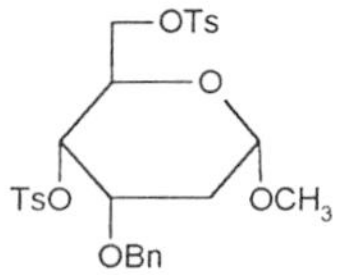	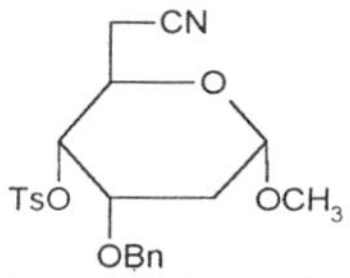	—	—	—	11

(continues)

TABLE I.7 (*continued*)

Educt	Product	Yield (%)	M.p. (°C)	$[\alpha]_D$	Ref(s).
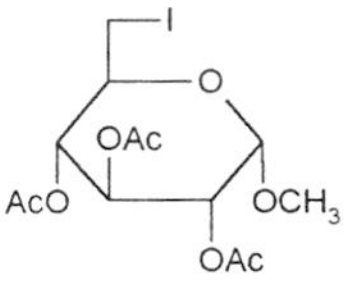	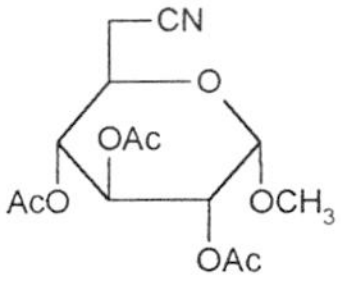	51	135–135.5	+139 (c = 1.88, CHCl₃)	12
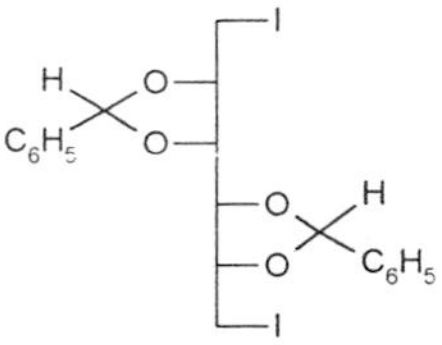	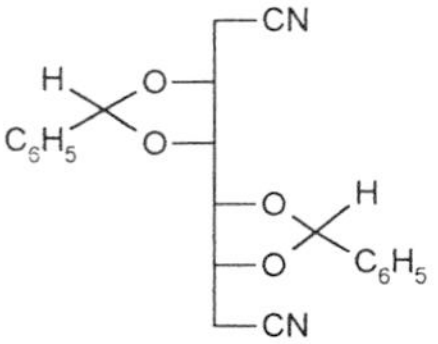	54	204–6	+82 (c = 0.45, CHCl₃)	12
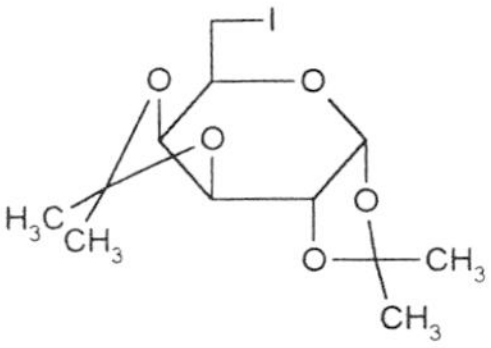	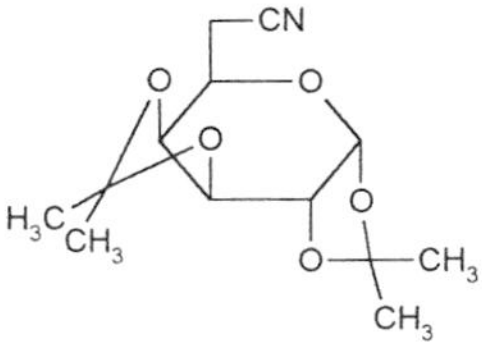	28	61–63	−67.7 (c = 0.85, CHCl₃)	12
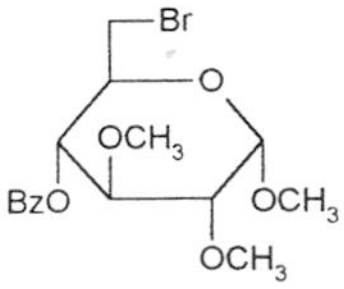	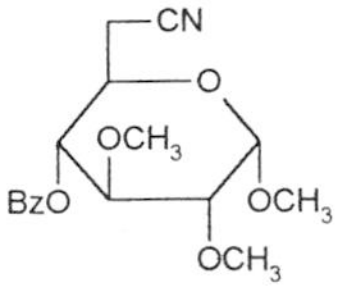	75	syrup	+44 (c = 11, CHCl₃)	13
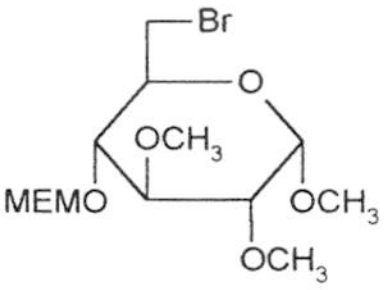	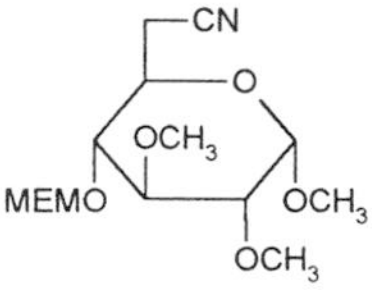	81	syrup	+168 (c = 0.3, CHCl₃)	13
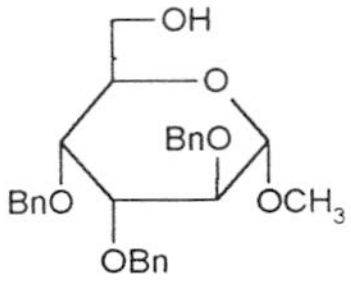	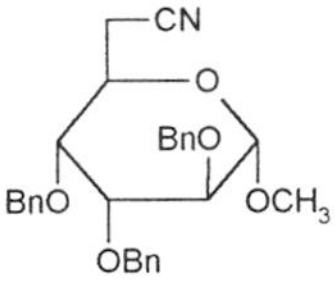	—	syrup	+85 (c = 1.6, CHCl₃)	14
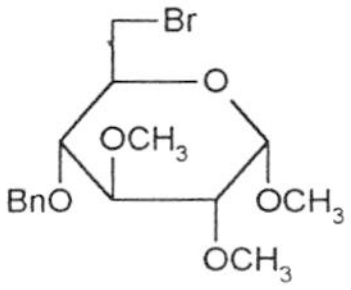	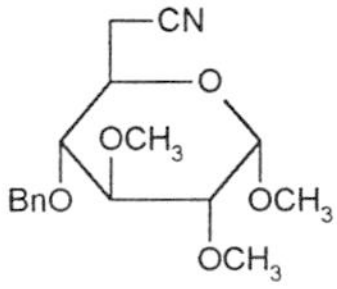	78	91–93	+152 (c = 1, CHCl₃)	13
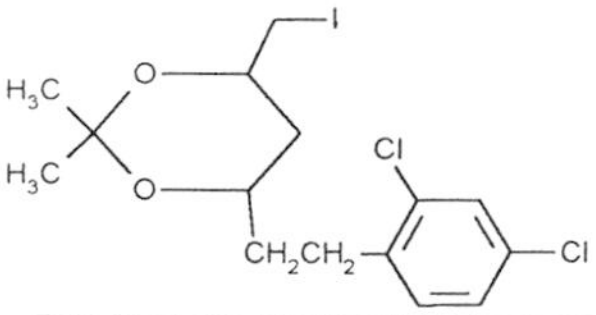	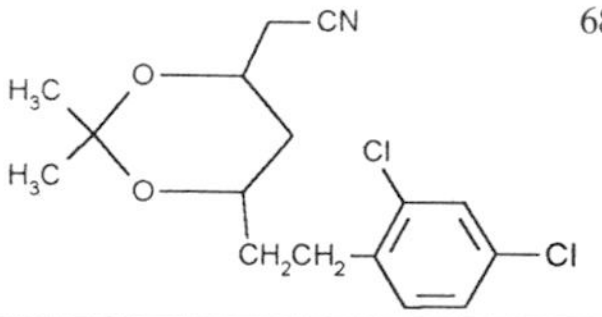	68	syrup	+134.7 (c = 0.1, CHCl₃)	15

(*continues*)

TABLE I.7 (*continued*)

Educt	Product	Yield (%)	M.p. (°C)	$[\alpha]_D$	Ref(s).
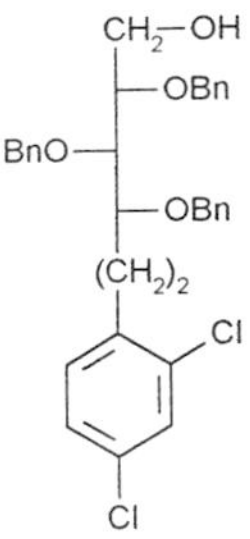	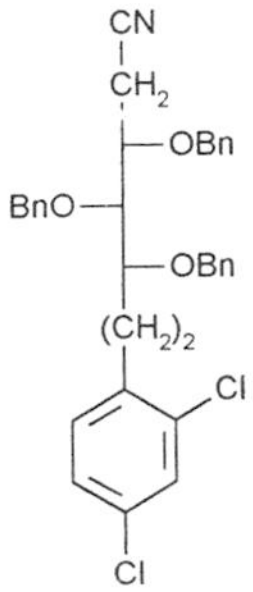	28	syrup	—	14
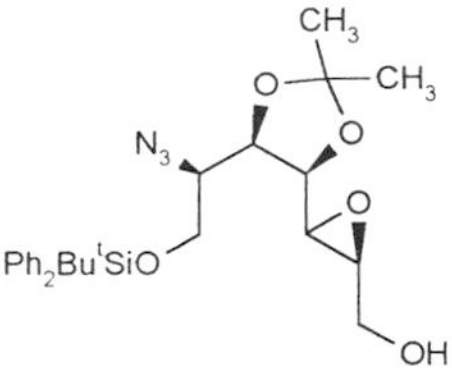	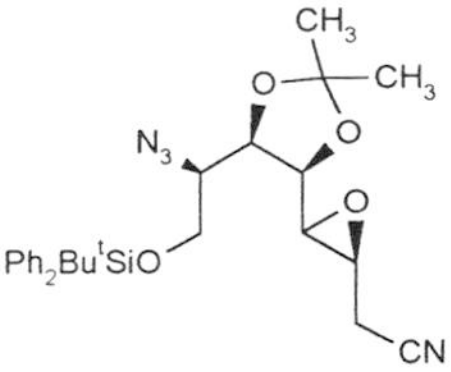	60	syrup	−30.8 (c = 0.40, CHCl₃)	17
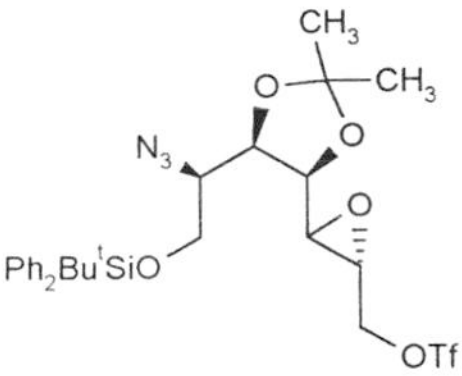	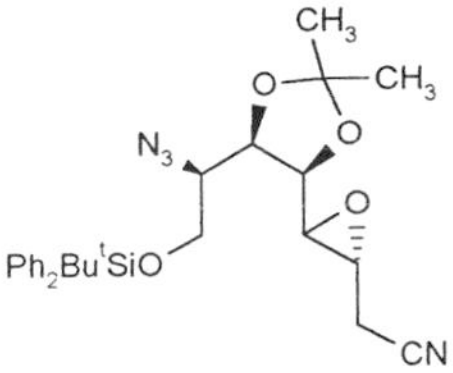	63	syrup	−15.2 (c = 1, CHCl₃)	17
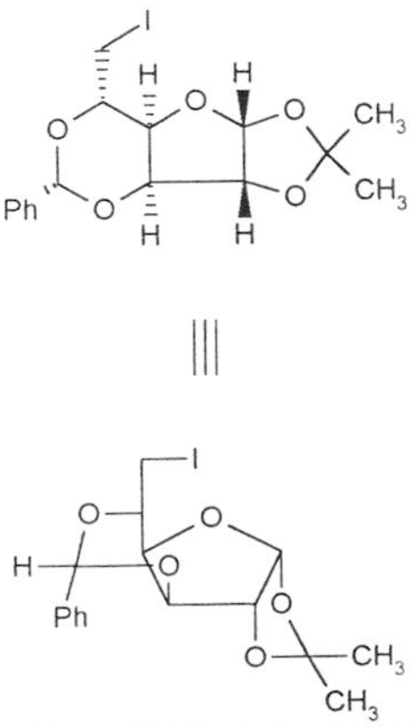	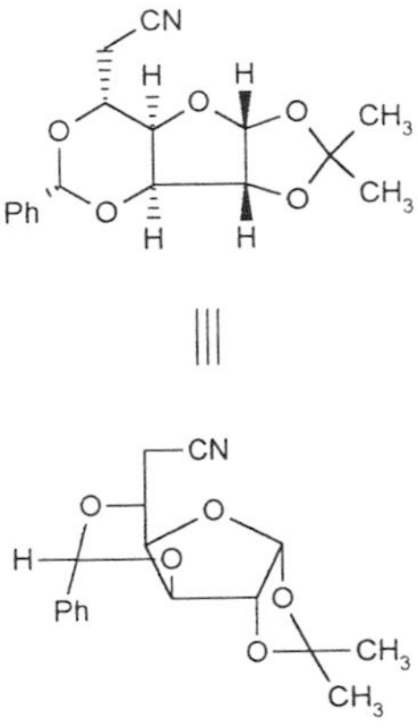	73	syrup	+6.1 (c = 1.4, CHCl₃)	18

(*continues*)

TABLE I.7 (*continued*)

Educt	Product	Yield (%)	M.p. (°C)	$[\alpha]_D$	Ref(s).
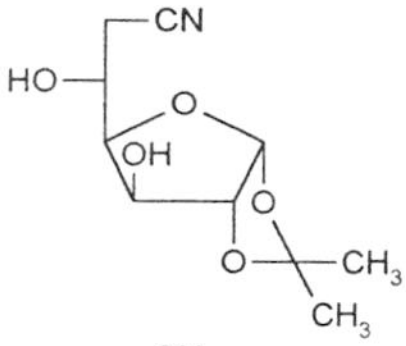 (furanose, HO—, CN, OH, O—C(CH₃)₂)	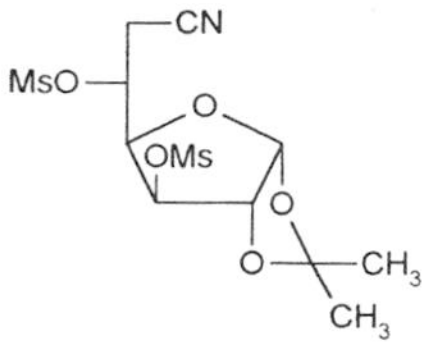 (furanose, MsO—, CN, OMs, O—C(CH₃)₂)	92	126	-50.2 (c = 20.75, CHCl₃)	5
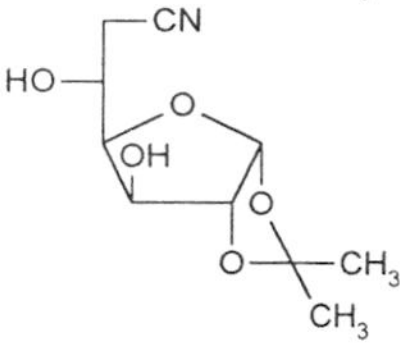 (furanose, HO—, CN, OH, O—C(CH₃)₂)	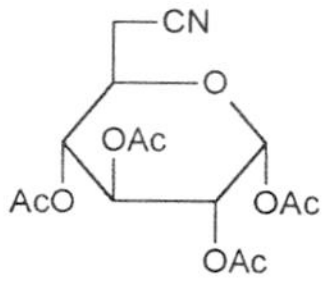 (pyranose, CN, OAc, AcO, OAc, OAc)	50	210	$+108.3$ (c = 1, CHCl₃)	10
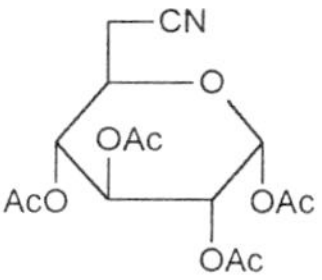 (pyranose, CN, O, OAc, AcO, OAc, OAc)	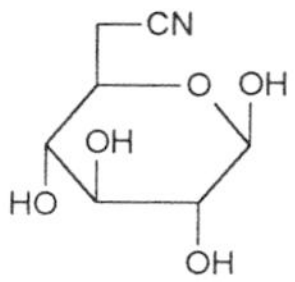 (pyranose, CN, O OH, OH, HO, OH)	81	147	$+17.5 \rightarrow 50.5$ (end value) (c = 2, H₂O)	10
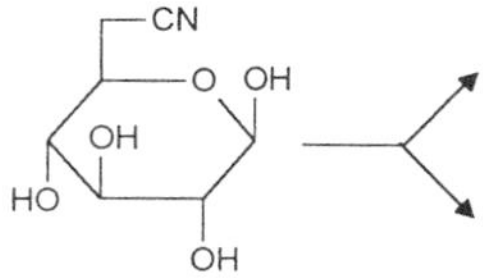 (pyranose, CN, O OH, OH, HO, OH)	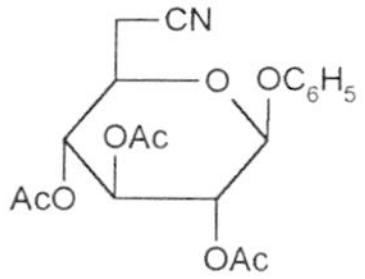 (pyranose, CN, O OC₆H₅, OAc, AcO, OAc)	66	182	-27.5 (c = 2, CHCl₃)	10
	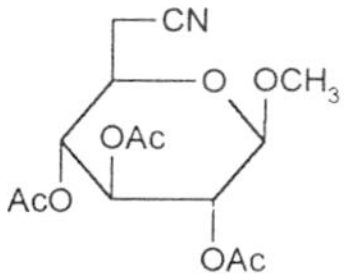 (pyranose, CN, O OCH₃, OAc, AcO, OAc)	90	144	-12.5 (c = 2, CHCl₃)	10
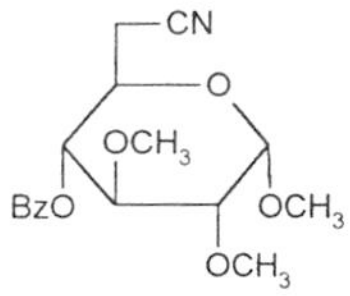 (pyranose, CN, O, OCH₃, BzO, OCH₃, OCH₃)	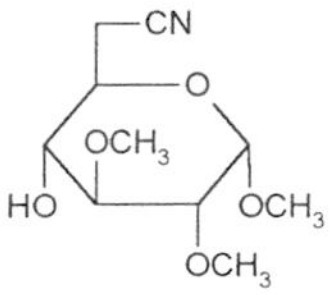 (pyranose, CN, O, OCH₃, HO, OCH₃, OCH₃)	80	syrup	$+99$ (c = 4.6, CHCl₃)	13
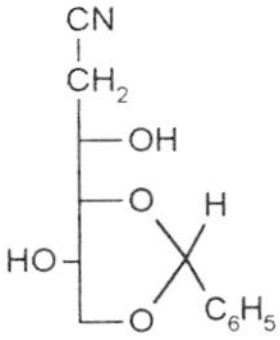 (CN, CH₂, —OH, O H, HO—, O C₆H₅)	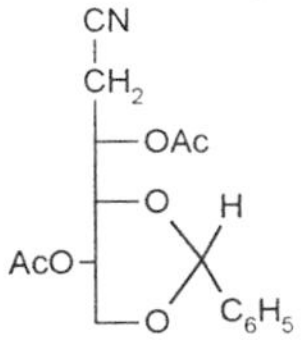 (CN, CH₂, —OAc, O H, AcO—, O C₆H₅)	91	125	$+63$ (c = 2.5, pyridine)	6
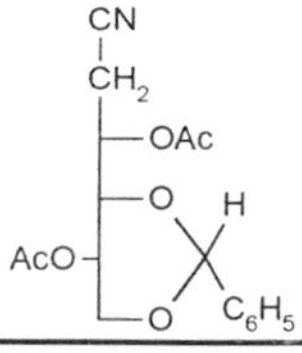 (CN, CH₂, —OAc, O H, AcO—, O C₆H₅)	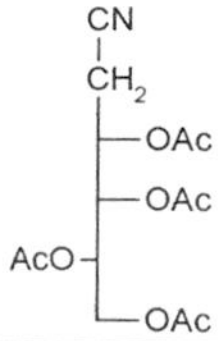 (CN, CH₂, —OAc, —OAc, AcO—, —OAc)	91	90	-29.6 (c = 2, pyridine)	6

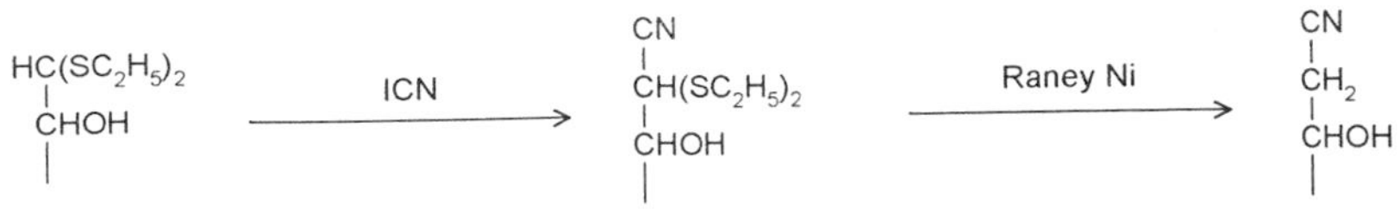

FIGURE 1.19

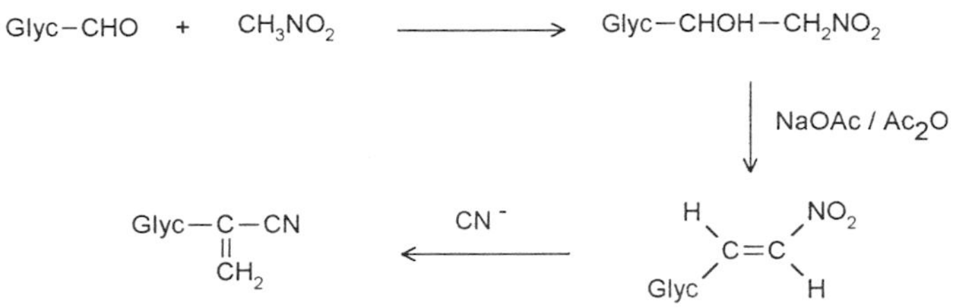

FIGURE 1.20

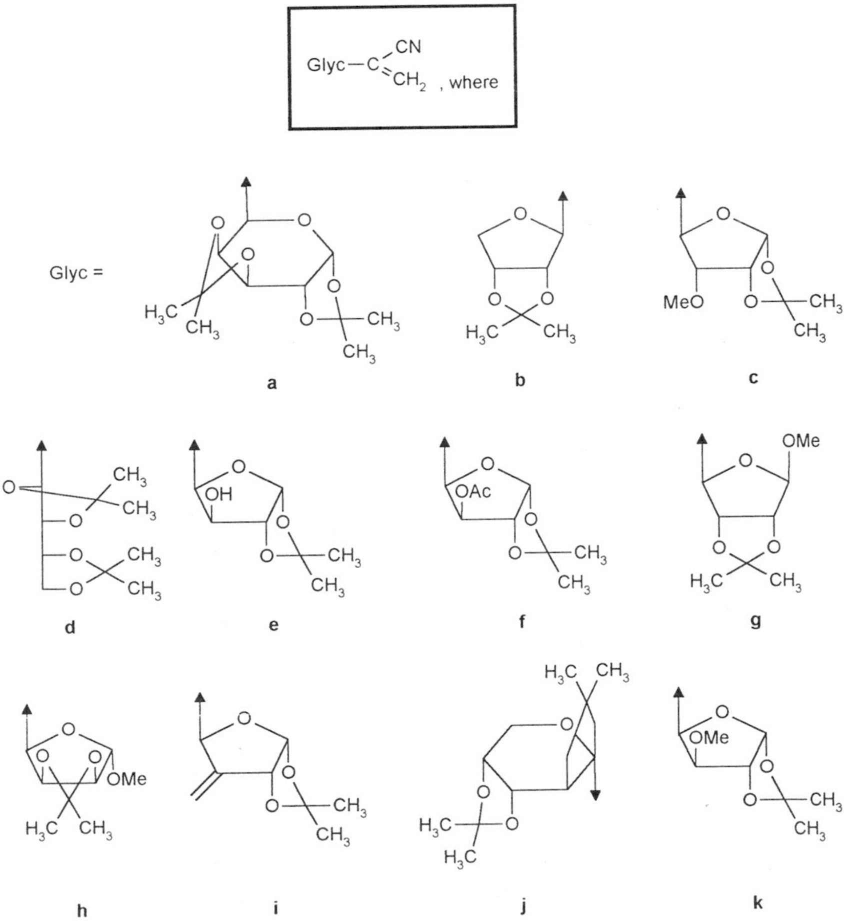

FIGURE 1.21

shown in Figure 1.20. This procedure is particularly useful for the synthesis[20] of a variety of 5-*C*-methyleneurononitriles with different substitution patterns, as shown in Figure 1.21.

REFERENCES TO SECTION I.2.2

1. M. E. Jung and T. J. Shaw, *J. Am. Chem. Soc.* **102**, 6304 (1980).
2. R. J. Bayly and J. C. Turner, *J. Chem. Soc.*, p. 704 (1966).
3. C.-Y. Shine, R. R. MacGregor, R. E. Lade, C.-H. Wan, and A. P. Wolf, *Carbohydr. Res.* **74**, 323 (1979).
4. I. F. Pelyvás, C. Monneret, and P. Herczegh, *Synthetic Aspects of Aminodeoxy Sugars of Antibiotics* Springer-Verlag, Heidelberg, 1988.
5. H. Weidmann and H. Schwarz, *Monatsh. Chem.* **103**, 218 (1972).
6. R. Grewe and H. Pachaly, *Chem. Ber.* **87**, 46 (1954).
7. D. Brett, I. M. Downie, and J. B. Lee, *J. Org. Chem.* **32**, 855 (1954).
8. Yu. A. Zhdanov, Yu. A. Alexeev, H. A. Kurdanov, and G. E. Guterman, *Zh. Obshch. Khim.* **42**, 481 (1972).
9. G. W. J. Fleet and D. R. Witty, *Tetrahedron: Asymmetry* **1**, 119 (1990).
10. R. Grewe and G. Rockstroh, *Chem. Ber.* **86**, 536 (1953).
11. K. Kakinuma, N. Otake, and H. Yonehara, *Tetrahedron Lett.* **21**, 167 (1980).
12. J. M. Sugihara, W. J. Teerlink, R. Macleod, S. M. Dorrence, and C. H. Springer, *J. Org. Chem.* **28**, 2079 (1963).
13. K. Jones and W. W. Wood, *Carbohydr. Res.* **155**, 217 (1986).
14. J. Kuszmann and B. Podányi, *Carbohydr. Res.* **225**, 247 (1992).
15. Gy. Hodosi, G. Galambos, B. Podányi, and J. Kuszmann, *Carbohydr. Res.* **225**, 269 (1992).
16. P. J. Garegg, J. Hofmann, B. Lindberg, and B. Samuelsson, *Carbohydr. Res.* **67**, 263 (1992).
17. S. Choi, I. Bruce, A. J. Fairbanks, G. W. J. Fleet, A. H. Jones, R. J. Nash, and L. E. Fellows, *Tetrahedron Lett.* **32**, 5517 (1991).
18. K. S. Akerfeldt and P. A. Bartlett, *J. Org. Chem.* **56**, 7133 (1991).
19. P. Herczegh, R. Bognár, and E. Timár, *Org. Prep. Proced. Int.* **10**, 211 (1978).
20. J. M. J. Tronchet and S. Zerelli, *J. Carbohydr. Chem.* **8**, 217 (1989).

I.2.3. Nitroalkane Syntheses

Carbohydrate chemistry utilizes a wide variety of synthetic methods for producing natural or unnatural sugars and their derivatives. The advantages and disadvantages of the addition of hydrogen cyanide to saccharides, described in Section 1.2.1, explain the reasons for further search for additional possibilities of chain extension. In the course of these studies, it was found that the well-known condensation[1] reaction of aldehydes with primary or secondary nitroalkanes can be adopted to carbohydrates.[2] This procedure involves two steps: a nitroaldol condensation (Henry reaction) and subsequent treatment with an acid to afford the carbonyl compounds (Nef reaction) as shown in Figure 1.22.

The reaction scheme clearly shows the formation of two diastereoisomeric nitroalcohols (**22.1** and **22.2**), which are separated in the form of salts as the transformation is catalyzed by a base (sodium alkoxides, barium

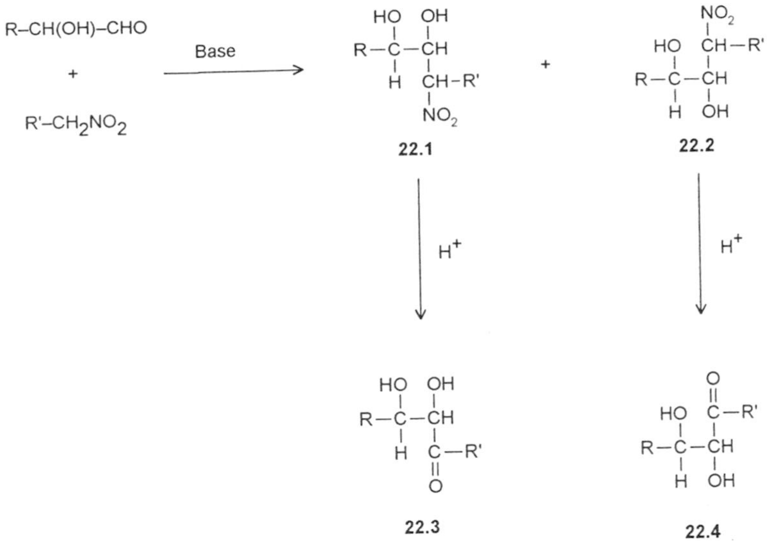

R–CH(OH)–CHO

\+

R'–CH$_2$NO$_2$

$\xrightarrow{\text{Base}}$

$$
\begin{array}{c}
\text{HO} \quad \text{OH} \\
\text{R}-\overset{|}{\underset{|}{\text{C}}}-\overset{|}{\underset{|}{\text{CH}}} \\
\text{H} \quad \text{CH}-\text{R'} \\
\text{NO}_2
\end{array}
$$

22.1

\+

$$
\begin{array}{c}
\text{NO}_2 \\
\text{HO} \quad \text{CH}-\text{R'} \\
\text{R}-\overset{|}{\underset{|}{\text{C}}}-\overset{|}{\underset{|}{\text{CH}}} \\
\text{H} \quad \text{OH}
\end{array}
$$

22.2

$\downarrow$ H$^+$ $\downarrow$ H$^+$

$$
\begin{array}{c}
\text{HO} \quad \text{OH} \\
\text{R}-\overset{|}{\underset{|}{\text{C}}}-\overset{|}{\underset{|}{\text{CH}}} \\
\text{H} \quad \text{C}-\text{R'} \\
\text{O}
\end{array}
$$

22.3

$$
\begin{array}{c}
\text{O} \\
\text{HO} \quad \text{C}-\text{R'} \\
\text{R}-\overset{|}{\underset{|}{\text{C}}}-\overset{|}{\underset{|}{\text{CH}}} \\
\text{H} \quad \text{OH}
\end{array}
$$

22.4

FIGURE 1.22

hydroxide), and this is seldom a disadvantage during the preparative operation. In the case of hexoses, the more favored and predominate product is that possessing the 2,4-*threo*-configuration—in accordance with Maltby's rule (see Section 1.2.1), but no such selectivity is observed for pentoses. In general, *gauche*-effects and *O/O* interactions in 1,3-parallel position have significant influence on the product distribution, and this has been well explored and demonstrated by the detailed systematic studies of Köll et al.[3,4] under standardized conditions. Then, in the next step the epimeric 1-deoxy-1-nitroalditols are transformed into the required saccharides (**22.3** and **22.4**; R' = H = aldoses, R' = alkyl = ketoses in Fig. 1.22) usually by treatment with a cold sulfuric acid solution.

In comparison to the Kiliani–Fischer method, nitroaldol condensation is preferred if the former method does not give the required epimer. To study the scope and limitations of the two procedures, parallel experiments have been carried out to obtain 1-^{14}C-labeled D-glucose from D-arabinose. The overall yield of the cyanohydrin synthesis is better,[5] but separation of the by-product, D-mannose, by means of fractional crystallization is very tedious. Separation of the isomers produced in the nitromethane synthesis[6] is carried out with the nitroalditols; thus radiochemically pure 1-^{14}C-D-glucose can be more conveniently obtained. However, it is disadvantageous in many cases that the equilibrium is shifted toward the starting aldose, which is, in addition, purely soluble, so that the nitromethane synthesis fails, as in the case of D-glucose. Application of dipolar aprotic solvents, such as N,N-dimethylformamide, promotes the conversion as shown in the following sections.

Characterization of the intermediary 1-deoxy-1-nitroalditols is a crucial problem during related syntheses. Chemical degradation to a known aldose is quite complicated in the case of higher sugars, but optical methods [optical rotatory dispersion (ORD) or preferably, circular dichroism (CD)] allow the assignation of the configuration of the produced epimeric nitroalditols. In the CD spectra a Cotton effect is observed at 310 nm whose sign is dependent only on the configuration of carbon C-2; a *negative* CD curve is observed for the (2R)-nitroalditols, whereas it is *positive* in the case of the (2S)-diastereoisomers.[7,8]

1.2.3.1. Chain Extension with Nitromethane

Most of the chain-extension experiments have been carried[9] out with nitromethane, the simplest nitroalkane. Free aldoses, or protected saccharides carrying a free-aldehyde moiety, were condensed with nitromethane in aqueous or methanolic solutions in the presence of a base to the 1-deoxy-1-nitroalditol with a chain extended by *one* further carbon atom. The products are generally separated by fractional crystallization of the deionized salt mixtures. From the previously published results it can be concluded that the nitromethane chain extension of free aldoses proceeds less selectively than the cyanohydrin synthesis, and in most cases steric hindrance of the substituted educts plays a decisive role in the process. Condensation of the β-methyl glycoside of 2,3-di-O-benzyl-D-*xylo*-pentodialdo-1,4-furanose (**23.1**) with nitromethane gives rise[10] exclusively to the *gluco*-product (**23.2**) with 81% yield, whereas from the corresponding α anomer (**23.3**) a 1:6 L-*ido*:D-*gluco* mixture (**23.4** and **23.5**) is obtained (Fig. 1.23). At the same time, exclusive formation of the D-*gluco* sugar **24.2** is observed[11] when the reaction with the *xylo* compound **24.1** is accom-

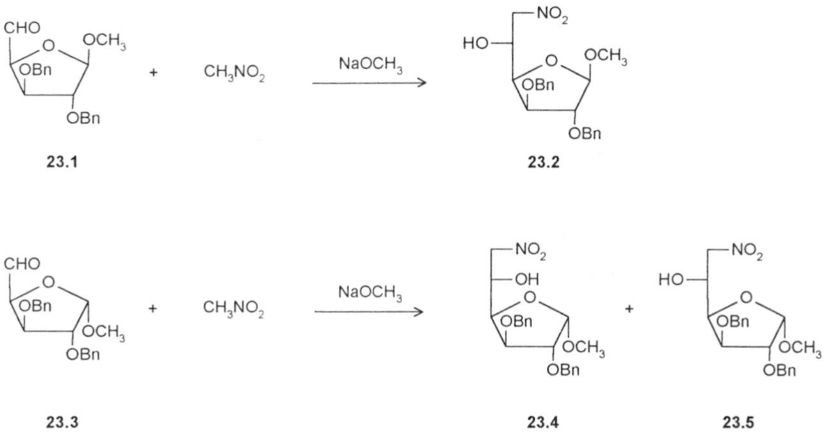

FIGURE 1.23

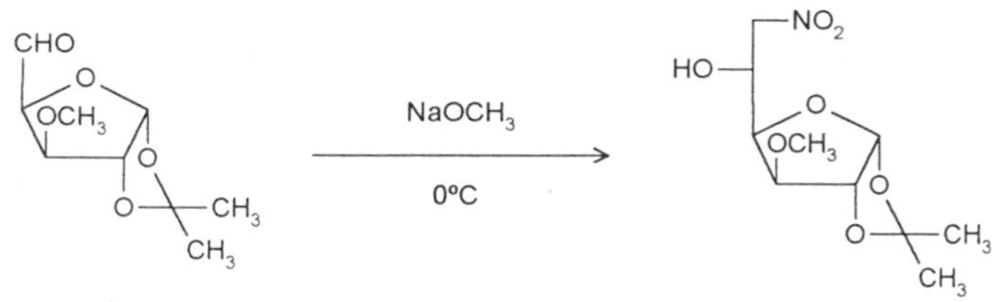

FIGURE 1.24

plished at 0°C (Fig. 1.24). Both isomers are produced if the dialdehydosugar with D-*ribo* configuration is employed, or the reaction is executed at higher temperatures.

A very efficient procedure[12] reported for the synthesis of the two rare sugars L-glucose and L-mannose is based on a related methodology.

A typical example for the nitromethane-condensation is the chain extension of D-galactose (Fig. 1.25) to obtain 1-deoxy-1-nitro-D-*glycero*-L-*manno*-heptitol **(25.1)** and 1-deoxy-1-nitro-D-*glycero*-L-*gluco*-heptitol **(25.2)**.

> *1-Deoxy-1-nitro-D-*glycero-L-manno-*heptitol (25.1) and 1-deoxy-1-nitro-D-glyc-ero-L-gluco-*heptitol (25.2)*[13]   To a suspension of D-galactose (50 g) in dry methanol (10 ml) and nitromethane (130 ml) a cold solution of sodium methoxide (prepared from 13 g of sodium and 300 ml of methanol) is added. The mixture warms spontaneously to 50°C, and after stirring for 1 day it is cooled to −20°C; then the sodium salts of the deoxynitroheptitols are filtered off and washed with methanol. The wet salt mixture is dissolved in water (500 ml) and deionized by passing through a column filled with Amberlite IR-100 cation-exchange resin. The eluate is concentrated, the separated crystals are filtered off, and the addition of ethanol to the syrupy residue gives further crystalline material. Recrystallization of the less soluble crystalline product from water leads to the isolation of 13.3 g (18.4%) of the L-*manno*-heptitol **25.1** in the form of monohydrate, m.p. 158–159°C. After drying over phosphorous pentoxide for 24 h, the anhydrous product has m.p. 165–166°C, $[\alpha]_D^{20}$ +6.3 (c = 4 in water). Recrystallization of the more soluble crystal fractions first from aqueous ethanol and then from ethanol gives 4.5 g (6.6%) of a product mixture (m.p. 147–

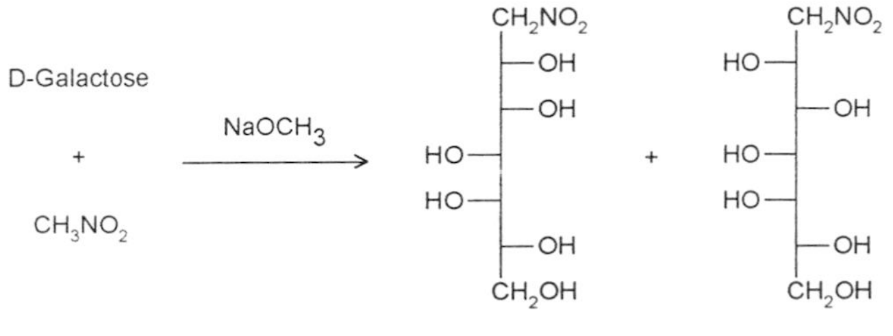

25.1   **25.2**

FIGURE 1.25

152°C) and 16.6 g (24.8%) of the L-*gluco*-heptitol (**25.2**), m.p. 152–153°C, $[\alpha]_D^{20}$ +7.8 (c = 4 in water).

D-Glycero-L-gluco-*heptose*[11] In this procedure 2 g of 1-deoxy-1-nitro-D-*glycero*-L-*gluco*-heptitol is dissolved in 1 N sodium hydroxide (10 ml), and this solution is added dropwise to a solution of concentrated sulfuric acid (1.2 ml) dissolved in water (1.6 ml) at 50°C. After stirring for a few minutes, the reaction mixture is deionized by passing through columns filled with Amberlite IR-120 (H⁺) and Duolite A-4 (OH⁻) ion-exchange resins. The eluate and the washings are concentrated *in vacuo* and mixed with a solution of phenylhydrazine (1.2 ml) in 25% acetic acid. Separation of the phenylhydrazone starts in a few minutes, and after remaining overnight the product is filtered and washed with cold water and ethanol to give 1.8 g (78%), m.p. 191–192°C. Conventional treatment of the phenylhydrazone with benzaldehyde and seeding gives pure D-*glycero*-L-*gluco*-heptose monohydrate, m.p. 83–85°C, $[\alpha]_D^{20}$ −13.7 (c = 4 in water, in equilibrium).

Detailed investigations have shown that in certain cases Me₂SO, as the solvent, has a favorable effect on the yield of the transformation, as shown by the example of the condensation of D-galactose with nitromethane.[3,14]

Condensation of D-galactose with nitromethane in Me₂SO To a solution of D-galactose (40 g) in DMSO (350 ml) and nitromethane (105 ml), anhydrous calcium sulfate (15 g) and 12% methanolic sodium methoxide (250 ml) are added. After remaining for 4 h, the *aci*-nitro salts are precipitated by the addition of ether (dried over sodium) at 4°C, then the creamy precipitate is filtered with suction, washed well with ether, and extracted with water. Following removal of insoluble CaSO₄ the filtrate is passed through a column filled with Amberlite IR-120 (H⁺) resin and concentrated to result in the crystallization of the monohydrate of 1-deoxy-1-nitro-D-*glycero*-L-*manno*-heptitol (**25.1**), and sometimes an orange syrup is also separated. The physical data of the pure product, recrystallized twice (16.5 g, 30%), are m.p. 155–157°C and $[\alpha]_D$ +6 (c = 2 in water). The orange syrup can be crystallized from a small volume of ethanol, and after repeated recrystallization pure 1-deoxy-1-nitro-D-*glycero*-L-*gluco*-heptitol (**25.2**) (4.8 g, 9%) is obtained, m.p. 152–153°C, $[\alpha]_D^{24}$ +7.7 (c = 2 in water).

Condensation of 2,5-anhydro-3,4,6-tri-*O*-benzyl-D-allose (**26.1**) with nitromethane (Fig. 1.26) showed that under kinetic control the reaction afforded a single product: 3,6-anhydro-4,5,7-tri-*O*-benzyl-1-deoxy-1-nitro-D-*glycero*-D-*altro*-heptitol (**26.2**).[15,16]

3,6-Anhydro-4,5,7-tri-O-benzyl-1-deoxy-1-nitro-D-glycero-D-altro-heptitol (**26.2**)[16] To a stirred, cold (0°C) mixture of 2,5-anhydro-3,4,6-tri-*O*-benzyl-D-allose

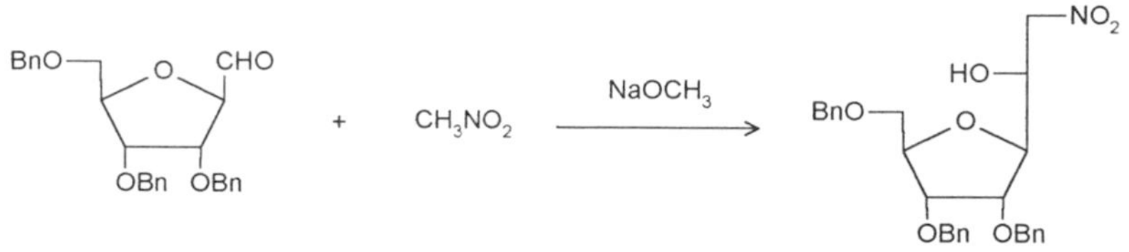

26.1   **26.2**

FIGURE 1.26

(**26.1**) (2.77 g, 6.4 mmol) in methanol (200 ml) and nitromethane (20 ml), 10 ml of 0.48 M sodium methoxide in methanol is added dropwise, and after stirring at 0°C for 1 h, it is neutralized with Dowex 50 (H$^+$) resin, filtered, and concentrated. The residue is dissolved in chloroform, and washed with water and the organic layer is dried. After removal of the solvent by distillation under reduced pressure the residue is crystallized from ether by the addition of hexane to give 2.35 g (74%) of **26.2,** m.p. 42–44°C, $[\alpha]_D^{20}$ −12.4 ($c = 0.18$ in chloroform).

On treatment of 1-deoxy-1-nitroalditols with hydrogen peroxide in aqueous solution and in the presence of catalytic amounts of molybdate, tungstate, or vanadate ions, the corresponding aldoses are produced, but no such conversion proceeds in the absence of these catalysts.[17] The transformation of the nitrohexitol (**27.1**) derived from L-arabinose into the rare, unnatural sugar L-mannose (**27.2**) is shown in Figure 1.27.

> *Preparation of L-mannose (**27.2**)*[17]   To a solution of the sodium salt of the nitrohexitol **27.1** derived[18] from L-arabinose (15 g) in water (120 ml), sodium molybdate (0.25 g) is added and then gradually treated with a 15% hydrogen peroxide (40 ml) solution to ensure that the temperature of the reaction mixture does not rise over 30°C. It is kept at room temperature for 20 h, 0.2 g of 5% Pd/C is added, and the mixture is allowed to remain for an additional day. After filtration, a solution of phenylhydrazine (11 ml) in methanol (20 ml) is added and the precipitated L-mannose phenylhydrazone (13 g, 48%), is filtered off after ~5 h.

The nitromethane syntheses with aldoses and *aldehydo*-saccharides, reported in the literature thus far, are summarized in Table 1.8.[20–64]

The reaction conditions employed for the nitromethane syntheses listed in Table 1.8 were used to ensure that the major product of the chain extension was the required 1-deoxy-1-nitro-alditol, since earlier studies had revealed that application of either milder conditions or a longer reaction time may result in the formation of secondary products, which are mainly the anhydro derivatives of the 1-nitroalditols. These latter substances could be readily isolated when a concentrated aqueous solution of the C-2 epimeric mixture of the open-chain deoxy-nitroalditols (the primary products of the nitromethane addition) was subjected to boiling for a longer period of time (20–30 h). Under such circumstances a slow ring closure occurs with the formation of the 2,6-anhydro derivatives, of which the thermody-

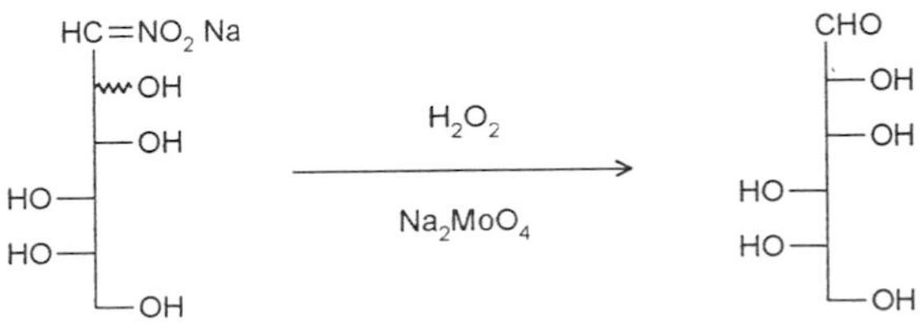

FIGURE I.27

TABLE 1.8 Nitromethane Syntheses with Aldose Derivatives

Educt	Nitroalcohol(s)	Aldose	Ref(s).
D-Glyceraldehyde	1-Deoxy-1-nitro-D-erythritol and -threitol		3
2,3-O-Isopropylidene glyceraldehyde			20
D-Erythrose	1-Deoxy-1-nitro-D-arabinitol and -ribitol	D-Arabinose	3,21,22
		1-¹⁴C-D-Arabinose	
		D-Ribose	
		1-¹⁴C-D-Ribose	23
L-Erythrose	1-Deoxy-1-nitro-L-arabinitol and -ribitol		24
2,4-O-Benzylidene-D-erythrose	3,5-O-Benzylidene-1-deoxy-1-nitro-D-arabinitol and -ribitol		21
2,4-O-Ethylidene-D-erythrose	3,5-O-Ethylidene-1-deoxy-D-arabinitol and -ribitol		25
D-Arabinose	1-Deoxy-1-nitro-D-mannitol and -D-glucitol	1-¹⁴C-D-Mannose	21,26
		1-¹⁴C-D-Glucose	6,27,28
L-Arabinose	1-Deoxy-1-nitro-L-mannitol and -L-glucitol	L-Mannose	29
		L-Glucose	19
2,4:3,5-Di-O-ethylidene-L-arabinose	1-Deoxy-3,5:4,6-di-O-ethylidene-1-nitro-L-iditol and -L-glucitol		30
4,6-O-Benzylidene-2,3,5-tri-O-acetyl-D-glucononitrile	4,6-O-Benzylidene-1-deoxy-1-nitro-D-mannitol		31
2,4-O-Benzylidene-L-xylose	2,4-O-Benzylidene-6-deoxy-6-nitro-D-glucitol	L-Glucose	32
D-Lyxose	1-Deoxy-1-nitro-D-glucitol		3,33
D-Ribose	1-Deoxy-1-nitro-D-allitol and -D-altritol		3,34,36
2,3-O-Isopropylidene-D-ribofuranose	1-Deoxy-1-nitro-3,4-O-isopropylidene-D-altritol and -D-allitol		37
5-Deoxy-D-xylose	1,6-Dideoxy-1-nitro-D-gulitol and -D-iditol		38,39
D-Rhamnose	1,7-Dideoxy-1-nitro-L-talo-heptitol		33
1,2-O-Cyclohexylidene-α-D-xylo-pentodialdo-1,4-furanose	1,2-O-Cyclohexylidene-6-deoxy-6-nitro-α-D-glucofuranose and -β-L-idofuranose		40
1,2-O-Isopropylidene-α-D-xylo-pentodialdo-1,4-furanose	6-Deoxy-1,2-O-isopropylidene-6-nitro-α-D-glucofuranose and -β-L-idofuranose	6-Deoxy-6-nitro-D-glucose and -L-idose	41–43
3-O-Alkyl-1,2-O-isopropylidene-α-D-xylo-pentodialdo-1,4-furanose	3-O-Alkyl-6-deoxy-1,2-O-isopropylidene-6-nitro-α-D-glucofuranose and -β-L-idofuranose		44
1,2-O-Isopropylidene-3-O-methyl-α-D-xylo-pentodialdo-1,4-furanose	6-Deoxy-1,2-O-isopropylidene-3-O-methyl-6-nitro-α-D-glucofuranose and -β-L-idofuranose		45,46

3-O-Benzyl-1,2-O-isopropylidene-α-D-xylo-pentodialdo-1,4-furanose	3-O-Benzyl-6-deoxy-1,2-O-isopropylidene-6-nitro-β-L-idofuranose and -α-D-glucofuranose	47
3-O-Benzyl-1,2-O-isopropylidene-α-D-ribo-pentodialdo-1,4-furanose	3-O-Benzyl-6-deoxy-1,2-O-isopropylidene-6-nitro-β-L-talofuranose and -α-D-allofuranose	48
3-O-Benzyl-1,2-O-isopropylidene-β-L-arabino-pentodialdo-1,4-furanose	3-O-Benzyl-6-deoxy-1,2-O-isopropylidene-6-nitro-β-L-altrofuranose and -α-D-galactofuranose	47
Ethyl 2-acetamido-2-deoxy-1-thio-α-D-xylo-pentodialdo-1,4-furanose	Ethyl 2-acetamido-2,6-dideoxy-1-thio-6-nitro-α-D-glucofuranoside and β-L-idofuranoside	48
Differently protected aldehydoaldoses	Protected nitroalcohols	49,50
D-Allose	1-Deoxy-1-nitro-D-glycero-D-allo-heptitol and 7-Deoxy-7-nitro-D-glycero-L-allo-heptitol	3
D-Altrose	1-Deoxy-1-nitro-D-glycero-D-gluco-heptitol and -D-manno-heptitol	3,51
D-Glucose	1-Deoxy-1-nitro-D-glycero-D-gulo-heptitol	3,31,52
D-Mannose	1-Deoxy-1-nitro-D-glycero-D-talo-heptitol and -D-galacto-heptitol	D-glycero-D-talo-Heptose and D-glycero-D-galacto-Heptose	20,53,54
D-Galactose	1-Deoxy-1-nitro-D-glycero-L-manno-heptitol and -L-gluco-heptitol	14,55,64
2-O-Benzyl-D-galactose	3-O-Benzyl-1-deoxy-1-nitro-D-glycero-L-manno-heptitol	57
4,6-O-Benzylidene-D-glucopyranose	5,7-O-Benzylidene-1-deoxy-1-nitro-D-glycero-D-gulo-heptitol	58
2-Acetamido-2-deoxy-3,4,5,6-di-O-isopropylidene-D-glucose	3-Acetamido-1,3-dideoxy-4,5:6,7-di-O-isopropylidene-1-nitro-D-glycero-D-ido-heptitol	3-Acetamido-3-deoxy-4,5:6,7-di-O-isopropylidene-D-glycero-D-ido-heptose	59
2-Acetamido-2-deoxy-D-mannose	3-Acetamido-1,3-dideoxy-1-nitro-D-glycero-D-galacto-heptitol	60
Methyl 2,3-di-O-acetyl-4-deoxy-β-L-threo-hex-4-enodialdo-1,5-piranoside	Methyl 2,3-di-O-acetyl-4,7-dideoxy-7-nitro-D-(and -L-)glycero-β-L-threo-hept-4-enopyranoside	61
D-Idose	1-Deoxy-1-nitro-D-glycero-L-gulo-heptitol and -L-ido-heptitol	62
D-glycero-D-galacto-Heptose	1-Deoxy-1-nitro-D-erythro-L-manno-octitol and 1-Deoxy-1-nitro-D-erythro-L-gluco-octitol	D-erythro-L-manno-Octose	20,62
D-erythro-L-manno-Octose	1-Deoxy-1-nitro-D-arabino-L-galacto-nonitol and -L-talo-nonitol	D-arabino-L-galacto-Nonose	63

namically more stable epimer is predominant. Besides these compounds cyclization of the open-chain 1-deoxy-1-nitroalditols into 2,5-anhydrides was also observed.

Similar to the nitroalditols, three maxima appear in the CD spectra of the anhydro derivatives, but the bands intensities are usually significantly larger for the former substances. A shoulder is observed at 310 nm, the n $\rightarrow$ π^* transition is at ~275 nm, and the more intense band appears at 210 nm.[56]

Detailed studies[66] have shown that related dehydration of C-2 epimeric 1-deoxy-1-nitroalditols gives rise to a single anhydro derivative, and this is the derivative in which the nitromethyl group is *equatorially* oriented. In such cases the steric arrangement of the C-1 and C-2 substituents is conformationally the most favored, as in the example given in Figure 1.28, showing the transformation[66] of the mannitol (**28.1**) and glucitol (**28.3**) into the same compound: 2,6-anhydro-1-deoxy-1-nitro-D-mannitol (**28.2**).

> *Preparation of 2,6-anhydro-1-deoxy-1-nitro-D-mannitol (**28.2**)*[66]   A solution of 20 g of 1-deoxy-1-nitro-D-mannitol (**28.1**) (or glucitol, **28.3**) in water (200 ml) is boiled until the specific optical rotation value is constant (~2 days). Concentration of the solution results in the crystallization of the product (**28.2**) (11.5 g, 63%), m.p. 170–171°C, $[\alpha]_D^{25}$ −52.5 (c = 4 in water).

Dehydration of the 1-deoxy-1-nitroalditols **29.1** and **29.2**, derived from D-ribose, is not as simple as in the preceding case, since separation of the products (**29.3** and **29.4**) requires column chromatographic technique (Fig. 1.29).

> *2,5-Anhydro-1-deoxy-1-nitro-D-altritol (**29.3**) and 2,5-anhydro-1-deoxy-1-nitro-D-allitol (**29.4**)*[37,66]   A mixture of D-ribose (15 g, 0.1 mol) in methanol (100 ml) and nitromethane (6 ml, 0.11 mol) and potassium carbonate (13.8 g, 0.1 mol) is stirred until all the starting sugar has reacted (~6 h; thin-layer chromatography (TLC: 1 : 3 CCl$_4$–acetone). After dilution with water, the mixture is deionized with Amberlite IR-120 (H$^+$) resin which is then filtered off; then the filtrate concentrated and the residue is codistilled several times with ethanol to give 3.28 g (17%) of 2,5-anhydro-1-deoxy-1-nitro-D-altritol (**29.3**), which can be recrystallized from 2-propanol to afford 1.39 g (10%) of the pure product, m.p. 139–140°C, $[\alpha]_D^{22}$ +79 (c = 1 in water). The residue obtained on evaporation of the mother liquor is

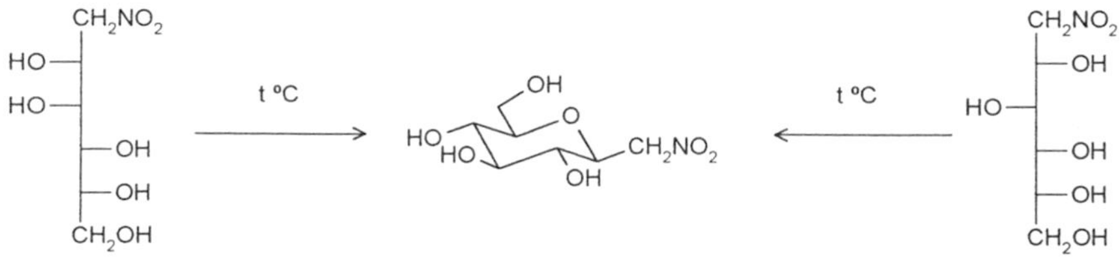

FIGURE I.28

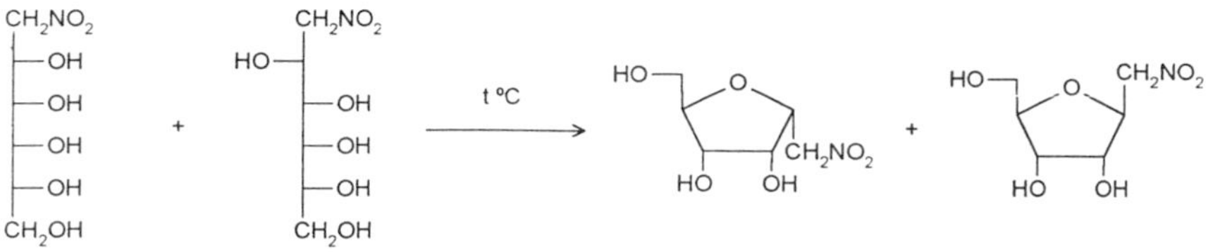

FIGURE 1.29

subjected to column chromatography (eluant: ethyl acetate) to yield 12 g (62%) of 2,5-anhydro-1-deoxy-1-nitro-D-allitol, $[\alpha]_D^{22}$ −7 (c = 1.5 in water).

The corresponding pair of pyranosyl derivatives is prepared according to a method[37,66] that uses DMSO as the solvent. The synthesis of 2,6-anhydro-1-deoxy-1-nitro-D-*glycero*-D-*manno*-heptitol (**30.2**) has also been performed[56] in DMSO (Fig. 1.30).

> *2,6-Anhydro-1-deoxy-1-nitro-D-glycero-D-manno-heptitol (30.2) from D-galactose (30.1)*[56]   To a solution of D-galactose (**30.1**) (50 g) in DMSO (200 ml) a mixture of nitromethane (100 ml) and sodium methoxide solution (prepared from 12.5 g of sodium and 350 ml of dry methanol) is added and stirred for 1 day. The precipitate separating on addition of *n*-butanol (100 ml) is filtered off, washed with cold methanol (2 × 50 ml), and added to a mixture of water (100 ml), cation-exchange resin (H⁺; 150 g), and dry ice (50 g). The resin is filtered off and washed with water (3 × 100 ml), and the fitrate–washing combination is passed through a 30 × 2 cm column filled with cation-exchange resin. The eluate is concentrated to ~50 ml, heated at 100°C for 30 h, decolorized with charcoal, filtered, and mixed with 151 g of Dowex 1 × 4 (297 × 149 μm) anion-exchange resin. After remaining for 1 h with occasional rinsing, the resin is filtered off and washed with water (1 liter). The washed resin is stirred with 100 ml of water and warmed to 20°C, and 100 g of dry ice is added to cool down (but not freeze) the mixture. The resin is filtered off and washed with water (3 × 100 ml), and the combined aqueous solution is concentrated to obtain 41 g (66%) of crude **30.2,** which is then recrystallized from methanol. The pure product has m.p. 198–200°C and $[\alpha]_D^{20}$ +37 (c = 2 in water). Workup of the mother liquor gives three additional stereoisomers, as minor products.

The chain extension of aldehydes with nitromethane can also be catalyzed with potassium fluoride[67] and crown ethers. If the target compound

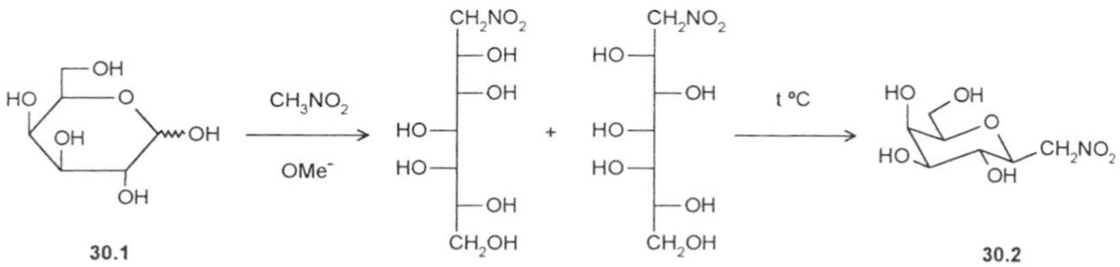

FIGURE 1.30

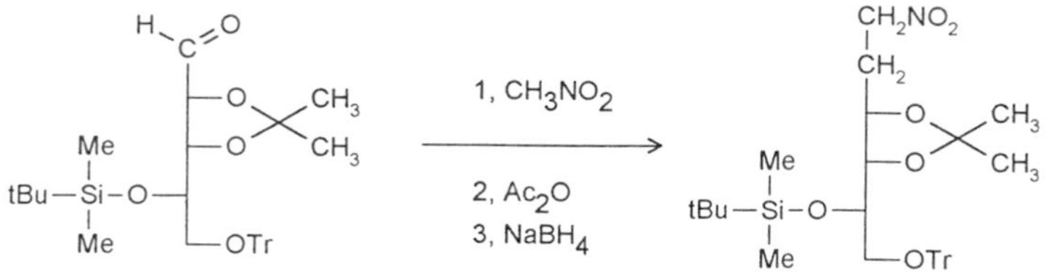

FIGURE 1.31

is the C-2 deoxy derivative, the epimeric 1-deoxy-1-nitroalditols are *O*-acetylated and then reduced into the required nitroalkane. In the field of carbohydrates, the conversion of aldehydes into saturated nitro compounds was executed with protected *aldehydo*-sugars, and this methodology has been used most successfully[68] for chain extension, as shown in Figure 1.31.

> *5-O-(tert-Butyldimethylsilyl)-1,2-dideoxy-3,4-O-isopropylidene-1-nitro-6-O-triphenylmethyl-L-arabino-hexitol (31.2)*[68] To a solution of the *aldehydo*-L-arabinose derivative **31.1** [freshly prepared from 4-O-(*tert*-butyldimethylsilyl)-2,3-O-isopropylidene-5-O-triphenylmethyl-L-arabinose diethyl dithioacetal (5 g, 7.7 mmol)] in dry 2-propanol (25 ml) nitromethane (2 ml, 37 mmol), anhydrous potassium fluoride (50 mg, 0.86 mmol) and 18-crown-6 (120 mg, 0.45 mmol) are added and the mixture is stirred at room temperature. The progress of the reaction is monitored by TLC (10 : 1 benzene–ether). The solvent is distilled off, the foamy residue is dissolved in dry ether (30 ml), and acetic anhydride (2 ml) and 4-dimethylaminopyridine (60 mg, 0.5 mmol) are added. After 50 min TLC (97 : 3 benzene–ether) shows the presence of two more polar products. Ether is distilled off, 100 ml of dry ethanol is added, the mixture is cooled down on an ice bath and 2.2 g (58 mmol) of sodium borohydride is cautiously added. TLC (benzene) shows the formation of a new product (whose spot is situated inbetween the spots of the former two compounds). After completion of the reaction the solvent is distilled off, hexane (100 ml) and water (50 ml) are added, and the mixture is cooled down on an ice bath and acidified with 10% aqueous aceteic acid. The aqueous layer is separated, and washed with hexane (2 × 100 ml), the combined organic layer is washed with water (3 × 100 ml), washed with saturated aqueous sodium hydrogen-carbonate solution until neutral, washed again with water, and dried over MgSO$_4$. The thick syrup obtained on evaporation is subjected to column chromatography (eluant: 8 : 100 ethyl acetate–hexane) to afford 3.8 g (83% calculated to the starting dithioacetal) of pure **31.2**, $[\alpha]_D^{22}$ −1.1 (c = 10 in chloroform).

1.2.3.2. Chain Extension with Nitroethane

Extension of the carbon chain with two carbon atoms necessitates the application of nitroethane. Despite the available modern techniques, the separation and structure elucidation of the four theoretically possible isomers produced in such reactions are sometimes rather tedious.

Condensation of 1,2 : 3,4-di-*O*-isopropylidene-α-D-*galacto*-hexodialdo-1,5-pyranose (**32.1**) with nitroethane (Fig. 1.32) resulted in three isomeric 7,8-dideoxy-7-nitroalditols (**32.2**) that could be isolated in the form of

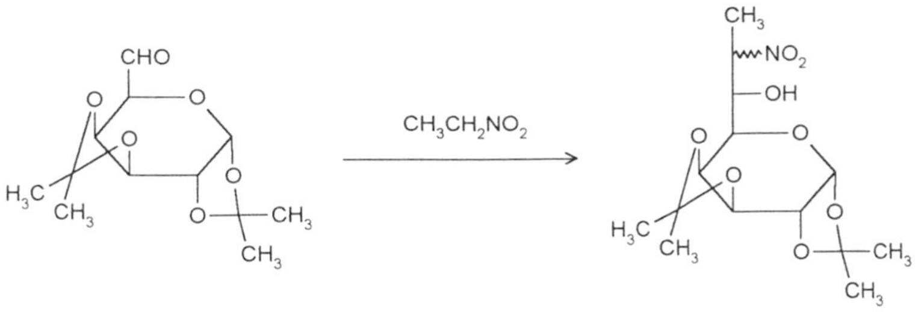

FIGURE 1.32

the corresponding acetates.[69] A similar mixture of isomers (Fig. 1.33), consisting of 6,7-dideoxy-1,2-*O*-isopropylidene-3-*O*-methyl-6-nitro-D,L-*glycero*-D-*gluco* and L-*ido*-heptofuranose (**33.2**), is produced[70] from 1,2-*O*-isopropylidene-3-*O*-methyl-α-D-*xylo*-pentodialdo-1,4-furanose (**33.1**) on condensation with nitroethane. In the reaction shown in Figure 1.34, a nonseparable mixture of the isomeric (*tert*-butyldimethylsilyl)-6,7-dideoxy-2,3-*O*-isopropylidene-6-nitroheptofuranosides (**34.2**) was obtained[71] in 60% overall yield from the dialdose (**34.1**). In the case of D-mannose (**35.1**), the formation of only two isomers is observed[72] (Fig. 1.35) and treatment of the unseparated, crystalline mixture of 1,2-dideoxy-2-nitrooctitols (**35.2**) with dilute sulfuric acid gives rise to a single product: 1-deoxy-D-*glycero*-D-*galacto*-octulose (**35.3**).

> *1-Deoxy-D-glycero-D-galacto-octulose (35.3)*   A cold solution of sodium hydroxide (18 g, 0.45 mol) in water (20 ml) is mixed with 125 ml of methanol, and this solution is added to a suspension of D-mannose (**35.1**, 40 g, 0.22 mol) in methanol (175 ml) and nitroethane (100 ml). From the resulting clear solution, precipitation of the nitronate salt begins in ~1 h, and this is complete in a week to obtain, after filtration, 60 g of the crude product, m.p. 135–140°C. A solution of the crude nitronate (30 g, 0.11 mol) in water (100 ml) is added dropwise to a soluiton of sulfuric acid (13.4 ml, 0.25 mol) in water (10 ml). When the gas evolution is complete, the solution is consecutively passed through a column of 600-ml of a Bio Rad AG

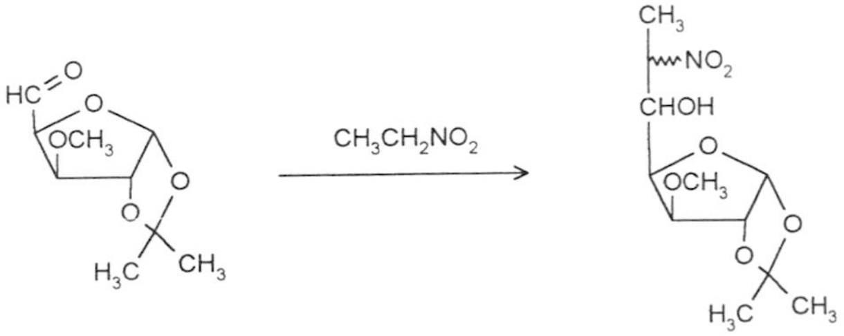

FIGURE 1.33

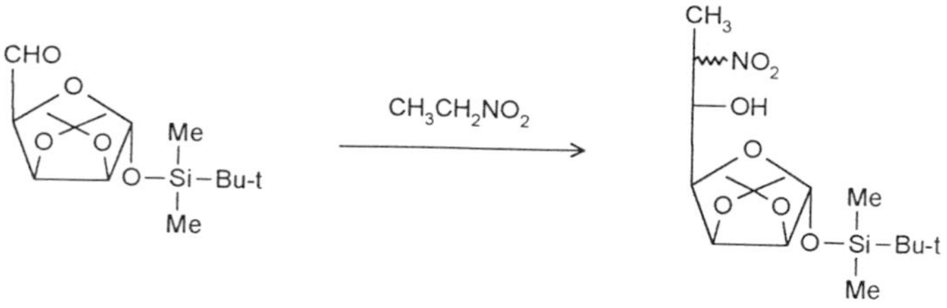

FIGURE I.34

3-X4 (OH⁻) anion-exchange column, and then a 600-ml Dowex 50 (H⁺) cation-exchange column and the deionized solution is neutralized with a small amount of Dowex 1 (HCO₃) and concentrated to a syrup. Crystallization from ethanol gives 13.6 g (55% calculated for D-mannose) of **35.3**, m.p. 149–151°C, $[\alpha]_D^{23}$ +87 (in water, end value).

By means of the fractional crystallization of the acidified *aci*-nitro salt mixture, the two epimeric 1,2-dideoxynitrooctitols can be isolated.

In agreement with the previous work, nitroethane condensation of D-galactose gave two products in a 3:2 ratio, which could be isolated (in 24% yield) as a crystalline substance and then separated[73] in the form of crystalline acetyl derivatives.

1.2.3.3. Chain Extension with Nitroethanol

When aldoses are submitted to a condensation reaction with nitroethanol under the conditions described in the previous sections, ketoses extended by two carbon atoms in the chain are obtained. So far this method has been attempted only with the four D-series pentoses, and the ketoses were obtained[74] with moderate yields (Table 1.9) even when the isomeric 2-deoxy-2-nitroheptitols were not separated.

The reaction of 1,2-dideoxy-3,4-O-isopropylidene-1-nitro-L-*glycero*-tetritol (**36.1**) with O-benzyl-L-lactaldehyde (**36.2**) gave (Fig. 1.36) three isomeric heptitols (**36.3**), and on catalytic hydrogenation and subsequent

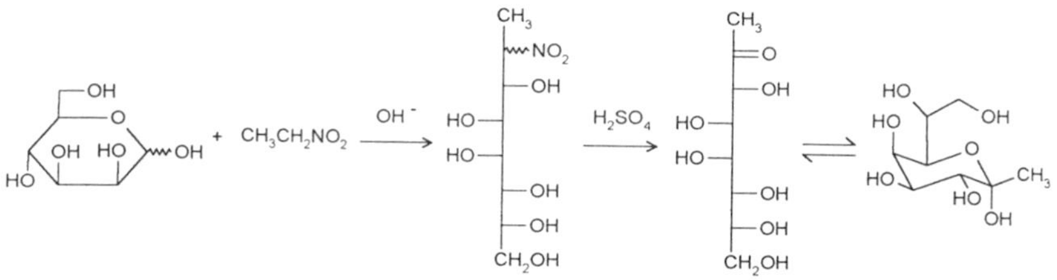

FIGURE I.35

TABLE 1.9   Nitroethanol Condensations Carried Out with Pentoses[74]

Pentose	Product	Yields (%)
D-Arabinose	D-*gluco*-Heptulose	11
	D-*manno*-Heptulose	4
D-Xylose	2,7-Anhydro-β-D-*ido*-heptulopyranose	18.9
D-Ribose	2,7-Anhydro-β-D-*altro*-heptulopyranose	4.8
D-Lyxose	D-*galacto*-Heptulose	7.7
	D-*talo*-Heptulose	1.7

acetylation, three aminodeoxyheptitols (**36.4**) could be isolated, each with ~15% yield.[75]

The nitroaldol condensation of 2-*O*-benzyl-D-glyceraldehyde (**37.1**) with the nitroacetal **37.2** in the presence of tetrabutylammonium fluoride catalyst (Fig. 1.37) allowed the preparation[76] of 2-amino-2-deoxypentoses (*arabino : ribo* ratio 88 : 12).

1.2.3.4. Chain Extension with Nitroalkane Carboxylic Acids

In the presence of ammonium acetate catalyst, 2,3 : 4,5-di-*O*-isopropylidene-*aldehydo*-D-arabinose (**38.1**) undergoes condensation (Fig. 1.38) with ethyl nitroacetate (**38.2**) to afford[77] a mixture of 2-deoxy-3-hydroxy-4,5 : 6,7-di-*O*-isopropylidene-2-nitro-L-*arabino*-heptonic acids (**38.3**), whereas a double addition occurs in the presence of other amines.

Methyl nitroacetate (**39.2**) was used for the chain extension (Fig. 1.39) of 5-deoxy-D-xylose (**39.1**), which resulted in a single isomer. According to spectroscopic studies,[37] this compound must be methyl 3,6-anhydro-2,7-dideoxy-2-nitro-D-*glycero*-L-*talo*- (or L-*galacto*)-heptonate (**39.3**).

Methyl nitropropionate is applied when extension of the carbon chain by three carbon atoms is required. With this ester (**40.2**), 2,3-di-*O*-benzyl-4,5-*O*-isopropylidene-*aldehydo*-L-arabinose (**40.1**) gives a mixture of diastereoisomeric octonic acids (**40.3**) in the presence of diisopropylamine catalyst as shown in Figure 1.40.

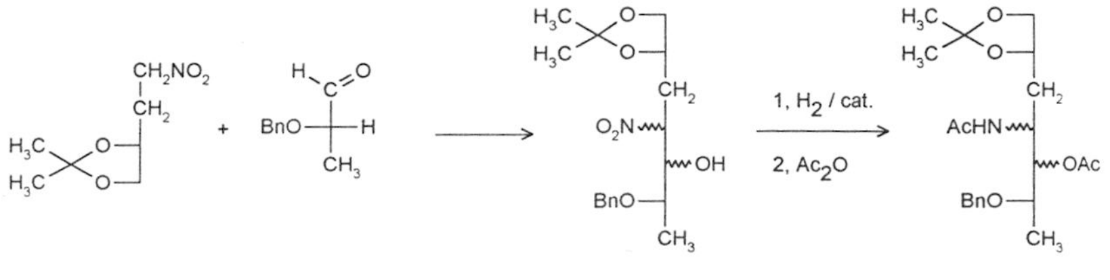

36.1   **36.2**   **36.3**   **36.4**

FIGURE 1.36

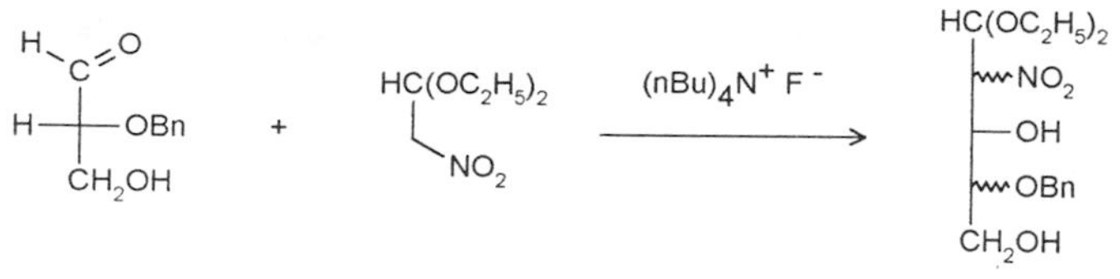

37.1 37.2 37.3

FIGURE 1.37

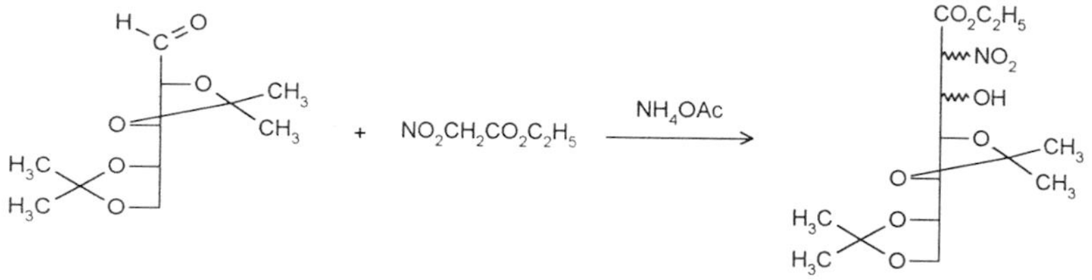

38.1 38.2 38.3

FIGURE 1.38

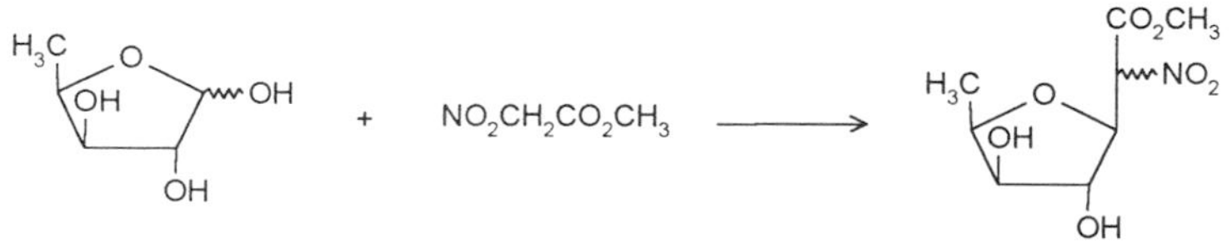

39.1 39.2 39.3

FIGURE 1.39

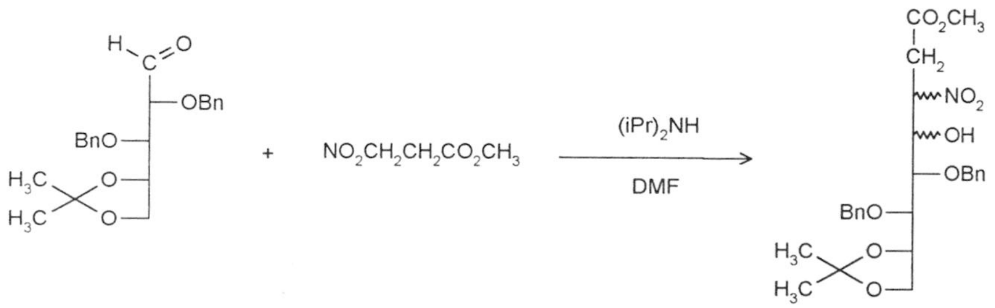

40.1 40.2 40.3

FIGURE 1.40

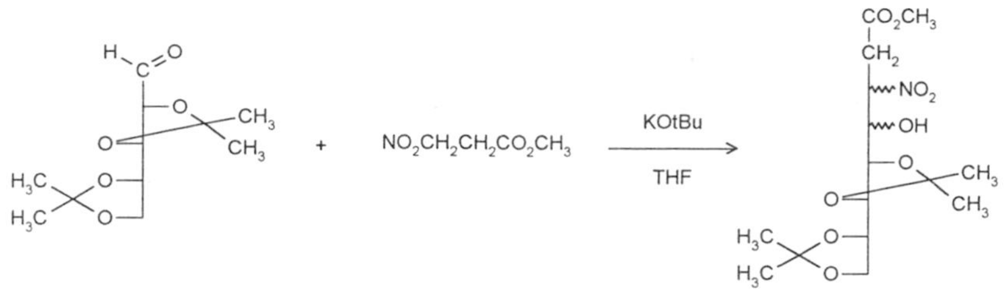

FIGURE I.41

2,3:4,5-Di-O-isopropylidene-*aldehydo*-L-arabinose (**41.1**) can be readily condensed, as well, (Fig. 1.41) with methyl nitropropionate to a mixture of dideoxyoctonic acids (**41.2**). This reaction is complete in less than 30 min when potassium *tert*-butoxide is applied as the catalyst.[78]

Condensation of C_3-aldehydes with methyl nitropropionate is a very important tool for the total synthesis of naturally occurring aminodeoxy hexoses, the sugar components of various antibiotics.[79] Protected lactaldehydes, such as (2S)-[tetrahydro-2H-pyran-2(R,S)-yl-oxy]propanal[80] (**42.1**) (see Fig. 1.42) or (2S)-benzyloxypropanal[81] have been transformed into methyl 2,3,6-trideoxy-3-nitrohexonates, subjects for further conversion into the rare 3-amino-2,3,6-trideoxy-L-hexose building units of antibiotics.

The reaction of **42.1** with methyl nitropropionate (Fig. 1.42) gives a mixture of methyl 2,3,6-trideoxy-3-nitro-L-hexonates (**42.2**) in a non-

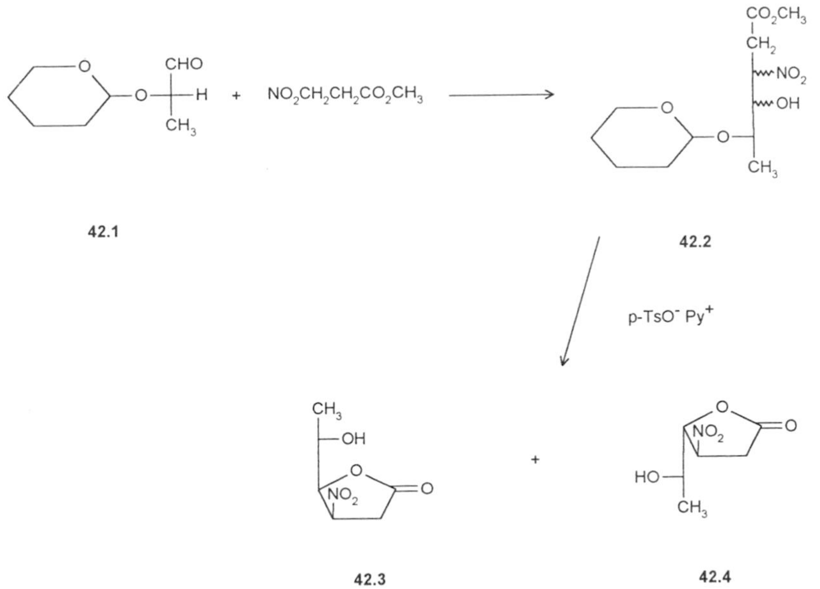

FIGURE I.42

chelate-controlled reaction, whose treatment with pyridinium toluenesulfonate affords a mixture of hexonolactones with L-*lyxo* (**42.3**) and L-*ribo* (**42.4**) configurations.[80] The product distribution in the reaction of *O*-benzyl lactaldehyde and methyl nitropropionate in the presence of various catalysts is summarized in Table 1.10 according to the results of the Hanessian group.[81] The selectivity of the nitroaldol reaction could be further influenced[81] by the application of the D- or L-enantiomer of methyl nitropropionate.

The methyl 3-nitro-2,3,6-trideoxyhexonates with L-*ribo*, L-*lyxo*, and L-*arabino* configurations have been employed[79] for the synthesis of L-*ristosamine*, L-*daunosamine,* and L-*acosamine,* respectively.

The nitroaldol reaction has also served as the key step in an ingenious synthesis of *sinefungin.* Thus, the potassium fluoride–catalyzed condensation of methyl 2,3-*O*-isopropylidene-β-D-*ribo*-pentodialdo-1,4-furanose with *tert*-butyl α-(*p*-toluenesulfonamido)-δ-nitrovalerate readily furnished the required key intermediate to *sinefungin.*[82]

1.2.3.5. Nitroaldol Condensation of Monosaccharides Containing Nitromethyl Groups

The discovery and isolation of higher sugars built up from 8–10 carbon atoms and carrying various functional groups called for widening the scope of the nitromethane condensation reaction. It was soon recognized that carbohydrate derivatives containing a nitromethyl function are also suitable for chain extensions. Thus, condensation of methyl 2,3,4-tri-*O*-acetyl-6-

TABLE 1.10 Influence of Catalyst on the Product Ratio of Nitroaldol Reaction of O-Benzyllactaldehyde with Methyl Nitropropionate

		Ratio of products			
		$\begin{array}{c}CO_2CH_3\\ H{-}\!\!\!-\!\!\!-H\\ O_2N{-}\\ HO{-}\\ BnO{-}\\ CH_3\end{array}$	$\begin{array}{c}CO_2CH_3\\ H{-}\!\!\!-\!\!\!-H\\ {-}NO_2\\ {-}OH\\ BnO{-}\\ CH_3\end{array}$	$\begin{array}{c}CO_2CH_3\\ H{-}\!\!\!-\!\!\!-H\\ {-}NO_2\\ HO{-}\\ BnO{-}\\ CH_3\end{array}$	$\begin{array}{c}CO_2CH_3\\ H{-}\!\!\!-\!\!\!-H\\ O_2N{-}\\ {-}OH\\ BnO{-}\\ CH_3\end{array}$
Catalyst	Temperature (°C)	L-*ribo*	L-*lyxo*	L-*arabino*	L-*xylo*
Catalytic KO*t*Bu	0°C	1	Traces	2	1
KO*t*Bu	0°C	2	Traces	1	1
KO*t*Bu/MgBr$_2$	0°C	1	Traces	1	3
KO*t*Bu/MgBr$_2$	0°C	1	Traces	3	1
KO*t*Bu/Me$_3$SiCl/F$^-$	−78°C	1	0	1	0
Neutral Al$_2$O$_3$	25°C	15	Traces	1	1.5

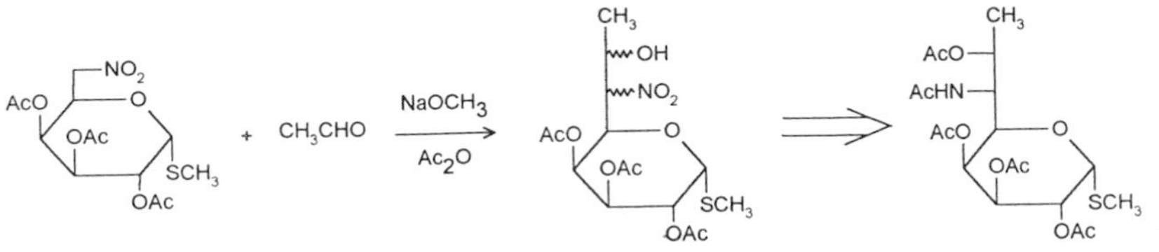

FIGURE 1.43

deoxy-6-nitro-1-thio-α-D-galactopyranoside (**43.1**) with acetaldehyde (Fig. 1.43) gave the octose **43.2**, which could be transformed[83] into the protected *methyl lincosaminide* derivative **43.3**, the carbohydrate component of the antibiotic *lincomycin*.

To increase the antibacterial activity of the antibiotic *fortimycin B*, modification of the structure by the introduction of a bulky lipophilic group was established by means of the nitroaldol condensation strategy (Fig. 1.44). The reaction of methyl 2-acetamido-6-nitro-2,3,4,6-tetradeoxy-α-D-

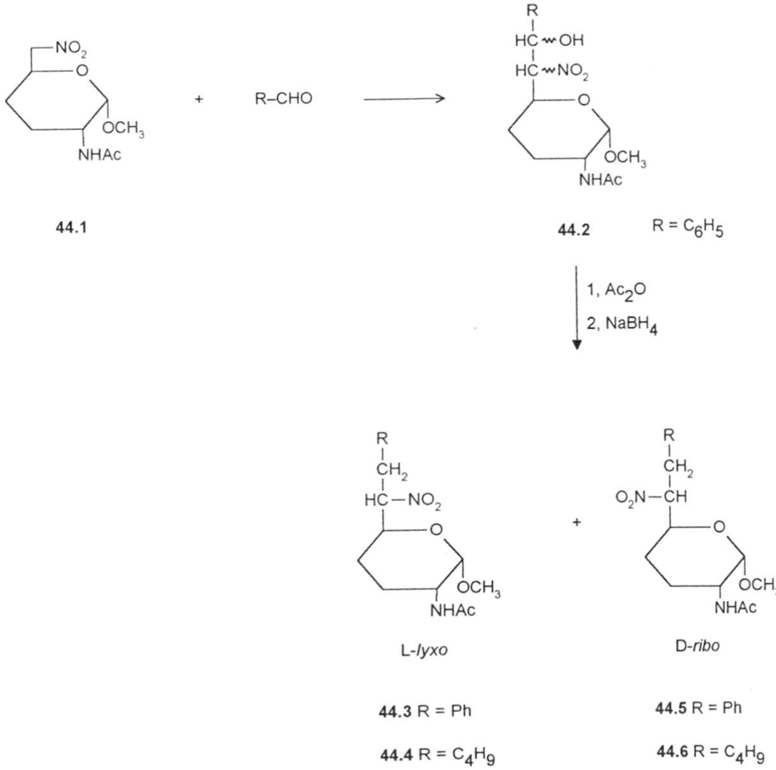

FIGURE 1.44

erythro-hexopyranoside (**44.1**) with benzaldehyde in the presence of sodium methoxide catalyst gave rise to an unseparable mixture (**44.2**) of nitroaldols. Acetylation and subsequent reduction with sodium borohydride then furnished methyl 2-acetamido-6-nitro-2,3,4,6,7-pentadeoxy-7-phenyl-β-L-*lyxo* (and α-D-*ribo*)-heptopyranoside (**44.3** and **44.5**, respectively). Separation of this mixture with chromatography led to the isolation of 54% of the α-*ribo*-isomer **44.5**. It is to be noted that this reaction did not proceed in acetonitrile in the presence of potassium or cesium fluoride catalysts.

> *Methyl 2-acetamido-6-nitro-2,3,4,6,7-pentadeoxy-7-phenyl-α-D-ribo-heptopyranoside (44.5)*[84] A mixture of **44.1** (1.5 g), benzaldehyde (0.7 ml) and 1 M sodium methoxide (6.7 ml) in methanol (3 ml) is stirred at 0°C for 2 h. Following neutralization with Amberlite IR-120 (H⁺) resin, the reaction mixture is concentrated, the residue is dissolved in acetic anhydride (10 ml) and cooled, and boron trifluoride etherate (1.5 ml) is added. After stirring for 1 h, the mixture is poured into ice water (100 ml) and extracted with dichloromethane (150 ml). The organic layer is washed with saturated NaHCO₃ solution (300 ml) and water (100 ml), dried, and evaporated. The residue is dissolved in DMSO (18 ml), a suspension of sodium borohydride (0.2 g) in DMSO (2 ml) is added, and the mixture is stirred for 30 min. It is then acidified with Amberlite IR-120 (H⁺) resin and extracted with chloroform (100 ml), the extract is dried and concentrated, and the residue is purified by column chromatography with 90 : 10 chloroform–methanol as the eluant, to obtain 1.13 g (54%) of **44.5** and 0.6 g of the starting sugar **44.1**.

Condensation of **44.1** with butyraldehyde in the presence of cesium fluoride catalyst (Fig. 1.44) proceeds in a very similar manner, and after removal of the hydroxyl group, methyl 2-acetamido-6-nitro-2,3,4,6,7,8,9,10-octadeoxy-β-L-*lyxo*- (**44.4**) and α-D-*ribo*-decopyranoside (**44.6**) are obtained.[85]

When carbohydrate derivatives are applied as both partners of the nitroaldol condensation, functionalized higher sugars can be prepared in a straightforward fashion. For example, as shown in Figure 1.45, 3,5-*O*-benzylidene-6,7-dideoxy-1,2-*O*-isopropylidene-7-nitro-α-D-*gluco*-hepto-1,4-furanose (**45.1**), easily available in crystalline form, reacts with 2,3 : 4,5-di-*O*-isopropylidene-*aldehydo*-D-arabinose to afford[86] a two-component mixture of the isomeric 6,7-dideoxy-7-nitro-dodecafuranoses (**45.3**). Analogous condensation of **45.1** with 2,4-*O*-ethylidene-D-erythrose (**45.4**) leads to two isomeric 6,7-dideoxy-7-nitroundecofuranoses (**45.5**).

The key step (Fig. 1.46) of the synthesis of the carbohydrate portion of the antibiotic *ezomycin* involves the condensation of 5-deoxy-1,2-*O*-isopropylidene-3-*O*-(methylthio)methyl-5-nitro-α-D-ribofuranose (**46.1**) with 2,3-*O*-isopropylidene-L-glyceraldehyde (**46.2**) in the presence of potassium fluoride catalyst.[87] Reduction and subsequent acetylation of the resulting octofuranose mixture (**46.3**) gave a separable mixture of three (compounds **46.4–46.6**) of the theoretically possible four isomers in 71% overall yield. In this case application of potassium fluoride catalyst did not ensure a stereoselective reaction.[87]

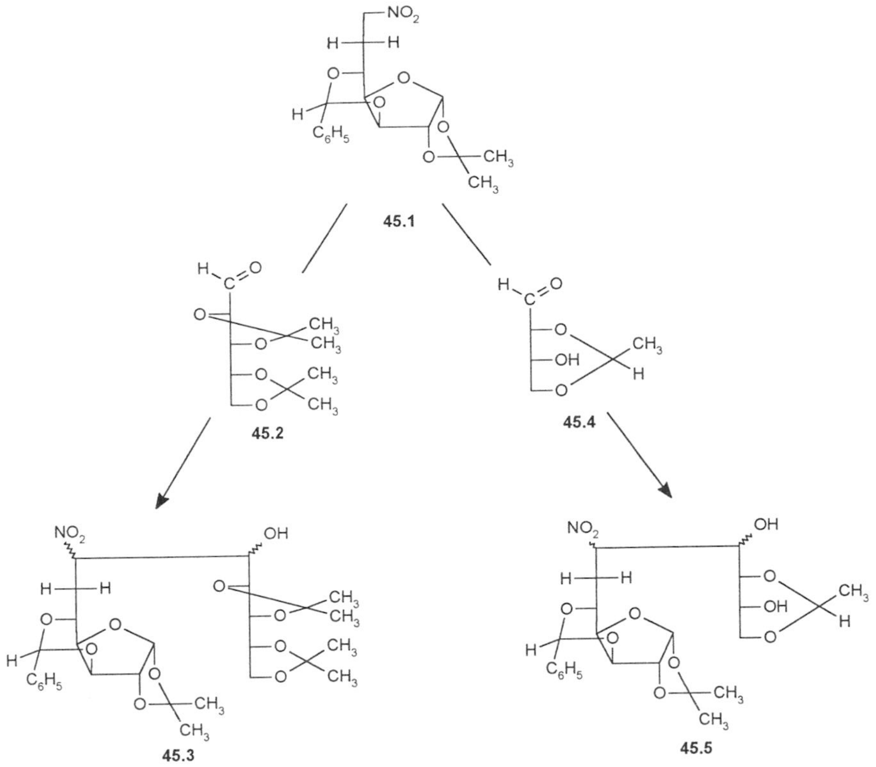

FIGURE I.45

5-Acetamido-5-deoxy-1,2:7,8-di-O-isopropylidene-3-O-(methylthio)methyl-β-L-erythro-L-talo-octofuranose-(1,4) **(46.5)** *and 5-acetamido-5-deoxy-1,2:7,8-di-O-isopropylidene-3-O-(methylthio)methyl-β-L-threo-L-talo-octofuranose-(1,4)* **(46.4)**[87] To a solution of the nitro sugar **46.1** (1 g) and 2,3-O-isopropylidene-L-glyceraldehyde **(46.2)** (0.75 g) in toluene (3 ml) anhydrous potassium fluoride (0.25 g) and tetrabutylammonium fluoride are added and the reaction mixture is stirred at room temperature for 2.5 h. It is then diluted with ethyl acetate, washed with water several times, dried, and concentrated. The residue is dissolved in a mixture of ethyl acetate (20 ml) and acetic anhydride (1 ml) and hydrogenated at 53.9 Pa for 20 h over Raney-Ni T-4 catalyst.[88] The catalyst is filtered off, sodium carbonate (5 g) is added, and the mixture is stirred for 1 h. The precipitate is filtered off, the filtrate is concentrated to a syrup that is dissolved in methanol (20 ml), and acetic anhydride (1 ml) is added. After remaining at room temperature for 10 min, the mixture is evaporated, then coevaporated with toluene and the residue is subjected to column chromatography with ethyl acetate eluant to obtain a mixture (1.01 g, 67%) of **46.5** and **46.6** and 0.072 g (4.7%) of **46.4**. The mixture of the former two compounds is dissolved in toluene (10 ml) and the solution is kept at −20°C overnight. The precipitated crystals of **46.5** are recrystallized from toluene to obtain the pure product with m.p. 138–139°C, $[\alpha]_D^{23}$ +25.9 (c = in chloroform) and syrupy **46.4**, $[\alpha]_D^{25}$ +44.0 (c = 1.08 in chloroform).

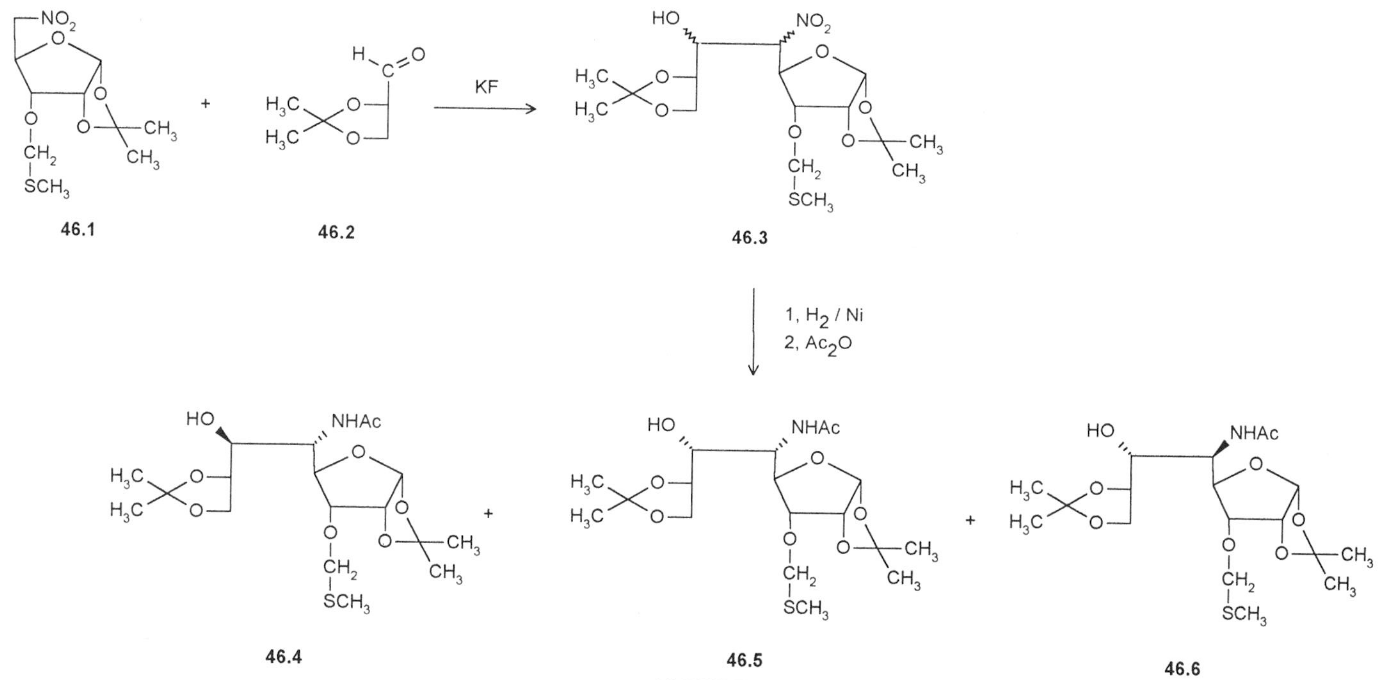

FIGURE I.46

Condensation of 6,7-dideoxy-1,2:3,4-di-O-isopropylidene-7-nitro-α-D-galacto-heptopyranose (**47.1**) with 2,3:4,5-di-O-isopropylidene-aldehydo-D-arabinose (**47.2**) in the presence of sodium methoxide gives rise to three 6,7-dideoxy-7-nitro-1,2:3,4:9,10:11,12-tetra-O-isopropylidene-α-D-dodecapyranoses (**47.3–47.5**), shown in Figure 1.47 and the fourth isomer (**47.6**) could not be detected[89] in the reaction mixture.

With the goal of total synthesis of the antibiotic *tunicamycin,* a similar chain extension was carried out (Fig. 1.48) with 2-benzyloxycarbonylamino-2,6,7-trideoxy-3,4-O-isopropylidene-α-D-galacto-hepto-1,5-pyranose (**48.1**). Thus, in the nitroaldol condensation of **48.1** with 1,2-O-isopropylidene-3-O-benzyl-α-D-allofuranos-1,4-ulose (**48.2**), two isomeric, protected 7-nitro-β-L-dodecodialdo-(12R)-furanose-(12,9)-pyranosides(1,5) (**48.3**) were produced,[90] whose configuration was not clarified.

It is interesting to note that a *reversed functionalization* of the reaction partners, namely, the nitroaldol condensation of 3-O-acetyl-5-deoxy-1,2-O-isopropylidene-5-nitro-α-D-ribofuranose with methyl 2-benzyloxycarbonylamino-2-deoxy-3,4-O-isopropylidene-α-D-galactopyranoside gave a *single* isomer: methyl 9-O-acetyl-2-benzyloxycarbonylamino-2,7-dideoxy-3,4:10,11-di-O-isopropylidene-7-nitro-β-L-undecodialdo-(11R)-furanose-(11,8)-pyranoside-(1,5).[91]

When methyl 5-deoxy-2,3-O-isopropylidene-5-nitro-β-D-ribofuranoside (**49.1**) was treated with methyl 2-(benzyloxycarbonyl)amino-2-deoxy-3,4-O-isopropylidene-α-D-galacto-dialdo-1,5-pyranoside (**49.2**) in the presence of potassium fluoride catalyst for 1 h (Fig. 1.49), a single, crystalline product was isolated in 61% yield, whose structure was assigned as methyl 2-(benzyloxycarbonyl)amino-2,7-dideoxy-3,4:9,10-di-O-isopropylidene-7-nitro-β-D-*glycero*-L-*altro*-D-*galacto*-undecadialdo-[methyl-(11R)-furanoside-(8,11)]-pyranoside-(1,5) (**49.3**).[92]

Considering the practical advantages, Seebach modified the Henry reaction by executing the fluoride–ion-catalyzed condensation of the aldehyde with silylnitronates.[93] This method could be successfully extended to carbohydrates, as well, and thus Martin has applied extremely mild conditions ($-78°$C, 12 h) for the chain extension of *aldehydo*-sugars with the trimethysilyl ester of 1-*aci*-nitropropane. The reaction does not require a large excess of the silylnitronate: 1.1 eq of the reagent is sufficient for completion of the transfromation.[94]

Still another modification of the Henry reaction is the introduction of phenylthionitromethane for condensation with the *aldehydo*-sugars. The advantages of this strategy, elaborated by Barrett,[95] are shown in Figure 1.50, illustrating the preparation of the key intermediate, methyl 5,6-dideoxy-2,3-O-isopropylidene-6-nitro-6-(phenylthio)-β-D-*ribo*-hex-5(Z)-enofuranoside (**50.3**) in the total synthesis of the antibiotic *polyoxin C.*

Methyl 5,6-dideoxy-2,3-O-isopropylidene-6-nitro-6-(phenylthio)-β-D-ribo-hex-5(Z)-enofuranoside (50.3)[95] To a solution of phenylthionitromethane (1.82 g,

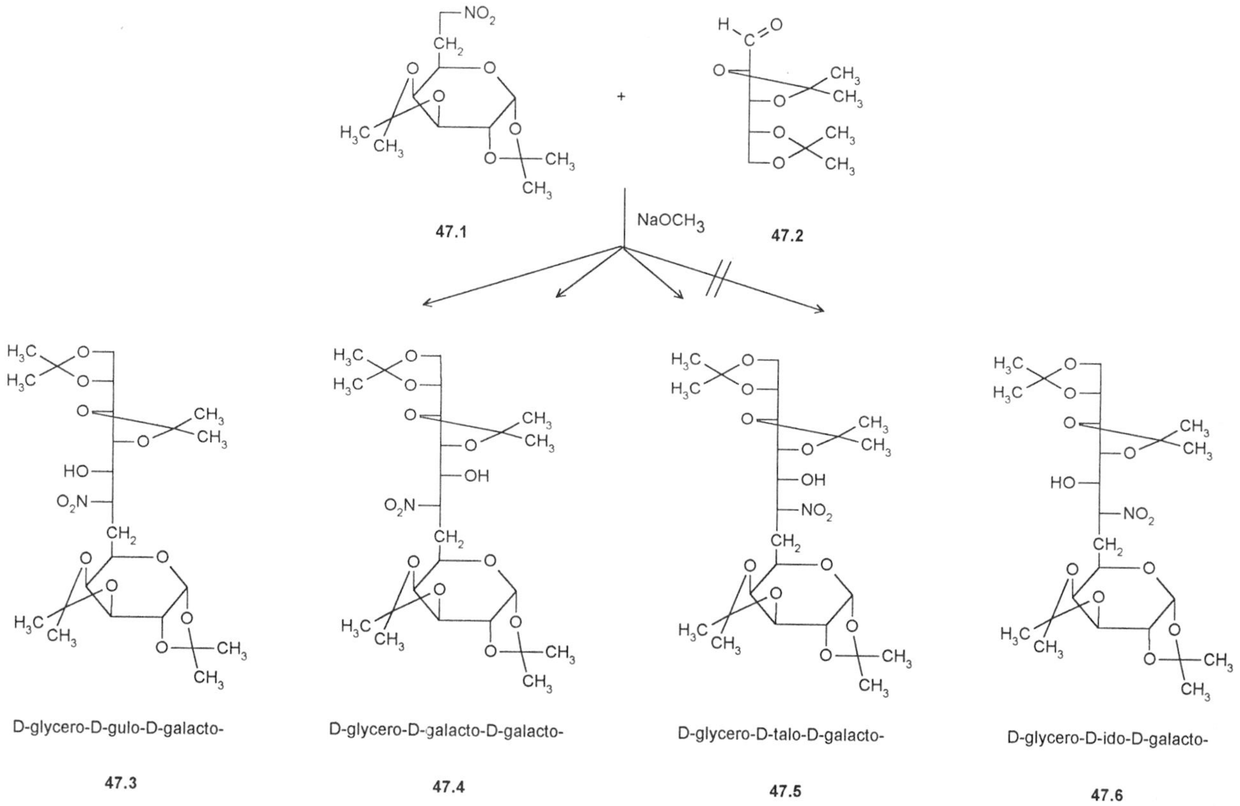
NaOCH3
47.1
47.2
D-glycero-D-gulo-D-galacto-
47.3
D-glycero-D-galacto-D-galacto-
47.4
D-glycero-D-talo-D-galacto-
47.5
D-glycero-D-ido-D-galacto-
47.6

FIGURE 1.47

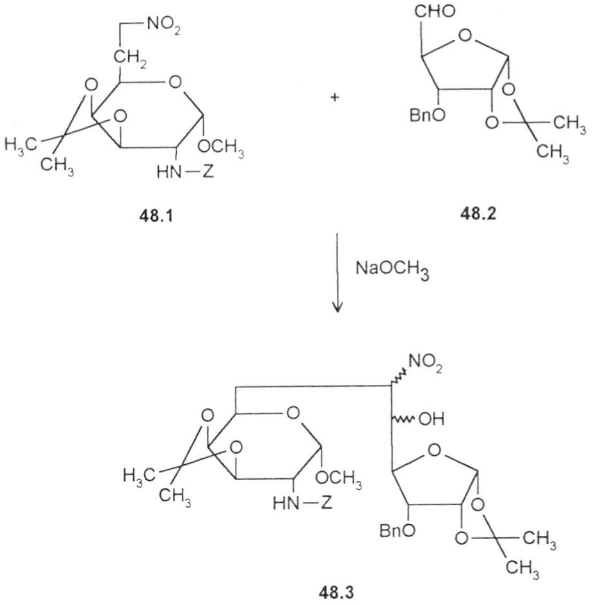

48.1   48.2

NaOCH₃

48.3

FIGURE 1.48

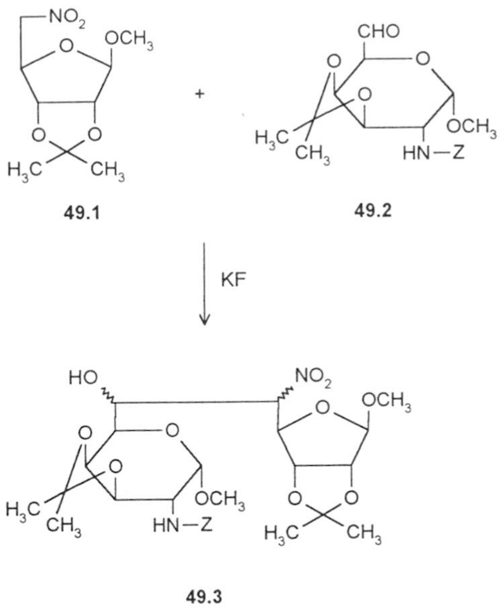

49.1   49.2

KF

49.3

FIGURE 1.49

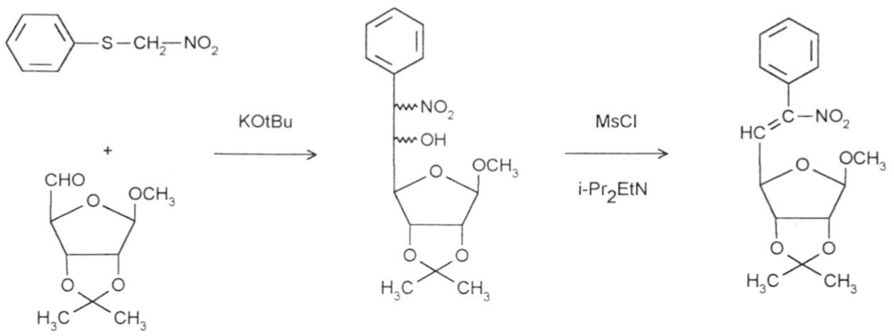

FIGURE 1.50

10.73 mmol) in a mixed-solvent system of 1 : 1 THF/t-BuOH (90 ml) at 0°C is added potassium $tert$-butoxide (1 M in t-BuOH; 0.1 eq, 1.1 ml). To the resulting suspension, methyl 2,3-O-isopropylidene-β-D-$ribo$-pentodialdo-1,4-furanoside (**50.1**, 2.17 g, 10.73 mmol) in anhydrous THF (25 ml) is added; the reaction mixture is allowed to warm to 25°C and maintained for 12 h, then poured into water (100 ml) and extracted with ether (3 × 50 ml). The combined organic layer is dried (MgSO$_4$), and concentrated, and the residue is filtered through a pad of silica, flushing with dichloromethane (200 ml). The eluant is evaporated, and to a solution of the residual sugar (**50.2**) in anhydrous dichloromethane (90 ml), methanesulfonyl chloride (2.5 ml, 32.19 mmol) is added at −78°C, followed by diisopropylethylamine (3.0 ml, 32.19 mmol). The reaction mixture is allowed to warm to −30°C, maintained for 30 min and then poured into cold saturated aqueous NaHCO$_3$ (100 ml), and the organic layer is separated. The aqueous phase is extracted with dichloromethane (2 × 50 ml), and the combined organic layer is dried (MgSO$_4$) and evaporated. The residue is subjected to column chromatography on silicagel (eluant: 3 : 7 ether–hexanes) to give the nitroolefin **50.3** (3.53 g, 93%) as a yellow crystalline solid, m.p. 103°C (from ether–hexanes), [α]$_D$ −55.7 (c = 1.235 in chloroform).

1.2.3.6. Nitroaldol Condensations with 1-Deoxy-1-Nitroaldoses

1-Deoxy-1-nitrosugars, available[96] only quite recently, are also suitable starting materials for chain extensions with aldehydes or $aldehydo$-sugars, such as 1,2 : 3,4-di-O-isopropylidene-α-D-$galacto$-hexopyranos-1,5-ulose.[97] The resulting nitro compounds are very useful targets for transformation into ketoses[97] in a subsequent step, or into "C-glycosidic compounds" on denitration[98] with tributylstannane.

As an example, Figure 1.51 shows the reaction of 1-deoxy-2,3-O-isopropylidene-1-nitro-5-O-trityl-D-ribofuranose (**51.1**) with formaldehyde to furnish an anomeric mixture (**51.2** and **51.3**) of the desired D-psicofuranose derivatives.

2-Deoxy-3,4-O-isopropylidene-2-nitro-6-O-trityl-α- (51.2) and β-D-psicofura-nose (51.3)[97] To a solution of the 1-deoxy-1-nitroribofuranose derivative **51.1** (923 mg, 2 mmol; available in the form of an anomeric mixture) in methanol (10 ml), paraformaldehyde (600 mg, 20 mmol) and potassium carbonate (28 mg,

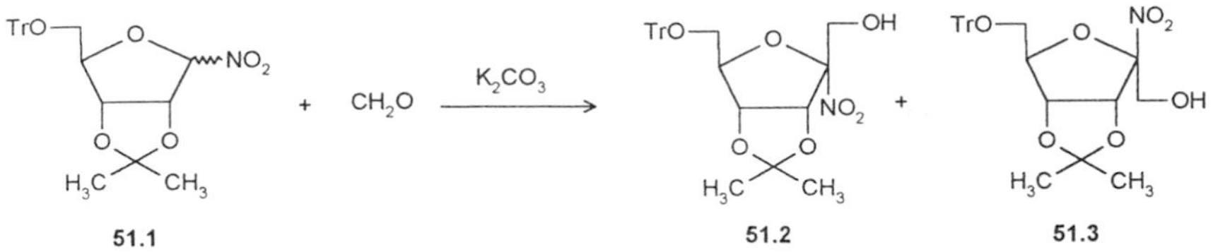

FIGURE I.5I

0.2 mmol) are added, and the mixture is stirred at room temperature for 140 min. It is then concentrated under diminished pressure; the residue is taken up with water, extracted with ether, the organic layer is evaporated, and the residue (1 g) is submitted to column chromatography on a silicagel column (60 g) with 1 : 2 ethyl acetate–hexane as the eluant. The first fraction contains the pure β-isomer **51.3** (18 mg, 2%), $[\alpha]_D$ +3.0 (c = 1.4 in chloroform), followed by an anomeric mixture (105 mg, 11%), and the last fraction consists of the pure α anomer **51.2** (730 mg, 74%), as an amorphous powder, $[\alpha]_D$ −25.5 (c = 1.1 in chloroform).

Condensation of 1-deoxy-2,3 : 5,6-di-O-isopropylidene-1-nitro-α-D-mannofuranose (**52.1**) with the dialdose derivative **52.2** (Fig. 1.52) furnished the dodeculose **52.3** in a diastereoselective reaction, and the structure of the product could be unequivocally proved by X-ray measurements.

> *7-Deoxy-1,2 : 3,4 : 8,9 : 11,12-tetra-O-isopropylidene-7-nitro-β-D-manno-D-gly-cero-α-D-galacto-dodeco-1,5-pyranos-7-ulo-7,10-furanose (52.3)*[97] To a mixture of the deoxynitrofuranose **52.1** (289 mg, 1 mmol) and 1,2 : 3,4-di-O-isopropylidene-α-D-*galacto*-hexopyranos-1,5-ulose (**52.2**, 516 mg, 1 mmol) in dichloromethane (5 ml) tetrabutylammonium fluoride is added in three portions (114, 74, and 30 mg, 0.69 mmol) at 20-min intervals at room temperature. The mixture is stirred for a further 45 min, and concentrated, and the yellow, syrupy residue is submitted to column chromatography (eluant: 1 : 3 ethyl acetate–hexanes). The first fraction contains the unreacted ulose **52.2** (196 mg, 0.76 mmol), followed by a mixture (64 mg) of two nonidentified by-products. The third fraction (496 mg, 90%) contains the crude title product **52.3**, which is recrystallized from ether–hexanes to afford the pure sugar (427 mg, 78%), m.p. 172.5–173°C, $[\alpha]_D^{20}$ −15.2 (c = 1.0 in chloroform).

On solvolysis, or treatment with sodium hydrogencarbonate in N,N-dimethylformamide, the deoxynitro disaccharide **52.3** can be readily transformed (Fig. 1.52) into 1,2 : 3,4 : 8,9 : 11,12-tetra-O-isopropylidene-D-*manno*-D-*glycero*-α-D-*galacto*-dodeco-1,5-pyranos-7-ulo-7,10-furanose[97] (**52.4**), or—after O-acetylation—the resulting sugar is reduced with tri-n-butyl stannane into 6-acetoxy-7,10-anhydro-1,2 : 3,4 : 8,9 : 11,12-tetra-O-isopropylidene-α-D-*erythro*-L-*manno*-D-*galacto*-dodeco-1,5-pyranose (**52.5**), which is produced from an intermediary radical as the more stable product.[98]

The transformation shown in Figure 1.53 is also based on the previous principle, allowing a straightforward route[99] to N-*acetylneuraminic acid* by means of the nitroaldol condensation of the 1-deoxy-1-nitro-D-glucosamine (**53.1**) derivative with 1,2-O-cyclohexylidene-D-glyceraldehyde (**53.2**) to give the chain-extended nonitol **53.3**.

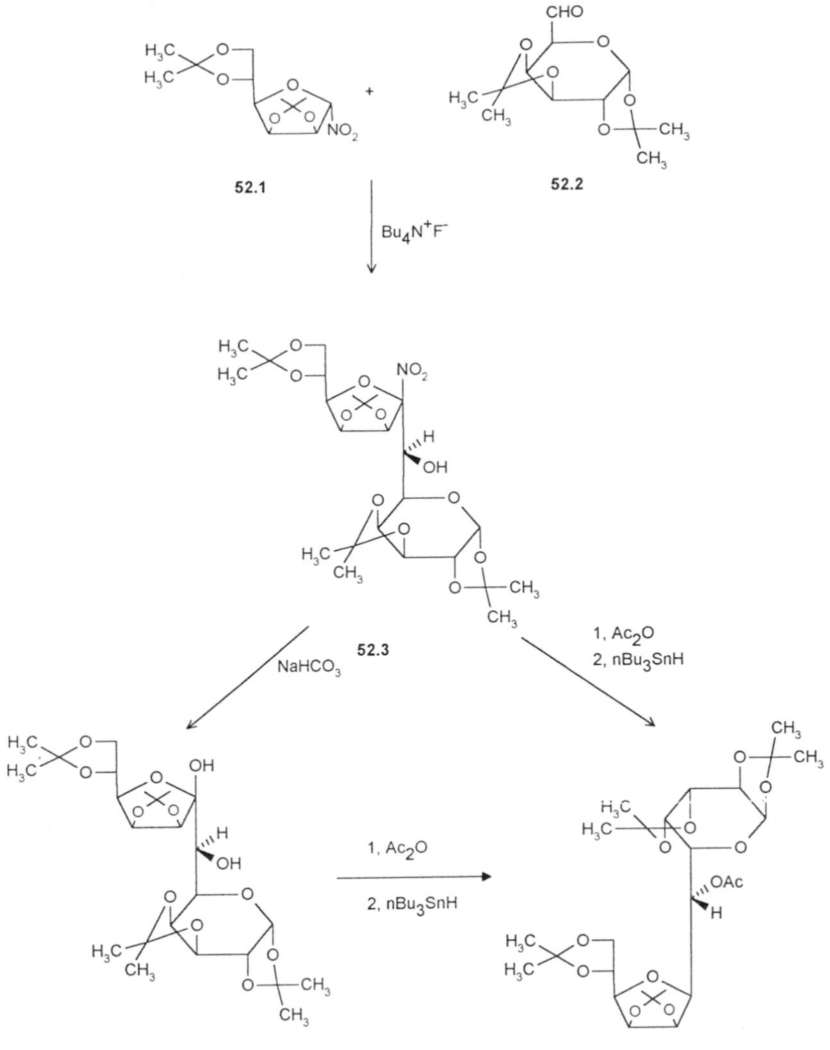

FIGURE I.52

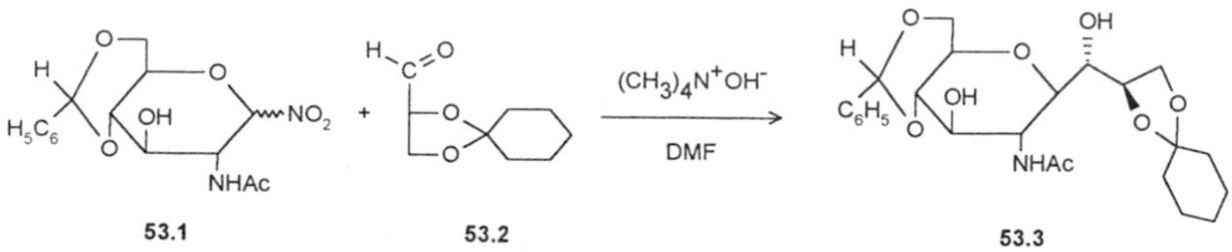

FIGURE I.53

(4R)-5-Acetamido-4,8-anhydro-7,9-O-benzylidene-1,2-O-cyclohexylidene-5-deoxy-4-nitro-D-gluco-L-erythro-nonitol (53.3)[99]   To a solution of the 1-deoxy-1-nitro-D-glucosamine derivative (**53.1,** 4.0 g, 11.8 mmol) in *N,N*-dimethylformamide (30 ml) a mixture of tetramethylammonium hydroxide in methanol (0.3 ml, 1.5 mol) and 2,3-*O*-cyclohexylidene-D-glyceraldehyde (**53.2,** 1.5 g, 8,8 mmol) is added, and the same amount of these reagents added, again, three times at 45 min intervals. The reaction mixture is stirred for an additional hour, and the solvents are removed under reduced pressure. The residue is purified by means of column chromatography on 500 g of silicagel (eluant: 1 : 1 ethyl acetate–hexanes) to afford pure **53.3** as a foam, $[\alpha]_D^{20}$ + 17.4 (*c* = 1.1 in chloroform). The product can be converted into the crystalline diacetate (m.p. 148–149°C, $[\alpha]_D^{20}$ −3.8 (*c* = 1.1 in chloroform) by treatment with acetic anhydride in pyridine.

1.2.3.7. Nitroaldol Condensation with *C*-Glycopyranosyl-Nitromethane Derivatives

2,6-Anhydro-1-deoxy-1-nitroheptitols ("*C*-glycopyranosyl-nitromethanes"), which can be formally regarded[100] as *C*-glycosidic compounds, are also excellent educts for chain extension with the nitroaldol condensation methodology. Such transformations have been effected[56,65,101,102] with the available 2-acetamido-2-deoxy-2,6-anhydro-1-deoxy-1-nitroheptitols possessing D-*gluco*-, D-*allo*-, D-*altro*-, D-*galacto*- and D-*manno* configurations.

When a solution of 2,6-anhydro-7-deoxy-7-nitro-L-*glycero*-L-*galacto*-heptitol (**54.1,** "*C*-galactopyranosyl-nitromethane") in Me$_2$SO is treated[103] with formaldehyde in the presence of sodium methoxide (Fig. 1.54), a mixture of 3,7-anhydro-2-deoxy-2-nitro-D-*threo*-L-*galacto*-octitol (**54.2**) and the corresponding *erythro*-isomer (**54.3**) is produced, and an analogous

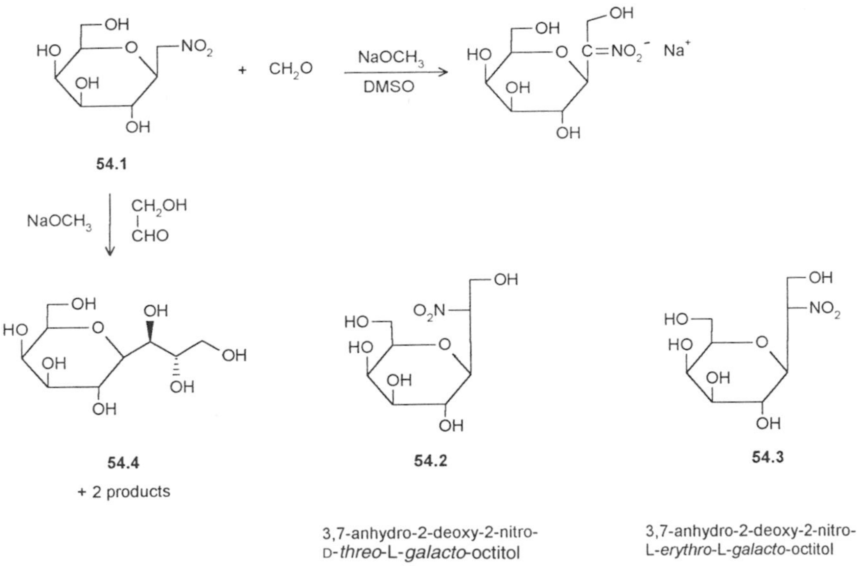

54.1

54.4
+ 2 products

54.2

3,7-anhydro-2-deoxy-2-nitro-
D-*threo*-L-*galacto*-octitol

54.3

3,7-anhydro-2-deoxy-2-nitro-
L-*erythro*-L-*galacto*-octitol

FIGURE I.54

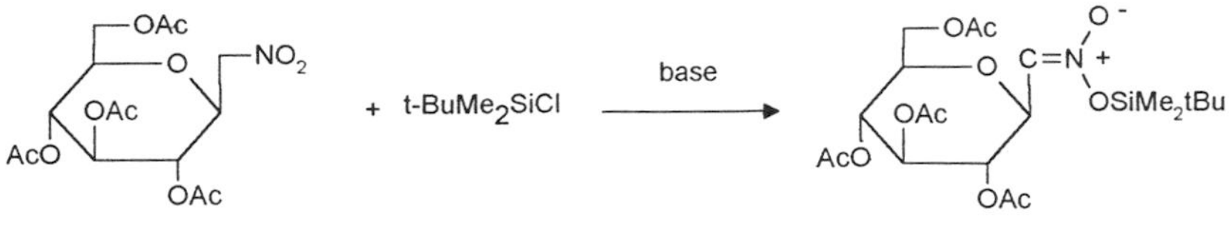

55.1 55.2

Base	Solvent	Yields (%)
Et_3N	C_6H_5-CH_2Cl_2	30
LDA	THF	53
NaH	THF	59
DBU	CH_2Cl_2	95

FIGURE 1.55

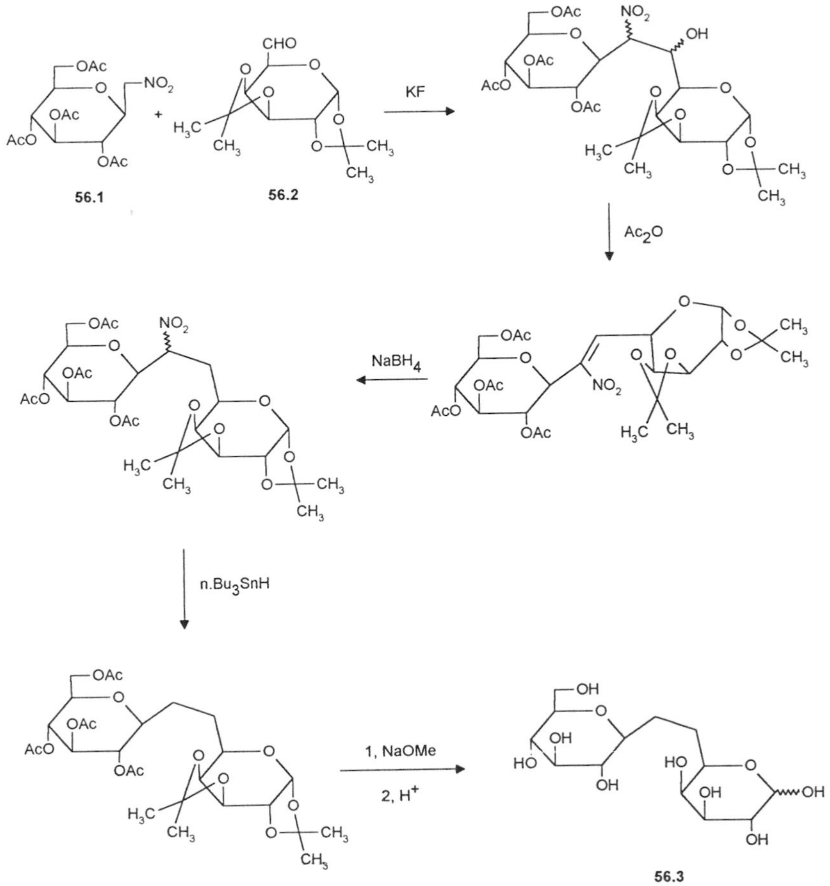

FIGURE 1.56

reaction of the glucopyranose analog has also been reported.[104] With the addition of glycolaldehyde, the formation of four isomeric nitrononitols was expected; three of these were observed when the sugar **54.1** was submitted to nitroaldol condensation. X-Ray measurements on the single crystalline product isolated showed[105] the structure of this chain-extended sugar to be 4,8-anhydro-3-deoxy-3-nitro-D-*lyxo*-D-*gluco*-nonitol (**54.4**).

Martin *et al.*[106,107] have applied the "silylnitronate" chain-elongation procedure also for the family of sugars discussed earlier. Figure 1.55 shows the results of a related transformation of the *gluco*-sugar **55.1** into the nitronate **55.2** in the presence of various bases and solvents.

Silylnitronates readily react with aromatic aldehydes, but an analogous nitroaldol condensation with *aldehydo*-sugars proceeds more advantageously in the presence of potassium fluoride and 18-crown-6. Such an example, when both reaction partners are sugar derivatives, is shown in Figure 1.56. By applying the nitromethyl glucose **56.1** and the *galacto*-dialdose **56.2**, and following conventional synthetic transformations, 8,12-anhydro-6,7-dideoxy-D-*glycero*-D-*gulo*-D-*galacto*-tridecose (**56.3**), the *carbasugar analog* of the disaccharide β-D-Glcp-(1 → 6)-D-Galp could be synthesized.

REFERENCES TO SECTION I.2.3

1. *Houben-Weyl, Methoden der Organischen Chemie*, Vol. X/1. p. 251 (1971),
2. J. C. Sowden, *Adv. Carbohydr. Chem.* **6**, 291 (1951); J. M. Webber, *ibid.* **17**, 15 (1962); H. H. Baer, *Adv. Carbohydr. Chem. Biochem.* **24**, 64 (1969).
3. P. Köll, C. Stenns, W. Seelhorst, and H. Brandenburg, *Justus Liebigs Ann. Chem.*, p. 201 (1991).
4. P. Köll, H. Brandenburg, W. Seelhorst, C. Stenns, and H. Kogelberg, *Justus Liebigs Ann. Chem.*, p. 207 (1991).
5. D. E. Koshland, Jr. and F. H. Westheimer, *J. Am. Chem. Soc.* **71**, 1139 (1949); **72**, 3383 (1950).
6. J. C. Sowden, *Science* **109**, 229 (1949); *J. Biol Chem.* **180**, 55 (1949).
7. J. C. Sowden and H. O. L. Fischer, *J. Am. Chem. Soc.* **69**, 1048 (1947).
8. C. Satoh and A. Kiyomoto, *Carbohydr. Res.* **3**, 248 (1966); C. Satoh, A. Kiyomoto, and T. Okuda, *Carbohydr. Res.* **5**, 140 (1967).
9. J. Stanek, M. Cerny, J. Kocourek, and J. Pacák, *The Monosaccharides*, p. 148, Publ. House Czech. Acad. Scie., Prague, 1963; A. C. Richardson in *Int. Rev. Sci.: Org. Chem.*, *Ser. Two* **7**, 136 (1976).
10. B. O. Gusev, T. Mitrofanova, O. N. Tolkachev, and R. P. Evstigneeva, *Khim. Prir. Soedin.*, p. 8 (1972).
11. J. M. J. Tronchet, K. D. Pallie, and F. Barbalat-Rey, *J. Carbohydr. Chem.* **4**, 29 (1985).
12. J. C. Sowden, *Methods Carbohydr. Chem.* **1**, 132 (1962).
13. J. C. Sowden and D. R. Strobach, *J. Am. Chem. Soc.* **82**, 954 (1960).
14. L. Hough and S. H. Shute, *J. Chem. Soc.*, p. 4633 (1962).
15. H. P. Albrecht, D. P. Repke, and J. G. Moffatt, *J. Org. Chem.* **38**, 1836 (1973).
16. D. B. Repke, H. P. Albrecht, and J. G. Moffatt, *J. Org. Chem.* **40**, 2481 (1975).
17. V. Bílik, *Collect. Czech. Chem. Commun.* **39**, 1621 (1974).

18. J. C. Sowden, *Methods Carbohydr. Chem.* **1,** 132 (1962).
19. A. P. Kozikowski, Y. Kitagawa, and J. P. Springer, *J. Chem. Soc., Chem. Commun.,* p. 1460 (1983).
20. J. C. Sowden and R. R. Thompson, *J. Am. Chem. Soc.* **80,** 2236 (1958).
21. J. C. Sowden, *J. Am. Chem. Soc.* **72,** 808 (1950).
22. D. H. Murray and G. C. Butler, *Can. J. Chem.* **37,** 1776 (1959).
23. D. A. Rappoport and W. Z. Hassid, *J. Am. Chem. Soc.* **73,** 5524 (1951).
24. K. D. Carlson, C. R. Smith, Jr., and I. A. Wolff, *Carbhydr. Res.* **13,** 391 (1970).
25. J. C. Sowden, U.S. Patent 2,530,342 (1950); *Chem. Abstr.* **45,** 2971 (1951).
26. C. Satoh and A. Kiyomoto, *Chem. Pharm. Bull.* **12,** 615 (1964).
27. J. C. Sowden and H. O. L. Fischer, *J. Am. Chem. Soc.* **69,** 1963 (1947).
28. H. Paulsen and W. Grewe, *Chem. Ber.* **106,** 2114 (1973).
29. J. C. Sowden and H. O. L. Fischer, *J. Am. Chem. Soc.* **66,** 1312 (1944).
30. J. C. Sowden and H. O. L. Fischer, *J. Am. Chem. Soc.* **67,** 1733 (1945).
31. J. Yoshimura and H. Ando, *Nippon Kagaku Zasshi* **85,** 138 (1964); *Chem. Abstr.* **61,** 16140d (1964).
32. J. C. Sowden and H. O. L. Fischer, *J. Am. Chem. Soc.* **69,** 1048 (1947).
33. W. W. Zorbach and A. Ollapally, *J. Org. Chem.* **29,** 1790 (1964).
34. R. N. Ray, *J. Indian Chem. Soc.* **65,** 880 (1988).
35. T. Takamoto, H. Omi, T. Matsuzaki, and R. Sudoh, *Carbohydr. Res.* **60,** 97 (1978).
36. M. B. Perry and V. Daoust, *Can. J. Chem.* **51,** 3039 (1973).
37. T. Sakakibara, T. Takamoto, T. Matsuzaki, H. Omi, U. Win Maung, and R. Sudoh, *Carbohydr. Res.* **95,** 291 (1981).
38. H. Paulsen, *Justus Liebigs Ann. Chem.* **665,** 166 (1963).
39. J. M. Grosheintz and H. O. L. Fischer, *J. Am. Chem. Soc.* **70,** 1476 (1948).
40. J. M. Grosheintz and H. O. L. Fischer, *J. Am. Chem. Soc.* **70,** 1479 (1948).
41. R. L. Whistler and R. E. Pyler, *Carbohydr. Res.* **12,** 201 (1970).
42. J. M. J. Tronchet, K. D. Pallie, J. Graf-Poncet, J. F. Tronchet, G. H. Werner and A. Zerial, *Eur. J. Med. Chem.—Chim. Ther.* **21,** 111 (1986).
43. J. Kovár and H. H. Baer, *Can. J. Chem.* **51,** 1801 (1973).
44. J. M. J. Tronchet, K. D. Pallie, and F. Barbalat-Rey, *J. Carbohydr. Chem.* **4,** 29 (1985).
45. T. Iida, M. Funabashi, and J. Yoshimura, *Bull. Chem. Soc. Jpn.* **46,** 3203 (1973).
46. M. Funabashi, K. Kobayashi, and J. Yoshimura, *J. Org. Chem.* **44,** 1619 (1979).
47. M. Iwakawa, J. Yoshimura, and M. Funabashi, *Bull. Chem. Soc. Jpn.* **54,** 496 (1981).
48. S. Ogawa, K. L. Rinehart, Jr., G. Kimura, and R. P. Johnson, *J. Org. Chem.* **39,** 812 (1974).
49. J. M. J. Tronchet, S. Zerelli, N. Dolatshaki, and H. Türler, *Chem. Pharm. Bull.* **36,** 3722 (1988).
50. A. R. Moorman, T. Martin, and R. T. Borchardt, *Carbohydr. Res.* **113,** 233 (1983).
51. R. K. Hulyalkar, J. K. N. Jones, and M. B. Perry, *Can. J. Chem.* **41,** 1490 (1963).
52. D. T. Williams and M. B. Perry, *Can. J. Chem.* **41,** 1490 (1963).
53. J. C. Sowden and R. Schaffer, *J. Am. Chem. Soc.* **73,** 4662 (1951).
54. V. Bílik, J. Alföldi, and K. Bíliková, Czech. Pat. CS 263,174 (1989); *Chem. Abstr.* **113,** 244212g (1990).
55. O. P. Singh and G. A. Adams, *Carbohydr. Res.* **12,** 261 (1970).
56. L. Petruš, S. Bystricky, T. Sticzay, and V. Bílik, *Chem. Zvesti* **36,** 103 (1982).
57. J. C. Sowden and H. O. L. Fischer, *J. Am. Chem. Soc.* **68,** 1511 (1946).
58. L. Benzing and M. B. Perry, *Can. J. Chem.* **56,** 691 (1978).
59. J. Yoshimura, H. Sakai, N. Oda, and H. Hashimoto, *Bull. Chem. Soc. Jpn.* **45,** 2027 (1972).
60. D. Horton and A. Liav, *Carbohydr. Res.* **24,** 105 (1972).
61. J. Kovár and H. H. Baer, *Can. J. Chem.* **48,** 2377 (1970).
62. J. V. Karabinos and C. S. Hudson, *J. Am. Chem. Soc.* **75,** 4324 (1953).
63. J. C. Sowden and D.R. Strobach, *J. Am. Chem. Soc.* **82,** 956 (1960).

64. M. Teuber, R. D. Bevill, and M. J. Osborn, *Biochemistry* **7**, 3303 (1968).
65. J. C. Sowden and M. L. Oftedahl, *J. Org. Chem.* **26**, 1974 (1974); A. Förtsch, H. Kogelberg, and P. Köll, *Carbohydr. Res.* **164**, 391 (1987).
66. P. Köll, J. Kopf, D. Wess, and H. Brandenburg, *Justus Liebigs Ann. Chem.*, p. 685 (1988).
67. R. H. Wollenberg and S. J. Miller, *Tetrahedron Lett.* **19**, 3219 (1978).
68. G. Just and D. R. Payette, *Tetrahedron Lett.* **21**, 3219 (1980); D. R. Payette, and G. Just, *Can. J. Chem.* **59**, 269 (1981); G. Just and H. Oh, *ibid.*, p. 2729.
69. G. B. Howarth, D. G. Lance, W. A. Szarek, and J. K. N. Jones, *Can. J. Chem.*, **47**, 75 (1969); X. Wang and P. H. Gross, *Justus Liebigs Ann. Chem.*, p. 1367 (1995); N. Ono, M. Bougauchi, and K. Maruyama, *Tetrahedron Lett.* **33**, 1629 (1992).
70. J. M. J. Tronchet, K. D. Pallie, and F. Barbalat-Rey, *J. Carbohydr. Chem.* **4**, 29 (1985).
71. K. Brewster, J. M. Harrison, T. D. Inch, and N. Williams, *J. Chem. Soc., Perkin Trans. 1*, p. 21 (1987).
72. W. S. Chilton, W. C. Lontz, R. B. Roy, and C. Yoda, *J. Org. Chem.* **21**, 3222 (1971).
73. M. Mancera, E. Rodriguez, I. Roffé, and J. A. Galbis, *J. Org. Chem.* **53**, 5648 (1988).
74. J. C. Sowden, *J. Am. Chem. Soc.* **72**, 3225 (1950); J. C. Sowden and D. R. Strobach, *J. Am. Chem. Soc.* **80**, 2532 (1958).
75. T. Suami, K. Tadano, A. Suga, and Y. Ueno, *J. Carbohydr. Chem.* **3**, 429 (1984).
76. V. Wehner and V. Jäger, *Angew. Chem.* **102**, 1180 (1990); *Angew. Chem., Int. Ed. Engl.* **29**, 1169 (1990).
77. V. I. Kornilov, B. B. Paidak, and Ju. A. Zhdanov, *Zh. Obshch. Khim.* **43**, 189 (1973).
78. G. Just and P. Potvin, *Can. J. Chem.* **58**, 2173 (1980).
79. I. F. Pelyvás, C. Monneret, and P. Herczegh, *Synthetic Aspects of Aminodeoxy Sugar of Antibiotics* Springer-Verlag, Heidelberg, 1988.
80. S. Brandänge and B. Lindquist, *Acta Chem. Scand. Ser. B* **B39**, 589 (1985).
81. S. Hanessian and J. Kloss, *Tetrahedron Lett.* **26**, 1261 (1985).
82. M. P. Maguire, P. L. Feldman, and H. Rapoport, *J. Org. Chem.* **55**, 948 (1990).
83. B. J. Magerlein, *Tetrahedron Lett.* **11**, 33 (1970).
84. Y. Fukuda, H. Sasi, and T. Suami, *Bull. Chem. Soc. Jpn.* **54**, 1830 (1981).
85. K. Kanai, J. Nishigaki, S. Ogawa, and T Suami, *Bull. Chem. Soc. Jpn.* **60**, 261 (1987).
86. Y. Fukuda, H. Sasai, and T. Suami, *Bull. Chem. Soc. Jpn.* **54**, 1830 (1981).
87. O. Sakanaka, T. Ohmori, S. Kozaki, T. Suami, T. Ishii, S. Ohba, and Y Saito, *Bull. Chem. Soc. Jpn.* **59**, 1753 (1986); O. Sakanaka, T. Ohmori, S. Kozaki, and T. Suami, *ibid.*, p. 3523.
88. S. Nishimura, *Bull. Chem. Soc. Jpn.* **32**, 61 (1959).
89. Y. Fukuda, H. Kitasato, H. Sasai, and T. Suami, *Bull. Chem. Soc. Jpn.* **55**, 880 (1982).
90. Y. Fukuda, H. Sasai, and T. Suami, *Bull. Chem. Soc. Jpn.* **55**, 1574 (1982).
91. H. Asai, K. Matsuno, and T. Suami, *J. Carbohydr. Chem.* **4**, 99 (1985).
92. T. Suami, Y. Fukuda, J. Yamamoto, Y. Saito, M. Ito, and S. Ohba, *J. Carbohydr. Chem.* **1**, 9 (1982).
93. E. W. Colwin, A. K. Beck, and D. Seebach, *Helv. Chim. Acta* **64**, 2264 (1981); D. Seebach, A. K. Beck, T. Mukhopadhay, and E. Thomas, *ibid.* **65**, 1101 (1982).
94. O. R. Martin, F. E. Khamis, H. A. El-Shenawy, and S. P. Rao, *Tetrahedron Lett.* **30**, 6139 (1989).
95. A. G. M. Barrett and S. A. Lebold, *J. Org. Chem.* **55**, 3853 (1990).
96. B. Aebischer and A. Vasella, *Helv. Chim. Acta* **66**, 789 (1983).
97. B. Aebischer, J. H. Bieri, R. Prewo, and A. Vasella, *Helv. Chim. Acta* **65**, 2251 (1982).
98. F. Baumberger and A. Vasella, *Helv. Chim. Acta* **66**, 2210 (1983).
99. R. Julina, I. Müller, A. Vasella, and R. Wyler, *Carbohydr. Res.* **164**, 415 (1987).
100. M. H. D. Postema, *Tetrahedron* **48**, 8545 (1992).
101. K. N. Drew and P. H. Gross, *Tetrahedron* **47**, 6113 (1991).
102. X. Wang and P. H. Gross, *J. Org. Chem.* **60**, 1201 (1995).

103. M. Petrušová, E. Lattová, M. Matulová, and L. Petruš, *Chem. Papers* **45,** 120 (1992).
104. M. Petruš and J. N. BeMiller, *Carbohydr. Res.* **230,** 197 (1992).
105. P. Köll, J. Kopf, M. Morf, B. Zimmer, M. Petrušová, and L. Petruš, *Carbohydr. Res.* **224,** 273 (1992).
106. O. R. Martin, F. E. Khamis, and S. P. Rao, *Tetrahedron Lett.* **30,** 6143 (1989).
107. O. R. Martin and W. Lai, *J. Org. Chem.* **58,** 176 (1993).

1.2.4. Chain Extension with Diazoalkanes

1.2.4.1. Hydrolysis of Diazoketones

The chain extension methodology leading through diazoketones (Fig. 1.57) is based on the well-known transformation[1] of acid halides (**57.1**) with diazoalkanes (**57.2**), and involves conversion of the diazoketone (**57.3**) thus produced into halogenoketoses (**57.4**), ketoses (**57.5**), or deoxyketoses (**57.6**) by treatment with hydrogen halides, or acetic acid or by applying simple hydrolytic conditions, respectively.

The reaction of aldonic acid chlorides with excess diazomethane proceeds easily; for example, 2,3,4,5,6-penta-*O*-acetyl-D-gluconyl chloride (**58.1**) readily gives 3,4,5,6,7-penta-*O*-acetyl-1-deoxy-1-diazo-D-*gluco*-heptulose (**58.2**) in moderate yield,[2] as shown in Figure 1.58.

> *3,4,5,6,7-Penta-O-acetyl-1-deoxy-1-diazo-D-gluco-heptulose (58.2)*[2]   To a solution of diazomethane (2.1 g, 0.23 mol) in dry ether a solution of the chloride **58.1** (5 g, 10 mmol) in 50 ml of dry ether is added dropwise with stirring at 0°C. After remaining at room temperature for 3 h, the solvent is distilled off to result in the crystallization of the product on cooling. The pure diazoketone **58.2** (2.5 g) is

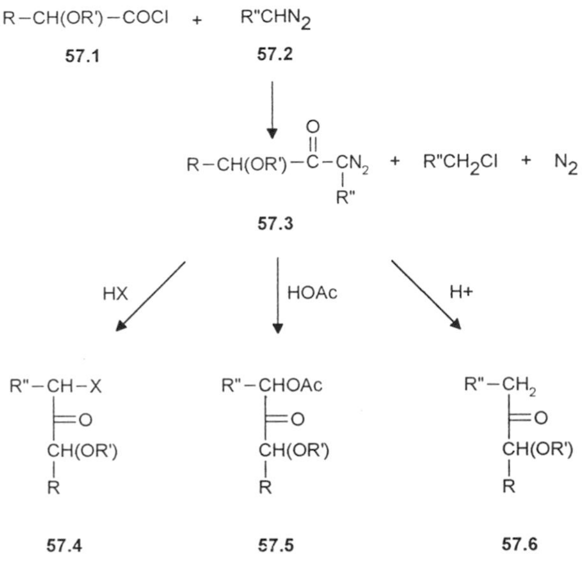

FIGURE 1.57

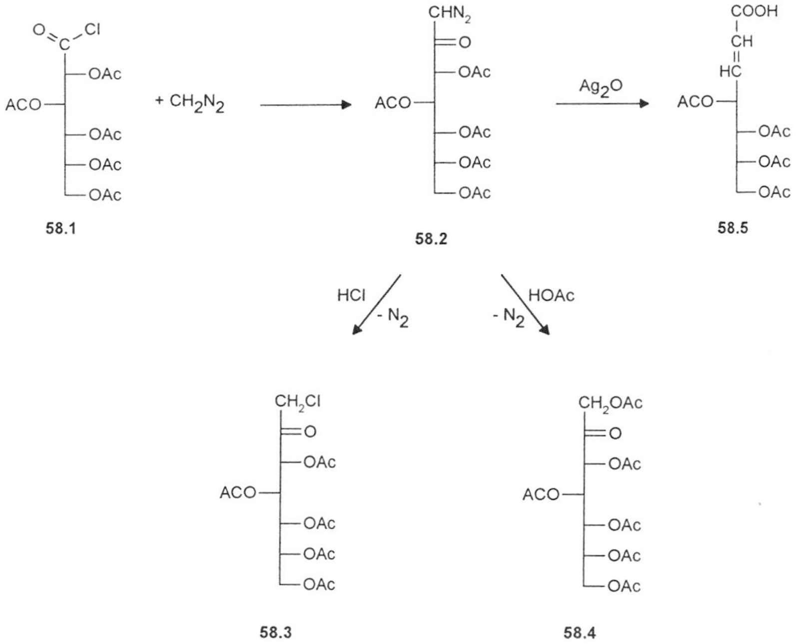

FIGURE I.58

obtained after recrystallization from ether, m.p. 106–106.5°C, $[\alpha]_D^{30}$ +65.8 ($c = 4$ in chloroform).

An analogous reaction of diacetyl-L-tartaric chloride gives rise[3] to the 1-methyl ester of L-*threo*-di-*O*-acetyl-5-diazo-5-deoxy-4-pentulonic acid.

On treatment with hydrogen halides or acetic acid, the diazoketone produced in the reaction is transformed into the corresponding halogeno-methyl[4] or acetoxy ketone,[5] and such conversions are illustrated, again, through the example of the diazoglucoheptulose (**58.2**) (Fig. 1.58).

*3,4,5,6,7-Penta-O-acetyl-1-chloro-1-deoxy-D-*gluco-*heptulose (58.3)*[4] One gram of the diazoketone **58.2** is suspended in ether (15 ml), and dry hydrochloric acid gas is passed through until a clear solution is produced. It is kept at room temperature for 2 h, the excess HCl is removed by extraction with aqueous sodium hydrogencar-bonate, the organic phase is dried (Na₂SO₄) and diluted with the same volume of petroleum ether, and the precipitated crystals are filtered and washed with petroleum ether to isolate 0.6 g of **58.3**, m.p. 100–101°C, $[\alpha]_D^{22}$ −5.5 ($c = 5$ in chloroform).

*1,3,4,5,6,7-Hexa-O-acetyl-D-*gluco-*heptulose (58.4)*[5] A solution of the diazoke-tone **58.2** (5.0 g) in acetic anhydride (100 ml) is boiled under reflux for 10–15 min until no evolution of nitrogen is observed (in the drop-counter tube equipped on top of the condenser). The hot reaction mixture is poured onto crushed ice and extracted with chloroform (4 × 50 ml). The organic layer is washed until neutral, dried over CaSO₄, and decolorized with carbon. Removal of the solvent results in the spontaneous crystallization of the product **58.4** as yellow needles, which are recrystallized from 60 ml of 1 : 4 ethanol–water, and diluted with the same volume of hot water. Yield 3.7 g (70%), m.p. 103.5–105°C, $[\alpha]_D^{22}$ +18.7 (c = 2.7 in chloroform). Following three further recrystallizations, highly pure product is obtained with m.p. 104–105°C, $[\alpha]_D^{22}$ +18.7 (c = 2.7 in chloroform).

The same sugar (**58.4**) is obtained when the bromo analog of **58.3** is submitted to similar exchange reaction.

The present procedure allows simple syntheses of the following keto sugars: D-erythrulose,[6] D-ribulose,[7] D-sorbose,[8] L-sorbose,[9] D-fructose,[4] L-fructose,[10] D-psicose,[11] D-*galacto*-heptulose (*D-perseulose*),[12] L-*galacto*-heptulose (*L-perseulose*),[13] L-*manno*-heptulose,[14] D-*altro*-heptulose,[15] D-*glycero*-D-*gulo*-octulose,[16] D-*galacto*-octulose,[17] D-*glycero*-L-*manno*-octulose,[18] D-*glycero*-L-*gluco*-octulose,[18] D-*glycero*-D-*galacto*-octulose,[19] D-*erythro*-L-*manno*-nonulose,[20] and D-*erythro*-L-*gluco*-nonulose.[20]

The diazoketones, derived from diazoalkanes, readily undergo silver oxide–induced Wolff rearrangement[21] to lead to unsaturated acids via elimination. For example, related transformation of the diazoketone **58.2** gives[4,22] 4,5,6,7-tetraacetoxy-D-*arabino*-hept-2-enoic acid **58.5,** as shown in Figure 1.58.

4,5,6-Tri-*O*-acetyl-2,3-dideoxy-L-*threo*-hex-2-enoic acid (**59.3**), the key intermediate[9] to *rhodinose,* can be obtained in a similar fashion, specifically, from the 1-diazo-hex-2-ulose (**59.2**), available from the acid chloride **59.1** derived from L-xylose (Fig. 1.59).

*3,4,5,6-Tetra-O-acetyl-1-deoxy-1-diazo-L-xylo-hex-2-ulose (**59.2**)*[9] A solution of 2,3,4,5-tetra-*O*-acetyl-L-xylonyl chloride (**59.1**) in dry ether is added dropwise to an ethereal solution of diazomethane prepared from 6.1 g of nitrosomethyl urea. Crystallization of the product starts immediately and is complete on cooling. Recrystallization from acetone–ether affords pure **59.2** (7.4 g, 91%), m.p. 124–126°C, $[\alpha]_D^{25}$ −45 (c = 1.09 in chloroform).

*4,5,6-Tri-O-acetyl-2,3-dideoxy-L-threo-hex-2-enoic acid (**59.3**)*[9] To a suspension of **59.2** (2.6 g) in water (100 ml) freshly prepared silver oxide (0.5 g) is added at 65°C. When the gas evolution is finished, a further amount of the catalyst (0.5 g) is gradually added over a period of 45 min. The mixture is filtered, treated with Amberlite IR-120 (H⁺), concentrated to 30 ml, and extracted with chloroform. The organic layer is dried and concentrated, and the residue is purified on a silicagel

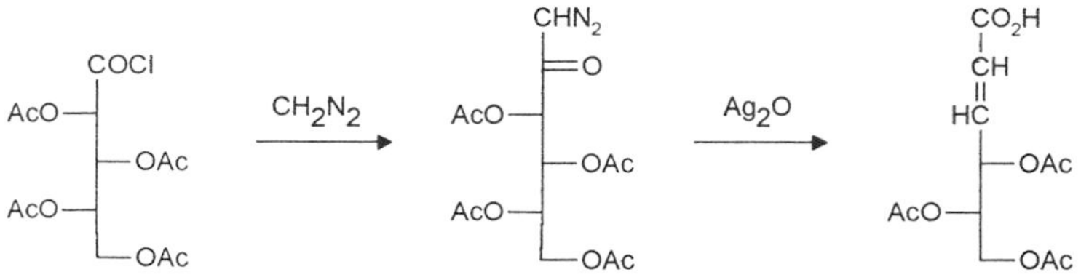

FIGURE 1.59

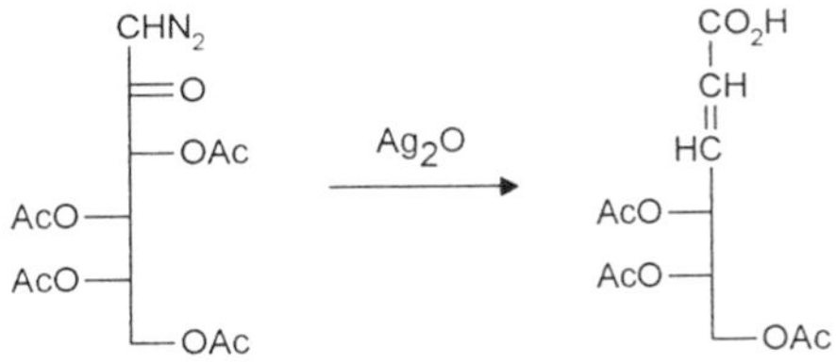

FIGURE 1.60

column (eluant: 40 : 1 dichloromethane–methanol) to obtain pure **59.3** (1.0 g, 48%) as a colorless syrup, $[\alpha]_D^{25}$ −26.8 (c = 2.25 in chloroform).

From 3,4,5,6-tetra-O-acetyl-1-diazo-1-deoxy-L-*arabino*-hex-2-ulose (**60.1**) 4,5,6-tri-O-acetyl-2,3-dideoxy-L-*erythro*-hex-2-enoic acid (**60.2**) can be obtained[22] in a similar manner (Fig. 1.60).

The diazoketone derivatives of sugars can be readily transformed into the corresponding methyl ethers on treatment with methanol in the presence of boron trifluoride etherate. Thus, from 7,8-dideoxy-7-diazo-1,2:3,4-di-O-isopropylidene-α-D-*galacto*-6-octulopyranose (**61.1**), the two 7-O-methyl ethers (**61.2** and **61.3**) are obtained[17] (Fig. 1.61).

1.2.4.2. Addition of Diazomethane to *aldehydo*-Sugars

Homologization of aldehydes to ketones can also be achieved by the addition of diazoalkanes to aldehydes. The intermediate of such a noncatalyzed process[23] (Fig. 1.62) is a *betaine-type* compound (**62.1**), which is most susceptible to loss of nitrogen, giving rise to the methylketone **62.2** or, as a by-product, the respective anhydro derivative (**62.3**).

The progress of this reaction has been studied[24] in detail with 2,3-O-isopropylidene-D-glyceraldehyde, with respect to, for instance, the influence of the solvent. Addition of diazomethane produced 1-deoxy-3,4-O-isopropylidene-D-*glycero*-tetrulose as the major product. The reaction of this aldehyde with methyl diazoacetate has also been studied. It has been found

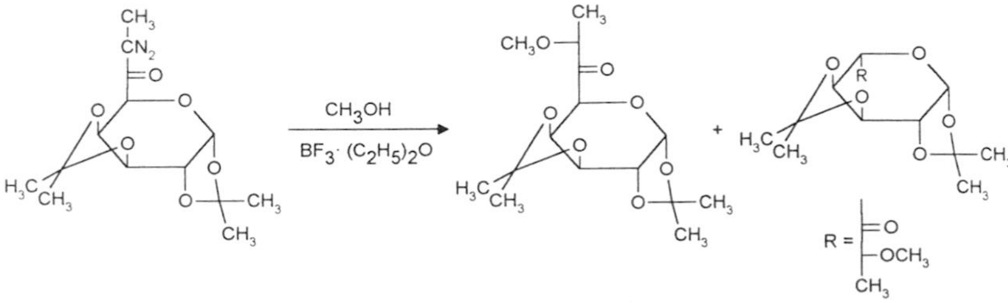

FIGURE 1.61

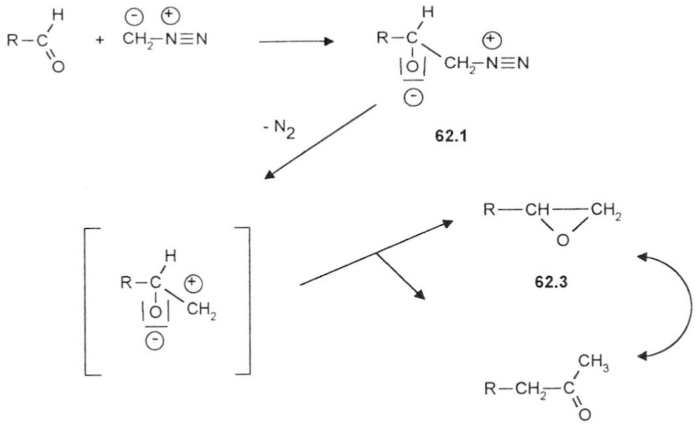

FIGURE 1.62

that the noncatalyzed process gives an 84:16 mixture of the (3S,4R)- and (3R,4R)-4,5-O-isopropylidene-2-diazo-3,4,5-trihydroxypentanoates, and this is explained by an easier approach of the reagent from the *si* side in the more favorable conformation of the *aldehydo* compound.[25]

In practice, this conversion has turned out to be rather useful for a saccharide derivative whose structure has recently been revised. Thus, Grindley[26] showed that the structure of the extended-chain sugar obtained according to the Brigl procedure[27] from "tetrabenzoyl-*aldehydo*-D-glucose" (**63.1**) must be as depicted by formula **63.2** (Fig. 1.63). In a similar, easily reproducible reaction, methyl di-O-acetyl-L-threuronate (**64.1**) can be converted[3] to methyl 2,3-di-O-acetyl-5-deoxy-L-*threo*-4-penturonate (**64.2**), as shown in Figure 1.64.

Further homologization can be conveniently achieved if excess diazomethane is employed in the chain-extension procedure. For example, from the enantiomeric 2,3,4,5-tetra-O-acetyl-*aldehydo*-arabinoses, 4,5,6,7-tetra-

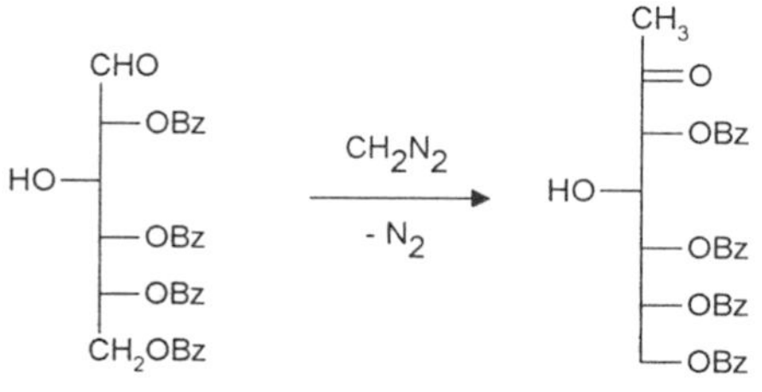

FIGURE 1.63

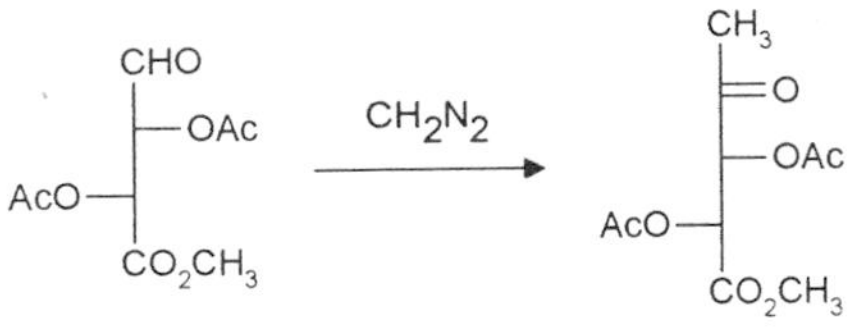

FIGURE 1.64

O-acetyl-1,2-dideoxy-D- and L-*arabino*-heptuloses have been prepared.[28] An analogous procedure (Fig. 1.65) with the *aldehydo*-galactose **65.1** serves for a convenient synthesis[29] of 4,5,6,7,8-penta-O-acetyl-1,2-dideoxy-D-*galacto*-octulose (**65.2**).

> *4,5,6,7,8-Penta-O-acetyl-1,2-dideoxy-D-galacto-octulose (65.2)*[29]   A solution of penta-O-acetyl-*aldehydo*-D-galactose (**65.1**, 8 g) in dry chloroform is treated with 2.2 M ethereal diazomethane with cooling, and the mixture is left at room temperature overnight. It is then filtered, and the filtrate is concentrated to a syrup, which crystallizes on trituration (yield: 7.0 g, m.p. 97–100°C). Recrystallization from a sixfold volume of 50% aqueous ethanol gives small plates of pure **65.2** (5.4 g), m.p. 99–100°C, $[\alpha]_D^{25}$ −10 (c = 4 in chloroform).

In modern carbohydrate chemistry the chain extensions with diazoalkanes play an important role in the synthesis of C-disaccharides as well, since an appropriate diazosaccharide is an excellent reaction partner for the extension of the sugar chain with a longer unit. Spanish chemists[30] based the synthesis of the key intermediate to *2-deoxytunicamine* on a related procedure (Fig. 1.66). Thus, 6-diazo-6-deoxy-1,2;3,4-di-O-isopropylidene-D-galactopyranose (**66.1**), available in a few simple steps, was reacted with methyl 2,3-O-isopropylidene-β-D-*ribo*-pentodialdo-1,4-furanose (**66.2**) to obtain a mixture of the C-disaccharide ketone **66.3** and the epoxide **66.4**—in agreement with those discussed in the introduction of this section. From the anhydro sugar (**66.4**), the target compound, *2-deoxy-tunicamine,* was prepared in a straightforward way.[30]

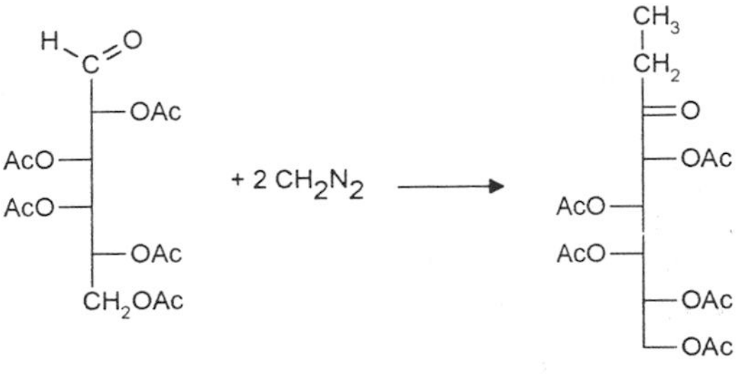

FIGURE 1.65

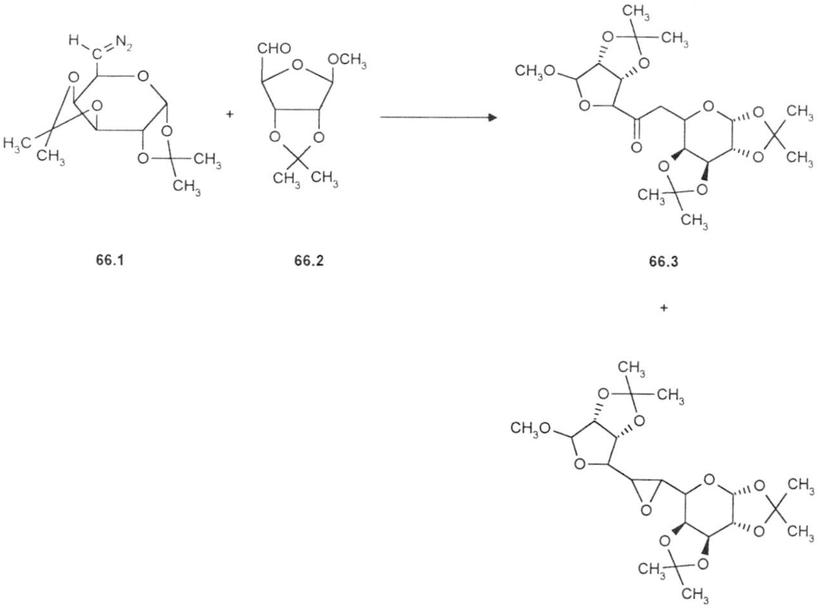

FIGURE 1.66

Condensation of 6-diazo-6-deoxy-1,2:3,4-di-O-isopropylidene-D-galactopyranose
(66.1) with methyl 2,3-O-isopropylidene-β-D-ribo-pentodialdo-1,4-furanoside
(66.2)[30] To a solution of the furanoside **66.2** (1 g) in ether (10 ml) a solution of
the diazo compound **(66.1)** (1.7 g) is added dropwise at 0°C. After stirring for 6 h,
the reaction is complete, and column chromatography of the crude mixture on
silicagel (eluant: 10 : 1 hexane–ethyl acetate) provides 1.8 g (82%) of an unresolvable
1 : 1 mixture of two products. Crystallization of this mixture from hexane–ethyl
acetate gives methyl 5-C-(6-deoxy-1,2:3,4-di-O-isopropylidene-D-galactopyranos-
6-yl)-5-keto-2,3-O-isopropylidene-β-D-ribo-furanoside **(66.3)**, m.p. 124°C, $[\alpha]_D^{20}$
-108.2 ($c = 3.31$ in chloroform), and methyl (1,2:3,4:9,10-tri-O-isopropylidene-6,7-
anhydro-L-*glycero*-L-*allo*-D-*galacto*-undecodialdo-1,5-pyranoside)-11,8-β-furanoside
(66.4), $[\alpha]_D^{20}$ -66.0 ($c = 0.5$ in chloroform).

For the execution of C−C chain extension with a diazoketone, a catalytic procedure has also been elaborated by Kametani and coworkers.[31]
This methodology is based on the rhodium(II)acetate-induced generation
of a carbene, which ensures chain extension with phenyl thioglycosides.
The advantages of this procedure are: (1) the use of phenyl thioglycosides
as starting materials can restrict the reaction site by the preferential participation of the sulfur atom with the carbenoid, (2) the introduction of various
functionalities can be accomplished by manipulation of the organosulfur
groups of the product, (3) the reaction can be performed under neutral
condition, and (4) the C−C bond formation would be stereoselective if this

reaction proceeded via the oxonium intermediate generated by a proposed reaction mechanism as shown in Figure 1.67.

> *General procedure for the intermolecular carbenoid displacement reaction*[31]   A solution of 1 mmol of the protected thioglycoside and 3 eq of dimethyl α-diazomalonate (474 mg) in methylene chloride (20 ml) in the presence of rhodium(II)acetate (30 mg) is refluxed for 2 h. After evaporation of the solvent, the residue is chromatographed on a silicagel column using benzene–ethyl acetate to give the *C*-glycosyl compounds.

Related *C*-glycosylation of a few thioglycosides is shown in Fig. 1.68

Ethyl diazopyruvate could also be employed for the chain extension of mono-saccharides in a Lewis acid–catalyzed process, which gives rise to the esters of 2,4-diketocarboxylic acids. According to Herczegh,[32] the $SnCl_2$-catalyzed reaction provides the products as shown by the equation below:

$$R-CHO + N_2CHCOCO_2C_2H_5 \xrightarrow[20°C]{SnCl_2} R-C(O)=C(OH)-C(O)OC_2H_5$$

> *Chain extension of* aldehydo-*sugar derivatives with ethyl diazopyruvate in a catalyzed process*[32]   To a solution of the aldehyde (4 mmol) and ethyl diazopyruvate (4.1 mmol) in dichloromethane (10 ml), tin(II)chloride (70 mg, 0.37 mmol) is added and the mixture is stirred at room temperature for 3 h. After dilution with the same solvent (50 ml), it is washed successively with saturated aqueous $NaHCO_3$ and dilute EDTA solutions. The product is filtered on Kieselgel 60 using 7:3 hexane–ethyl acetate and then 95:5 dichlorormethane–methanol mixtures.

When the hydroxyaldehydes carry benzyl protecting groups, the relative quantity of the primary products is decreased and secondary processes may predominate, to result in ethyl 2-hydroxytetrahydrofuran-2-carboxylates. It is interesting to note that such conversions, catalyzed by boron trifluoride etherate, are carried out[33,34] with the preponderance of the cyclic products even at temperatures as low as −78°C.

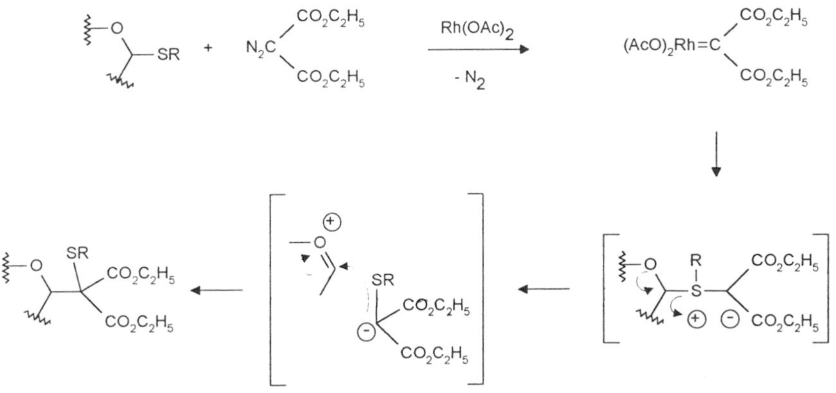

FIGURE I.67

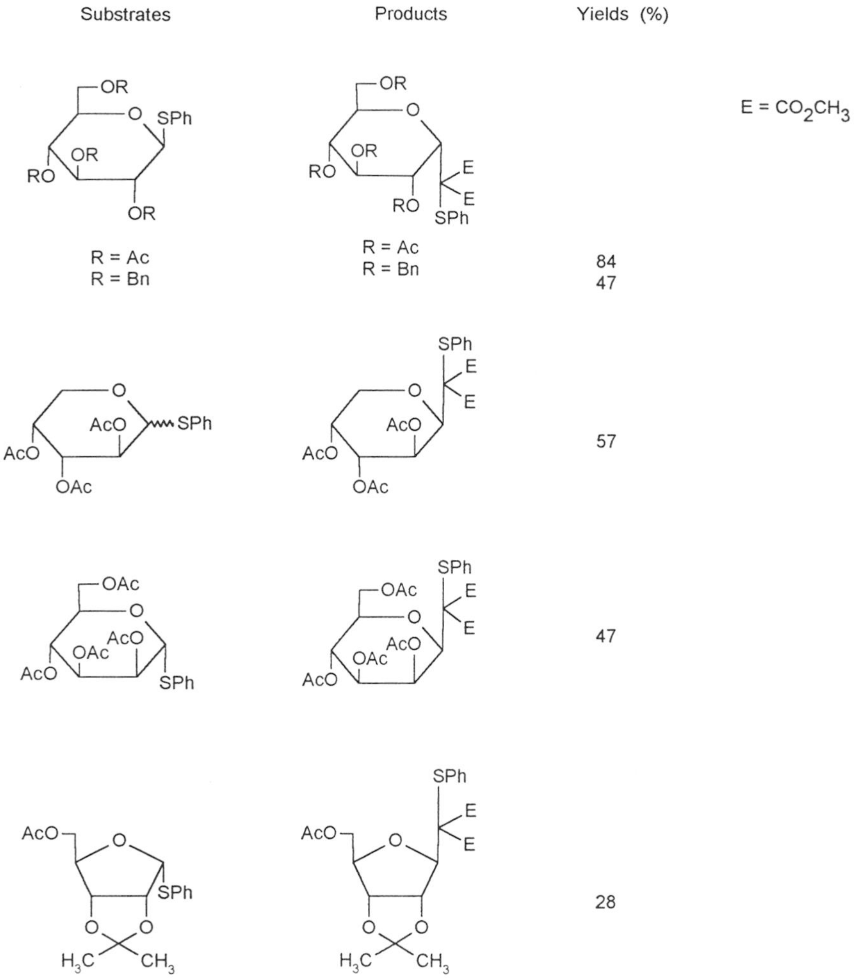

Substrates　　　　　　Products　　　　Yields (%)

$E = CO_2CH_3$

R = Ac
R = Bn

R = Ac
R = Bn

84
47

57

47

28

FIGURE 1.68

REFERENCES TO SECTION 1.2.4

1. B. Eistert, in *Neuere Methoden der präparativen organischen Chemie Vol. I*, p. 395. Verlag Chemie, Berlin, 1944; W. Ried, *Fortschr. Chem. Forsch.* **5,** 1 (1965); G. Hilgetag and A. Martini, *Weygand/Hilgetag, Organisch-chemische Experimentierkunst*, p. 982. Barth Verlag, Leipzig, 1970; A. L. Fridman, T. S. Issmailova, V. S. Salesov, and S. S. Novikov, *Usp. Khim.* **41** 722 (1972).
2. M. L. Wolfrom, D. I. Weisblat, W. H. Zophy, and S. W. Waisbrot, *J. Am. Chem. Soc.* **63,** 201 (1941).

3. A. J. Ultée and J. B. J. Soons, *Recl. Trav. Chim. Pays-Bas* **71**, 565 (1952); F. Weygand and R. Schmiechen, *Chem. Ber.* **92**, 535 (1959).
4. M. L. Wolfrom, S. M. Waisbrot, and R. L. Brown, *J. Am. Chem. Soc.* **64**, 1701 (1942).
5. M. L. Wolfrom, S. W. Waisbrot, and R. L. Brown, *J. Am. Chem. Soc.* **64**, 2329 (1942).
6. K. Iwadare, *Bull. Chem. Soc. Jpn.* **14**, 131 (1939); M. L. Wolfrom and R. B. Bennett, *J. Org. Chem.* **30**, 458 (1965).
7. D. L. MacDonald, J. D. Crum, and R. Barker, *J. Am. Chem. Soc.* **80**, 3379 (1958).
8. M. L. Wolfrom, S. M. Olin, and E. F. Evans, *J. Am. Chem. Soc.* **66**, 204 (1944).
9. W. J. Humphlett, *Carbohydr. Res.* **7**, 431 (1968); R. Knollmann and I. Dyong, *Chem. Ber.* **108**, 2021 (1975).
10. M. L. Wolfrom and A. Thompson, *J. Am. Chem. Soc.* **68**, 791 (1946).
11. M. L. Wolfrom, A. Thompson, and E. F. Evans, *J. Am. Chem. Soc.* **67**, 1793 (1945).
12. M. L. Wolfrom, R. L. Brown, and E. F. Evans, *J. Am. Chem. Soc.* **65**, 1021 (1943).
13. M. L. Wolfrom, J. M. Berkebile, and A. Thompson, *J. Am. Chem. Soc.* **71**, 2360 (1949).
14. M. L. Wolfrom and H. B. Wood, *J. Am. Chem. Soc.* **73**, 730 (1951).
15. M. L. Wolfrom, J. M. Berkebile, and A, Thompson, *J. Am. Chem. Soc.* **74**, 2197 (1952).
16. M. L. Wolfrom and A. Thompson, *J. Am. Chem. Soc.* **68**, 1453 (1946).
17. S. M. David, *Carbohydr. Res.* **38**, 147 (1974); S. M. David and J.-C. Fischer, *ibid.* **50**, 239 (1976).
18. M. L. Wolfrom and P. W. Cooper, *J. Am. Chem. Soc.* **71**, 2668 (1948).
19. M. L. Wolfrom and P. W. Cooper, *J. Am. Chem. Soc.* **72**, 1345 (1950).
20. M. L. Wolfrom and H. B. Wood, *J. Am. Chem. Soc.* **77**, 3096 (1955).
21. L. Wolff, *Justus Liebigs Ann. Chem.* **394**, 23 (1912).
22. D. Charon, *Carbohydr. Res.* **11**, 447 (1969); I. Dyong and W. von der Heydt, *Justus Liebigs Ann. Chem.* **735**, 138 (1970); R. A. Gakhokidse, N. N. Sidamonidse, and Ch. W. Tan, *Zh. Obshch. Khim.* **58**, 911 (1988).
23. B. Eistert, *Neuere Methoden der präparativen organischen Chemie I*, pp. 359–402. Verlag Chemie, Berlin, 1944; C. D. Gutsche, *Org. React. (N.Y.)* **8**, 394 (1954).
24. S. Hagen, T. Anthonsen, and L. Kilaas, *Tetrahedron* **35**, 2583 (1979).
25. F. J. López-Herrera, M. Valpuesta-Fernández, and S. Garcia-Clacos, *Tetrahedron* **46**, 7165 (1990).
26. T. B. Grindley and R. Ponnampalam, *Can. J. Chem.* **58**, 1365 (1980).
27. P. Brigl, H. Mühlschlegel, and R. Schinle, *Ber. Dtsch. Chem. Ges.* **64**, 2921 (1931).
28. M. L. Wolfrom, J. D. Crum, J. B. Miller, and D. I. Weisblat, *J. Am. Chem. Soc.* **81**, 243 (1959).
29. M. L. Wolfrom, D. J. Weisblat, E. F. Evans, and J. B. Miller, *J. Am. Chem. Soc.* **79**, 6454 (1957).
30. F. Sarabia-Garcia, F. J. López-Herrera, and M. S. Pino González, *Tetrahedron* **51**, 5491 (1995); F. J. López-Herrera, F. Sarabia-Garcia, and M. S. Pino González, *Tetrahedron Lett.* **35**, 2933 (1994); F. Sarabia-Garcia and F. J. López-Herrera, *Tetrahedron* **52**, 4757 (1996).
31. T. Kametani, K. Kawamura, and T. Honda, *J. Am. Chem. Soc.* **109**, 3010 (1987).
32. P. Herczegh, I. Kovács, L. Szilágyi, and F. Sztaricskai, *Synlett*, p. 705 (1991).
33. S. R. Angle, G. P. Wei, Y. K. Ko, and K. Kubo, *J. Am. Chem. Soc.* **117**, 8041 (1995).
34. D. D. Dhavale, N. N. Bhujbal, P. Joshi, and S. G. Desai, *Carbohydr. Res.* **263**, 303 (1994).

1.2.5. Chain Extension with Malonester Derivatives

This method is based[1] on the Knoevenagel condensation of aldehydes and ketones with compounds containing an active methylene group, to result in unsaturated carboxylic acid derivatives susceptible of transformations to aldoses[2] with higher carbon chains:

$$R-CHO \rightarrow R-CH=CH-COR' \rightarrow R-CHOH-CHOH-CO_2R'$$
$$\downarrow$$
$$R-CHOH-CHOH-CHO$$

This section also includes the reaction of the salts of active methylene compounds with glycosyl halides, as the products of such transformations are the same as those depicted by the preceding equation, as well as those of a related Wittig reaction (see Section 1.2.6), as shown in Figure 1.69.

This type of ring-chain isomerization then explains the term "C-glycosidic compound" applied for the products existing in the cyclic form.

1.2.5.1. Condensation of Open-Chain Monosaccharides with Active Methylene Compounds (Knoevenagel–Doebner Reaction)

The *aldehydo*-derivatives of monosaccharides readily react[2] with malonic acid in pyridine in the presence of a catalytic amount of piperidine.

General procedure for the condensation of aldehydo-*alkylidene monoses with malonic acid*[2]   A mixture of 0.04 mol of the alkylidene-*aldehydo* sugar derivative, 0.045 mol of malonic acid, and a few drops of piperidine (~1%) in dry pyridine is warmed to 100°C for 0.5–1 h. It is then kept at room temperature for overnight, concentrated under diminished pressure, and recrystallized from the appropriate

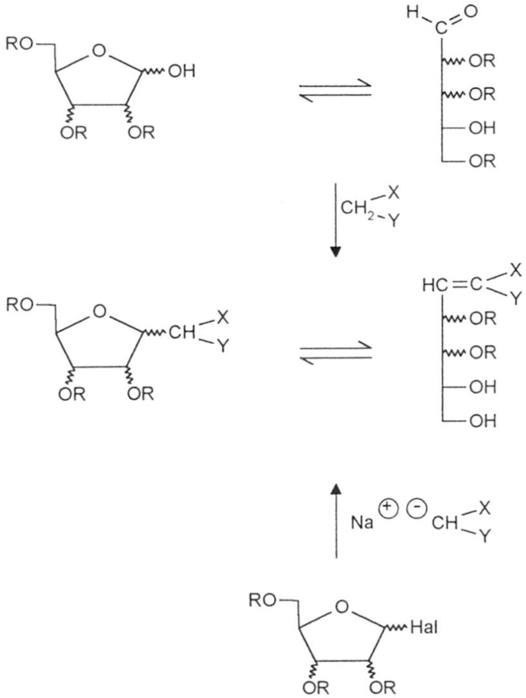

FIGURE I.69

solvent (see Table 1.11). Hydrolysis of the acetal protecting groups can be achieved on hydrolysis with 25–30 parts of 50% acetic acid at 100°C for 30 min.

When an ester of malonic acid is employed for the condensation reaction, no decarboxylation of the product occurs and the compounds shown in Table 1.12[2–4] (see also Table 1.11), can be synthesized according to the following equation:

$$R-CHO + CH_2(CO_2CH_3)_2 \rightarrow R-CH=CH(CO_2CH_3)_2 + H_2O$$

General procedure for preparation of Knoevenagel condensation products from aldehydo *sugars and diethyl malonate*[5] A mixture of the *aldehydo*-sugar (17.6 mmol), dimethyl malonate (20.1 ml, 76 mmol), and acetic anhydride (63 ml) in pyridine (90 ml) is kept at room temperature for 36 h. It is then diluted with ethyl

TABLE 1.11 Knoevenagel–Doebner Condensation with Open-Chain Monosaccharides

	Yield (%)	Physical parameters		Ref.
		M.p. (°C)	$[\alpha]_D$	
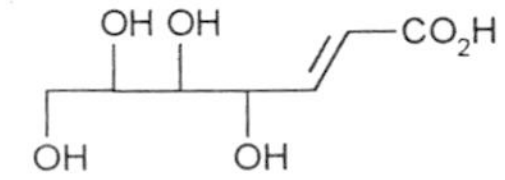	—	175 (EtOH)	−18.3 (c = 0.87, H₂O)	2
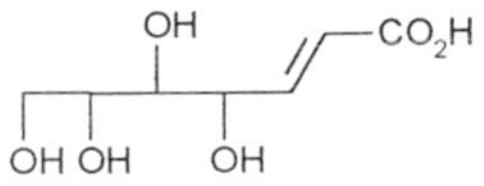	—	Amorphous (ion-exchange chromatographic purification)	−15.8 (c = 1.01, pyridine)	2
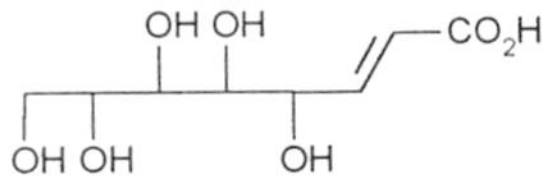	—	203–205 (heptane)	−19.4 (c = 0.98, H₂O)	2
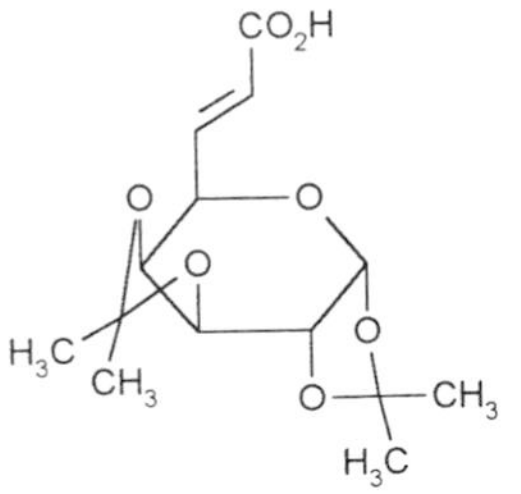	56	198–198.9 (ether/ hexane)	−131.3 (c = 1.6, CHCl₃)	3
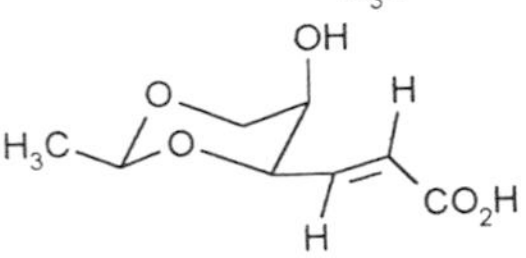	26	127–128 (CHCl₃)	−77 (c = 1, CHCl₃)	4
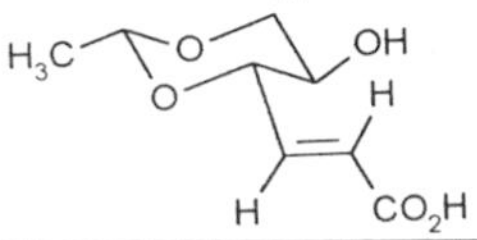	40	93–95 (CHCl₃)	−55 (c = 1, CHCl₃)	4

TABLE 1.12 Condensation Products of *aldehydo*-Sugars with Dimethyl Malonate[5]

Starting material	Product	$[\alpha]_D^{24}$
2,4,5-Tri-*O*-acetyl-3-*O*-benzyl-*aldehydo*-D-xylose	Methyl (4*S*,5*R*,6*R*)-4,6,7-triacetoxy-5-benzyloxy-2-methoxycarbonyl-2-heptenoate	+10.0 (*c* = 1.15, CHCl₃)
2,3,4-Tri-*O*-benzyl-5-*O*-*tert*-butyldimethylsilyl-*aldehydo*-D-ribose	Methyl (4*S*,5*S*,6*R*)-4,5,6-tris-benzyloxy-7-[(*tert*-butyldimethylsilyl)oxy]-2-methoxycarbonyl-2-heptenoate	−5.6 (*c* = 0.78, CHCl₃)
2,3,4-Tri-*O*-benzyl-5-*O*-*tert*-butyldiphenylsilyl-*aldehydo*-D-xylose	Methyl (4*S*,5*R*,6*R*)-4,5,6-tris-benzyloxy-7-[(*tert*-butyldiphenylsilyl)oxy]-2-methoxycarbonyl-2-heptenoate	—
4-*O*-*tert*-Butyldiphenylsilyl-2,3-*O*-isopropylidene-*aldehydo*-D-erythrose	Methyl (4*S*,5*R*)-6-[(*tert*-butyldiphenylsilyl)oxy]-4,5-(isopropylideneoxy)-2-methoxycarbonyl-2-hexenoate	+18.5 (*c* = 0.74, CHCl₃)
3-*O*-Benzyl-1,2-*O*-isopropylidene-α-D-*xylo*-pentodialdo-1,4-furanose	Methyl 3-*O*-benzyl-5,6-dideoxy-1,2-isopropylidene-6-C-methoxycarbonyl-α-D-*xylo*-hepto-1,4-furaneuronate	—
2,3,4-Tri-*O*-benzyl-5-*O*-*tert*-butyldiphenylsilyl-*aldehydo*-D-arabinose	Methyl (4*R*,5*S*,6*R*)-4,5,6-tris-benzyloxy-7-[(*tert*-butyldiphenylsilyl)oxy]-2-methoxycarbonyl-2-heptenoate	—

acetate and extracted with water (3 × 300 ml). The aqueous phases are, separately, reextracted with 300–300 ml of ethyl acetate, and the combined organic layer is dried (Na_2SO_4). Following evaporation, the residue is purified by means of column chromatography (eluant: 1 : 3 ethyl acetate–hexane) to obtain syrupy products.

Knoevenagel–Doebner syntheses have also been performed with the monomethyl ester of malonic acid, and the resulting α,β-unsaturated chain-extended products have been shown as very useful for the preparation[6] of the methyl esters of 3-O-methyl aldonic acids by treatment with sodium methoxide. Related chain extension (Fig. 1.70) of 2,3-O-isopropylidene-D-glyceraldehyde (**70.1**) or 2,3:4,5-di-O-isopropylidene-D-arabinose (**70.2**) give, under very mild conditions, methyl *trans*-2,3-dideoxy-4,5-O-isopropyl-idene-D-*glycero*-pent-2-enoate (**70.3**)[6] or methyl *trans*-2,3-dideoxy-4,5:6,7-di-O-isopropylidene-D-*arabino*-hept-2-enoate (**70.4**),[7] respectively.

Data in the literature show a many-sided reactivity of 2,3-O-isopropyli-dene-D-glyceraldehyde in the Knoevenagel–Doebner condensation reaction. Depending on the reaction conditions, various products are formed with methyl malonate, cyanoacetic acid, or acetoacetic acid, and the structure of the products could be elucidated[8–10] in many cases. In general, it is established that a noncatalyzed reaction of the preceding simple sugar first gives and adduct, which transforms into a furane derivative on treatment with acids. In piperidine-catalyzed condensations, unsaturated compounds are produced and are then converted[11] into trioxaspiro[4.4]non-7-enes at different rates.

A similar trend has been observed with the condensations of 2,3:4,5-di-O-isopropylidene-*aldehydo*-D-xylose[12] and 2,3:4,5-di-O-isopropylidene-*aldehydo*-D-arabinose. The latter sugar afforded (Fig. 1.71) an α,β- (**71.1**) and a β,γ- (**71.2**) unsaturated compound and an enol (**71.3**) as the primary products[13] with acetylacetone.

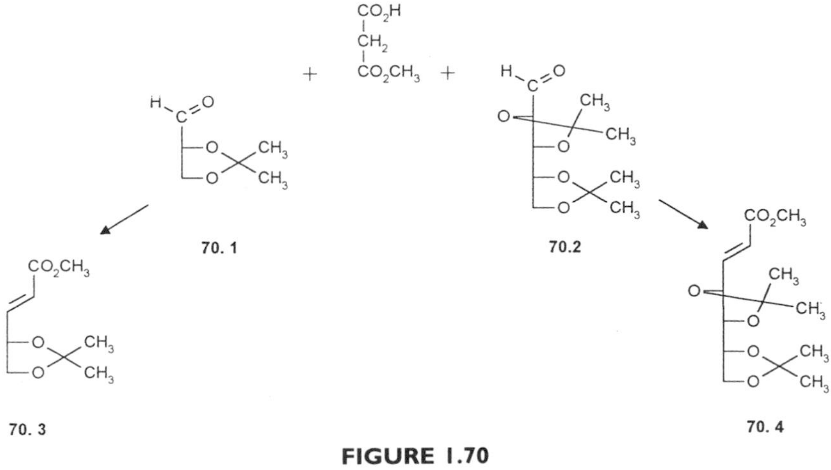

FIGURE I.70

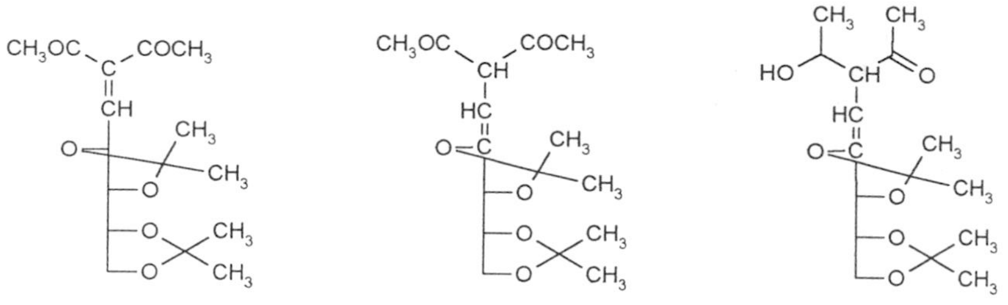

71.1   71.2   71.3

FIGURE 1.71

In base-catalyzed Knoevenagel–Doebner reactions, the catalyst induced epimerization[14–16] at C-2 of the starting sugar (which corresponds
to C-4 in the product) in a few cases. Thus, when the condensation reactions
of 2,3:5,6-di-O-isopropylidene-D-mannofuranose (**72.1**) with methyl malonate (**72.2**) are catalyzed with piperidine, instead of the expected product
with *manno*-configuration, methyl *trans*-2,3-dideoxy-4,5:7,8-di-O-isopro-
pylidene-D-*gluco*-oct-2-enoate (**72.3**) is produced[6,7] (Fig. 1.72).

Methyl trans-2,3-dideoxy-4,5:7,8-di-O-isopropylidene-D-gluco-oct-2-en-
oate (**72.3**)[7]   A mixture of the mannofuranose **72.1** (13 g, 50 mmol) and monomethyl
malonate (**72.2**, 10.7 g, 100 mmol) in pyridine (20 ml) piperidine (1.4 ml) is added
and bolied under reflux for 18 h. After reaction times of 4 and 10 h, an additional
7.5 ml (150 mmol) amount of the malonate is added and the conversion is monitored
by means of TLC (1 : 5 ethyl acetate–hexane) or GC (column package: 3% diethyl-
eneglycol succinate on WAW Chromosorb, 80 mesh). When the reaction is complete,
the solvent is removed under diminished pressure and the residue is boiled with
hexane (100 ml) for 30 min. After filtration the extract is cooled to 0°C when a
syrup separates. After cooling of the remaining solution to −40°C, crystals of the
product are separated. Repeated extraction of the syrup with hexane furnishes
further crops of the crystalline **72.3** (overall yield: 11 g, 70%), m.p. 75–76°C, $[\alpha]_D^{20}$
−9 (c = 1.3 in methanol). Chromatographic separation of the crude product allowed
the isolation, in a ~4% overall yield, of methyl (2,3:5,6-di-O-isopropylidene-β- and
α-D-mannofuranosyl)acetates, as well.

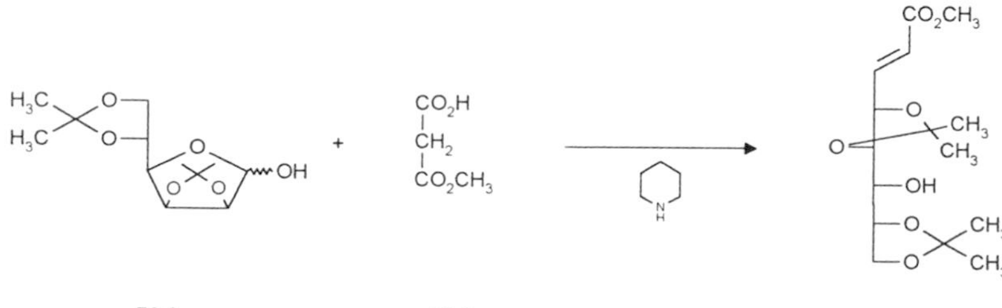

72.1   72.2   72.3

FIGURE 1.72

In agreement with these results, analogous transformation of 2,3-*O*-isopropylidene-D-ribofuranose readily furnished 54% of methyl *trans*-2,3-dideoxy-4,5-*O*-isopropylidene-D-*arabino*-hept-2-enoate, and—most interestingly—the by-products were identified[6,7] as methyl 2-(5-*O*-acetyl-2,3-*O*-isopropylidene-D-ribofuranosyl)acetates.

The chain extension of 2,5-anhydro-3,4-*O*-isopropylidene-D-arabinose with methyl acetoacetate and pentane-2,4-dione has also been investigated,[15] and the formation of a series of spiro-*C*-glycosidic compounds have been observed. When the catalyst is piperidine and the condensation is carried out without warming, a high yield of the product can be achieved according to the following easily reproducible procedure:

*(4R,5S)-5-(2,3-*O-*Isopropylidene-α-*D-*erythrofuranosyl)-4-methoxycarbonyl-3-methylcyclohex-2-en-1-one*[15] A mixture of 2,5-anhydro-3,4-*O*-isopropylidene-D-arabinose (1 g, 5.78 mmol), methyl acetoacetate (1.35 g 11.6 mmol), and piperidine (0.2 ml) is kept at room temperature for at least 4 weeks. Crystallization occurs slowly. The product is purified by means of column chromatography (1:3 ethyl acetate–hexane) on silicagel (100 g), to give the title sugar as white needles (1.6 g, 89.3%), m.p. 178–180°C (from ethanol), $[\alpha]_D^{20}$ +184 (c = 0.1 in chloroform).

The reaction of *aldehydo*-saccharides with the esters of cyanoacetic acid or with ethyl acetoacetate is an effective and valuable tool for chain extension. As an example, Figure 1.73 shows the piperidine-catalyzed condensation[16] of 2,3:4,5-di-*O*-isopropylidene-*aldehydo*-D-arabinose (**73.1**) with ethyl acetoacetate (**73.2**) to afford 1-acetyl-1-(ethoxycarbonyl)-3,4:5,6-di-*O*-isopropylidene-D-*arabino*-hexos-1-ene (**73.3**).

*1-Acetyl-1-(ethoxycarbonyl)-3,4:5,6-di-*O-*isopropylidene-*D-arabino-*hexos-1-ene* (**73.3**)[16] A mixture of the *aldehydo*-sugar (**73.1**) (2.3 g, 0.01 mol), ethyl acetoacetate (1.33 g, 0.01 mol) and 3 drops of diethylamine in toluene (50 ml) is kept at 0°C for 7 days, and during this period a small volume of water is separated. The organic layer is separated and concentrated to a syrup *in vacuo* at 40°C, and the residue is submitted to high-vacuum fractional distillation. Following distillation of the excess of ethyl acetoacetate and the residual solvent, the title compound (**73.3**) is obtained as the major fraction at 105–110°C (bath temperature) and at 6.65 × 10^{-2} Pa as a pale yellow syrup. Yield 2.53 g (74%), n_D^{20} 1.4640, $[\alpha]_D^{19}$ +24.2 (c = 2.92 in methanol).

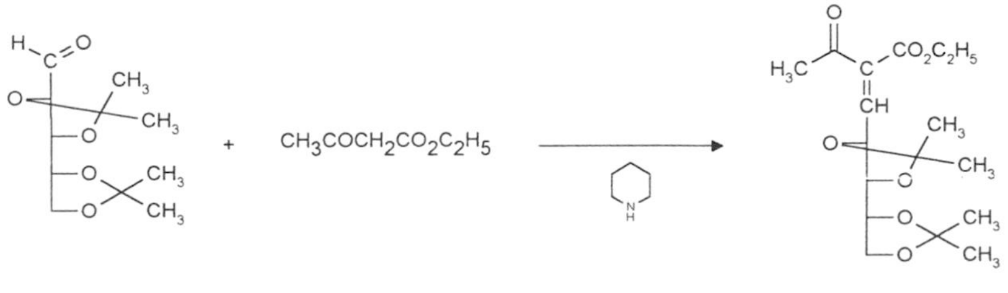

| 73.1 | 73.2 | 73.3 |

FIGURE 1.73

It is surprising that the *aldehydo*-sugar **74.1,** carrying acetyl protecting groups, reacts with two molecules of ethyl acetoacetate (Fig. 1.74) to furnish[17] 85% of the product **74.2.**

> *Diethyl   (1S,2R,3R,4R)-2,4-dimethyl-3-[D-pentaacetoxypentyl-(1)]-glutarate (74.2)*[17]   Penta-*O*-acetyl-*aldehydo*-D-glucose (**74.1,** 10 mmol) is mixed with ethyl acetoacetate (2.6 g, 20 mmol) and 1 drop of diethylamine, and the mixture is kept at −6°C for 14 days. The yellow syrup is separated from the unreacted educt, and the filtrate is washed with ligroin to remove excess of the reagent. The residual syrup is dissolved in chloroform, washed with aqueous NaHSO₃ and water, dried (Na₂SO₄), and concentrated. To a solution of the residue in ether, petroleum ether is added to give 5.5 g (85%) of **74.2,** $[\alpha]_D^{20}$ +25.8 (*c* = 1 in chloroform).

Analogous condensation[17] of **74.1** with ethyl *β*-aminocrotonate proceeds similarly to give the 3,5-diethyl ester of (1*R*,2*R*,3*R*,4*R*)-2,6-diamino-4-[pentaacetoxypentyl-(1)]-heptadiene-(2,5)-dicarboxylic acid.

Another catalyst have also been found suitable to effect Knoevenagel condensation of *aldehydo*-sugars. Israeli authors[18] have reported that TiCl₄ is rather useful for the synthesis of the chain-extended derivatives of *aldehydo*-aldoses carrying benzylidene protecting groups.

> *General procedure for the condensation of the O-benzylidene derivatives of* alde-hydo-*sugars with active methylene compounds in the presence of titanium tetrachlo-ride*[18]   A solution of TiCl₄ (1.1 ml) in dry carbon tetrachloride (2.5 ml) is added to 20 ml of dry tetrahydrofuran; precipitation is observed. To this mixture is added a solution containing 5 mmol of the active methylene compound and 5 mmol of the benzylidene-protected sugar derivative in tetrahydrofuran (12.5 ml), followed by the slow addition (1 h, with stirring at 0°C) of a solution of 1.6 ml (20 mmol) of pyridine in 3.5 ml of dry tetrahydrofuran. The reaction mixture is left to be stirred at 0°C for 48–72 h while protected from moisture. Then 50 ml of water is added and the mixture is extracted with chloroform. The organic solution is washed with aqueous sodium chloride, dried (Na₂SO₄), and concentrated, and the residual mixture is separated by means of column chromatography.

It has been found that the chain extension of partially protected or unprotected monosaccharides with active methylene compounds leads to complex product mixtures. With diethyl acetonedicarboxylate, simple sug-

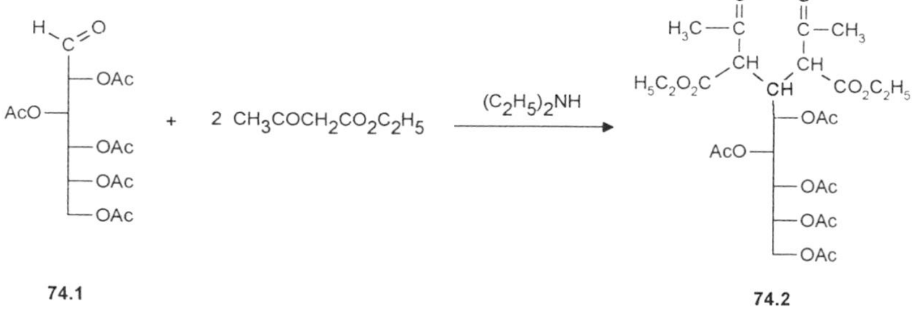

FIGURE I.74

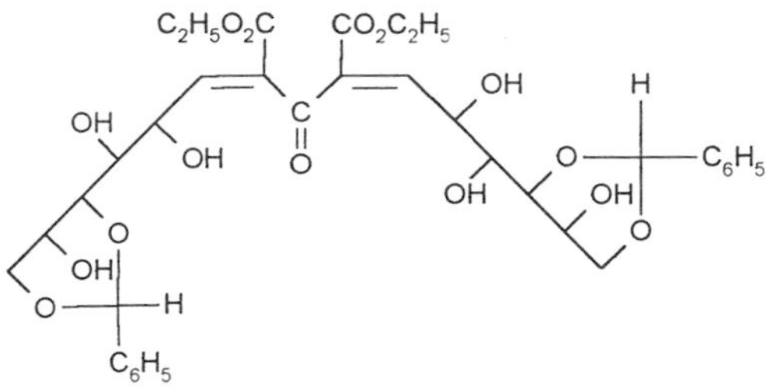

FIGURE 1.75

ars give bis-condensation products in the presence of piperidine catalyst.[19] For example, from 4,6-O-benzylidene-D-glucopyranose the pentadecose shown in Figure 1.75 is produced.

The monocondensation products usually cannot be obtained in crystalline form; thus, in many cases these are transformed into polyhydroxyalkyl-heterocycles[20] in a subsequent step.

Addition of diethyl oxalacetate (**76.1**) to 2,4:3,5-di-O-benzylidene-aldehydo-D-xylose (**76.2**) leads (Fig. 1.76) to the ethyl ester of crystalline 3-ethoxycarbonyl-3-deoxy-5,7:6,8-di-O-benzylidene-D-gulo-octulosonic acid (**76.3**). Confirmation of the gulo-configuration was carried out by conversion of the product **76.3** into O-methyl-L-malic acid and by transforma-

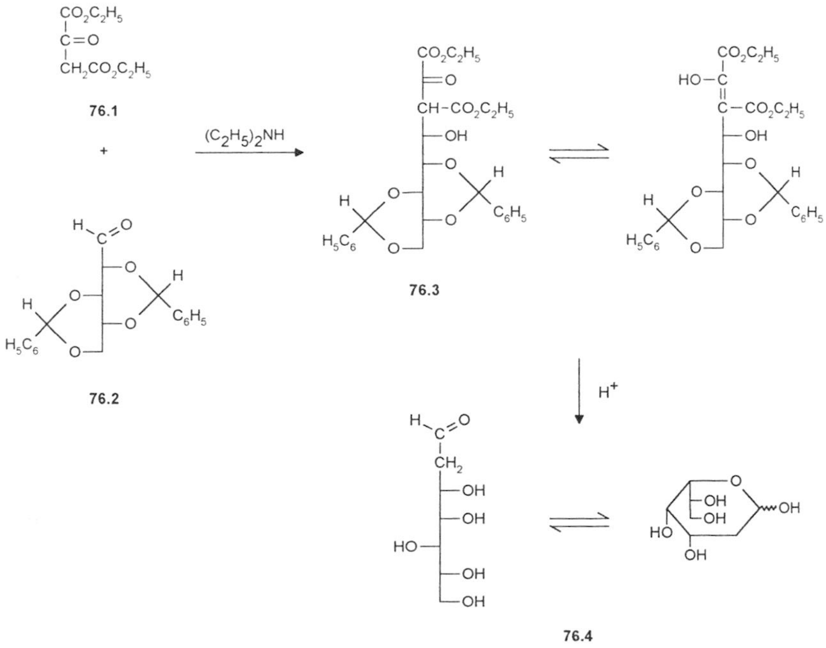

FIGURE 1.76

tion into the corresponding bis(p-bromophenacyl ester). On treatment with dilute hydrochloric acid in 1,4-dioxane, the ester **76.3** can be easily converted into syrupy 2-deoxy-D-*gulo*-heptose (**76.4**) with 85% yield.

Ethyl 3-ethoxycarbonyl-3-deoxy-5,7:6,8-di-O-benzylidene-D-gluco-octulosonate (76.3)[21] A mixture of the *aldehydo*-xylose derivative **76.2** (3.26 g, 0.01 mol), diethyl oxalacetate (**76.1**; 1.88 g, 0.01 mol), and diethylamine (0.5 ml) in chloroform (120 ml) is kept at 20°C for 3 days with occasional shaking, and during this time a clear solution is formed. The solvent is distilled off, and the syrupy residue is crystallized from methanol to obtain pure **76.3** (2.10 g, 41%) as needles, m.p. 168–169°C, $[\alpha]_D^{18}$ +86.1 (c = 1.85 in chloroform).

(2*E*,4*E*)(6*R*,7*R*)-4,6,7,8-Tetradeoxy-2-cyanooctadieneamide—produced in the reaction of D-glucose and cyanoacetamide—is of practical importance as its dehydration products (3-cyano-2-pyridones and 2-cyano-2-pyrrolidones) are UV-light-absorbing, electrochemically oxidizable or fluorescent compounds, useful for *postcolumn labeling* in high-performance liquid chromatography (HPLC). The acetyl derivative of the chain-extended product is easily available (with 48% yield) in the pyridine-catalyzed Knoevenagel condensation[22] of pentaacetyl-*aldehydo*-D-glucose with cyanoacetamide.

Figure 1.77 shows an interesting chain extension reaction of *aldehydo*-sugars, carrying *O*-benzylidene or isopropylidene protecting groups, with dibutyl cyanomethylphosphonate. According to this procedure, reported by Zhdanov,[23] 2,3-dideoxy-2-(dibutoxyphosphonyl)-4,5:6,7-di-*O*-isopropylidene-L-*arabino*-heptenonitrile (**77.3**) can be synthesized from the *aldehydo*-sugar **77.1** and the cyanomethylphosphonate **77.2**.

1.2.5.2. Chain Extension with Malonate Derivatives

The esters of malonic acid are extremely versatile reagents in organic chemistry; therefore, many attempts have been made to prepare their carbohydrate derivatives. Glycosyl halides readily react with malonates under glycosidation conditions, to form a C—C bond, and thus to produce anhydro-2-deoxy-2-alkoxycarbonylhexonates or -heptonates. Related deriva-

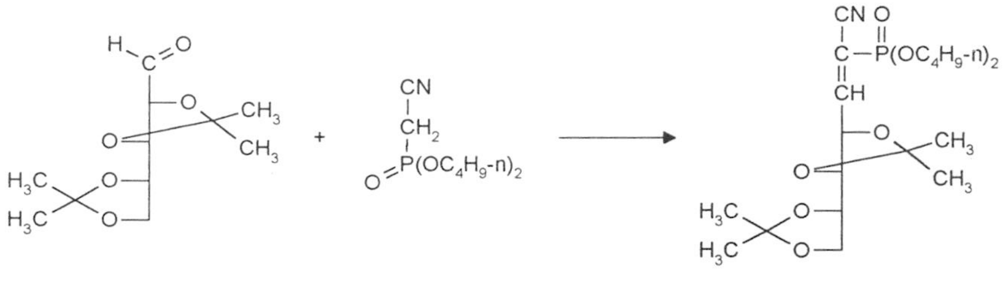

77.1   77.2   77.3

FIGURE 1.77

tives previously synthesized according to the following equation are collected in Table 1.13.[24-30]

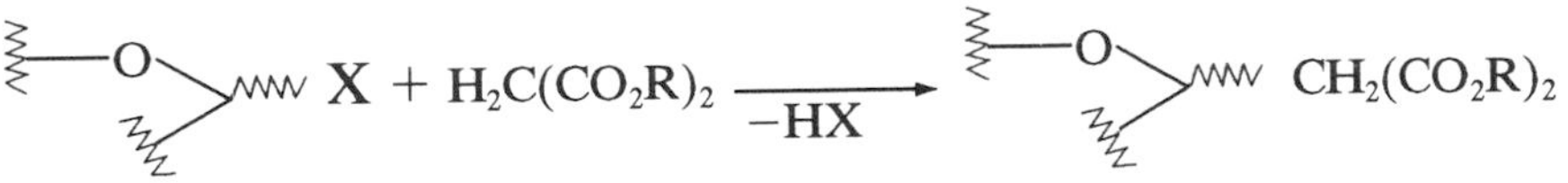

$$\text{—O} \diagdown \text{mw } X + H_2C(CO_2R)_2 \xrightarrow[-HX]{} \text{—O} \diagdown \text{mw } CH_2(CO_2R)_2$$

The chain-extended derivatives shown in Table 1.13 can be regarded as C-glycosidic compounds, whose formation—as well as the ratio of the anomers produced in the reaction—can be influenced[27] by bases, and the use of a very simple reaction step permits the isolation of the thermodynamically more stable product, as shown in the following example.

> *Diethyl 2-(2,3,4,6-tetra-O-benzyl-β-D-glucopyranosyl)-malonate*[31] To a solution of diethyl 2-(2,3,4,6-tetra-O-benzyl-α-D-glucopyranosyl)-malonate (1 mmol) in a small volume of methanol is added sodium methoxide in methanol (0.94 mmol, 15 ml), and the reaction is monitored by TLC (4 : 1 hexane–ethyl acetate). After 30 min the mixture is neutralized and the crude product is recrystallized from diisopropyl ether–petroleum ether to furnish 88% of the pure β anomer, m.p. 50°C, $[\alpha]_D^{20}$ +3.2 (c = 1 in chloroform).

An additional possibility for synthesizing similar malonester analogs is the reaction of sugar derivatives, carrying a free anomeric hydroxyl group, with the sodium salt of an active methylene compound (malonitrile, cyanoacetate, or malonate). As shown in Figure 1.78, such transformations also provide the C-glycoside of the methylene derivative.[32]

> *General procedure for the preparation of* C-*glycofuranosyl malonates*[32]   Method A A solution of the malonic acid derivative (15 mmol) in THF (15 ml) is added to a suspension of 50% sodium hydride (720 mg, 15 mmol) in dry THF (20 ml) at 0°C in argon atmosphere, and then 5 mmol of the sugar derivative is added. After overnight stirring, the mixture is poured onto saturated aqueous ammonium chloride solution (20 ml) and extracted with dichloromethane (3 × 100 ml). The organic layer is washed with water (2 × 30 ml) and aqueous Na_2CO_3 (50 ml) and dried over $MgSO_4$. The solvent is distilled off, and the crude product is purified by means of column chromatography (eluant: 1 : 12 ethyl acetate–hexane or 4 : 1 toluene–ether).
>
> Method B To a solution of the sugar derivative (5 mmol) in benzene or dichloromethane (20 ml), 10% aqueous NaOH solution (20 ml) and tetrabutylammonium hydrogensulfate (1.86 g, 5 mmol) are added, followed by the addition of the malonic acid derivative, and the mixture is stirred vigorously for 3 h while monitoring with TLC as shown in method A.

Barbituric acid, the cyclic ureide of malonic acid, also contains an active methylene group, and therefore can be used in chain-extension experiments. Thus, when glucosamine hydrochloride (**79.1**) is heated with barbituric acid (**79.2**) in water, 5-(2-amino-2-deoxy-β-D-glucopyranosyl)-barbituric acid (**79.3**) is obtained[33] (Fig. 1.79).

> *5-(2-Amino-2-deoxy-β-D-glucopyranosyl)-barbituric acid (**79.3**)*[33] A solution of D-glucosamine hydrochloride (**79.1**, 1.1 g, 5 mmol) in water (20 ml) is mixed with sodium carbonate (0.27 g, 2.5 mmol) and barbituric acid (**79.2**, 0.64 g, 5 mmol),

TABLE 1.13 C-Glycosyl-Malonester Derivatives Obtained from Glycosyl Halides

Educt	Product	Yield (%)	α/β ratio	Ref.
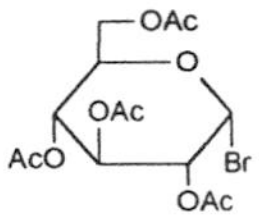 (structure: pyranose, OAc, OAc, AcO, OAc, Br)	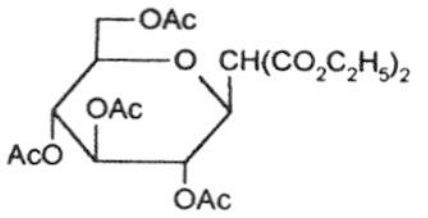 (structure: OAc, OAc, AcO, OAc, O—CH(CO$_2$C$_2$H$_5$)$_2$)	20	—	24
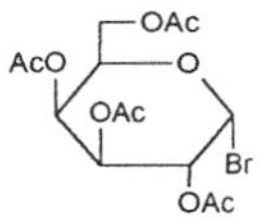 (structure: OAc, AcO, OAc, Br, OAc)	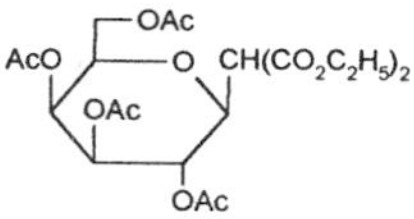 (structure: OAc, AcO, OAc, OAc, O—CH(CO$_2$C$_2$H$_5$)$_2$)	19	—	25
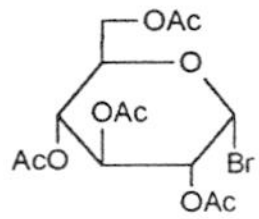 (structure: OAc, OAc, AcO, Br, OAc)	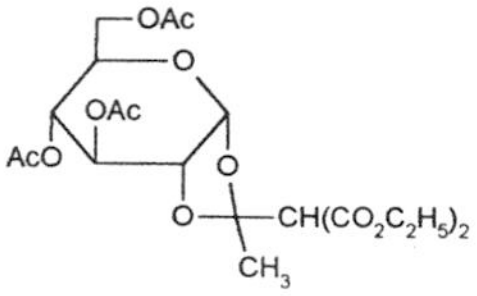 (structure: OAc, OAc, AcO, O—C(CH$_3$)—CH(CO$_2$C$_2$H$_5$)$_2$)	80–100	—	24
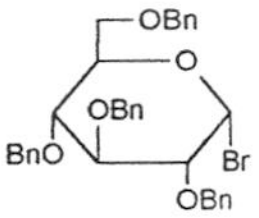 (structure: OBn, OBn, BnO, Br, OBn)	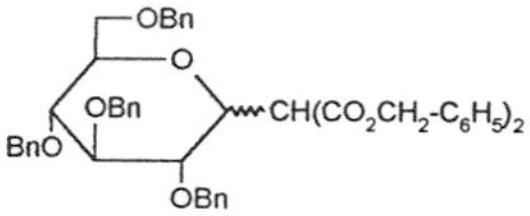 (structure: OBn, OBn, BnO, OBn, CH(CO$_2$CH$_2$-C$_6$H$_5$)$_2$)	81–92	23:77– 72:28	24
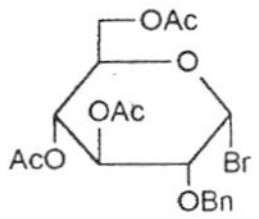 (structure: OAc, OAc, AcO, Br, OBn)	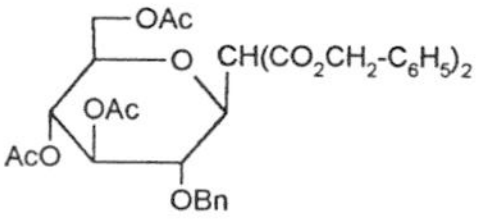 (structure: OAc, CH(CO$_2$CH$_2$-C$_6$H$_5$)$_2$, OAc, AcO, OBn)	21	—	26
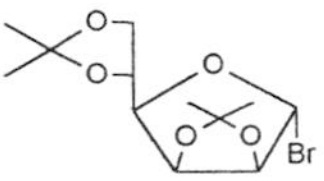 (furanose isopropylidene structure, Br)	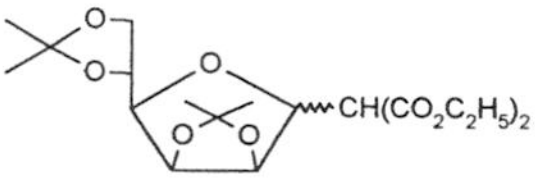 (furanose isopropylidene structure, CH(CO$_2$C$_2$H$_5$)$_2$)	quantitative	9:1	24
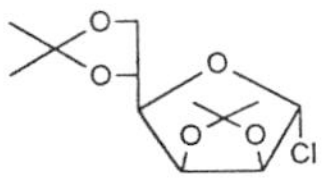 (furanose isopropylidene structure, Cl)	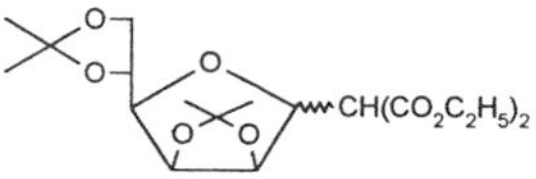 (furanose isopropylidene structure, CH(CO$_2$C$_2$H$_5$)$_2$)	80	9:1	27
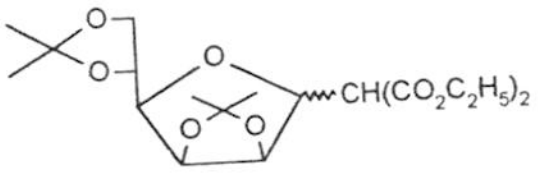 (furanose isopropylidene structure, CH(CO$_2$C$_2$H$_5$)$_2$)	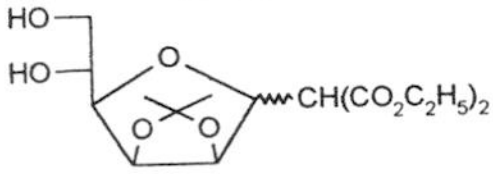 (structure: HO, HO, CH(CO$_2$C$_2$H$_5$)$_2$)	57	—	24
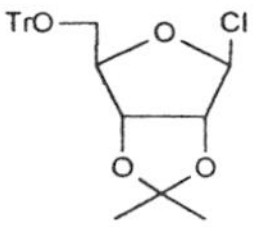 (structure: TrO, Cl, isopropylidene)	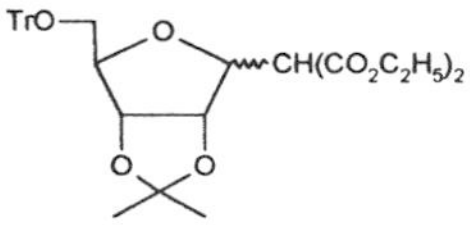 (structure: TrO, CH(CO$_2$C$_2$H$_5$)$_2$, isopropylidene)	~100 90	9:1 10:1	27 28
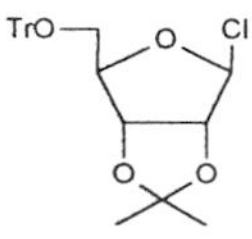 (structure: TrO, Cl, isopropylidene)	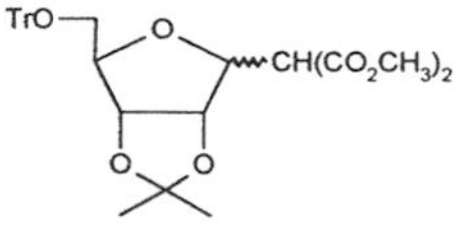 (structure: TrO, CH(CO$_2$CH$_3$)$_2$, isopropylidene)	94	12:7	27

(*continues*)

TABLE 1.13   (*continued*)

Educt	Product	Yield (%)	α/β ratio	Ref.
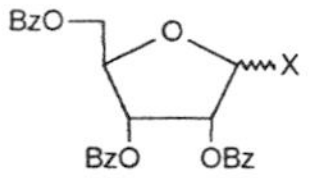	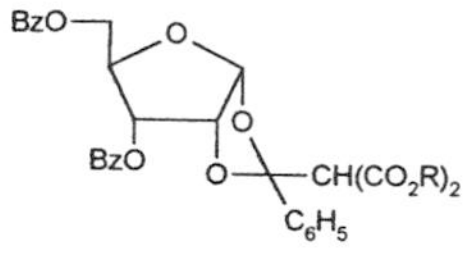 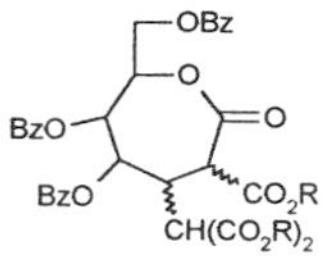	See original publication		29
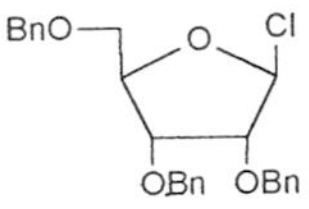	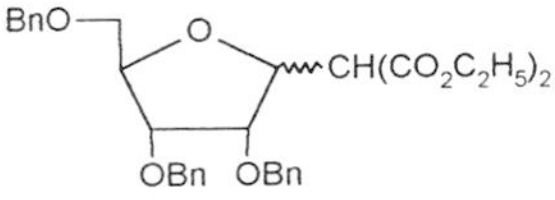 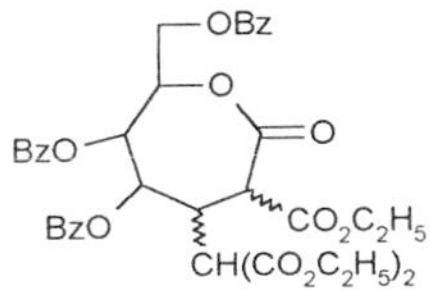	See original publication		29
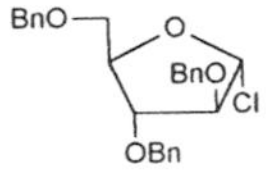	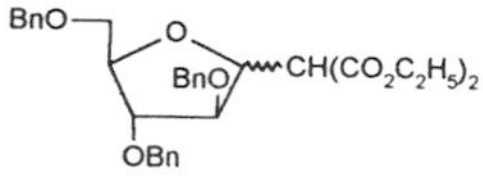	Quanitative	1 : 1	29
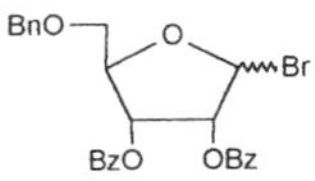	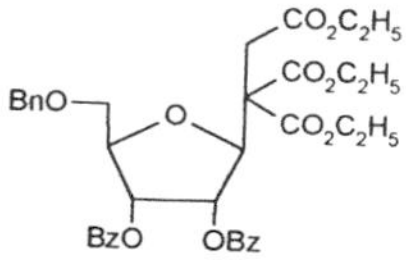 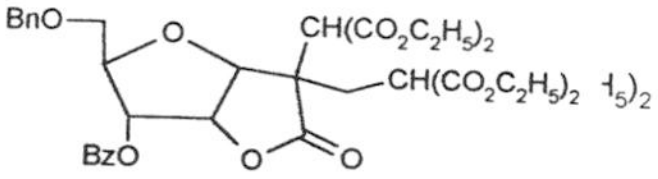	80	—	29
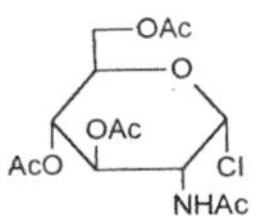	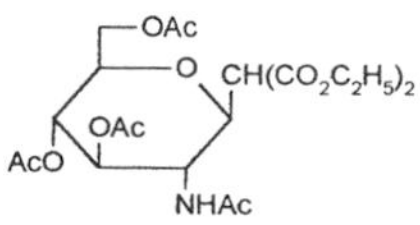	—	—	30

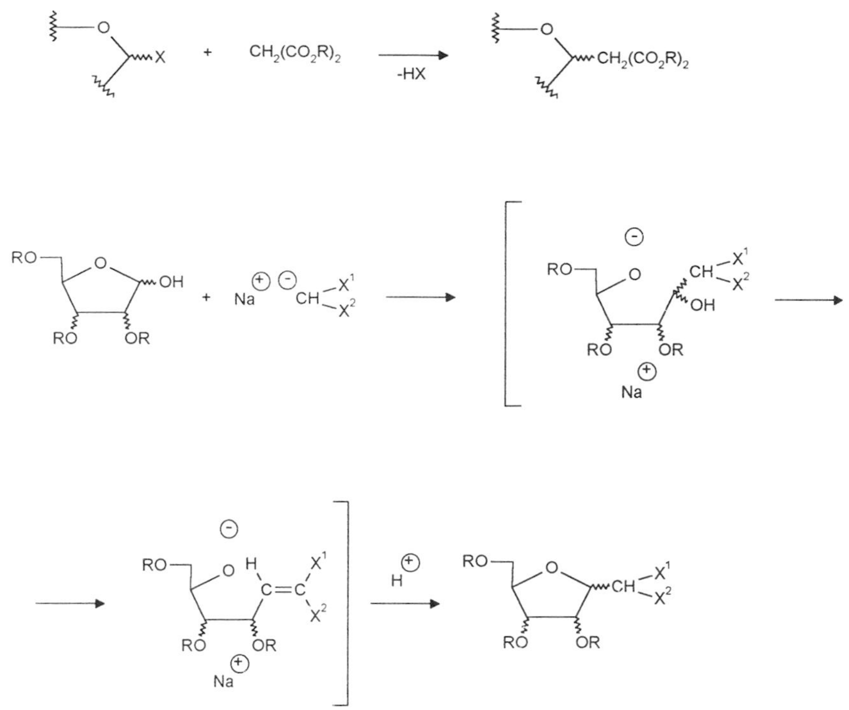

FIGURE I.78

and the mixture is kept at 50°C until the formation of a clear solution. It is then warmed for an additional period of 10 h and then cooled, and the crystals of the product **79.3** (1.08 g, 70%) are filtered off and recrystallized from water, m.p. 200°C, $[\alpha]_D^{22}$ −7 (c = 0.7 in 1 N NaOH).

The glycopyranosyl-barbituric acids thus obtained are suitable candidates for the development of further C−C bonds. With this in mind, Wulff[34] examined various alkylation reactions (Fig. 1.80) of the sodium salt of 5-β-D-glucopyranosyl-1,3-dimethylbarbituric acid (**80.1**) and studied the specific chemical reactions of the resulting 5,5-disubstituted barbituric acids (**80.2**),

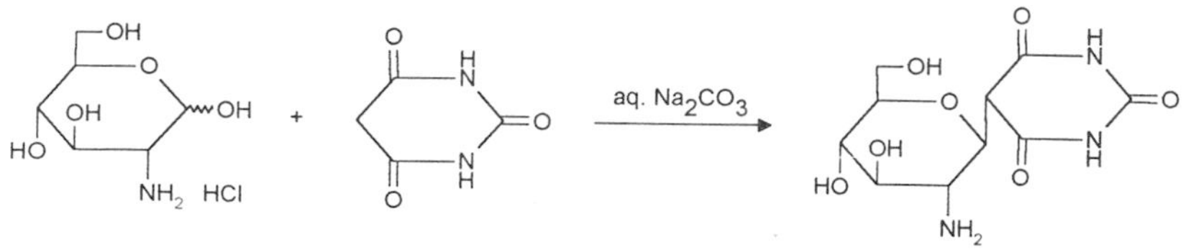

FIGURE I.79

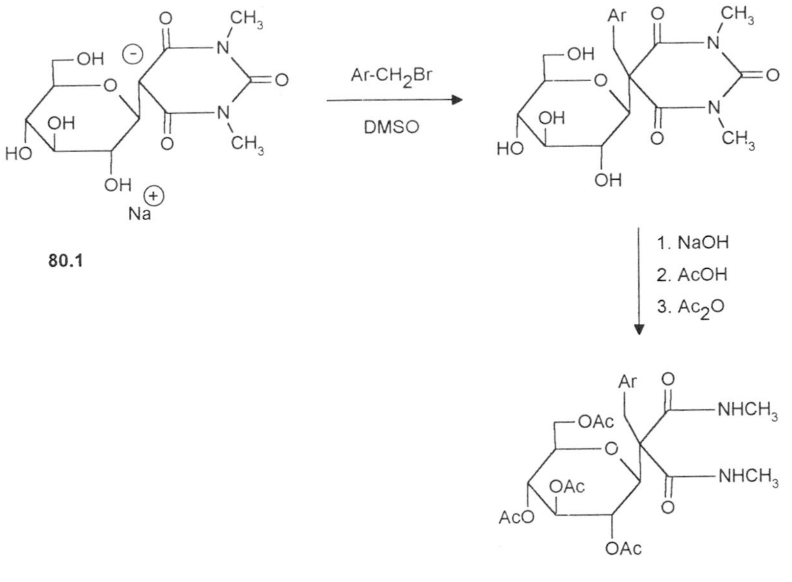

80.1

80.2

80.3

FIGURE 1.80

and among them, conversion into the multifunctionalized *C*-glycosidic compound **80.3**.

Zhdanov and Bogdanova[35] have found that the 5-*O*-glycopyranoside derivatives of barbituric acid are easily available from hexoses (D-glucose, D-mannose, and D-galactose) on treatment of the corresponding *aldehydo*-aldose with barbituric acid in hot aqueous ethanol.

1,3-Dimethylbarbituric acid is a suitable target for conversion, as either the free acid or its sodium salt, into the 5-glycosyl-1,3-dimethylbarbituric acids **81.1** and **81.2** (or their sodium salts) according the the Zhdanov method. Acetylation of these compounds then leads[35] either to cyclic *C*-glycosidic compounds (such as in the case of D-ribose to furnish **81.3**) or to acyclic analogs, such as **81.4,** obtained form D-xylose (Fig. 1.81).

The observations discussed in the preceding paragraphs have been successfully applied[36] for the synthesis of the *C*-glycoside-type antibiotic *pyrazomycin.* The key step in this procedure (Fig. 1.82) is the C−C bond formation between 2,3-*O*-isopropylidene-5-*O*-(*p*-nitrobenzoyl)-β-D-ribofuranosyl bromide (**82.1**) and the active methylene compound diethyl 1,3-acetonedicarboxylate (**82.2**), followed by straightforward steps to *pyrazomycin* (**82.7**).

*Condensation of 2,3-O-isopropylidene-5-O-(p-nitrobenzoyl)-β-D-ribofuranosyl bromide (**82.1**) with diethyl 1,3-acetonedicarboxylate (**82.2**)[36]* To a stirred suspen-

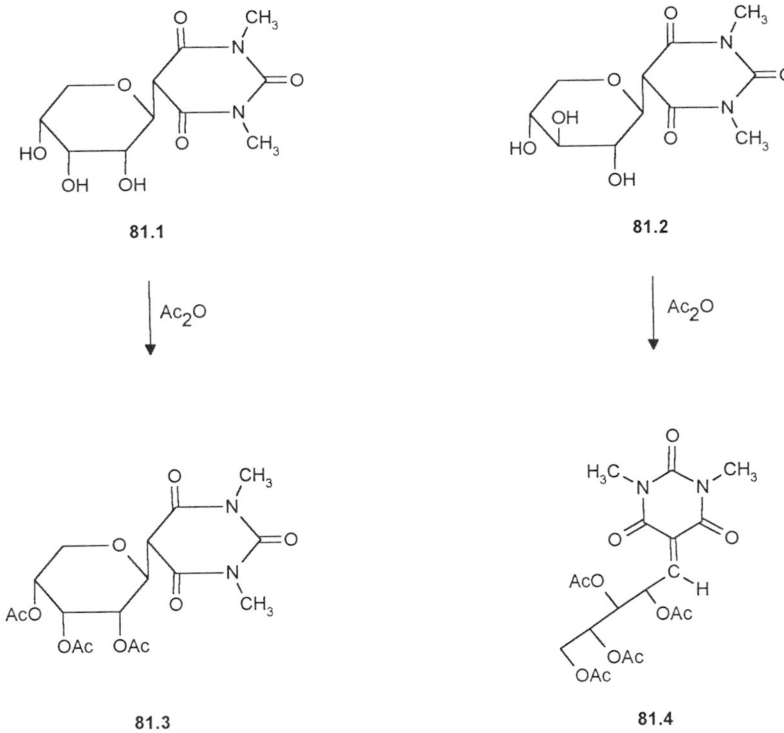

FIGURE 1.81

sion of potassium hydride (805 mg, 20.1 mmol) in dry benzene (40 ml), 4 ml of diethyl 1,3-acetonedicarboxylate (**82.2**) is added dropwise under argon atmosphere, followed by a solution of 18-crown-6 (3.75 g, 14.2 mmol) in 30 ml of benzene. After hydrogen evolution has ceased, a larger excess (22 ml) of diethyl 1,3-acetonedicarboxylate is added in one portion. Then, a solution of the ribofuranosyl bromide **82.1** (5.93 g, 14.74 mmol) in 80 ml of dry benzene is added dropwise over a 30 min period. The reaction mixture is stirred under argon at room temperature for 16 h and diluted with ether (1 liter) and the ethereal phase is washed with water (3 × 300 ml), diluted with 300 ml of benzene, and dried over Na_2SO_4. After evaporation of the solvent under reduced pressure, excess of the reagent **82.2** is distilled off in a bulb-to-bulb apparatus at 80–85°C (0.1 mmHg). The residue is dissolved in a 10:1 mixture of toluene and ethyl acetate (15 ml) and chromatographed on a column containing 550 g of a mixture of 75% of Silicagel 60 and 25% of Silicagel PF_{254} (both from Merck). The column is developed with the following mixtures of toluene and ethyl acetate: 10:1 (3600 ml, fractions 1–149), 10:1.5 (2300 ml, fractions 150–265) and 10:3 (1300 ml, fractions 266–300). The eluate is monitored by TLC (10:1.75 toluene–ethyl acetate and 3:1 cyclohexane–ethyl acetate).

Fractions 80–114: Evaporation and drying *in vacuo* at 60°C (0.01 mmHg) affords 0.41 g (5.3%) of 3-[2,3-*O*-isopropylidene-5-*O*-(*p*-nitrobenzoyl)-β-D-ribofuranosyl]-oxy-2-pentenedioic acid diethyl ester (**82.3**) as a colorless syrup, $[\alpha]_D^{25}$ −96.8 (*c* = 1.12 in chloroform).

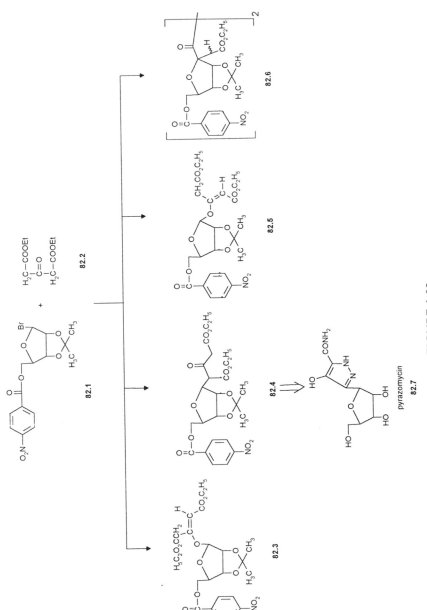

FIGURE I.82

Fractions 115–188: Evaporation and drying give 2.85 g of 2-[2,3-*O*-isopropyli-dene-5-*O*-(*p*-nitrobenzoyl)-α-D-ribofuranosyl)-oxoglutaric acid diethyl ester (**82.4**). An additional 0.45 g of the compound can be obtained on rechromatographing fractions 189–230, giving a total yield of 42.8%, colorless syrup, $[\alpha]_D^{25}$ +44.8 (*c* = 0.94 in chloroform).

Fractions 231–310: These fractions (combined with the remainder from fractions 189–230) are rechromatographed on 450 g of silicagel mixture (see the preceding

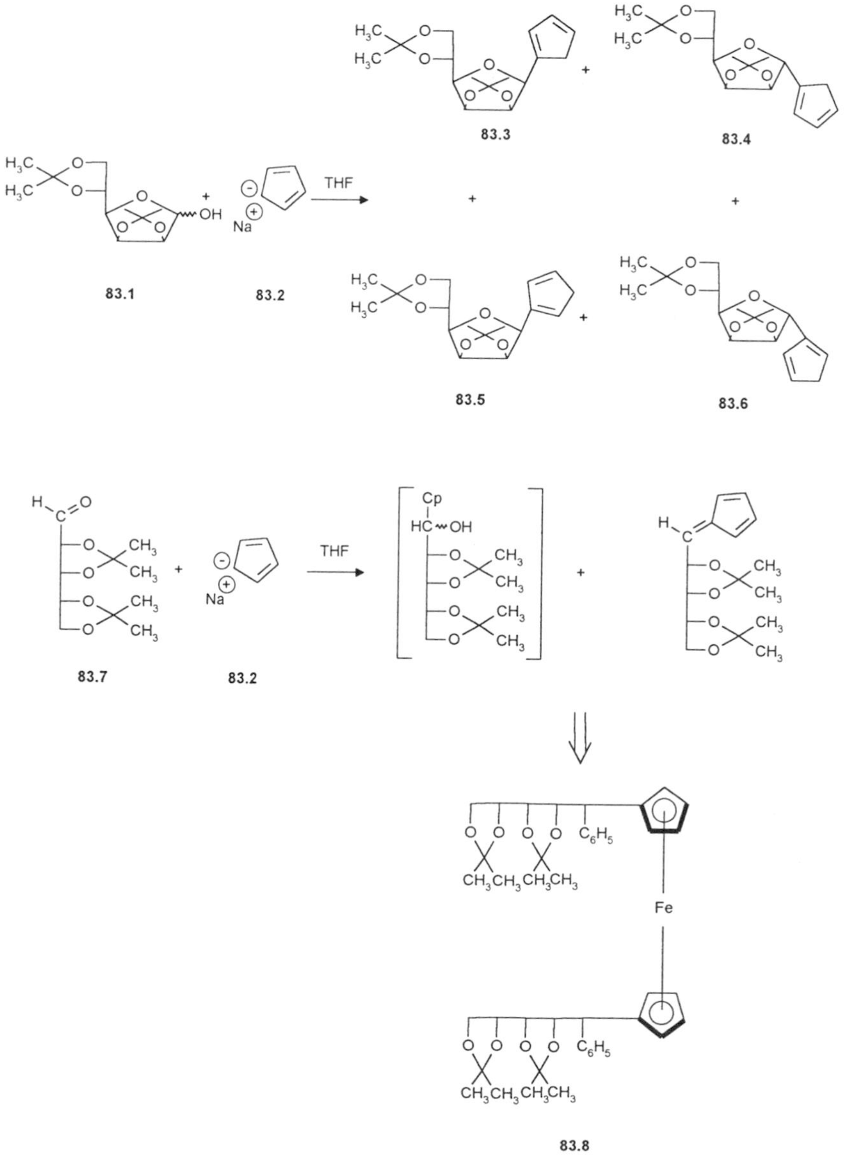

FIGURE I.83

procedures). The column is eluted with ethyl acetate–cyclohexane 1 : 3 (4.2 liters) and 3 : 7 (3 liters). On evaporation, appropriate fractions yielded 1.625 g (21.1%) of 3-[2,3-*O*-isopropylidene-5-*O*-(*p*-nitrobenzoyl)-α-D-ribofuranosyl]-oxy-2-penten-edioic acid diethyl ester (**82.5**), $[\alpha]_D^{25}$ +41.7 (*c* = 1.13 in chloroform).

Later fractions afford 1.49 g (23.9%) of 2,4-bis-[2,3-*O*-isopropylidene-5-*O*-(*p*-nitrobenzoyl)-α-D-ribofuranosyl]-3-oxoglutaric acid diethyl ester (**82.6**), $[\alpha]_D^{25}$ +45.5 (*c* = 1.12 in chloroform).

Vasella *et al.*[37] have described the preparation of *glycosylcyclopentadienes* (cyclopentadienyl-*C*-glycosides) starting from the cyclopentadienyl anion. Figure 1.83 shows the reaction of 2,3:5,6-di-*O*-isopropylidene-β-D-mannofuranose (**83.1**) with cyclopentadienyl-sodium (**83.2**) to lead to epimeric glycosylcyclopentadienes (**83.3–83.6**), consisting of mixtures of the 1,3- and 1,4-cyclopentadienes. A similar transformation occurs with 2,3:4,5-di-*O*-isopropylidene-*aldehydo*-D-ribose (**83.7**), which can be converted,[37] in a few synthetic steps, to polyhydroxyalkylferrocenes, such as **83.8**.

REFERENCES TO SECTION I.2.5

1. G. Jones, *Org. React. (N.Y.)* **15**, 204 (1967).
2. N. K. Kochetkov and B. A. Dimitriev, *Tetrahedron* **21**, 803 (1965).
3. J. M. J. Tronchet and M. A. M. Massoud, *Helv. Chim. Acta* **62**, 1632 (1979).
4. M. V. Fernández, F. J. López-Herrera, T. L. Cobos, and G. P. Escribano, *Carbohydr. Res.* **118**, 286 (1983).
5. K. Tadano, H. Maeda, M. Hoshino, Y. Imura, and T. Suami, *J. Org. Chem.* **52**, 1946 (1987); K. Tadano, H. Kimura, M. Hoshino, S. Ogawa, and T. Suami, *Bull. Chem. Soc. Jpn.* **60**, 3673 (1987).
6. F. J. López-Herrera and M. S. Pino González, *Tetrahedron* **42**, 6033 (1986).
7. F. J. López-Herrera and M. S. Pino González, *Carbohydr. Res.* **152**, 283 (1986).
8. F. J. López-Aparicio and F. J. López-Herrera, *An. Quím.* **72**, 931 (1975).
9. F. J. López-Aparicio, M. Gomez-Guillén, and I. Izquierdo Cubero, *An. Quím.* **73**, 1168 (1977).
10. F. J. López-Aparicio, M. Gomez-Guillén, and I. Izquierdo Cubero, *An. Quím.* **72**, 938 (1976).
11. F. J. López-Aparicio, F. J. López-Herrera, and J. S. Ballesteros, *Carbohydr. Res.* **69**, 55 (1979).
12. F. J. López-Herrera, M. Valpuesta Fernández, and R. Garcia Segura, *An. Quím. Ser. C* **81**, 232 (1985).
13. F. J. López-Herrera, M. Valpuesta Fernández, and R. Garcia Segura, *An. Quím. Ser. C* **82**, 135 (1986).
14. F. J. López-Aparicio, J. A. López Sastre, and J. Molina Molina, *An. Quím.* **78**, 73 (1982).
15. F. J. López-Herrera, M. Valpuesta-Fernández, and R. Garcia Segura, *Carbohydr. Res.* **127**, 217 (1984).
16. H. Zinner, E. Wittenburg, and G. Rembarz, *Chem. Ber.* **92**, 1614 (1959).
17. F. Micheel and W. Möller, *Justus Liebigs Ann. Chem.* **670**, 63 (1963).
18. E. Breuer, D. Melumad, S. Sarel, E. Margalith, and E. Katz, *J. Med. Chem.* **26**, 30 (1983).
19. P. E. Papadakis, *J. Org. Chem.* **20**, 630 (1955).
20. P. E. Papadakis, *J. Org. Chem.* **26**, 199 (1961).
21. H. Zinner and J. Weber, *J. Prakt. Chem.* **316**, 13 (1974).

22. S. Honda, K. Kakehi, K. Fujikawa, Y. Oka, and M. Takahashi, *Carbohydr. Res.* **183,** 59 (1988).
23. Ju. A. Zhdanov, L. A. Uslova, and L. M. Maksimushkina, *Zh. Obshch. Khim.* **52,** 937 (1982).
24. S. Hanessian and A. G. Pernet, *Can. J. Chem.* **52,** 1264 (1974).
25. M. L. Sinnott, G. T. Tzotzos, and S. E. Marshall, *J. Chem. Soc., Perkin Trans. 2,* p. 1665(1982).
26. F. Nicotra, F. Ronchetti, and G. Russo, *J. Org. Chem.* **47,** 4459 (1982).
27. H. Ohrui, G. H. Jones, J. G. Moffatt, M. L. Maddox, A. T. Christensen, and S. K. Byram, *J. Am. Chem. Soc.* **97,** 4602 (1975).
28. H. Ohrui and J. J. Fox, *Tetrahedron Lett.* **14,** 1951 (1973).
29. S. Hanessian and A. G. Pernet, *Can. J. Chem.* **52,** 1280 (1974).
30. K.-I. Kim and R. I. Hollingsworth, *Tetrahedron Lett.* **35,** 1031 (1994).
31. P. Allevi, M. Anastasia, P. Ciuffreda, A. Fiecchi, and A. Scala, *J. Chem. Soc., Perkin Trans. 1,* p. 1275 (1989).
32. F. Germain, Y. Chapleur, and B. Castro, *Synthesis,* p. 119 (1983).
33. M. A. Gonzalez, J. L. J. Requejo, J. C. P. Albarran, and J. A. G. Perez, *Carbohydr. Res.* **158,** 53 (1986).
34. G. Wulff and G. Clarkson, *Carbohydr. Res.* **257,** 81 (1994).
35. Ju. A. Zhdanov and G. V. Bogdanova, *Khim. Geterotsikl. Soedin.* **1,** 56 (1966); *Chem. Abstr.* **65,** 2337c (1966).
36. S. De Bernardo and M. Weigele, *J. Org. Chem.* **41,** 287 (1976).
37. P. Vedso, R. Chauvin, Z. Li, B. Bernet, and A. Vasella, *Helv. Chim. Acta* **77,** 1631 (1994).

1.2.6. Chain Extension with Phosphoranes: Olefination Reactions for Synthesis of Chain-Extended Monosaccharides

The discovery of phosphoranes (also called *phosphoniumylides*) and their utilization in C—C bond formation brought about a frenetic development in synthetic organic chemistry.[1,2] Carbohydrate chemists have since used this strategy, and a review paper[3] published in 1972 shows that in the first 19 years of application of this extremely versatile procedure, many results were obtained, mainly in the field of monosaccharides.[1,3]

The present section primarily attempts to summarize the methods used to date that involve Wittig reaction of hydroxyaldehydes as the key step. The first step of this procedure, used for the preparation of a plethora of natural organic compounds, is based on the generation of a phosphonium-ylide (**84.2**) from a phosphonium salt (**84.1**), followed by addition to a carbonyl compound (**84.3**) as shown in Figure 1.84.

When steps A and B proceed simultaneously the process is a $\pi_s^2 + \pi_a^2$-type [2+2]-cycloaddition reaction, responsible for the formation of *cis* products or *cis–trans* mixtures. If the phosphorane contains a stabilizing group, production of the betaine **84.4** is reversible and the thermodynamically more stable *trans*-isomer is obtained. However, the ratio of the isomers can be influenced by the addition of lithium salts or by changing the solvent.

For the synthesis of nonbranched, chain-extended products, the reaction of cyclic carbohydrates and ω-aldosuloses (both carrying free anomeric hydroxyl group) with phosphoranes may also be the choice,[2] when the carbonyl-olefination strategy gives rise to sugars with a C=C unit.

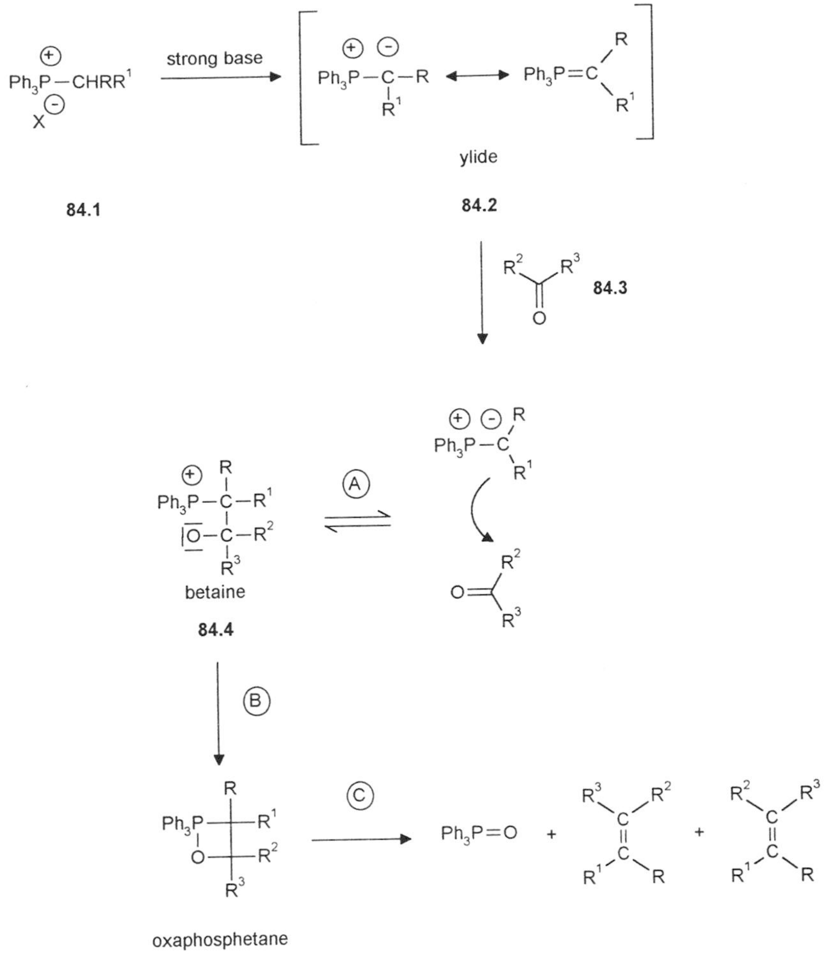

FIGURE 1.84

With γ- and δ-hydroxyaldehydes—i.e., furanosides (**85.1**) and pyrano-sides—a crucial question of the chain extension is the result of the carbonyl olefination, namely, addition of the OH group to the double bond (Michael addition, resulting in ring closure: **85.2** → **85.3**), as shown in Figure 1.85. In most cases this cannot be avoided in the presence of strong bases; in fact, such a reaction, which can be used to furnish[4] "*C*-glycosidic compounds" (**85.4**), may even be preferred for the preparation of related substances.

1.2.6.1. Chain Extension with Nonstabilized Ylides

Carbonyl olefination with nonstabilized ylides appears to lead to chain-extended products with *Z*-configuration, but this experimental fact cannot be explained in full details. Nevertheless, the formation of an intermediary

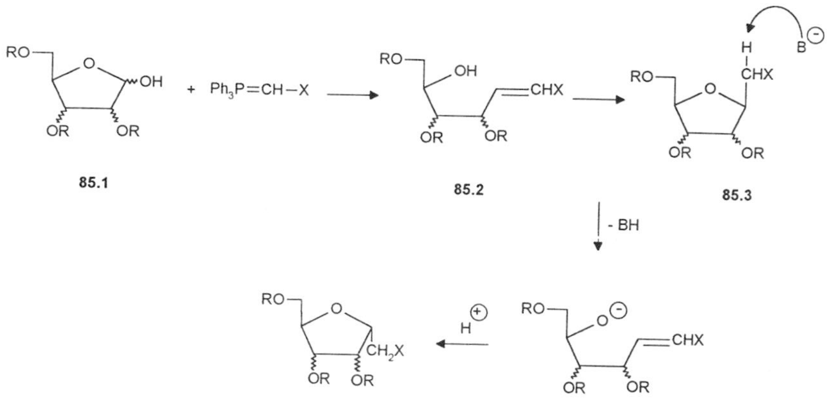

85.1   85.2   85.3

- BH

85.4

FIGURE 1.85

1,2-oxaphosphetane is observed, but the steps of its further conversion[1,5] have not been unequivocally clarified.

1.2.6.1.1. Carbonyl Olefination of Hydroxyaldehydes with Alkylidenephosphoranes

Both D- and L-glyceraldehydes, serving as important starting materials in chiral syntheses, have frequently been used as educts for various chain-extension procedures.[6] Elongation of the D-enantiomer by a single carbon atom, to furnish (S)-1,2-O-isopropylidene-3-buten-1,2-diol,[7,8] is shown in the following example.

> (S)-1,2-O-Isopropylidene-3-buten-1,2-diol[7]   To a solution of methylenetriphe-nylphosphorane in benzene, prepared as described by Schlosser et al.[9] is added, dropwise, a solution of 2,3-O-isopropylidene-D-glyceraldehyde (18.3 g) in benzene (50 ml) over a period of 1 h with cooling, so that the temperature of the mixture does not exceed 10°C. After an additional 1 h the ylide excess is decomposed by the addition of acetone in benzene until a colorless solution is obtained. After filtration, benzene is distilled off by using a Vigreux column; the resulting syrup is stirred vigorously with 1 liter of hexane to precipitate triphenylphosphine oxide. The mixture is then filtered, and the filtrate is washed with water, dried over 4Å molecular sieves, and distilled with the aid of a Vigreux column for removal of the solvents and to obtain the syrupy product (10.5 g, 59.5%), b.p. 50–52°C (6.66 kPa). The optical rotation value of the product further purified by means of preparative GC is $[\alpha]_D^{24}$ +30.96 (c = 0.98 in 2-propanol).

An analogous reaction of 2,3-O-isopropylidene-D-glyceraldehyde with ethylidenetriphenylphosphorane produces a 98:2 Z:E mixture of the corresponding pentene derivative,[10] and a similar product ratio is observed when hexylidenetriphenylphosphorane is used for the chain extension.[11] For the preparation[12] of (S)-(1,2-isopropylidenedioxy)-hept-3(Z)-ene, methyllithium has been employed as the base.

(S)-(1,2-Isopropylidenedioxy)-hept-3(Z)-ene[12]   A solution of *n*-butyltriphenyl-
phosphonium bromide (30.67 g) in dry THF (307 ml) is mixed at 0°C with a solution
of methyllithium (1.69 g, 1 eq) in ether (80 ml). To the stirred mixture is slowly
added a solution of 6.5 g of freshly distilled 2,3-*O*-isopropylidene-D-glyceraldehyde
in THF (50 ml) over a 1-h period, after which the red color of the ylide just
disappears. The solvents are evaporated under diminished pressure, and petroleum
ether (b.p. 30–40°C) is added to the residue. Triphenylphosphine oxide is filtered
off, and evaporation of the filtrate gives 6.2 g of the crude, yellow syrupy product
that is purified by means of distillation, b.p. 62°C (0.67 kPa).

To obtain the corresponding octadecene-derivative *n*-butyllithium is
applied.[13]

(S)-(1,2-Isopropylidenedioxy)-octadec-3(Z)-ene[13]   To a solution of pentadecyl-
triphenylphosphonium bromide (100 g, 180.64 mmol) in THF (400 ml) is slowly
added, over a 10-min period, a solution of *n*-butyllithium in hexane (1.6 N, 110 ml,
176 mmol). To the yellow solution of the phosphorane is added at $-78°C$ a solution
of 2,3-*O*-isopropylidene-D-glyceraldehyde (30 g, 230.8 mmol) in THF (80 ml). The
mixture is kept at $-78°C$ for 2 h, and then at room temperature for 14 h. After
concentration the residue is diluted with water (200 ml) and extracted with pentane.
The organic layer is washed with water, dried over $MgSO_4$, and purified with column
chromatography (eluant: 1:4 ethyl acetate–hexane) to obtain 47.4 g (80%) of the
syrupy title product, $[\alpha]_D^{20}$ +4 (c = 5.72 in chloroform).

The diene **86.2** can be similarly prepared[14] (Fig. 1.86) from the dialdofuranose **86.1.**

3,5,6-Trideoxy-1,2-O-isopropylidene-α-D-glycero-hex-3,5-dienofuranose (86.2)[14]
To a stirred solution of methylenetriphenylphosphonium bromide (15 g, 42 mmol)
in dry THF (250 ml), 40 mmol of *n*-butyllithium in hexane is added under argon
atmosphere. After stirring at room temperature for 30 min, a solution of 1,2-*O*-
isopropylidene-α-D-*glycero*-pent-3-eno-*dialdo*-1,4-furanose (**86.1**) in THF (20 ml)
is added. After 15 min the mixture no longer contains the starting sugar (TLC:
ether); it is then diluted with water (100 ml) and extracted with ether (3 ×
250 ml). The combined organic layer is washed with aqueous Na_2CO_3 until neutral,
and the crude product obtained on usual workup is purified by means of column
chromatography (eluant: ether) to obtain the pure dienofuranose **86.2,** as a syrup,
$[\alpha]_D^{20}$ −149.1 (c = 1.06 in chloroform).

Data in the literature show that extension of the carbonyl-olefination
method for tetrose derivatives is quite useful in glycolipid chemistry to
obtain *sphingosine* analogs. Thus, 2,4-*O*-benzylidene-D-threose has been

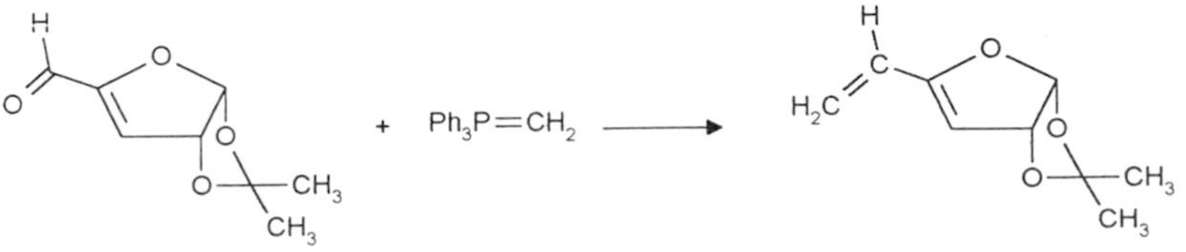

FIGURE I.86

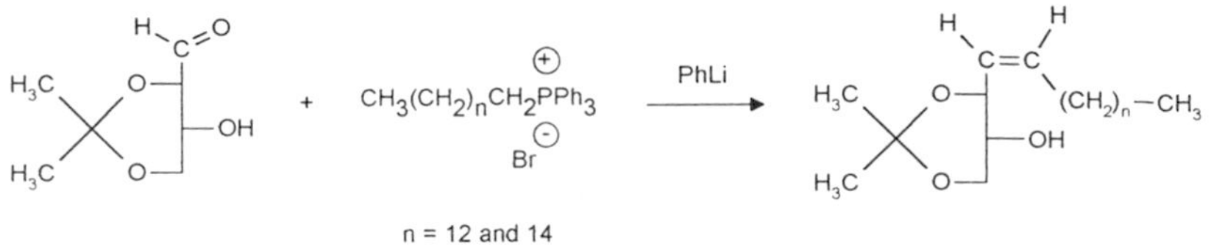

n = 12 and 14

87.1   87.2   87.3

FIGURE I.87

converted[15] into a $4:1$ $Z:E$ alkene mixture with tetradecyltriphenylphosphonium bromide and potassium *tert*-butoxide; under photochemical conditions, this olefinic product ratio can be changed to $1:10$.

2,4-O-Isopropylidene-D-threose (**87.1**) is an excellent starting sugar for conversion into *sphingosine* derivatives (Fig. 1.87). By applying tetradecyl or hexadecyltriphenylphosphonium bromide (**87.2**; n = 12 or 14, respectively) and appropriate reaction conditions, the isomeric chain-extended products **87.3** can be readily separated.[16]

> *(2R,3R,4E)-1,3-O-Isopropylidene-4-octadecene-1,2,3-triol and its (2R,3R,4Z)-analog*[16] To a stirred solution of tetradecyltriphenylphosphonium bromide (18.8 g) in dry THF (100 ml), a solution of phenyllithium (17.4 ml; 2 M in 7 : 3 cyclohexane–ether) is added in a nitrogen stream. The clear, red solution of the ylide thus obtained is cooled to −60°C and mixed with a solution of 2,4-O-isopropylidene-D-threose (4.7 g) in THF (19 ml). After stirring for 30 min at −30°C, 27.7 ml of the preceding phenyllithium solution is added, and the deep-red solution, produced in the reaction is kept at room temperature for 40 min, then poured into ice water and extracted with ether, and the organic phase is washed with water, dried, and concentrated. Column chromatography with alcohol-free chloroform gives 3.67 g (40%) of the (*E*)-isomer, m.p. 44.5–45.5°C, $[\alpha]_D$ −26 (c = 0.7 in chloroform) and 3.21 g (35%) of the (*Z*)-isomer, m.p. 44.5–45.5°C, $[\alpha]_D$ −3 (c = 0.4 in chloroform).

Further examples of this chain-elongation procedure are the transformation[17] of 2,2,4(*S*)-trimethyl-1,3-dioxolan-4-carbaldehyde into (4*S*,5*S*)-[2-(1,3-dioxolan-2-yl)ethenyl]-2,2,5-trimethyl-1,3-dioxolane, or its chain extension[18] with *N*-carbobenzyloxyalanine.

Studies on the chain extension of aldoses carrying free anomeric hydroxyl group (**88.1**) with nonstabilized phosphoranes have revealed that the products are 1-alkenes (**88.2**), which retain the configuration of the educt (Fig. 1.88). A summary of related transformations is shown in Table 1.14.[19–30]

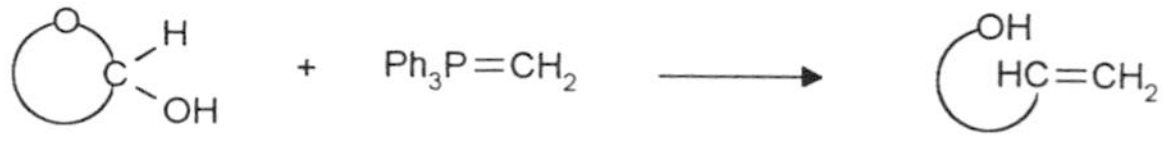

88.1   88.2

FIGURE I.88

TABLE 1.14 Partially Protected C-1 Unsaturated Alditols Obtained by Olefination of Reducing Monosaccharides with Methylenetriphenylphosphorane

Product	Ref(s).
3,4,5,7-Tetra-*O*-benzyl-1,2-dideoxy-D-*gluco*-hept-1-enitol	19–22
4,5,7-Tri-*O*-benzyl-1,2-dideoxy-D-*gluco*-hept-1-enitol	23
3,4,5,7-Tera-*O*-benzyl-1,2-dideoxy-D-*manno*-hep-1-enitol	22,24
3,4,5,6,7-Penta-*O*-benzyl-1,2-dideoxy-D-*galacto*-hep-1-enitol	22
3,4,6-Tri-*O*-benzyl-1,2-dideoxy-D-*ribo*-hex-1-enitol	22,23
4,6-Di-*O*-benzyl-1,2,3-trideoxy-D-*erythro*-hex-1-enitol	22,23
1,2,3-Trideoxy-6-*O*-triphenylmethyl-D-*erythro*-hex-1-enitol	22
3,4,6-Tri-*O*-benzyl-1,2-dideoxy-D-*arabino*-hex-1-enitol	25–27
3,4-Di-*O*-benzyl-6-*O*-triphenylmethyl-1,2-dideoxy-D-*ribo*-hex-1-enitol	28
6-*O*-*tert*-Butyldiphenylsilyl-1,3,4-trideoxy-D-(and -L-)-*erythro*-hex-1-enitol	29
3,4,6-Tri-*O*-benzyl-1,2-dideoxy-L-*xylo*-hex-1-enitol	30

When the chain extension of 2,3,5-tri-*O*-benzyl-D-ribose with methyltriphenylphosphonium bromide and *n*-butyllithium into 3,4,6-tri-*O*-benzyl-1,2-dideoxy-D-*ribo*-hex-1-enitol was carried out, epimerization to the *arabino*-compound was observed.[25,31] At the same time, this latter sugar, synthesized from 2,3,5-tri-*O*-benzyl-D-arabinose, proved to be stable toward bases.

2-Amino-2-deoxy-D-glucose derivatives with a free hydroxyl group at the anomeric position suffer extensive degradation on attempted chain extension[32] with alkylidenephosphoranes. However, under phase-transfer conditions (formamide–1,4-dioxane, K_2CO_3) no such fragmentation occurs, and *N*-acetyl-D-glucosamine (**89.1**) gives (*E*)-3-acetamido-1,2,3-trideoxy-1-phenyl-D-*gluco*-hept-1-enitol (**89.2**) with benzyltriphenylphosphonium chloride (Fig. 1.89) together with the *manno*-product **89.3,** formed on C-2 epimerization. This finding clearly explains the similar product distribution observed[33] in an analogous Wittig reaction of *N*-acetyl-D-mannosamine (**89.4**).

The scope and limitations of the carbonyl-olefination methodology in the field of carbohydrates have been studied mostly on starting materials that are readily available from pentoses or hexoses and are easily convertible into substances carrying an aldehyde function. For the chain extension of *aldehydo*-aldoses with alkylidenephosphoranes, a general procedure was reported by Anderson and Fraser-Reid.[34]

General procedure for the Wittig reaction of aldehydo-*sugars*[34]   A three-necked round-bottomed flask is equipped with a septum, vacuum tubing with a tap, a

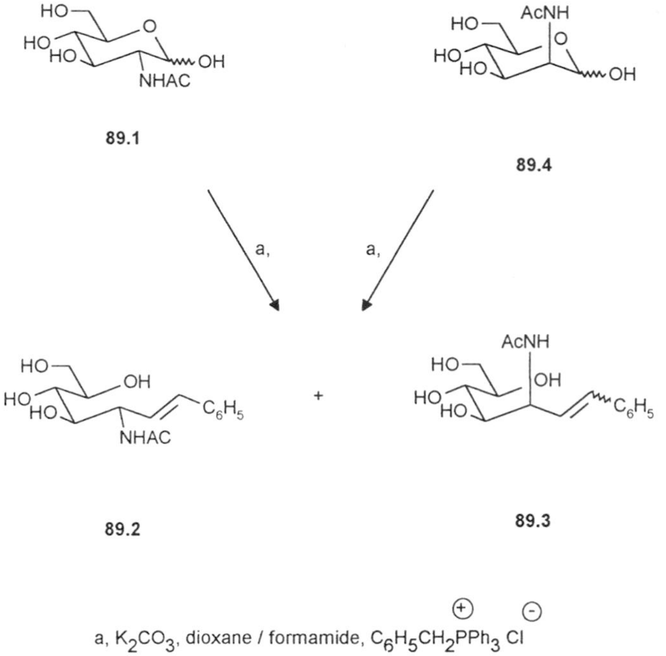

89.1

89.4

89.2

89.3

a, K_2CO_3, dioxane / formamide, $C_6H_5CH_2PPh_3 \overset{\oplus}{} Cl \overset{\ominus}{}$

FIGURE I.89

magnetic stirrer, and a stopper. The dry solvent (~15 ml/1 g of the carbonyl compound) and the required phosphonium salt (1.3 eq) are placed in the flask, which is then flushed with a stream of nitrogen or argon to remove air. Through the septum, n-butyllithium (1 mmol/mmol of the phosphonium salt) is injected into the flask and the mixture is stirred for 30 min. Then a solution of the carbonyl compound in the same solvent (~2 ml/1 g of the substance) is injected slowly into the mixture. After stirring for 90 min, the reaction is quenched by the addition of a small volume of water, the solvents are distilled off, and after conventional workup the semisolid residue is purified by means of column chromatography.

RajanBabu[35] has published an additional procedure for the Wittig reaction of *aldehydo*-sugars.

Another general procedure for the Wittig reaction of aldehydo-*sugars*[35]   To a three-necked flask (dried with heating) equipped with a dropping funnel, a thermocouple lead, and a septum, the recrystallized, dried phosphonium salt and anhydrous THF are added, so that a 0.5 M suspension is obtained. The solution is cooled to −20°C, and 1.6 M n-butyllithium (0.98 eq) is added dropwise from the funnel, which is then rinsed with a small volume of THF. The stirred mixture is warmed to room temperature to obtain a clear solution (~1 h), and then a 0.5 M solution of the saccharide (0.5 eq) in THF is added at −20°C. The mixture is allowed to warm to room temperature and stirred for 16 h, a reflux condenser is placed on the flask, and the mixture is warmed at 50°C for 15 min. Then it is cooled, pure acetone is added, and after stirring for 5 min, a solution of the saccharide (120 ml ether/mmol of the saccharide) is added and the precipitate is filtered through a pad of Celite.

The filter cake is washed with ether and the combined ethereal solution is washed with saturated aqueous $NaHCO_3$, aqueous NaCl, and water. Following drying and evaporation, the residue is purified by means of column chromatography with an ethyl acetate–hexane mixture.

Table 1.15[36–85] lists the literature results of chain extensions carried out with tetrose, pentose, and hexose derivatives using alkylidenephosphoranes.

The experience obtained with the preceding carbohydrate derivatives and the nonstabilized phosphoranes offered further extension of this type of carbonyl-olefination methodology. In a review paper Secrist, Barnes, and Wu discussed[86] the syntheses of naturally occurring higher sugars based on the Wittig method described in the preceding paragraphs. The idea to derive both partners of the olefination reaction from suitable carbohydrate derivatives has also emerged,[86] and in such a case the product would be a functionalized olefin as shown by the following equation:

$$(Saccharide)-CH=PPh_3$$
$$+ \; (saccharide)'-CHO \rightarrow saccharide-CH=CH-saccharide'$$

For the execution of a related reaction, methyl 5-deoxy-2,3-O-isopropylidene-5-(triphenylphosphonio)-β-D-ribofuranoside (**90.2**) was found as a suitably reactive phosphonosugar that did not undergo β-elimination. This compound can be transformed into a reddish-brown ylide (**90.3**), whose reaction with aldehydes gives rise exclusively to olefins with α-L-*lyxo* configuration (Fig. 1.90), as proved by detailed structural investigation.

> *Methyl 5-deoxy-2,3-O-isopropylidene-5-(triphenylphosphonio)-β-D-ribofurano-side iodide (**90.2**)*[86]   A solution of methyl 5-deoxy-5-iodo-2,3-O-isopropylidene-β-D-ribofuranoside (**90.1**, 4.0 g, 13 mmol) and triphenylphosphine (3.67 g, 14 mmol) in sulfolane (4.5 ml) is heated at 110°C for 64 h. The yellow solution is diluted first with chloroform (80 ml) and then with ether ($\sim$700 ml). The mixture is cooled at -78°C until the precipitation of the salt **90.2** is complete; the salt is then filtered off and washed with ether to give 6.16 g (84%) of colorless crystals. Recrystallization from ethyl acetate–methanol yields the pure iodide, m.p. 177.5–179°C.

Detailed studies have shown that the ylide **90.3**, generated from the salt **90.2** with n-butyllithium, is transformed into the α-L-*lyxo*-ylide **90.4** on acid treatment. Consequently, the reaction of this latter compound with simple aldehydes, such as benzaldehyde, p-chlorobenzaldehyde, and butyraldehyde, results in hex-5-enofuranosides **90.5** with the same configuration. The self-condensation of **90.4**, proceeding with a moderate yield and leading to the 5,9-dienofuranoside (**90.6**), was also observed.

> *Methyl 5,6,9,10-tetradeoxy-2,3:7,8-di-O-isopropylidene-D-glycero-β-D-gulo-deca-5,9-dienofuranoside (**90.6**)*[86]   A 3 M solution of the salt **90.2** (360 mg, 0.625 mmol) in a 2 : 1 mixture of THF/HMPA is cooled to -50°C and 0.726 mmol of n-butyllithium is added under nitrogen atmosphere. After stirring for 3 min, 0.5 g of Dowex 50

TABLE 1.15 Carbonyl Olefination of *aldehydo*-Sugars with Alkylidenphosphoranes

Educt	Phosphorane	Ref(s).
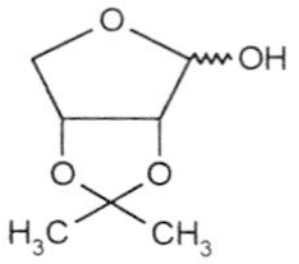	$Cl(CH_2)_3CHPPh_3$	36
	$H_2C{=}PPh_3$	37
		38
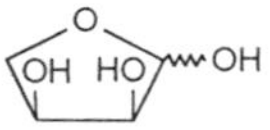	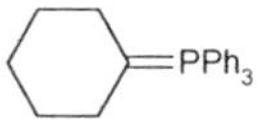	39
	$RCH{=}PPh_3$	34,40
	$(R = C_5H_{11}{-}C_{10}H_{21})$	
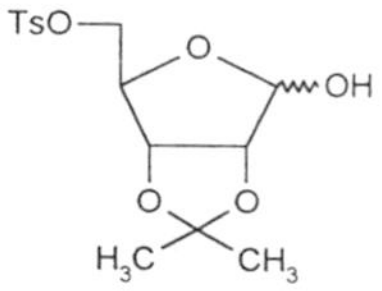	$iPrPPh_3$	41
	$RCH{=}PPh_3$	
	$(R = C_4H_9 - C_9H_{19})$	42
	$CH_3CH_2CH{=}PPh_3$	43
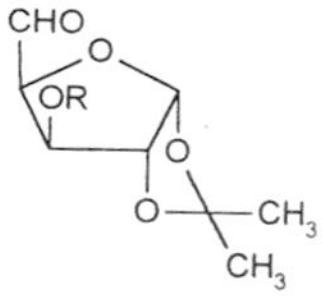	$H_2C{=}PPh_3$	44,45
	$CH_3(CH_2)_{13}CH{=}PPh_3$	46
	$CH_3CH_2CH{=}PPh_3$	47,48
	$CH_3CH_2CH_2CH{=}PPh_3$	49
	$CH_3(CH_2)_5CH{=}PPh_3$	50
	$CH_3(CH_2)_{12}CH{=}PPh_3$	51
	$C_7H_5PPh_3$	52
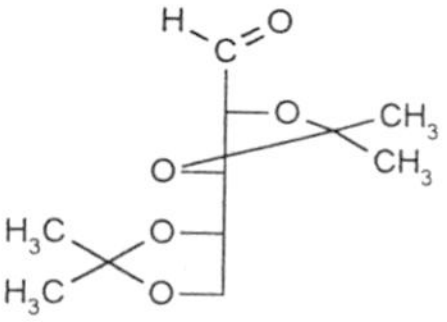	$H_2C{=}PPh_3$	53
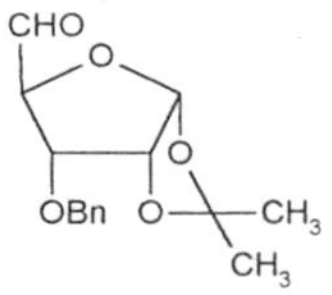	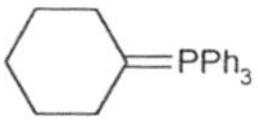	54

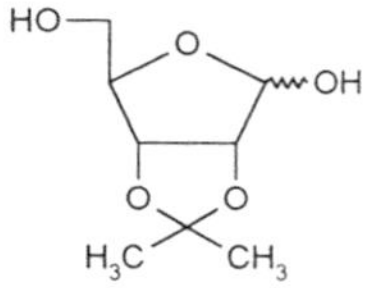

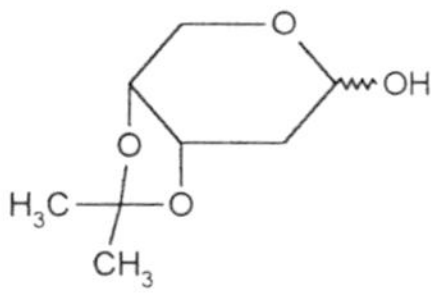

(continues)

TABLE 1.15 (*continued*)

Educt	Phosphorane	Ref(s).
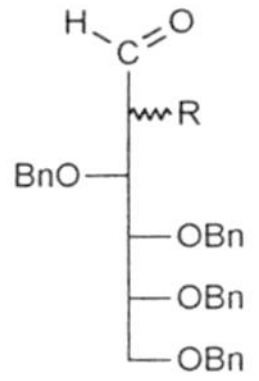	$H_2C=PPh_3$	55
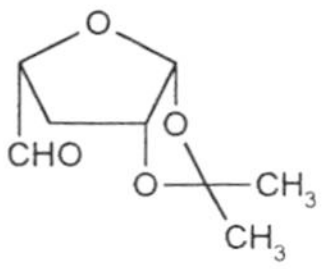	$CH_3(CH_2)_3=PPh_3$	50
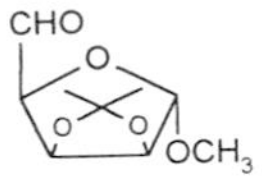	$CH_3(CH_2)_{13}CH=PPh_3$	46
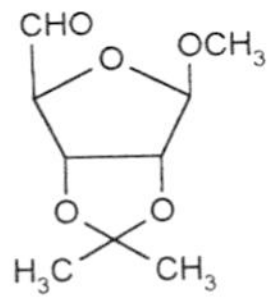	$CH_3(CH_2)_{13}CH=PPh_3$	46
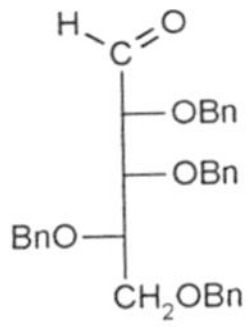	$CH_3(CH_2)_{13}CH=PPh_3$	56
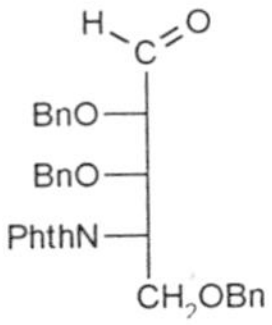	$CH_3(CH_2)_{11}CH=PPh_3$	57
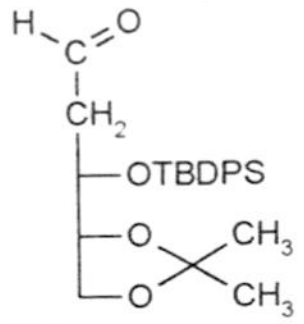	$CH_3(CH_2)_4CH=PPh_3$	58
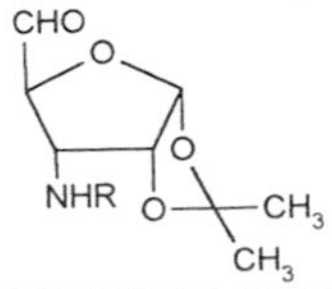	$CH_3(CH_2)_{12}CH=PPh_3$ $CH_3(CH_2)_{13}CH=PPh_3$	59 60

(*continues*)

TABLE 1.15 (*continued*)

Educt	Phosphorane	Ref(s).
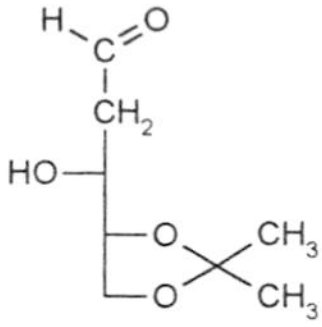	$C_5H_{11}CH=PPh_3$	61
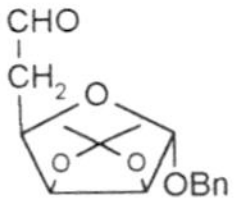	$CH_3(C(S)HOH)(CH_2)_8CH=PPh_3$	62
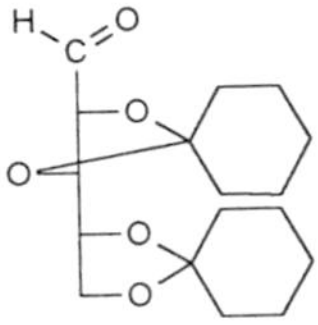	$RCH=PPh_3$	63,64
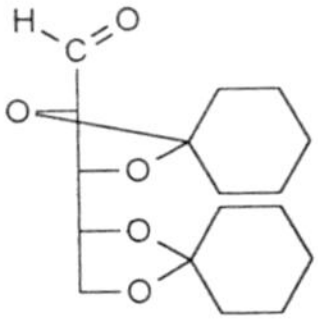	$RCH=PPh_3$	65
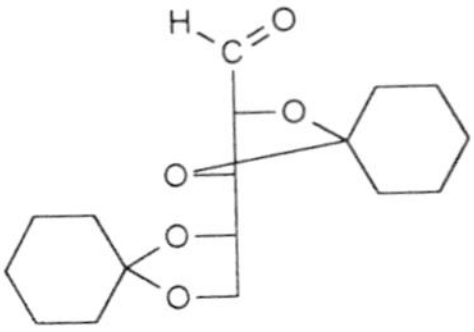	$RCH=PPh_3$	66
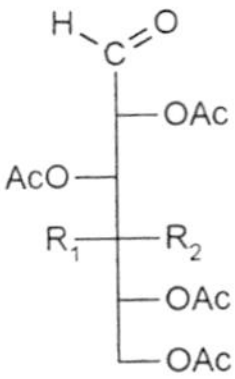	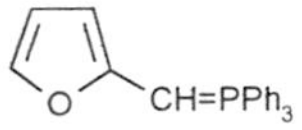 $CH=PPh_3$	67
	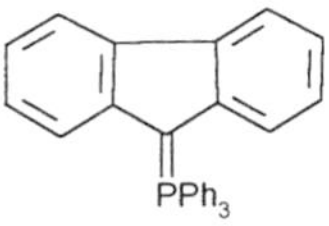 PPh_3	68
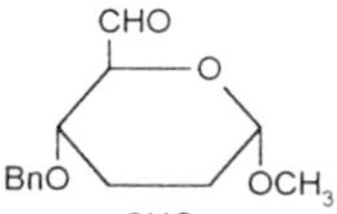	$CH_3(CH_2)_2CH=PPh_3$	69
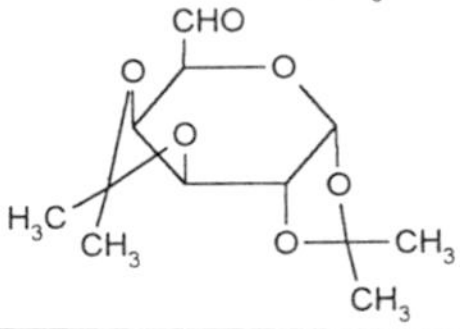	$H_2C=PPh_3$	71
	$CH_3CH=PPh_3$	72
	$CH_3CH_2CH=PPh_3$	73
	$(CH_3)_2CH(CH_2)_3CH=PPh_3$	73

(*continues*)

TABLE 1.15 (*continued*)

Educt	Phosphorane	Ref(s).
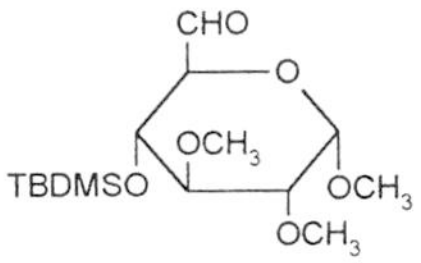	$(CH_3)_3SiCH_2CH=PPh_3$	74
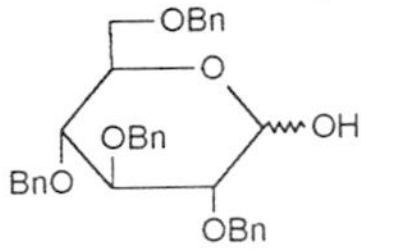	$H_2C=PPh_3$	35
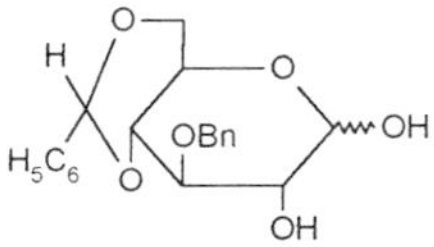	$H_2C=PPh_3$	35
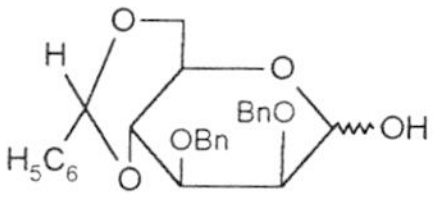	$H_2C=PPh_3$	35
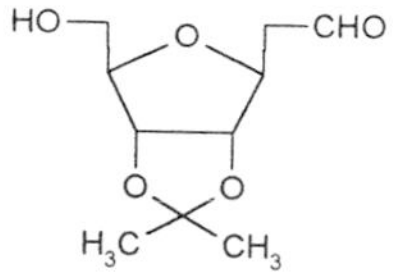	$CH_3CH=PPh_3$	75
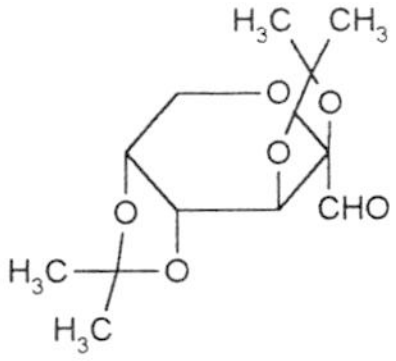	$H_2C=PPh_3$	76
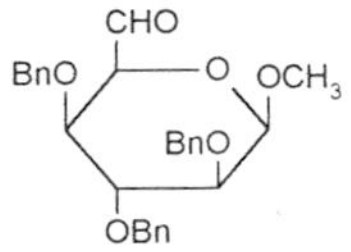	$H_2C=PPh_3$	77
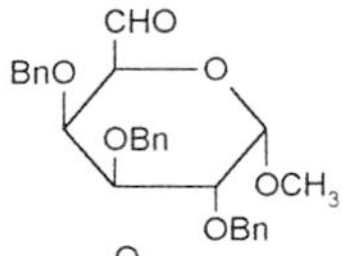	$H_2C=PPh_3$	77
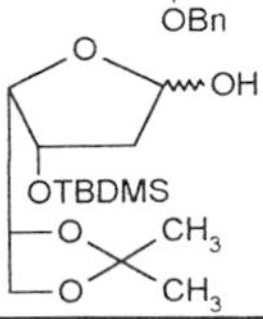	$CH_3CH_2CH=PPh_3$	78

(*continues*)

TABLE 1.15 (*continued*)

Educt	Phosphorane	Ref(s).
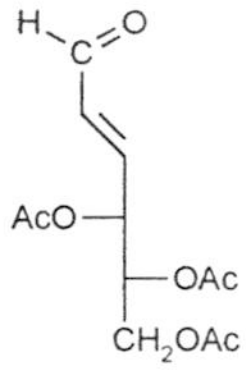	$CH_3(CH_2)_6CH=PPh_3$	79
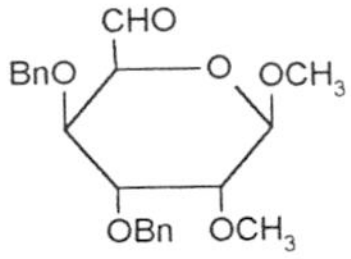	$(CH_3)_2CHCH=PPh_3$	80
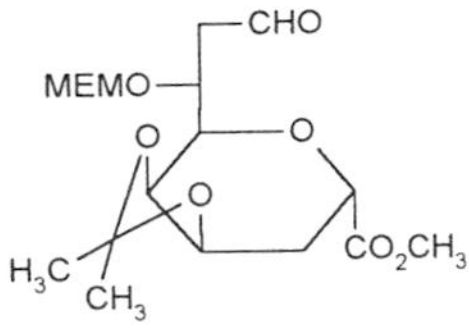	$CH_3CH=PPh_3$	81
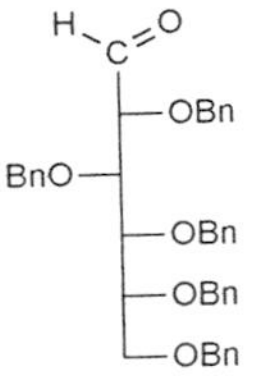	$CH_3CH=PPh_3$	82
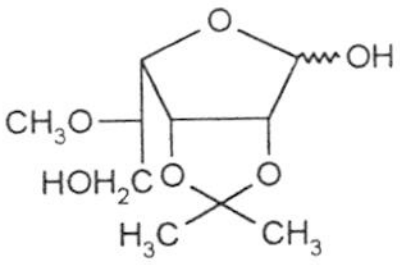	$(CH_3)_2C=PPh_3$	83
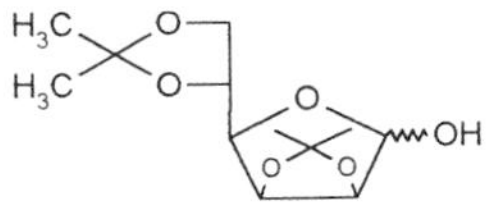	$H_2C=PPh_3$	84,85

(H^+) cation-exchange resin is added when the solution becomes slightly yellow. It is diluted with benzene at $-10°C$, the resin is filtered off and washed with the same solvent and the combined filtrate is washed with water, dried, and concentrated. Preparative TLC of the residue (eluent: 3:1 petroleum ether–ether) gives 65 mg (64%) of the pure dienofuranoside **90.6** as a colorless syrup.

Using this method, several hexose derivatives have been converted to phosphonio sugars as useful sources for obtaining the corresponding ylides. Two of these saccharides (**91.1** and **91.2**), derived[87] from appropriately protected galactose derivatives, are shown in Figure 1.91.

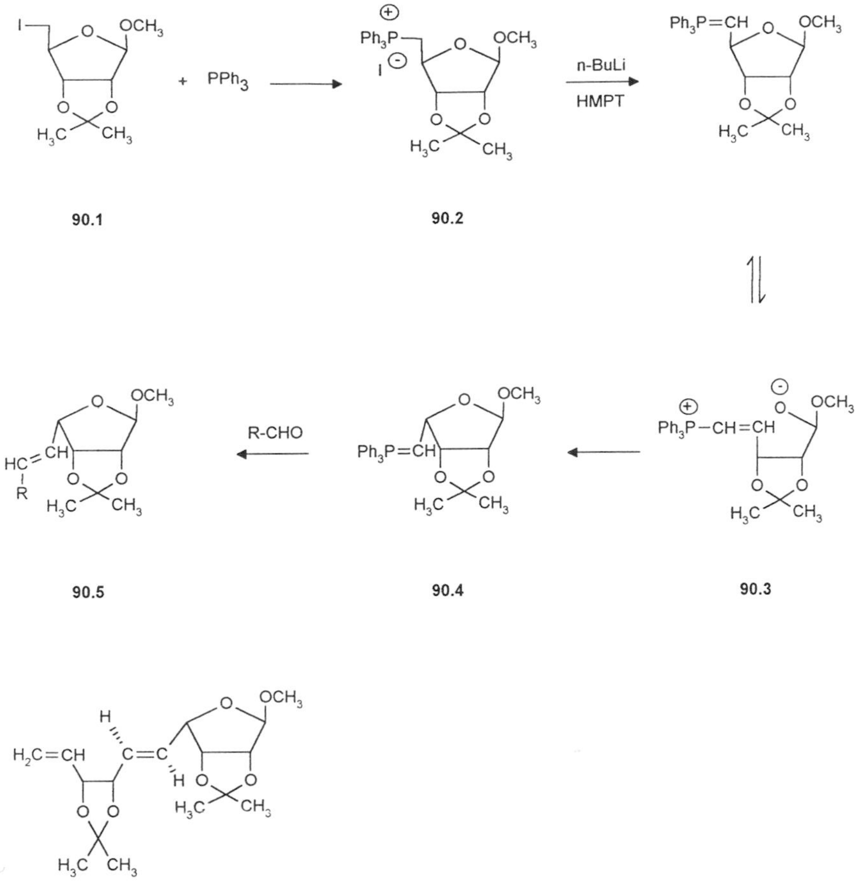

90.1   **90.2**

90.5   **90.4**   **90.3**

90.6

FIGURE 1.90

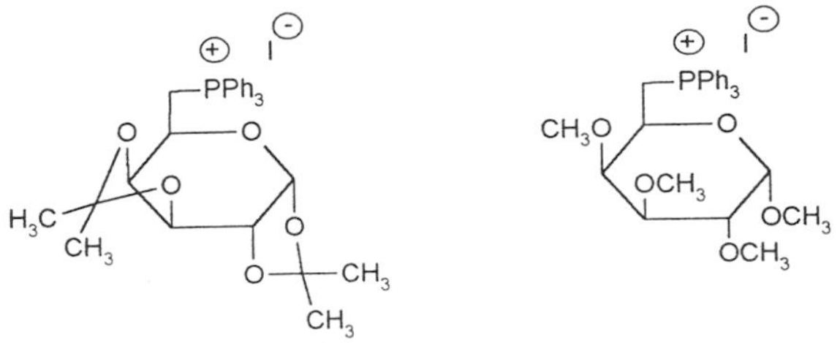

91.1   **91.2**

FIGURE 1.91

These phosphonium salts can be readily transformed into the respective ylides, which are to be immediately converted to the required olefin.

A general procedure for the generation of ylides and their reaction with aldehydes[87]
A ~2-M solution of the phosphonium salt in 2 : 1 THF/HMPA is cooled to −60°C, and 1 eq of *n*-butyllithium is added through a septum under nitrogen atmosphere. After 0.5–1 min, 1.2–1.5 equivalents of the aldehyde is added and the mixture is allowed to warm to −10°C over a 45-min period. (Liquid aldehydes are applied without solvent, and the solid ones are dissolved in THF.) Then a 1 : 1 mixture petroleum ether–wet ether is added, the precipitated triphenylphosphine oxide is filtered off and washed with the same solvent mixture, and the combined filtrate is concentrated. The residue is taken up with a 1 : 1 petroleum ether–ether mixture; washed with water, saturated aqueous NaHSO₃, and again with water; dried (MgSO₄), and the residue is purified by means of column chromatography.

By employing this general procedure[87] (*Z*)-(1-methyl-2,3-*O*-isopropylidene-β-D-*ribo*-tetrofuranos-4-yl)-2-(1,2:3,4-di-*O*-isopropylidene-α-D-*galacto*-pentopyranos-5-yl)-ethylene (**92.1**) was prepared with 64% yield from the phosphonium salt **91.1**. From this latter salt and 2,3:4,5-di-*O*-isopropylidene-*aldehydo*-D-arabinose (*Z*)-6,7-dideoxy-1,2:3,4:8,9:10,11-tetra-*O*-isopropylidene-D-*arabino*-α-D-*galacto*-undec-6-enopyranose (**92.3**) was obtained, and upon exposure to UV light, both (*Z*)-isomers were converted into the respective (*E*)-isomers **92.2** and **92.4** (Fig. 1.92).

(E)-6,7-Dideoxy-1,2:3,4:8,9:10,11-tetra-O-isopropylidene-D-arabino-α-D-galacto-undec-6-enopyranose (92.4)[87] A mixture of the (*Z*)-isomer **92.3** (410 mg, 0.9 mmol), diphenyl disulfide (400 mg, 1.83 mmol) and cyclohexane (3 ml) is irradiated with a medium-pressure 450-W Hanovia lamp (No. 676 A36) for 40 min at room temperature, after which the solution is warmed up. The solvent is distilled off, and the residue is separated by means of preparative TLC (3 runs in 3 : 1 petroleum ether–ether) to obtain 248 mg (60 %) of **92.4** and 43 mg (10%) of the educt **92.3**. Recrystallization from hexane affords a pure analytic sample of **92.4** with m.p. 100–101°C, $[\alpha]_D^{25}$ −86.6 (*c* = 0.38 in chloroform).

This type of carbonyl olefination, utilizing the reaction of *aldehydo*-sugars and sugar phosphinoalkenes, has been employed in the synthesis of various natural products structurally related to saccharides. The following examples illustrate the utility of the present methodology.

The key step (Fig. 1.93) in the synthesis[88] of (+)-*anamarin* (**93.4**) is the reaction of 6-deoxy-2,3:4,5-di-*O*-isopropylidene-*aldehydo*-L-glucose (**93.1**) with the dihydropyranylidenephosphorane **93.2** to afford a 9 : 1 mixture of the (*E*)-olefin **93.3** and the corresponding (*Z*)-isomer. The (−)-isomer of **93.3** was prepared[89] from the D-enantiomer of **93.1** and, interestingly, formation of the (*E*)-olefin is not reported.

For the synthesis of a tridecose derivative the 6,7-anhydrooctose **94.1** was reacted[90] with the phosphonium salt **94.2** (Fig. 1.94). Detailed studies have shown that the 1 : 1 *E/Z* ratio of the product **94.3** can be changed to 1 : 5 by employing lithium hexamethyldisilylamide in THF/HMPA instead of lithium diethylamide.

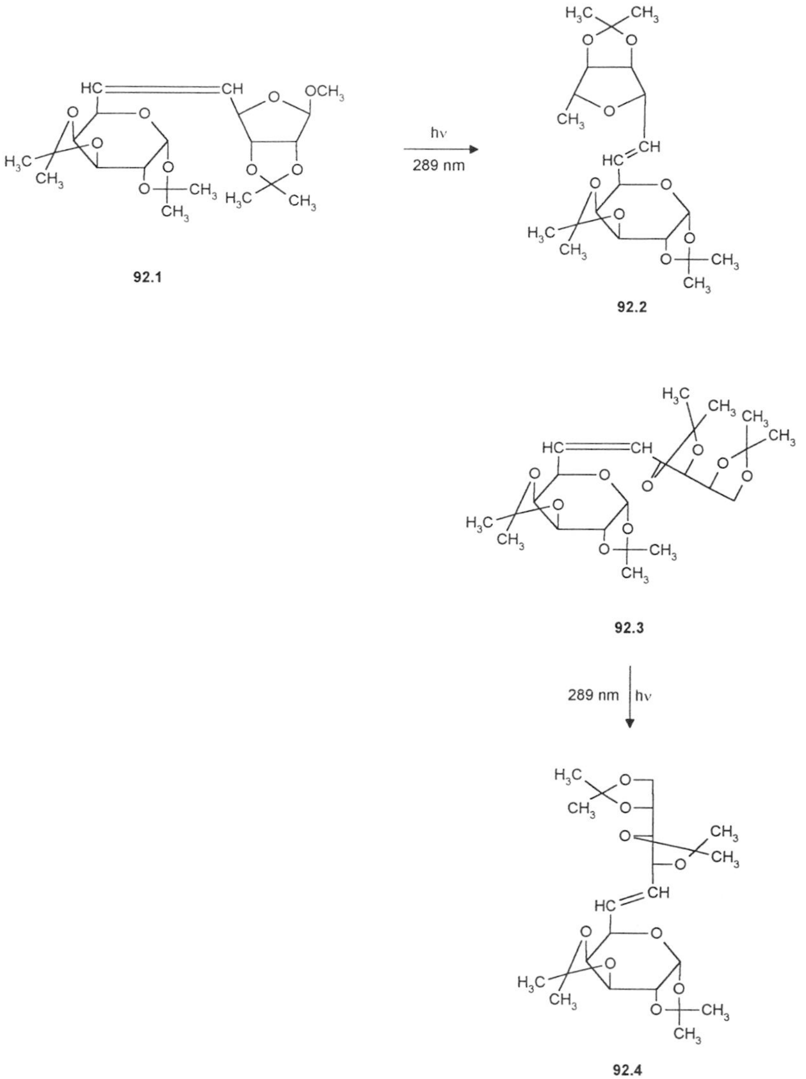

FIGURE 1.92

The reaction 2,3-di-*O*-benzyl-5,6-*O*-isopropylidene-*aldehydo*-D-arabinose (**95.1**) with the phosphonium salt **95.2**, derived from 1,6-anhydro-D-glucose, afforded[91] the (*Z*)-ethylene **95.3** exclusively (Fig. 1.95), and a similar *Z*-selectivity was observed[92] during the Wittig chain extension to result in methyl 4-acetamido-2,3,6,7,8,9,10,11-octa-*O*-acetyl-4-deoxy-α-D-*glycero*-D-*gluco*-undecopyranoside.

It is also interesting to mention that the key step (Fig. 1.96) in the synthesis of *methyl nonaacetyl-L-hicosaminide*, i.e., olefination[92] (see also

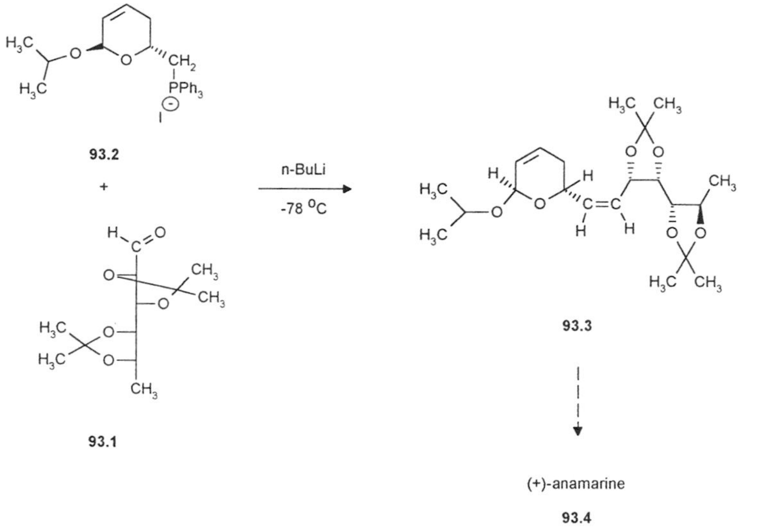

FIGURE 1.93

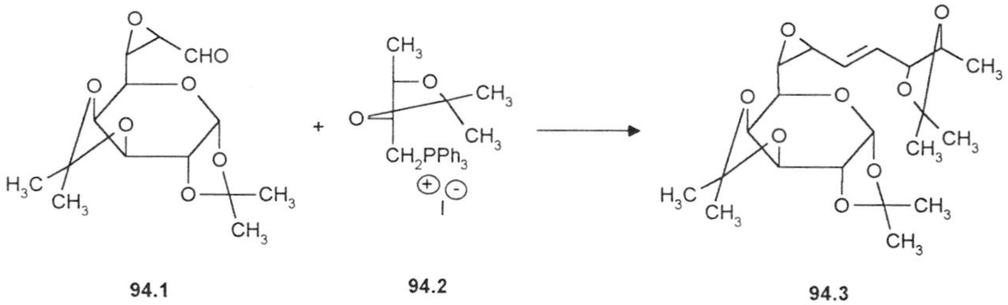

FIGURE 1.94

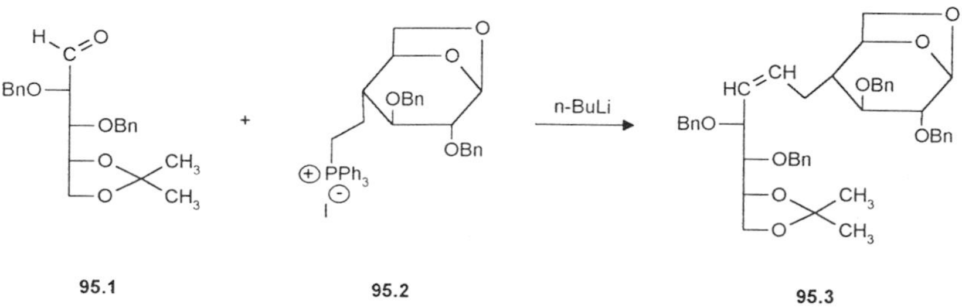

FIGURE 1.95

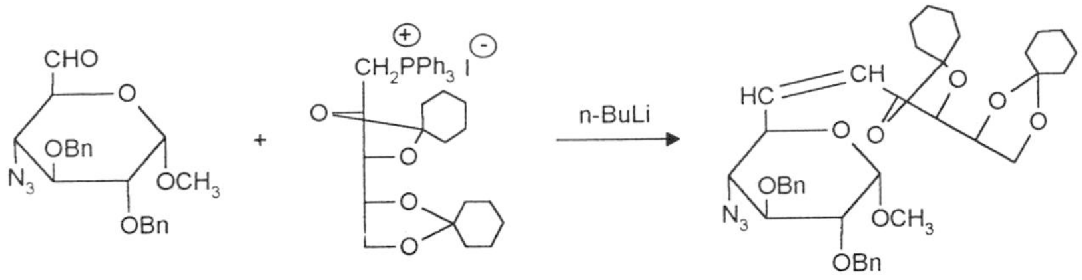

FIGURE 1.96

Jarosz[93]) of methyl 4-azido-4-deoxy-2,3-di-*O*-benzyl-α-D-glucopyranos-6-ulose (**96.1**) with 2,3:4,5-di-*O*-cyclohexylidene-1-deoxy-1-(triphenylphosphonio)-D-arabinitol (**96.2**), also led to the *Z*-product (**96.3**) exclusively.

The chain extension procedure based on Wittig methodology is also suitable for the preparation of the so-called *C*-disaccharides. This principle is illustrated on Figure 1.97, which shows bromonium ion–induced 6-*endo–trig* cyclization of the *E*-olefin **97.4**, derived from the phosphonium salt **97.1** and the *aldehydo*-D-arabinose **97.2** via **97.3**, leading to α-*methyl 1',2'-dideoxycellobioside* (**97.5**).[94]

1.2.6.1.2. Carbonyl Olefination of Hydroxyaldehydes and Saccharides with Alkoxy- and Alkylthiomethylenephosphoranes

Besides the academic importance of the chain-extension procedures based on the reaction of hydroxyaldehydes and sugars (**98.1**) with alkoxy and alkylthiomethylenephosphoranes (**98.2**), this plausible transformation is of practical significance as well, since the alkoxy- or alkylthio-1-alkenes (**98.3**) produced in the reaction can be easily hydrolyzed into 2-deoxy sugars (**98.4**) as shown in Figure 1.98.

A simple and useful example for this transformation is the synthesis of L-*arabino*-2,3:4,5-di-*O*-isopropylidene-1(*Z*)-(*p*-tolyloxy)-hexene, whose hydrolysis gives rise to a rare saccharide, 2-deoxy-L-gulose.[95]

L-Arabino-2,3:4,5-*Di-O-isopropylidene-1(Z)-(p-tolyloxy)-hexene*[95] To a suspension of *p*-tolyloxymethylenephosphonium chloride (5.5 mmol) in dry ether (10 ml) a solution of phenyllithium (5.5 mmol) in ether (15 ml) is added under nitrogen atmosphere when the color of the mixture turns deep red. To this suspension is added dropwise, during 10–15 min, a solution of 2,3:4,5-di-*O*-isopropylidene-*aldehydo*-L-arabinose (4.3 mmol) in ether (10 ml), when the mixture turns gradually colorless. It is stirred for an additional 30 min under nitrogen and concentrated. The residue is extracted with benzene (70 ml), washed with water, dried over MgSO₄, and evaporated. Purification of the residue (2.53 g) is performed with column chromatography (eluant: 100:2 chloroform–methanol) to give 0.89 (67%) of the yellow, syrupy title product and 1.21 g (87%) of triphenylphosphine oxide.

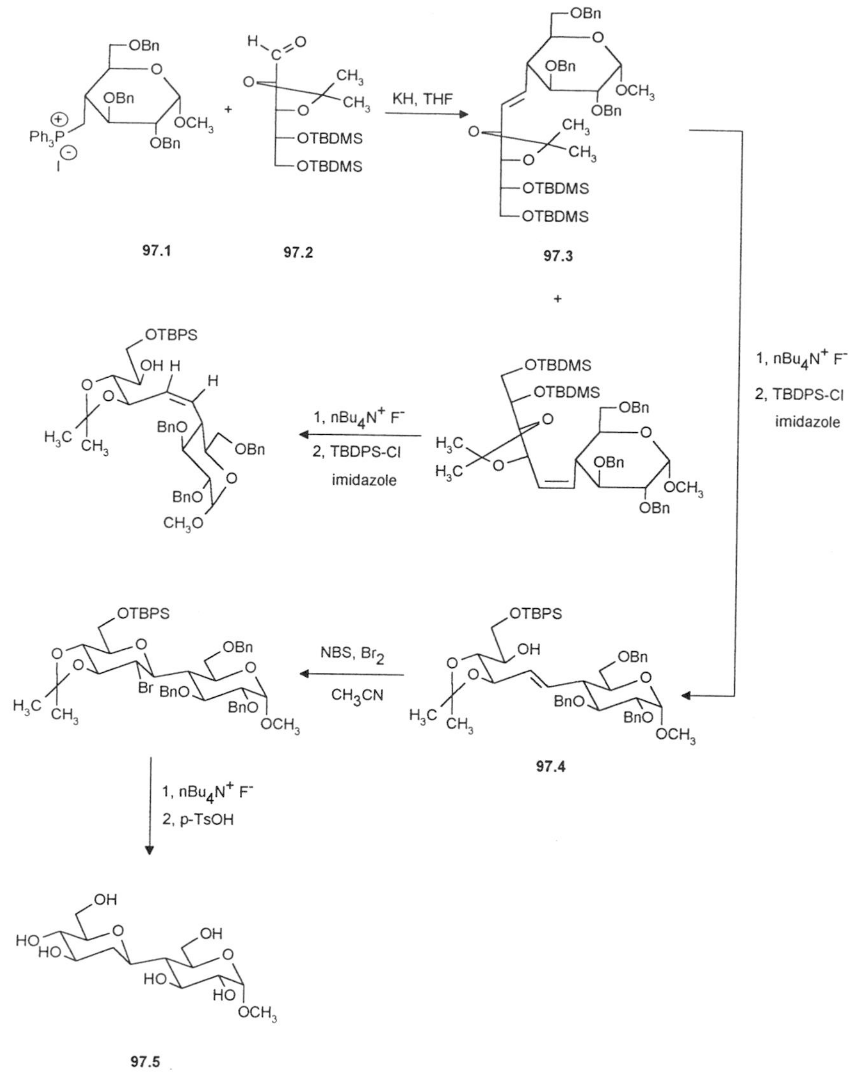

α-Methyl 1',2'-dideoxycellobioside

FIGURE 1.97

Some additional transformations based on this principle are summarized in Table 1.16.[96–113]

1.2.6.1.3. Carbonyl Olefination with the Reaction between Saccharides and Mono- or Dihalogenophosphoranes

This procedure is discussed here as a method for preparation of acetylene derivatives carrying chiral centers from suitable halomethylene ana-

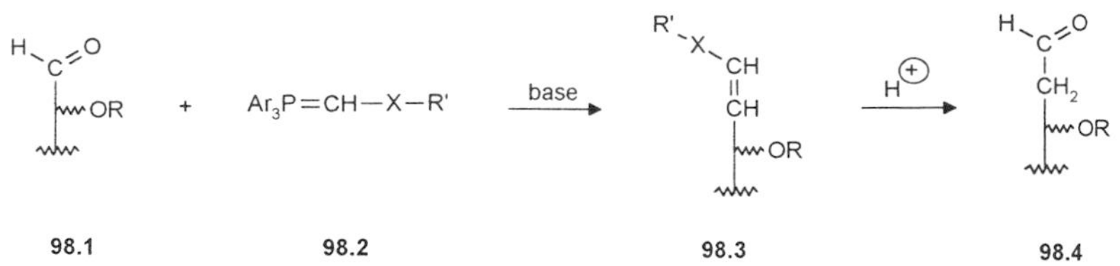

98.1   **98.2**   **98.3**   **98.4**

FIGURE 1.98

logs, produced in the chain-extension reaction of saccharides with halogenated methylenephosphoranes.[114–121] By employing a practical one-pot operation, there is no need to separate the geometric isomers of the primarily produced haloalkene derivatives.

A related chloromethylenation method is shown by an example of a protected D-glucose derivative (Fig. 1.99).

> *(E) and (Z)-1,2-Dideoxy-1-chloro-3,4:5,7-di-O-isopropylidene-D-*gluco-*hept-1-enitol (99.2 and 99.3)*[121a] A suspension of chloromethylenetriphenylphosphorane (3.16 g, 7.2 mmol) in dry THF (8 ml) is mixed, under nitrogen atmosphere, with a 1.6 M solution of *n*-butyllithium in hexane (4.5 ml). To the deep-red mixture, HMPA (1.26 ml, 7.2 mmol) and a solution of 2,3:4,6-di-O-isopropylidene-D-glucopyranose (**99.1**, 470 mg, 1.8 mmol) in dry THF (8 ml) are added. After 1.5 h, the reaction is complete; 100 ml of a saturated aqueous solution of NaHCO$_3$ is added and the mixture is extracted with dichloromethane. The separated organic layer is dried and evaporated under diminished pressure, and the crude product is purified by means of column chromatography (70 : 30 : 0.1 hexane–ethyl acetate–triethylamine) to obtain 132 mg of the faster-moving (E)-isomer **99.2**, $[\alpha]_D^{20}$ −55 (c = 1.0 in chloroform) and 130 mg of the slower-moving (Z)-compound **99.3**, m.p. 95°C (from hexane), $[\alpha]_D^{20}$ −3 (c = 0.3 in chloroform). The overall yield of the two geometric isomers is 50%.

The same reaction was carried out with the corresponding galactose derivative to furnish[121a] an overall yield of 70%.

The chain-extended products derived with the preceding methodology are summarized in Table 1.17.[114–121]

1.2.6.1.4. Carbonyl Olefination of Carbohydrates with Semistabilized Ylides

In the carbohydrate field, relatively few examples have been reported for the application of the semistabilized arylidenetriphenylphosphoranes. From 2,4-O-benzylidene-L-xylose, 2,6,7-trideoxy-7-C-(2,4-dichlorophenyl)-D-*xylo*-heptonic acid was prepared[122] and its conversion into C-glycosidic compounds was investigated[123]. Unprotected monosaccharides can also be reacted with benzylidenetriphenylphosphorane in hot 1,4-dioxane according to the Wittig methodology, and useful procedures (with ~70% yield) for such a reaction with D-arabinose, L-xylose, D-glucose, and D-galactose have been reported.[124]

> *Olefination of aldoses with benzylidenetriphenylphosphorane*[124] A solution of benzylidenetriphenylphosphonium chloride (11.6 g, 30 mmol) and potassium *tert*-butoxide (3.36 g, 30 mmol) in dry 1,4-dioxane (120 ml) is stirred at room temperature for 30 min and then at 80°C for 30 min. Then the sugar (15 mmol) is added, and

TABLE 1.16 Carbonyl Olefination of Hydroxyaldehydes and Saccharides with Alkoxy and Alkylthiomethylenephosphoranes

Educt	Phosphorane	Ref(s).
	$PhSCH=PPh_3$	96
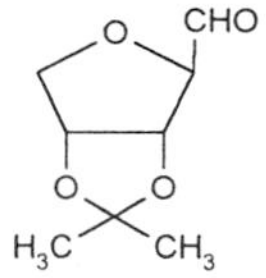	$CH_3SCH=PPh_3$	97
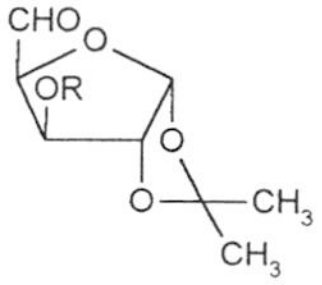	$CH_3SCH=PPh_3$	98
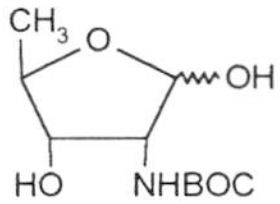	$CH_3OCH=PPh_3$	99
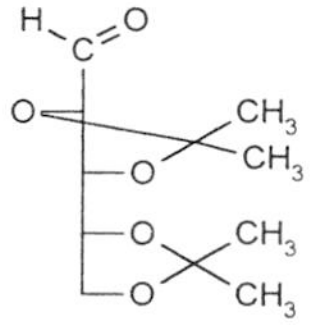	$CH_3SCH=PPh_3$ $PhSCH=PPh_3$ $CH_3OCH=PPh_3$	100 100 101
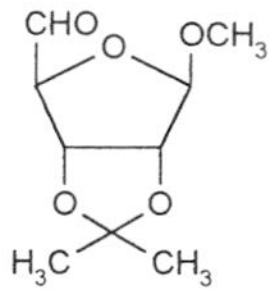	$CH_3C(OCH_3)=PPh_3$	102
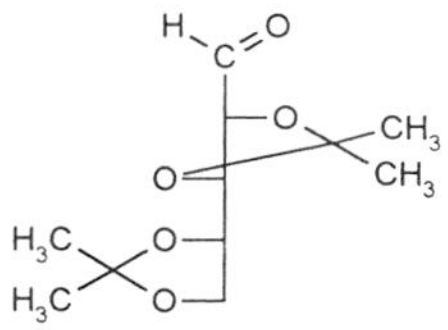	$CH_3OCH=PPh_3$ $CH_3SCH=PPh_3$	53 103
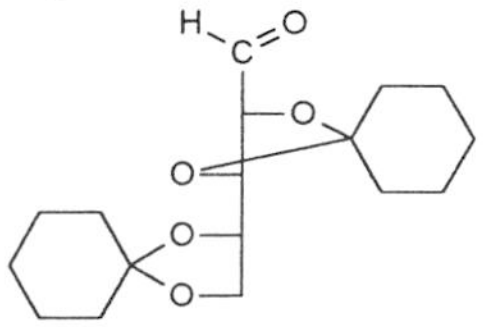	$CH_3OCH=PPh_3$	104
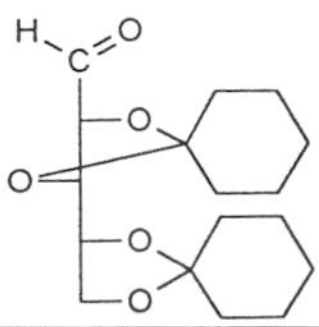	$CH_3OCH=PPh_3$	105

(continues)

TABLE 1.16 (*continued*)

Educt	Phosphorane	Ref(s).
	PhSCH=PPh₃	106,107
	PhSCH=PPh₃	108
	CH₃OCH=PPh₃	109
	CH₃OCH=PPh₃	109
	CH₃OCH=PPh₃	109
	PhSCH=PPh₃	110
	CH₃OCH=PPh₃	111
	CH₃OCH=PPh₃	112
	CH₃OCH=PPh₃	113

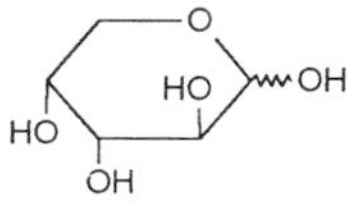

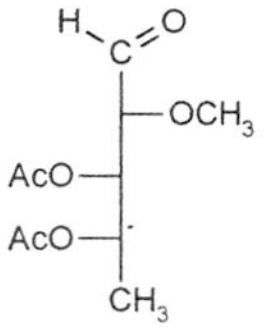

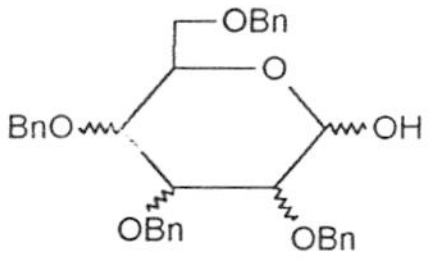

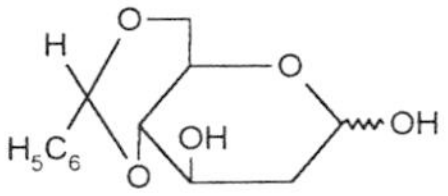

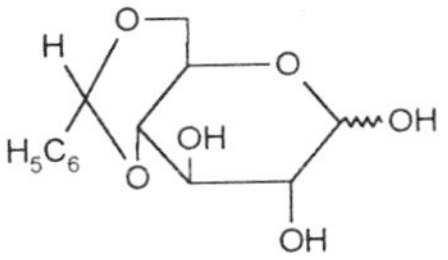

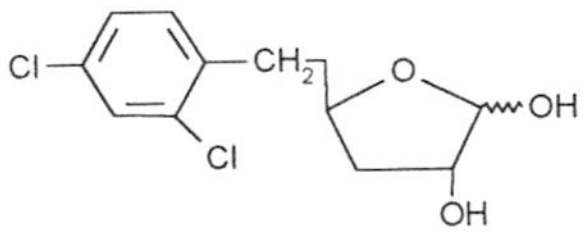

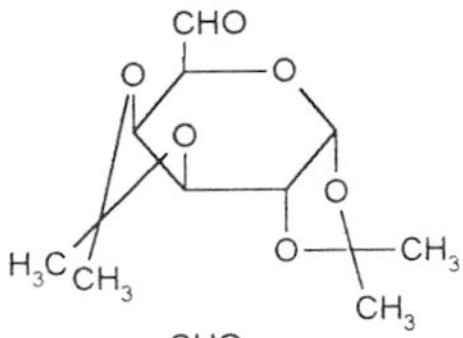

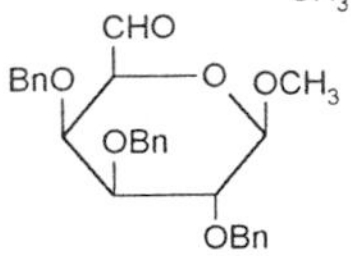

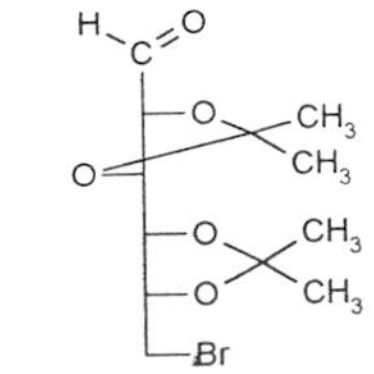

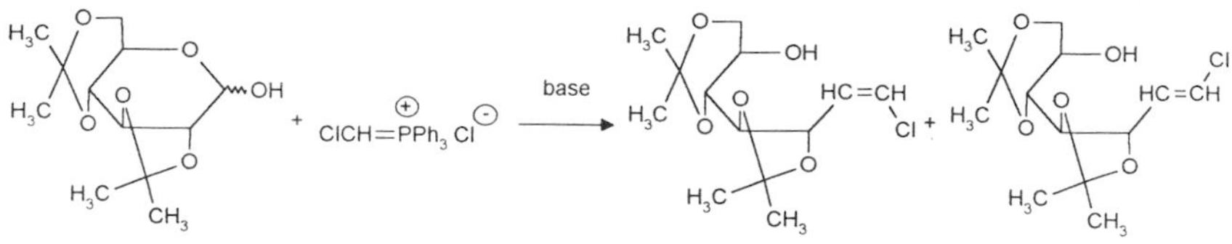

FIGURE 1.99

the solution is heated to reflux for 2 h. It is cooled to room temperature, the excess of the ylide is destroyed by the addition of 10 ml of water, and the solvent is evaporated under reduced pressure. The *trans*-configurated D-*galacto* derivative is obtained on recrystallization of the residue from methanol (workup by chromatography yielded an unseparable 95:5 (*E*)/(*Z*) mixture). The other compound is purified by column chromatography (eluant: 5:1 dichloromethane–methanol).

1,2-*O*-Isopropylidene-3-*O*-methyl- (or benzyl)-α-D-*xylo*-pentodialdo-1,4-furanose have been successfully converted[125] with 3-pyridylmethylene- and 2-benzimidazolydenetriphenylphosphorane into the corresponding chain-extended products, and this procedure can also be exectuted[126] under phase-transfer conditions.

The practical importance of this above methodology and, most particularly, of the transformation of free reducing saccharides with pyrimidinyl-methylenephosphoranes, is that this type of the Wittig reaction leads[127,128] directly, or at least in two simple steps, to homo-*C*-nucleosides. Pyrrolo [3,2-*d*]pyrimidine-*C*-nucleosides have been synthesized[127] by treatment of 2,3-*O*-isopropylidene-5-*O*-trityl-D-ribofuranose (**100.1**) with [(2,4-dimethoxy-5-nitropyrimidin-6-yl)-methylene]triphenylphosphorane, and other *C*-nucleosides have also been prepared (Fig. 1.100) by the Wittig reaction of the ribofuranose **100.1** with [(6-chloropyrimidin-4-yl)methylene]triphenyl-phosphorane (**100.2**).

*Chain extension of 2,3-O-isopropylidene-5-O-trityl-D-ribofuranose (**100.1**) with [(6-chloro-pyrimidin-4-yl)methylene]triphenylphosphorane (**100.2**)[128]* A mixture of the protected ribofuranose **100.1** (2.60 g, 6 mmol) and the phosphorane **100.2** (2.57 g, 6.6 mmol) in 20 ml of acetonitrile is refluxed for 2 h, then the solvent is distilled off. The residue is submitted to column chromatography on a 250-g silicagel column (eluant: 9:1 hexane–ethyl acetate), to afford, first 0.46 g (14%) of 4-chloro-6-(2′,3′-*O*-isopropylidene-5′-*O*-trityl-α-D-ribofuranosyl)methylpyrimidine (**100.3**) as a foam, then the corresponding β anomer **100.4** (2.1 g, 64%), and finally 0.2 (6%) of (*Z*)-4-chloro-6-(1′,2′-dideoxy-5-hydroxy-3′,4′-*O*-isopropylidene-6′-*O*-trityl-D-*ribo*-hex-1′-enyl)pyrimidine (**100.5**), as a foam. Further elution of the column with 4:1 hexane–ethyl acetate gave 0.23 g (7%) of the (*E*)-isomer of **100.5**.

Additional chloropyrimidinylphosphoranes have also been involved in these studies, and transformation[128] of olefins into homo-*C*-nucleosides with 1,8-diazabicyclo[5.4.0]un-dec-7-ene was carried out, as well.

TABLE 1.17 Chain-Extended Products of Carbonyl Olefination with Reaction between Saccharides and Mono- and Dihalogenophosphoranes

Educt	Phosphorane	Ref(s).
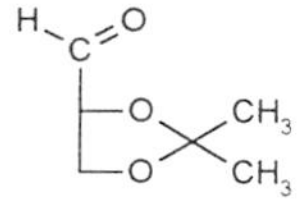	$Br_2C{=}PPh_3$	114
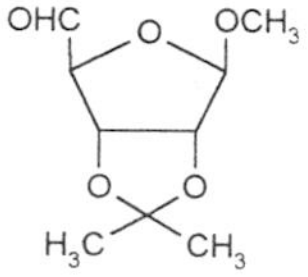	$Br_2C{=}PPh_3$ $F_2C{=}PPh_3$ $Cl_2C{=}P(NMe_2)_3$	115 116 117
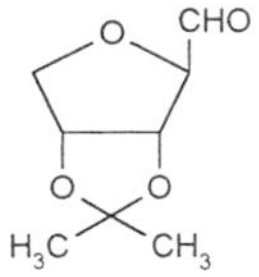	$Br_2C{=}PPh_3$ $F_2C{=}P(NMe_2)_3$	118 117
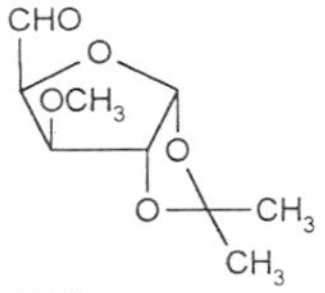	$Br_2C{=}PPh_3$ $ClFC{=}PPh_3$ $Cl_2C{=}PPh_3$	119,120 117 117
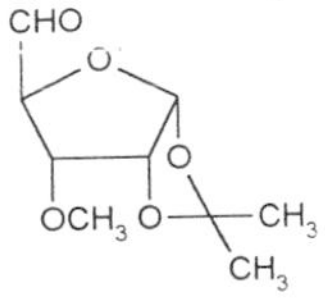	$Cl_2C{=}PPh_3$ $F_2C{=}P(NMe_2)_3$	117 116
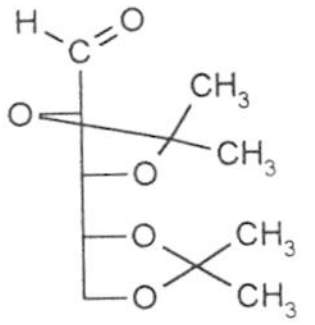	$Cl_2C{=}PPh_3$ $F_2C{=}P(NMe_2)_3$	117 116
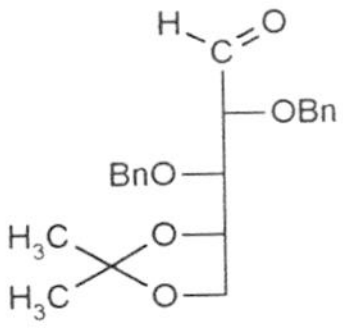	$ClCH{=}PPh_3$	121
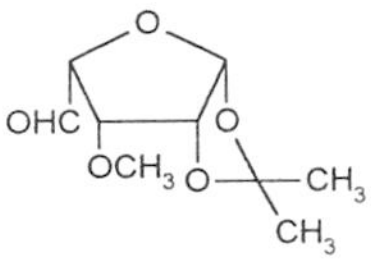	$F_2C{=}P(NMe_2)_3$	116

(*continues*)

TABLE 1.17 (continued)

Educt	Phosphorane	Ref(s).
	HFC=P(NMe₂)₃	117
	Br₂C=PPh₃	116
	Br₂C=PPh₃	115
	Cl₂C=PPh₃	117

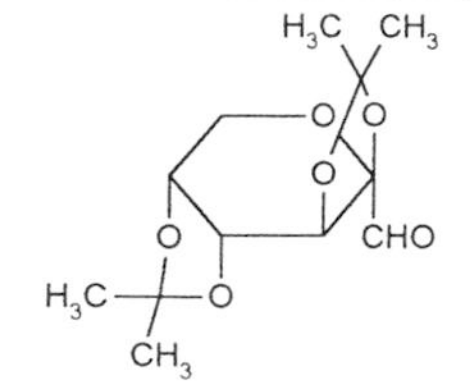

$HFC=P(NMe_2)_3$

$Br_2C=PPh_3$

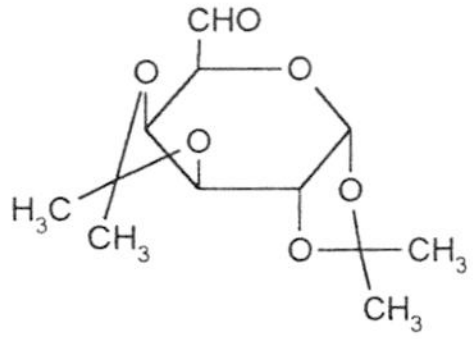

$Br_2C=PPh_3$

$Cl_2C=PPh_3$

100.1   100.2

100.3   100.4   100.5

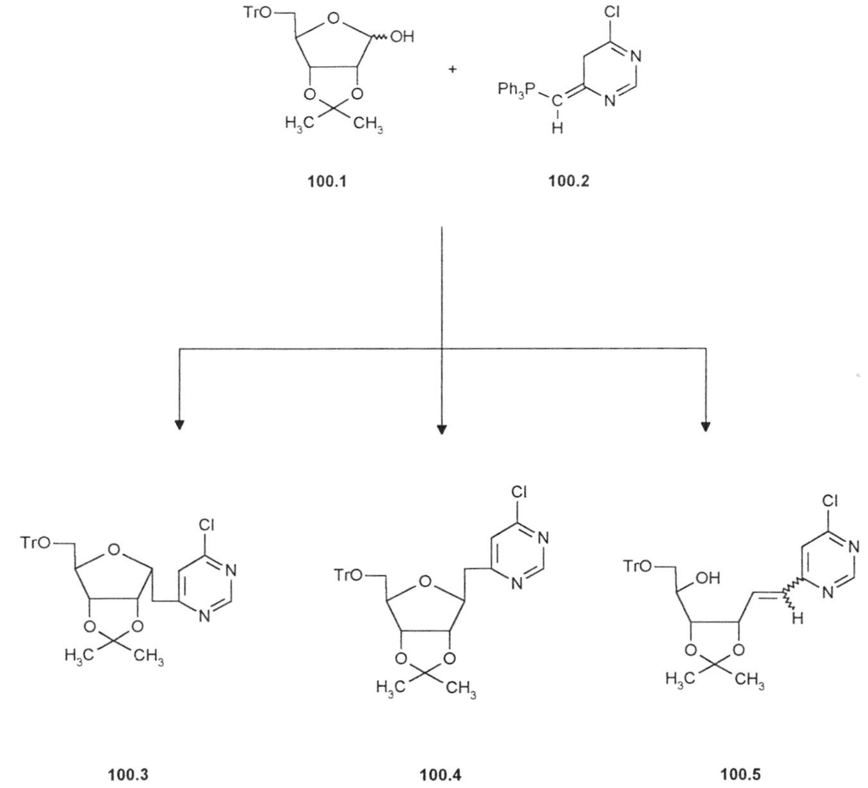

FIGURE 1.100

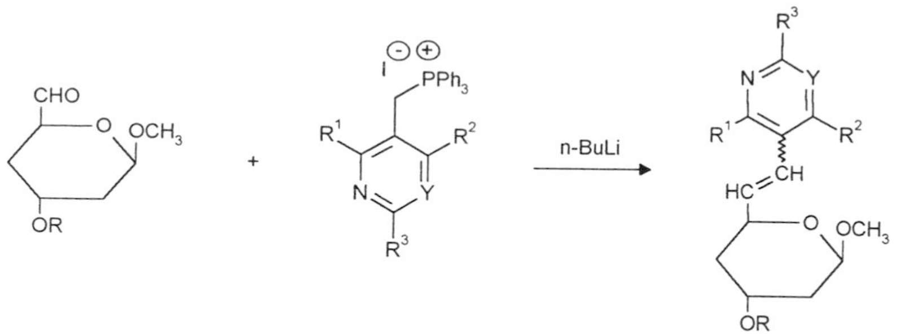

101.1 **101.2** **101.3**

R = Si(C$_6$H$_5$)$_2$C(CH$_3$)$_3$ Y = CH,N

FIGURE 1.101

During studies of the reaction of uloses with pyrimidin-5-yl- and pyridin-3-yl-phosphoranes (**101.2;** Fig. 1.101), 3-O-(*tert*-butyldiphenylsilyl)-2,4-dideoxy-β-D-*erythro*-hexopyranos-1,5-ulose (**101.1**)[129] was transformed[130] into an (E)/(Z) mixture of the oct-6,7-enoses **101.3.**

> *General procedure for the preparation of 7-heteroaryl-oct-6,7-enoses*[130]   A 1.6 M solution of *n*-butyllithium in hexane (12 ml, 19.2 mmol) is added dropwise to a solution of the phosphonium salt (17.5 mmol) in THF (100 ml) at 0°C. The reaction mixture is stirred for 30 min, a solution of the sugar **101.1** (7.29 g, 18.4 mmol) in THF (40 ml) is added, and stirring is continued for an additional 1 h. After dilution with water, the pH of the mixture is adjusted to ~5 with acetic acid and extracted with ether. The combined organic layer is washed with saturated aqueous NaHCO$_3$, and after workup the products are purified by means of column chromatography.

Table 1.18 contains the 7-heteroaryl-oct-6,7-enose derivatives prepared according to the procedure[130] described in the preceding paragraphs.

1.2.6.1.5. Synthesis of Dienes by Carbonyl Olefination

On treatment with allylidene- and crotylidenephosphoranes, *aldehydo*-aldose derivatives are readily converted into the corresponding dienes,[131] useful as chiral educts for Diels–Alder reactions. The preparation of the (E/Z)-diene derived from 2,3-O-isopropylidene-D-glyceraldehyde has been reported,[132] and an improved procedure[133] for the synthesis (Fig. 1.102) of (E/Z)-5,6:7,8-di-O-isopropylidene-L-*arabino*-octa-1,3-dienitol (**102.3**) is described in the following procedure.

> (E/Z)-5,6:7,8-Di-O-*isopropylidene*-L-arabino-*octa-1,3-dienitol* (**102.3**)[133]   To a suspension of allyltriphenylphosphonium bromide (**102.2;** 23 g, 0.06 mol) in dry ether (300 ml) a solution of phenyllithium in hexane (4 M, 18 ml) is added under nitrogen atmosphere, and after stirring for 1 h a solution of 2,3:4,5-di-O-isopropylidene-*aldehydo*-L-arabinose (**102.1;** 6.9 g, 0.03 M) in dry ether (50 ml) is added. Following stirring for 16 h, water is added, the ethereal layer is separated, and the aqueous phase is extracted with ether. The combined organic layer is dried

TABLE 1.18 Synthesized 7-Heteroaryl-oct-6,7-enoses[130]

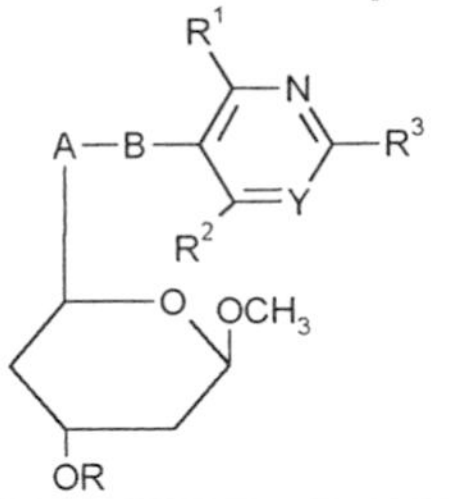

R = Si(C$_6$H$_5$)$_2$C(CH$_3$)$_3$		A-B = (E/Z) −CH = CH−	
Y	R^1	R^2	R^3
CH	CH$_3$	4-FC$_6$H$_4$	CH$_3$
CH	CH$_3$	4-ClC$_6$H$_4$	CH$_3$
CH	CH$_3$	4-FC$_6$H$_4$	C$_6$H$_5$
CH	i-C$_3$H$_7$	4-FC$_6$H$_4$	C$_6$H$_5$
CH	i-C$_3$H$_7$	4-FC$_6$H$_4$	CH$_3$
CH	i-C$_3$H$_7$	4-FC$_6$H$_4$	i-C$_3$H$_7$
CH	i-C$_3$H$_7$	4-FC$_6$H$_4$	t-C$_4$H$_9$
CH	i-C$_3$H$_7$	4-FC$_6$H$_4$	c-C$_6$H$_{11}$
CH	i-C$_3$H$_7$	4-FC$_6$H$_4$	C$_6$H$_5$
CH	i-C$_3$H$_7$	4-FC$_6$H$_4$	4-FC$_6$H$_4$
CH	i-C$_3$H$_7$	4-FC$_6$H$_4$	2,5-(CH$_3$)$_2$C$_6$H$_3$
CH	i-C$_3$H$_7$	4-FC$_6$H$_4$	3,5-(CH$_3$)$_2$C$_6$H$_3$
CH	i-C$_3$H$_7$	4-CH$_3$OC$_6$H$_4$	C$_6$H$_5$
CH	i-C$_3$H$_7$	4-CF$_3$C$_6$H$_4$	C$_6$H$_5$
CH	t-C$_4$H$_9$	4-FC$_6$H$_4$	C$_6$H$_5$
CH	c-C$_6$H$_{11}$	4-FC$_6$H$_4$	C$_6$H$_5$
CH	4-FC$_6$H$_4$	i-C$_3$H$_7$	C$_6$H$_5$
N	CH$_3$	4-FC$_6$H$_4$	CH$_3$
N	CH$_3$	4-ClC$_6$H$_4$	CH$_3$
N	i-C$_3$H$_7$	4-FC$_6$H$_4$	i-C$_3$H$_7$
N	i-C$_3$H$_7$	4-FC$_6$H$_4$	c-C$_6$H$_{11}$
N	i-C$_3$H$_7$	4-FC$_6$H$_4$	C$_6$H$_5$
N	i-C$_3$H$_7$	4-FC$_6$H$_4$	4-FC$_6$H$_4$
CH	CH$_3$	4-FC$_6$H$_4$	CH$_3$
CH	CH$_3$	4-FC$_6$H$_4$	C$_6$H$_5$
N	CH$_3$	4-ClC$_6$H$_4$	CH$_3$
CH	C$_2$H$_5$	4-FC$_6$H$_4$	C$_6$H$_5$
CH	i-C$_3$H$_7$	4-FC$_6$H$_4$	C$_6$H$_5$
N	CH$_3$	4-FC$_6$H$_4$	CH$_3$

(MgSO$_4$) and concentrated under reduced pressure, and the residue is submitted to column chromatography (eluant: 95:5 hexane–acetone) to furnish 4.76 g (62%) of yellow syrupy **102.3**, as a mixture of (E) and (Z)-isomers.

The research work aimed at the synthesis of certain natural products necessitated the preparation of specific dienes to be derived from carbohydrates. For example, the reaction of 2-deoxy-4,5-O-isopropylidene-D-*threo-*

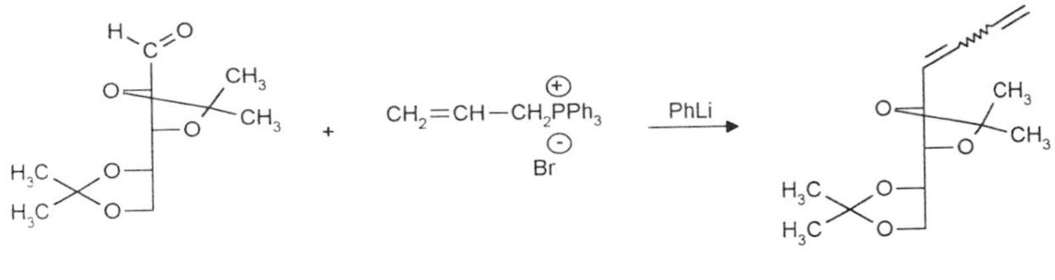

102.1   **102.2**   **102.3**

FIGURE 1.102

pentose (**103.1**) with (Z)-3-(hexen-1-ylidene)triphenylphosphorane (**103.2**) at −60°C gave rise[134] to a mixture of the (Z,Z)- and (E,Z)-diene isomers (**103.3**) with 70% yield (Fig. 1.103).

The chain extension of ω-aldehydo-sugar diethyl dithioacetals into the respective dienes can also be accomplished[135,136] with allyltriphenylphosphorane. Thus, Figure 1.104 illustrates the Wittig reaction of 2,3,4-tri-O-benzyl-D-xylo-pentodialdose diethyl dithioacetal (**104.1**) to furnish (2S,3R,4R)-octa-5(E/Z),7-dien-1-al diethyl dithioacetal (**104.2**).[135] After liberation of the aldehyde function of **104.2,** the resulting **104.3** is also a suitable candidate for Wittig chain extension with methylenephosphorane, leading to the nona-1,6(E/Z),8-triene **104.4.**

> (2R,3S,4R)-Octa-5(E/Z),7-dien-1-al diethyl dithioacetal (**104.2**)[135] A suspension of allyltriphenylphosphonium bromide (1.5 g, 4 mmol) in toluene (30 ml) is mixed with a solution of n-butyllithium in hexane (3.84 mmol) under nitrogen atmosphere. After stirring for 1 h, a solution of the diethyl dithioacetal **104.1** (1.8 g, 3.4 mmol) in toluene (5 ml) is added and the reaction mixture is stirred for 1 h. It is then filtered through a pad of Celite, and the filtrate is washed with water, dried over MgSO₄, and concentrated. Column chromatography of the residue (eluant: 9 : 1 hexane–ethyl acetate) yields 0.7 g (37.2%) of the title diene **104.2** as a 6:4 (Z/E) mixture.

> (3S,4R,5R)-Tribenzyloxy-nona-1,6(E,Z)-8-triene (**104.4**)[135] To a solution of methyltriphenylphosphonium bromide (0.321 g, 0.9 mmol) in toluene (10 ml) a solution of n-butyllithium in hexane (1.6 M, 0.56 ml) is added dropwise under nitrogen atmosphere. Then 0.262 g (0.59 mmol) of (2S,3R,4R)-tribenzyloxy-octa-5(E,Z),7-dien-1-al (**104.3**) is added and the mixture is stirred for 1 h. Following filtration, the filtrate is concentrated and the residue is purified by means of column

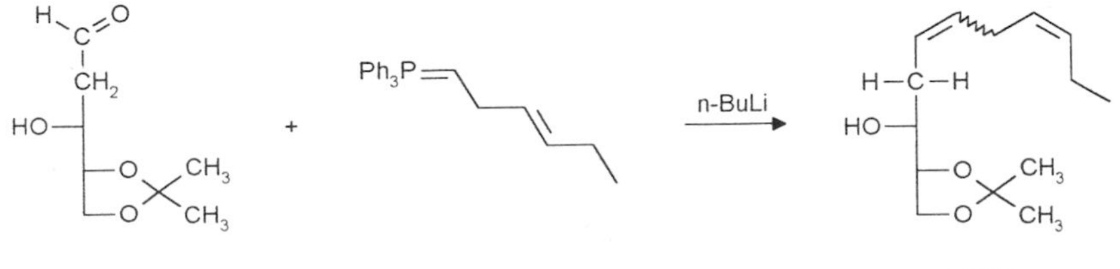

103.1   **103.2**   **103.3**

FIGURE 1.103

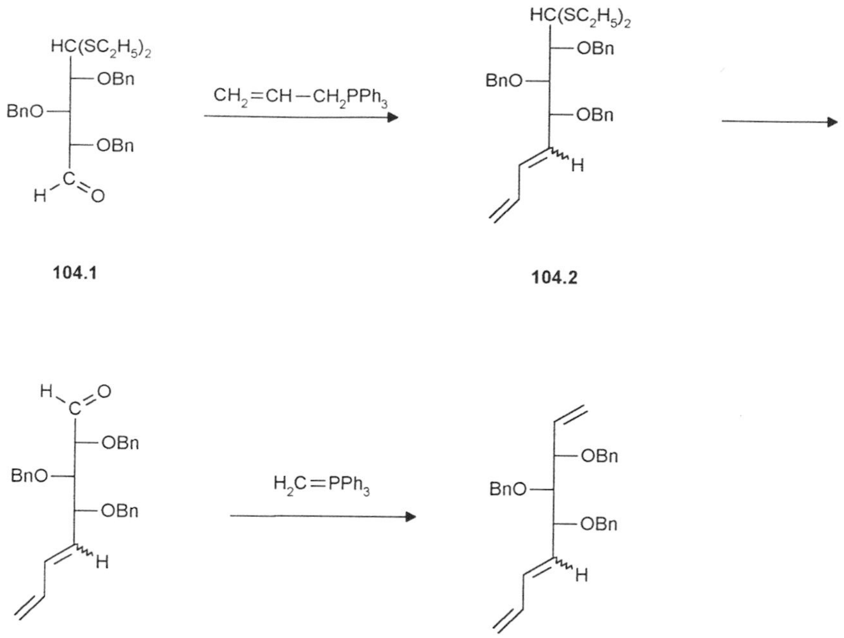

FIGURE 1.104

chromatography (eluant: 9:1 hexane–ethyl acetate) to obtain 0.2 g (62.6%) of the syrupy triene **104.4** (*E/Z* ratio ~2:3).

This principle can be successfully applied for the preparation of a higher homolog: (3*R*,4*R*,5*R*,6*S*)-3,4:5,6-di-*O*-isopropylidene-deca-1,7(*E*,*Z*),9-triene-3,4,5,6-tetraol,[136] for compound (**105.1**), as well as for the conversion of this latter into the bis-diene **105.2**, serving as a common intermediate in *prostaglandin* chemistry[137] (Fig. 1.105).

1.2.6.2. Extension of the Saccharide Chain with (Oxoalkylidene)Phosphoranes

The relative stability of phosphoranes, which can be roughly described by the negative charge distribution at the ylide carbon, is considerably enhanced by the presence of a carbonyl group ("semistabilized ylide"). Thus, in contrast to the nonstabilized methylenephosphoranes, (2-oxoalkylidene)phosphoranes and their positional isomers can be regarded as moderately reactive phosphoranes.

In principle, the reaction of an *aldehydo*-saccharide (**106.1**) with (oxoalkylidene)- or (oxoarylidene)phosphoranes (**106.2**) leads to an unsatu-

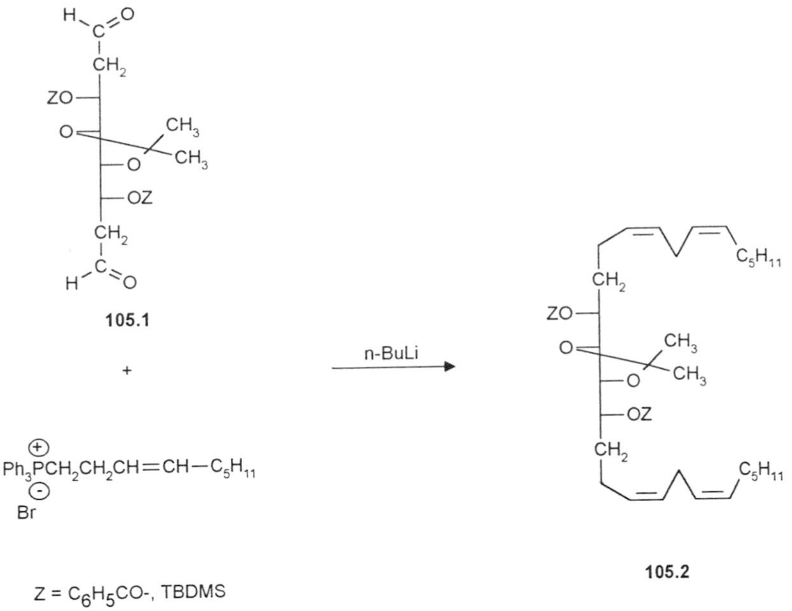

Z = C_6H_5CO-, TBDMS

FIGURE 1.105

rated ketone, specifically, a chain-extended C-1 substituted ketose (**106.3**), as shown in Figure 1.106.

> *General procedure for the preparation of α,β-unsaturated C-1-substituted ketoses*[138] A solution of the penta-O-acetyl-*aldehydo*-hexose (1–1.2 mmol) and the corresponding phosphorane (1.2–1.4 mmol) in chloroform is heated under reflux for 2–4 h, and the completion of the reaction is monitored by means of TLC (3:2 chloroform–benzene or 13:10 chloroform–toluene). The solvent is distilled off, and the residue is crystallized from methanol or from a 1:4 acetone–methanol mixture. The syrupy products are O-deacetylated, and triphenylphosphine oxide is removed by washing with organic solvents. The residue is then reacetylated with pyridine–acetic anhydride to obtain the C-1 substituted ketoses shown in Table 1.19.

The key intermediate in the synthesis of the rare monosaccharide 2,3-dideoxy-D-*glycero*-pentofuranose[139,140] is the unsaturated sugar;

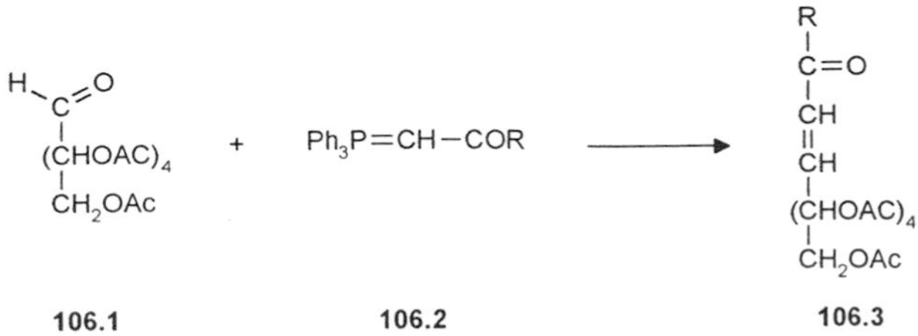

106.1   106.2   106.3

FIGURE 1.106

TABLE I.19 1-C-Substituted, Acetylated α,β-Unsaturated Higher-Carbon Ketoses[138]

Configuration of Aldose	Substituent at C-1	Yield (%)	M.p. (°C)
D-*gluco*	Methyl	23	119–120
D-*galacto*	Methyl	—	142–143
D-*gluco*	Phenyl	40	Syrup
D-*galacto*	Phenyl	79	134–135
D-*gluco*	p-Nitrophenyl	60	Syrup
D-*galacto*	Phenyl	79	134–135
D-*galacto*	p-Ethoxyphenyl	54	135–136
D-*galacto*	p-Bromophenyl	65	152–153
D-*galacto*	2,3,4-Trimethoxyphenyl	33	115–117
D-*galacto*	1-Furyl	69	133–134
D-*galacto*	1-Thienyl	70	160–161

(E)-2,3-dideoxy-4,5-O-isopropylidene-*aldehydo*-D-*glycero*-pent-2-enose (**107.3**), which is also conveniently available by a well-elaborated Wittig reaction (Fig. 1.107) of the protected glyceraldehyde **107.1** with the (2-oxoalkylidene)phosphorane (**107.2**). Note that this chain-extension reaction proceeds with E-selectivity as high as 95%.

> (E)-2,3-Dideoxy-4,5-O-isopropylidene-aldehydo-D-glycero-*pent-2-enose*
> (*107.3*)[139,140] A mixture of freshly distilled 2,3-O-isopropylidene-D-glyceraldehyde
> (**107.1**, 60 g, 0.47 mol) and (triphenylphosphoranylydene)acetaldehyde (**107.2**,
> 146.8 g, 0.47 mol) in dry benzene (150 ml) is stirred at room temperature for 10 h.
> The solvent is distilled off under reduced pressure, and the residue is extracted
> with a 1:7 mixture of ethyl acetate–cyclohexane until the extract is almost colorless
> (~1.5 liter). Following evaporation *in vacuo*, most of triphenylphosphine oxide
> crystallizes from the deep-brown syrup; it is then filtered off and washed with a
> small volume of cyclohexane, the filtrate is concentrated, and the residue is submitted
> to vacuum distillation to afford 32.5 g (55%) of pure **107.3**, b.p. 60–64°C at 0.033 kPa.

The transformation of aldehydes with 2-(1,3-dioxan-2-yl)ethyltriphenylphosphorane[141] (**108.2**) offers an outstanding opportunity for the introduction of a *three-carbon unit* with excellent Z-stereoselectivity, as

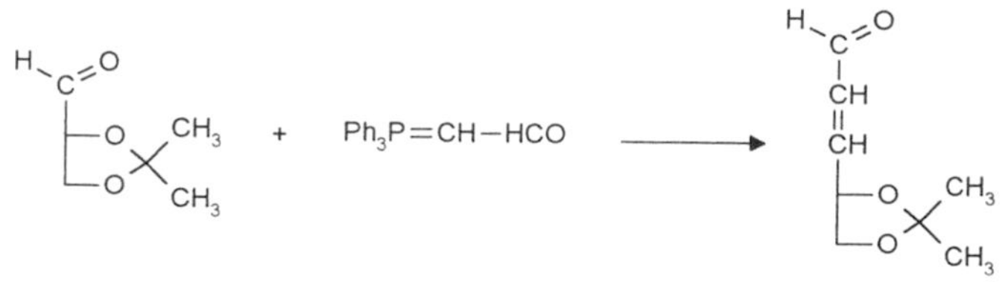

107.1   **107.2**   **107.3**

FIGURE I.107

shown in Figure 1.108 by the related reaction[142] of 2,3-*O*-isopropylidene-D-erythrose (**108.1**).

> *Benzoic acid (+)-(4R-cis)(Z)-2,2-dimethyl-5-[(1,3-dioxan-2-yl)-1-propenyl]-1,3-dioxolan-4-methyl ester (**108.4**)*[142]   To a solution of 2-(1,3-dioxan-2-yl)ethyltriphe-nylphosphonium bromide (129.9 g, 0.284 mol) in dry THF (325 ml) a solution of *n*-butyllithium in hexane (1.6 M, 177.5 ml) is added dropwise at −25°C over a 15-min period. The dropping funnel is rinsed with 25 ml of dry THF into the mixture. The color of the reaction mixture changes to yellow and then brown, and the mixture is stirred for 20 min at −25°C. This solution of the phosphorane **108.2** is added dropwise to a solution of crude 2,3-*O*-isopropylidene-D-erythrose (**108.1;** 22.7 g, 0.142 mol) in dry THF (150 ml) at −25°C over a 30-min period. The dropping funnel is rinsed, again, with 25 ml of THF into the mixture. The resulting orange solution is stirred at −25°C for 30 min, allowed to warm to room temperature, and stirred for 25 min. Following careful addition of water (21 ml), the straw-yellow mixture is poured into a separatory funnel containing 560 ml of water and 700 ml of ether. The organic layer is separated, and the aqueous phase is extracted three times with ether. After the usual workup, a syrup (68.7 g) containing crystals is obtained, which is dissolved in dry pyridine (200 ml) and benzoylated at −5°C by the dropwise addition of benzoyl chloride (24 g, 0.17 mol). A solid is separated, and the mixture is stirred at the same temperature for 3 h and then poured into a saturated aqueous solution of NaHCO₃ (1.1 liters) and extracted with ether three times. Following the usual workup, a mixture of a syrup and crystals (94 g) is obtained and is treated with a mixture of toluene (66 ml) and hexane (190 ml). The suspension thus produced is filtered, and the filter cake (triphenylphosphine oxide) is washed with a cold 2.9 : 1 mixture of hexane and toluene. The filtrate and the washing are combined and concentrated under diminished pressure (first with a water pump and then in high vacuum) to obtain 54.2 g of the crude product as a syrup. This substance is purified, in two equal portions, on 500–500 g of silicagel by gradient elution with 19 : 1, 9 : 1 and 4 : 1 mixtures of toluene–ethyl acetate to furnish 40.8 g (79.3%) of the pure ester **108.4**, b.p. 135–140°C (bath temperature) at 0.04 kPa, $[\alpha]_D^{25}$ +48.7 (*c* = 1.03 in chloroform).

The *p*-tolylsulfonyl ester can be obtained in a similar fashion from the intermediary alcohol **108.3**. With application of a similar procedure with 2,4-*O*-ethylidene-D-threose, the chain extension and subsequent benzoylation produces the benzoic acid ester of (2*R*,4*S*,5*R*)-(*Z*)-4-[3-(1,3-dioxan-2-yl)-1-propenyl]-2-methyl-1,3-dioxan-5-ol. It is to be noted that when the corresponding *p*-toluenesulfonic acid ester was prepared, isomerization to the (*E*) geometric isomer was observed.[142]

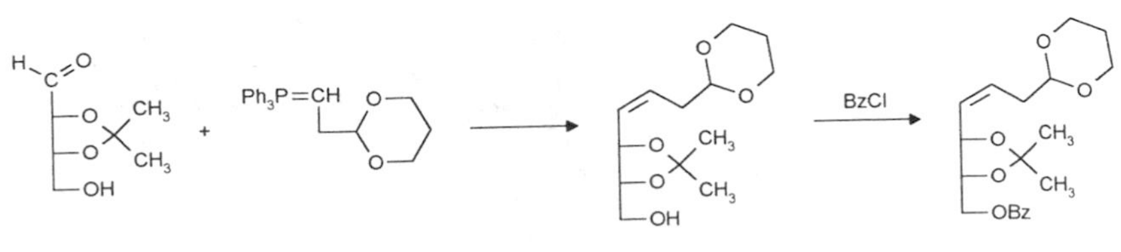

FIGURE 1.108

In studies on the influence of the solvent on the chain extension of various uloses it was found that in chloroform the proportion of the (Z)-isomer was small, and in DMF the (E)-isomer was present exclusively.[143] After warming of (Z)-5,6,8-trideoxy-1,2-O-isopropylidene-3-O-methyl-α-D-$xylo$-oct-5-enofuranos-1,4-diulose (**109.1**) in Me_2SO, a thermal isomerization into **109.2** was observed[144] (Fig. 1.109). An analogous isomerization of the (E)-isomer **109.3** into **109.4** occurred in hot DMF in the presence potassium fluoride and 12-crown-4.

(2-Oxoalkylidene)phosphoranes can also be prepared from saccharide derivatives, thus offering a useful route to higher-carbon carbohydrates. For this purpose the three phosphoranes: (1,2-O-isopropylidene-3-O-methyl-α-D-xylofuranuronoylmethylene)triphenylphosphorane[145] (**110.1**), (1,2:3,4-di-O-isopropylidene-α-D-galactopyranuronoyl)-(triphenylphosphoranyli-dene)-methane[146] (**110.2**) and (1,2,3,4-tetra-O-benzyl-α-D-galactopyra-nuronoyl)-(triphenylphosphoranylidene)-methane[147] (**110.3**) are available (Fig. 1.110).

*Preparation of (1,2:3,4-di-O-isopropylidene-α-D-galactopyranuronoyl)-(triphe-nylphosphoranylidene)-methane (**110.2**)[146]* To a solution of 1,2:3,4-di-O-isopro-pylidene-α-D-galactopyranuronic acid (1.65 g, 6.0 mmol) in THF (10 ml), carbonyldi-imidazole (1.04 g, 6.41 mmol) is added, and after the CO_2 evolution has finished, it is added to a solution of methylenetriphenylphosphorane in benzene [derived from methylenetriphenylphosphonium bromide (7.1 g, 19.9 mmol) with n-butyl-

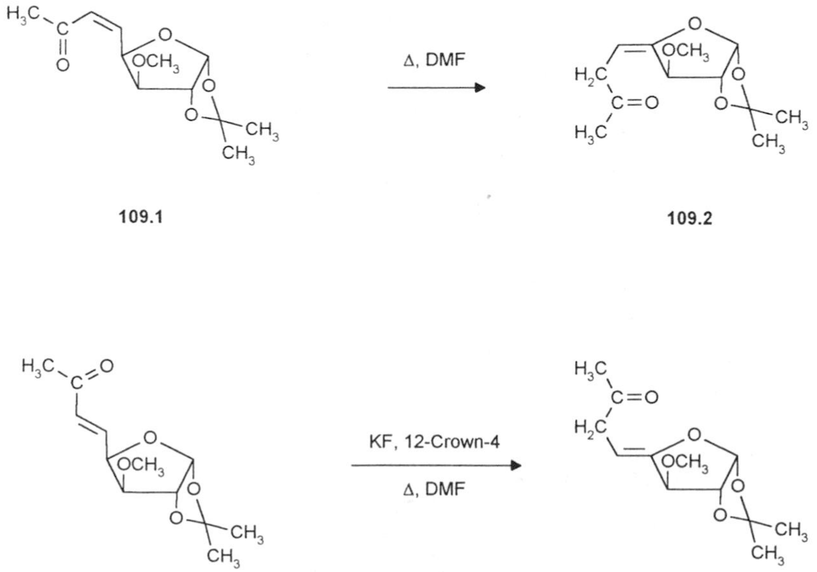

109.1   Δ, DMF   109.2

109.3   KF, 12-Crown-4   Δ, DMF   109.4

FIGURE I.109

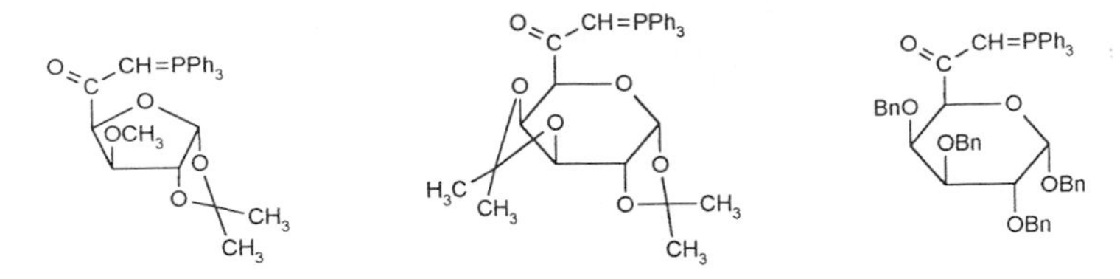

FIGURE 1.110

lithium (2.5 M, 7.4 ml)]. When the reaction is complete (TLC), 50 ml of aqueous ammonium chloride is added and the organic layer is separated. This is washed with water, dried, and concentrated. Column chromatography of the residue (eluant: 1:1 petroleum ether–ethyl acetate) gives the crystalline product **110.2**, m.p. 119–121°C, $[\alpha]_D^{23}$ −113.6 ($c = 0.25$ in chloroform).

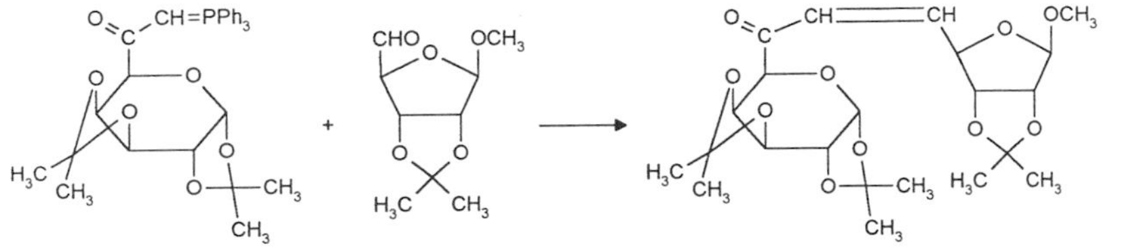

The reaction of the sugar phosphorane **110.2** with the *dialdo*-ribofuranose derivative **110.4** leads[146] to the chain-extended, unsaturated "*C*-disaccharide" **110.5**.

> *Methyl 2,3-O-isopropylidene-5-deoxy-5-C-[7-deoxy-1,2:3,4-di-O-isopropylidene-α-D-galactoheptopyranos-6-ulose-7(E)-ylidene]-β-D-ribofuranoside* (**110.5**)[146] A mixture of the phosphorane **110.2** (1.86 g, 3.5 mmol) and methyl 2,3-*O*-isopropylidene-β-D-*ribo*-pentodialdo-1,4-furanose (**110.4**; 0.71 g, 38 mmol) in toluene (15 ml) is refluxed for 1 h, when TLC (1:1 ethyl acetate–petroleum ether) shows the disappearance of the starting materials and the appearance of a UV-absorptive new spot. Following the usual workup, column chromatography of the crude product (eluant: 3:7 ethyl acetate–petroleum ether) gives 1.25 g (78%) of pure syrupy **110.5**, $[\alpha]_D^{23}$ −106 ($c = 2.2$ in chloroform).

The products of the carbonyl-olefination reaction of hydroxyaldehydes and *aldehydo*-monosaccharides with (oxoalkylidene)phosphoranes are shown in Table 1.20.[148–192]

Special attention should be devoted to an additional Wittig chain-extension procedure, elaborated by Dondoni *et al.*[193] for the construction of stereochemically defined polyhydroxy chains attached to a furanose or pyranose moiety. The basic step in this method is, again, the preparation of the suitable Wittig reagent (Fig. 1.111) from 2-bromoacetylthiazole (**111.1**),

TABLE 1.20 Carbonyl Olefination of Hydroxyaldehydes and *aldehydo*-Monosaccharides with (Oxoalkylidene)phosphoranes

Educt	Phosphorane	Ref(s).
(glyceraldehyde diol, $H_2C=O$ with two OH)	$ArCOCH=PPh_3$	148
(aldehyde with acetonide, isopropylidene dioxolane)	$Ph_3P=CHCHO$	149
	$Ph_3P=CHCH(OC_2H_5)_2$	149
	$Ph_3P=CHCH_2CH(OC_2H_5)_2$	150
	$Ph_3P=CHCOCH_3$	151,152
	$Ph_3P=CHCOCH_2CH_3$	153
	(pyranose with OBn, BnO, OBn, $CH=PPh_3$, C=O)	154
(aldehyde with isopropylidene and OCHPh$_2$)	$Ph_3P=CHCHO$	133
(aldehyde with isopropylidene, OTBDMS)	$Ph_3P=CHCOC(CH_3)_2OTBDMS$	155
(furanose CHO, OR, isopropylidene)	$Ph_3P=CHCHO$	156
	$Ph_3P=C(Br)COR$	157
	$Ph_3P=CHCOCH_3$	143
	(pyranose with $CH=PPh_3$, C=O, BnO, OBn, OCH$_3$, OBn)	147
(pyranose with OH, OH, H_3C, CH$_3$)	$Ph_3P=CHCOCH_3$	158
(aldehyde with bis-cyclohexylidene dioxolane)	$Ph_3P=CHCHO$	159

(*continues*)

TABLE 1.20 (*continued*)

Educt	Phosphorane	Ref(s).
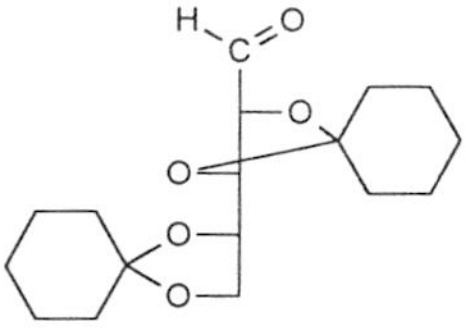	Ph$_3$P=CHCHO	159
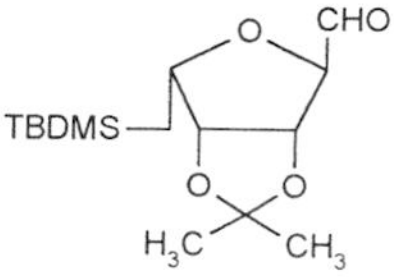	Ph$_3$P=CHCOCH$_3$	160
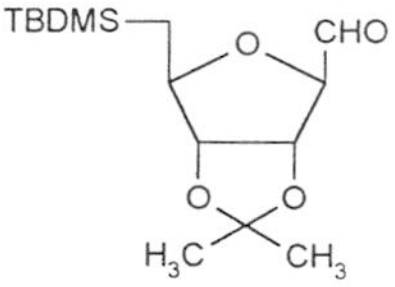	Ph$_3$P=CHCOCH$_3$	160
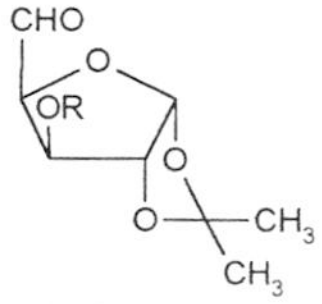	Ph$_3$P=CHCOAr Ph$_3$P=CHCOCH$_3$	161,162 163,164
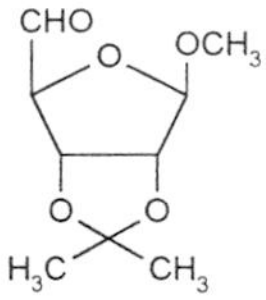	Ph$_3$P=CHCOCH$_3$	165
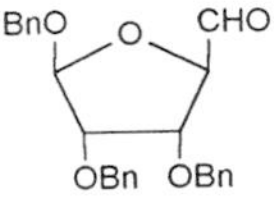	Ph$_3$P=CHCOCH$_3$	166
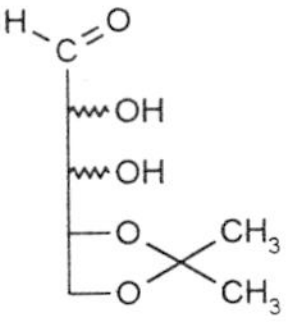	Ph$_3$P=CHCOCH$_3$	167
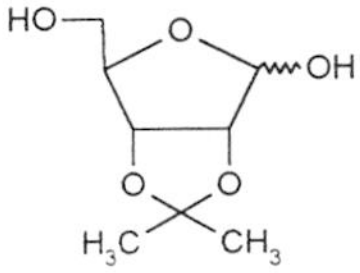	Ph$_3$P=CHCOCH$_3$ Ph$_3$P=C(X)COR Ph$_3$P=CHCOCH$_2$CONHR	168 169 170
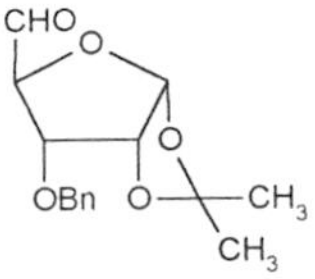	Ph$_3$P=CHCHO Ph$_3$P=CHCOCH$_3$	171,172 143

(*continues*)

TABLE 1.20 (*continued*)

Educt	Phosphorane	Ref(s).
	Ph₃P=CHCOCH₃	173
	Ph₃P=CHCOCH₃	173
	Ph₃P=CHCOCH₃	173
	Ph₃P=CHCHO Ph₃P=CHCOCH₃	172 173
	Ph₃P=CHCOCH₃	173
	Ph₃P=CHCOCH₃	173
Hexoses	Ph₃P=CHCOC₆H₄OCH₃(p)	174
Saccharides with free anomeric OH	Ph₃P=CHCOC₆H₄OCH₃(p)	175
	Ph₃P=CHCOAr	176
	Ph₃P=CHCOCH₃ Ph₃P=CHCOAr Ph₃P=C(R)COCH₃ Ph₃P=CHCHO Ph₃P=CH—	177,178 177 179 180,181,179 178

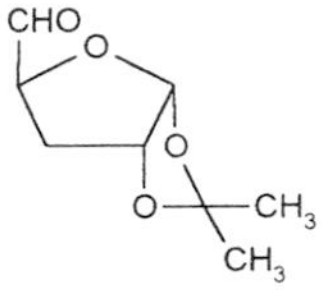

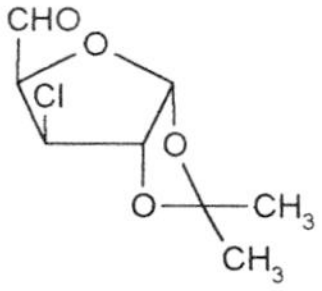

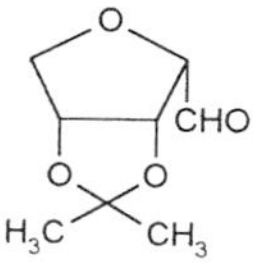

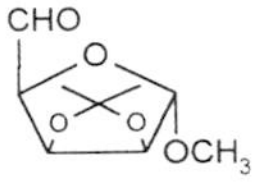

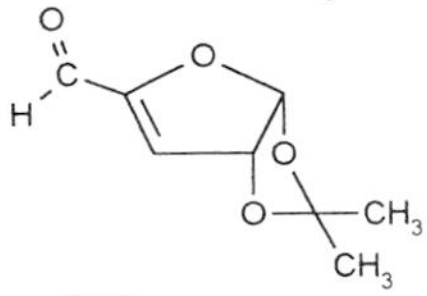

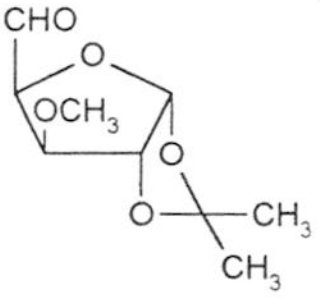

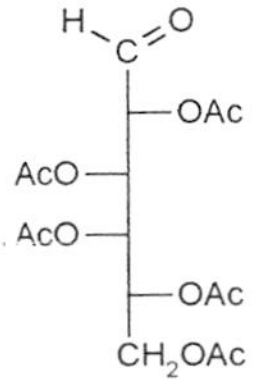

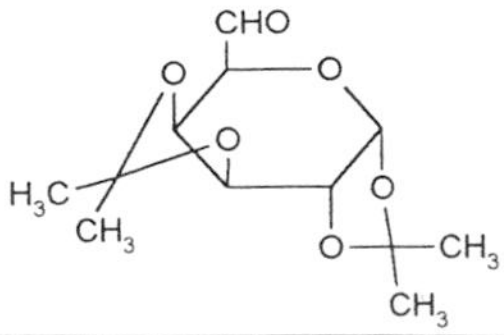

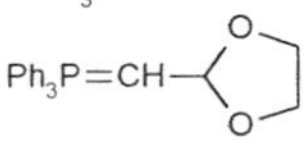

(*continues*)

TABLE 1.20 (continued)

Educt	Phosphorane	Ref(s).
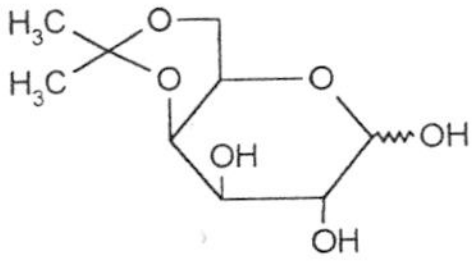	$Ph_3P{=}CHCOCH_3$	182
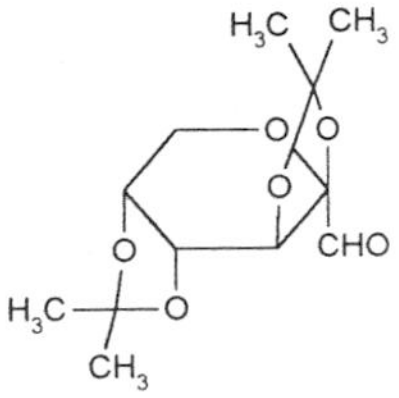	$Ph_3P{=}CHCOCH_3$ $Ph_3P{=}CHCOAr$	176 176
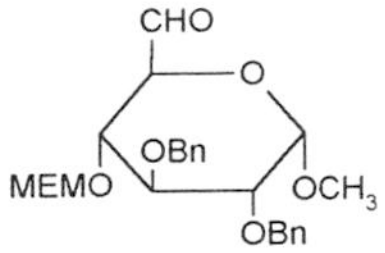	$Ph_3P{=}CHCHO$ $Ph_3P{=}CHCH(OC_2H_5)_2$	182,183 182,183
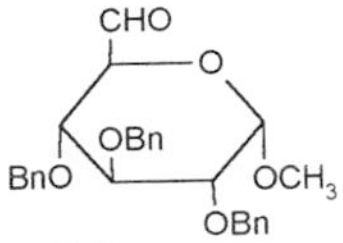	$Ph_3P{=}CHCHO$	184
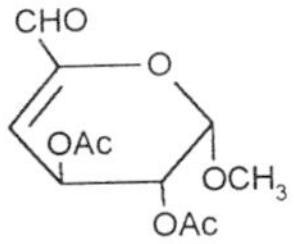	$Ph_3P{=}CHCOCH_3$	185
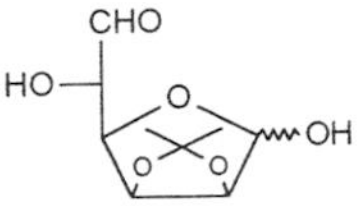	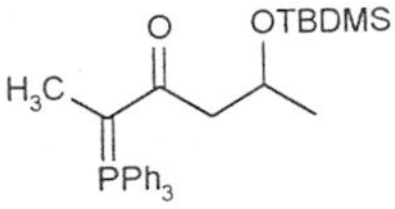	186
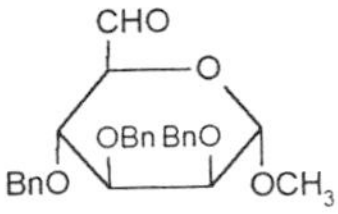	$Ph_3P{=}CHCHO$	184
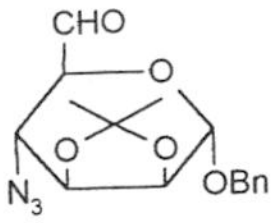	$Ph_3P{=}CHCHO$	187
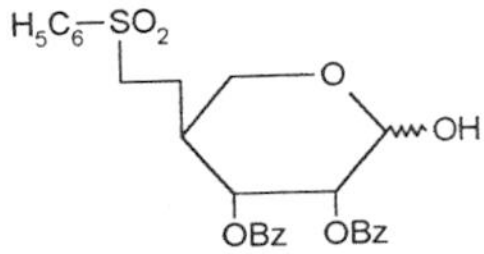	$Ph_3P{=}CHCOCH_3$	188
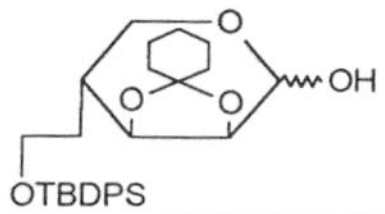	$Ph_3P{=}CHCOCH_3$	189

(continues)

TABLE 1.20   (*continued*)

Educt	Phosphorane	Ref(s).
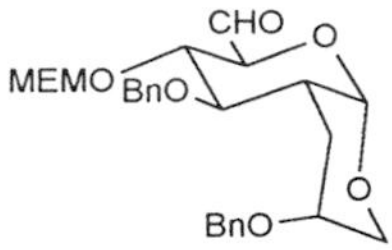	$Ph_3P{=}CHCH(OC_2H_5)_2$	190
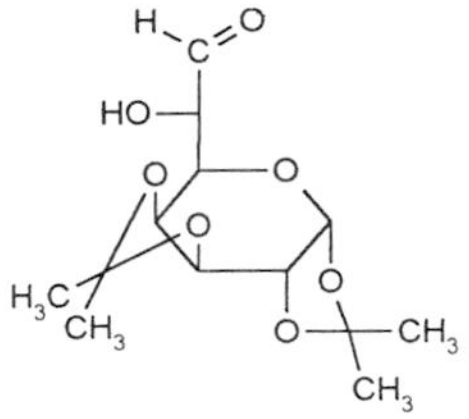	$Ph_3P{=}CHCHO$	191
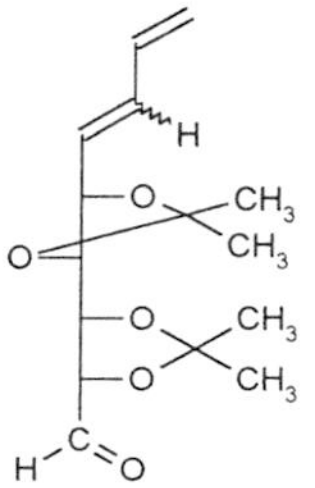	$Ph_3P{=}CHCOCH_3$	136
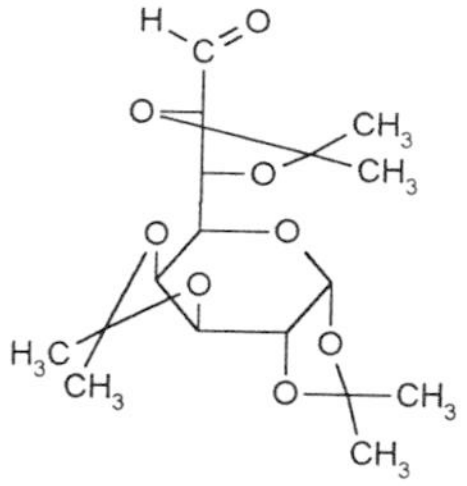	$Ph_3P{=}CHCHO$	192
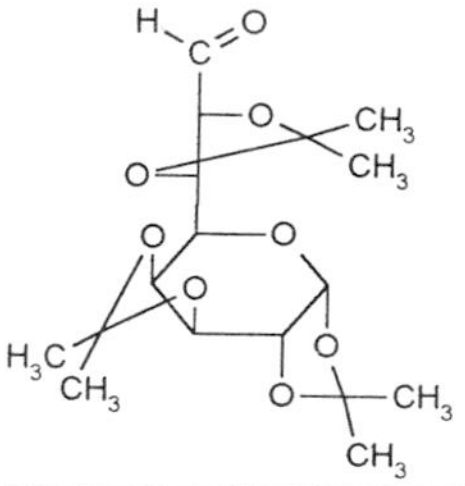	$Ph_3P{=}CHCHO$	192

followed by the carbonyl olefination with the resulting stable phosphorane: 2-thiazolylcarbonylmethylenetriphenylphosphorane (**111.3**). For example, olefination of 2,3-*O*-isopropylidene-D-glyceraldehyde (**111.4**) with the phosphorane **111.3** gives rise[194] to the (*E*)-vinyl-ketone **111.5** in 87% yield.

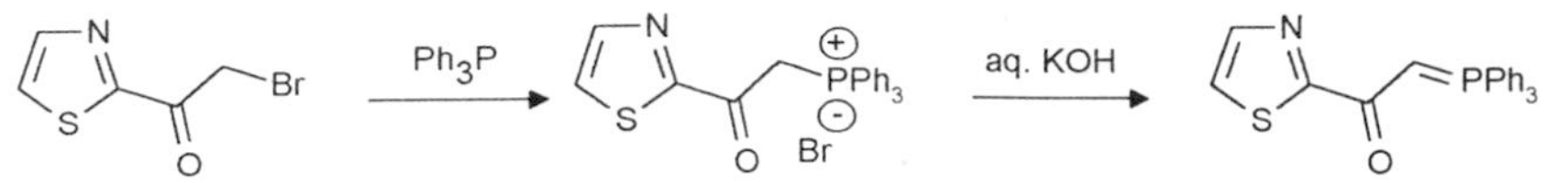

FIGURE 1.111

2-Thiazolylcarbonylmethylenetriphenylphosphorane (111.3)[193]   (*Caution*: This reaction has to be carried out under an efficient hood.) A 300-ml three-necked, round-bottomed flask, containing a magnetic stirring bar, is equipped with a 200-ml pressure-equalizing dropping funnel. Argon gas is flushed through the dry apparatus for a few minutes, and then the tube is connected to a ballon filled with argon to maintain the inert-gas atmosphere. The flask is charged with a solution of 2-(trimethylsilyl)thiazole (10.5 g, 67 mmol) in dry dichloromethane (100 ml) and then immersed in an ice bath. A solution of bromoacetyl bromide (13.5 g, 67 mmol) in dry dichloromethane (50 ml) is added dropwise with stirring, and the mixture is stirred at room temperature for 3 h. Saturated aqueous $NaHCO_3$ is added under vigorous stirring to render the pH slightly basic. The organic layer is separated, and the aqueous phase is extracted with dichloromethane (3 × 50 ml). The combined organic layer is washed with brine and dried over Na_2SO_4, and the solvent is evaporated. The residue is purified by means of column chromatography on silicagel (eluant: 9 : 1 hexane–ether) to give 11.31 g (82%) of 2-bromoacetylthiazole (**111.1**) as a white solid, m.p. 48–49°C. In another procedure, a solution of **111.1** (11.31 g) in benzene (300 ml) is placed in an apparatus similar to that described above, and under argon atmosphere triphenylphosphine (18.34 g, 70 mmol) is added in portions with stirring. Then the mixture is stirred at room temperature for 12 h, and the precipitate is filtered off, washed several times with benzene and *n*-pentane, and dried under reduced pressure for 2 h. This crude, slightly hygroscopic phosphonium salt **111.2** (25.67 g, 100%, m.p. 120–122°C) is used without further purification for the generation of the phosphorane **111.3** as follows. To a well-stirred suspension of the phosphonium bromide (**111.2**) in water aqueous 1 N sodium hydroxide (~70 ml) is added slowly to adjust the pH to near 10. The resulting deep-orange mixture is stirred at room temperature for 30 min and the precipitate is collected by filtration, washed several times with water, and dried under reduced pressure in a desiccator over P_2O_5 to furnish 21.23 g (100%) of the phosphorane **111.3** as a slightly hygroscopic orange solid, m.p. 188–190°C.

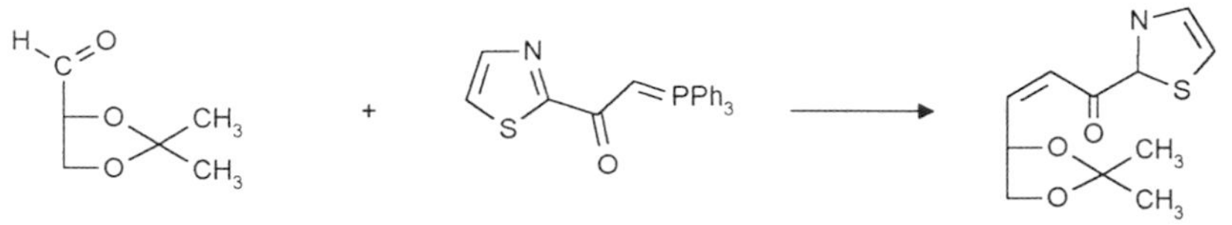

Carbonyl-olefination of 2,3-O-isopropylidene-D-glyceraldehyde (111.4) with the phosphorane 111.3[194]   A 200-ml round-bottomed flask, containing a magnetic stirring bar, is flushed with argon gas for a few minutes and then connected to a ballon filled with argon to maintain the inert-gas atmosphere. The flask is charged with a mixture of 2,3-O-isopropylidene-D-glyceraldehyde (**111.4**, 3.5 g, 26.9 mmol) and the phosphorane **111.3** (10.2 g, 26.4 mmol) in 60 ml of freshly distilled chloroform. The reaction mixture is stirred at room temperature for 20–24 h, after which the reaction is judged to be completed by TLC (8:2 ether–petroleum ether). The solvent is distilled off under reduced pressure, ether (150 ml) is added to the residue, and the resulting mixture is filtered. The solvent is evaporated, and the residual crude material is submitted to column chromatography on silicagel (eluant: 9:1 petroleum ether–ether) to obtain 5.49 g (87%) of the pure syrupy (E)-vinylketone **111.5**, $[\alpha]_D$ +21.9 (c = 1.69 in chloroform).

By a *syn*-diastereoselective 1,4-conjugate addition of benzyl oxide anion, the vinyl ketone **111.5** allows the preparation of polyalkoxyalkylketones, which are convertible into ulosonic acids. Related transformations have been carried out with 2,3:4,5-O-isopropylidene-*aldehydo*-D-arabinose[194] and 6-O-TBPS-2,4:3,5-di-O-isopropylidene-*aldehydo*-D-mannose.[195]

In the Wittig reaction of 1,2:3,4-di-O-isopropylidene-α-D-*galacto*-hexodialdo-1,5-pyranoside both the (Z)- and (E) isomers are present in the reaction mixture, and by performing numerous experiments, investigators have found[196] that the C-7, C-8, and C-9 homologs react with the phosphorane in toluene at room temperature to give the corresponding olefins in good yield and variable E/Z selectivity depending on the dialdose employed.

The key reaction, discussed earlier, which leads to olefinic sugars such as **111.5,** represents the basis of the methodology[196–198] called the "thiazole route to long-chain alkene sugars."

1.2.6.3. Elongation of the Sugar Chain with Alkoxycarbonylmethylenephosphoranes

The chain extension of an *aldehydo*-sugar with alkoxycarbonyl-methylenephosphoranes, known as *stabilized phosphoranes,* affords α,β-unsaturated carboxylic acid esters, and thus this method permits a simultaneous introduction of a C=C bond and an ester function into the saccharide chain.[1] This type of the Wittig reaction is one of the most versatile procedures for the controlled introduction of a carbon–carbon bond from a carbonyl precursor, and therefore this reaction has found significant use in the carbohydrate field as a route to higher-carbon sugar derivatives through subsequent functionalization (e.g., epoxidation, cycloaddition reactions).

The appropriate carbohydrate derivatives (i.e., *aldehydo*-sugars or sugars with a free anomeric hydroxyl group) are easy to react with stabilized phosphoranes, since the stable and less reactive ylides require relatively more energic (and easier-to-control) conditions than do those discussed in the previous sections. At the same time—because of the ester function introduced—this type of chain extension may proceed with intramolecular

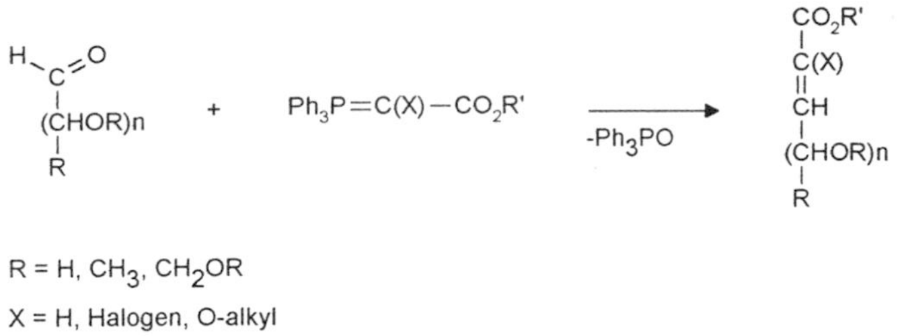

R = H, CH$_3$, CH$_2$OR

X = H, Halogen, O-alkyl

FIGURE 1.112

side reactions, such as ring closure to *C*-glycosidic compounds (Michael addition) or other cyclic products, including carbocycles or indolizine derivatives, if an amino function is also present in the molecule.

It is known that related transformations (Fig. 1.112) give rise to the thermodynamically more stable *trans*-isomers, and this is why the early papers described the isolation of the corresponding (*E*)-isomers exclusively.

By examining the reaction of nonprotected simple pentoses with ethoxycarbonylmethylenetriphenylphosphorane, Horton[199] has suggested that the oxaphosphethane **113.1** is responsible for the formation of the saccharide derivatives shown in Figure 1.113.

The chain-extension reaction of *aldehydo*-pentoses and *aldehydo*-hexoses with carboxyalkylenephosphoranes is an extremely versatile tool for the synthesis of heptoses, octoses, and higher-carbon sugars. The unsatu-

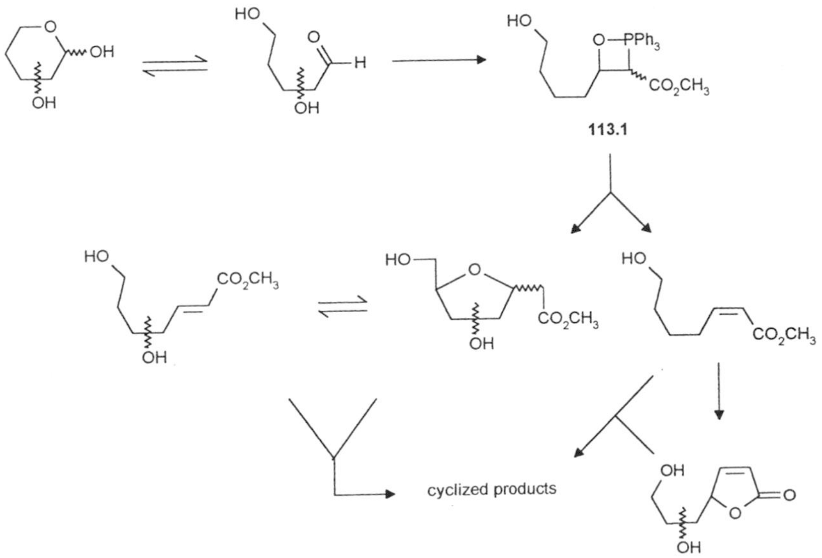

FIGURE 1.113

rated ester derivatives can be prepared according to the following general procedure.[200-208]

> *Chain extension of* aldehydo-*sugars with alkoxycarbonylmethylenephosphoranes*
> A mixture of the phosphorane (0.011 mol) and the *aldehydo*-sugar (0.01 mol) in benzene (30 ml) is refluxed for 90 min. The solvent is distilled off, and the residue is crystallized from methanol. The yield can be increased by column chromatography of the residue obtained after evaporation of the mother liquor. The physical data of a few related products are summarized in Table 1.21.

Because of the low solubility of the starting monosaccharides, the free 2,3-dehydro-2,3-dideoxyonic acid esters have been prepared in DMF solutions. In such cases the formation of *C*-glycosidic compounds, which were separated by column chromatography was also observed.[207]

To increase the yields of the Wittig transformations with pentoses, a potentially advantageous effect of metal ions, as complexing agents, has also been studied. It was found that in a complicated reaction leading to an equilibrium mixture of products, metal ions may form complexes with not only the starting sugars but also with the reaction products (see Fig. 1.113), and may thus change the net outcome of the reaction. For example, when the Wittig reaction was performed with D-arabinose in the presence of cupric acetate, the outcome was quite different from that observed in the absence of metal ion. The major product was the dehydroheptonic acid ester, isolated in good yield (50%), and almost double that obtained without the added cupric acetate.[199]

TABLE 1.21 Crystalline *trans*-2,3-Dehydro-2,3-Dideoxyaldonic Acid Ethylesters[207]

Product	Yield (%)	M.p. (°C)	$[\alpha]_D$ (c = 1, CHCl$_3$)
4,5,6,7-Tetra-*O*-acetyl-*trans*-2,3-dehydro-2,3-dideoxy-L-*arabino*-heptonic acid ethylester	75	83–84	−35.9
4,5,6,7,8-Penta-*O*-acetyl-*trans*-2,3-dehydro-2,3-dideoxy-D-*gluco*-octonic acid ethylester	84	127–129	+19.1
4,5,6,7,8-Penta-*O*-acetyl-*trans*-2,3-dehydro-2,3-dideoxy-D-*galacto*-octonic acid ethylester	77.5	161	+11.5
trans-2,3-Dehydro-2,3-dideoxy-D-*arabino*-heptonic acid ethylester	60.5	133–135	+14.45 (H$_2$O)
trans-2,3-Dehydro-2,3-dideoxy-D-*ribo*-heptonic acid ethylester	45.5	61–64	−21 (AcOH)
trans-2,3-Dehydro-2,3-dideoxy-D-*gluco*-heptonic acid ethylester	46.5	115–116	−11.6 (AcOH)
trans-2,3-Dehydro-2,3-dideoxy-D-*glycero*-D-*gulo*-nononic acid ethylester	31.5	108–110	−24.5 (AcOH)

According to Lyga,[209] the change of the solvent was so successful as to enhance the yield of the desired product, and this is shown by the following example.

> *Ethyl (E)-2,3-Dideoxy-D-arabino-hept-2-enoate* A suspension of D-arabinose (17.2 g, 0.115 mol) and ethoxycarbonylmethylenetriphenylphosphorane (40 g, 0.115 mol) in 1,4-dioxane is heated at reflux for 3 h. The resulting clear solution is concentrated under diminished pressure to afford a white solid that is triturated in 100 ml of warm 1:1 ether–petroleum ether. The solid is then collected and recrystallized from 95% ethanol to afford 17 g (67%) the title compound, as a white solid, m.p. 138–139°C, $[\alpha]_D^{25}$ +15.4 (c = 0.4 in methanol); see also Table 1.21.

The execution of the Wittig reaction was simplified by an *in situ* generation of the phosphorane reagent in toluene solution,[210] which resulted in the increase of the yield of the aldooctenoates, as shown in the following general procedure.

> *General procedure for the preparation of aldooctenoates*[211] To a suspension of zinc (2 eq) in toluene a solution of tri-*n*-butylphosphine (2 eq), the bromoacetic acid ester (2 eq) and the starting material is added dropwise. The progress of the reaction is monitored by TLC in chloroform–acetone mixtures. When the reaction is complete, the residue, obtained on evaporation of the reaction mixture, is directly subjected to column chromatography on silicagel pretreated with triethylamine.

For the sake of completeness, it is to be noted that 4,5,6,8-tetra-*O*-acetyl-D-*galacto*-octonic acid ethyl ester (**114.3**) can be obtained (Fig. 1.114) from 2,3,4,6-tetra-*O*-acetyl-α-D-galactopyranose (**114.1**) with ethoxymethylenetriphenylphosphorane. Subsequent acetylation then gives rise[207,212] to the peracetate **114.4**. Related transformations are included in Table 1.22.

A synthesis of (+)-*biotin,* an important natural product, also involves carbonyl olefination of a sugar derivative. Thus, Vogel *et al.*[213] have shown that the olefination of a partially protected aldose with a complex phosphorane can be directed and controlled so that only *one* of the stereoisomers is produced. In principle, the reaction[213] of 2-*O*-benzoyl-3,4-*O*-isopropylidene-D-arabinose (**115.1**) and methyl 4-(triphenylphosphoranediyl)crotonate (**115.2**) results in not only an (*E/Z*) mixture of the open-chain nonadiene ester (**115.3**) is obtained (Fig. 1.115), but also the expected formation of the 5,9-anhydrononenic acid derivative **115.4.**

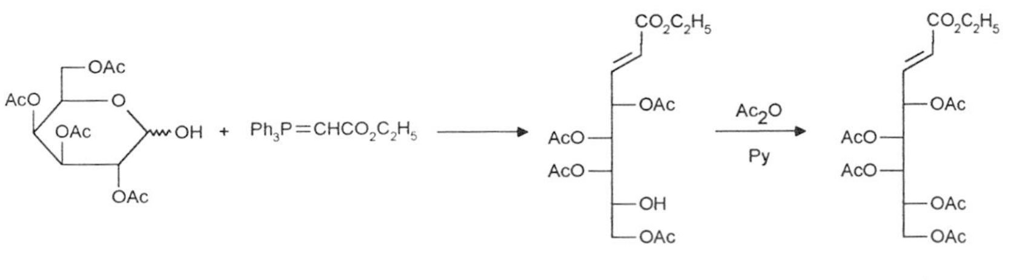

FIGURE 1.114

TABLE 1.22 Carbonyl Olefination of Saccharide Derivatives with Methoxycarbonylmethylenetriphenylphosphorane

Educt	Reaction time (h)	Yield (%)	Z/E ratio (from ^{1}H-NMR spectra)
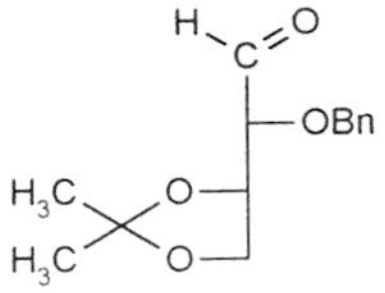	24	77	11:1
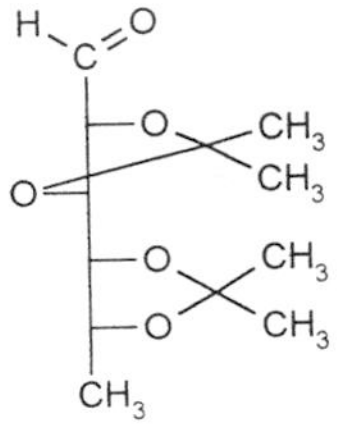	1	70	7:1
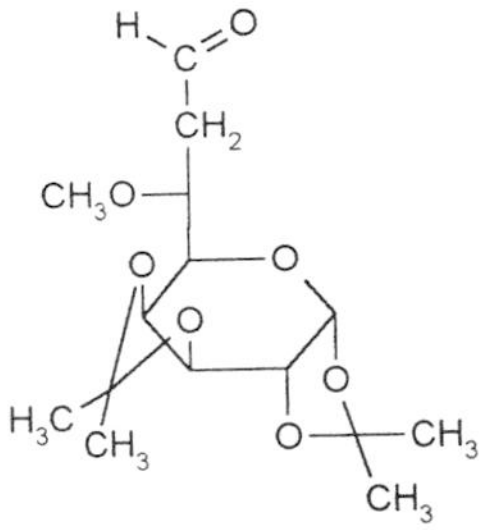	2.25	88	5:4
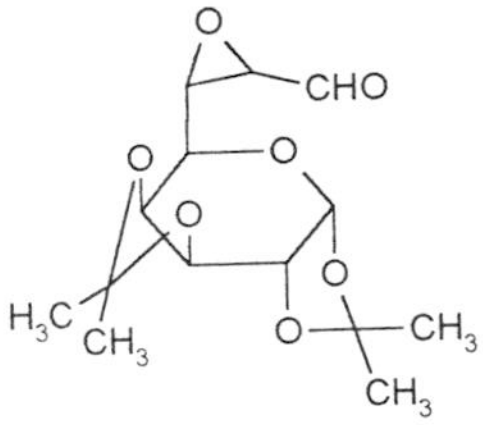	0.75	82	4.3:1
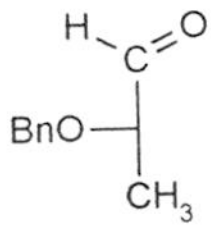	2	82	3.7:1
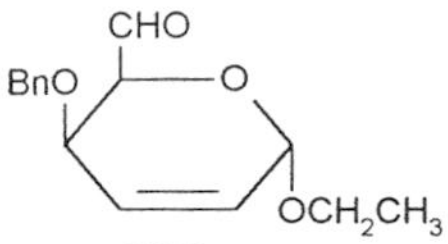	3	78	100:1
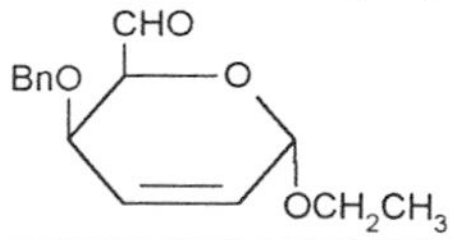	2	76	90:1

(continues)

TABLE 1.22 (*continued*)

Educt	Reaction time (h)	Yield (%)	Z/E ratio (from ^{1}H-NMR spectra)
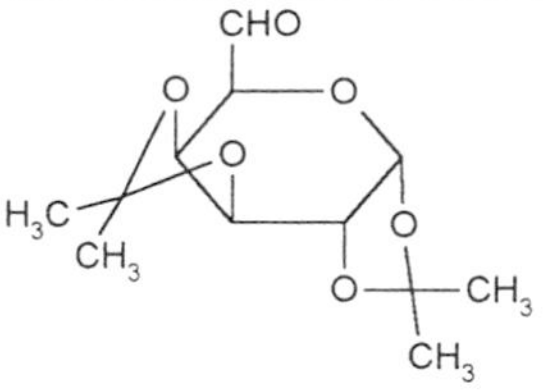	4	80	20 : 1
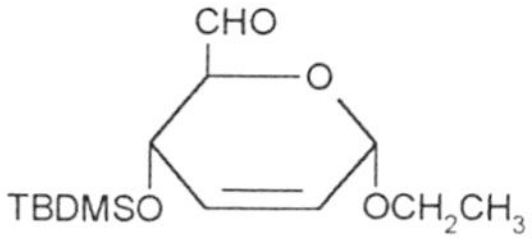	1	92	1 : 3.5
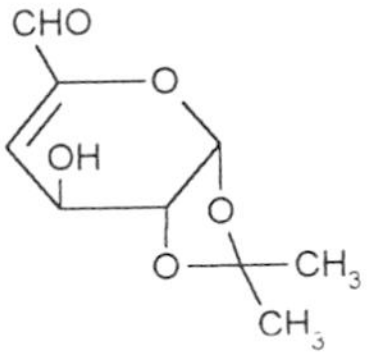	1.5	73	1 : 1.7

2-O-Benzoyl-1-deoxy-3,4-O-isopropylidene-1-[3-(methoxycarbonyl)allyl]-D-arab-inose (115.4)[213]   A mixture of 2-*O*-benzoyl-3,4-*O*-isopropylidene-D-arabinose (**115.1**, 1.0 g, 3.4 mmol) and methyl 4-(triphenylphosphoranediyl)crotonate (**115.2**, 3.70 g, 10.2 mmol) in dry benzene (20 ml) is heated at reflux for 6 h under argon atmosphere, and the cooled mixture is poured into ether (200 ml). After filtration and concentration of the filtrate, the residue is chromatographed on silicagel (120 g) with ether as the eluant to obtain a 7:3 mixture (**115.4**) of the α- and β anomers (0.74 g, 85%), $[\alpha]_D^{20}$ −2.05 (*c* = 2.6 in dichloromethane). The specific rotation value may be varied, depending on the anomeric ratio.

(6R,7R,8S)-6-Benzoyloxy-9-hydroxy-7,8-(isopropylidenedioxy)-2,4-nonadienic acid methyl ester (115.3)[213]   To a solution of 2-*O*-benzoyl-3,4-*O*-isopropylidene-D-arabinose (**115.1**, 20 g, 68 mmol) in dichloromethane (700 ml) methyl 4-(triphenyl-phosphoranediyl)crotonate (**115.2**, 74 g, 205 mmol) is added, and the mixture is refluxed for 6 h and then evaporated under argon atmosphere. The crude pruduct is submitted to column chromatography on silicagel with ether to eluate, first a pale yellow syrup consisting of the α,β and *cis–trans* isomers of **115.4**, then a complex mixture, and finally 5.9 g of a yellow syrup (*cis–trans* mixture). A solution of this latter (5.6 g) in ether is applied onto the top of a 400-g silicagel column and eluted with a 9:1 ether–hexane mixture to allow isolation of 3.46 g of colorless syrupy **115.3**, which crystallizes partially on standing for several weeks, $[\alpha]_D^{20}$ +11.6 (*c* = 2.6 in dichloromethane).

Regarding the supposed[1] betaine-type intermediate of the carbonyl-olefination process, a *syn*-elimination in polar solvents (e.g., in alcohols) is most likely to result, mainly in *cis*-olefins. When the transformation of

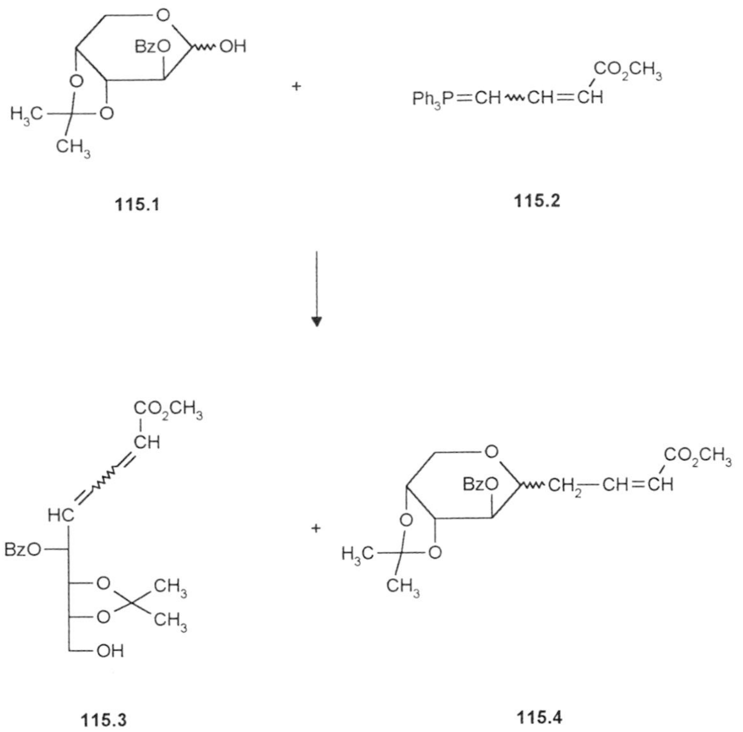

115.1   **115.2**

115.3   **115.4**

FIGURE I.115

1,2:3,4-di-O-isopropylidene-D-galactopyranos-1,5-ulose with methoxycarbonylmethylenetriphenylphosphorane was studied at 25°C in isopropanol,
ethanol, and methanol the (Z)-selectivity was observed to increase; i.e.,
10:1, 22:1 and 35:1, respectively, and in methanol the reaction proceeded
with a 100:1 (Z)-selectivity when the temperature was lowered to −8°C.

> *Carbonyl olefination of saccharide derivatives with methoxycarbonylmethylenetri-*
> *phenyl-phosphorane*[214] A mixture of the saccharide derivative (1 mmol) and
> methoxymethylenetriphenylphosphorane (3 eq) in methanol is stirred at room
> temperature for the reaction time given in Table 1.22. The solvent is distilled off,
> the residue is taken up with dichloromethane (in a volume as small as possible),
> and this is applied on top of a silicagel column to be eluted with a hexane–ethyl
> acetate mixture in which the fastest-moving spot is with R_f = ~0.25 on TLC.
> The geometric isomers of compounds shown in Table 1.22 can be separated using
> this procedure.

Detailed studies[215] on the related reaction of 2,3-O-isopropylidene-4-
O-methyl-5-O-methoxymethyl-*aldehydo*-D-ribose with alkoxycarbonylmethylenetriphenylphosphoranes have revealed that in ethanol the pre-

dominant products are the (Z)-α,β-unsaturated esters, while in dichloromethane the (E)-isomers are produced almost exclusively.

Examinations on three of the four pentoses carrying free anomeric hydroxyl group established[215] that the free hydroxyl group at C-4 significantly influences the stereochemical outcome of the carbonyl olefination—most probably due to hydrogen-bond formation. In the case of 2,3-O-isopropylidene-D-ribose and -D-xylose, the Z/E ratio is strongly shifted toward the (Z)-form, whereas the preponderant product from 2,3,4-tri-O-benzyl-D-arabinose is the (E)-isomer. It has also been reported that the acetal protecting group affects the E/Z product distribution.[216]

The chain extension of saccharide derivatives with alkoxycarbonylmethylenetriphenylphosphoranes and related reagents is summarized in Table 1.23.[217-340]

Diphenyl(triphenylphosphoranylidene)methylenephosphonate (**116.1**), a stabilized phosphorane available from—among other compounds—diphenyl chloromethylphosphonate and triphenylphosphine,[341] represents a special reagent in this group, as it can be used for chain extensions leading to sugar–phosphonates (**116.2**) bearing an olefinic function (see Fig. 1.116). The utility of this methodology is shown by a related reaction of 2,3,4,5,6-penta-O-acetyl-$aldehydo$-D-glucose.

(E)-3,4,5,6,7-Penta-O-acetyl-1,2-dideoxy-1-diphenylphosphono-D-gluco-hept-1-enitol[342]   A mixture of 2,3,4,5,6-penta-O-acetyl-$aldehydo$-D-glucose (1.07 g, 3 mmol), diphenyl(triphenylphosphoranylidene)methylenephosphonate (1.52 g, 3 mmol), and dry benzene (200 ml) is heated at reflux for 8 h. Then the solvent is distilled off, and the residue is extracted five times with ether; a part of the triphenylphosphine oxide remains undissolved. The ethereal solution is concentrated, and the residue is purified by fractional crystallization from ethanol–petroleum ether to furnish 0.9 g (50%) of the pure title compound, m.p. 103–106°C, $[\alpha]_D^{20}$ +14.2 (c = 1.0 in chloroform).

Additional phosphonic acid derivatives have already been prepared:

(Z)-1,2-Dideoxydiphenylphosphono-3,4:5,6-di-O-isopropylidene-D-
 $arabino$-hex-1-enitol,[342] $[\alpha]_D^{20}$ −8.1 (c = 1.0 in chloroform)

(Z)-3,5-O-Ethylidene-1,2-dideoxy-1-monophenyl-4-O-
 cyclophosphono-D-$erythro$-pent-1-enitol, [342] $[\alpha]_D^{20}$ −3.5 (c = 1.0 in chlorofom), m.p. 149–151°C

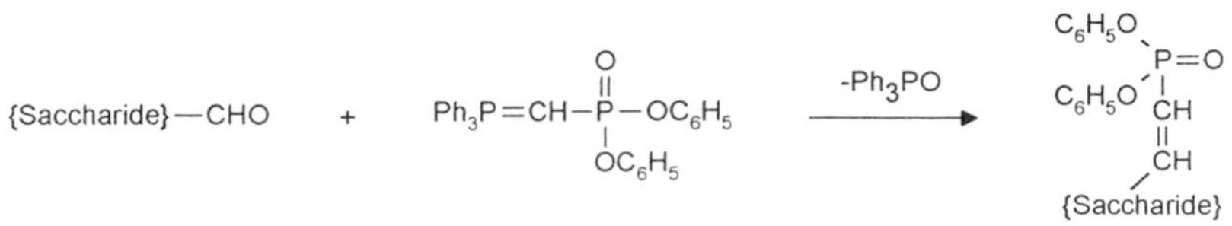

116.1   116.2

FIGURE 1.116

TABLE 1.23 Chain Extension of Saccharide Derivatives with Alkoxycarbonylmethylenetriphenylphosphoranes and Related Reagents

Starting saccharide	Phosphorane	Ref(s).
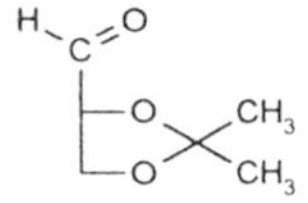	$Ph_3P=CHCO_2CH_3$ $Ph_3P=CHCO_2C_2H_5$ $Ph_3P=CHCN$	217,218 149,218–220 221
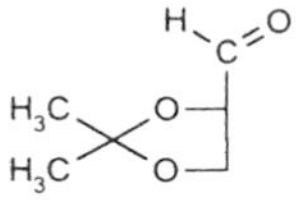	$Ph_3P=CHCO_2C_2H_5$	218,222
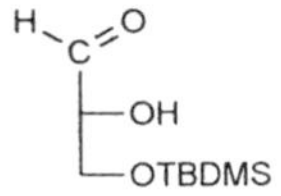	$Ph_3P=CHCO_2C_2H_5$	223
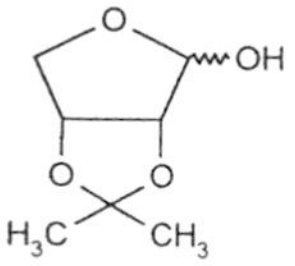	$Ph_3P=CHCO_2C_2H_5$ $Ph_3P=CH(CH_2)_2CO_2C_2H_5$	224 225
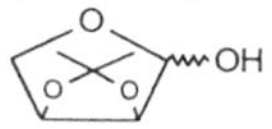	$Ph_3P=CH-CH=CHCO_2C_2H_5$	226
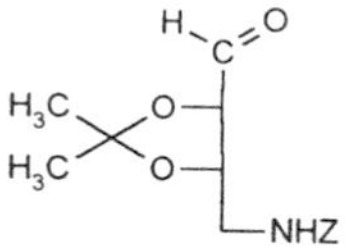	$Ph_3P=CH(CH_2)_2CO_2C_2H_5$	227
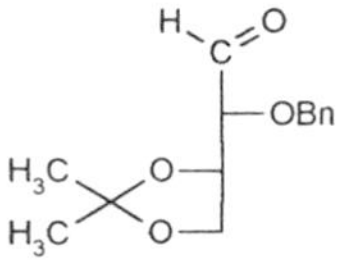	$Ph_3P=CHCO_2CH_3$	218
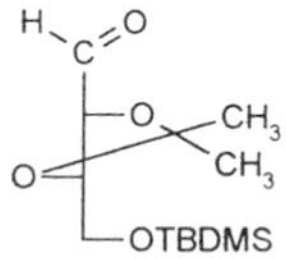	$Ph_3P=CHCO_2CH_3$	228
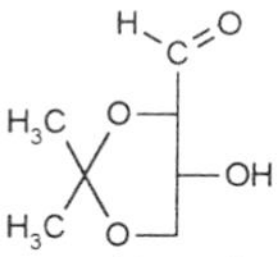	$Ph_3P=CHCO_2CH_3$	229
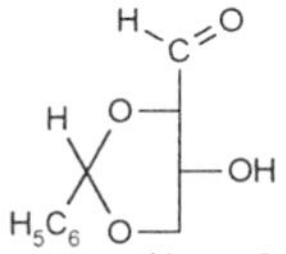	$Ph_3P=CHCO_2H$	230
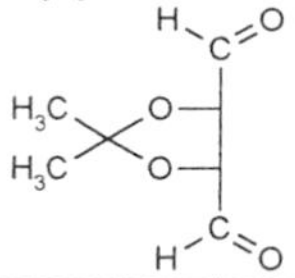	$Ph_3P=CHCO_2CH_3$	231

(*continues*)

TABLE I.23 (*continued*)

Starting saccharide	Phosphorane	Ref(s).
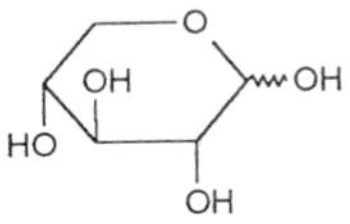	$Ph_3P=CHCO_2C_2H_5$	199,232
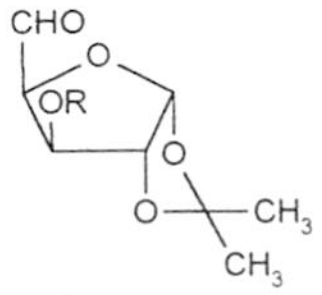	$Ph_3P=CHCO_2CH_3$ $Ph_3P=CHCO_2C_2H_5$ $Ph_3P=C(Br)CO_2C_2H_5$ $Ph_3P=C(Hal)CN$	233,234 143,235,236 157,237 238
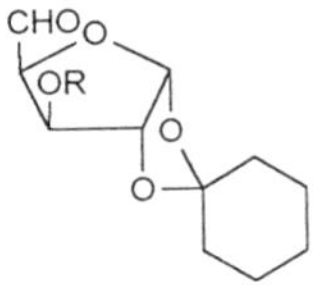	$Ph_3P=CHCO_2C_4H_9\text{-}n$	239
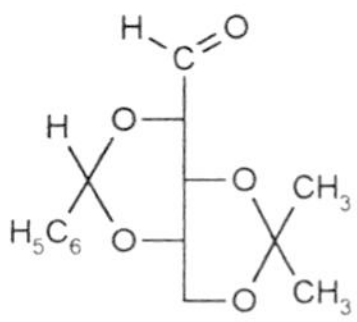	$Ph_3P=CHCO_2CH_3$	216
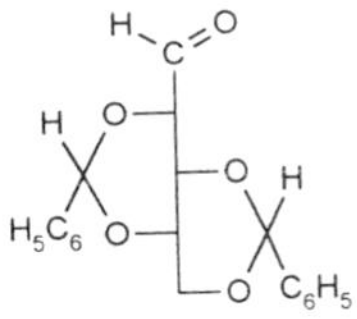	$Ph_3P=CHCO_2CH_3$	216
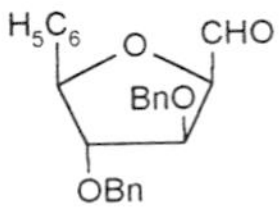	$Ph_3P=CHCO_2CH_3$	240
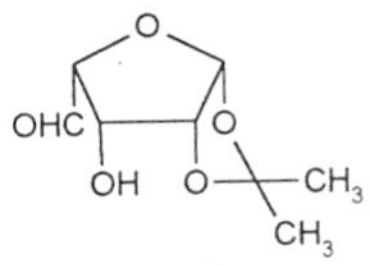	$Ph_3P=CHCO_2C_2H_5$	236
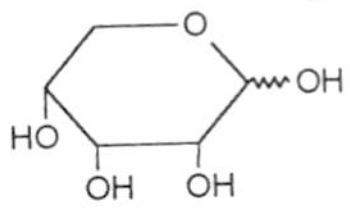	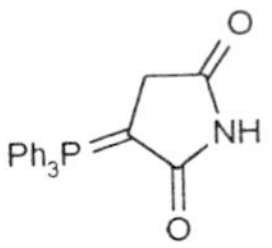 Ph_3P	241
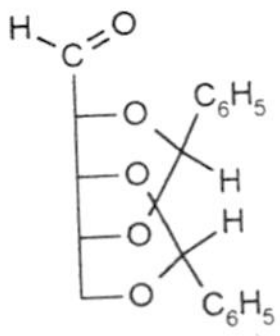	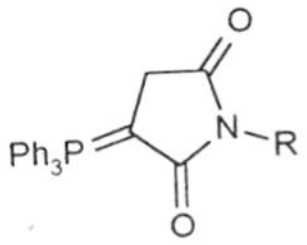 Ph_3P	242

(*continues*)

TABLE 1.23 *(continued)*

Starting saccharide	Phosphorane	Ref(s).
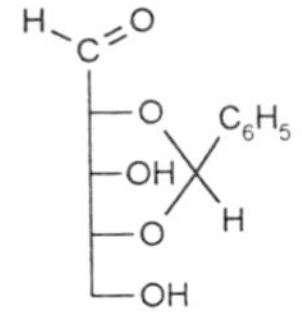 (aldehyde saccharide with O–C(C$_6$H$_5$)(H), OH, O, OH)	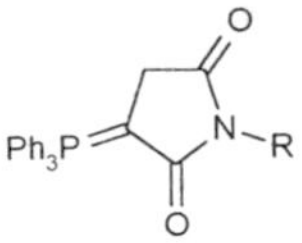 $Ph_3P{=}$ (succinimide-type ring, N–R)	242
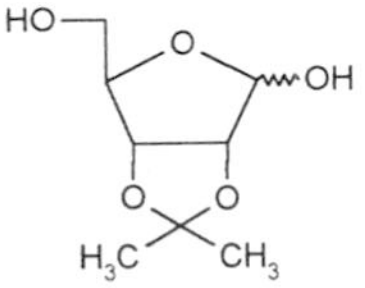 (furanose, HO–, –OH, isopropylidene H$_3$C/CH$_3$)	$Ph_3P{=}CHCO_2CH_3$	243,244
	$Ph_3P{=}CHCN$	243
	$Ph_3P{=}CHCO_2C_2H_5$	243,245,246
	$Ph_3P{=}C(Br)CO_2C_2H_5$	245
	$Ph_3P{=}CHCOCOC_2H_5$	245
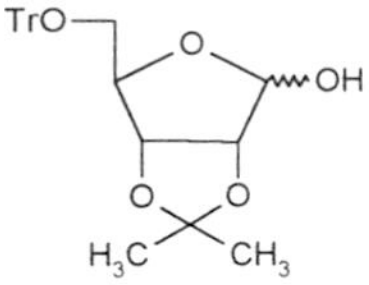	$Ph_3P{=}CHCO_2CH_3$	243,247–249
	$Ph_3P{=}C(Br)CO_2CH_3$	250
	$Ph_3P{=}C(X)CO_2CH_3$	248,251
(TrO– furanose, isopropylidene)	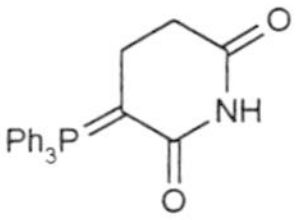 $Ph_3P{=}$ (glutarimide-type ring, NH)	252
	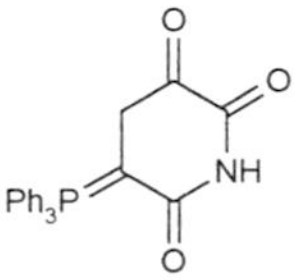 $Ph_3P{=}$ (dioxo-piperidine ring, NH)	253
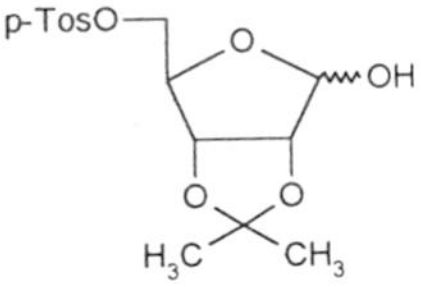 (p-TosO– furanose, isopropylidene)	$Ph_3P{=}CHCO_2C_2H_5$	254
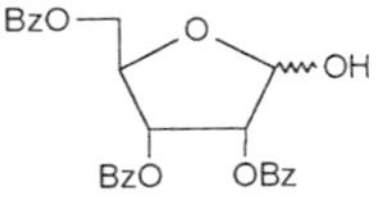 (BzO– furanose, BzO, OBz)	$Ph_3P{=}CHCO_2C_2H_5$	255
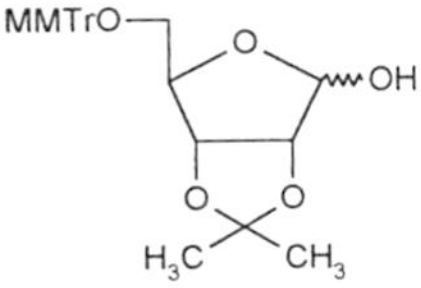 (MMTrO– furanose, isopropylidene)	$Ph_3P{=}CHCO_2C_2H_5$	256
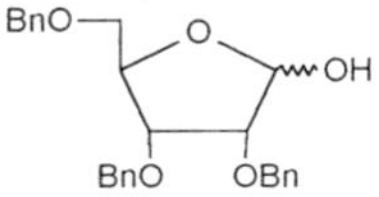 (BnO– furanose, BnO, OBn)	$Ph_3P{=}CHCO_2CH_3$	243
	$Ph_3P{=}C(Cl)CO_2C_2H_5$	257
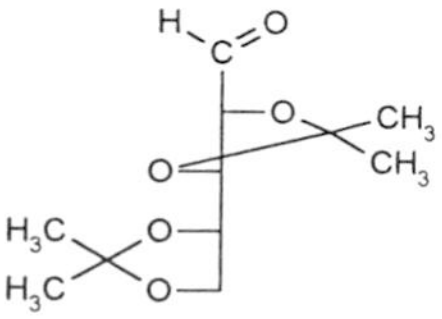 (aldehyde saccharide with O–C(CH$_3$)$_2$, O, H$_3$C, H$_3$C, O)	$Ph_3P{=}CHCO_2C_2H_5$	258
	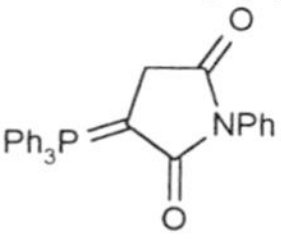 $Ph_3P{=}$ (succinimide-type ring, NPh)	242,259
	$Ph_3P{=}CHCOCO_2CH_3$	260

(continues)

TABLE 1.23 (*continued*)

Starting saccharide	Phosphorane	Ref(s).
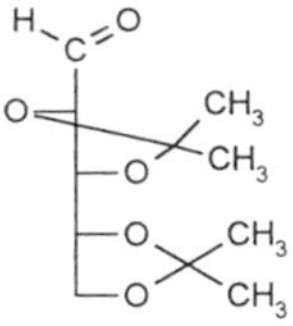	$Ph_3P=CHCOCO_2C_2H_5$ $Ph_3P=CHCOCO_2C_4H_9\text{-}t$ $Ph_3P=C(OC_2H_5)CO_2C_2H_5$ $Ph_3P=CHCN$ 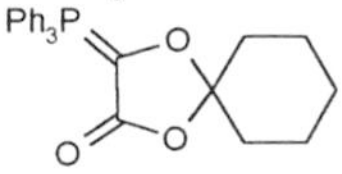 $Ph_3P=CHCO_2CH_3$	261,262 263 264 100 265 266
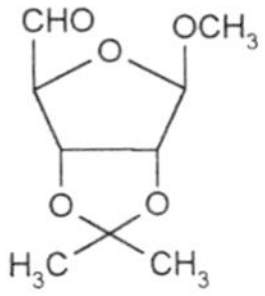	$Ph_3P=CHCO_2CH_3$	267
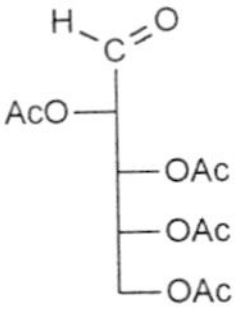	$Ph_3P=CHCO_2CH_3$ $Ph_3P=CHCN$	25 267
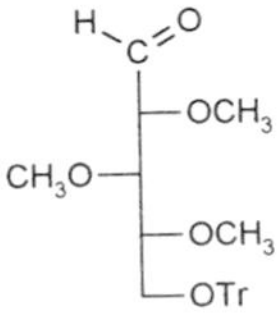	$Ph_3P=CHCO_2CH_3$	268
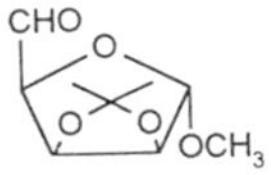	$Ph_3P=CHCO_2CH_3$	234
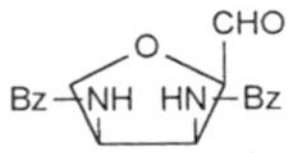	$Ph_3P=CH\!-\!CH=CHCO_2C_2H_5$	269
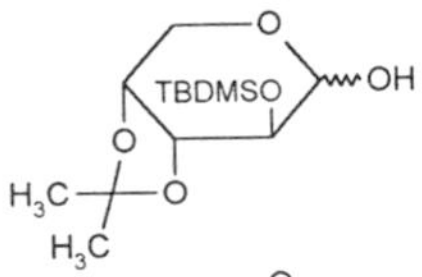	$Ph_3P=CHCO_2CH_3$	270
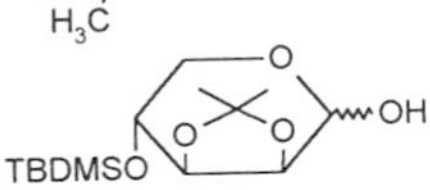	$Ph_3P=CHCO_2CH_3$	270
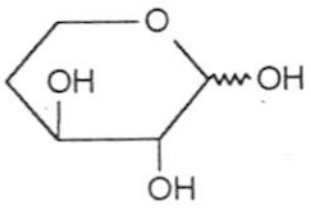	$Ph_3P=CHCO_2CH_2\text{-Tos-}p$	271
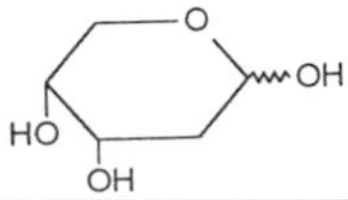	$Ph_3P=CHCO_2C_2H_5$	272,273

(*continues*)

TABLE 1.23 (*continued*)

Starting saccharide	Phosphorane	Ref(s).
	Ph₃P=CH(CH₂)₃CO₂H	274
	Ph₃P=CHCO₂C₂H₅	275
	Ph₃P=CHCO₂C₂H₅	276
	Ph₃P=CHCO₂C₂H₅	277
	Ph₃P=CHCO₂CH₃ Ph₃P=CHCO₂C₂H₅ Ph₃P=CHCOCO₂CH₃	143,243,278–280 278,281,282 283
	Ph₃P=C(OBn)CO₂Bn	284
	Ph₃P=CHCO₂C₂H₅	285
	Ph₃P=CHCO₂C₂H₅	285
	Ph₃P=CHCO₂C₂H₅	280,285,286

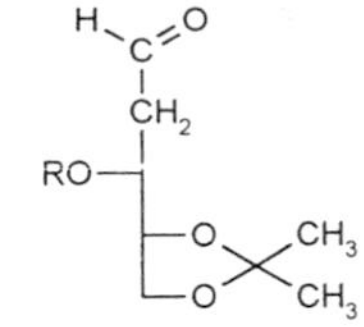

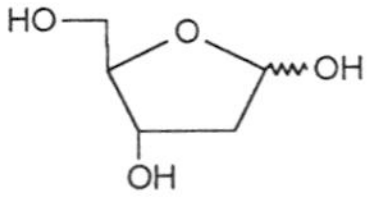

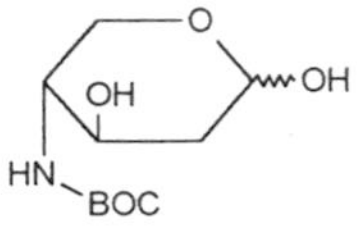

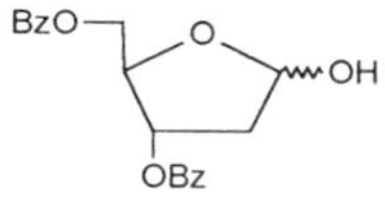

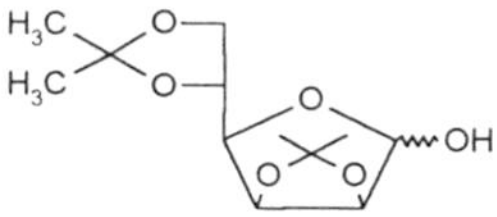

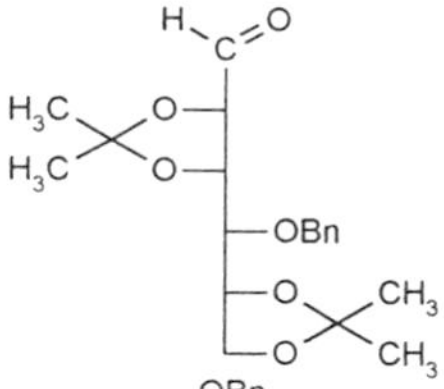

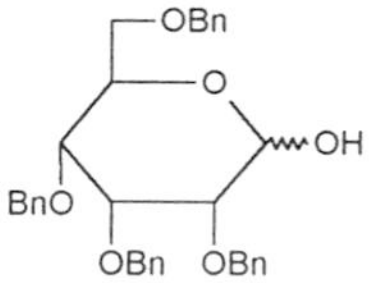

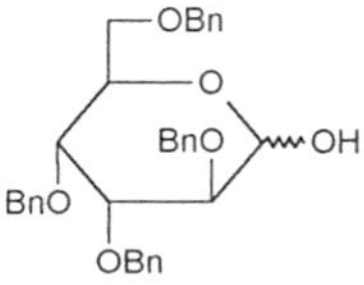

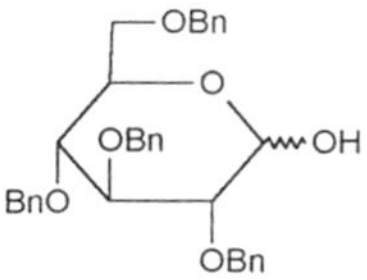

(*continues*)

TABLE 1.23 *(continued)*

Starting saccharide	Phosphorane	Ref(s).
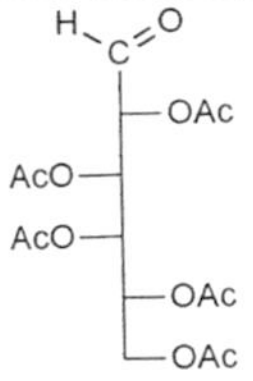	$Ph_3P{=}CHCO_2C_2H_5$	287
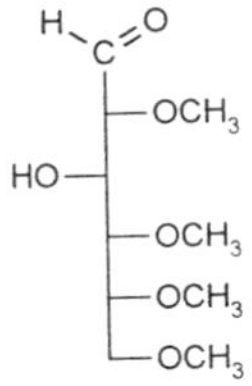	$Ph_3P{=}CHCO_2C_2H_5$	288
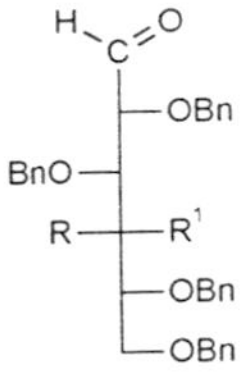 R = OBn, R^1= H R = H, R^1 = OBn	$Ph_3P{=}CHCO_2C_2H_5$	289
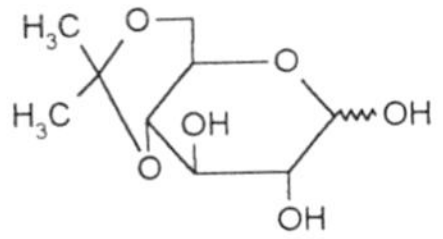	$Ph_3P{=}CHCOCH_2CO_2C_2H_5$	290
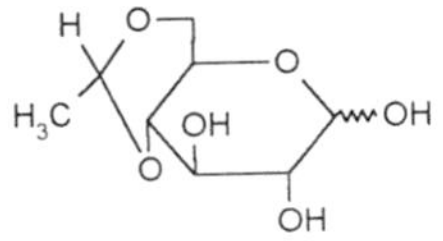	$Ph_3P{=}CHCO_2CH_3$	291,292
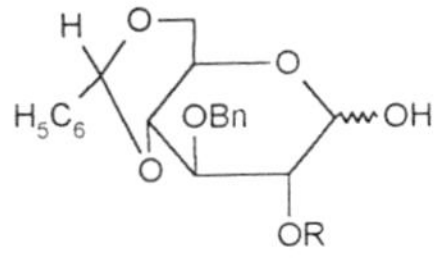	$Ph_3P{=}CHCO_2C_2H_5$	293
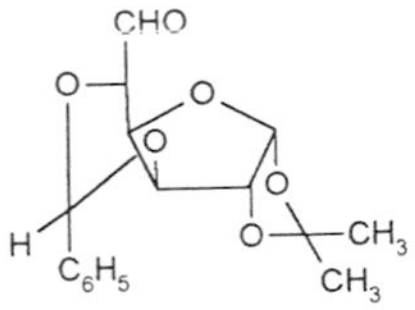	$Ph_3P{=}CHCO_2C_2H_5$	294
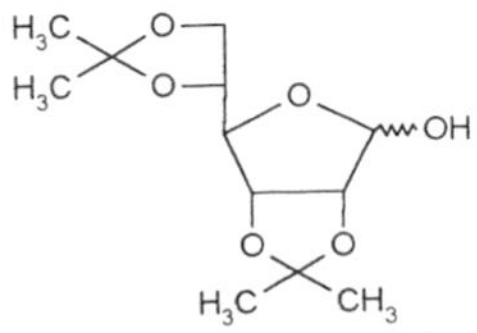	$Ph_3P{=}CHCO_2C_2H_5$	295

(continues)

TABLE 1.23 (*continued*)

Starting saccharide	Phosphorane	Ref(s).
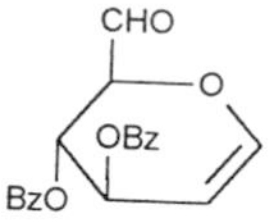	$Ph_3P{=}CHCO_2C_2H_5$	296,297
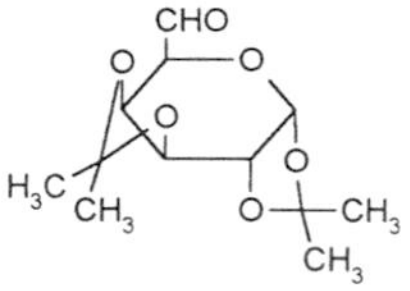	$Ph_3P{=}C(X)CO_2R$ $Ph_3P{=}CHCO_2CH_3$	298 296,299
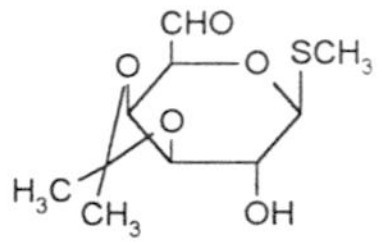	$Ph_3P{=}C(Br)CO_2CH_3$	300
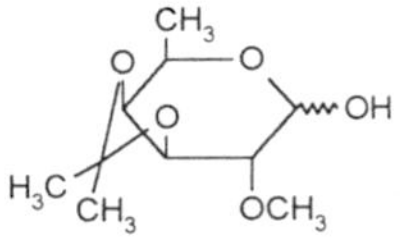	$Ph_3P{=}CHCO_2C_2H_5$	301
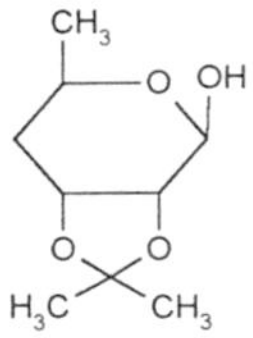	$Ph_3P{=}CHCOSC_2H_5$	302
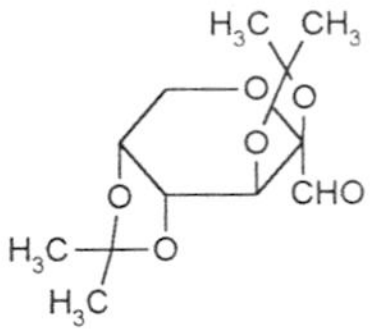	$Ph_3P{=}CHCO_2C_2H_5$	303
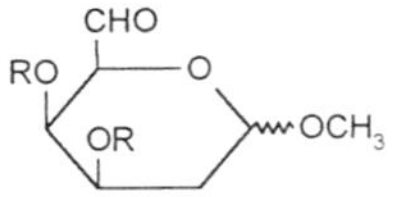	$Ph_3P{=}CHCH_2{-}CH{=}CH(CH_2)_3CO_2CH_3$	304
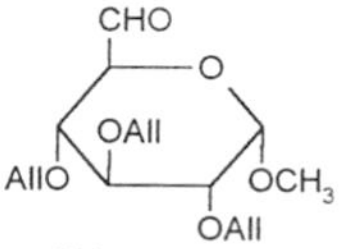	$Ph_3P{=}CHCO_2C_2H_5$	305
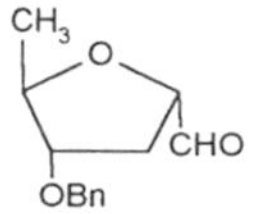	$Ph_3P{=}CHCO_2C_2H_5$	306
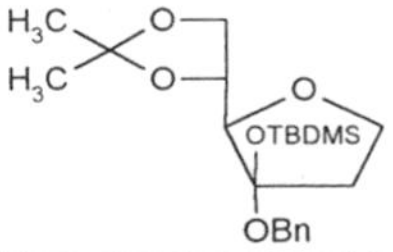	$Ph_3P{=}CHCO_2CH_3$	307

(continues)

TABLE 1.23 *(continued)*

Starting saccharide	Phosphorane	Ref(s).
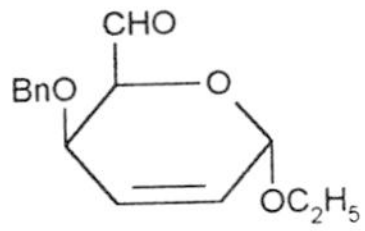	$Ph_3P{=}CHCO_2CH_3$	308
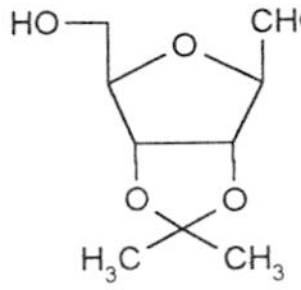	$Ph_3P{=}CHCO_2C_2H_5$	309
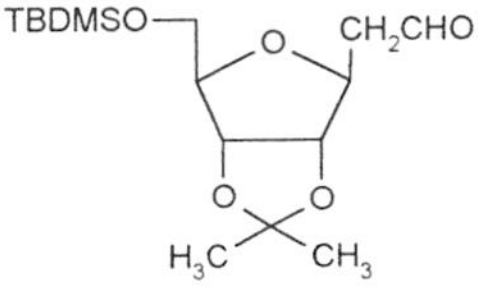	$Ph_3P{=}CHCO_2CH_3$	310
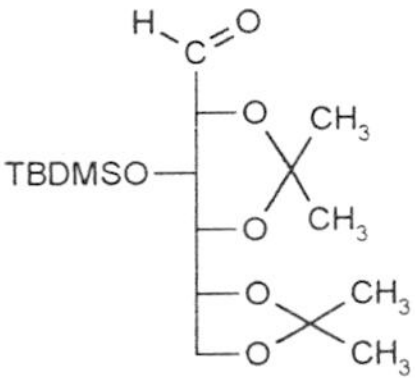	$Ph_3P{=}CHCO_2CH_3$	311
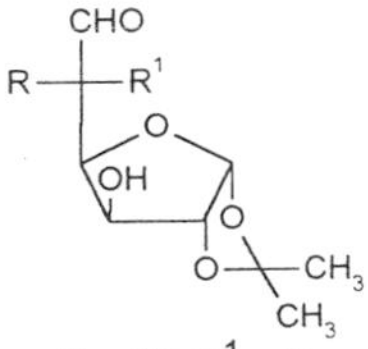 R = OH, R^1 = H R = H, R^1 = OH	$Ph_3P{=}CHCO_2C_2H_5$	312
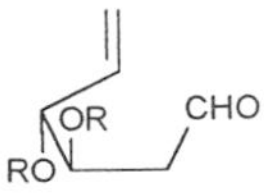	$Ph_3P{=}CHCO_2C_2H_5$	313
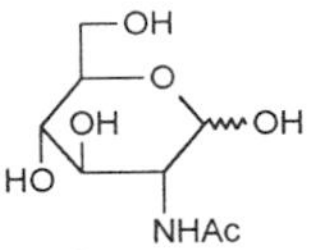	$Ph_3P{=}CHCO_2CH_3$	314
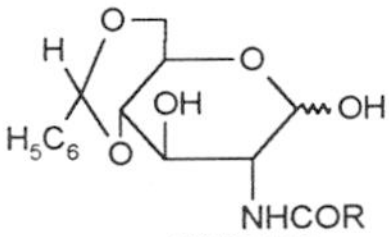	$Ph_3P{=}CHCO_2CH_3$ $Ph_3P{=}CHCO_2C_2H_5$	314 315–317
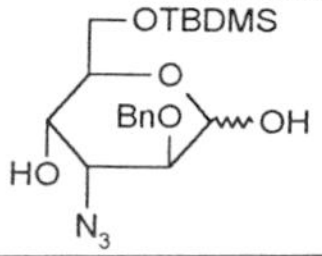	$Ph_3P{=}CHCO_2C_2H_5$	318

(continues)

TABLE 1.23   *(continued)*

Starting saccharide	Phosphorane	Ref(s).
	$Ph_3P{=}CHCO_2C_2H_5$	319
	$Ph_3P{=}CHCO_2C_2H_5$	320
	$Ph_3P{=}CHCO_2Bn$	321
	$Ph_3P{=}CHCO_2CH_3$	322
	$Ph_3P{=}CHCO_2C_2H_5$	323
	$Ph_3P{=}CHCO_2C_2H_5$	324
	$Ph_3P{=}CHCO_2C_2H_5$	325
	$Ph_3P{=}C(OC_2H_5)CO_2C_2H_5$	326
	$Ph_3P{=}C(OC_2H_5)CO_2C_2H_5$	327

(continues)

TABLE 1.23 (*continued*)

Starting saccharide	Phosphorane	Ref(s).
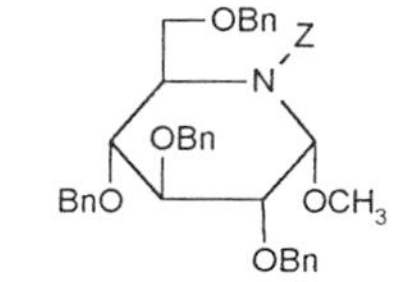	$Ph_3P=CHCO_2C_2H_5$	328
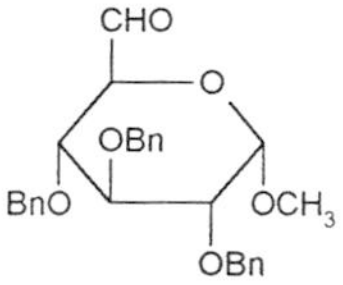	$Ph_3P=CHCO_2C_2H_5$	329
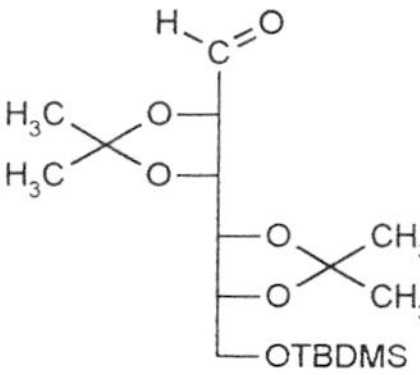	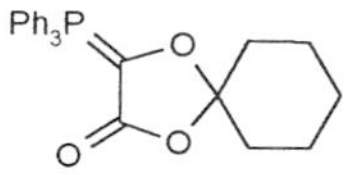	265
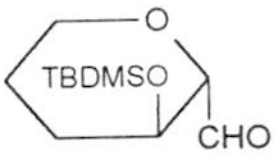	$Ph_3P=CH(CH_2)_2CO_2C_2H_5$	330
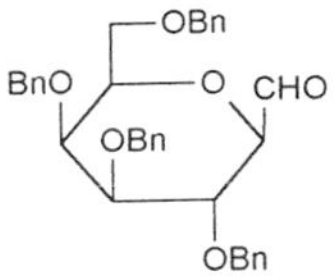	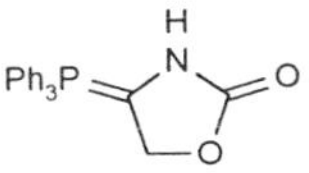	331
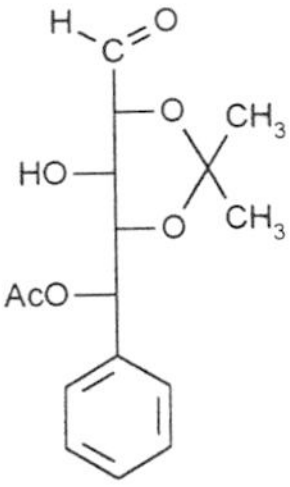	$Ph_3P=CHCO_2CH_3$	332
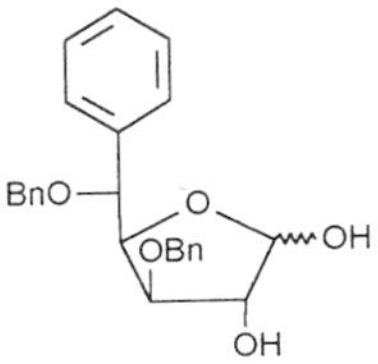	$Ph_3P=CHCO_2C_2H_5$	333
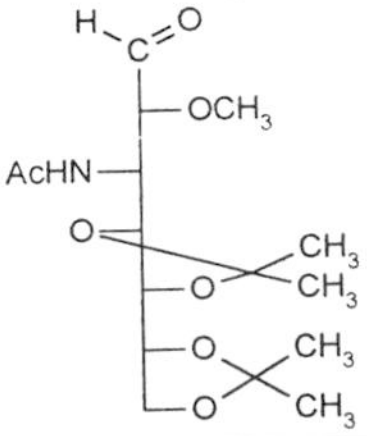	$Ph_3P=C(OC_2H_5)CO_2C_2H_5$	334

(*continues*)

TABLE 1.23 *(continued)*

Starting saccharide	Phosphorane	Ref(s).
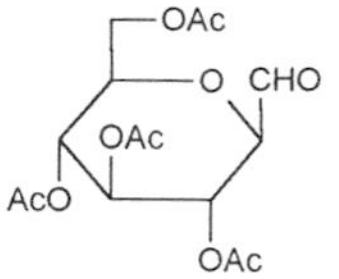	$Ph_3P{=}CHCO_2C_2H_5$	335
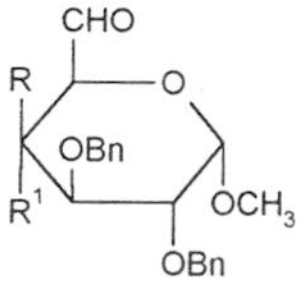 R = OBn, R^1 = H R = H, R^1 = OBn	$Ph_3P{=}CHCO_2CH_3$	336
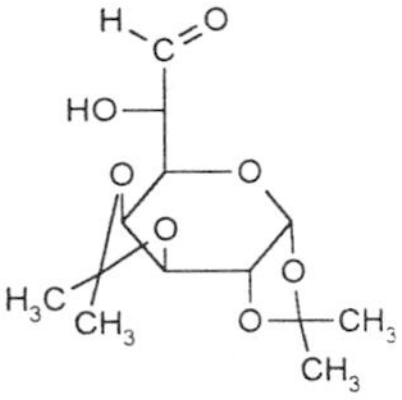	$Ph_3P{=}CHCO_2CH_3$	191
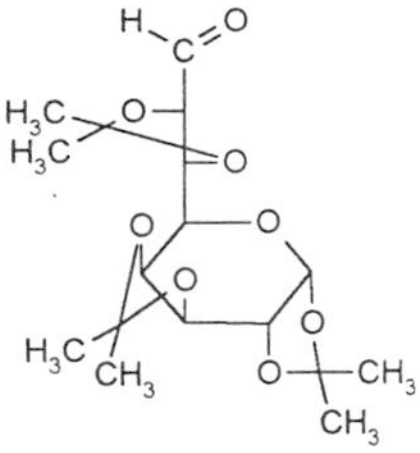	$Ph_3P{=}CHCO_2CH_3$	192,337
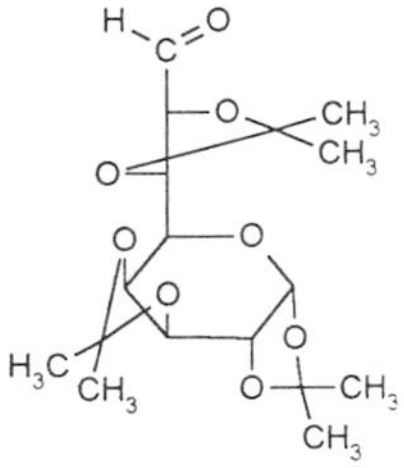	$Ph_3P{=}CHCO_2CH_3$	192
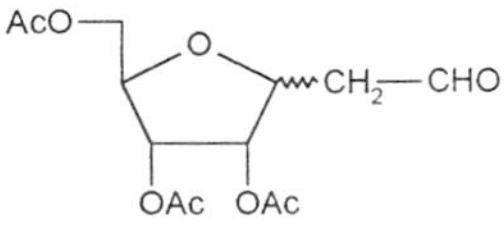	$Ph_3P{=}CHCO_2Bu\text{-}t$	338
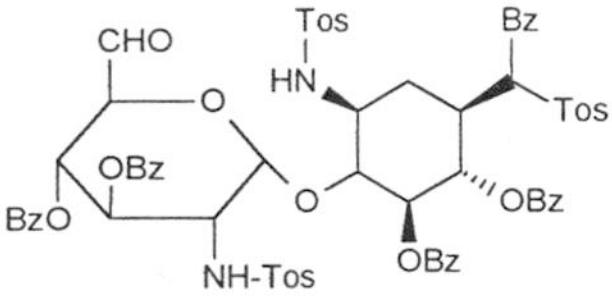	$Ph_3P{=}CHCO_2C_2H_5$	339

(continued)

TABLE 1.23 (continued)

Starting saccharide	Phosphorane	Ref(s).
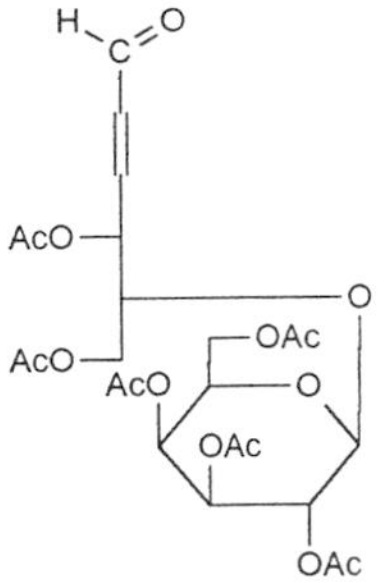	$Ph_3P{=}CHCO_2C_2H_5$	340

Methyl 2,3-di-*O*-acetyl-5,6-dideoxy-6-(*O,O*-diphenyl)phosphono-α-D-
  arabino-hex-5-enofuranoside,[343] $[\alpha]_D^{20}$ +31.9 (*c* = 0.68 in
  chloroform), m.p. 52°C (in a sealed tube)
Diphenyl-D-*altro*-2,5-anhydro-3,4-*O*-isopropylidene-6-*O*-trityl-
  deoxyhexanophosphonate and diphenyl-D-*allo*-2,5-anhydro-3,4-*O*-
  isopropylidene-6-*O*-trityl-deoxyhexanophosphonate[344]
(*E*)-2,3,5-Tri-*O*-benzyl-1,2-dideoxy-1-diphenylphosphono-4-*O*-(*tert*-
  butyldimethylsilyl)-D-*ribo*-hex-1-enitol.[345]

1.2.6.4. Chain Extension of Saccharides with Phosphoryl-Stabilized Carbanions

The olefination reaction of various PO-activated reagents can also be
used for chain extension. In general,[1,346] such a process involves the formation of an unsaturated compound (**117.3**) from a PO-activated carbanion
(**117.1**) and an aldehyde (**117.2**) or ketone with splitting off of the PO-
activated reagent in the form of the next-higher oxidation state, as shown
in Figure 1.117.

Application of this methodology, called the *Horner–Wittig* or *Wadsworth–Emmons* reaction, is very well documented, for example, in the
volumes of Houben-Weyl.[347] The supposed mechanism of the PO-activated
olefination can be explained by a reaction scheme such as that in Figure
1.118, which demonstrates that the product must be a mixture of the (*E*)-
and (*Z*)-olefins. The attack of the PO-activated carbanion (**118.1**) on the
carbonyl group (**118.2**) gives rise to an oxyanion (**118.3**) in a reversible
process, which is then transformed into the (*E/Z*)-olefin **118.5** via a four-
center intermediate **118.4**. The stereochemical outcome of the reaction is
determined by the combination of the individual reaction steps.

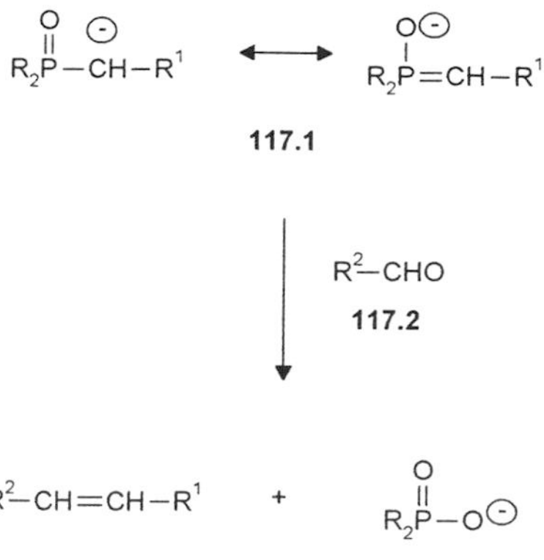

117.1

R²–CHO
117.2

R²–CH=CH–R¹ +

117.3 **117.4**

FIGURE 1.117

1.2.6.4.1. Chain Extension of Saccharides with Phosphonates

The reaction of phosphonic acid esters, carrying an activated methylene group at α-position to the phosphorous atom, with carbonyl compounds in the presence of various bases, results in olefins with simultaneous loss of a phosphoric acid ester:

$$R-CH_2-P(O)(OR^1)_2 + R^2-CHO \longrightarrow R-CH=CH-R^2 + HOP(O)(OR^1)_2$$

It is known that mainly (E)-olefins are produced[1,348] from aldehydes substituted with an electron-withdrawing group and dialkyl phosphonates, but the presence of an oxygen-function at α- or β-position may infuence the ratio of the geometric isomers.

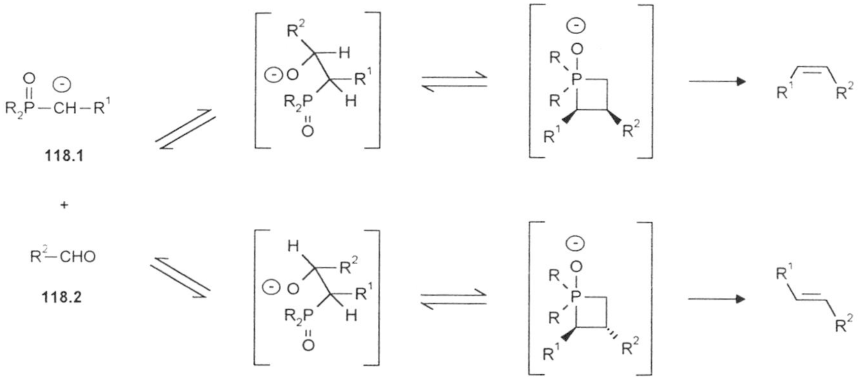

118.1

+

R²–CHO

118.2

118.3 **118.4** **118.5**

FIGURE 1.118

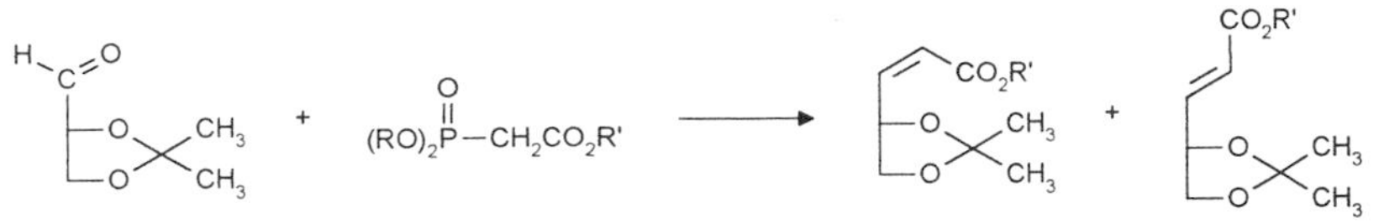

119.1   **119.2**   **119.3**   **119.4**

FIGURE 1.119

The chain extension of 2,3-O-isopropylidene-D-glyceraldehyde (**119.1**) with trimethyl phosphonoacetate (**119.2**) in the presence of sodium hydride leads[348] to 90% of a 7:1 (E/Z) mixture of the unsaturated esters **119.3** and **119.4** (see Fig. 1.119). With ethyl diisopropylphosphonoacetate and potassium *tert*-butoxide (as the base), this ratio changes[349] to 120:1, whereas the reaction of the sugar **119.1** with the sodium salt of trimethyl phosphonoacetate in THF in the presence of acetic acid gives[350] the (Z)-isomer **119.4** exclusively.

In the case of O-benzyl-L-lactaldehyde (**120.1**), the product distribution can be easily shifted toward the desired stereoisomer by selecting the proper reagent and reaction conditions. With trimethyl phosphonoacetate/NaH, a 1:1 mixture of the chain-extended products (**120.2** and **120.3**) is obtained. At the same time, the (Z)-pent-2-enoic ester (**120.3**) is the predominant ($E:Z = 1:5$) when the reagents are methyl di-O-(β,β,β-trifluoroethyl)-phosphonate and potassium hexamethyldisilazanide.[351]

General procedure for the preparation of methyl (2Z,4S)-4-benyzloxypent-2-enoates[351] To a mixture of potassium hydride (1 mmol) in dry THF (2 ml) a solution of methyl di-O-(β, β, β-trifluoroethyl)phosphonoacetate (1 mmol) in dry THF (2 ml) is added dropwise at −78°C. Then a solution of O-benzyl-L-lactaldehyde (1 mmol) in 2 ml of dry THF is added, and stirring is continued for an additional 40 min. The mixture is diluted with ether (3 ml), and the reaction is quenched with aqueous ammonium chloride (3 ml). It is then allowed to warm to room temperature, and the organic layer is separated, washed with aqueous Na$_2$CO$_3$ until neutral,

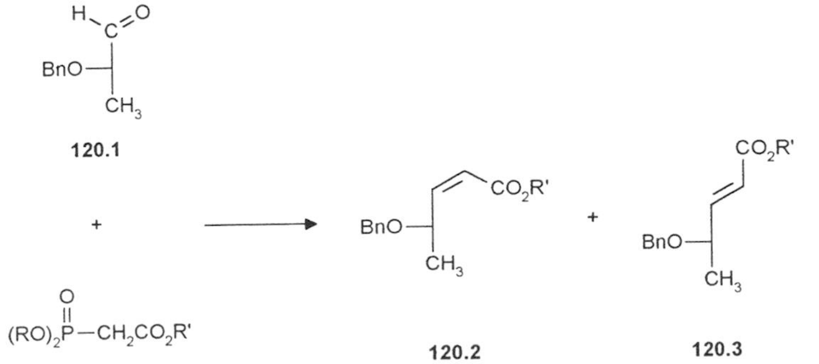

120.1

                     120.2   **120.3**

FIGURE 1.120

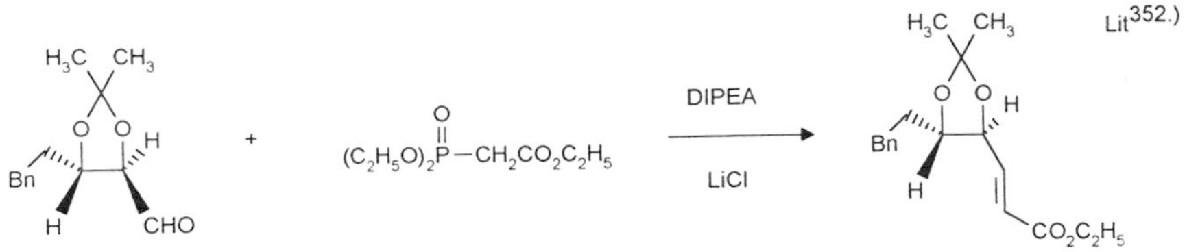

FIGURE 1.121

dried, and concentrated. The residue is submitted to column chromatography with a hexane–ethyl acetate eluant.

When this procedure is executed with sodium hydride and triethyl phosphonoacetate instead of the reagents mentioned previously, 2-(*E*)-products are obtained exclusively, and similar results have been obtained with the Horner–Emmons reactions shown in Figures 1.121 and 1.122.[352–354]

The chain extension[355] shown in Figure 1.123 is a synthetic route to a hex-2-enoic acid derivative **123.3**, in which the reaction partner of the starting saccharide **123.1** is the anion generated from trimethyl phosphonoacetate (**123.2**).

> *Ethyl 6-[(tert-butyldimethylsilyl)oxy]-4(S),5(S)-(isopropylidenedioxy)-hex-2(E)-enoate (**123.3**)[355]* To a 60% suspension of sodium hydride (182 mg in mineral oil) in benzene (10 ml), a solution of trimethyl phosphonoacetate (**123.2**, 827 mg, 4.54 mmol) in benzene (2 ml) is added at 0°C with stirring. Stirring is continued for an additional 1 h, and then a solution of 4-O-(*tert*-butyldimethylsilyl)-2,3-O-isopropylidene-L-threose (**123.1**, 1.245 g, 4.54 mmol) in benzene (4 ml) is added dropwise over a period of 5 min. After stirring for 1 h, the mixture is poured into 50 ml of ice water, the organic layer is separated, and the aqueous phase is extracted with benzene (3 × 50 ml). The combined organic layer is washed with water,

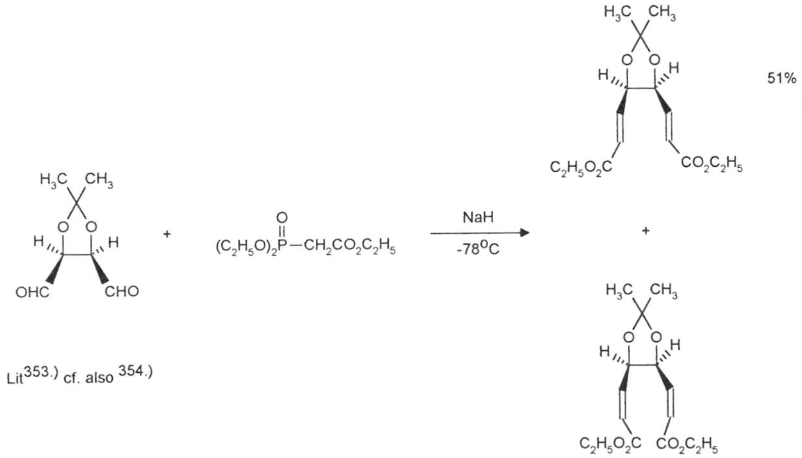

FIGURE 1.122

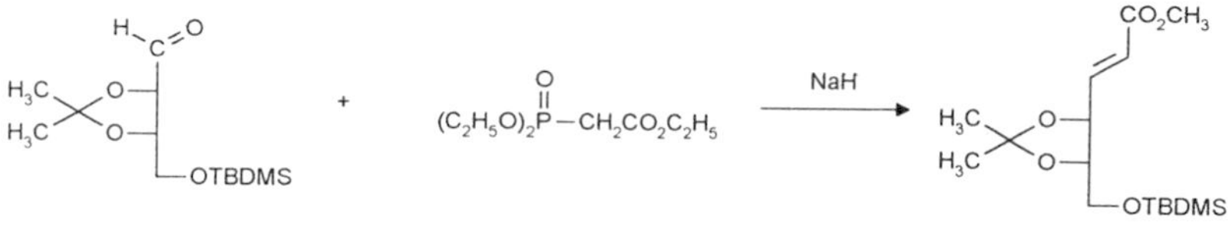

123.1   **123.2**   **123.3**

FIGURE 1.123

dried (MgSO$_4$), and concentrated, and the residue is purified by means of column chromatography with a 1:8 ethyl acetate–hexane eluant to obtain 1.43 g (95%) syrupy **123.3**, which contains less than 1% of the (Z)-isomer $[\alpha]_D^{20}$ −12.7 (c = 2.3 in methanol).

Table 1.24 lists further PO-activated Horner–Emmons olefination reactions of saccharides with relatively simple (mostly alkyl-substituted) phosphonates and gives some details on the experimental conditions.[356–378]

An important contribution to this field is a procedure for the preparation of higher-carbon sugars, which *allows the synthesis of natural products* with a longer carbon skeleton (C$_{20}$, or higher) by the Horner–Emmons coupling of saccharide–phosphonic acids with *aldehydo*-saccharides.

To illustrate this methodology, Figure 1.124 shows a convenient route to the C$_{15}$-enolether **124.3** from the *aldehydo*-heptose **124.1** and the sugar phosphonate **124.2**, as described by Paquet and Sinay.[379]

In another related work (Fig. 1.125) Indian authors[380] have converted four different educts into the sugar–ketophosphonates **125.2**, whose Horner–Emmons olefination with the *aldehydo*-saccharides **125.1** led to the long-chain enones (**125.3**) carrying a sugar moiety at both the carbonyl and the olefinic carbons. These latter compounds, regarded as the sugar analogs of *aromatic chalcones,* could be obtained by treatment of the keto-phosphonates (**125.2**) with cesium carbonate in 2-propanol.

This route was also accessible for the first synthesis of monosaccharide derivatives having 19 and 21 carbon atoms in the skeleton, and among others, the *"longest monosaccharide of 1994"* (**126.3**) was prepared[381] from the C$_{12}$-dialdose **126.1** and the C$_9$-phosphonate **126.2**, as shown in Figure 1.126.

From Figures 1.123–1.126 it is clear that the carbon atoms necessary for the chain extension of a saccharide may arise from sugar–phosphonates, which are generally transformed to the suitable ulose–phosphonates, capable of intramolecular PO-activated olefination. The chain-extended phosphonate **127.2**, derived from benzyl 2,3-O-isopropylidene-5-O-trifluoromethanesulfonyl-α-D-lyxofuranoside (**127.1**), as shown in Figure 1.127, was treated with sodium methoxide, when—on ring-closure—the O-isopropylidene derivative of *methyl shikimate* (**127.3**) is produced.[382]

TABLE I.24 Chain Extension of Saccharides with Phosphonates

Educt	Product	Reaction conditions, yield	Physical parameters	Refs.
		$(CH_3O)_2P(O)CH_2COCH_3$, K_2CO_3 9%, 20°C	—	356
		$(CH_3)_2P(O)CH \overset{OR}{\underset{CO_2C_2H_5}{\mid}}$ $(Me_3Si)_2NLi$, -78°C THF	R=TBDMS $E:Z = 5:1$; (E) m.p. 51-52°C	357
			$R = Cl_3CC \overset{CH_3}{\underset{CH_3O}{\mid}} C \overset{\mid}{\underset{C=O}{\mid}}$ $E:Z = 3:1$	357
		$(CH_3O)_2P(O)CH_2COCH_3$, NaH 22 °C, benzene, 30 min 83%	$E:Z = 20:1$	358
		$(CH_3O)_2P(O)CH_2COCH_3$, NaH 25°C, toluene	—	358
		1, $(C_2H_5O)_2P(O)CF_2H$, LDA THF, -78°C 2, $C_6H_5OC(S)Cl$ 83%	—	359

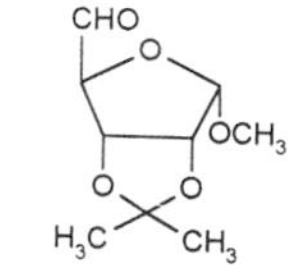	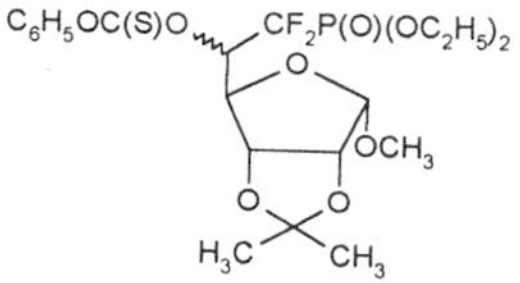	1, $(C_2H_5O)_2P(O)CF_2H$, LDA THF, -78°C 2. $C_6H_5OC(S)Cl$ 87%	—	359
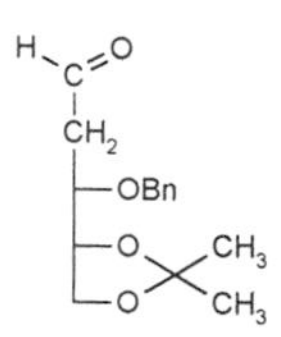	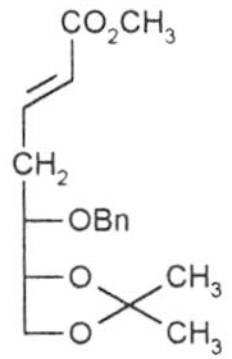	$(C_2H_5O)_2P(O)CH_2CO_2C_2H_5$, NaH 28°C, THF, 1 h 81%	$[\alpha]_D^{21} = +17$	360
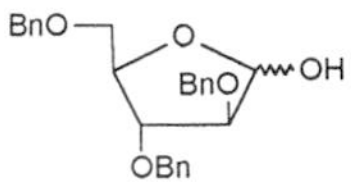	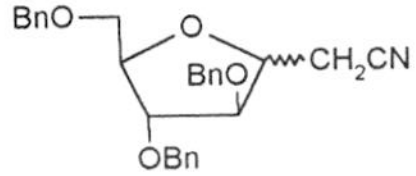	1 eq, $LiN(SiMe_3)_2$, THF 70%	$\alpha : \beta = 26 : 74$	361
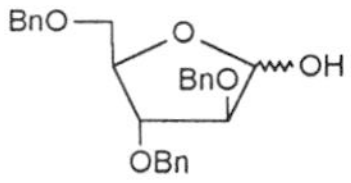	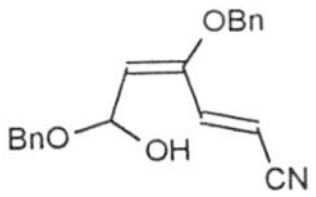	1 eq, $LiN(SiMe_3)_2$, THF, 20h 43%	$[\alpha]_D^{20} = +22.9$	361
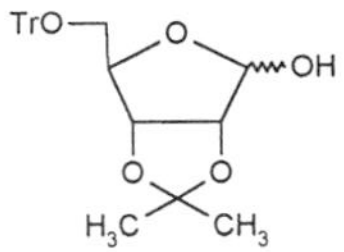	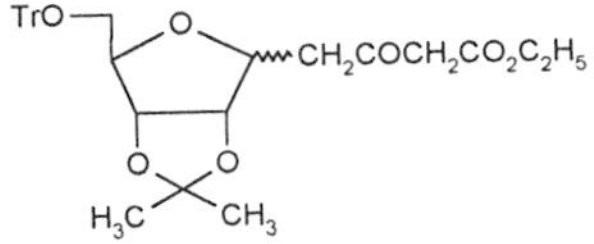	NaH, dimethoxyethane 90 min., reflux	$\alpha : \beta = 2 : 1$	362
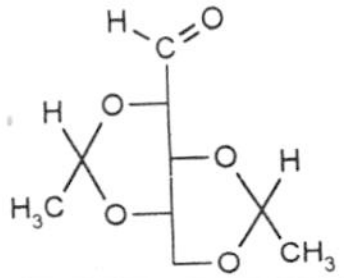	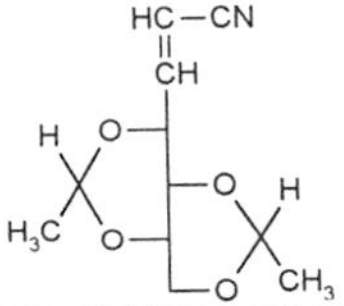	benzene:DMSO = 3:1, Na_2CO_3 39%	$[\alpha]_D^{20} = -13.2$ $(c = 1, CHCl_3)$	363

165

TABLE 1.24 (continued)

Educt	Product	Reaction conditions, yield	Physical parameters	Refs.
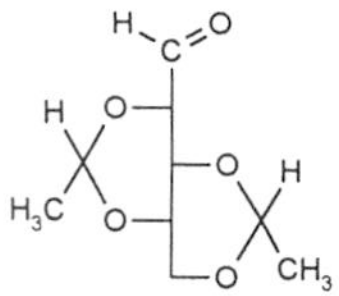 (structure)	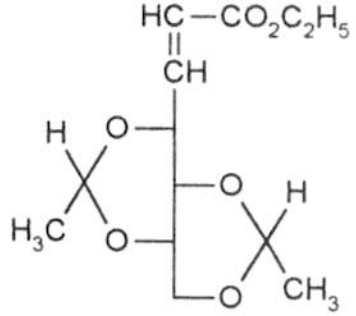 HC—CO₂C₂H₅ / =CH (structure)	benzene:DMSO = 3:1, Na₂CO₃ 48%	$[\alpha]_D^{20} = -10.3$ ($c = 1$, CHCl₃)	363
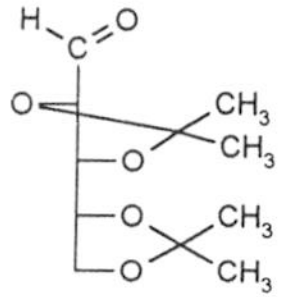 (structure)	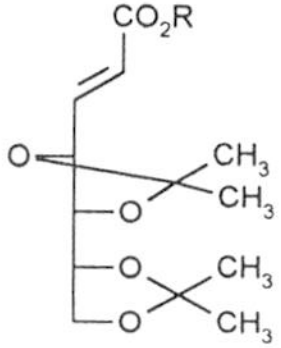 CO₂R (structure)	NaH, benzene, (RO)₂P(O)CH₂CO₂R 20°C, 1h	R = CH₃ $[\alpha]_D^{19} = -1.1$ ($c = 3$, C₂H₅OH) R = C₂H₅ $[\alpha]_D^{25} = +3.2$ ($c = 2.5$, C₂H₅OH)	364
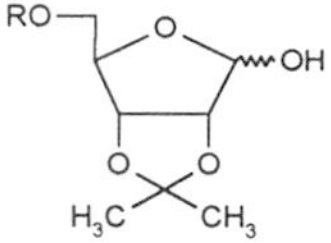 (structure) R = H, Tr, TBDMS	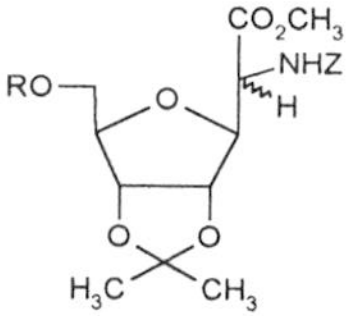 CO₂CH₃ / NHZ (structure)	with three different methods (CH₃O)₂P(O)HC—NHZ / CO₂CH₃	cf. original publication	365 Further derivatives: 366
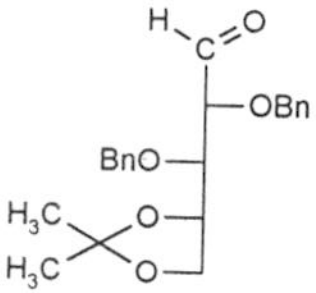 (structure)	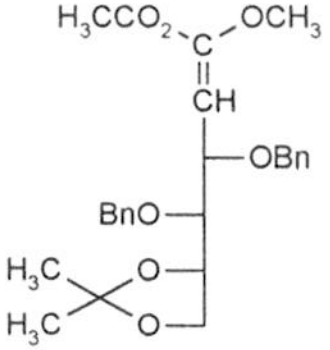 H₃CCO₂C—OCH₃ / =CH (structure)	(CH₃)₂P(O)CH(OCH₃)CO₂CH₃	E : Z = 65 : 35	367
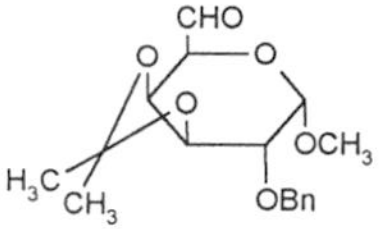 (structure)	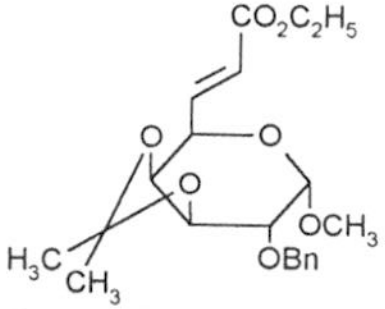 CO₂C₂H₅ (structure)	NaH, (C₂H₅O)₂P(O)CH₂CO₂C₂H₅ THF, 20°C	—	368

166

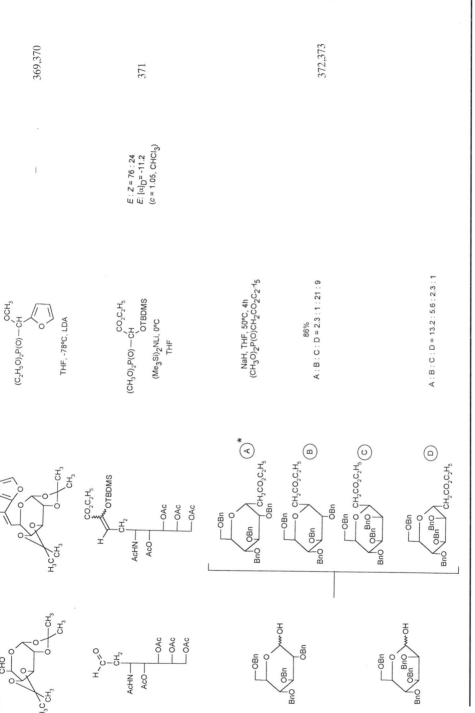

369,370

$(C_2H_5O)_2P(O)$—CH—$\overset{OCH_3}{\underset{}{}}$

THF, -78°C, LDA

371

$E : Z = 76 : 24$
$E: [\alpha]_D = -11.2$
$(c = 1.05, CHCl_3)$

$(CH_3O)_2P(O)$—CH—$\overset{CO_2C_2H_5}{\underset{OTBDMS}{}}$

$(Me_3Si)_2NLi, 0°C$
THF

372,373

NaH, THF, 50°C, 4h
$(CH_3O)_2P(O)CH_2CO_2C_2H_5$

86%

A : B : C : D = 2.3 : 1 : 21 : 9

A : B : C : D = 13.2 : 5.6 : 2.3 : 1

(continues)

167

TABLE I.24 (continued)

Educt	Product	Reaction conditions, yield	Physical parameters	Refs.
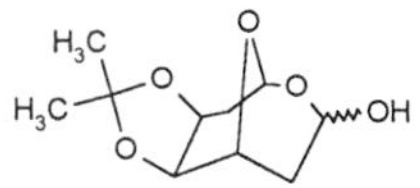 (structure)	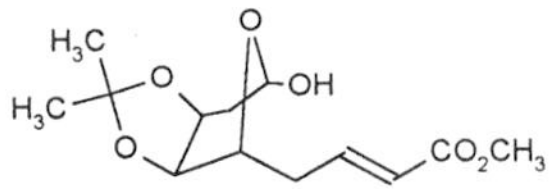 (structure with CO₂CH₃)	Na[(CH₃O)₂P(O)CHCO₂CH₃], THF −78°C 72%	only the E-isomer $[\alpha]_D^{25} = +20$ ($c = 0.64$, CHCl₃)	374
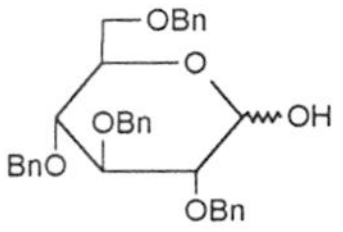 (structure)	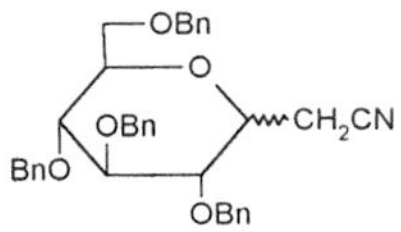 (structure with CH₂CN)	55%	$\beta : \alpha = 2 : 1$	373
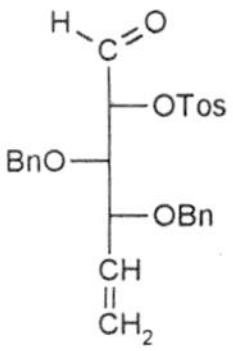 (structure)	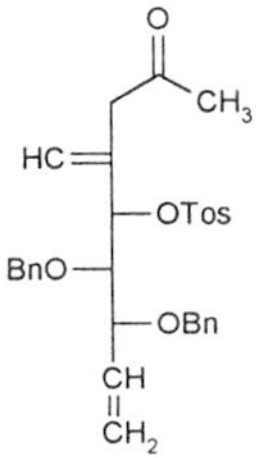 (structure)	(C₂H₅O)₂P(O)CH₂C(O)CH₃ n-BuLi, ether, −78°C, 6h	m.p. 99 - 101°C $[\alpha]_D^{20} = +85$ ($c = 1$, CHCl₃)	375
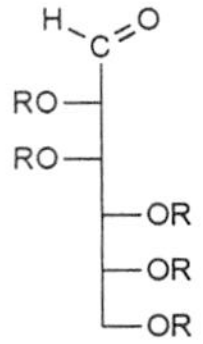 (structure)	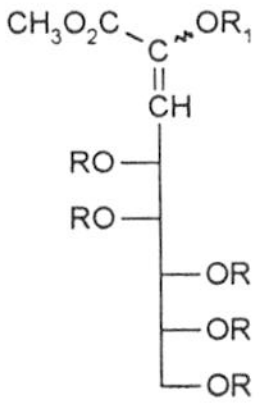 (structure)	LiN(SiMe₃)₂, −78°C 2h, (CH₃O)₂P(O)CH(OR₁)CO₂CH₃ 29 - 77%	—	376

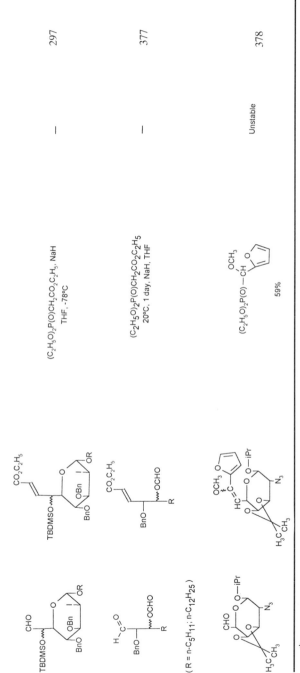

$(C_2H_5O)_2P(O)CH_2CO_2C_2H_5$, NaH
THF, -78°C

—

297

$(C_2H_5O)_2P(O)CH_2CO_2C_2H_5$
20°C, 1 day, NaH, THF

—

377

$(C_2H_5O)_2P(O)$—CH(OCH$_3$)(furyl)

59%

Unstable

378

($R = n\text{-}C_5H_{11}$; $n\text{-}C_{12}H_{25}$)

*The methyl esters have also been synthesized.

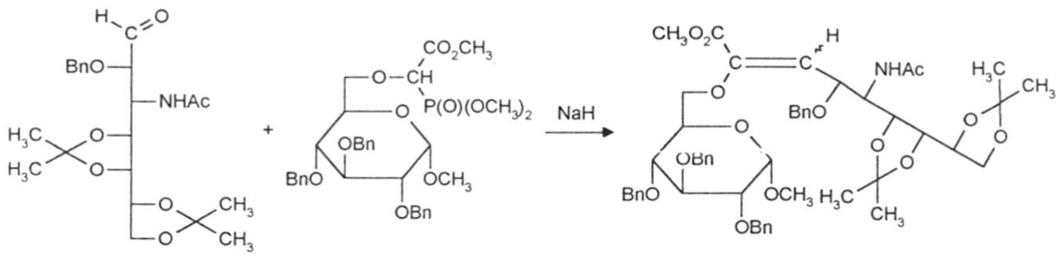

FIGURE I.124

Additional examples for PO-activated intramolecular olefinations have been reported.[383-389]

An easily reproducible procedure for the preparation of sugar–phosphonates has been recently reported by Paulsen and von Deyn[390] (see Fig. 1.128).

*Dimethyl3,4,5-tri-O-benzyl-1-deoxy-6,7-O-isopropylidene-D-glycero-D-gulo-hep-titol-1-phosphonate (**128.2**) and dimethyl 3,4,5-tri-O-benzyl-1-deoxy-6,7-O-isopro-pylidene-D-glycero-D-ido-heptitol-1-phosphonate (**128.3**)[390]* To a solution of di-methyl methylphosphonate (12 ml, 0.11 mol) in dry THF (300 ml), 69 ml of a 1.6 M solution of *n*-butyllithium in hexane is added dropwise at −78°C under nitrogen atmosphere. The mixture is warmed to room temperature, stirred for 10 min, and cooled again to −78°C, and a solution of 2,3,4-tri-O-benzyl-5,6-O-isopropylidene-*aldehydo*-D-glucose (**128.1**, 18.3 g, 37.3 mmol) in dry THF (200 ml) is added dropwise and stirring is continued for additional 1 h, when transformation of the *aldehydo*-sugar has been completed. For workup, 8 ml of acetic acid is added, the mixture is concentrated and redissolved in dichloromethane, and the organic layer is washed with water, dried over $MgSO_4$, and concentrated. The crude syrupy product is purified by means of column chromatography (eluant: 15:1 toluene–ethanol) to furnish 20.5 g (89%) of the mixture of **128.2** and **128.3**.

Methylene–bisphosphonates are also popular PO-activated reagents in chain-extension reactions. Thus, 2,3:4,5-di-*O*-isopropylidene-*aldehydo*-D-arabinose (**129.1**) readily furnishes 1-diethylphosphono-1,2-dideoxy-3,4:5,6-di-*O*-isopropylidene-D-*arabino*-(*E*)-hex-1-enitol (**129.3**) on chain extension[391] (Fig. 1.129) with the anion of diethyl methane–bis-phospho-nate (**129.2**).

*1-Diethylphosphono-1,2-dideoxy-3,4:5,6-di-O-isopropylidene-D-arabino-(E)-hex-1-enitol (**129.3**)[391]* To a stirred mixture of sodium hydride (145 mg, 60% in mineral oil) in dry ethyleneglycol dimethylether (25 ml), diethyl methane–bis-phosphonate (**129.2**, 0.35 g, 3.0 mmol) in ethyleneglycol dimethylether (15 ml) is added and the reaction mixture is stirred for 1 h. After cooling to 10°C, a solution of 2,3:4,5-di-*O*-isopropylidene-*aldehydo*-D-arabinose (**129.1**, 700 mg, 3 mmol) in ethyleneglycol dimethylether (25 ml) is added, and stirring is continued for an additional 1 h. The mixture is then poured into 250 ml of ice water, extracted with ether (5 × 100 ml), the organic layer is dried (Na_2SO_4) and concentrated, and the crude product

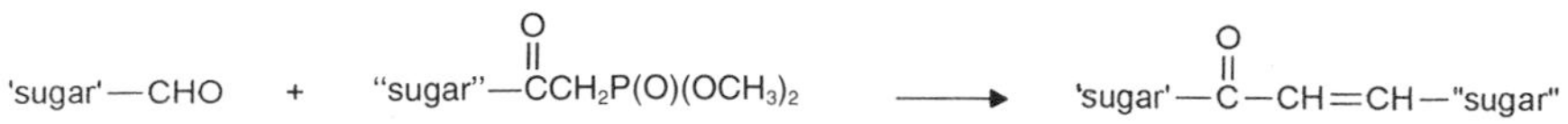

$$\text{'sugar'—CHO} \quad + \quad \text{"sugar"—} \overset{\overset{\text{O}}{\|}}{\text{C}} \text{CH}_2\text{P(O)(OCH}_3)_2 \quad \longrightarrow \quad \text{'sugar'—} \overset{\overset{\text{O}}{\|}}{\text{C}} \text{—CH=CH—"sugar"}$$

125.1   **125.2**   **125.3**

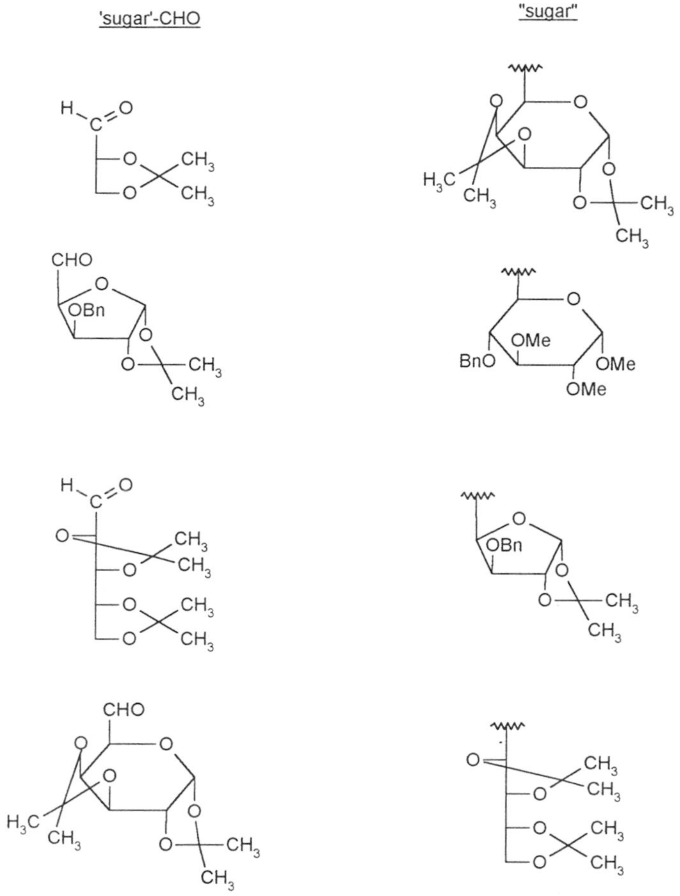

FIGURE 1.125

is crystallized from hot *n*-pentane to give 800 mg (72%) of the title compound **129.3**, m.p. 49–51°C, $[\alpha]_D^{20}$ +2.0 (c = 1 in chloroform).

2,4-*O*-Ethylidene-D-erythrose also gives[391] the (*E*)-product, with 31% yield, in an analogous reaction. An additional example for a related transformation is the chain extension of 2,3,5-tri-*O*-benzyl-4-*O*-(*tert*-butyldimethylsilyl)-*aldehydo*-D-arabinose to furnish[345] 31% of (*E*)-2,3,5-tri-

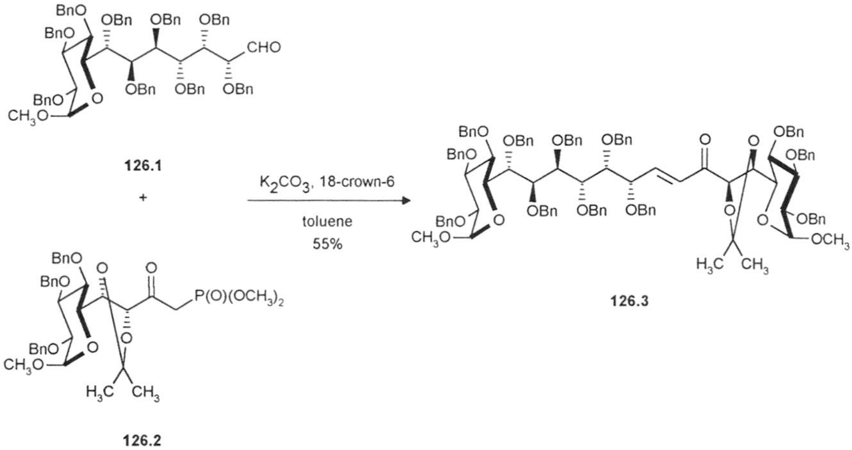

FIGURE 1.126

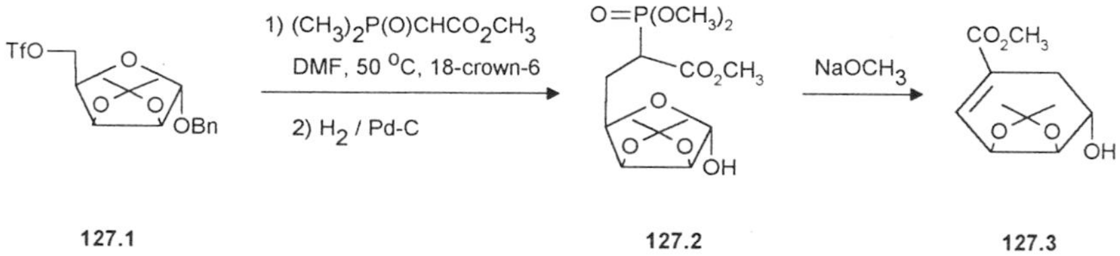

FIGURE 1.127

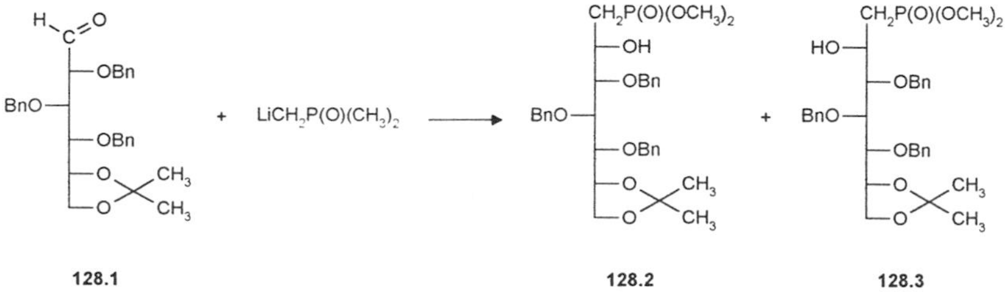

FIGURE 1.128

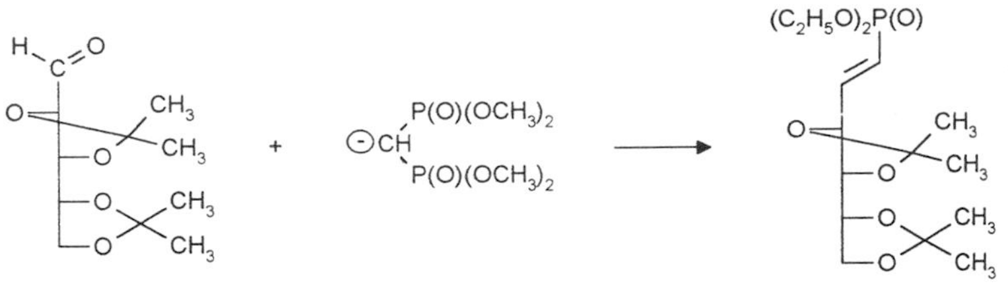

129.1   **129.2**   **129.3**

FIGURE 1.129

O-benzyl-1,2-dideoxy-1-diethylphosphono-4-*O*-(*tert*-butyldimethylsilyl)-D-*ribo*-hex-1-enitol.

The lithiated fluoromethylene–bis-phosphonate (**130.2**) has been reported in a preliminary paper[392] as applicable for the chain elongation (Fig. 1.130) of methyl 2,3-*O*-isopropylidene-β-D-*ribo*-pentodialdo-1,4-furanoside (**130.1**) to afford the (*E*)-vinylphosphonate **130.3** and the rearranged product **130.4**. The preparation of several another phosphonates is described by Paquet and Sinay[379] and Paulsen and Bartsch.[393]

A novel possibility for PO-activated olefination is associated with the utilization of alkoxyalkyl diarylphosphine oxides (Fig. 1.131). The lithiated cyclohexyloxymethyl diphenylphosphine oxide **131.2** was reacted with 2,3,5-tri-*O*-benzyl-D-arabinose (**131.1**) in THF solution at −78°C, and subsequent treatment with potassium hydride at 40°C resulted in a 1:2 (*E/Z*) mixture of the enolether **131.3** with 75% yield.[394] The methoxymethyl analog of **131.2** has been employed by Polish chemists[370] for similar transformations, and the chain extension of 2,3,5-tri-*O*-benzyl-D-arabinose and -D-ribose have been also carried out[395] with the phosphinoxides **132.1** (Fig. 1.132).

The sulfonyl- and sulfonylphosphoryl-stabilized carbanions represent the last sub-group of the PO-stabilized carbanions useful for the chain extension of monosaccharides (Fig. 1.133). While Peterson olefination of 2,3-*O*-isopropylidene-D-glyceraldehyde (**133.1**) with phenyltrimethylsilyl-sulfone (**133.2**) gives[396] 72% of an (*Z/E*) sulfone mixture (**133.3** and **133.4**),

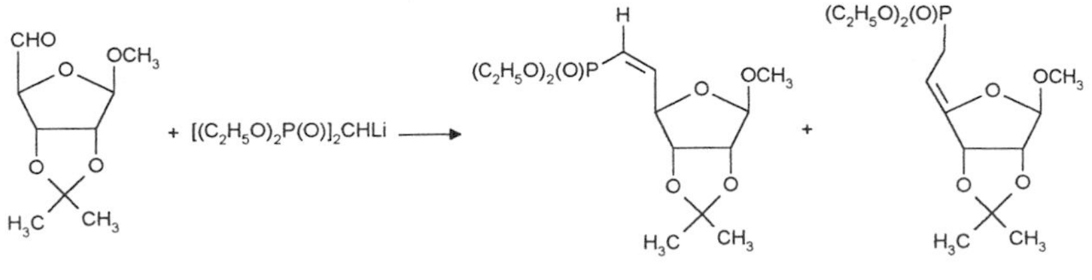

130.1   **130.2**   **130.3**   **130.4**

FIGURE 1.130

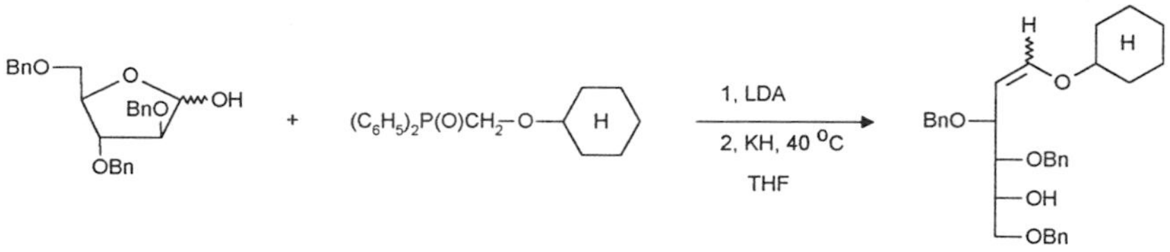

131.1   131.2   131.3

FIGURE 1.131

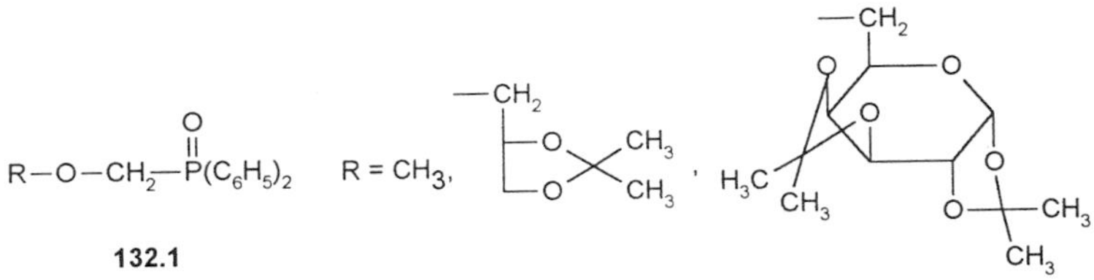

132.1

FIGURE 1.132

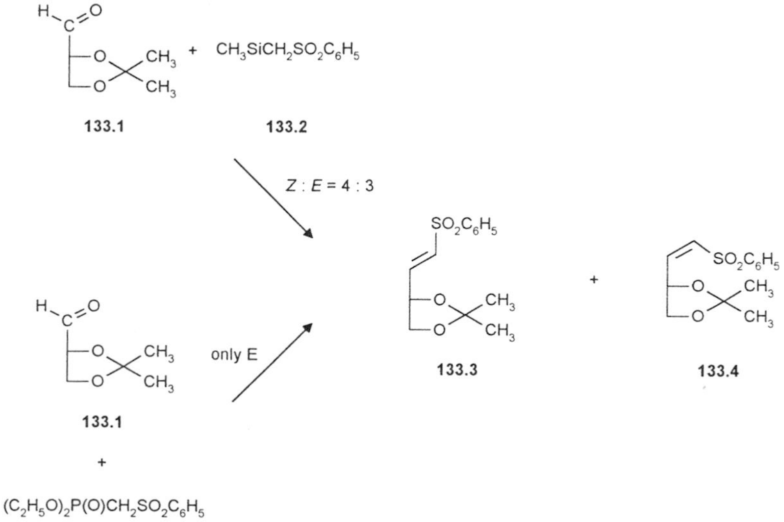

133.1   133.2

$Z : E = 4 : 3$

only E

133.3   133.4

133.1

+

$(C_2H_5O)_2P(O)CH_2SO_2C_6H_5$

133.5

FIGURE 1.133

the (*E*)-olefin (**133.4**) is produced exclusively when the transformation is performed[397] with diethyl(phenylsulfonyl)methanephosphonate (**133.5**).

> *(Z,E)-(4'S)-2-(2,2'-Dimethyl-1',3'-dioxolan-4'-yl)-vinyl phenylsulfone (133.3 and 133.4)*[396] A solution of phenyltrimethylsilylsulfone (**133.2**, 1 mmol) in dimethoxyethane (5 ml) is cooled to −78°C and an equimolar amount of *n*-butyllitium is added under argon atmosphere. The yellowish solution is kept at −78°C for 20 min, and then a solution of 2,3-*O*-isopropylidene-D-glyceraldehyde (**133.1**, 1 mmol) in a small volume of dimethoxyethane is added dropwise. The temperature is allowed to raise to room temperature, aqueous ammonium chloride is added, and the organic layer is separated, dried and concentrated. Column chromatography of the residue gives 72% of an (*Z/E*) mixture (**133.3** and **133.4**) of the title product.

> *(E)-(4'S)-(2,2'-Dimethyl-1',3'-dioxolan-4'-yl)-vinyl phenylsulfone (133.4)*[397] To a mixture of diethyl(phenylsulfonyl)methylphosphonate (**133.5**, 10.2 g, 35 mmol) in THF (50 ml), potassium *tert*-butoxide (3.7 g, 33 mmol) is added at 0°C, and the mixture is cooled to −78°C, and then treated with a dropwise addition of a solution of 2,3-*O*-isopropylidene-D-glyceraldehyde (**133.1**, 4 g, 30 mmol) in 15 ml of THF. After stirring for 2 h, the reaction is quenched with aqueous NaHSO₄ and the mixture is allowed to warm to room temperature. It is then extracetd with ether, and the organic layer is separated, washed with water and aqueous Na₂CO₃, dried over MgSO₄, and concentrated. Column chromatography of the residue yields 4.05 g of the pure (*E*)-olefin **133.4**, $[\alpha]_D^{25}$ +14.08 (*c* = 1.15 in chloroform).

By employing 1,2-*O*-isopropylidene-3-*O*-benzyl-α-D-ribofuranos-1,4-ulose (**134.1**) and one equivalent (1 eq) of lithium chloride, the same procedure (Fig. 1.134) gave[397] 63% of 3-*O*-benzyl-5,6-dideoxy-(*E*)-5,6-didehydro-1,2-O-isopropylidene-6-phenylsulfonyl-α-D-glucofuranose {**134.2**, m.p. 110–111°C, $[\alpha]_D^{25}$ +18 (*c* = 1 in chloroform)}.

Starting from aldehydes and dialkoxyphosphoryl methylsulfones, the Horner–Wadsworth–Emmons carbonyl olefination allows the preparation of vinylsulfones that can be transformed, in a subsequent Michael addition, into glycosylmethylsulfones. The first related work published reported[398] the transformation of the 4-deoxy-D-*xylo*-hexose derivatives (**135.1**) with diethyl (phenylsulfonyl)methylphosphonate (**135.2**) to result in the C-glycosylsulfones **135.3** as shown in Figure 1.135.

By treatment with sodium hydride, the α,β-sulfone mixture **135.3** can be converted into the β-isomer, and further studies[399] have revealed that

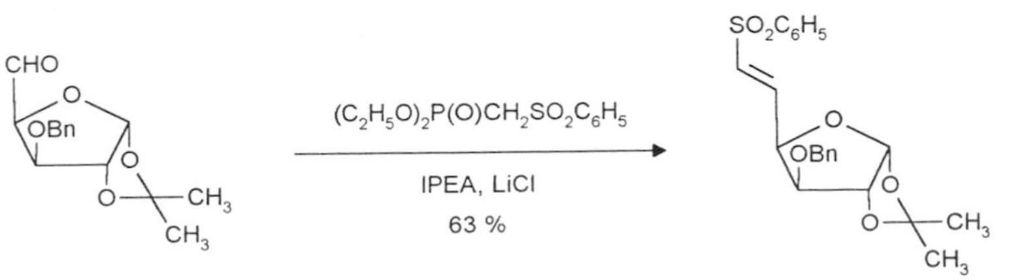

134.1

$(C_2H_5O)_2P(O)CH_2SO_2C_6H_5$

IPEA, LiCl

63 %

$SO_2C_6H_5$

134.2

FIGURE 1.134

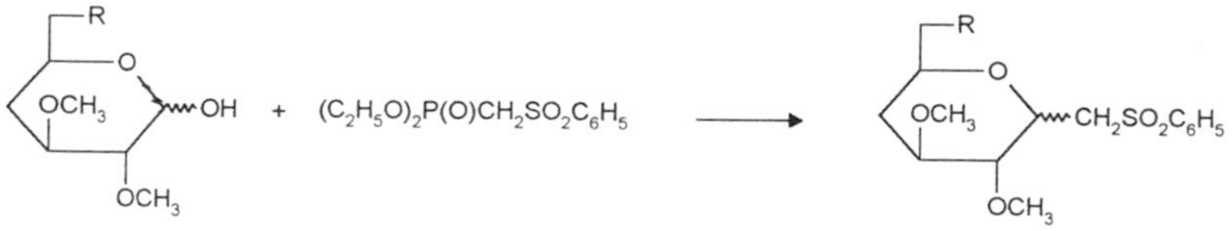

135.1   135.2   135.3

FIGURE 1.135

this strategy can be employed for the chain extension of additional sugars, such as D-glucose, 2-deoxy-D-glucose and 4,6-O-ethylidene-D-glucose.

3-(Diethylphosphono)acrolein diethyl dithioacetal (**136.2**) represents a specific reagent among the PO-activated phosphorous compounds, as it is suitable for chain extension by *three carbon atoms*. For example, Figure 1.136 shows that the product of the olefination[400] with **136.2** is the C_8-ketene dithioacetal **136.3** when the starting sugar is 2,3:4,5-di-O-isopropylidene-*aldehydo*-D-arabinose (**136.1**).

A *modern preparative synthesis* of 2-deoxy-D-ribose, worked out by Rapoport,[401] is based on the convenient chain extension (Fig. 1.137) of 2,4-O-ethylidene-D-erythrose (**137.1**), available by the oxidation of 4,6-O-ethylidene-D-glucose, with the anion of (dimethylphosphoryl)methyl phenylsulfone (**137.2**). The resulting (pent-2-en-1-yl) phenyl sulfoxide **137.3** can be then readily converted into 2-deoxy-D-ribose.

(E/Z)-(3R,4R)-3,5-(Ethylidenedioxy)pent-2-en-1-yl phenyl sulfoxide (137.3)[401]
To a solution of (dimethylphosphoryl)methyl phenylsulfoxide (2.48 g, 10 mmol) in dry THF (20 ml), 11 ml of a *n*-hexane solution of butyllithium is added dropwise at −70°C over a period of 3 h. Stirring is continued at −70°C for an additional 4 h, and then a solution of 2,4-O-ethylidene-D-erythrose (**137.1**, 2.0 g, 10 mmol) in dry THF (25 ml) is added and the stirred mixture is allowed to warm to room temperature. Stirring is continued overnight, the solvent is distilled off, and the residue is mixed with water (25 ml) and extracted with 3 × 15 ml of chloroform. The combined organic solution is washed with water (15 ml), dried over MgSO₄, and concentrated to give 75–87% of the isomeric mixture **137.3**.

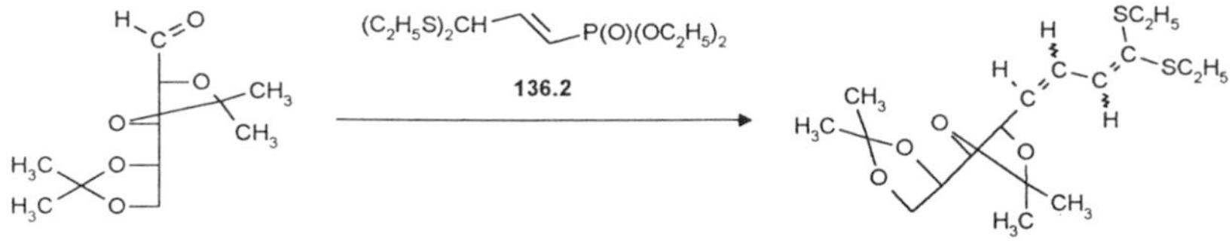

136.1   136.3

FIGURE 1.136

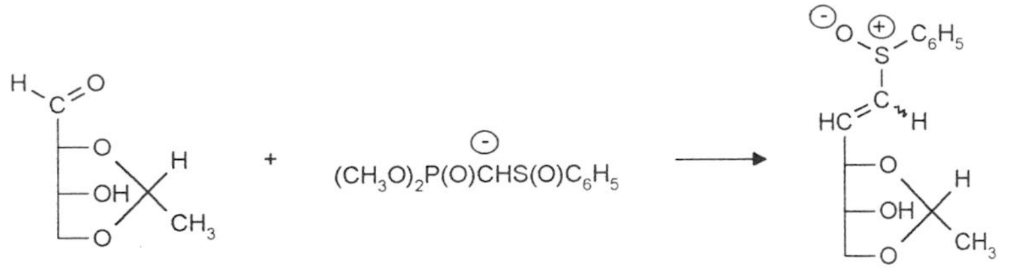

137.1   137.2   137.3

FIGURE 1.137

REFERENCES TO SECTION 1.2.6

1. *Houben-Weyl, Methoden der Organischen Chemie,* Vol. 5/1b, p. 383, 1972; Vol. 5/1c, p. 575, 1970;Vol E/1 pp 616, 710, 1982.
2. S. Trippett, *Q. Rev., Chem. Soc.* **17,** 406 (1963); A. Maercker, *Org. React. (N.Y.)* **14,** 270 (1965); A. W. Johnson, *Ylide Chemistry.* Academic Press, New York, 1966; M. Schlosser, *Top. Stereochem.* **5,** 1 (1970); J. Reucroft and P. G. Sammes, *Q. Rev., Chem. Soc.* **25,** 135 (1971); J. Boutagy and R. Thomas, *Chem. Rev.* **74,** 87 (1974); H. Pommer, *Angew. Chem.* **89,** 437 (1977); *Angew. Chem., Int. Ed. Engl.* **16,** 423 (1977); W. S. Wadsworth, Jr., *Org. React. (N.Y.)* **25,** 73 (1977); J. I. G. Cadogan, *Organophosphorous Reagents in Organic Synthesis.* Academic Press, New York, 1979; H. J. Bestmann, *Pure Appl. Chem.,* **51,** 515 (1979); **52,** 771 (1980); H. Pommer and P. C. Thieme, *Top. Curr. Chem.* **109,** 165 (1983); H. J. Bestmann and O. Vostrowsky, *ibid.* p. 85; W. E. Mc Even, B. D. Beaver, and J. V. Cooney, *Phosphorus and Sulfur* **25,** 255 (1985); B. E. Maryanoff and A. B. Reitz, *Chem. Rev.* **89,** 863 (1989).
3. Yu. A. Zhdanov, Yu. E. Alexeev, and V. G. Alexeeva, *Adv. Carbohydr. Chem. Biochem.* **27,** 227 (1972).
4. S. Hanessian and A. G. Pernet, *Adv. Carbohydr. Chem. Biochem.* **33,** 111 (1976); M. H. D. Postema, *Tetrahedron* **48,** 8545 (1992).
5. E. Vedejs and C. F. Marth, *J. Am. Chem. Soc.* **112,** 3905 (1990).
6. J. Jurczak, S. Pikul, and T. Bauer, *Tetrahedron* **42,** 447 (1986).
7. R. J. Crawford, S. B. Lutener, and R. D. Cockroft, *Can. J. Chem.* **54,** 3364 (1976).
8. A. P. Kozikowski and A. K. Gosh, *J. Am. Chem. Soc.* **104,** 5788 (1982).
9. M. Schlosser, G. Müller, and K. F. Christmann, *Angew. Chem.* **78,** 678 (1966); *Angew. Chem., Int. Ed. Engl.* **5,** 667 (1966).
10. R. K. Boeckman, Jr., J. J. Napier, E. W. Thomas, and R. I. Saito, *J. Org. Chem.* **48,** 4153 (1983).
11. J. C. Carratero and L. Goshez, *Tetrahedron Lett.* **29,** 2059 (1988).
12. F. Johnson, K. G. Paul, D. Favara, D. Ciabatti, and V. Guzzi, *J. Am. Chem. Soc.* **104,** 2190 (1982).
13. J. Mulzer and C. Brand, *Tetrahedron* **42,** 5961 (1986).
14. K. M. Sun and B. Fraser-Reid, *Synthesis,* p. 28 (1982).
15. K. Ohashi, Y. Yamagiwa, T. Kamikawa, and M. Kates, *Tetrahedron Lett.* **29,** 1185 (1988).
16. M. Kiso, A. Nakamura, Y. Tomita, and A. Hasegawa, *Carbohydr. Res.* **158,** 101 (1986).
17. S. Servi, *J. Org. Chem.* **50,** 5865 (1985).
18. K. Kamiyama, Y. Urano, S. Kobayashi, and M. Ohno, *Tetrahedron Lett.* **28,** 3123 (1987).

19. J.-R. Pougny, M. A. M. Nassr, and P. Sinay, *Chem. Commun.*, p. 375 (1981).
20. J.-M. Lancelin, J.-R. Pougny, and P. Sinay, *Carbohydr. Res.* **136**, 369 (1985).
21. P. S. Liu, *J. Org. Chem.* **52**, 5717 (1987).
22. F. Nicotra, L. Panza, F. Rochetti, G. Russo, and L. Thoma, *Carbohydr. Res.* **171**, 49 (1987).
23. F. Nicotra, R. Perego, F. Ronchetti, G. Russo, and L. Thoma, *Gazz. Chim. Ital.* **114**, 193 (1984).
24. F. Nicotra, R. Perego, F. Ronchetti, G. Russo, and L. Thoma, *Carbohydr. Res.* **131**, 180 (1984).
25. B. E. Maryanoff, S. O. Nortey, R. R. Inners, S. A. Campbell, A. B. Reitz, and D. Liotta, *Carbohydr. Res.* **171**, 259 (1987).
26. F. Freeman and K. D. Robarge, *Carbohydr. Res.* **171**, 1 (1987).
27. A. B. Reitz, S. O. Nortey, and B. E. Maryanoff, *Tetrahedron Lett.* **26**, 3915 (1985).
28. F. Nicotra, L. Panza, F. Rochetti, and L. Thoma, *Tetrahedron Lett.* **25**, 5937 (1984).
29. K. C. Nicolaou, R. A. Daines, J. Menishi, W. S. Li, D. P. Papahatjis, and T. K. Chakraborty, *J. Am. Chem. Soc.* **109**, 2205 (1987).
30. W. H. Pearson and J. V. Hines, *Tetrahedron Lett.* **32**, 5513 (1991).
31. W. V. Dahlhoff, *Justus Liebigs Ann. Chem.*, p. 109 1992).
32. A. Giannis, P. Münster, K. Sandhoff, and W. Steglich, *Tetrahedron* **44**, 7177 (1988).
33. A. Giannis and T. Henk, *Justus Liebigs Ann. Chem.*, p. 789 (1991)
34. R. G. Anderson and B. Fraser-Reid, *J. Org. Chem.* **50**, 478 (1985).
35. T. V. RajanBabu, T. Fujunaga, and G. S. Reddy, *J. Am. Chem. Soc.* **111**, 1759 (1989); T. Oshitari and S. Kobayashi, *Tetrahedron Lett.* **36**, 1089 (1995).
36. W. H. Pearson and K.-C. Lin, *Tetrahedron Lett.* **31**, 7571 (1990).
37. K. Burgess and I. Henderson, *Tetrahedron Lett.* **31**, 6949 (1990).
38. W. R. Baker and S. L. Condon, *Tetrahedron Lett.* **33**, 1581 (1992).
39. H. Kotsuki, A. Miyazaki, and M. Ochi, *Tetrahedron Lett.* **32**, 4503 (1991).
40. V. Kumar and S. Dav, *Tetrahedron* **43**, 5933 (1987).
41. M. F. Chen and C.-N. Hsiao, *Tetrahedron Lett.* **33**, 3567 (1992).
42. S.-K. Kang, Y.-S. Kim, J.-S. Lim, K.-S. Kim, and S.-G. Kim, *Tetrahedron Lett.* **32**, 363 (1991).
43. S.-K. Kang, D.-H. Lee, and J.-M. Lee, *Synlett*, p. 591 (1990).
44. N. Baggett, J. M. Webber, and N. R. Whitehouse, *Carbohydr. Res.* **22**, 227 (1972).
45. D. G. Lance and W. A. Szarek, *Carbohydr. Res.* **10**, 306 (1969).
46. A. Kjaer, D. Kjaer, and T. Skrydstrup, *Tetrahedron* **42**, 1439 (1986).
47. R. C. Anderson and B. Fraser-Reid, *J. Org. Chem.* **50**, 4786 (1985).
48. G. V. M. Sharma and S. R. Vepachedu, *Tetrahedron* **47**, 519 (1991).
49. S.-K. Kang and H.-S. Cho, *Tetrahedron Lett.* **32**, 367 (1991).
50. R. C. Anderson and B. Fraser-Reid, *J. Org. Chem.* **50**, 4781 (1985).
51. K. Koike, M. Numata, M. Sugimoto, Y. Nakahara, and T. Ogawa, *Carbohydr. Res.* **158**, 113 (1986).
52. G. V. M. Sharma and S. R. Vepachedu, *Tetrahedron Lett.* **31**, 4931 (1990).
53. J. M. J. Tronchet, E. Doelker, and B. Baehler, *Helv. Chim. Acta* **52**, 308 (1969); P. Alleri, F. Cajone, P. Ciuffreda, and M. Anastasia, *Tetrahedron Lett.* **36**, 1347 (1995).
54. M. Nakano, S. Atsuuka, Y. Koike, S. Tanaka, H. Funabashi, J. Hashimoto, and H. Morishima, *Tetrahedron Lett.* **31**, 1569 (1990).
55. H. Sugimura and K. Osumi, *Tetrahedron Lett.* **30**, 1571 (1989).
56. R. Gigg and C. D. Warren, *J. Chem. Soc. C,* p. 1879 (1966); M. Morita, M. Motoki, K. Akimota, T. Natori, T. Sakai, E. Sawa, K. Yamaji, Y. Koezuka, E. Kobayashi, and H. Fukushima, *J. Med. Chem.* **18**, 2176 (1995).
57. J. Gigg and R. Gigg, *J. Chem. Soc. C,* p. 1876 (1966).
58. Y. Leblanc, B. J. Fitzsimmons, J. Adams, F. Perez, and J. Rokach, *J. Org. Chem.* **51**, 789 (1986).

59. E. J. Reist and P. H. Christie, *J. Org. Chem.* **35**, 3521 (1970).
60. E. J. Reist and P. H. Christie, *J. Org. Chem.* **35**, 4127 (1970).
61. P. Rollin and J.-R. Pougny, *Tetrahedron* **42**, 3479 (1986).
62. G. Quinkert, E. Fernholz, P. Eckes, D. Neumann, and G. Dürner, *Helv. Chim. Acta* **72**, 1753 (1989).
63. Yu. A. Zhdanov and V. G. Alexeeva, *Zh. Obshch. Khim.* **37**, 1408 (1967).
64. Yu. A. Zhdanov and V. G. Alexeeva, *Zh. Obshch. Khim.* **39**, 405 (1969).
65. Yu. A. Zhdanov, Yu. E. Alexeev, V. G. Alexeeva, E. L. Korol, V. A. Tyumenev, I. I. Popov, and V. A. Polenov, *Dokl. Akad. Nauk SSSR* **244**, 1122 (1979); *Chem. Abstr.* **90**, 204382u (1979).
66. Yu. A. Zhdanov and V. G. Alexeeva, *Zh. Obshch. Khim.* **38**, 1951 (1968).
67. Yu. A. Zhdanov, G. N. Dorofeenko, and L. A. Uzlova, *Zh. Obshch. Khim.* **35**, 181 (1964).
68. Yu. A. Zhdanov, L. A. Uzlova, and G. N. Dorofeenko, *Zh. Vses. Khim. Obva.* **10**, 600 (1965); *Chem. Abstr.* **64**, 3671d (1965).
69. L. Stamatatos, P. Sinay, and J.-R. Pougny, *Tetrahedron* **40**, 1713 (1984).
70. H. Lay, J. Lehmann, L. Ziser, and W. Reutter, *Carbohydr. Res.* **195**, 145 (1989).
71. H. H. Lee, P. G. Hodgson, R. J. Bernacki, W. Korytnyk, and M. Sharma, *Carbohydr. Res.* **176**, 59 (1988).
72. S. Lesage and A. S. Perlin, *Can. J. Chem.* **56**, 3117 (1978).
73. A. G. Tolstikov, O. F. Prokopenko, L. M. Halilov, L. V. Spirikhin, A. A. Panasenko, V. N. Odinokov, and G. A. Tolstikov, *Zh. Org. Khim.* **27**, 798 (1991).
74. S. J. Danishefsky, M. P. De Ninno, G. B. Philips, R. E. Zelle, and P. A. Lartey, *Tetrahedron* **42**, 2809 (1986).
75. J. S. Yadav and M. C. Chander, *Tetrahedron Lett.* **31**, 4349 (1990).
76. R. W. Lowe, W. A. Szarek, and J. K. N. Jones, *Carbohydr. Res.* **28**, 281 (1973).
77. K. Tatsuta, Y. Niwata, K. Umezawa, K. Toshima, and M. Nakata, *Tetrahedron Lett.* **31**, 1171 (1990); *J. Antibiot.* **44**, 456 (1991); *Carbohydr. Res.* **222**, 189 (1991).
78. G. V. M. Sharma and S. M. Rao, *Tetrahedron Lett.* **33**, 2365 (1992).
79. A. G. Tolstikov, N. V. Hahlina, L. V. Spirikhin, L. M. Halilov, A. A. Panasenko, V. N. Odinokov, and G. A. Tolstikov, *Zh. Org. Khim.* **27**, 792 (1991).
80. H. Hashimoto, H. Ohrui, and H. Meguro, *J. Org. Chem.* **57**, 5042 (1992).
81. J. Tadanier, C.-M. Lee, D. Whittern, and N. Wickburg, *Carbohydr. Res.* **201**, 185 (1990).
82. H. Nagano and H. Yasai, *Chem. Lett.*, p. 1045 (1992).
83. N. Chida, J. Tobe, and S. Ogawa, *Tetrahedron Lett.* **32**, 1063 (1991).
84. A. G. M. Barrett, B. C. B. Bezuidenhout, A. F. Gasiecki, A. R. Howell, and M. A. Russell, *J. Am. Chem. Soc.* **111**, 1392 (1989).
85. A. Haudrechy and P. Sinay, *Tetrahedron Lett.* **31**, 5765 (1990).
86. J. A. Secrist, III, K. D. Barnes, and S.-R. Wu, *ACS Symp. Ser.* **386**, 93 (1989); J. A. Secrist, III and S.-R. Wu, *J. Org. Chem.* **42**, 4084 (1977).
87. J. A. Secrist, III and S.-R. Wu, *J. Org. Chem.* **44**, 1434 (1979).
88. K. Lorenz and F. W. Lichtenthaler, *Tetrahedron Lett.* **28**, 6437 (1987).
89. S. Valverde, A. Hernandez, B, Herradon, R. M. Rabanal, and M. Martin-Lomas, *Tetrahedron* **43**, 3499 (1987).
90. S. Valverde, B. Herradon, R. M. Rabanal, and M. Martin-Lomas, *Can. J. Chem.* **65**, 332 (1987).
91. S. A. Babirad, Y. Wang, and Y. Kishi, *J. Org. Chem.* **52**, 1370 (1987); Y. Wang, S. A. Babirad, and Y. Kishi, *ibid.* **57**, 468 (1992).
92. J. A. Secrist, III and K. D. Barnes, *J. Org. Chem.* **45**, 4526 (1980).
93. S. Jarosz, *Carbohydr. Res.* **224**, 73 (1992).
94. R. W. Armstrong and B. R. Teegarden, *J. Org. Chem.* **57**, 915 (1992).
95. M. F. Shostakovskii, N. N. Aseeva, and A. I. Polyakov, *Izv. Akad. Nauk SSSR*, p. 892 (1970).

96. J. R. Hanske and H. Rapoport, *J. Org. Chem.* **44**, 2472 (1979).
97. J. M. J. Tronchet, N. Le-Hong, and F. Perret, *Helv. Chim. Acta* **53**, 154 (1970).
98. J. M. J. Tronchet, B, Baehler, H. Eder, N. Le-Hong, F. Perret, J. Poncet, and J.-B. Zumwald, *Helv. Chim. Acta* **56**, 1310 (1973).
99. Y. Hamada, A. Kawai, and T. Shiohiri, *Chem. Pharm. Bull.* **33**, 5601 (1985).
100. J. M. J. Tronchet and B. Baehler, *Helv. Chim. Acta* **55**, 2112 (1972).
101. B. H. Dimitriev, N. N. Asaeva, and N. K. Kochetkov, *Izv. Akad. Nauk SSSR, Ser. Khim.* p. 1342 (1968).
102. K. M. Sun and B. Fraser-Reid, *Can. J. Chem.* **58**, 2732 (1980).
103. J. M. J. Tronchet, S. Jaccard-Thorndahl, and B. Baehler, *Helv. Chim. Acta* **52**, 308 (1969).
104. Yu. A. Zhdanov and V. G. Alexeeva, *Zh. Obshch. Khim.* **38**, 2594 (1968).
105. Yu. A. Zhdanov and V. G. Alexeeva, *Carbohydr. Res.* **10**, 184 (1969).
106. H. J. Bestmann and J. Angerer, *Tetrahedron Lett.* **9**, 3665 (1969).
107. H. J. Bestmann and J. Angerer, Farbwerke Hoechst AG, Ger. Pat. 1,929,215 (1970); *Chem. Abstr.* **75**, 20902x (1971).
108. R. L. Tolman and L. H. Peterson, *Carbohydr. Res.* **189**, 113 (1989).
109. T. V. RajanBabu, T. Fukunaga, and G. S. Reddy, *J. Am. Chem. Soc.* **111**, 1759 (1989).
110. T. J. Lee, *Tetrahedron Lett.* **26**, 4994 (1985).
111. K. Eklind, P. J. Garegg, B. Lindberg, and A. Pilotti, *Acta Chem. Scand. Ser. B*, **B28**, 260 (1974); B. M. Trost and T. A Grese, *J. Org. Chem.* **56**, 3189 (1991); J. Ramza and A. Zamojski, *Carbohydr. Res.* **228**, 205 (1992); Z. Pakulski and A. Zamojski, *Pol. J. Chem.* **68**, 1109 (1994).
112. J. W. Krajewski, P. Gluzinski, S. Jarosz, A. Zamojski, J. Bleidelis, A. Mishnyov, and A. Kemme, *Carbohydr. Res.* **144**, 183 (1985).
113. J. Marco-Contelles, C. Pozuelo, M. L. Jimeno, L. Martinez, and A. Martinez-Grau, *J. Org. Chem.* **57**, 2625 (1992).
114. M. R. Ord, C. M. Piggin, and V. Thaller, *J. Chem. Soc., Perkin Trans. 1*, p. 687 (1975).
115. J. M. J. Tronchet, A. P. Bonenfant, F. Perret, A. Gonzalez, J.-B. Zumwald, E. M. Martinez, and B. Baehler, *Helv. Chim Acta* **63**, 1181 (1980).
116. J. M. J. Tronchet, A. Bonenfant, and F. Barbalat-Rey, *Carbohydr. Res.* **67**, 564 (1978).
117. J. M. J. Tronchet and A.-P. Bonenfant, *Helv. Chim. Acta* **63**, 1644 (1980).
118. J. M. J. Tronchet, A. Gonzalez, J.-B. Zumwald, and F. Perret, *Helv. Chim. Acta* **57**, 1505 (1974).
119. J. M. J. Tronchet, B. Baehler, H. Eder, N. Le-Hong, F. Perret, J. Poncet, and J.-B. Zumwald, *Helv. Chim. Acta* **56**, 1310 (1973).
120. K. Kakinuma, *Tetrahedron Lett.* **18**, 4431 (1977).
121. J. Rochigneux, M.-L. Fontanel, J.-C. Malauda, and A. Dutheau, *Tetrahedron Lett.* **32**, 2617 (1991).
121a. M. Mella, L. Panza, F. Ronchetti, and L. Toma, *Tetrahedron* **44**, 1673 (1988).
122. J. Kuszmann and B. Podányi, *Carbohydr. Res.* **225**, 247 (1992).
123. J. Kuszmann, B. Podányi, and Gy. Jerkovich, *Carbohydr. Res.* **232**, 17 (1992).
124. T. Henk, A. Giannis, and K. Sandhoff, *Justus Liebigs Ann. Chem.*, p. 167 (1992).
125. J. M. J. Tronchet, M.-T. Campanini, J. Denoyelle, and J.-B. Zumwald, *Helv. Chim. Acta* **56**, 2567 (1973).
126. Yu. A. Zhdanov, V. A. Polenov, E. L. Korol, I. I. Popov, and V. G. Alekseeva, *Dokl. Akad. Nauk SSSR* **262**, 887 (1982).
127. T. L. Gupps, D. S. Wise, Jr., and L. B. Townsend, *J. Org. Chem.* **51**, 1058 (1986).
128. N. Katagiri, K. Takashima, and T. Kato, *J. Chem. Soc., Perkin Trans. 1*, p. 201 (1983); F. J. López Herrera, M. S. Pino González, and R. P. Aguas, *ibid.*, p. 2401 (1989); A. Dondoni and D. Perrone, *J. Org. Chem.* **60**, 4749 (1995), and references cited therein.
129. Y.-L. Yang and J. R. Falck, *Tetrahedron Lett.* **23**, 4305 (1982).
130. G. Beck, K. Kesseler, E. Baader, W. Bartmann, A. Bermann, E. Granzer, H. Jendralla, B. von Kerékjártó, R. Krause, E. Paulus, W. Schubert, and G. Weiss, *J. Med. Chem.* **33**, 52 (1990).

131. Yu. A. Zhdanov and V. G. Alexeeva, *Zh. Obshch. Khim.* **39**, 112 (1969); A. Lubineau, J. Augé, and N. Lubin, *J. Chem. Soc., Perkin Trans 1*, p. 3011 (1990).
132. M. Zsély, Ph.D. Thesis, University of Debrecen, 1989.
133. S. Y. Ko, A. W. M. Lee, S. Masamune, L. A. Reed, III, K. B. Sharplesss, and F. J. Walker, *Tetrahedron* **46**, 245 (1990).
134. J. R. Pougny and P. Rollin, *Tetrahedron Lett.* **28**, 2977 (1987).
135. P. Herczegh, M. Zsély, L. Szilágyi, Gy. Batta, I. Bajza, and R. Bognár, *Tetrahedron* **45**, 2793 (1989).
136. P. Herczegh, M. Zsély, L. Szilágyi, Z. Dinya, and R. Bognár, *Tetrahedron*, **45**, 5995 (1989); P. Herczegh, M. Zsély, L. Szilágyi, I. Bajza, Á. Kovács, Gy. Batta, and R. Bognár, *ACS Symp. Ser.* **112**, 494 (1992).
137. M. Saniere, Y. Le Merrer, B. Barbe, T. Koscielnak, and J. J. C. Depezay, *Tetrahedron* **45**, 7317 (1989).
138. Ya. A. Zhdanov, L. A. Uzlova, and G. N. Dorofeenko, *Carbohydr. Res.* **3**, 69 (1966).
139. E. Diekmann, K. Friedrich, and J. Lehmann, *Justus Liebigs Ann. Chem.*, p. 1247 (1989).
140. D. Horton, A. Liav, and S. E. Walker, *Carbohydr. Res.* **28**, 201 (1973); T. Katsuki, A. W. M. Lee, P. Ma, V. S. Martin, S. Masamune, K. B. Sharpless, D. Tuddenham, and F. J. Walker, *J. Org. Chem.* **47**, 1378 (1982).
141. J. C. Stowell and D. R. Keith, *Synthesis*, p. 132 (1979).
142. N. Cohen, B. L. Banner, R. J. Lopresti, F. Wong, M. Rosenberger, Y.-Y. Liu, E. Thom, and A. A. Liebman, *J. Am. Chem. Soc.* **105**, 3661 (1983).
143. J. M. J. Tronchet and B. Gentile, *Helv. Chim. Acta* **62**, 2091 (1979).
144. J. M. J. Tronchet, B. Gentile, and T. Nguyen-Xuan, *Helv. Chim. Acta* **62**, 110 (1979).
145. Yu. A. Zhdanov and V. A. Polenov, *Carbohydr. Res.* **16**, 466 (1971).
146. S. Jarosz, D. Mootoo, and B. Fraser-Reid, *Carbohydr. Res.* **147**, 59 (1986).
147. S. Jarosz, *Tetrahedron Lett.* **29**, 1193 (1988).
148. Yu. A. Zhdanov, G. N. Dorofeenko, G. A. Korolchenko, and A. E. Osolin, *Zh. Obshch. Khim.* **36**, 492 (1966).
149. T. Katsuki, A. W. M. Lee, P. Ma, V. S. Martin, S. Masamune, K. B. Sharpless, D. Tuddenham, and E. Walker, *J. Org. Chem.* **47**, 1373 (1982).
150. S. David, J. Eustache, and A. Lubineau, *J. Chem. Soc., Perkin Trans. 1*, p. 2274 (1974).
151. J. Leonard and G. Ryan, *Tetrahedron Lett.* **28**, 2525 (1987).
152. I. I. Cubero, M. D. P. Olea, and D. G. Poza, *Carbohydr. Res.* **138**, 135 (1985).
153. I. I. Cubero and M. T. P. López-Espinosa, *Carbohydr. Res.* **173**, 41 (1988).
154. M. Carcano, F. Nicotra, L. Panza, and G. Russo, *Chem. Commun.*, p. 642 (1989).
155. I. Savage and E. J. Thomas, *Chem. Commun.*, p. 717 (1989).
156. J. M. J. Tronchet, C. Cottet, B. Gentile, E. Mihály, and J.-B. Zumwald, *Helv. Chim. Acta* **56**, 1802 (1973).
157. J. M. J. Tronchet, O. R. Martin, and J. B. Zumwald, *Helv. Chim. Acta* **62**, 1303 (1979).
158. B. Schönenberger, W. Summermatter, and C. Ganter, *Helv. Chim. Acta* **65**, 2333 (1982).
159. Yu. A. Zhdanov and V. G. Alexeeva, *Zh. Obshch. Khim.* **39**, 112 (1969).
160. G. W. J. Fleet and L. C. Seymour, *Tetrahedron Lett.* **28**, 3015 (1987).
161. Yu. A. Zhdanov, Yu. E. Alexeev, and G. N. Dorofeenko, *Zh. Obshch. Khim.* **36**, 1742 (1966).
162. Yu. A. Zhdanov, Yu. E. Alexeev, and G. N. Dorofeenko, *Zh. Obshch. Khim.* **37**, 98 (1967).
163. Yu. A. Zhdanov, Yu. E. Alexeev, and G. N. Dorofeenko, *Zh. Obshch. Khim.* **37**, 2635 (1967).
164. Yu. A. Zhdanov, Yu. E. Alexeev, and G. N. Dorofeenko, *Zh. Obshch. Khim.* **38**, 231 (1968).
165. K. S. Kim and W. A. Szarek, *Carbohydr. Res.* **100**, 169 (1982).
166. D. B. Repke, H. P. Albrecht, and J. G. Moffatt, *J. Org. Chem.* **40**, 2481 (1975).
167. S. Pikul, J. Raczko, K. Ankner, and J. Jurczak, *J. Am. Chem. Soc.* **109**, 3981 (1987).

168. K. M. Sun, R. D. Dawe, and B. Fraser-Reid, *Carbohydr. Res.* **171,** 35 (1987).
169. M. C. Clingerman and J. A. Secrist, III, *J. Org. Chem.* **48,** 3141 (1983).
170. N. Katagiri, K. Takashima, T. Haneda, and T. Kato, *J. Chem. Soc., Perkin Trans. 1,* p. 553 (1984).
171. D. Horton and J.-H. Tsai, *Carbohydr. Res.* **75,** 151 (1979).
172. J. S. Brimacombe and A. K. M. S. Kabir, *Carbohydr. Res.* **150,** 35 (1986).
173. V. A. Polenov and Yu. A. Zhdanov, *Zh. Obshch. Khim.* **37,** 2455 (1967).
174. Yu. A. Zhdanov and V. A. Polenov, *Zh. Obsch. Khim.* **39,** 119 (1969).
175. Yu. A. Zhdanov, L. N. Uslova, G. N. Dorofeenko, and G. I. Kravchenko, *Zh. Obshch. Khim.* **36,** 1025 (1965).
176. E. Martinez, J. Usoz, and M. Perez de Eulate, *Carbohydr. Res.* **85,** 307 (1980).
177. J. M. J. Tronchet and M. A. M. Massoud, *Helv. Chim Acta* **62,** 1632 (1979).
178. K. Olejniczak and R. W. Frank, *J. Org. Chem.* **47,** 380 (1982).
179. J. S. Brimacombe, R. Hanna, A. K. M. S. Kabir, F. S. Bennett, and I. D. Taylor, *J. Chem. Soc., Perkin Trans. 1,* p. 815 (1986).
180. S. Jarosz, J. Glodek, and A. Zamojski, *Carbohydr. Res.* **163,** 289 (1987).
181. R. M. Rabanal, J. Escudero, M. Martin-Lomas, S. Valverde, A. Perales, and J. Fayos, *Carbohydr. Res.* **141,** 49 (1985).
182. B. F. Molino, L. Magdzinski, and B. Fraser-Reid, *Tetrahedron Lett.* **24,** 5819 (1983).
183. B. F. Molino and B. Fraser-Reid, *Can. J. Chem.* **65,** 2834 (1987).
184. J. C. Barnes, J. S. Brimacombe, A. K. M. S. Kabir, and T. J. R. Weakly, *J. Chem. Soc., Perkin Trans. 1,* p. 3391 (1988).
185. D. Horton and A. Liav, *Carbohydr. Res.* **24,** 105 (1972).
186. R. E. Ireland and R. D. Wardle, *J. Org. Chem.* **52,** 1780 (1987).
187. B. P. Bashyal, G. W. J. Fleet, M. J. Gough, and P. W. Smith, *Tetrahedron* **43,** 3083 (1987).
188. M. V. Rao and M. Nagarayan, *J. Org. Chem.* **53,** 1432 (1988).
189. A. P. Kozikowski, R. J. Schmiesing, and K. L. Sorgi, *J. Am. Chem. Soc.* **102,** 6578 (1980).
190. B. Fraser-Reid, B. F. Molino, L. Magdzinski, and D. R. Mootoo, *J. Org. Chem.* **52,** 4505 (1987).
191. J. S. Brimacombe and A. K. M. S. Kabir, *Carbohydr. Res.* **158,** 81 (1986).
192. J. S. Brimacombe, R. Hanna, and A. K. M. S. Kabir, *J. Chem. Soc., Perkin Trans. 1,* p. 823 (1986).
193. A. Dondoni, *Modern Synthetic Methods* (R. Scheffold, ed.), pp. 377–438 Verlag Helvetica Chimica Acta, Basel, 1992.
194. A. Dondoni, A. Marra, and P. Merino, *J. Am. Chem. Soc.* **116,** 3324 (1994); A. Dondoni, P. Merino, and J. Orduna, *Tetrahedron Lett.* **32,** 3247 (1991).
195. A. Dondoni and A. Marra, *Carbohydr. Lett.* **1,** 43 (1994).
196. A. Dondoni, G. Fantin, M. Fogagnolo, and P. Merino, *J. Carbohydr. Chem.* **9,** 735 (1990).
197. A. Dondoni, G. Fantin, M. Fogagnolo, and P. Merino, *Tetrahedron* **46,** 6167 (1990).
198. A. Dondoni and P. Merino, *Synthesis,* p. 196 (1992).
199. D. Horton and D. Koh, *Carbohydr. Res.* **250,** 231 (1993).
200. N. K. Kochetkov and B. A. Dmitriev, *Chem. Ind. (London),* p. 2147 (1962).
201. Yu. A. Zhdanov, G. N. Dorofeenko, and L. Uslova, *Zh. Obshch. Khim.* **33,** 3444 (1963).
202. N. K. Kochetkov and B. A. Dmitriev, *Chem. Ind. (London),* p. 864 (1983).
203. N. K. Kochetkov and B. A. Dmitriev, *Izv. Akad. Nauk SSSR, Ser. Khim.,* p. 669 (1964).
204. Yu. A. Zhdanov, G. N. Dorofeenko, and L. A. Uslova, *Zh. Obshch. Khim.* **35,** 181 (1965).
205. N. K. Kochetkov and B. A. Dmitriev, *Izv. Akad. Nauk SSSR, Ser. Khim.,* p. 274 (1966).
206. B. A. Dmitriev, N. E. Bairamova, and N. K. Kochetkov, *Izv. Akad. Nauk SSSR, Ser. Khim.,* p. 2691 (1967).
207. N. K. Kochetkov and B. A. Dmitriev, *Tetrahedron* **21,** 803 (1969).
208. D. Miljkovic, M. Popsavin, V. Popsavin, N. Vukojevic, and J. Harangi, *J. Serb. Chem. Soc.* **55,** 307 (1990); *Chem. Abstr.* **114,** 62588d (1991).

209. J. W. Lyga, *Org. Prep. Proced. Int.* **24,** 73 (1992).

210. A. Mbongo, C. Fréchou, D. Beaupére, R. Uzan, and G. Demailly, *Carbohydr. Res.* **246,** 361 (1993).

211. C. Liévre, C. Fréchou, and G. Demailly, *Tetrahedron Lett.* **36,** 6467 (1995).

212. N. K. Kochetkov, and B. A. Dmitriev, *Dokl. Akad. Nauk SSSR* **151,** 106 (1963).

213. F. G. M. Vogel, J. Paust, and A. Nürrenbach, *Justus Liebigs Ann. Chem.,* p. 1972 (1980).

214. S. Valverde, M. Martin-Lomas, B. Herradon, and S. García-Ochoa, *Tetrahedron* **43,** 1895 (1987).

215. T. H. Webb, L. M. Thomasco, S. T. Schlachter, J. J. Gaudino, and C. S. Wilcox, *Tetrahedron Lett.* **29,** 6823 (1988).

216. M. J. Wanner, G. J. Kromen, and U. K. Pandit, *Heterocycles* **22,** 1483 (1984).

217. M. Matsunaga, T. Sakamaki, H. Nagaoka, and Y. Yamada, *Tetrahedron Lett.* **24,** 3009 (1983).

218. S. Valverde, B. Hernadon, and M. Martin-Lomas, *Tetrahedron Lett.* **26,** 3731 (1985); J. Leonard, S. Mohialdin, and P. A. Swain, *Synth. Commun.* **19,** 3529 (1989).

219. R. Kuhn and R. Brossmer, *Angew. Chem.* **74,** 252 (1962); *Angew. Chem., Int. Ed. Engl.* **2,** 252 (1962).

220. C. K. Chu, J. W. Beach, G. V. Ullas, and Y. Kosugi, *Tetrahedron Lett.* **29,** 5349 (1988).

221. G. V. Ullas, C. K. Chu, M. K. Alin, and Y. Kosugi, *J. Org. Chem.* **53,** 2413 (1988).

222. C. Hubschwerlen, *Synthesis,* p. 962 (1986).

223. T. Ibuka, M. Tanaka, S. Mishii, and Y. Yamamoto, *J. Am. Chem. Soc.* **111,** 4864 (1989).

224. J. G. Buchanan, A. R. Edgar, and B. D. Hewitt, *J. Chem. Soc., Perkin Trans. 1,* p. 2371 (1987).

225. R. B. Bennett, III, J.-R. Choi, W. D. Montgomery, and J. K. Cha, *J. Am. Chem. Soc.* **111,** 2580 (1989).

226. T. Hudlicky, H. Luna, J. D. Price, and F. Rulin, *J. Org. Chem.* **55,** 4683 (1990).

227. Y. G. Kim and J. K. Cha, *Tetrahedron Lett.* **30,** 5721 (1989).

228. H. Iida, N. Yamazaki, and C. Kobayashi, *J. Org. Chem.* **52,** 3337 (1987).

229. M. V. Férnandez, F. J. López-Herrera, T. L. Cobos, and G. P. Escribano, *Carbohydr. Res.* **118,** 286 (1983).

230. S. R. Baker, D. W. Clissold, and A. McKillop, *Tetrahedron Lett.* **29,** 991 (1988).

231. A. Krief, W. Dumont, and P. Pasau, *Tetrahedron Lett.* **29,** 1079 (1988).

232. B. A. Dmitriev, A. Ya. Cherniak, and K. Kochetkov, *Zh. Obshch. Khim.* **41,** 2754 (1971).

233. J. S. Brimacombe and A. K. M. S. Kabir, *Carbohydr. Res.* **150,** 35 (1986).

234. R. C. Prakash and S. P. Rao, *Tetrahedron Lett.* **32,** 7473 (1991).

235. Y. Kawahata, S. Takatsuka, N. Ikekawa, M. Murata, and S. Omura, *Chem. Pharm. Bull.* **4,** 3102 (1986).

236. D. Tulshian, R. J. Doll, M. F. Stansberry, and A. T. McPhail, *J. Org. Chem.* **56,** 6819 (1991).

237. J. M. J. Tronchet, O. Martin, J.-B. Zumwald, N. Le-Hong, and F. Perret, *Helv. Chim. Acta* **8,** 1735 (1975).

238. J. M. J. Tronchet and O. R. Martin, *Carbohydr. Res.* **85,** 187 (1980).

239. Yu.A Zhdanov, Yu. E. Alexeev, and G. N. Dorofeenko, *Zh. Obshch Khim.* **36,** 1742 (1966).

240. J.-P. Gesson, J.-C. Jacquesy, and M. Mondon, *Tetrahedron* **45,** 2627 (1989).

241. G. M. Barrett, H. B. Broughton, S. K. Attwood, and A. A. L. Gunatilaka, *J. Org. Chem.* **51,** 495 (1986).

242. R. E. Harmon, G. Wellman, and S. K. Gupta, *Carbohydr. Res.* **11,** 574 (1969).

243. H. Ohrui, G. H. Jones, J. G. Moffat, M. L. Maddox, A. T. Christensen, and S. K. Byram, *J. Am. Chem. Soc.* **97,** 4602 (1975).

244. F. J. López Herrera and M. S. Pino-González, *Carbohydr. Res.* **152,** 283 (1986).

245. G. Just, M. Ramjeesingh, and T. J. Lick, *Can. J. Chem.* **54,** 2940 (1976).

246. P. D. Kane and J. Mann, *J. Chem. Soc. Chem. Commun.,* p. 224 (1983).

247. J. Cousineau and J. A. Secrist, III, *J. Carbohydr. Nucleosides Nucleotides* **3**, 185 (1976).
248. M. C. Clingerman and J. A. Secrist, III, *J. Org. Chem.* **48**, 3141 (1983).
249. F. J. López Herrera, M. S. Pino González, M. N. Sampedro, and R. M. Dominguez Aciego, *Tetrahedron* **45**, 269 (1989).
250. M. S. Pino González, R. M. Dominguez Aciego, and F. J. López Herrera, *Tetrahedron* **44**, 3715 (1988).
251. N. Katagiri, T. Haneda, and N. Takahashi, *Heterocycles* **22**, 2195 (1984).
252. M. J. Wanner and G. J. Koomen, *Synthesis*, p. 325 (1988).
253. M. J. Wanner and G. J. Koomen, *Tetrahedron Lett.* **31**, 907 (1990).
254. D. H. R. Barton, J. Camara, X. Cheng, S. D. Géro, J. Cs. Jászberényi, and B. Quiclet-Sire, *Tetrahedron* **48**, 9261 (1992).
255. E. J. Corey, D. A. Clark, G. Goto, A. Marfat, C. Miosowski, B. Samuelsson, and S. Hammerström, *J. Am. Chem. Soc.* **102**, 1436 (1980).
256. S. B. Mandal and B. Achari, *Synth. Commun.* **23**, 1239 (1993).
257. N. Katagiri, T. Haneda, R. Niwa, and T. Kato, *Chem. Pharm. Bull.* **33**, 2691 (1985).
258. B. A. Dmitriev, N. E. Bairamova, A. A. Kost, and N. K. Kochetkov, *Izv. Akad. Nauk SSSR, Ser. Khim.*, p. 2491 (1967).
259. J. M. J. Tronchet and B. Gentile, *Helv. Chim. Acta* **62**, 977 (1979).
260. B. A. Dmitriev, N. E. Bairamova, L. W. Backinowsky, and N. K. Kochetkov, *Dokl. Akad. Nauk SSSR* **173**, 350 (1967); *Chem. Abstr.* **67**, 54381b (1967).
261. T. K. M. Shing, *Tetrahedron Lett.* **33**, 1307 (1992).
262. T. K. M. Shing, *Tetrahedron* **48**, 6777 (1992).
263. N. K. Kochetkov, B. A. Dmitriev, and L. V. Backinowsky, *Carbohydr. Res.* **11**, 193 (1969).
264. M. N. Mirzayanova, L. P. Davidova and G. I. Samokhvalov, *Dokl. Akad. Nauk SSSR* **173**, 367 (1967); *Chem. Abstr.* **67**, 54368c (1967).
265. R. Ramage, G. W. Rose, and A. M. MacLeod, *Tetrahedron Lett.* **29**, 4877 (1988).
266. D. Horton, T. Machinami, and Y. Takagi, *Carbohydr. Res.* **121**, 135 (1983).
267. A. B. Reitz, A. D. Jordan, Jr., and B. E. Marynoff, *J. Org. Chem.* **52**, 4800 (1987); A. J. Cooper and R. G. Salomon, *Tetrahedron Lett.* **31**, 3813 (1990).
268. J. C. van den Bos, W. J. Vloon, G. J. Koomen, and U. K. Pandit, *Tetrahedron* **47**, 6787 (1991).
269. H. Ohrui, H. Kuzuhara, and S. Emoto, *Agric. Biol. Chem.* **35**, 750 (1971).
270. E. J. Enholm and A. Trivellas, *J. Am. Chem. Soc.* **111**, 6463 (1989).
271. K. Ohta and O. Mitsunobu, *Tetrahedron Lett.* **32**, 517 (1991).
272. J. Rokach, C.-K. Lau, R. Zamboni, and Y. Guindon, *Tetrahedron Lett.* **22**, 2763 (1981).
273. Y. Guindon, R. Zamboni, C.-K. Lau, and J. Rokach, *Tetrahedron Lett.* **33**, 739 (1982).
274. B. J. Fitzsimmons and J. Rokach, *Tetrahedron Lett.* **35**, 3043 (1984).
275. Y. Leblanc, B. J. Fitzsimmons, R. Zamboni, and J. Rokach, *J. Org. Chem.* **53**, 265 (1988).
276. S. Kano, T. Yokomatsu, and S. Shibuya, *Heterocycles* **31**, 13 (1990).
277. D. P. Marriott and J. R. Bantick, *Tetrahedron Lett.* **22**, 3657 (1981).
278. P. M. Collins, W. G. Overend and T. S. Shing, *J. Chem. Soc., Chem. Commun.*, p. 297 (1982).
279. A. Claesson, *J. Org. Chem.* **52**, 4414 (1987); G. J. P. H. Boons, P. A. M. van der Klein, G. A. van der Marel, and J. H. van Boom, *Recl. Trav. Chim. Pays-Bas* **109**, 273 (1990).
280. F. Nicotra, F. Ronchetti, and G. Russo, *J. Org. Chem.* **47**, 5381 (1982).
281. Yu. A. Zhdanov and L. A. Uslova, *Zh. Obshch. Khim.* **41**, 1396 (1971).
282. A. A. Akhrem, E. I. Kvasiuk, I. A. Mikhailopulo, and P. I. Prikopa, *Zh. Obshch. Khim.* **47**, 1206 (1977).
283. F. J. López Herrera and C. Uraga Baelo, *Carbohydr. Res.* **139**, 95 (1985).
284. W. Frick, T. Krülle, and R. R. Schmidt, *Justus Liebigs Ann. Chem.*, p. 435 (1991); T. K. M. Shing, *Tetrahedron: Asymmetry* **5**, 2405 (1994); T. Krülle, O. Holst, and H. Brade, *Carbohydr. Res.* **247**, 145 (1993); T. Krülle, R. R. Schmidt, H. Brade, and O. Holst, *Carbohydr. Res.* **254**, 141 (1994).

285. F. Nicotra, F. Ronchetti, G. Russo, and L. Toma, *Tetrahedron Lett.* **25,** 5697 (1984).

286. F. Nicotra, F. Ronchetti, and G. Russo, *J. Org. Chem.* **47,** 4459 (1982).

287. J. Molina Molina, A. Sanz Tejedor, and J. A. López Sastre, *An. Qím., Ser. C* **80,** 111 (1984).

288. S. Valverde, S. Garcia-Ocha, and A. Martin-Lomas, *Carbohydr. Res.* **147,** C1 (1986).

289. H. M. Park, D. M. Piatak, J. R. Peterson, and A. M. Clark, *Can. J. Chem.* **70,** 1662 (1992).

290. K. M. Sun, R. D. Dawe, and B. Fraser-Reid, *Carbohydr. Res.* **171,** 35 (1987).

291. B. Fraser-Reid, R. D. Dawe, and D. B. Tulshian, *Can. J. Chem.* **57,** 1746 (1979).

292. R. D. Dawe and B. Fraser-Reid, *J. Org. Chem.* **49,** 522 (1984).

293. L. A. Reed, III, Y. Ito, S. Masamune, and K. B. Sharpless, *J. Am. Chem. Soc.* **104,** 6468 (1982).

294. D. Hendry, L. Hough, and A. C. Richardson, *Tetrahedron* **44,** 6143 (1988).

295. D. K. Thompson, C. N. Hubert, and R. H. Wightman, *Tetrahedron* **49,** 3827 (1993).

296. G. D. Vité, R. Alonso, and B. Fraser-Reid, *J. Org. Chem.* **54,** 2286 (1989).

297. R. A. Alonso, D. G. Vité, R. E. McDevitt, and B. Fraser-Reid, *J. Org. Chem.* **57,** 573 (1992).

298. J. M. J. Tronchet and M. A. M. Massoud, *Helv. Chim. Acta* **62,** 1632 (1979).

299. J. S. Brimacombe, R. Hanna, A. K. M. S. Kabir, F. Bennett, and I. D. Taylor, *J. Chem. Soc., Perkin Trans. 1,* p. 815 (1986).

300. J. M. J. Tronchet and M. A. M. Massoud, *Heterocycles* **24,** 1265 (1986).

301. R. W. Franck, C. S. Subramaniam, T. V. John, and J. F. Blount, *Tetrahedron Lett.* **25,** 2439 (1984).

302. G. E. Keck, E. P. Boden, and M. R. Riley, *J. Org. Chem.* **54,** 896 (1989).

303. K. H. Aamlid, L. Hough, and A. C. Richardson, *Carbohydr. Res.* **202,** 117 (1990).

304. S. Lumin, P. Yadagiri, and J. R. Falck, *Tetrahedron Lett.* **29,** 4237 (1988).

305. M. Bessodes, D. Komiotis, and K. Antonakis, *J. Chem. Soc., Perkin Trans. 1,* p. 41 (1989).

306. S. Hanessian, P. C. Zyler, D. Demailly, and Y. Chapleur, *J. Am. Chem. Soc.* **103,** 6243 (1981).

307. E. J. Corey and G. Goto, *Tetrahedron Lett.* **21,** 3463 (1980).

308. S. Valverde, M. Martin-Lomas, and B. Herradon, *J. Carbohydr. Chem.* **6,** 685 (1987).

309. G. Just, A. Martel, K. Grozinger, and M. Ramjeesingh, *Can. J. Chem.* **53,** 131 (1975).

310. T. Sato and R. Noyori, *Bull. Chem. Soc. Jpn.* **53,** 1195 (1980).

311. R. J. Ferrier and P. C. Tyler, *Carbohydr. Res.* **136,** 249 (1985).

312. A. Berger, K. Dax, G. Gradnig, V. Grassberger, and A. E. Stütz, *J. Carbohydr. Chem.* **11,** 217 (1992).

313. S. Valverde, S. Garcia-Ochoa, and A. M. Gomez, *Carbohydr. Res.* **225,** 155 (1992).

314. B. A. Dmitriev and N. K. Kochetkov, *Izv. Akad. Nauk SSSR, Ser. Khim.,* p. 2483 (1967).

315. F. Nicotra, G. Russo, F. Ronchetti, and L. Thoma, *Carbohydr. Res.* **124,** C5 (1983).

316. A. Giannis and K. Sandhoff, *Carbohydr. Res.* **171,** 201 (1987).

317. H. Vyplel, D. Scholz, I. Macher, K. Schindlmaier, and E. Schütze, *J. Med. Chem.* **34,** 2759 (1991).

318. K. Tadano, M. Morita, Y. Hotta, S. Ogawa, B. Winchester, and I. Cenci di Bello, *J. Org. Chem.* **53,** 5209 (1988).

319. K. Tadano, Y. Hotta, M. Morita, T. Suami, B. Winchester, and I. Cenci di Bello, *Bull. Chem. Soc. Jpn.* **60,** 3667 (1987).

320. E. M. Acton, K. Ryan, and T. H. Smith, *Carbohydr. Res.* **97,** 235 (1981).

321. M. A. R. C. Bulusu and P. Waldstätten, *Tetrahedron Lett.* **33,** 1859 (1992).

322. A. G. Tolstikov, N. V. Khakhalina, E. E. Savateeva, L. Spirikhin, L. M. Khalilov, V. N. Odinokov, and G. A. Tolstikov, *Bioorg. Khim.* **16,** 1670 (1990).

323. N. Yasuda, H. Tsutsumi and T. Tayaka, *Chem. Lett.,* p. 31 (1985).

324. J. Gigg, R. Gigg, and C. D. Warren, *J. Chem. Soc. C,* p. 1882 (1966).

325. D. Hendry, L. Hough, and A. C. Richardson, *Tetrahedron* **44,** 6153 (1988).

326. M. N. Mirzayanova, L. N. Davidova, and G. I. Samokhvalov, *Zh. Obshch. Khim.* **38,** 1954 (1986).

327. M. N. Mirzayanova, L. N. Davidova, and G. I. Samokhvalov, *Zh. Obshch. Khim.* **40,** 693 (1970).

328. P. S. Liu, R. S. Rogers, M. S. Kong, and P. S. Sunkara, *Tetrahedron Lett.* **32,** 5853 (1991).

329. O. Duclos, A. Duréault, and J. C. Dépezay, *Tetrahedron Lett.* **33,** 1059 (1992).

330. K. C. Nicolaou, D. G. McGarry, P. K. Somers, B. H. Kim, W. W. Ogilvie, G. Yiannikouros, C. V. C. Prasad, C. A. Veale, and R. R. Hark, *J. Am. Chem. Soc.* **112,** 6263 (1990).

331. C. R. Bertozzi, D. G. Cook, W. R. Kobertz, F. Gonzalez-Scarano, and M. D. Bednarski, *J. Am. Chem. Soc.* **114,** 10639 (1992).

332. T. K. M. Shing, Z.-H. Zhou, and T. C. W. Mak, *J. Chem. Soc., Perkin Trans. 1,* p. 1907 (1992).

333. K. R. C. Prakash and S. P. Rao, *Tetrahedron* **49,** 1505 (1993).

334. J.-M. Beau, P. Sinay, J. P. Kamerling, and J. F. G. Vliegenthart, *Carbohydr. Res.* **67,** 65 (1978).

335. O. R. Martin, F. E. Khamis, and S. P. Rao, *Tetrahedron Lett.* **30,** 6143 (1989).

336. J. C. Barnes, J. S. Brimacombe, and G. McDonald, *J. Chem. Soc., Perkin Trans. 1,* p. 1483 (1989).

337. J. S. Brimacombe and A. K. M. S. Kabir, *Carbohydr. Res.* **152,** 335 (1986).

338. T. L. Cupps, D. S. Wise, and L. B. Townsend, *Carbohydr. Res.* **115,** 59 (1983).

339. O. R. Martin and W. A. Szarek, *Carbohydr. Res.* **230,** 195 (1984).

340. A. G. Tolstikov, O. F. Prokopenko, L. M. Khalilov, V. N. Odinokov, and G. A. Tolstikov, *Zh. Org. Khim.* **27,** 788 (1991).

341. G. H. Jones, E. K. Hamamura, and J. G. Moffatt, *Tetrahedron Lett.* **9,** 5731 (1986); H. P. Albrecht, G. H. Jones, and J. G. Moffatt, *J. Am. Chem. Soc.* **92,** 5511 (1971).

342. H. Paulsen, W. Bartsch, and J. Thiem, *Chem. Ber.* **104,** 2545 (1971).

343. F. M. Unger, D. Stix, E. Möderndorfer, and F. Hammerschmid, *Carbohydr. Res.* **67,** 349 (1978).

344. R. W. McClard, *Tetrahedron Lett.* **24,** 2631 (1983).

345. B. E. Maryanoff, S. O. Nortey, R. R. Inners, S. A. Campbell, A. B. Reitz, and D. Liotta, *Carbohydr. Res.* **171,** 259 (1987).

346. W. S. Wadshworth, *Org. React. (N.Y.)* **25,** 73 (1977).

347. *Houben-Weyl, Methoden der Organischen Chemie,* Vol. 5/1b, pp. 395, 895,1972; Vol. 12/1, pp. 262, 523; Vol. E/2, p. 300, 1982; Vol E/11, pp. 779, 1235, 1983.

348. H. Pommer and P. C. Thieme, *Top. Curr. Chem.* **109,** 165 (1983).

349. N. Minami, S. S. Ko, and Y. Kishi, *J. Am. Chem. Soc.* **104,** 1109 (1982).

350. B. M. Trost, S. Mignani, and T. N. Nanniga, *J. Am. Chem. Soc.* **110,** 1602 (1988).

351. A. Bernardi, S. Cardani, C. Scolastico, and R. Villa, *Tetrahedron* **44,** 491 (1988).

352. P. P. Waanders, L. Thijs, and B. Zwanenburg, *Tetrahedron Lett.* **28,** 2409 (1987).

353. A. Krief, W. Dumont, and P. Pasau, *Tetrahedron Lett.* **29,** 1079 (1988).

354. N. Ikemoto and S. L. Schreiber, *J. Am. Chem. Soc.* **112,** 9657 (1990); S. Saito, Y. Morikawa, and T. Moriwake, *J. Org. Chem.* **55,** 5424 (1990).

355. H. Iida, N. Yamazaki, and C. Kibayashi, *J. Org. Chem.* **52,** 3337 (1987).

356. S. Ohira, S. Ishi, K. Shinohara, and H. Nozaki, *Tetrahedron Lett.* **31,** 1037 (1990).

357. R. Plantier-Royon, and D. Anker, *J. Carbohydr. Chem.* **10,** 239 (1991).

358. T. Katsuki, A. W. M. Lee, P. Ma, V. S. Martin, S. Masamune, K. B. Sharpless, D. Tuddenham, and F. J. Walker, *J. Org. Chem.* **47,** 1378 (1982).

359. S. F. Martin, D. W. Dean, and A. S. Wagman, *Tetrahedron Lett.* **33,** 1839 (1992).

360. H. Maehr, A. Perrotta, and J. Smallheer, *J. Org. Chem.* **53,** 832 (1988).

361. A. B. Reitz, A. D. Jordan, Jr., and B. E. Maryanoff, *J. Org. Chem.* **52,** 4800 (1987).

362. N. Katagiri, K. Takashima, T. Haneda, and T. Kato, *J. Chem. Soc., Perkin Trans. 1,* p. 553 (1984).

363. Yu. A. Zhdanov, L. A. Uslova and L. M. Maximushkina, *Zh. Obshch. Khim.* **53** 484 (1983).

364. I. W. Lawston and T. D. Inch, *J. Chem. Soc., Perkin Trans. 1,* p. 2629 (1983).
365. A. Lieberknecht, J. Schmidt, and J. J. Stezowski, *Tetrahedron Lett.* **32,** 2113 (1991).
366. U. Schmidt, A. Lieberknecht, U. Kazmaier, H. Griesser, G. Jung, and J. Metzger, *Synthesis,* p. 49 (1991).
367. A. Saroli and A. Doutheau, *Tetrahedron Lett.* **28,** 5501 (1987).
368. S. Knapp and P. J. Kukkola, *J. Org. Chem.* **55,** 1632 (1990).
369. J. W. Krajewski, P. Gluzinski, Z. Urbanczyk-Lipkowska, J. Ramza, and A. Zamojski, *Carbohydr. Res.* **200,** 1 (1990).
370. J. Ramza and A. Zamojski, *Carbohydr. Res.* **228,** 205 (1992).
371. G. Estenne, A. Saroli, and A. Doutheau, *J. Carbohydr. Chem.* **10,** 181 (1991).
372. P. Allevi, P. Ciuffreda, D. Colombo, G. Speranza, and P. Manitto, *J. Chem. Soc., Perkin Trans. 1,* p. 1281 (1989).
373. D. Monti, P. Grammatica, G. Speranza, and P. Manitto, *Tetrahedron Lett.* **28,** 5047 (1987).
374. D.-P. Neff, Y. Chen, and P. Vogel, *Helv. Chim. Acta* **74,** 508 (1991).
375. R. J. Ferrier and P. Prasit, *J. Chem. Soc., Perkin Trans. 1,* p. 1645 (1983).
376. H. Itoh, T. Kaneko, K. Tanam, and K. Yoda, *Bull. Chem. Soc. Jpn.* **61,** 3356 (1988); H. Itoh, *Noguchi Kenkyusho Jiho,* p. 37 (1988); *Chem. Abstr.* **111,** 154236o (1989).
377. S.-K. Kang, H.-S. Cho, H.-S. Sim, and B.-K- Kim, *J. Carbohydr. Chem.* **11,** 807 (1992).
378. J. Ramza and A. Zamojski, *Tetrahedron* **48,** 6123 (1992).
379. F. Paquet and P. Sinay, *Tetrahedron Lett.* **25.** 3071 (1984).
380. K. Narkunan and M. Nararajan, *J. Org. Chem.* **59,** 6386 (1994).
381. S. Jarosz, *Tetrahedron Lett.* **35,** 7655 (1994).
382. G. W. J. Fleet and T. K. M. Shing, *J. Chem. Soc., Chem. Commun.,* p. 849 (1983).
383. S. Mirza and A. Vasella, *Helv. Chim. Acta* **67,** 1562 (1984).
384. M.-I- Lim and V. E. Marquez, *Tetrahedron Lett.* **24,** 4051 (1983).
385. H.-J. Altenbach, W. Holzapfel, G. Smerat, and S. H. Finkler, *Tetrahedron Lett.* **26,** 6329 (1985).
386. V. E. Marquez, M. I. Lim, C. K.-H. Tseng, A. Markovac, M. A. Priest, M. S. Khan, and B. Kaskar, *J. Org. Chem.* **53,** 5709 (1988).
387. R. Huber and A. Vasella, *Tetrahedron* **46,** 33 (1990).
388. G. W. J. Fleet, T. K. M. Shing, and S. M. Warr, *J. Chem. Soc., Perkin Trans. 1,* p. 905 (1984).
389. S. Mirza and J. Harvey, *Tetrahedron Lett.* **32,** 4111 (1991).
390. H. Paulsen and W. von Deyn, *Justus Liebigs Ann. Chem.,* p. 125 (1987).
391. H. Paulsen, W. Bartsch, and J. Thiem, *Chem. Ber.* **104,** 2545 (1971).
392. G. M. Blackburn and A Rashid, *J. Chem. Soc., Chem. Commun.,* p. 40 (1989).
393. H. Paulsen and W. Bartsch, *Chem. Ber.* **108,** 1745 (1975).
394. K. Suzuki and T. Mukaiyama, *Chem. Lett.,* p. 683 (1982).
395. F. Nicotra, L. Panza, F. Ronchetti, G. Russo, and L. Thoma, *J. Chem. Soc., Perkin Trans. 1,* p. 1319 (1987).
396. D. Craig, S. V. Ley, N. S. Simpkins, G. H. Whitham, and M. J. Prior, *J. Chem. Soc., Perkin Trans. 1,* p. 1949 (1985).
397. B. M. Trost, P. Seoane, S. Mignani, and M. Acemoglu, *J. Am. Chem. Soc.* **111,** 7487 (1989).
398. N. J. Barnes, A. H. Davidson, L. R. Hughes, and G. Procter, *J. Chem., Soc. Chem. Commun.,* p. 1292 (1985).
399. A. H. Davidson, L. R. Hughes, S. S. Qureshi, and B. Wright, *Tetrahedron Lett.* **29,** 693 (1988).
400. G. Just, P. Potvin, and G. H. Hakimelahi, *Can. J. Chem.* **58,** 2780 (1980).
401. J. Hauske and H. Rapoport, *J. Org. Chem.* **44,** 2472 (1979).

1.2.7. Miscellaneous Methods for Extension of the Monosaccharide Chain

The conventional and most widely known methodologies for extension of the carbohydrate chain have been collected and described in the previous sections. The present section is aimed at discussing a variety of methods that cannot be classified into the former, larger groups of procedures, and that are now a bit outdated but still applicable in special cases, as well as many of those—although introduced—but have not been extensively employed in the carbohydrate field.

1.2.7.1. Chain Extension by Addition of Organometallic Compounds to an Aldehyde or Lactol Function of Saccharides

1.2.7.1.1. Extension of the Sugar Chain by the Addition of Grignard Reagents to aldehydo-Sugars

Starting from simple chiral aldehydes, such as glyceraldehyde, lactaldehyde or tartraldehyde, modern carbohydrate chemistry extensively employs acyclic stereoselective methods[1] for the construction of complex saccharides based on related procedures. The addition of organometallic reagents to *aldehydo*-sugars is a crucial step in the syntheses of higher-carbon carbohydrates and for the preparation of the chiral structural units of polyether antibiotics and other agents. Known models of asymmetric induction (chelation or nonchelation control) can be used to predict the diastereofacial selectivity of such reactions in a variety of saccharide substrates. The cyclic chelate model was proposed by Wolfrom and Hanessian[2] to account for the diastereofacial selectivity of Grignard reagents to 1,2-*O*-isopropylidene-3-*O*-benzyl-D-xylofuranos-1,4-ulose.

These stereochemical studies have been also carried out[3] with the simplest open-chain saccharide: 2,3-*O*-isopropylidene-D-glyceraldehyde. The reactions of this aldehyde with a large variety of carbanions (e.g., with alkyl and arylmagnesium halides, alkyllithium reagents, alkyltitanium isopropoxides) have been accomplished, and the stereochemical outcome of these transformations, including the influenece of various factors, have been determined by means of comprehensive analytic methods (HPLC, GC and NMR).

The following example (Fig. 1.138) shows the chain extension of 2,3-*O*-isopropylidene-D-glyceraldehyde (**138.1**) with diallyl zinc to give rise[4] to (2R,3S)- and (2R,3R)-1,2-*O*-isopropylidene-5-hexen-1,2,3-triol (**138.2** and **138.3**, respectively), and similar reactions of the sugar **138.1** with ethinyl and vinylmagnesium bromide have also been reported.[5]

> *Preparation of (2R,3S)- and (2R,3R)-1,2-O-isopropylidene-5-hexen-1,2,3-triol (138.2 and 138.3)*[4]   To a solution of allylmagnesium chloride (0.52 mol) in THF (700 ml), zinc chloride (36.2 g, 0.266 mol) is added in small portions at 0°C, and the resulting gray suspension is stirred for 30 min at room temperature and cooled

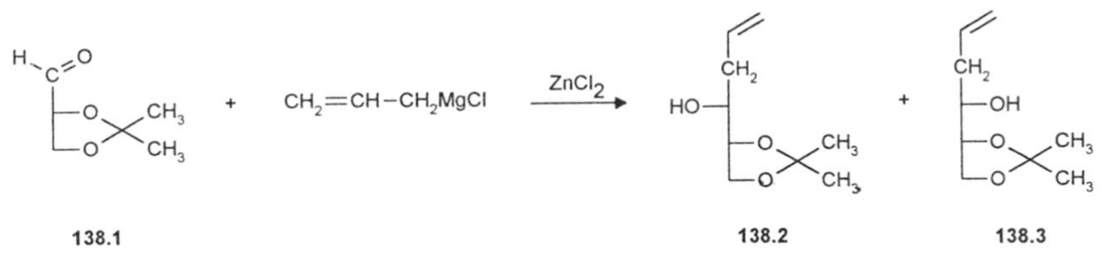

FIGURE 1.138

to $-10°C$. Then a solution of 2,3-O-isopropylidene-D-glyceraldehyde (**138.1**, 28.63 g, 0.22 mmol) in THF (150 ml) is added dropwise and stirring is continued at 20°C for 2h. After addition of aqueous ammonium chloride and conventional workup 31.11 g (82%) of an 85:15 mixture of **138.2** and **138.3** is obtained.

The chain extension of numerous monosaccharide derivatives, including sugars with free anomeric hydroxyl group and alduloses, with different Grignard reagents have been carried out, and these studies were also aimed at investigating the influence of various factors (complexation, solvent-effects, anomeric configuration, substitution pattern, etc.) on such of reactions. However, it is still difficult to predict a *general* outcome of the process in many cases. Nevertheless, in the light of the following results and examples, published in three detailed studies,[6–8] considerably useful (and somewhat generalizable) insight on the stereochemical outcome of the Grignard chain extensions can be gained.

As reported by Singh et al.,[6] the reaction of 2,3-O-isopropylidene-D-erythrofuranose (**139.1**), 2,3-O-isopropylidene-D-ribofuranose (**139.2**), 2,3:5,6-di-O-isopropylidene-D-allofuranose (**139.3**), 2,3:5,6-di-O-isopropylidene-D-mannofuranose (**139.4**) and 2,3-O-isopropylidene-D-lyxofuranose (**139.5**) with different Grignard reagents (Fig. 1.139 and Table 1.25) gives

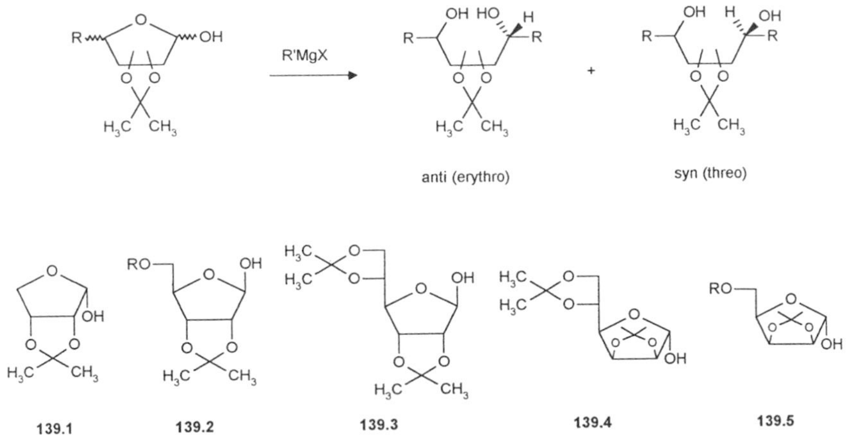

FIGURE 1.139

TABLE 1.25 Stereochemical Outcome of the Grignard Reactions of 2,3-O-isopropylidenefuranosides (see Fig. 1.139)

Entry	Substrate	Reagent	Conditions[a]	anti:syn[b]	Yield (%)
1	**139.1**	MeMgCl	THF/−78–0°C	5:5	88
2	**139.1**	MeLi	THF/−78–0°C	45:5	76
3	**139.1**	PhMgCl	THF/−78–0°C	98:2	97
4	**139.1**	PhLi	THF/−78–0°C	34:66	96
5	**139.1**	Vinyl MgCl	THF/−78–0°C	100:0	84
6	**139.1**	Allyl MgCl	THF/0°C	75:25	73
7	**139.1**	1-Hexynyl MgBr	THF/−78–0°C	100:0	74
8	**139.1**	1-Hexynyl Li	THF/RT	66:34	83
9	**139.2**, R = TBDMS	MeMgCl	THF/−78°C	98:2	85
10	**139.2**, R = TBDMS	MeLi	THF/−78°C	50:50	77
11	**139.2**, R = TBDMS	Vinyl MgCl	THF/−78°C	95:5	70
12	**139.2**, R = H	Allyl MgCl	THF/0°C	75:25	82
13	**139.2**, R = H	(Allyl)$_2$Zn	THF/0°C	96:4	86
14	**139.2**, R = H	1-Hexynyl MgBr	THF/RT	80:20	55
15	**139.2**, R = H	1-Hexynyl Li	THF/RT	75:25	67
16	**139.2**, R = TBDPS	1-Hexynyl Li	THF/0°C	75:25	66
17	**139.3**	MeMgCl	THF/0°C	93:7	90
18	**139.3**	MeLi	THF/−20°C	34:66	61
19	**139.4**	MeMgCl	THF/−78°C	100:0	95
20	**139.4**	MeLi	THF/−78°C	0:100	66
21	**139.4**	PhMgBr	THF/−78°C	99:1	70
22	**139.4**	PhLi	THF/−40°C	0:100	80
23	**139.5**, R = H	MeMgCl	THF/−78°C	95:5	90
24	**139.5**, R = H or TBDPS	MeLi	THF/−78°C to RT	No Reaction	0
25	**139.5**, R = H	Allyl MgBr	THF/−78°C	96:4	76
26	**139.5**, R = H or TBDPS	PhLi	THF/0°C to RT	No Reaction	0

[a]Reactions carried out with 2.2–3.0 equivalents of reagent, except for entries 23–26 (20 eq).
[b]All yields and ratios refer to pure isolated products.

rise mainly to the *anti*-product (Masamune nomenclature) with *erythro*-stereochemistry.

Related comprehensive studies[7] on deoxypentofuranosuloses indicated the role of the configuration of the anomeric carbon atom concerning the stereochemical outcome of the reaction. Thus, methylmagnesium halides, methyllithium, methylcerium, and MeTi(OiPr)$_3$ were reacted with pentodialdo-1,4-furanosides in an effort to determine whether the stereoselectivity of addition to the formyl group is the result of chelation or nonchelation control, and also to determine the effect of the anomeric configuration. It was found that the stereoselectivity of the addition is dependent on the configuration of the anomeric center, and the results obtained with methyl 3-*O*-benzyl-2-deoxy-α-D-*erythro*-pentodialdo-1,4-furanoside (**140.1**) and with the corresponding β anomer (**140.2**) are summarized in Figure 1.140.

Kim *et al.*[7] and Kilaas and coworkers[8] have also studied the addition of Grignard reagents to similar substrates; novel literature data[9–12] have also been reported in this field for the application simple Grignard reagents, and several works[13–20] deal with the transformations of *aldehydo*-sugars with alkyl- and arylmagnesium halides. The following easily reproducible procedure, elaborated by Gätzi and Reichstein,[21] describes the chain extension (Fig. 1.141) of 2,3:4,5-di-*O*-isopropylidene-*aldehydo*-D-arabinose (**141.1**) into the 6-deoxyalditols **141.2** and **141.3.**

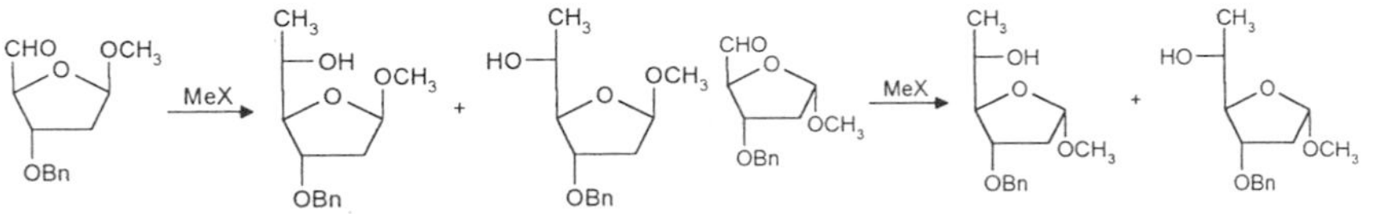

140.2 140.3 140.4 140.1 140.5 140.6

Entry	Reagent	Conditions: Solvent	Conditions: T (°C)	ratio[a] 140.3/140.4	yield[b] (%)
1	CH_3MgCl	THF	0	85/15	89
2	CH_3MgCl	THF	20	85/15	89
3	CH_3MgCl	THF	-45	85/15	93
4	CH_3MgBr	THF	0	82/18	91
5	CH_3MgBr	Ether	0	60/40	80
6	CH_3Li	Ether	-70	81/19	80
7	"$CH_3CeCl_2\cdot LiCl$"	THF	-70	85/15	44
8	$CH_3MgCl\cdot 2DMPU$[c]	THF	0	86/14	83
9	$CH_3MgBr\cdot 4DMPU$[c]	THF	0	83/17	53
10	$CH_3MgBr\cdot ZnCl_2$	THF	-70	75/25	30
11	$CH_3MgBr\cdot TiCl_4$	THF	-70	86/14	43
12	CH_3MgCl "hi salt"	THF	-10	84/15	100
13	CH_3MgCl "low salt"	THF	0	83/17	85
14	$CH_3Ti(OiPr)_3$	CH_2Cl_2	-50	93/7	76

[a] Determined by integration of the ^{1}H-NMR signals of the C-5—CH_3 in crude reaction mixtures.
[b] Isolated yield of both diastereomers.
[c] DMPU = dimethylpropyleneurea (1,3-dimethyl-3,4,5,6-tetrahydro-2(1*H*)-pyrimidinone).

Entry	Reagent	Conditions: Solvent	Conditions: T (°C)	ratio[a] 140.5/140.6
1	CH_3MgCl	THF	0	38/62
2	CH_3MgCl	THF	-40	38/62
3	CH_3MgBr	THF	0	45/55
4	CH_3MgBr	Ether	0	26/74
5	CH_3Li	Ether	-70	50/50
6	"$CH_3CeCl_2\cdot LiCl$"	THF	-70	45/55
7	$CH_3MgBr\cdot ZnCl_2$	THF	-70	33/67
8	$CH_3MgBr\cdot TiCl_4$	THF	-70	45/55
9	CH_3MgCl "hi salt"	THF	-10	45/55
10	CH_3MgCl "low salt"	THF	-10	45/55

[a] Determined by integration of the ^{1}H-NMR signals of the C-5—CH_3 in crude reaction mixtures.

FIGURE 1.140

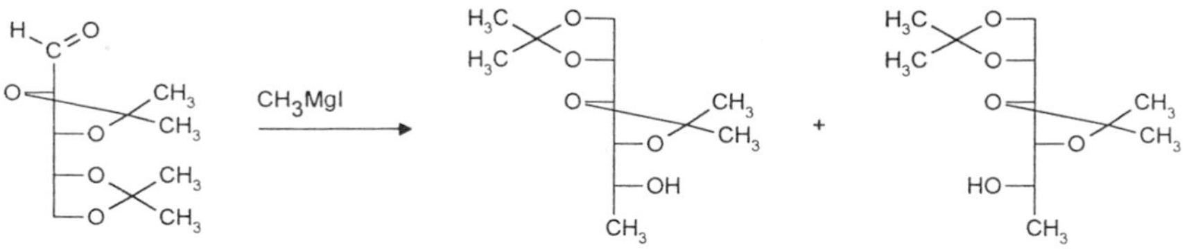

FIGURE 1.141

6-Deoxy-1,2:3,4-di-O-isopropylidene-D-mannitol (***141.2***) *and* -L-*gulitol* (***141.3***)[21]
In a round-bottomed flask equipped with a reflux condenser, magnesium turnings
(2 g), activated with iodine, are placed and 100 ml of dry ether is added. After
adding a small crystal of iodine, methyl bromide (passed through a washing device
filled with sulfuric acid) is led to the mixture until all the magnesium shavings
disappear, and during this time the reaction mixture is kept under a gentle reflux.
Heating under reflux is continued for further 5 min, and then a solution of 2,3:4,5-
di-O-isopropylidene-*aldehydo*-D-arabinose (**141.1**, 5.0 g) in dry ether is added, at
which point a vigorous reaction occurs. The mixture is refluxed for an additional
30 min, cooled, and quenched with saturated aqueous ammonium chloride with
external cooling on an ice bath. The aqueous layer is separated and extracted with
ether, and the combined organic phase is washed with aqueous ammonium chloride
and water, dried, and submitted to vacuum distillation. The colorless thick syrup
(4.7 g, 78%) collected at b.p. 81°C and 5.33 Pa is crystallized from pentane (15 ml):
crystallization is complete at −80°C. The crystals are washed with cold pentane to
give 1.7 g of the crude 6-deoxy-D-mannitol derivative **141.2,** m.p. 45–49°C. For
further purification, the crystalline substance is cautiously melted and a twofold
excess of pentane is added to result in the separation of pure **141.2** as large prisms,
m.p. 66.5–67°C [corrected], $[\alpha]_D^{19}$ +1 (c = 1.4 in methanol). The remaining syrup
consists of the L-gulitol derivative **141.3,** $[\alpha]_D^{19}$ +3 (c = 0.68 in methanol).

Aromatic Grignard reagents are generally employed for the chain extension of aldulose derivatives. As shown in Figure 1.142, the reaction
of 3-O-benzyl-1,2-O-isopropylidene-α-D-*xylo*-pentodialdo-1,4-furanose
(**142.1**) with phenylmagnesium bromide leads[22] to a mixture of 3-O-benzyl-
1,2-O-isopropylidene-5-C-phenyl-α-D-*gluco*- and -β-L-*ido*-pentofuranose
142.2 and **142.3**, respectively, readily separable by vacuum distillation.

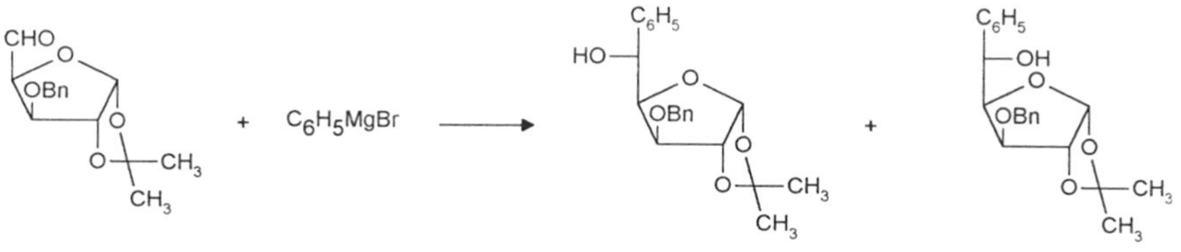

FIGURE 1.142

*Conversion of 3-O-benzyl-1,2-O-isopropylidene-α-D-xylo-pentodialdo-1,4-furan-ose (**142.1**) with phenylmagnesium bromide[22]*

A. *In ether*   To a solution of the ulose **142.1** (15 g) in ether (100 ml) is added a freshly prepared solution of the Grignard reagent (prepared according to the general procedure from 4.5 g of magnesium turnings and 18 ml of bromobenzene in 100 ml of ether, under controlled conditions), and the suspension is stirred under reflux for 2 h. It is then cooled, washed with dilute aqueous ammonium chloride solution, dried, and concentrated, and the residue is submitted to column chromatography (eluant: 4:1 benzene–ether) to give, first 1.0 g (5%) of the *gluco*-compound **142.2**, as the minor product, with $[\alpha]_D^{23}$ -76 ($c = 1$ in chloroform). The major product, 3-O-benzyl-1,2-O-isopropylidene-5-C-phenyl-β-L-*ido*-pentofuranose (**142.3**) is obtained by vacuum distillation at 0.013 kPa (bath temperature: 280°C), $[\alpha]_D^{23}$ -33.5 ($c = 2$ in chloroform).

B. *In THF*   To a solution of the dialdofuranose **142.1** (15.0 g) in 100 ml of THF, a solution of the freshly prepared Grignard reagent (prepared in the usual manner from 4 g of Mg and 15 ml of bromobenzene in 100 ml of THF) is added, and the mixture is heated under reflux for 1.5 h and then poured into dilute aqueous ammonium chloride solution. THF is distilled off, and the residual aqueous solution is extracted with chloroform. The organic layer is washed with water, dried, and then worked up as described in method *A* to obtain 1.8 g (13%) of the α-D-*gluco* (**142.2**) and 6.0 g (43%) of the β-L-*ido* (**142.3**) products.

The chain extension of saccharides with the required Grignard reagent is a rather useful procedure for obtaining complex and higher-carbon sugar analogs. Some results[23–30] with the application of vinylmagnesium halides are shown in Figure 1.143. In the procedure offered by Chapleur,[29] the formation of a single isomer—the oct-7-enopyranoside **143.2**—is reported.

*Methyl 4-O-benzyl-7,8-dideoxy-2,3-O-isopropylidene-α-D-manno-oct-7-enopyr-anoside (**143.2**)[29]*   To a cooled ($-60°C$) solution of oxalyl chloride (0.16 ml, 1.8 mmol) in dry THF (5 ml) is added a solution of Me$_2$SO (0.4 ml, 3.6 mmol) in dry THF (2 ml). After 5 min a solution of methyl 4-O-benzyl-2,3-O-isopropylidene-α-D-mannopyranoside (600 mg, 1.6 mmol) in dry THF (5 ml) is added dropwise at this temperature, and after stirring for 15 min, a solution of triethylamine (808 mg) in THF (2 ml) is added and the mixture is allowed to warm to room temperature during 5 min. The crude product of the oxidation: methyl 4-O-benzyl-2,3-O-isopropylidene-α-D-*manno*-hexodialdo-1,5-pyranose (**143.1**) is used directly in the next step for the chain extension. The solution of **143.1** is cooled to $-60°C$, and a solution of vinylmagnesium bromide in THF (1M, 8 mmol) is added and the mixture is stirred for 3 h. Ethanol (1 ml) and a saturated aqueous solution of ammonium chloride are added successively. The mixture is extracted with ether (3×50 ml) and the combined extract is washed with water (3×10 ml), dried over MgSO$_4$ and evaporated under reduced pressure to give a crude product that can be purified on a silicagel column (eluant: 2:8 acetone–hexane) to give the pure title oct-7-enopyranoside **143.2** (400 mg, 83%), m.p. 56–57°C, $[\alpha]_D$ $+27.5$ ($c = 0.3$ in chloroform).

Related chain extensions with ethynylmagnesium bromide[31–38] offers a *straightforward route* to saccharides carrying an acetylenic bond that are, in turn, rather useful for further chemical manipulations to obtain novel olefinic sugars or uronic acids. In the case of 2,3-O-isopropylidene-β-D-*ribo*-pentodialdo-1,4-furanoside (**144.1**), separation of the epimeric

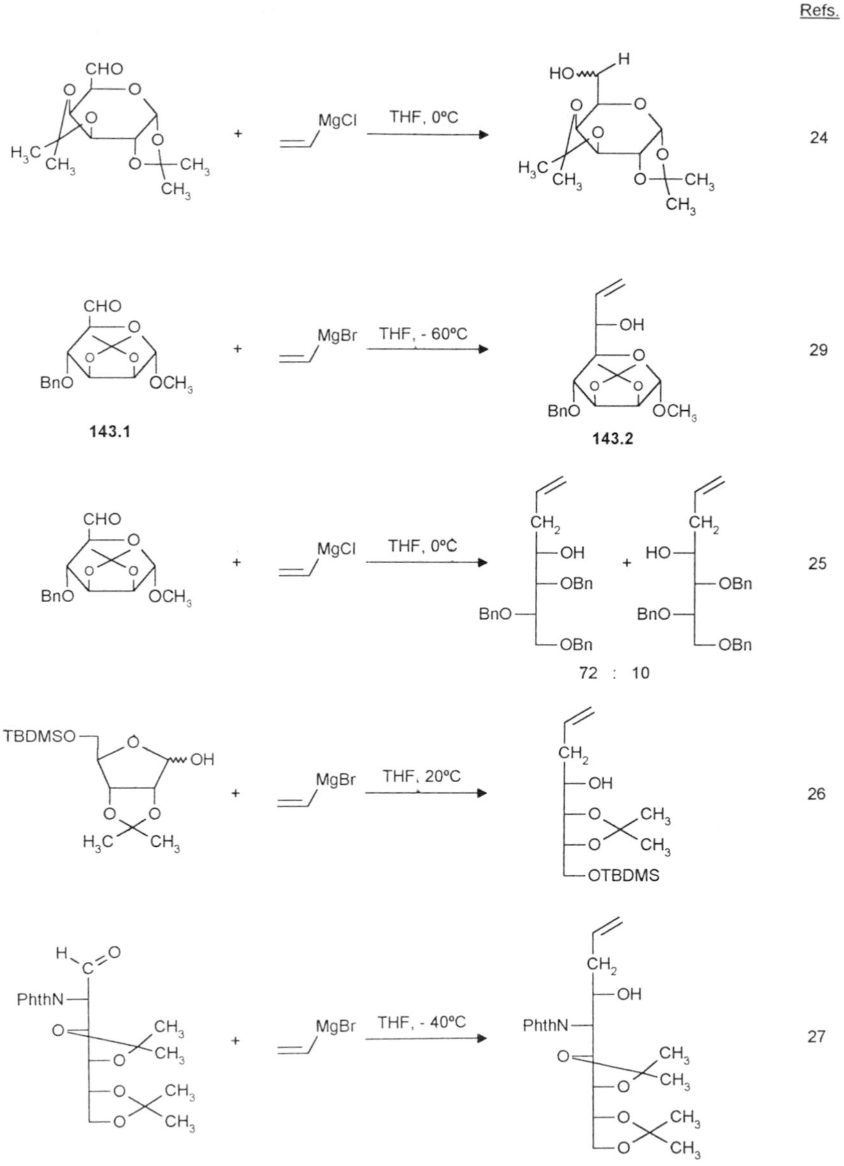

FIGURE I.143a

mixture of **144.2** and **144.3,** formed on ethynylation[32] (Fig. 1.144), is well elaborated by means of chromatography.

*Methyl 6,7-dideoxy-2,3-O-isopropylidene-β-D-allo- (**144.2**) and -α-L-talo-hept-6-yno-furanoside (**144.3**)*[32]   A solution of ethylmagnesium bromide, prepared from magnesium turnings (0.31 g) and ethyl bromide (1.5 ml) in dry THF (15 ml), is added dropwise to a stirred solution of dry acetylene in THF (15 ml). Dry acetylene

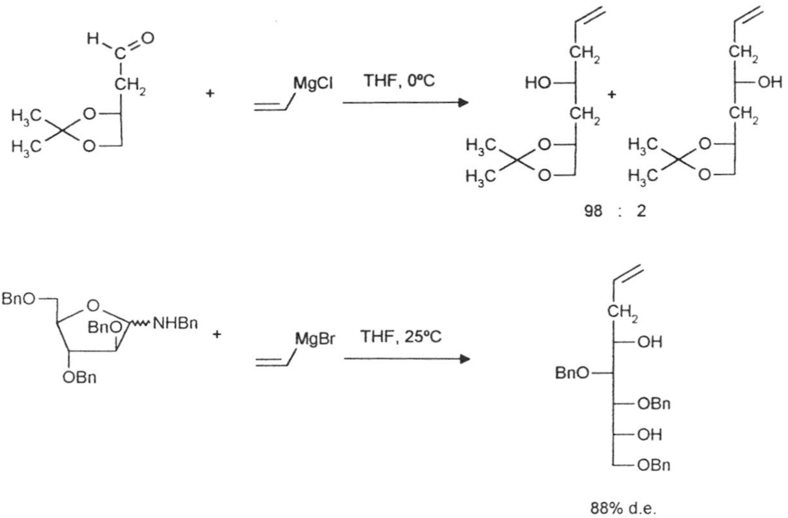

FIGURE 1.143b

is passed through the mixture during the addition and the next 60 min. After cooling to 0°C, a solution of methyl 2,3-*O*-isopropylidene-β-D-*ribo*-pentodialdo-1,4-furanoside (**144.1,** 1.3 g) in THF (10 ml) is added over a 30-min period. Acetylene is passed through the solution throughout the addition and for a further 3 h. Then the mixture is allowed to warm to room temperature, stirred overnight, and concentrated. A solution of the residue in ether (50 ml) is washed with saturated aqueous ammonium chloride (3 × 50 ml) at 0°C and water (50 ml), dried over MgSO₄, and concentrated. The resulting crystalline mixture of **144.2** and **144.3** (1.4 g) is fractionated by preparative gas–liquid chromatography (GLC) (column: 10% PEG-4000 on Chromosorb WAW, 190°C) to furnish 48% of pure **144.2,** as white needles, m.p. 93–94°C, $[\alpha]_D^{20}$ −96 (c = 0.5 in chloroform), T = 1.22 (cf. 1.00 for **144.3**); and **144.3** (52%), m.p. 63–64°C, $[\alpha]_D^{20}$ −13 (c = 0.5 in chloroform).

An additional, very useful procedure has been described by Czernecki *et al.*[39] utilizing trimethysilyl acetylene for analogous chain extensions (Fig. 1.144).

> *Methyl 2,3,4-tri-O-benzyl-7,8-dideoxy-L-glycero- and D-glycero-D-gluco-oct-7-ynopyranoside (**144.7 and 144.8**)*[39] The reaction is to be carried out under argon. Two batches of anhydrous magnesium bromide (24 mmol each) are prepared from magnesium turnings (0.6 g, 24 mmol) and 1,2-dibromoethane (2.1 ml, 24 mmol) in ether (15 ml) at room temperature. In a separate flask, (trimethylsilyl)acetylene (1.92 ml, 13.6 mmol) is added dropwise to a cooled (−5°C) solution of *n*-butyllithium (7.8 ml of a 1.6 M solution in hexane diluted with 15 ml of ether). After stirring for 15 min, this mixture is added to one batch of freshly prepared anhydrous MgBr₂. The resulting white suspension is cooled to −30°C. The second batch of MgBr₂ (24 mmol) is added to the dialdosugar **144.4** (1.43 g, 3.09 mmol) dissolved in ether (70 ml), and the preceding suspension is added to this mixture at −30°C. The mixture is allowed to attain room temperature before careful hydrolysis with saturated aqueous ammonium chloride (50 ml). Following decantation, the aqueous layer is extracted with ether (2 × 50 ml) and the combined organic layer is washed

FIGURE 1.144

with water until neutral and dried over MgSO$_4$. Evaporation of the solvent affords a syrup that is submitted to flash column chromatography (eluant 1:4.5 → 1:3 ethyl acetate–hexane) to furnish the trimethylsilyl derivatives **144.5** (1.41 g, 82%) and **144.6** (95 mg, 5.5%), as colorless syrups that are separately desilylated as follows. First, to a solution of **144.5** (1.41 g, 2.5 mmol) in THF (10 ml) is added a solution of Bu$_4$NF in THF (1.1 M, 4 ml) at room temperature. After completion of the reaction (~15 min), the solvent is evaporated and the residue is partitioned between water and toluene (2:5, 70 ml). The aqueous phase is extracted with toluene (2 × 10 ml), and the combined organic phase is dried over MgSO$_4$ and concentrated to a white foam. Flash column chromatography (with 1:2 ethyl acetate–hexane) yields 1.18 g (96%) of **144.7**, as white crystals, that is recrystallized from ether–hexane to obtain the pure product with m.p. 75°C, [α]$_D$ +9 (c = 1.0 in chloroform). Then desilylation of **144.6** (95 mg, 0.17 mmol), under the same conditions, and subsequent chromatographic purification gives 61 mg (74%) of **144.8**, that is recrystallized from ether–hexane to furnish an analytically pure sample with m.p. 86–87°C, [α]$_D$ +41 (c = 1.5 in chloroform).

Allylmagnesium halides have also been used for the chain extension of monosaccharides,[40] including 2-acetamido-2,4-dideoxy-D-hexopyranoses,[28] unnatural enantiomers of *castanospermine* and *1-epi-castanospermine*,[25] and *oxetanocine* analogs.[41] An important extension of this methodology is the utilization of Grignard reactions, permitting nucleophilic *hydroxymethyla-tion,* and in these cases Grignard reagents ensuring temporary protection and convenient recovery of the newly generated functionality are generally used. [Phenyl(dimethylsilyl)methyl]magnesium chloride has been shown[42] shown to be a suitable reagent for the chain extension of 1,2:3,4-di-*O*-isopropylidene-α-D-*galacto*-hexodialdo-1,5-pyranose, and allyloxymethyl-magnesium chloride (**145.2**) has been used for the synthesis[43] of the naturally occurring D- and L-*glycero*-D-*manno*-heptoses (Fig. 1.145).

Benzyl 7-O-allyl-2,3,4-tri-O-benzyl-β-L- (145.3) and α-D-glycero-D-manno-*heptopyranoside (145.4)*[43] To a suspension of magnesium turnings (1.76 g) and mercuric chloride (4–6 mg) in THF (8 ml), a few drops of allyloxymethyl chloride is added under argon atmosphere. When the Grignard reaction has started, a solution of allyloxymethyl chloride (5.9 g) in dry THF (15 ml) is added dropwise at 0°C. After stirring for 30 min, the mixture is cooled to −30°C, and benzyl 2,3,4-tri-O-benzyl-α-D-*manno*-hexodialdo-1,5-pyranose (**145.1**, 13 g) dissolved in THF (15 ml) is added dropwise, then stirring is continued at −20°C for 30 min. It is allowed to attain room temperature, and is kept at this temperature for 18 h, and cold aqueous ammonium chloride is added. The resulting mixture is extracted with ether several times, the organic phase is concentrated, and the residue is chromatographed on

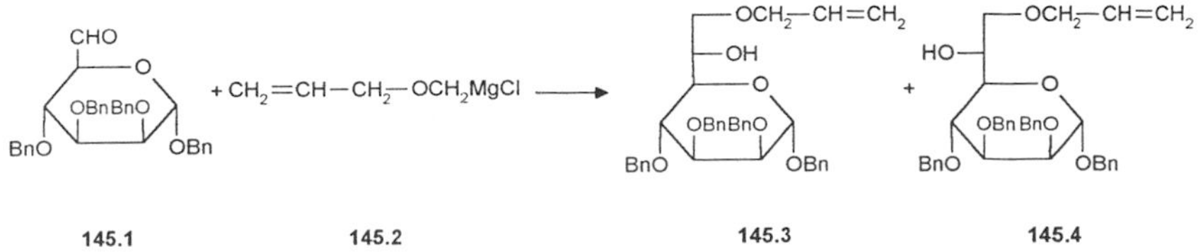

FIGURE 1.145

silicagel (eluant: 95:5 petroleum ether–ethyl acetate). The first fractions contain the β-L-derivative **145.3** (7.53 g, 51.5%), as a syrup, $[\alpha]_D^{27}$ +35 (c = 1.1 in chloroform), followed by the elution of the α-D-isomer **145.4** (2.26 g, 16%).

Removal of the protecting group of the products **145.3** and **145.4** gives the free heptoses, and the Grignard reagent **145.2** can be more advantageously applied than benzyloxymethylmagnesium chloride, whose application is associated with separation problems. For similar purposes Tamao[44] has introduced (isopropoxydimethylsilyl)methylmagnesium halides, and these employed reagents are now widely used.[45-52] A closely related chain extension with [phenyl(dimethylsilyl)methyl]magnesium chloride (**146.2**), proceeding also with high stereoselectivity and leading to a single isomer **146.3** from the hexodialdopyranoside **146.1,** is shown in Figure 1.146.

*Preparation of methyl 2,3,4-tri-O-benzyl-7-(phenyldimethylsilyl)silane-7-deoxy-*L-*glycero-α-D-mannopyranoside (146.3)*[51] A small amount of (phenyldimethylsilyl)methyl chloride (11.7 g, 60 mmol) in THF (45 ml) is added under a nitrogen atmosphere to dry magnesium turnings (1.46 g, 60 mmol), the reaction mixture is heated until reflux and, after the reaction is initiated by the addition of 1,2-dibromoethane (0.1 ml), the remaining chloride is added at such a rate as to maintain a gentle reflux. The resulting Grignard reagent (**146.2**) is transferred to a dry round-bottomed flask and a solution of the *aldehydo*-sugar **146.1** (previously dried by coevaporation with 2 × 20 ml of toluene) in dry THF (45 ml) is added dropwise to the cooled (0°C) Grignard reagent. After stirring for 2 h, TLC (1:2 ether–petroleum ether) indicated the complete conversion of **146.1** into **146.3** (R_f = 0.5). The mixture is then slowly poured into aqueous ammonium chloride (50 ml, 20%) and extracted with 200 ml of dichloromethane. The organic layer is washed with water (50 ml), dried over MgSO₄, and concentrated under reduced pressure to a syrup that is purified by means of column chromatography on silicagel (200 g) (eluant: petroleum ether → 9:1 petroleum ether–ethyl acetate → 4:1 petroleum ether–ethyl acetate). Concentration of the appropriate fractions gives 13.1 g (71%) of pure syrupy **146.3,** $[\alpha]_D$ +11.5 (c = 1 in chloroform), a target for transformation into the heptopyranoside **146.4.**

Silicon-containing Grignard reagents are known to react also with the free anomeric hydroxyl group of saccharides. A practical utilization of this recognition is represented by the chain extension (Fig. 1.147) of *tert*-butyl 2-acetamido-3-O-(*tert*-butyldimethylsilyl)-2,4-dideoxy-D-*xylo*-hexopyranuronate (**147.1**) with trimethylsilylmethylmagnesium chloride to

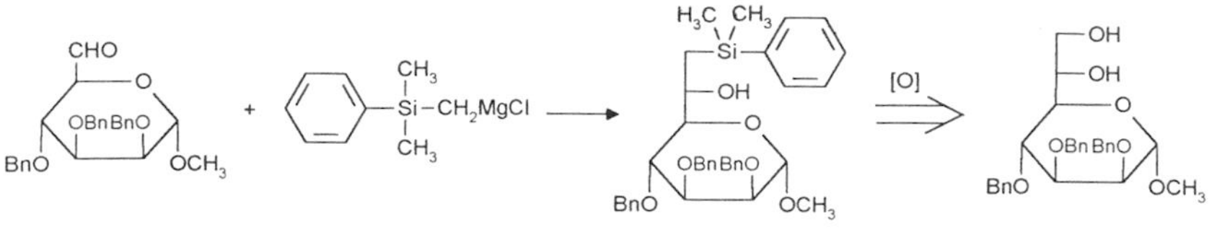

FIGURE 1.146

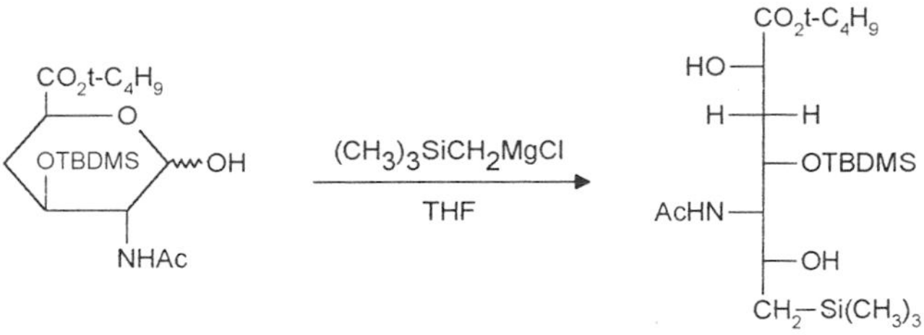

FIGURE I.147

result in the open-chain heptonic acid (**147.2**), a *precursor*[52] of the *sialidase-inhibitory* chiral piperidine carboxylic acids.

tert-*Butyl   5-acetamido-4-O-(tert-butyldimethylsilyl)-3,5,7-trideoxy-7-C-(trimethyl-silyl)-D-ido-heptonate (147.2)*[52]   A solution of the hexopyranuronate **147.1** (5 g, 12.8 mmol) in dry THF (20 ml) is added at 0°C over 30 min under argon to a solution of trimethylsilylmethylmagnesium chloride [prepared from magnesium (1.55 g, 64.17 mmol) and trimethylsilylmethyl chloride in 30 ml of dry THF]. The mixture is stirred for 1 h at 0°C and then for 3 h at room temperature, diluted with ethyl acetate (50 ml), poured into ice-cold saturated ammonium chloride solution, and extracted with ethyl acetate. The organic layer is washed with a saturated aqueous solution of ammonium chloride (pH 6) and worked up in the usual manner, the residue is coevaporated with toluene, and the residue is purified by chromatography (eluant: 4:1 ethyl acetate–hexane) to yield 5.2 g (85%) of pure **147.2**, that was crystallized from ether, m.p 138°C, $[\alpha]_D^{25}$ +15.5 ($c = 1.3$ in chloroform).

1.2.7.1.2. Extension of the Sugar Chain by Addition of Lithioorganic Compounds to aldehydo–*Sugar Derivatives*

From the previous section it is clear that the products of the Grignard reactions are to be related,[3,6,7] first, to those of the chain extensions performed with lithiumalkyls.

The reaction of 2,3-O-isopropylidene-D-glyceraldehyde with methyl-, *n*-butyl- and phenyllithium proceeds with a high *threo*-selectivity,[53] and this is also observed when 2,3:5,6-di-O-isopropylidene-D-mannofuranose is treated[54] with methyl-, ethyl-, and *n*-butyllithium. Transformation of 2,3-O-isopropylidene-D-glyceraldehyde with furyllithium have also been extensively studied[55–57] and related conversion of 2,3,5-tri-O-benzyl-D-ribofuranose has been reported.[58] The major product of the chain extension[59] of 6-deoxy-2,3-O-isopropylidene-β-D-allofuranoside with methyllithium is 6-deoxy-2,3-O-isopropylidene-β-D-*ribo*-pentodialdo-1,4-furanoside, and the α-L-*talo*-derivative has also been isolated as the minor product.

The key step in a synthesis of the *carbocyclic analog of D-ribose* is the reaction of 2,3-O-isopropylidene-5-O-methoxymethyl-D-ribofuranose

(**148.1**) with lithioacetylene to furnish[60] the chain-extended hept-1-ynitol as a 20:1 mixture of the diastereoisomers **148.2** and **148.3** (Fig. 1.148).

1,2-Dideoxy-4,5-O-(1-methylethylidene)-7-O-methoxymethyl-D-allo-hept-1-ynitol (148.2[60] To vigorously stirred THF (280 ml) at −78°C under nitrogen is added 3.7 liters of acetylene gas at a flow rate of 120 ml/min, then a solution of *n*-butyllithium (5.86 g, 91.5 mmol) in 50 ml of hexane is added by a syringe, and the resulting clear solution is stirred for 15 min. A solution of the sugar **148.1** (7.14 g, 30.5 mmol) in 25 ml of THF is added by cannulation, the cooling bath is removed and the mixture is allowed to warm to room temperature. After 8 h, the reaction is quenched with 30 ml of saturated aqueous ammonium chloride, neutralized to pH 7 with 10% aqueous hydrochloric acid and concentrated under reduced pressure. After dilution with 100 ml of water, the biphasic mixture is extracted with dichloromethane (3 × 200 ml), the combined organic extract is dried (MgSO₄), and concentrated to an orange oil that solidifies upon standing. The crude product appears to be a 20:1 mixture of the two diastereoisomers by NMR investigation. The solid is powdered in a minimum volume of ethyl acetate and rinsed until white. Filtration yields 5.18 g (64%) of the pure major diastereoisomer **148.2**. Concentration of the mother liquor under reduced pressure back to the orange solid and repetition of the powdering and rinsing procedure yield another 640 mg (8%) of pure **148.2**, bringing the overall yield up to 72%, m.p. 88–90°C, $[\alpha]_D^{22}$ −9.3 (*c* = 1.06 in chloroform).

More complicated lithioorganic compounds have also served as suitable agents for the chain extension of saccharides. Thus, ethoxyvinyllithium (**149.2**), generated *in situ* from ethyl vinylether and *tert*-butyllithium,[61] extends the skeletone of 1,2:3,4-di-*O*-isopropylidene-α-D-*galacto*-hexodialdo-1,5-pyranose (**149.1**) with two carbon atoms to afford the oct-7-enopyranose **149.3**, a key intermediate in a synthesis[62] of *methyl α-lincosaminide* (Fig. 1.149).

7,8-Dideoxy-7-ethoxy-1,2:3,4-di-O-isopropylidene-D,L-glycero-α-D-galacto-oct-7-enopyranose (149.3)[62] To a solution of ethyl vinyl ether (0.72 ml, 7.5 mmol) in dry THF (5 ml) is added at −78°C *tert*-butyllithium (3.13 ml of a 1.6 N solution in pentane, 5 mmol), and the mixture is allowed to warm to room temperature. It is then cooled again to −78°C, a solution of the hexodialdose **149.1** (1.29 g, 5 mmol) in 5 ml of THF is added, the reaction mixture is stirred at this temperature for a further 1 h, and the reaction is quenched with 10 ml of 20% aqueous ammonium chloride at 0°C. Then 15 ml of ether is added, and the aqueous layer is separated and extracted with 2 × 10 ml of ether. The combined organic layer is dried over

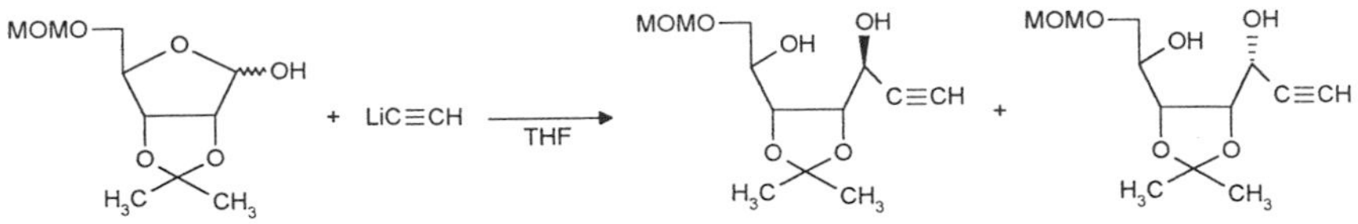

148.1   + LiC≡CH ——THF——→   148.2   +   148.3

20 : 1

FIGURE 1.148

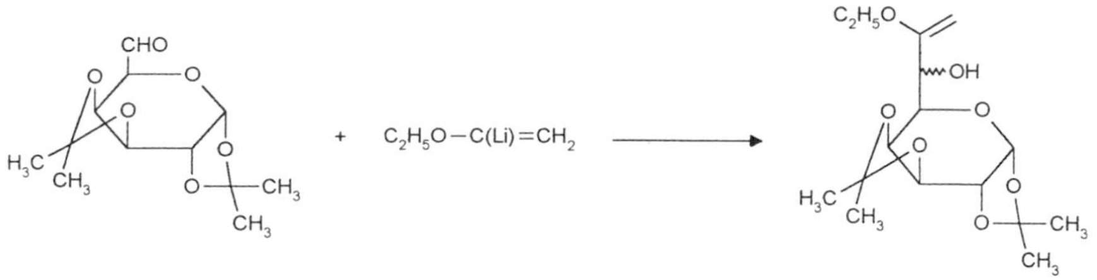

149.1 149.2 149.3

FIGURE 1.149

MgSO$_4$ and concentrated to obtain 1.42 g of the crude product, that is recrystallized from cyclohexane to furnish 0.75 g (45.4%) of pure **149.3,** m.p. 114–117°C. From the mother liquor 0.35 g (21.2%) of the product is obtained by column chromatography (eluant: ethyl acetate–petroleum ether).

The synthesis of *3-deoxy-D-manno-2-octulosonic acid* (*Kdo*) can also be effected by the chain extension of an *aldehydo*-sugar with a lithioorganic compound. On the basis of retrosynthetic analysis, and in the knowledge of the steps of the biosynthesis, generation of the deoxy function was effected[62] following chain extension (Fig. 1.150) of the starting sugar, 2,3:4,5-di-*O*-isopropylidene-*aldehydo*-D-arabinose (**150.1**). The reaction partner

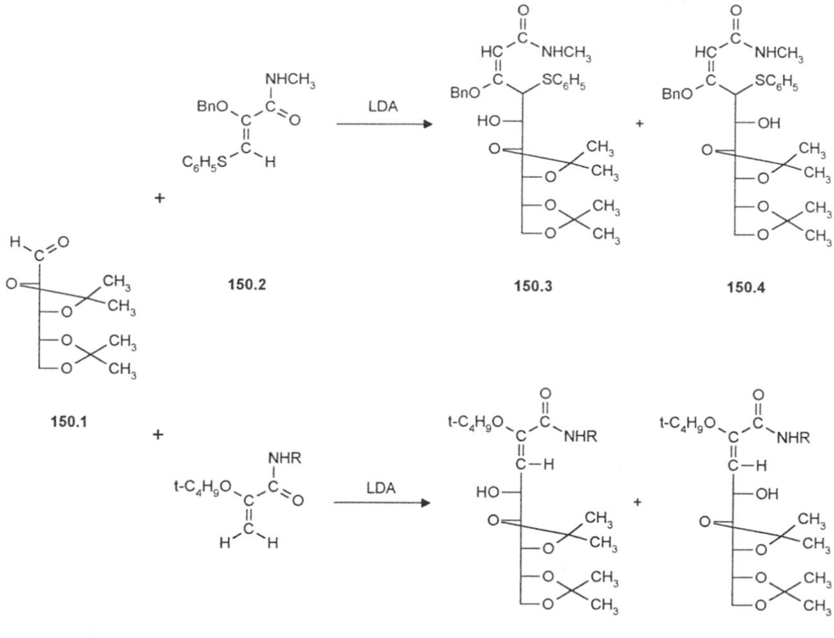

150.1 150.2 150.3 150.4 150.5 150.6 150.7

FIGURE 1.150

selected, was (Z)-2-(benzyloxy)-N-methyl-3-(phenylthio)acrylic amide **150.2**, carrying an easily lithiable phenylthio function at the β-position. Thus, bimolar lithiation of **150.2**, followed by its diastereoselective addition to the sugar **150.1**, led to the crystalline (2Z)-2-O-benzyl-3-deoxy-5,6:7,8-di-O-isopropylidene-N-methyl-3-(phenylthio)-D-*manno*-oct-2-enoamide **150.3** with 60% yield without chromatography. From the mother liquor the minor product, i.e., the D-*gluco*-derivative **150.4**, could also be isolated. Even higher yield of the major stereoisomer **150.3** can be achieved by adding HMPA as the cosolvent.[63]

> (2Z)-2-O-Benzyl-3-deoxy-5,6:7,8-di-O-isopropylidene-N-methyl-3-(phenylthio)-
> D-manno-oct-2-enoamide (**150.3**)[63]
>
> A. Lithium diisopropylamide (55.2 mmol) dissolved in a mixture of hexane and
> THF is added to a solution of (Z)-2-(benzyloxy)-N-methyl-3-(phenylthio)acryl-
> amide (**150.2**) in dry THF (180 ml) at −80°C. After 30 min, small crystals are
> separated and stirring is continued for 30 min. Then 2,3:4,5-di-O-isopropylidene-
> aldehydo-D-arabinose (**150.1**, 6.91 g, 30 mmol) is added and the stirred reaction
> mixture is kept at −80°C for 2 h. It is then warmed to −20°C, and after 5 h it is
> poured onto ice water. The pH is adjusted to 1 with concentrated hydrochloric
> acid, the mixture is extracted with ether (3 × 100 ml), and the organic phase is
> washed with saturated aqueous sodium hydrogencarbonate, dried (MgSO₄), and
> concentrated. The residue is dissolved in 20 ml of ethyl acetate, and slow addition
> of petroleum ether results in the crystallization of the product (5.3 g, 60%).
>
> B. A solution of the acrylamide **150.2** (4.0 g, 13.36 mmol) in THF (120 ml) is
> treated with lithium diisopropylamide (29.4 mmol) as described in method A. HMPA
> (7 ml, 40.2 mmol) is added to the resulting suspension of the dianion when the
> precipitate dissolves completely. After 1 h the sugar **150.1** (3.68 g, 16.03 mmol) is
> added, and after completion of the reaction workup is carried out as described in
> method A, to obtain 5.3 g (75%) of colourless crystalline **150.3**, m.p. 113–113.5°C,
> $[\alpha]_D^{21}$ +197 (c = 1 in chloroform).

If *tert*-butoxyacrylic amides (**150.5**) are employed as the functionalized β-lithioacrylic acid derivatives both epimers—the D-*manno*-oct-2-enosonic amide (**150.6**) and the corresponding *gluco*-derivative **150.7**—are produced.[64]

Schmidt et al.[65] have found that the reaction of 2,3:4,5-di-O-isopropylidene-*aldehydo*-D-arabinose with functionalized β-lithioacrylic ester educts, derived from pyrrolidine and alkyl acetylenedicarboxylates, proceeds with a diastereoselectivity opposite those discussed in the preceding paragraphs, and thus from the primary chain-extended product 3-deoxy-D-*gluco*-2-octulosonic acid (D-*gluco*-Kdo), an unnatural *configurational isomer of Kdo* can be obtained (Fig. 1.151).

Detailed studies have revealed that the educts produced from dialkyl acetylenedicarboxylates (**151.1**) and secondary amines (**151.2**) are mainly the mixtures of the E/Z isomers, wich can be transformed into the esters of (E)-2-(1-alkylamino)butenedicarboxylic acid (**151.3**) by thermal treatment. Then chain extension of 2,3:4,5-di-O-isopropylidene-*aldehydo*-D-arabinose (**151.5**) with the lithioanalog (**151.4**) of **151.3** leads to a mixture of

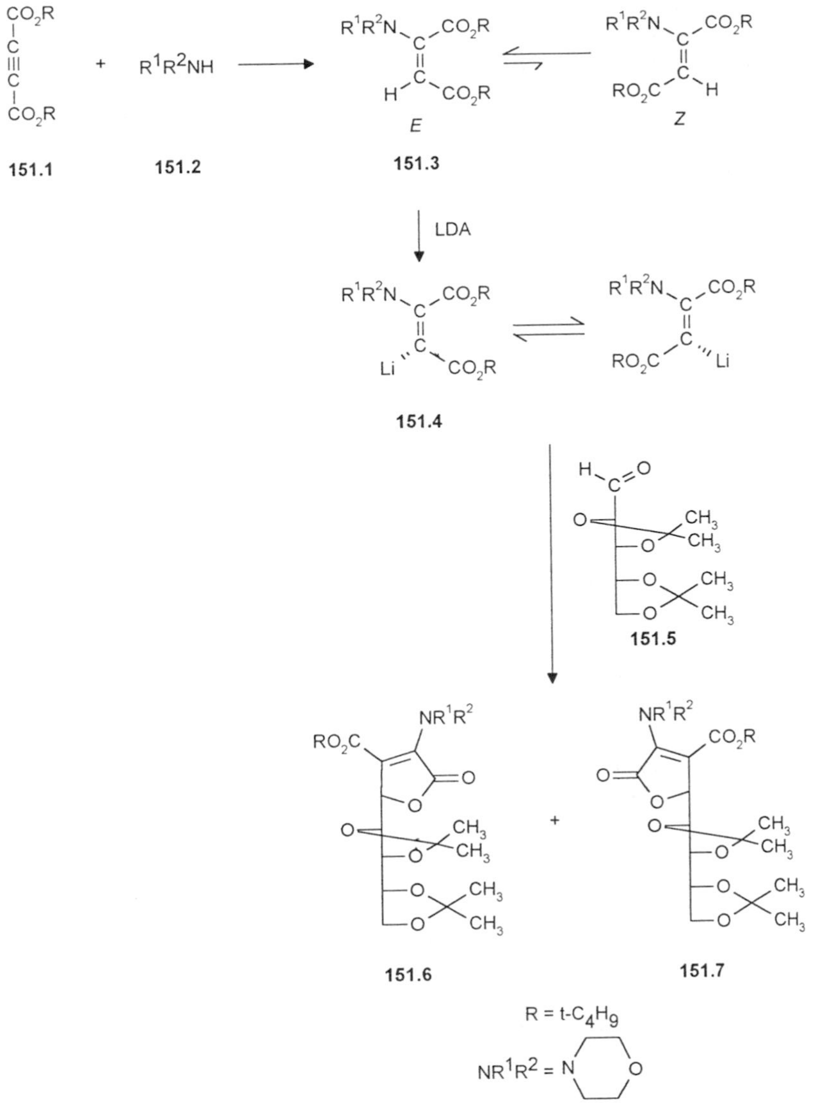

FIGURE 1.151

2,3-dideoxy-5,6:7,8-di-O-isopropylidene-3-(alkoxycarbonyl)-2-alkylamino-
D-*gluco*- (**151.6**) and D-*manno*-2-octeno-1,4-lactone (**151.7**).

> *Preparation of 2,3-dideoxy-3-(tert-butoxycarbonyl)-5,6:7,8-di-O-isopropylidene-2-(4-morpholinyl)-D-gluco- (151.6, R = t-butyl; NR¹R² = morpholinyl) and -D-manno-2-octeno-1,4-lactone (151.7, R = t-butyl; NR¹R² = morpholinyl)*[65] A mixture of di-*tert*-butyl acetylenedicarboxylate (1 g, 4.42 mmol) and morpholine (1.16 ml, 13.26 mmol) in ether is maintained at room temperature for 75 min, and

then the volatile components are distilled off at 1.33 kPa. The residue is taken up with petroleum ether at 0°C to obtain 0.659 g (48%) of di-*tert*-butyl (*E*)-2-(4-morpholinyl)-butenate (**151.3**, R = *tert*-butyl; R^1R^2 = morpholinyl) with m.p. 128–129°C. When the remaining material, or the preceding, original residue is heated under reflux in cyclohexane for 90 min, the syrupy (*Z*)-isomer of **151.3** can be obtained. Then 1 mmol of (**151.3**) dissolved in dry THF (5 ml) is lithiated with 1.2 mmol of LDA in dry THF (10 ml) at −90°C, and after 2 h a solution of the *aldehydo*-sugar **151.5** (1.5 mmol) in THF (5 ml) is added. The temperature is allowed to rise to −80°C, and the mixture is kept at this temperature for 2 h and then at −45°C for 12 h. It is poured into saturated aqueous ammonium chloride (100 ml), and the aqueous layer is extracted with ether (3 × 50 ml), dried over MgSO$_4$, and concentrated. The residue is taken up with a small volume of ether, concentrated and purified by means of flash column chromatography (eluant: 1:3 ethyl acetate–hexane) to obtain a 4:1 *gluco–manno* mixture. The *gluco*-compound (**151.6**) can be isolated by treating this mixture with petroleum ether, m.p. 116–118°C, $[\alpha]_D^{20}$ +46.6 (*c* = 1 in chloroform), but the *manno*-derivative **151.7** cannot be isolated in pure form.

Figure 1.152 gives several additional examples of chain extension with lithioorganic compounds.[67–72]

Nucleophilic acylation with 2-lithiodithiane, introduced by See-bach,[73,74] has emerged as a very important tool for chain extension of saccharide derivatives. This reagent and its recently developed related analogs are easily react with electrophilic substances such as carbonyl compounds, anhydro derivatives, or alkylhalides. The procedure involves the introduction of an 1,3-dithiane moiety, which contains a carbonyl group masked as a cyclic dithioacetal, to be regenerated on dedithioacetalation in the following step. The present methodology for saccharide chain extensions by the application of lithiated dithiane derivatives has *contributed significantly to the development* of synthetic carbohydrate chemistry.

The first example reported in this field was the reaction[75] (Fig. 1.153) of 1,2-*O*-isopropylidene-5,6-anhydro-α-D-glucofuranose (**153.1**, R = H) to give rise to 80% of 6-deoxy-6-*C*-(1,3-dithiane-2-yl)-1,2-*O*-isopropylidene-α-D-glucofuranose (**153.2, R = H**). The chain extension also proceeds readily with sugars carrying an aldehyde function.[76–78] With 2-methyl-1,3-dithiane (**154.2**) the chain extension proceeds more slowly, and Figure 1.154 shows a related transformation of 1,2:3,4-di-*O*-isopropylidene-D-galacto-pyranos-1,5-ulose (**154.1**) into 8-deoxy-1,2:3,4-di-*O*-isopropylidene-L-*glycero*-α-D-*galacto*-octos-7-ulose propylene dithioacetal (**154.3**), representing the key step of a synthesis[79] of *methyl α-L-lincosaminide*.

As an example of the cleavage of a terminal anhydro ring with 2-lithiodithiane (Fig. 1.153), the reaction[80] of 1,2-*O*-isopropylidene-3-*O*-methyl-5,6-anhydro-α-D-glucofuranose (**153.1**, R = CH$_3$) is to be carried out as follows.

Preparation[80] *of 6-deoxy-6-*C-*(1,3-dithian-2-yl)-1,2-O-isopropylidene-3-O-methyl-α-D-glucofuranose (153.2, R = CH$_3$)* A solution of 2-lithiodithiane (0.78 g) in DMF (8 ml) is added to a solution of the sugar **153.1** (R = CH$_3$) in HMPA

Refs.

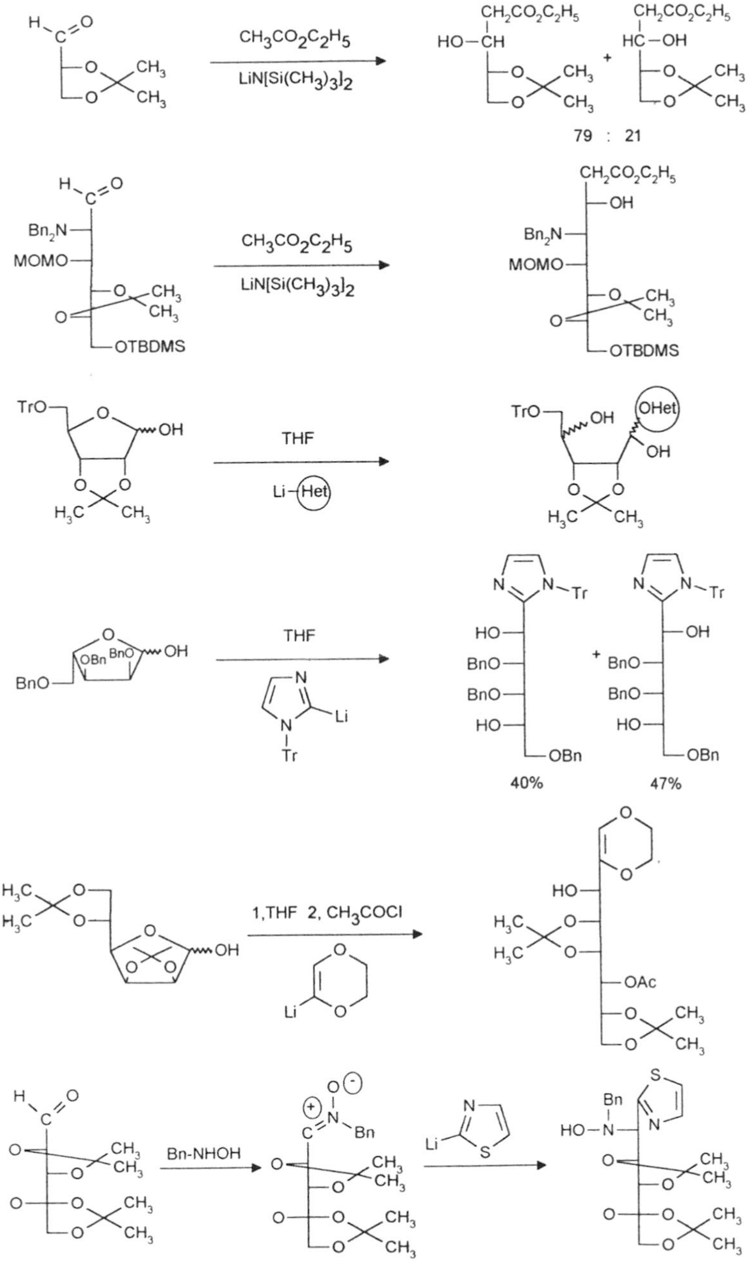

67

68

69

70

71

72

FIGURE 1.152

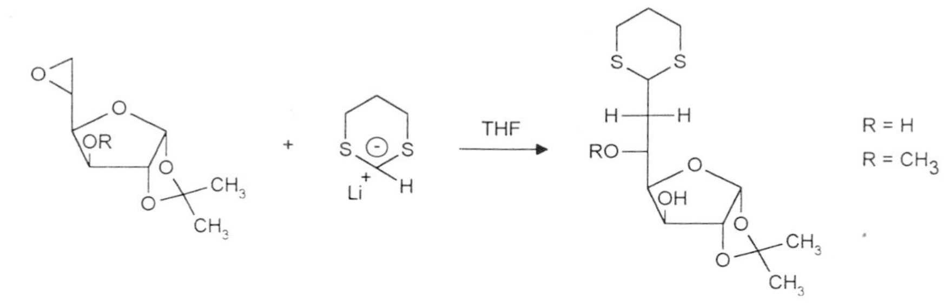

153.1 153.2

FIGURE 1.153

(5 ml). After remaining at −20°C for 3 h, the mixture is kept at 0°C overnight and diluted with ice water. It is then extracted with toluene, dried, and concentrated, and the residue is submitted to column chromatography (eluant: 2 : 3 ethyl acetate–petroleum ether) to obtain 1.7 g (85%) of syrupy **153.2** (R = CH_3).

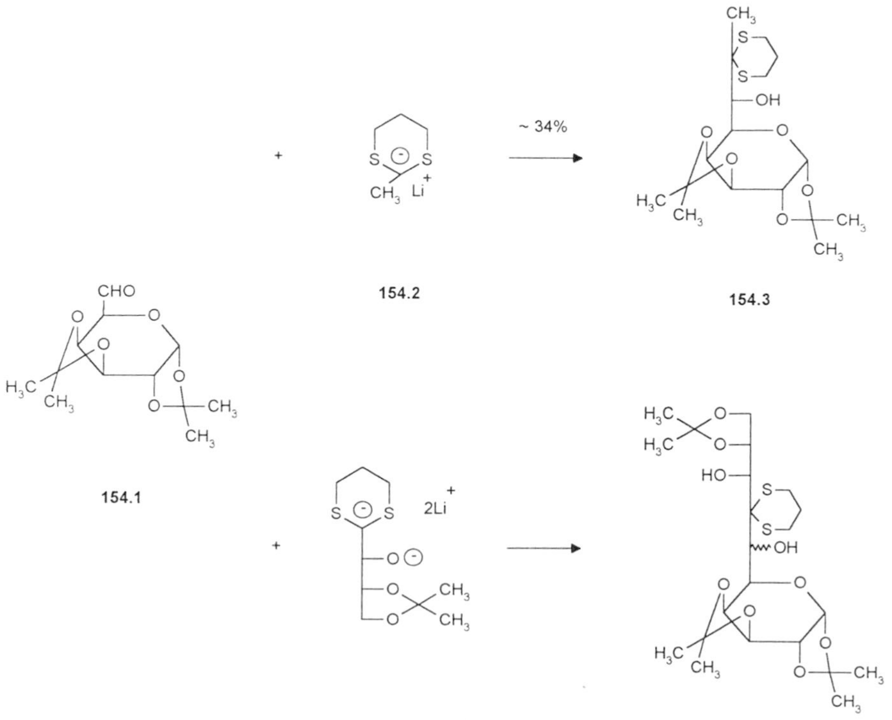

154.1 154.2 154.3 154.4 154.5

FIGURE 1.154

A stable dianion (**154.4**) could be generated from 3,4-O-isopropylidene-
D-erythrose trimethylene dithioacetal, and the chain extension (Fig. 1.154)
of the sugar **154.1** with this dianion gave[81] the functionalized decose **154.5.**

The stereoselectivity of the preceding chain elongation reactions with
2-lithio-1,3-dithiane derivatives can be attributed to chelation with the educt
(in THF as the solvent), and this is utilized in the preparation[82] of L-*glycero*-
D-*manno*-heptose. The three oxygen functions of 2,3:5,6-di-O-isopropyli-
dene-D-mannofuranose (**155.1**) at carbons C-1, C-2, and C-4 is coordinated
with the lithium reagent **155.2**, and the steric arrangement of this coordination is facilitated by the *manno*-configuration of the sugar (Fig. 1.155). In
such lithium chelations, the attack of the anion proceeds from the *si* side,
and thus with 2.5 eq of 2-lithio-1,3-dithiane, the transformation is highly
diastereoselective to furnish[82] 77% of 3,4:6,7-di-O-isopropylidene-D-
glycero-D-*galacto*-heptose trimethylene dithioacetal (**155.3**).

*Chain extension of 2,3:5,6-di-O-isopropylidene-D-mannofuranose (155.1) with
2-lithio-1,3-dithiane (155.2)*[82]   In a 2-liter three-necked round-bottomed flask, 1,3-
dithiane (82 g, 0.682 mol) is dissolved in THF (820 ml) under nitrogen atmosphere.
After cooling to −40°C, *n*-butyllithium (12.5 M in hexane, 60 ml, 0.75 mol) in
hexane (20 ml) is added dropwise over 30 min. The mixture is allowed to warm to
−20°C for a half an hour and then cooled, again, to −40°C. In another 2-liter three-
necked round-bottomed flask, the sugar **155.1** (71 g, 0.273 mol, previously dried in
high *vacuo*) is dissolved in THF (710 ml) and cooled to −40°C. The two flasks are
connected with a Teflon tubing (3 mm i.d.), and the solution of the lithiated dithiane
is transferred (by a slight pressure of N$_2$) into that of the sugar in a rate such that
the temperature does not exceed −50°C. The reaction mixture is stirred at −40°C

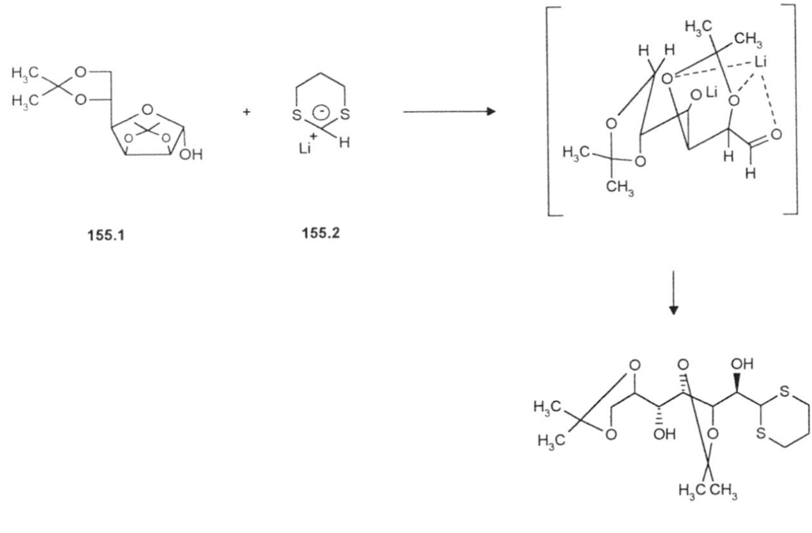

155.1   155.2

155.3

FIGURE 1.155

for 2 days then at −15°C for 3 days, and hydrolyzed with ice (20 g) in a 5-liter flask. After completion of the reaction, the mixture is concentrated, the residue is taken up with chloroform (500 ml), water (1 liter) is added, and the pH is adjusted to almost neutral by the addition of 2 N hydrochloric acid (370 ml). The organic layer is separated, washed with water (3 × 200 ml) and concentrated. The syrupy residue is dissolved in ether (1.2 liters), and after addition of petroleum ether (b.p. 60–70°C, ~0.6 liter) the product **155.3** is crystallized. Yield: 80 g (77%), m.p. 139°C, $[\alpha]_D^{20}$ −10 (c = 8.5 in pyridine).

By a careful separation procedure, the two additional isomers can also be isolated. A further, quite useful experimental description[59] reports on the formation of 97% of methyl 2,3-*O*-isopropylidene-α-L-*talo*-hexodialdo-1,4-furanoside trimethylene dithioacetal (**156.3**) and 3% of the corresponding β-D-*allo* isomer **156.4** on chain extension of methyl 2,3-*O*-isopropylidene-β-D-*ribo*-pentodialdo-1,4-furanoside **156.1** with 2-lithio-1,3-dithiane (**156.2**) (Fig. 1.156).

Chain extension of 2,3-O-isopropylidene-β-D-ribo-pentodialdo-1,4-furanoside (156.1) with 2-lithio-1,3-dithiane (156.2)[59]   A stirred solution of sublimated 1,3-dithiane (10.7 g, 89.5 mmol) in dry THF (150 ml) is cooled to −30 ± 5°C and a solution of *n*-butyllithium in hexane (1.47 M, 67 ml) is added through a syringe in a rate that corresponds to ~10 ml/min. The pale-yellow solution is stirred at −30°C for a further 1 h, cooled to −78°C, and to this solution is added, through a syringe, a solution of the sugar 156.1 (9.46 g, 46.8 mmol) in freshly distilled THF (50 ml) in a rate of ~5 ml/min. The temperature of the mixture is kept between −78 and −60°C for 1 h; at this time no unreacted *aldehydo*-sugar can be detected by TLC (99:1 chloroform–methanol). The reaction mixture is treated with saturated aqueous ammonium chloride (500 ml) and extracted with ethyl acetate. The organic phase is washed with aqueous NaHCO₃ and water, dried over MgSO₄, and concentrated. Separation of the mixture of the isomers **156.3** and **156.4** is carried out by chromatography (eluant: chloroform), to isolate, first, the less polar β-D-allose derivative **156.4** (0.45 g, 3%), m.p. 84–85°C (from ether–hexane), followed by the major product: methyl 2,3-*O*-isopropylidene-α-L-*talo*-hexodialdo-1,4-furanoside trimethylene dithioacetal (**156.3**), as a solidifying syrup (14.13 g, 97%), m.p. 73–74°C (from ether–hexane), $[\alpha]_D^{21}$ −44.4 (c = 0.9 in methanol).

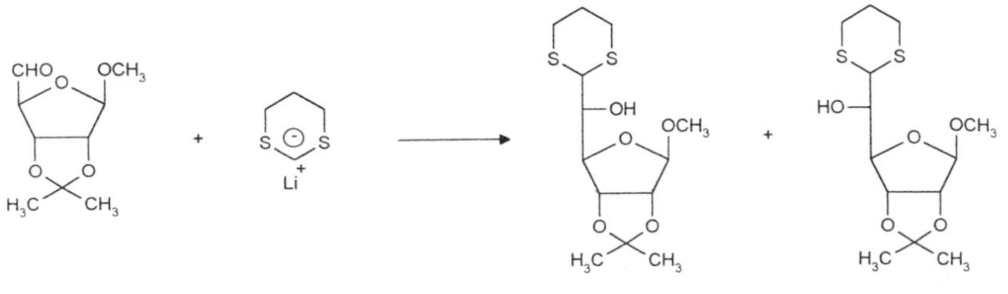

156.1   156.2   156.3   156.4

97 : 3

FIGURE 1.156

Lithiodithiane and its derivatives are also suitable for chain extensions by opening of an anhydro function.[83] Such a strategy is quite useful for the preparation of higher-carbon sugar lactones, which are *key intermediates to Kdo* and its homologs (discussed later). Thus, 1,2-anhydro-3,5:4,6-di-*O*-ethylidene-L-gulitol (**157.1**) was treated with the anion of 2-ethoxycarbonyl-1,3-dithiane (**157.2**) in benzene/DMF to give,[84] as a result of epoxide-ring opening and subsequent lactonization, 2-(1,3-dithiano)-2,3-dideoxy-5,7:6,8-di-*O*-ethylidene-L-*gulo*-octonic-1,4-lactone (**157.3**), as shown in Figure 1.157.

*2-(1,3-Dithiano)-2,3-dideoxy-5,7:6,8-di-O-ethylidene-L-gulo-octonic-1,4-lactone (**157.3**)*[84]   To a suspension of sodium hydride (0.45 g) in benzene (18 ml), 2-ethoxycarbonyl-1,3-dithiane (**157.2**; 2.78 g, 15 mmol) in 6 ml of DMF is added dropwise with external cooling (0°C) under argon atmosphere. The mixture is stirred for 30 min, and left at room temperature overnight, and then a solution of 1,2-anhydro-3,5:4,6-di-*O*-ethylidene-L-gulitol (**157.1**; 2.16 g, 10 mmol) in benzene (10 ml) is added. Stirring is continued for an additional 1 h, and the mixture is heated under reflux for 1 h. The pH of the cooled solution is adjusted to 1–2 by the addition of 10% aqueous sulfuric acid and is extracted with chloroform (3 × 20 ml). The combined extract is washed with water until neutral, dried over $MgSO_4$, and concentrated, and the residue is chromatographed on an aluminium oxide column (eluant: 14:1 benzene–ether). The fractions with $R_f = 0.55$ are combined and evaporated to furnish 1.2 g (33%) of the syrupy lactone **157.3**, $[\alpha]_D^{20}$ −4.9 ($c = 1.58$ in chloroform).

Less often the dithiane function is introduced by nucleophilic substitution, such as in the case of the preparation of 1-deoxy-1-*C*-(1,3-dithianyl)-D-erythritol from 2,4-*O*-ethylidene-1-halo-erythritols (HMPA, −20°C, 16 h), and a similar procedure has been used[85] to obtain 5-deoxy-5-*C*-(1,3-dithianyl)-2,3-*O*-isopropylidene-β-D-ribofuranose with 43% yield.

Nucleophilic substitution of the suitably protected mannitol **158.2** with the cyclic ethylene dithioacetal derivative **158.1** of glyoxylic acid (Fig. 1.158) afforded the key intermediate **158.3** of a *modern synthesis of Kdo,* reported by Shiba *et al.*[86] On removal of the protecting groups of **158.3** (Zemplén *O*-deacylation, dedithioacetalization with NBS, subsequent treatment with

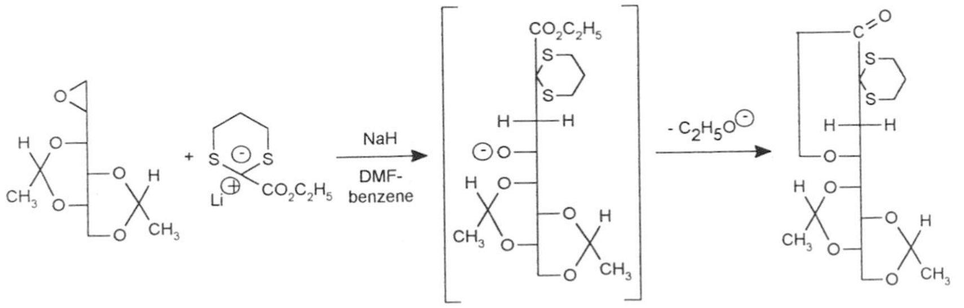

157.1   157.2

FIGURE 1.157

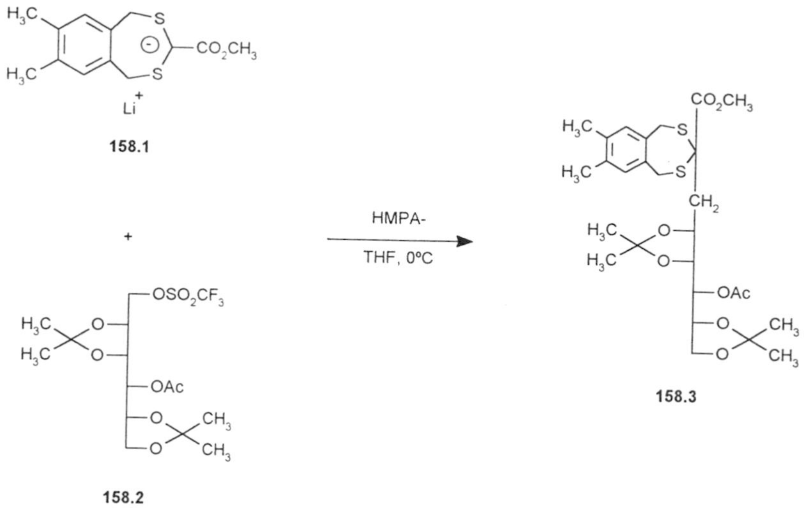

FIGURE 1.158

90% acetic acid, and alkaline hydrolysis with 0.1 N NaOH) readily furnished the target compound.

In another synthesis of *Kdo,* van Boom and coworkers[87] applied the reaction of a similar, lithiated ethylene dithioacetal derivative (**159.2**) of glyoxylic acid with the cyclic 1,4-sulfate (**159.1**) of 2,3:5,6-di-*O*-isopropylidene-D-mannitol (Fig. 1.159). This procedure affords the desired *Kdo,* with an overall yield of 57%, in five steps—including hydrolysis of the sulfate moiety and dedithioacetalization (with NBS) of the product **159.3**. By means of a similar ring-opening reaction of methyl 2,3-*O*-isopropylidene-α-D-mannofuranose-5,6-cyclosulfate (**159.4**) with 2-lithiodithiane (**159.5**), the derivatives of 6-deoxy-D-*manno*-heptose (such as **159.6**) are readily available.[88]

For the chain extension of the enone **160.1** Paulsen and Bünsch[88] have applied the lithiated ethylene dithioacetal of ethyl glyoxylate (**160.2**) to obtain the 1,4-addition products **160.3** and **160.4,** separable by chromatography (see Fig. 1.160).

*Ethyl 3,7-anhydro-6,8-benzylidene-4-deoxy-D-ribo-oct-2,5-diulosonate-2-ethylene dithioacetal (**160.3**) and the corresponding D-lyxo derivative (**160.4**)*[88] Diisopropylamine (1 ml, 7 mmol) is cooled to 0°C under nitrogen, and a solution of *n*-butyllithium in hexane (1.5 M, 4.4 ml, 6.6 mmol) is added. After 10 min, 5 ml of dry THF is added, and the mixture is stirred at room temperature for 10 min and cooled to −78°C. Then a solution of ethyl 1,3-dithiolane-2-carboxylate (1.07 g, 6 mmol) in THF (4 ml) is added dropwise over a period of 30 min and the mixture is stirred at this temperature for a further 30 min. This mixture is treated with a dropwise addition (over 30 min) of a solution of 1,5-anhydro-4,6-*O*-benzylidene-2-deoxy-D-*erythro*-hex-1-en-3-ulose (**160.1,** 1.4 g, 6 mmol) and stirred for further 90 min. Then 5 g of ammonium chloride is added, the reaction mixture is poured into 100 ml of aqueous ammonium chloride and extracted with chloroform, the

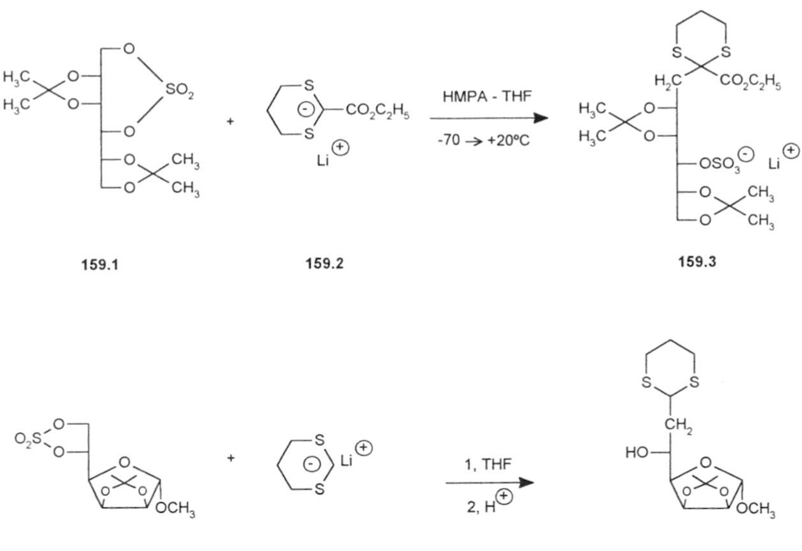

159.1   159.2   159.3

159.4   159.5   159.6

FIGURE 1.159

organic layer is washed with water several times and dried over MgSO$_4$, and the solvent is distilled off under reduced pressure. The residue, consisting of two major products with $R_f = 0.37$ and 0.27 (1 : 2 ethyl acetate–hexane), is submitted to column chromatography on silicagel (eluant: 1 : 2 ethyl acetate–hexane) and the pure products are crystallized from ether–hexane to afford 0.31 g (13%) of **160.3**, m.p. 160–

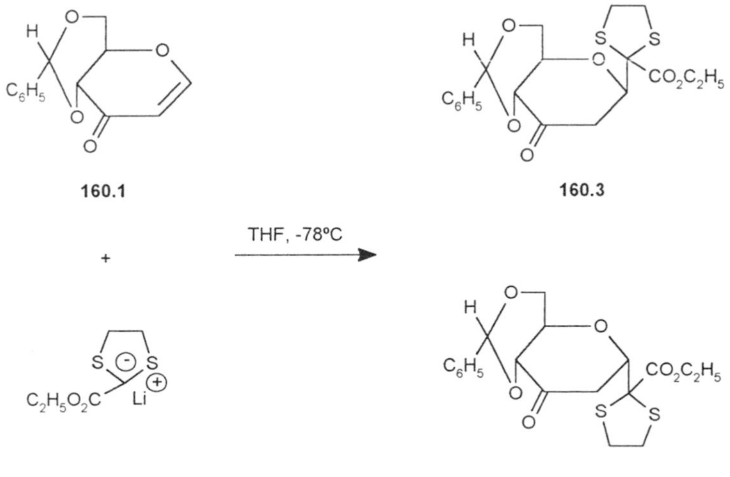

160.1   160.3

160.2   160.4

FIGURE 1.160

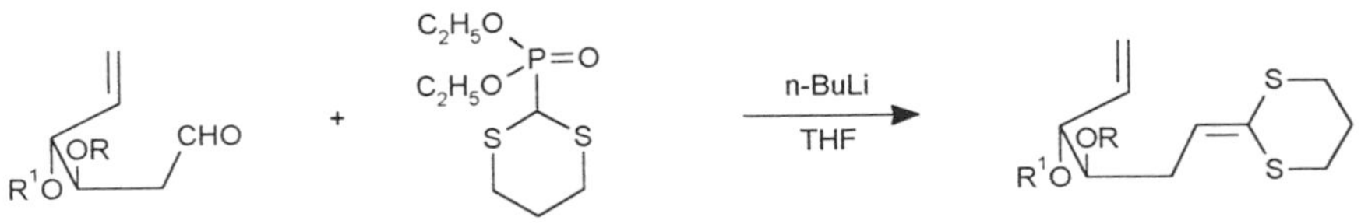

R = MOM
R^1 = TBDMS

FIGURE 1.161

161°C, $[\alpha]_D$ −19.4 (c = 0.5 in chloroform) and 0.92 g (37%) of **160.4**, m.p. 124–126°C, $[\alpha]_D$ −2.6 (c = 2.8 in chloroform).

Ferrier and Tyler[89] have described the chain extension of 4-O-(tert-butyl-dimethylsilyl)-2,5,6-trideoxy-3-O-(methoxymethyl)-D-*threo-aldehydo*-hex-5-enose (**161.1**) with diethyl 1,3-dithian-2-yl-phosphonate (**161.2**) to result in the chain-extended chiral diolefine (**161.3**), shown in Figure 1.161.

By employing 2-lithio-1,3-dithiane (**162.2**) as carbon nucleophile, several investigators treated[90,91] 2,3:5,6-di-O-isopropylidene-L-gulonolactone (**162.1**) with this reagent, and the crystalline product **162.3** of the transformation (Fig. 1.162) could be obtained[91] without chromatography, although in moderate yield.

1-(1,3-Dithian-2-yl)-2,3:5,6-di-O-isopropylidene-β-L-gulofuranose (**162.3**)[91]
To a solution of n-butyllithium [prepared from lithium (0.2 g, 0.03 mol) and n-butyl bromide (2.5 g, 0.02 mol)] in ether (30 ml), 200 ml of dry hexane is added and cooled to −75°C, and a solution of 1,3-dithiane (1.2 g, 0.01 mol) in THF (30 ml) is added dropwise over 30 min at −40°C. After stirring for 45 min at −75°C, a solution of the lactone **162.1** (2.5 g, 0.01 mol) in THF (100 ml) is added and

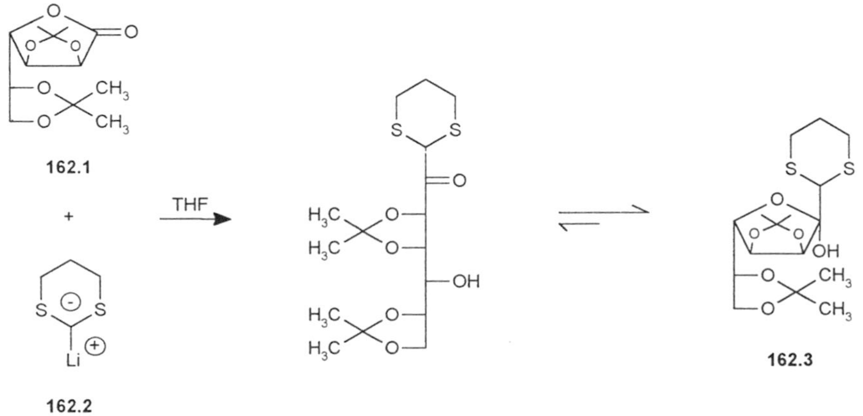

FIGURE 1.162

stirring is continued for an additional 3–4 h. Then aqueous ammonium chloride is added, the mixture is extracted with ether, and the organic layer is washed with water and dried over MgSO$_4$. Evaporation of the solvent results in the precipitation of 1.2 g (32%) of the pure title product **162.3,** as colorless needles with m.p. 131–135°C.

The reaction of the trimethylsilylated D-*glucono*-1,5-lactone **163.1** with 2-lithio-1,3-dithiane (**163.2**) was performed by Horton and Priebe[92] in a one-pot operation, and conventional acetylation of the product **163.3** gave rise to the cyclic tetraacetate **163.4,** the cyclic pentaacetate **163.6,** or the open-chain hexa-*O*-acetyl compound **163.5**–depending on the reaction conditions shown in Figure 1.163.

1-C-(1,3-Dithian-2-yl)-α-D-glucopyranose (163.3)[92]   To a solution of 1,3-dithiane (4.5 g, 37.4 mmol) in dry THF (180 ml), 39.3 mmol of *n*-butyllithium is added at −55°C under an argon atmosphere. The mixture is kep at −30 to −20°C for 2.5 h and cooled to −60°C, and then a solution of 2,3,4,6-tetra-*O*-(trimethylsilyl)-D-gluconolactone (**163.1**, 17.45 g, 37.4 mmol) in THF (60 ml) is added. After stirring for 5 h at −5 to −45°C, and then for one day at −14°C, the reaction mixture is

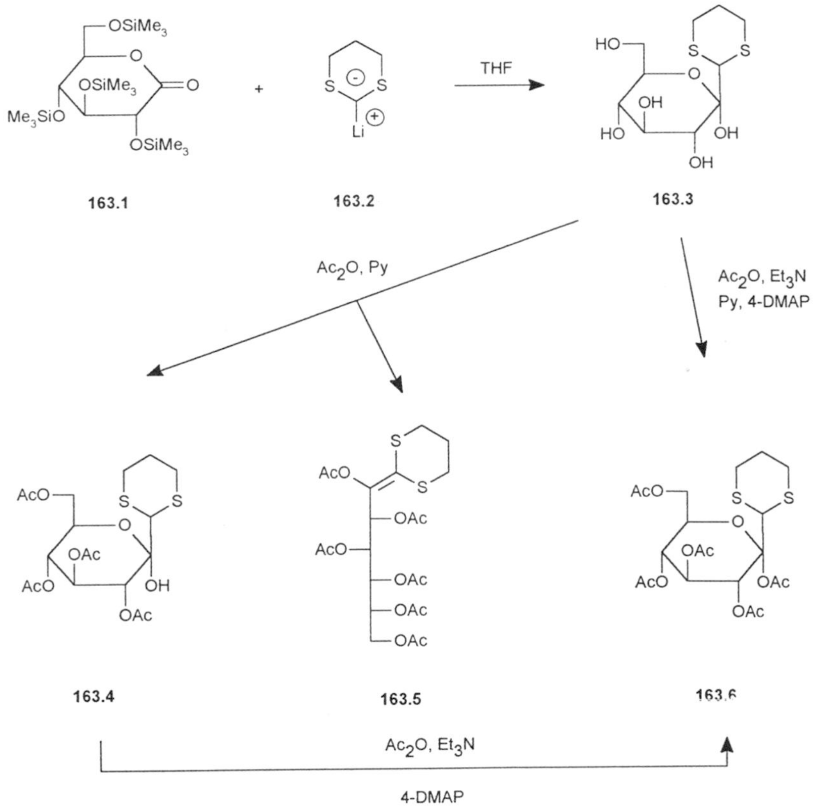

FIGURE 1.163

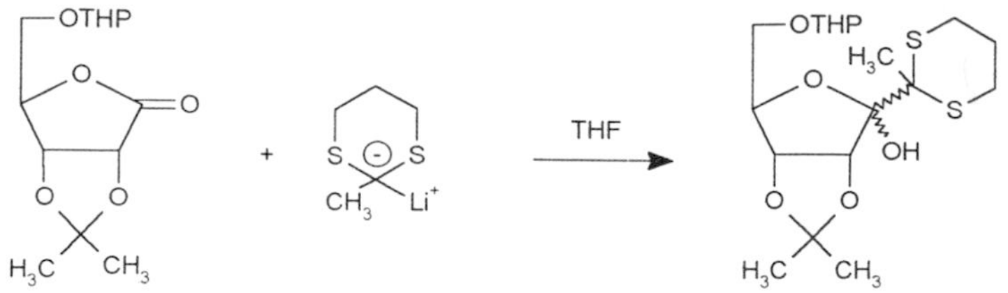

FIGURE 1.164

poured into 0.5 liter of water and extracted with pentane. The combined organic phase is washed with 7% aqueous KOH and water, dried and evaporated to a yellow syrup, that is heated under reflux in 500 ml of 50% aqueous methanol until a single spot appears (~2.5 h) on TLC (5:1 chloroform–methanol). The mixture is cooled, washed with pentane and evaporated to the pale-yellow syrupy product **163.3** (6.95 g, 62%), $[\alpha]_D^{25}$ +31 (c = 1 in chloroform).

The chain extension of the ribonolactone **164.1** to C-(1,3-dithian-2-methyl-2-yl)-2,3-O-isopropylidene-5-O-tetrahydropyranyl-D-ribofuranose (**164.2**) was carried out in an essentially similar way[79] (Fig. 1.164), and lithiated aromatic heterocycles have also been employed for related transformations of various sugar lactones.[93]

Attempts to broaden the scope of the chain extensions discussed above have led to the development of procedures in which the reagent to be lithiated is a sugar–dithioacetal. As an exmple, it has been shown[94] that— following lithiation—2-deoxy-3,4:5,6-di-O-isopropylidene-D-*arabino*-hexose diethyl dithioacetal (**165.1**) is susceptible to chain extension (Fig. 1.165) with methyl iodide (or benzyl bromide) to result in the heptulose derivative **165.2.**

1,3-Dideoxy-4,5:6,7-di-O-isopropylidene-D-arabino-heptulose diethyl dithioacetal (**165.2**)[94] A solution of 2-deoxy-D-*arabino*-hexose diethyl dithioacetal (2.0 g, 7.4 mmol) in acetone (35 ml) is treated with 3 drops of conc. sulfuric acid and the solution is stirred at ~25°C for 24 h. Concentrated, aqueous ammonia (1 ml, sufficient to basify the solution) is then added, the resulting suspension is filtered, and

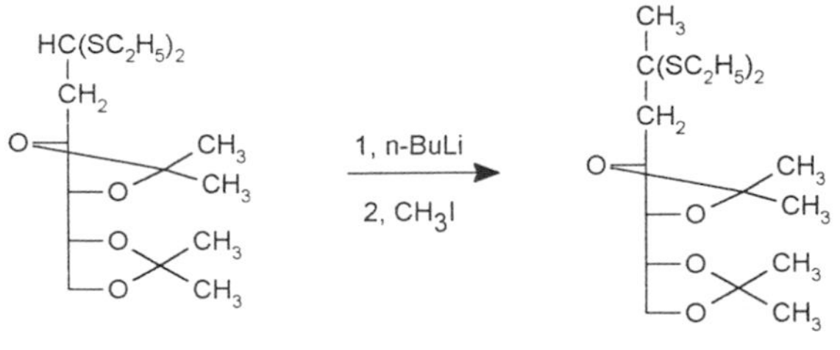

FIGURE 1.165

the filtrate is concentrated. The product, 2-deoxy-3,4:5,6-di-O-isopropylidene-D-arabino-hexose diethyl dithioacetal (**165.1**, 2.51 g, 97%), is obtained as a distillable thin syrup, b.p. 110–115°C (at 0.8 kPa), $[\alpha]_D^{25}$ −1.2 (c = 1.3 in chloroform). In a reaction vessel sealed with a septum and purged with nitrogen, a solution of **165.1** (0.5 g, 1.43 mmol) in dry oxolane (10 ml) is cooled to −30°C. n-Butyllithium (2.4 M in hexane, 1.3 ml, 3.12 mmol) is slowly added through a syringe and with stirring, and the solution is kept at −20 to −30°C for 2 h. Iodomethane (1 ml, 15.5 mmol) is then slowly added and the solution is allowed to warm to 0°C, and is kept at this temperature for 18 h. The yellowish solution is poured into water (20 ml), made neutral with acetic acid and extracted with pentane. The organic phase is washed with 5% aqueous KOH, NaHCO$_3$, and water; dried (K$_2$CO$_3$), and evaporated to the thin syrupy product **165.2**, (0.43 g, 83%), b.p. 110–115°C (at 0.8 kPa), $[\alpha]_D^{25}$ ±0, $[\alpha]_{Hg578,546,436,365}^{25}$ ±0 (c = 0.5 in chloroform).

A chain extension reaction, aimed at the introduction of a C-formyl function, was carried out with N,N-dimethylformamide, as the acylating agent,[95] and the anion of 2-deoxy-4,5-O-isopropylidene-D-erythro-pentose diethyl dithioacetal (**166.1**),[96] as shown in Figure 1.166.

> 3-Deoxy-5,6-O-isopropylidene-α,β-D-erythro-hexofuran-2-ulose 2,2-diethyl dithioacetal (**166.2**)[96]   To a cold (−20°C) solution of the dithioacetal **166.1** (522 mg, 1.86 mmol) in THF (20 ml) is added, under nitrogen atmosphere, a 2.2 N solution of n-butyllithium (2.7 ml, 5.94 mmol) in hexane. Stirring is continued at −35 to −40°C for 2 h, followed by the dropwise addition of DMF (0.5 ml, 11.8 mmol). The temperature is allowed to rise to −20°C, and stirring is continued at this temperature for 1 h. Water (2 ml) is then added, and the mixture is allowed to warm to room temperature. It is poured into water, the mixture is extracted with chloroform, and the organic phase is washed with water, dried over Na$_2$SO$_4$, and concentrated. The crude residue is purified by means of column chromatography (eluant: 3 : 1 petroleum ether–ethyl acetate) to give 0.36 g (65%) of the pure product **166.2** in form of a mixture of the α- and β anomers, $[\alpha]_D^{25}$ −14 (c = 2.4 in chloroform).

1.2.7.1.3. Chain Extension of Saccharides with Organosilicon, Organotin, and Organoboron Compounds

Like the methods discussed in the previous sections, the procedures described here are based on the addition of carbon nucleophiles to an aldehyde function, which can be present in acylated form, or as an alkylated hemiacetal (anomeric acyl compounds or glycosides). Because of the chiral centers of the saccharide molecules, asymmetric induction or diastereofacial selectivity highly influences the stereochemical outcome of these reac-

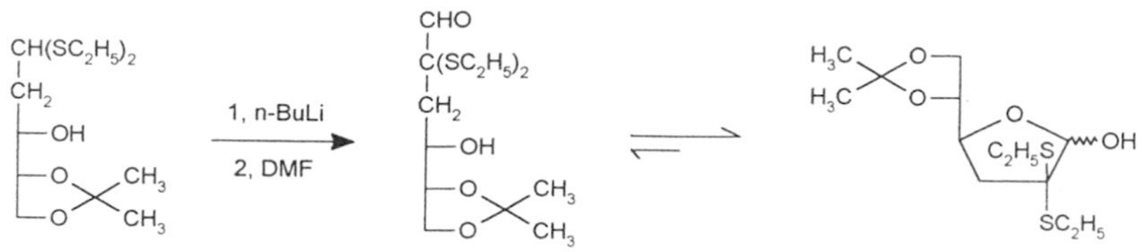

166.1   **166.2**

FIGURE 1.166

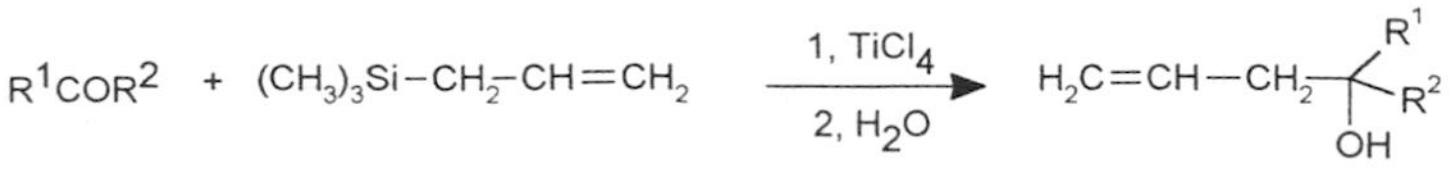

R1COR2 + (CH3)3Si–CH2–CH=CH2
1, TiCl4
2, H2O
H2C=CH–CH2
R1
R2
OH

FIGURE 1.167

tions, which have been studied and explained by various stereochemical models.[1,3,97]

Of the *organosilicon compounds* the most extensively used reagents for related chain extensions are the allyl- and propynylsilane derivatives. The idea of chain elongation of *aldehydo*-sugars with allylsilanes came from the work of Japanese chemists,[98] who have converted ketones into tertiary alcohols with allyltrimethylsilane under titanium tetrachloride-catalysis, as shown in Figure 1.167. Noyori *et al.*[99] have reported that for acetals an analogous chain extension procedure requires a catalytic amount of trimethylsilyl triflate.

From a practical point of view, the transformations involving the reaction of a formyl group, a free lactol—OH or a glycosidic center, as well as an anomeric *O*-acyl function of a saccharide with allyltrimethylsilane, are considered the most important. The product of such reactions is an anhydrodeoxyaldose (*C*-glycoside) extended with *three carbon atoms* in the chain. According to the studies of Sammakia[100] these are not formed with a direct displacement mechanism, and the observed diastereoselectivity is not due to the selective complexation of one of the two acetal oxygens, suggesting that the reaction proceeds predominantly by way of an oxocarbenium ion mechanism.

The great utility of these chain extensions is demonstrated by the huge number of literature references dealing with a related topic. Of the plethora of reported examples, Figure 1.168 shows a work of Kishi,[101] who found that the observed 53% yield can be improved up to 80% if, instead of the free, reducing sugar, the corresponding 1-*O*-(*p*-nitrobenzoate) is applied as the starting material.

The chain extension readily proceeds with open-chain sugars as well, and the reaction scheme illustrated in Figure 1.169, and involving the formation of hept-1-enitols (**169.2**) from L-tetroses (**169.1**) susceptible to ozonolysis to the desired L-hexose, has been found very useful for the synthesis[102]

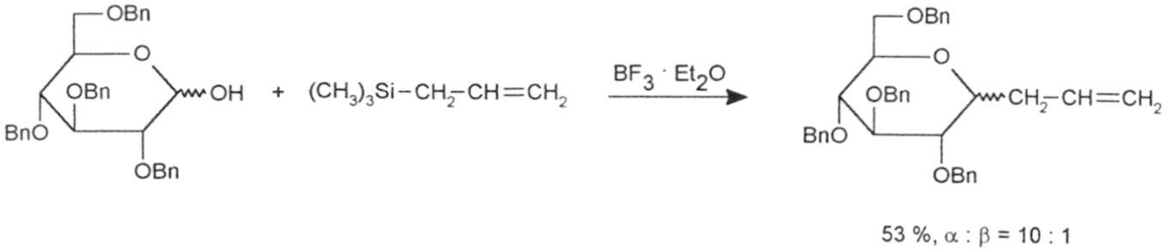

OBn
O
OBn
OH
BnO
OBn
+ (CH3)3Si–CH2–CH=CH2
BF3 · Et2O
OBn
O
OBn
CH2–CH=CH2
BnO
OBn
53 %, α : β = 10 : 1

FIGURE 1.168

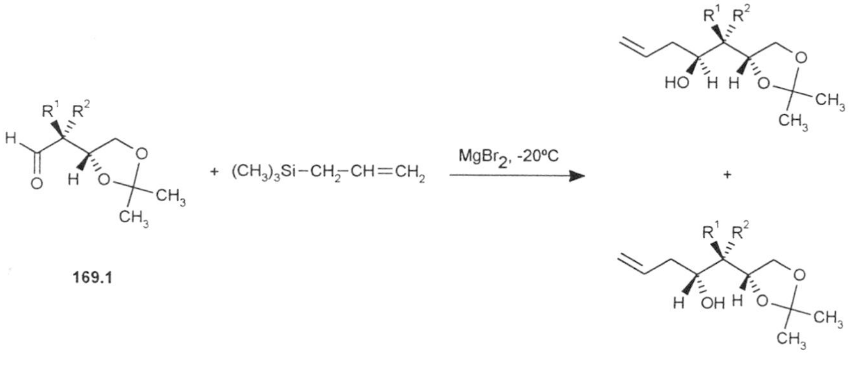

FIGURE 1.169

of the *rare L-hexoses.* Besides ensuring a favorable C-4—C-5 *syn*-stereochemistry, the role of the added magnesium bromide in this reaction is also to prevent undesired cleavage of the labile acetal protecting group, which occurs, indeed, when titanium tetrachloride is employed[102] in a similar transformation (see Fig. 1.170).

The application of trimethylsilyl trifluoromethanesulfonate was found to be very efficient in a diastereoselective chain extension[103] of 1-*O*-acetyl-2,3,5-tri-*O*-benzoyl-β-D-ribofuranose **(171.1)** into the octene derivatives **171.2** and **171.3** (Fig. 1.171).

> *Preparation of 4,7-anhydro-1,2,3-trideoxy-5,6,8-tri-O-benzoyl-D-altro-oct-1-ene* **(171.2)** *and the corresponding D-allo derivative* **(171.3)**[103] To a mixture of the ribofuranose **171.1** (5.04 g, 10 mmol) and trimethylsilyl trifluoromethanesulfonate (2.45 ml, 14 mmol) in nitromethane (50 ml) allyltrimethylsilane (2.38 ml) is added at 0°C under nitrogen atmosphere, and the reaction mixture is kept at 0°C for 5 h. Then the solvent is distilled off, the residual thick syrup is dissolved in ethyl acetate, and this solution is washed with saturated aqueous sodium hydrogencarbonate (2 × 30 ml) and saturated aqueous sodium chloride (30 ml) and dried over $MgSO_4$. After workup the syrupy residue is submitted to column chromatography (eluant: 95 : 5 toluene–ethyl acetate). According to TLC (15 : 1 hexane–ethyl acetate), the product (3.75 g, 83%) consists of the oct-1-enes (**171.2** and **171.3**) in a ratio of 8:1, and is separated on a Lobar column (particle size: B, eluant: 95:5 toluene–ethyl acetate) to give pure **171.2**, $[\alpha]_D^{23}$ +85 (c = 0.8 in chloroform) and **171.3**, $[\alpha]_D^{23}$ +39.8 (c = 1.8 in chloroform).

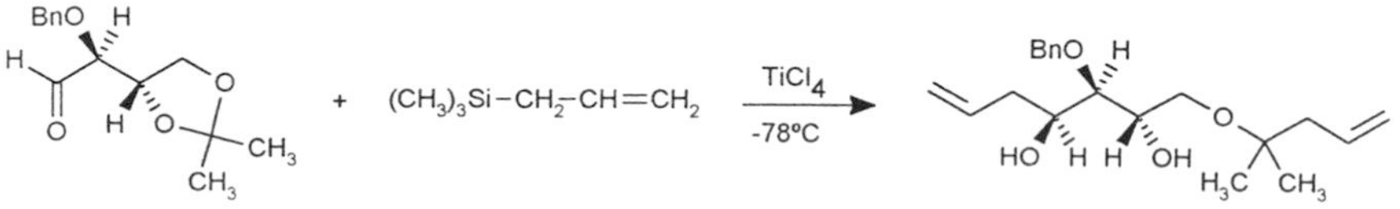

FIGURE 1.170

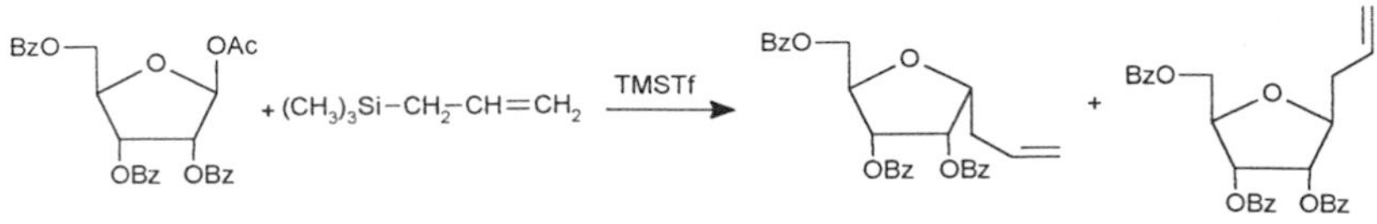

FIGURE I.171

An exclusive formation of the *altro*-isomer (**172.2**) was observed[104] when an analogous chain extension (Fig. 1.172) was carried out with the tri-*O*-benzyl analog (**172.1**) of **171.1** with allyltrimethylsilane in the presence of tritylperchlorate catalyst.

The diastereoselectivity of the chain extension reactions with allyltrimethylsilane was also studied on aldulose substrates with the primary goal of discovering the reaction conditions that would facilitate the selective formation of a single isomer. The results of these investigations,[105,106] made on the high-yielding Lewis acid–catalyzed processes are summarized in Table 1.26.

Table 1.27 summarizes[107] the influence of the reaction conditions (catalyst, solvent) on the outcome (yield, anomeric ratio) of the chain extension of penta-*O*-acetyl-*α*- and -*β*-D-galactopyranoses.

The chain extensions of saccharides with allyltrimethylsilane reported in the literature are listed in Table 1.28.[108–117] However, the data related to the results of an alternative methodology, namely, when a glycosyl halide is reacted with allyltrimethylsilane,[118] are not included in this table.

A further, successful extension of this reaction makes various functionalized saccharide derivatives easily available. In one of these approaches[119] glycals are reacted with allyltrimethylsilane, as the tendency for leaving groups at C-3 of glycals to be displaced by heteronucleophiles has been well known for a long time. The product of such a reaction[119,120] is a 2,3-unsaturated allyl-*C*-glycoside, and ulosyldienes are obtained from 2-hydroxyglycals. As an example, reported by Ferrier,[121] Figure 1.173 shows the chain extension of tetra-*O*-acetyl-2-hydroxyglycal (**173.1**) with allyltrimethylsilane leading to the nonadien-5-uloses **173.2** and **173.3**.

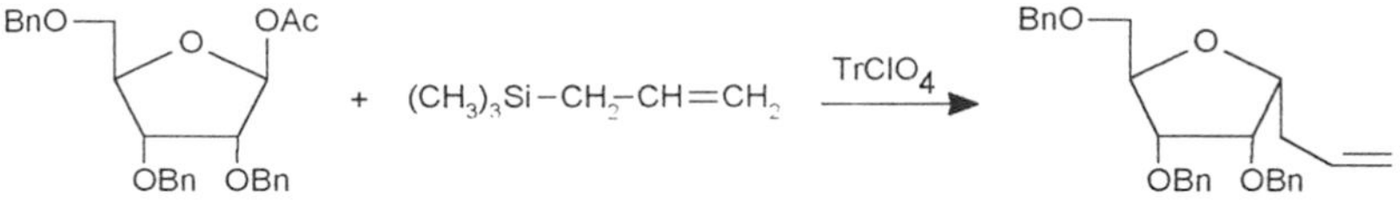

FIGURE I.172

TABLE 1.26   Chain Extension of Saccharides with Allyltrimethylsilane

Educt	Product	

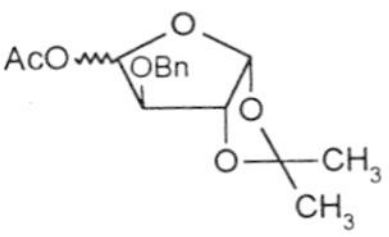

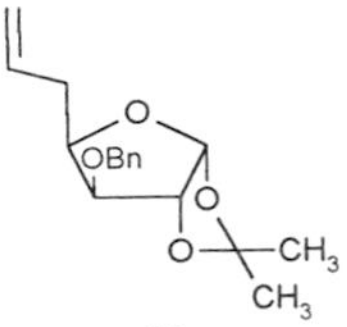

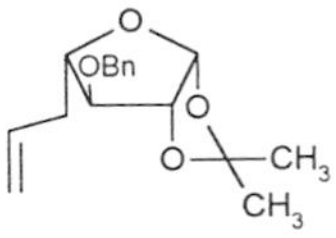

MgBr$_2$:   82   :   18
ZnBr$_2$:   15   :   85

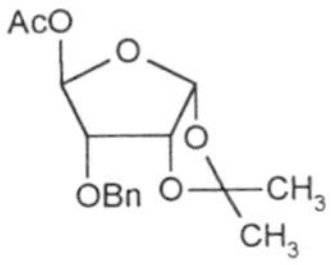

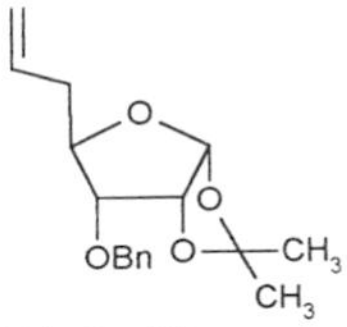

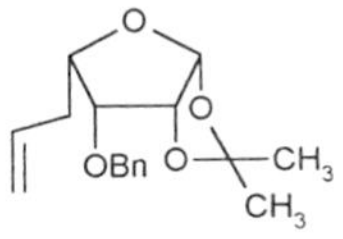

BF$_3$·(C$_2$H$_5$)$_2$O :   92   :   8
MgBr$_2$:   20   :   80

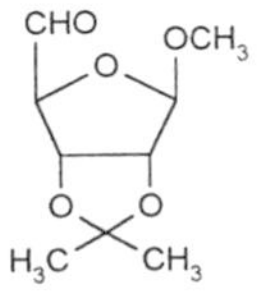

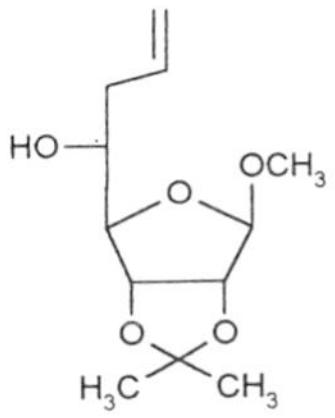

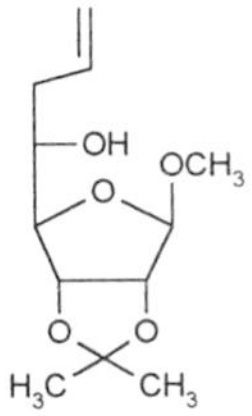

BF$_3$·(C$_2$H$_5$)$_2$O :   >20   :   1
TiCl$_4$:   <1   :   20

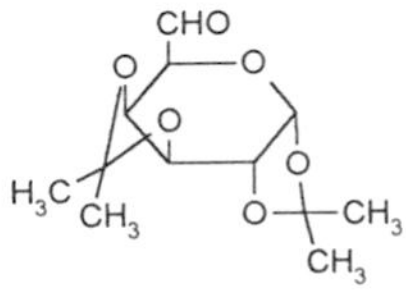

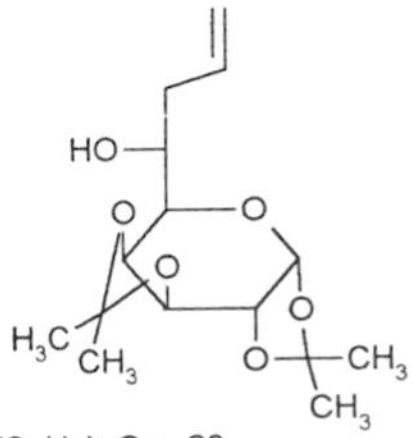

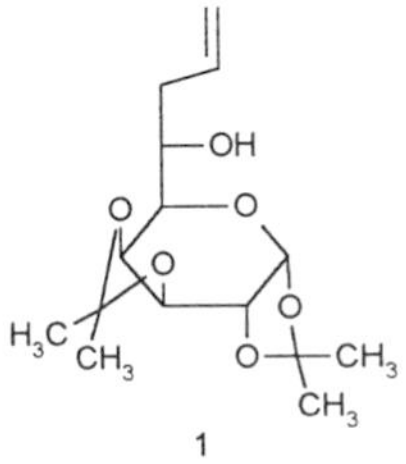

BF$_3$·(C$_2$H$_5$)$_2$O :   20   :   1
TiCl$_4$:   1   :   10

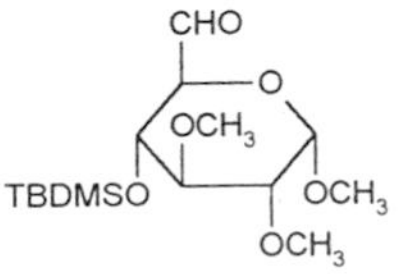

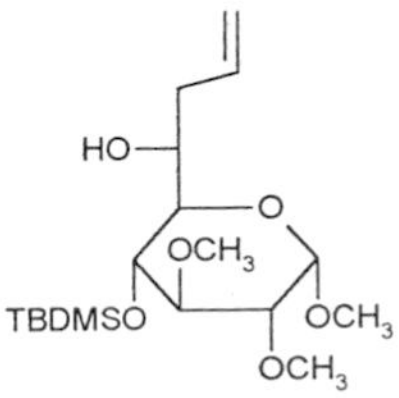

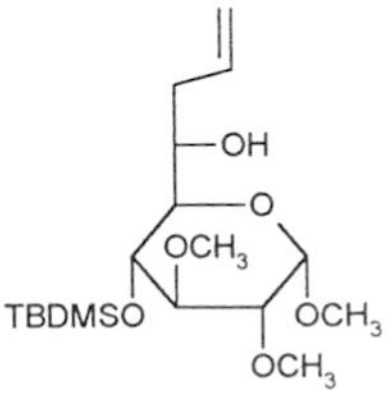

BF$_3$·(C$_2$H$_5$)$_2$O :   1   :   20
TiCl$_4$:   <1   :   20

TABLE 1.27 Reaction of Penta-O-acetyl-α-D- and Penta-O-acetyl-β-D-Galactopyranosides with Allyltrimethylsilane under Different Experimental Conditions[107]

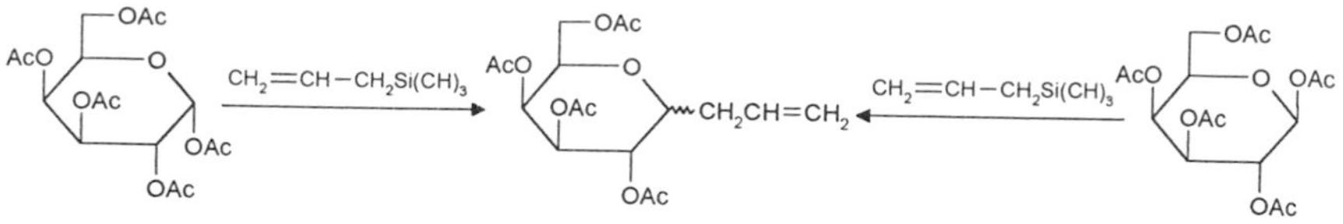

Starting galactosyl acetate	Catalyst	Solvent	Temperature °C	Time h	C-allyl product Yield (%)	C-allyl product α/β ratio
α	$BF_3 \cdot Et_2O$	CH_3CN	4	48	0	—
α	$BF_3 \cdot Et_2O$	CH_3CN	50	8	60	9:1
β	$BF_3 \cdot Et_2O$	CH_3CN	4	48	70	9:1
α	$BF_3 \cdot Et_2O$	$(ClCH_2)_2$	40	48	0	—
α	$BF_3 \cdot Et_2O$	$(ClCH_2)_2$	80	48	10	7:3
β	$BF_3 \cdot Et_2O$	$(ClCH_2)_2$	40	24	50	6:4
α	$ZnBr_2$	CH_3CN	80	48	0	—
β	$ZnBr_2$	CH_3CN	80	48	0	—
β	$ZnBr_2$	$(ClCH_2)_2$	80	24	70	6:4

1-O-Acetyl-2,6-anhydro-3,4,7,8,9-pentadeoxy-D-threo/L-erythro-nona-3,8-dien-5-ulose (173.2 and 173.3)[121] A mixture of tetra-O-acetyl-1,5-anhydro-D-*arabino*-hex-1-enitol (**173.1**, 2 g) and allyltrimethylsilane (1.4 g, 2 molar eq) in benzene (35 ml) is stirred at 20°C under nitrogen atmosphere, and boron trifluoride–diethyl ether (0.8 ml) is added over a 3-h period. The mixture is then washed with aqueous $NaHCO_3$ and water, dried ($MgSO_4$) and concentrated. Radial chromatography of the residue gives the title compound (0.51 g) as a 3:1 D-*threo* (**173.2**)/L-*erythro* (**173.3**) mixture and 1.0 g of the starting glycal **173.1**. This latter is treated as described above to afford a second fraction of the product mixture (total: 0.95 g, 75%), $[\alpha]_D^{20}$ −70 (in chloroform).

An alternative possibility[114,122,123] of the generation of the diene structure is when the organosilicon compound, to be reacted with the saccharide, already carries this named functionality. A related transformation,[122] carried out with (*E*)-2,4-pentadienyltrimethylsilane (**174.2**), is shown in Figure 1.174.

5-(Tetra-O-benzyl-α-D-glucopyranosyl)-(E)-1,3-pentadiene (174.3)[122] A solution of 2,3,4,6-tetra-O-benzyl-1-O-(*p*-nitrobenzoyl)-α-D-glucopyranose (**174.1,** 500 mg, 0.72 mmol) in dry acetonitrile (10 ml), is cooled to 0°C and boron trifluoride–diethyl ether (0.26 ml, 2.16 mmol) and freshly prepared (*E*)-penta-2,4-dienyltrimethylsilane (**174.2,** 0.39 ml, 2.16 mmol) are added. The mixture is stirred overnight under nitrogen, and the solvent is removed under reduced pressure. The residue is dissolved in dichloromethane; washed successively with water, saturated aqueous $NaHCO_3$ and water: dried ($MgSO_4$); and evaporated to a syrup, that is chromatographed on a silicagel column (eluant: 9:1 petroleum ether–ether). The

TABLE 1.28   Chain Extension of Saccharides with Allyltrimethylsilane

Educt	Product(s)	Ref(s).
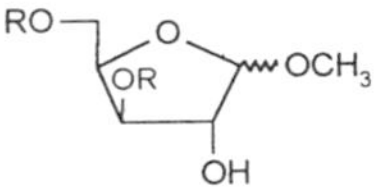	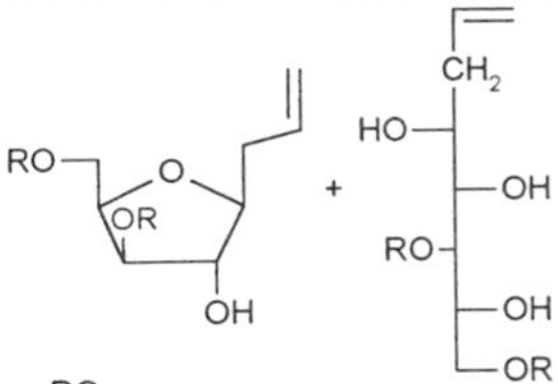	108
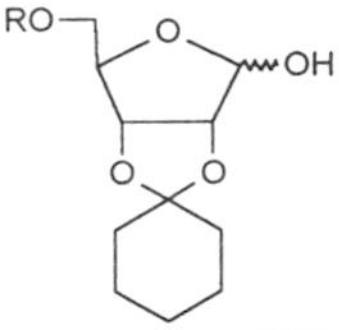	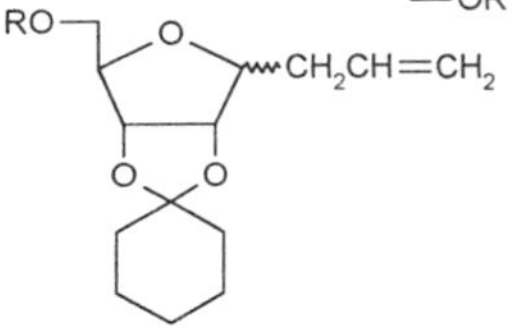	109
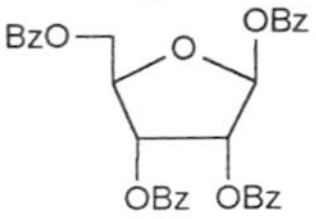	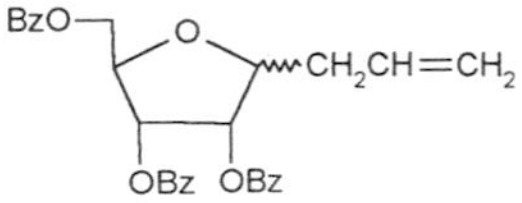	109 110
① R^1 = Ac, H, SO_2CH_3 R^2 = Bz R^3 = R = Ac ② R^3 = R^1 = R^2 = Bn, R = CH_3		111–114 115
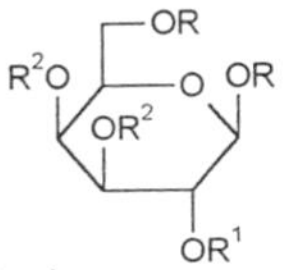 R = Ac R^1 = Ac, H, SO_2CH_3 R^2 = Bz	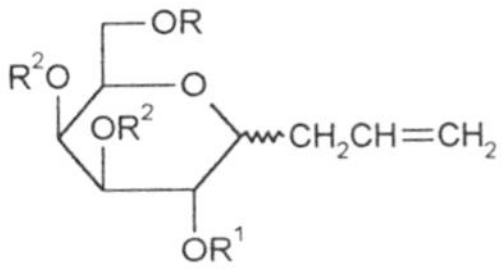	111
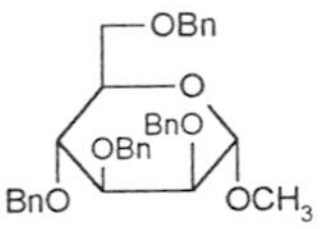	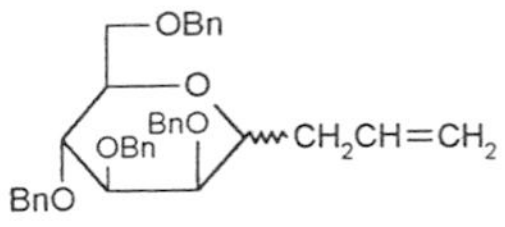	112 115
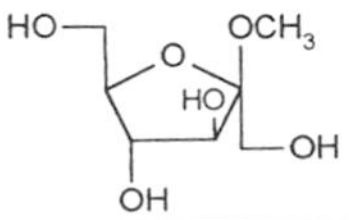	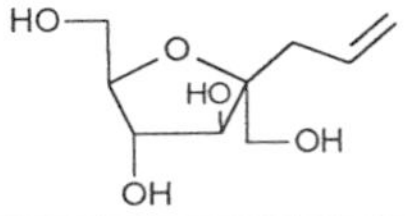	112

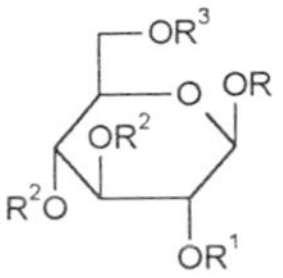

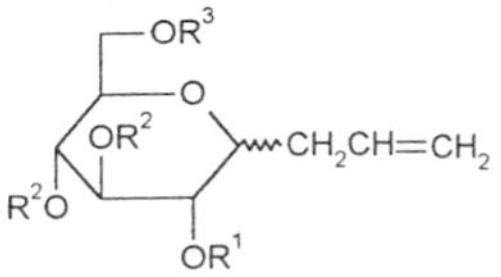

(continues)

TABLE 1.28 *(continued)*

Educt	Product(s)	Ref(s).
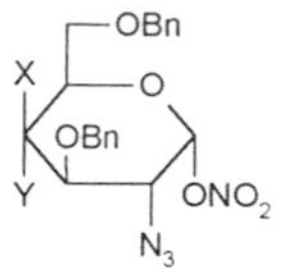	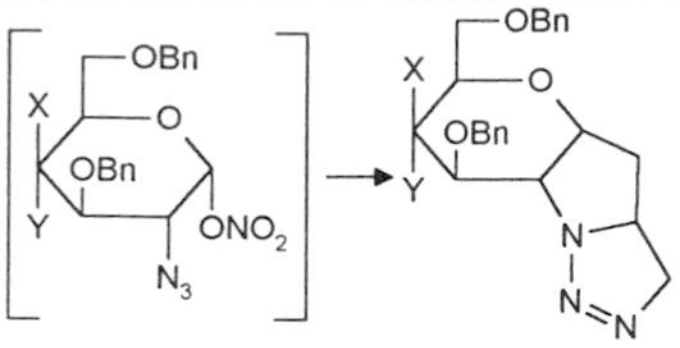	115
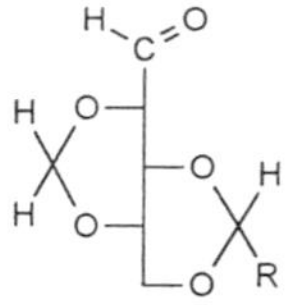	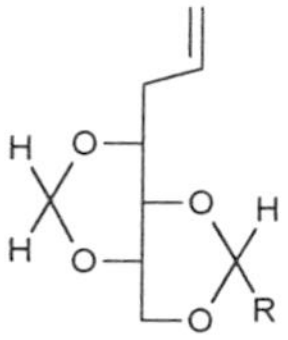 + tricyclic products	113
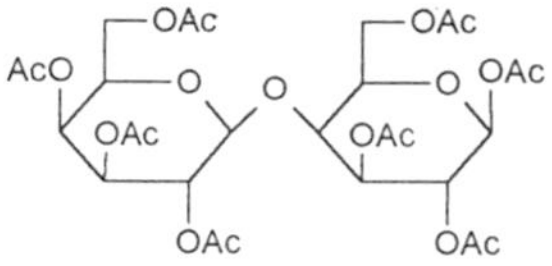	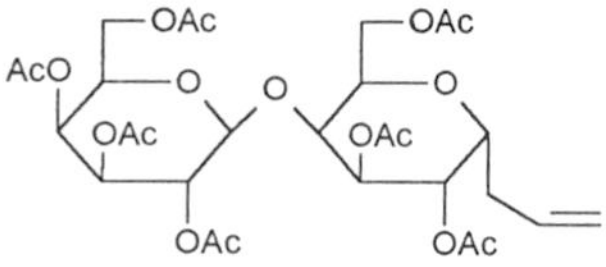	108
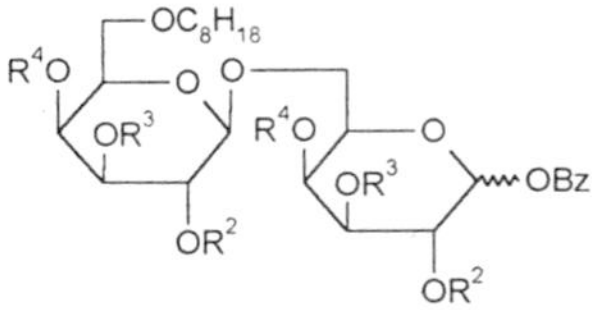 $R^2 = R^3 = R^4 = Bz$ $R^2 = R^3 = R^4 = Ac$ $R^2 = R^3 = R^4 = Bn$	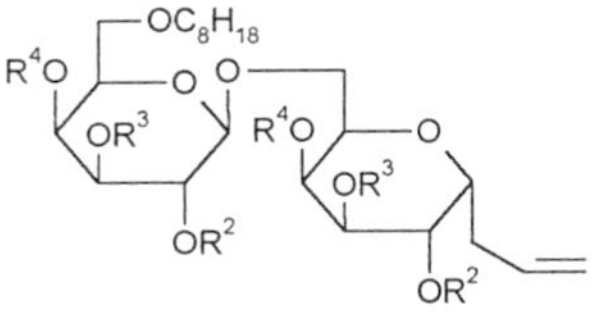	104

major product, **174.3,** can be isolated as a white solid (193 mg, 45%), that gives long needles on recrystallization from methanol, m.p. 79–80°C, $[\alpha]_D^{28}$ +61.4 (*c* = 1.7 in dichloromethane).

C-Glycosyl-allenes, containing a *cumulative* double-bond system, can also be synthesized[115,124-127] according to the procedure discussed above, by the reaction of 1-*O*-acyl aldoses or alkyl glycosides with propargyltri-

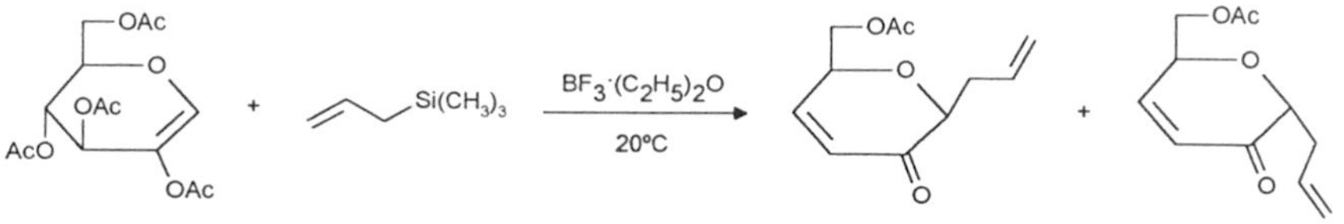

L-*erythro* D-*threo*

173.1 **173.2** **173.3**

FIGURE 1.173

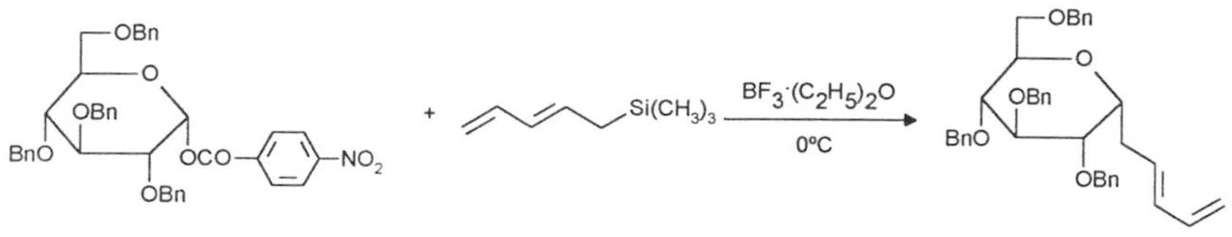

FIGURE I.174

methylsilane (see Fig. 1.175). The products (**175.1**) are used primarily for further conversion[115,127] of the C-glycosyl allenic unit into a $-CH_2CHO$ moiety.

With open-chain saccharides, the present chain extension is often accompanied by an additional reaction. Thus, when the 2,3-O-isopropylidene derivatives of *aldehydo*-aldoses (**176.1**) are treated with allylsilanes, vinylethers, or vinylsulfides (**176.2**) in the presence of boron trifluoride (Fig. 1.176), tetrahydrofuranes (such as **176.3**) may be produced, presumably resulting from intramolecular cyclization accompanied by migration of the isopropylidene group[117,128–132] (see also Fig. 1.170).

Organotin compounds have also emerged as important reagents for the chain extension of saccharides. Allytri-(n-butyl)stannane is used, in the presence of lithium perchlorate, for the chain extension of *aldehydo*-sugars into unsaturated higher-carbon saccharides,[133] such as the methyl 6-heptenosides shown in Figure 1.177.

Addition of tributyltin hydride to an acetylenic bond of a sugar results in an organotin olefin that, on treatment with n-butyllithium and subsequent reaction with an *aldehydo*-sugar, can be converted into most valuable chain-extended products, such as those available[134] from 6-O-benzyl-7,8-dideoxy-1,2:3,4-di-O-isopropylidene-L-*glycero*-α-D-*galacto*-oct-7-ynopyranose (**178.1**) by the reaction sequence shown in Figure 1.178. The ratio of the produced L-*ido* (**178.2**) and D-*gluco* (**178.3**) diastereoisomers can be relatively easily controlled[134] by the reaction temperature: at $-78°C$ this ratio is $3:1$ but it is $3:2$ at $0°C$.

The chain-extension principle described in the preceding paragraphs has been successfully applied by Jarosz and Fraser-Reid[135–137] for the synthesis of higher-carbon sugars (Fig. 1.179). Starting from 6,7-dideoxy-1,2:3,4-di-O-isopropylidene-α-D-*galacto*-hept-6-ynopyranose (**179.1**), the

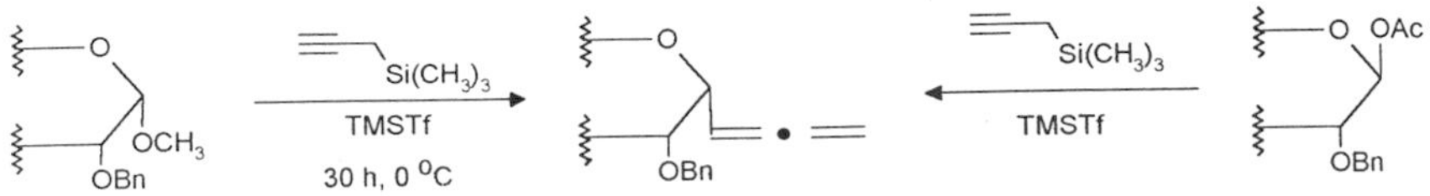

FIGURE I.175

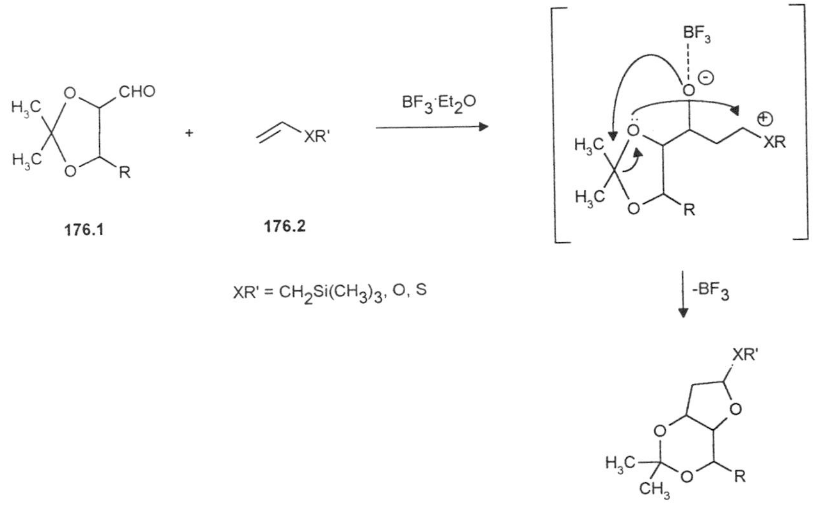

FIGURE 1.176

reaction could be designed and executed so that the anion of **179.1** gave a 33:67 mixture of the propargyl alcohols **179.3** and **179.4** with the *aldehydo-*sugar **179.2**. Subsequent hydrogenolysis of the product mixture then led to the *cis/trans* alcohols **179.5**. When the 6-ynopyranose was first treated with tributyltin hydride (**179.1** → **179.6**) and then coupled with the *aldehydo-*sugar **179.2** (with *n*-butyllithium), the epimeric *trans*-dodecenoses (**179.7** and **179.8**) were produced in a ratio of 72:28.

Saccharide derivatives with a C—Sn bonding are also available,[138-144] and these are susceptible to chain extension into higher-carbon sugars following transformation into the lithioorganic analogs. Thus, configurationally stable 2-deoxy-β- and -α-D-hexopyranosyl lithium compounds can be prepared and reacted with electrophilic compounds with retention of

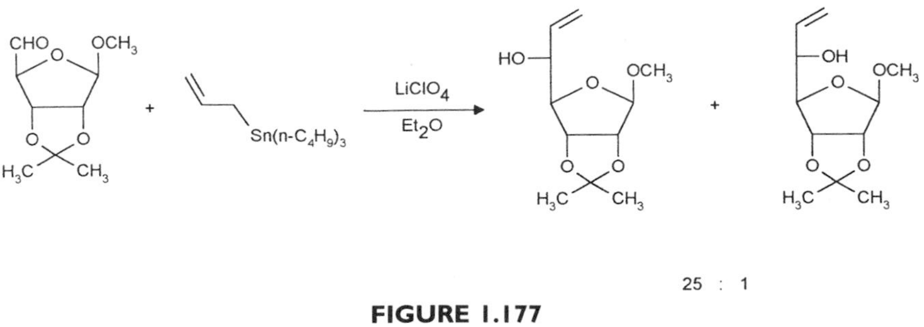

25 : 1

FIGURE 1.177

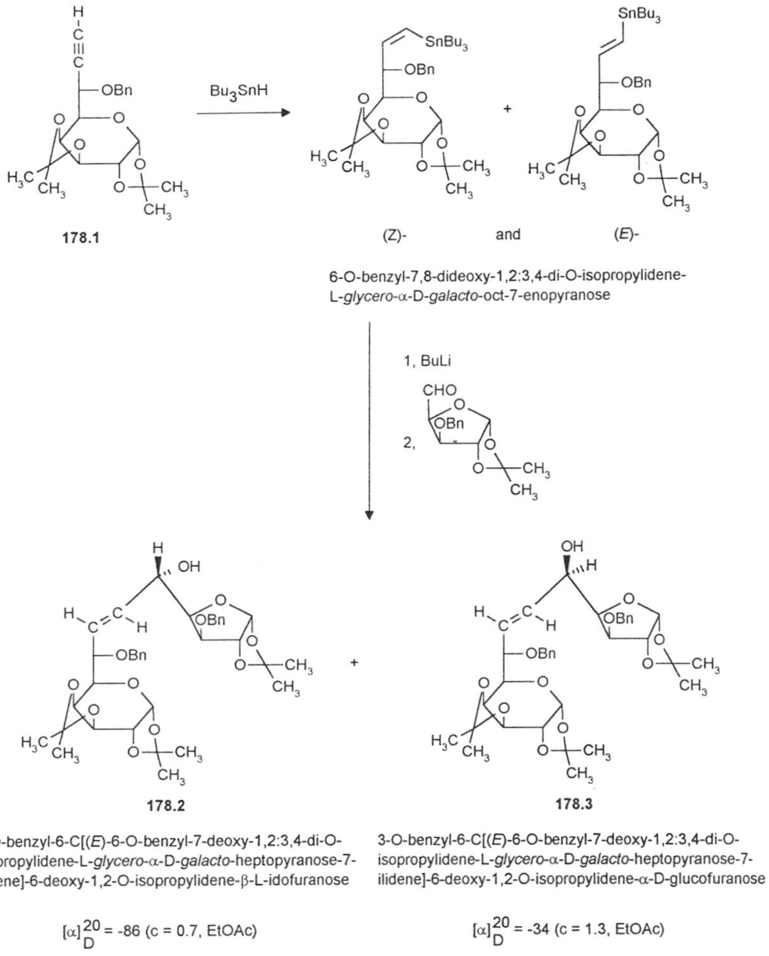

Bu3SnH
178.1
(Z)- and (E)-
6-O-benzyl-7,8-dideoxy-1,2:3,4-di-O-isopropylidene-L-*glycero*-α-D-*galacto*-oct-7-enopyranose
1, BuLi
2,
178.2
178.3
3-O-benzyl-6-C[(E)-6-O-benzyl-7-deoxy-1,2:3,4-di-O-isopropylidene-L-*glycero*-α-D-*galacto*-heptopyranose-7-ilidene]-6-deoxy-1,2-O-isopropylidene-β-L-idofuranose
3-O-benzyl-6-C[(E)-6-O-benzyl-7-deoxy-1,2:3,4-di-O-isopropylidene-L-*glycero*-α-D-*galacto*-heptopyranose-7-ilidene]-6-deoxy-1,2-O-isopropylidene-α-D-glucofuranose
$[\alpha]_D^{20}$ = -86 (c = 0.7, EtOAc)
$[\alpha]_D^{20}$ = -34 (c = 1.3, EtOAc)

FIGURE 1.178

the configuration.[138] The results of the studies of Beau[139] on the chain extension of glycosylstannanes with various anhydro compounds are summarized in Table 1.29.

The preparation of the chiral polyhydroxyalkyl pyrans and dihydropyrans was carried out in the presence (procedure A) or in the absence (procedure B) of 2-thienyl-cyanocuprate under boron trifluoride catalysis.

In further studies in this field, 1-tributylstannyl-D-glucals were coupled efficiently to different organic halides in the presence of Pd(0) catalyst, and this mild process is very useful for the preparation[142] of 1-*C*-aryl-D-glucals. Stereospecific Pd/Cu cocatalyzed cross-couplings of tributylstannyl glucopyranosides with thiono- and thiolochloroformates afford good yields

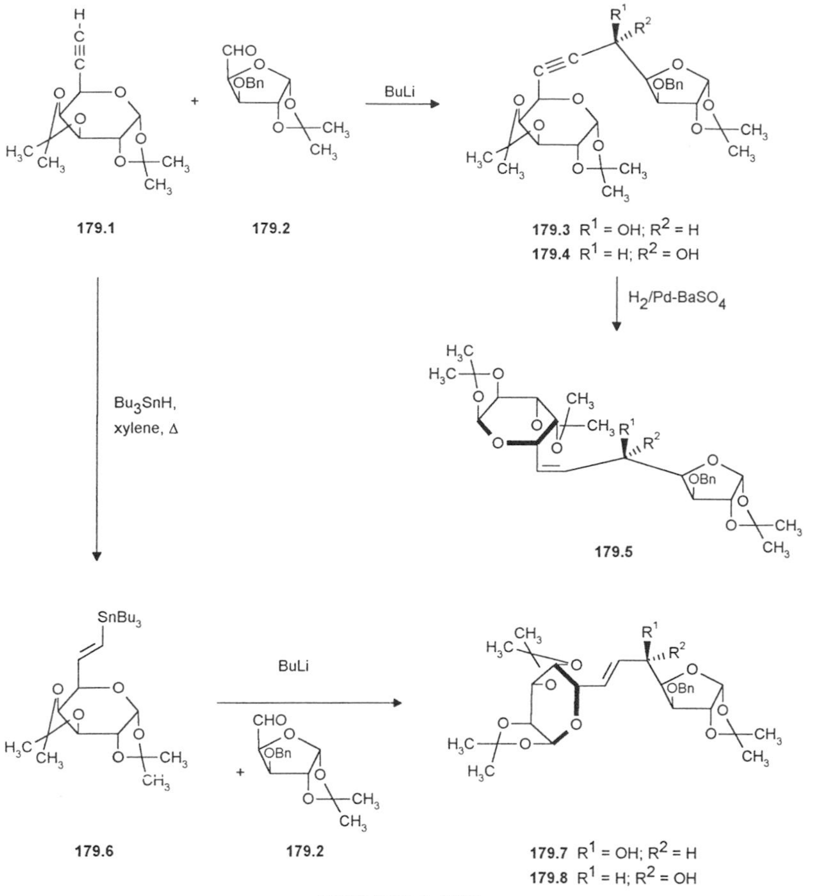

FIGURE 1.179

of *C*-glucosylthiocarboxylates.[140] *C*-Glycosylcarboxylates (2,6-anhydrohep-tonic acids) are obtained by conversion of the stannylated glycopyranosides into the lithioderivatives, followed by carboxylation with carbon dioxide.

According to the procedure of Fuchs,[141] related coupling reactions for the chain-extension of anomeric stannanes (available as described by Si-nay[138]) with enones can be executed via glycosyl copper reagents as shown in Figure 1.180.

1-(3',4',6'-Tri-O-benzyl-2'-deoxy-β-D-glucopyranosyl)butan-3-one (***180.2***)[141]
A solution of 316 mg (0.446 mmol) of 1-tributylstannyl-3,4,6-tri-*O*-benzyl-β-D-*ara-bino*-hexopyranoside (**180.1**)[138] in 2.2 ml of dry THF at −78°C is treated with 0.18 ml (2.49 M, 0.456 mmol) of *n*-butyllithium in hexane followed by stirring at this temperature for 10 min. The yellow solution is transferred via a cooled cannula to a solution of 101 mg (0.491 mmol) of copper(I)bromide–dimethyl sulfide in 0.5 ml of diisopropyl sulfide and 0.6 ml of THF at −78°C pretreated with 1 drop

(~10 μl) of 2.0 M isopropylmagnesium chloride in THF as described previously, followed by stirring at $-78°C$ for 15 min. To the brown solution is added 26 mg (31 μl, 0.372 mmol) of neat methyl vinyl ketone and then 70 mg (60 μl, 0.491 mmol) of boron trifluoride etherate. The reaction mixture is stirred at $-78°C$ for 10 min, followed by warming to $-50°C$ for 5 min and to $0°C$ for 2 min. The solution is then added to 50 ml of 1:1 NH_3-NH_4Cl solution, diluted with dichloromethane (30 ml), and stirring is continued at ambient temperature for 30 min. The aqueous layer is extracted with dichloromethane, the combined organic layer is dried (Na_2SO_4) and concentrated *in vacuo* to a colorless syrup, which is submitted to column chromatography on silicagel [12 g, 200–400 mesh, eluant: 100 ml of 10% (v/v) and then 16% (v/v) ethyl acetate in hexane] to afford 100 mg (55%) of the *C*-glycosidic compound **180.2,** as a colorless syrup.

The stereoselective addition of *allylboron reagents* to dialkoxyalde-hydes leads to 1-*C*-(prop-2-enyl)dialkoxyalkane derivatives, of which the C_5 and C_6 representatives are extremely useful[1,3,145] for the synthesis of *ω-deoxymonosaccharides*. This procedure can be well utilized for the prepa-ration of certain *deoxysugars* as shown by the example of 2-deoxy-D-*erythro*-pentose (Fig. 1.181). Treatment of 2,3-*O*-isopropylidene-D-glyceraldehyde (**181.1**) with 2-allyl-4,4,5,5-tetramethyl-1,3,2-dioxaborolane (**181.2**) gives rise[146] to an epimeric mixture (**181.3**) of 2,3-*O*-isopropylidene-1-*C*-(prop-2-enyl)-D-*threo*- and D-*erythro*-glycerol, from which the desired deoxypentose can be prepared. The stereoselectivity of the addition can be influenced[147] by the addition of isopropyl D- or L-tartarate, but chiral boron reagents have also been efficiently employed for this purpose.[148,149] The *threo/erythro* ratio in the product mixture **181.3** is ~15:25, which may slightly change by varying the reaction conditions (solvent, temperature), and almost the same ratio of the products (**181.5**) is observed in a similar addition[150] of the boron compound **181.2** to 2,3-*O*-cyclohexylidene-D-glyceraldehyde (**181.4**).

By applying an appropriate borolane reagent (**182.1**), one can adopt the preceding chain extension principle for the diastereoselective synthesis[151] of the protected D-*fucose derivative* **182.2** (Fig. 1.182).

(*Z*)-γ-Methoxymethylallylboronate (**183.1**), available by the reaction of allylmethoxy methyl ether and $FB(OCH_3)_2$, has been coupled with 2,3-*O*-cyclohexylidene-D-glyceraldehyde to obtain 75–80% of the homoallyl alcohol **183.2**, the key intermediate in a chiral synthesis[152] of *sesbanimide* (Fig. 1.183), with a diastereoselectivity higher than 20:1.

An analogous transformation[153] of 4-deoxy-2,3-*O*-isopropylidene-L-threose (**184.1**) with the chiral boronate **184.2** offers one of the synthetic routes (Fig. 1.184) to the homoallyl alcohol **184.3**, a target for further conversion into *2,6-dideoxy-D-lyxo-hexose* (**184.4**).

A total synthesis of *L-oleandrose* from two C_3 building blocks ap-plies[154] the reaction of *O*-benzyl-L-lactaldehyde (**185.1**), with 4,5-dimethyl-2-[(*Z*)-3-methoxy-2-propenyl]-1,3,2-dioxaborolane (**185.2**) to furnish, with 84% yield, a mixture of three C_6-triols (Fig. 1.185), from which the de-sired stereoisomer, (3*S*,4*S*,5*S*)-5-benzyloxy-4-hydroxy-3-methoxy-1-hexene

TABLE 1.29 Chain-Extension of Glycosylstannanes

Stannane[a]	Epoxide (eq)	Procedure[b]	Product	Yield (%)[c] isomer ratio[d]
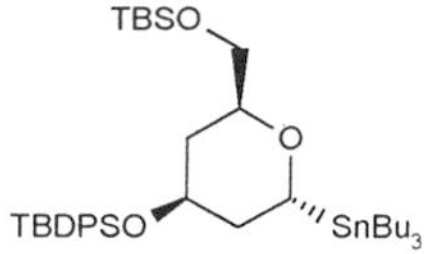	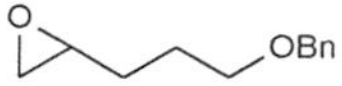 (1.5)	B	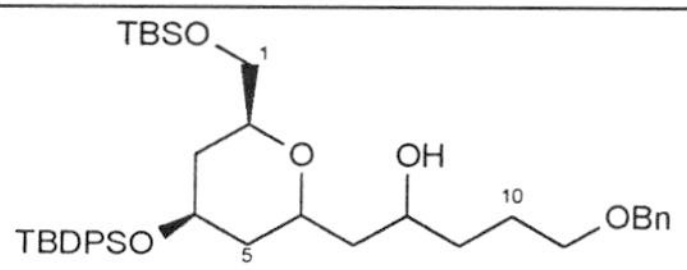	30 (2:3)
	(1.5)	A		71 (2:1)
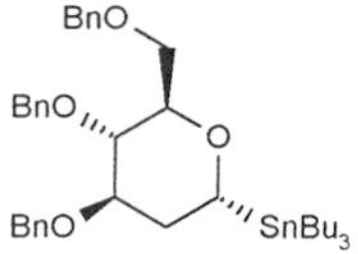	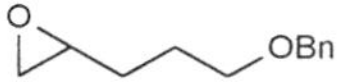 (1.5)	A	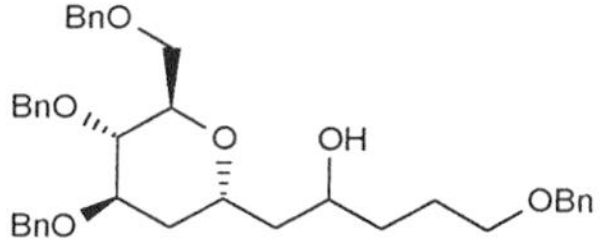	71 (3:2)
	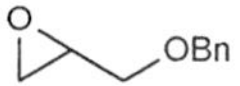 (1.5)	A	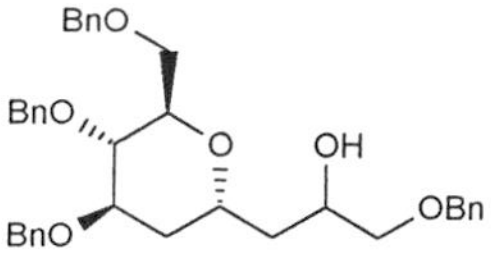	67 (n.d.)
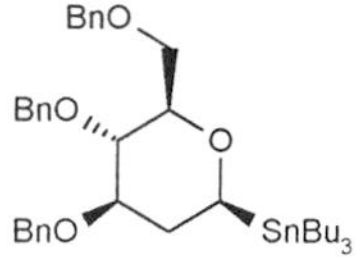	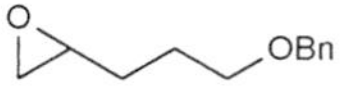 (1.5)	A	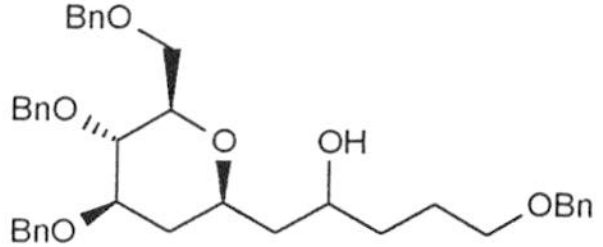	63 (1:1)
	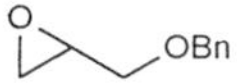 (1.5)	A	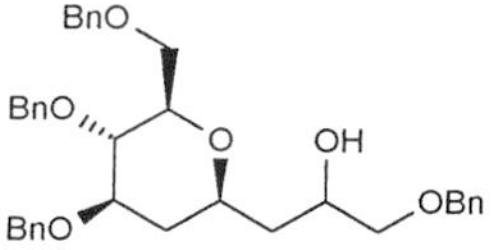	50 (1:1)

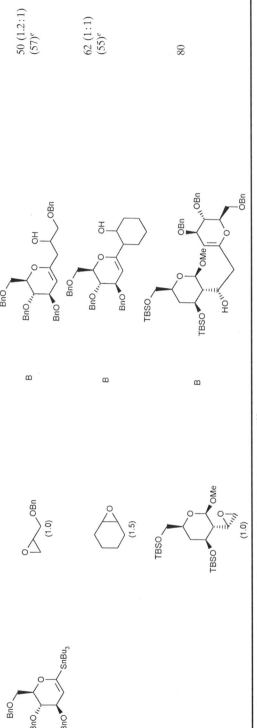

50 (1.2:1)
(57)^e

62 (1:1)
(55)^e

80

^{a}Prepared according to the literature cited in Lesimple *et al.*[138]
^{b}For procedures A and B, see text.
^{c}Isolated yields are given.
^{d}Deduced from ^{1}H-n.m.r. and isolated yields.
^{e}Yield obtained using procedure A.
Abbreviations: TBS—*tert*-butyldimethylsilyl; TBDPS—*tert*-butyldiphenylsilyl.

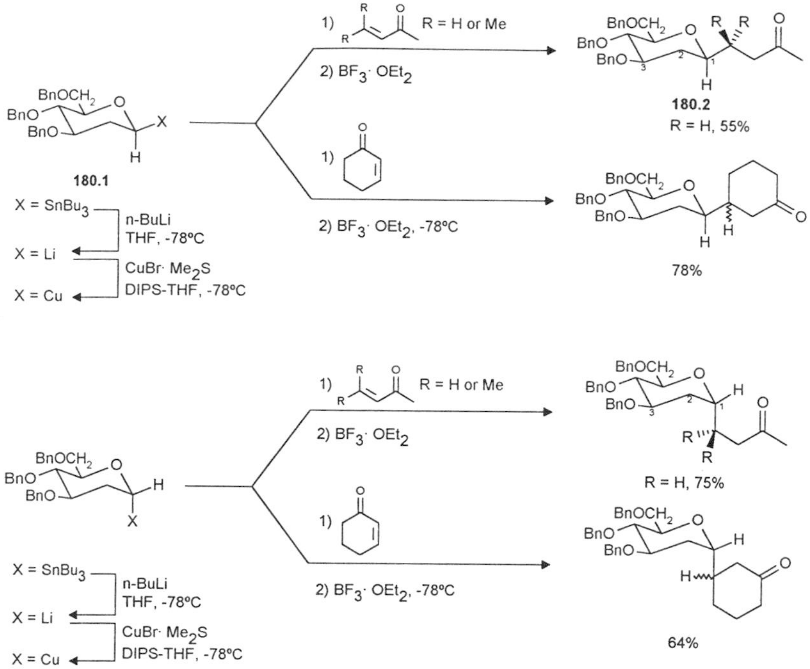

FIGURE 1.180

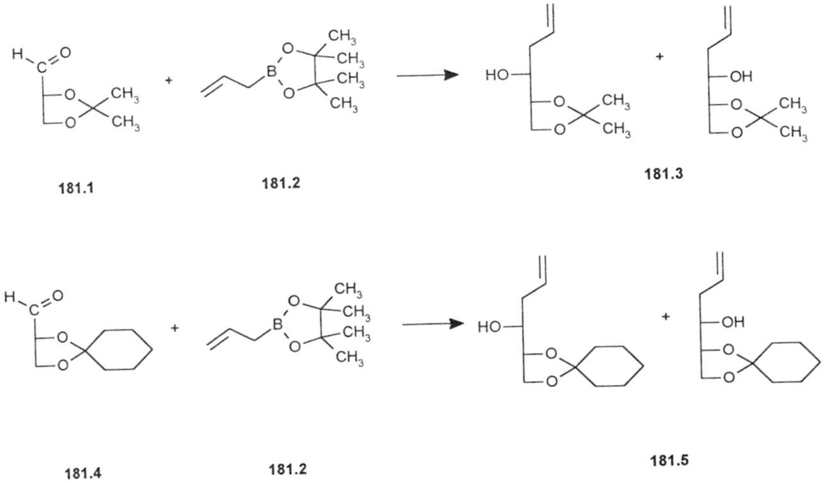

FIGURE 1.181

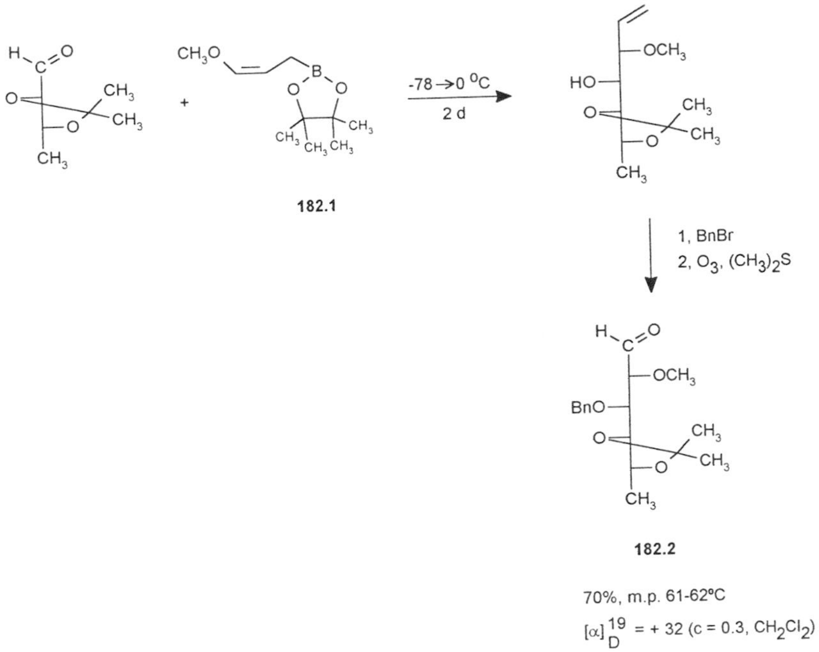
-78→0 °C
2 d
182.1
1, BnBr
2, O_3, $(CH_3)_2S$
182.2
70%, m.p. 61-62°C
$[\alpha]_D^{19}$ = + 32 (c = 0.3, CH_2Cl_2)

FIGURE 1.182

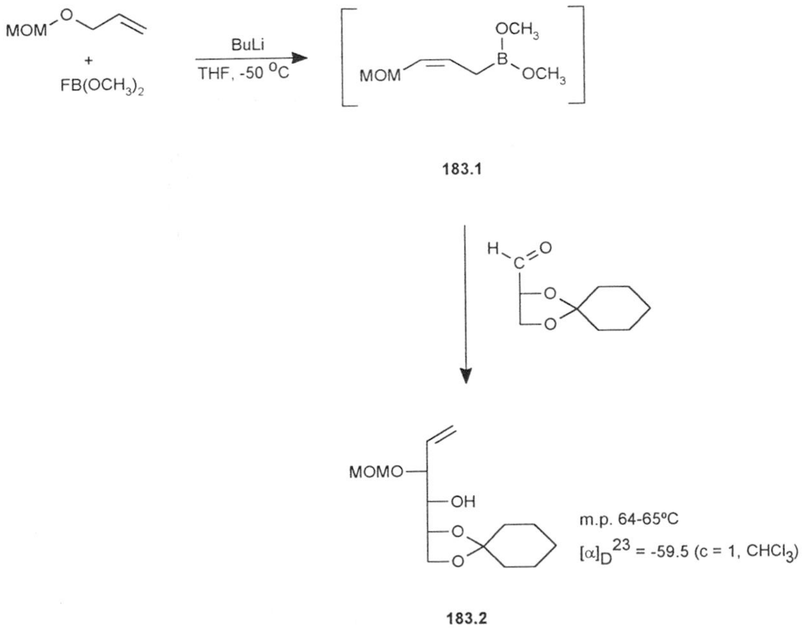
MOM
+
$FB(OCH_3)_2$
BuLi
THF, -50 °C
183.1
MOMO
OH
m.p. 64-65°C
$[\alpha]_D^{23}$ = -59.5 (c = 1, $CHCl_3$)
183.2

FIGURE 1.183

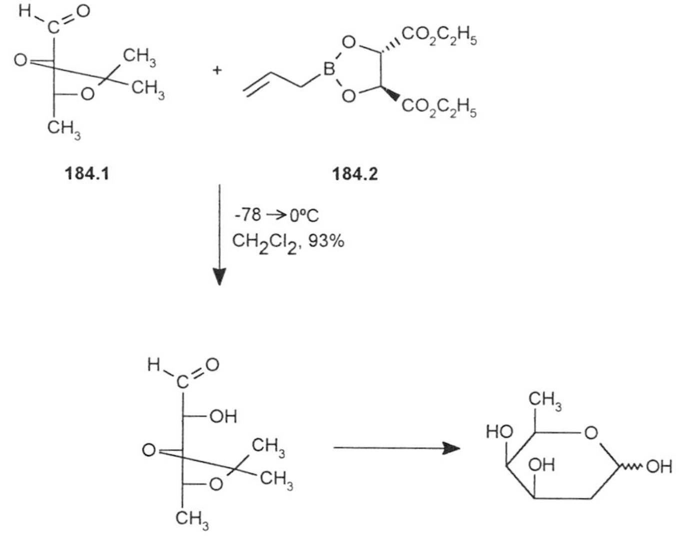

184.1   +   **184.2**

-78 → 0°C
CH_2Cl_2, 93%

184.3   **184.4**

FIGURE 1.184

(185.3), needed for the next step of the synthetic procedure, could be readily separated.

*Preparation of (3S,4S,5S)-5-benzyloxy-4-hydroxy-3-methoxy-1-hexene (**185.3**)*[154]
To a cold (−78°C), stirred solution of 3-methoxypropane (4.3 g, 60 mmol) in dry THF (40 ml) is added under argon atmosphere, via a syringe, *sec*-butyllithium (1.1 M in cyclohexane, 54.5 ml, 60 mmol) to produce a cloudy yellow mixture, which is stirred for 15 min before the addition of 4,5-dimethyl-2-fluoro-1,3-dioxa-2-boracyclopentane (2.4 M in benzene, 25 ml, 60 mmol), discharging the yellow color. Stirring is continued for 30 min at −78°C, and then 3.3 g (20.4 mmol) of (2S)-(phenylmethoxy)propanal (**185.1**) is added. The solution is allowed to slowly warm to room temperature, and stirring is continued for 7 days. Then addition of 20 ml (3.0 M in acetone) of (EtOH)$_3$N solution produced a white fine precipitate, which, after an additional hour of stirring, is removed by filtration through a pad

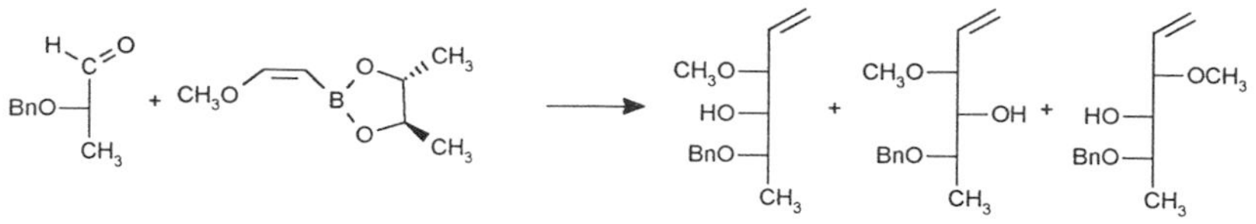

185.1   **185.2**   (3R,4S,5S)   (3R,4R,5S)   (3S,4S,5S)

185.3

FIGURE 1.185

of Celite. The filtrate is concentrated to a thick syrup that is washed onto the top of a short column of silicagel with dry acetone and allowed to stand for several hours before elution with 55% of ethyl acetate in hexane, gradually increasing the solvent polarity until all the desired triol is collected (as determined by TLC analysis of the eluant). This material is concentrated (11.2 g) and purified by medium-pressure liquid chromatography (MPLC) (linear gradient elution, 5–50% ethyl acetate in hexane), affording 4.1 g (84%) of the desired triol **185.3**, $[\alpha]_D^{22}$ +43.13 (neat oil) along with two minor products in a ratio of 8.7 : 1.2 : 1.0.

On the basis of mechanistic knowledge and stereochemical considerations, the preceding chain extension of O-benzyl-L-lactaldehyde can be carried out so that three of the four *2,6-dideoxy-L-hexose isomers* are available. Addition of *(Z)*- or *(E)*-4,4,5,5-tetra-methyl-2-[3-(2-trimethylsilyl) ethoxy-2-propenyl]-1,3,2-dioxaborolane to O-benzyl-L-lactaldehyde leads[155] to the 3,4,5-trihydroxylated hex-1-enes with *arabino, xylo, ribo,* and *lyxo* configurations. With the *(Z)*-borolane (**186.1**), a 82 : 18 *arabino/ xylo* mixture (**186.2** and **186.3**) is obtained, whereas a 4 : 6 *ribo/lyxo* (**186.5/ 186.6**) asymmetric induction is observed with the *(E)*-isomer **186.4** (Fig. 1.186). By appropriate functionalization, three of the four 3,4,5-trihydroxy-1-hexenes have been converted into *2,6-dideoxy-*L-*arabino,* L-*ribo,* and L-*lyxo-hexose* (Fig. 1.186).[155]

(2S,3S,4R)- *and (2S,3R,4S)-2-Benzyloxy)-4-(tert-butyldimethylsilyl)-5-hexen-3-ol (186.5 and 186.6)*[156] To a solution of the *(E)*-dioxaborolane **186.4** (15.9 mmol) in petroleum ether (30 ml, b.p. 40–60°C) is added *(S)*-2-benzyloxypropanal (2.23 g, 13.6 mmol). After stirring for 4 days at room temperature, ether (25 ml) is added and the mixture is treated with triethylamine (2.03 g, 13.6 mmol) for 12 h. The precipitate is filtered and washed with ether (3 × 15 ml), and the combined filtrate is concentrated and chromatographed on silicagel (45 g, eluant: dichloromethane) to furnish 4.15 g (94%) of the *ribo*-alcohol **186.5** containing 4% of the *lyxo*-isomer **186.6** Analytic samples were obtained by GC (column: SE 30 at 180°C).

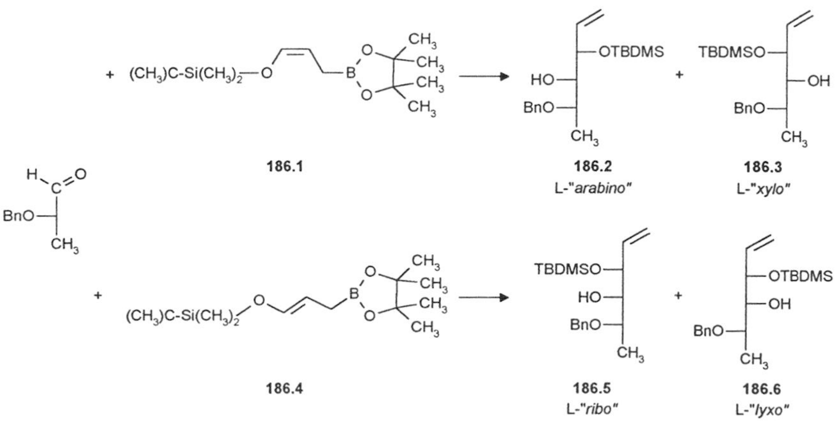

FIGURE 1.186

Asymmetric allyboration[157] of *threo*-(2*R*,3*S*)-4-(*tert*-butyldiphenylsilyoxy)-2,3-epoxybutanal (**187.1**) and its *erythro*-(2*S*,3*S*)- isomer (**187.2**) have been found suitable as the basis for a general procedure (Fig. 1.187) for the synthesis of the *2-deoxyhexose stereoisomers*.[158] This new and highly stereoselective approach relies on two asymmetric transformations: (1) the Sharpless asymmetric epoxidation and (2) the asymmetric allylboration reaction, which can presumably be used to achieve diastereofacial selection in the addition of allyl- or γ-alkoxyalkyl units to epoxyaldehydes. This principle of asymmetric allylboration has also been used for the synthesis of the *AB-disaccharide unit of olivomycin A*.[159]

1.2.7.2. Chain Extension of *aldehydo*-Sugars with Thiazole, Furan, and Pyrrole Derivatives

Retrosynthetic considerations indicate that thiazole, oxazole, and pyrrole metalated at position C-2 correspond to a synthetic equivalent of the formyl anion. Detailed studies have revealed that these equivalents are suitable for the chain extension of alkoxyaldehydes, and that the *thiazole compounds* 2-lithiothiazole or 2-trimethylstannylthiazole do not ensure selective reaction and/or are not reactive enough. It has also been shown[160] that the newly created chiral center has *anti*-configuration, according to the *Felkin–Anh model* of asymmetric induction. As masked aldehydes, the resulting 2-polyhydroxyalkylthiazoles can be readily converted into the next "sugar homolog" in three synthetic steps (formation of quaternary salt, reduction, and subsequent hydrolysis). Then the whole procedure (Fig. 1.188) can be repeated with the product to access the next sugar of the

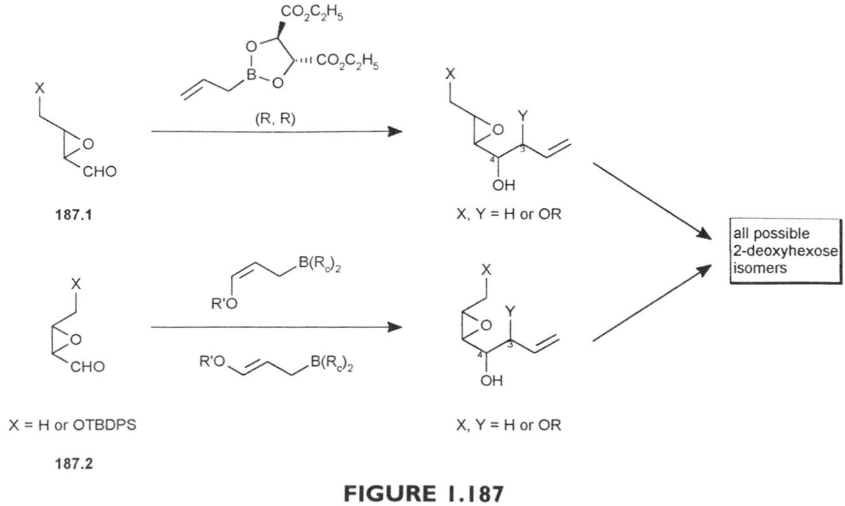

FIGURE 1.187

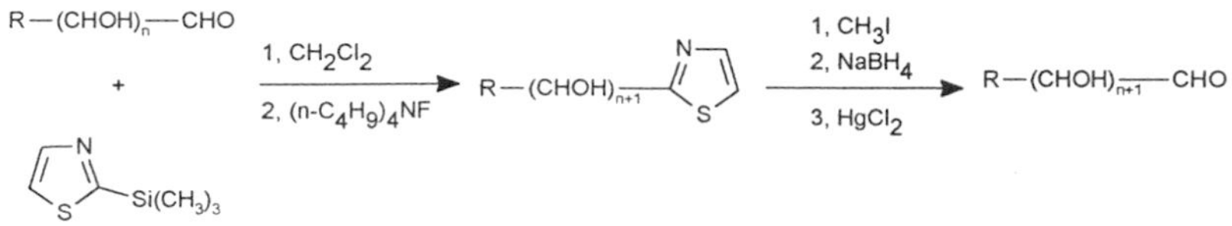

FIGURE I.188

series, and thus this *iterative* methodology has allowed the construction of a 2-polyhydroxyalkylthiazole with a 10-carbon skeleton, as the longest.[160]

> *General procedure for the addition of 2-trimethylsilylthiazole to aldehydes (see Fig. 1.188)*[160]   A mixture of the *aldehydo*-sugar (5 mmol) and 2-trimethylsilylthia-zole[161] (1.17 g, 7.5 mmol) in dry dichloromethane (25 ml) is stirred at 0–20°C for 12 h. The solvent is distilled off, and tetrabutylammonium fluoride (7.5 mmol) dissolved in THF (30 ml) is added to the residue. After 2 h, the solvent is removed under diminished pressure, the residue is taken up with water and extracted with dichloromethane, and the organic layer is dried (Na_2SO_4). The residue is purified by means of column chromatography (eluant: 7:3 cyclohexane–ethyl acetate).

The products[160–162] of the addition of 2-trimethylsilylthiazole to *aldehydo*-sugar derivatives have been collected in Table 1.30.

The examples shown in Table 1.30 represent the capacity of the "thia-zole method," offering an *iterative* approach to 1,2-polyols. A fully stereo-controlled chain extension cannot be realized in this way, because of the *anti*-selectivity of addition of the reagent to the formyl group. However, this disadvantage can be overcome[162,163] by oxidation of the product **189.1** into the ketone **189.2,** which can then be reduced with either *K*- or *L*-Selectride to the desired isomer **189.3,** which is not directly available by the "thiazole method" (Fig. 1.189).

An alternative solution is the direct preparation of the 2-thiazolylketone and subsequent reduction (as previously) to the *syn*-2-thiazolylalcohol. An example of such a methodology[162,164] is shown in Figure 1.190. From ethyl (*S*)-*O*-(benzyloxymethyl)-L-lactate (**190.1**) and 2-bromo-thiazole (**190.2**), 2-[(*S*)-2-(benzyloxymethoxy)-propionyl]thiazole (**190.3**) is obtained with 90% yield, and this is reduced with *L*-Selectride to a 93:7 mixture (95%) of (1*R*)-2-*O*-(benzyloxymethyl)-3-deoxy-1-(2-thiazolyl)-L-glycerol (**190.4**) and its (1*S*)-epimer. Dondoni and Merino[165] have described several analogous chain extensions.

In the transformations discussed above, the thiazole heterocycle serves as a masked formyl equivalent (for a related chain extension of nitrones, see Dondoni *et al.*[166,167]). In similar reactions *furan* ensures a C_4 unit, and as the furan ring can be diversely substituted,[168] such a methodology is of great synthetic value for chain extensions. The chloroacetic acid–catalyzed reaction[169] of 2,3-*O*-isopropylidene-D-glyceraldehyde (**191.1**) with furan (**191.2**) gives rise to 37% of an 85:15 mixture of the diastereoisomeric

TABLE 1.30 The Addition of 2-Trimethylsilylthiazole on aldehydo-Derivatives of Sugars

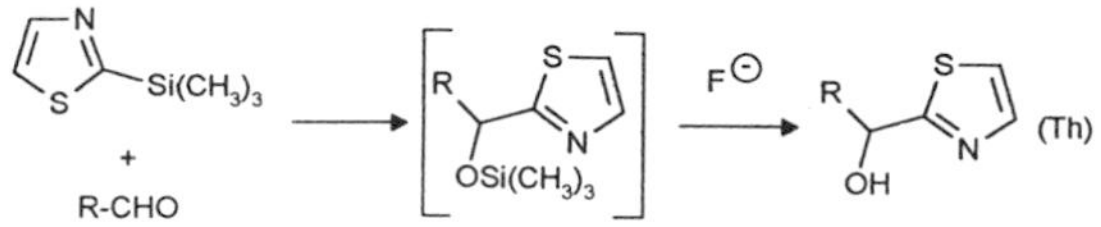

$$\text{(thiazole)}-Si(CH_3)_3 \;+\; R\text{-CHO} \longrightarrow \left[R \overset{\displaystyle \text{(thiazole)}}{\underset{OSi(CH_3)_3}{\big|}} \right] \overset{F^\ominus}{\longrightarrow} R \overset{\text{(thiazole)}}{\underset{OH}{\big|}} \;\; (Th)$$

Educt	Reaction temperature (°C)	Product diastereoselectivity (%)	M.p. (°C)	Yield (%)
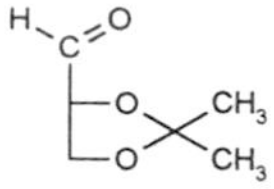 aldehyde with O–C(CH₃)₂–O acetonide	0	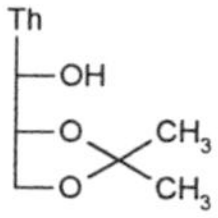 Th, —OH, O–C(CH₃)₂–O; anti, > 95	114–116	96
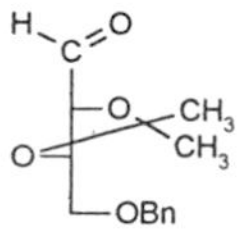 aldehyde with O–C(CH₃)₂, O=, OBn	0	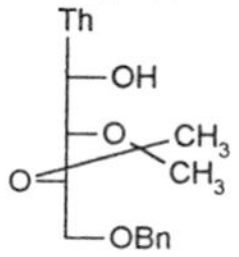 Th, —OH, O=C(CH₃)₂, OBn; anti, 90	Oil	89
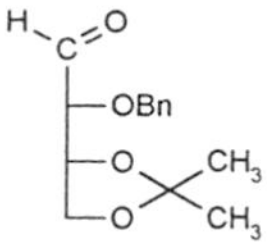 aldehyde with OBn, O–C(CH₃)₂–O	20	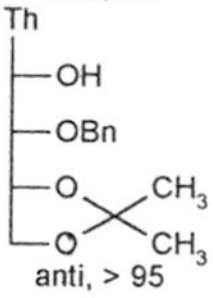 Th, —OH, —OBn, O–C(CH₃)₂–O; anti, > 95	105–107	92
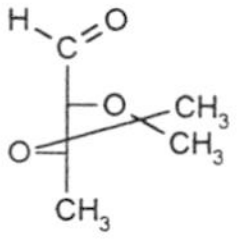 aldehyde with O–C(CH₃)₂, O=, CH₃	20	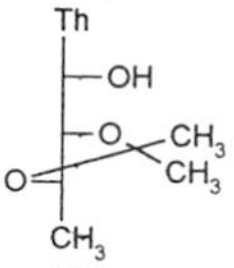 Th, —OH, O=C(CH₃)₂, CH₃	Oil	76
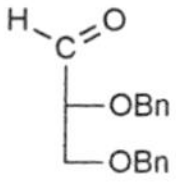 aldehyde with —OBn, —OBn (R, S)	0	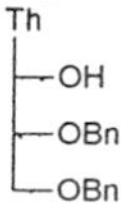 Th, —OH, —OBn, —OBn; anti, 67	Oil	75
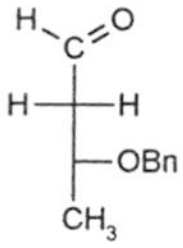 aldehyde with H—H, —OBn, CH₃ (R, S)	0	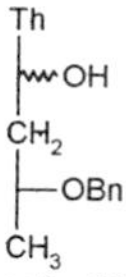 Th, OH, CH₂, OBn, CH₃; syn : anti = 50 : 50	Oil	70
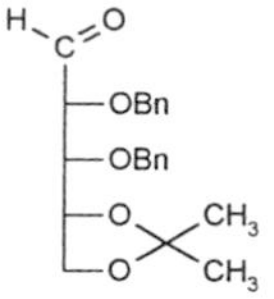 aldehyde with —OBn, —OBn, O–C(CH₃)₂–O	20	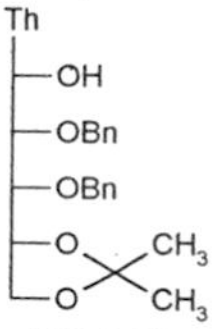 Th, —OH, —OBn, —OBn, O–C(CH₃)₂–O; anti, > 95	Oil	94

(continues)

TABLE I.30   (*continued*)

Educt	Reaction temperature (°C)	Product diastereoselectivity (%)	M.p. (°C)	Yield (%)
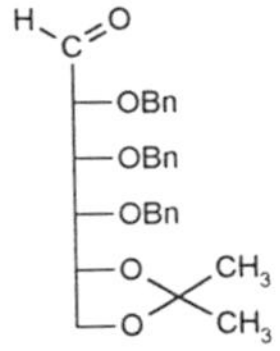 (structure: H−C=O, OBn, OBn, OBn, O−C(CH₃)₂−O)	20	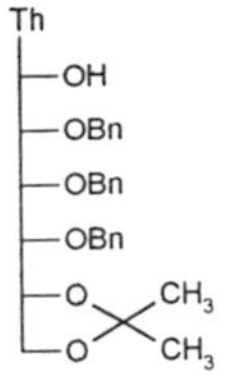 Th, OH, OBn, OBn, OBn, O−C(CH₃)₂−O, anti, 90	Oil	81
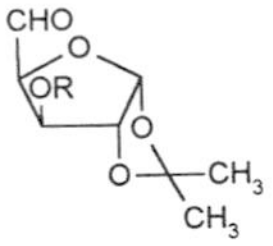 (structure: CHO, OR, O−C(CH₃)₂) R = CH₃ R = Bn	0 0	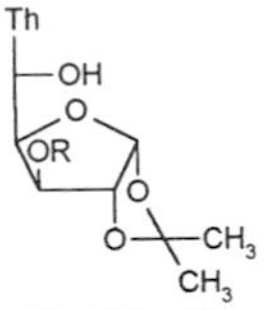 Th, OH, OR, O−C(CH₃)₂ R = CH₃ > 95 R = Bn > 95	Syrup Syrup	84 86
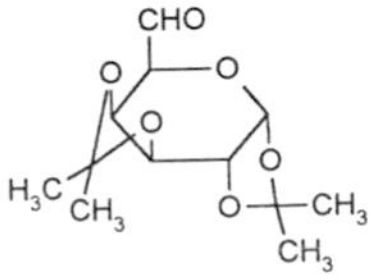 (structure: CHO, H₃C−CH₃, O−C(CH₃)₂)	0	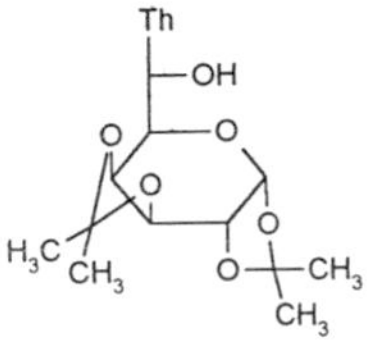 Th, OH, H₃C−CH₃, O−C(CH₃)₂, anti, > 95	170–172	85
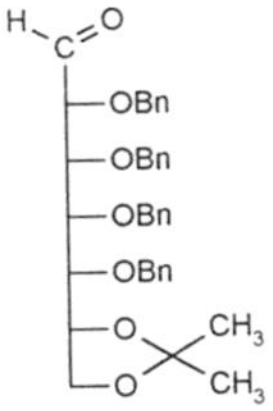 (structure: H−C=O, OBn, OBn, OBn, OBn, O−C(CH₃)₂−O)	20	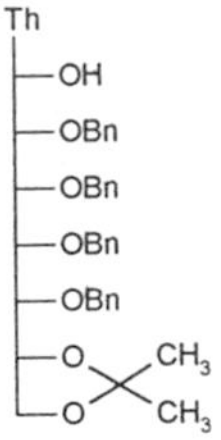 Th, OH, OBn, OBn, OBn, OBn, O−C(CH₃)₂−O, anti, > 95	Oil	83
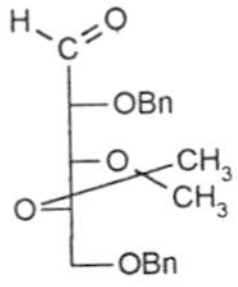 (structure: H−C=O, OBn, O−C(CH₃)₂, O=, OBn)	20	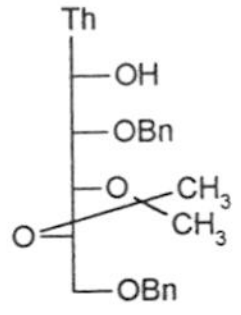 Th, OH, OBn, O−C(CH₃)₂, O=, OBn, anti, > 86	Oil	70

(*continues*)

TABLE I.30 (*continued*)

Educt	Reaction temperature (°C)	Product diastereoselectivity (%)	M.p. (°C)	Yield (%)
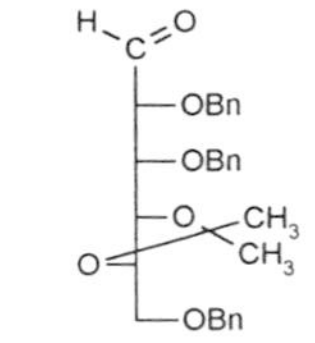	20	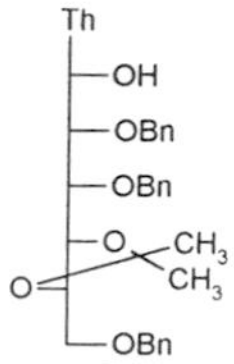 anti, 95	Oil	55
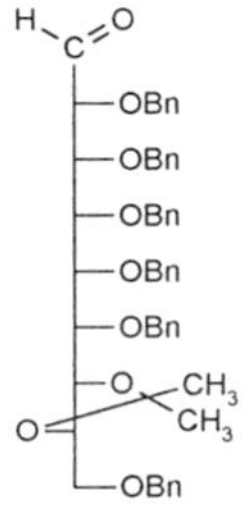	20	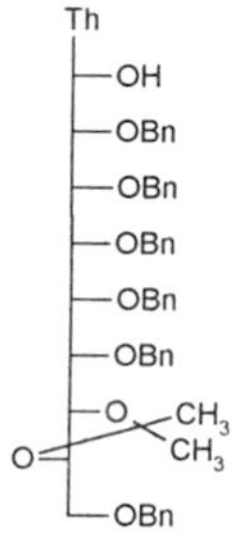 anti, > 95	Oil	80
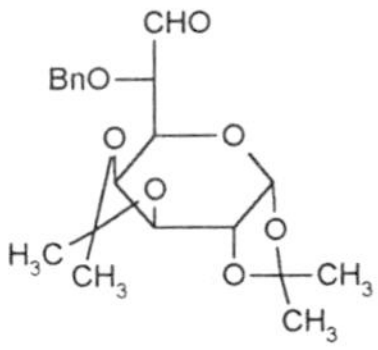	20	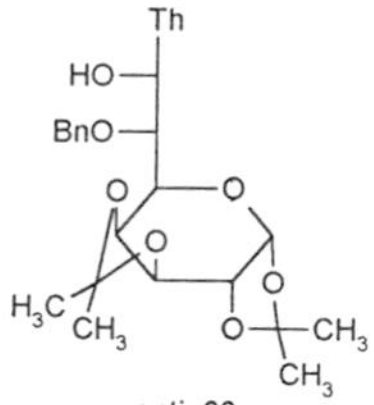 anti, 80	82–85	71
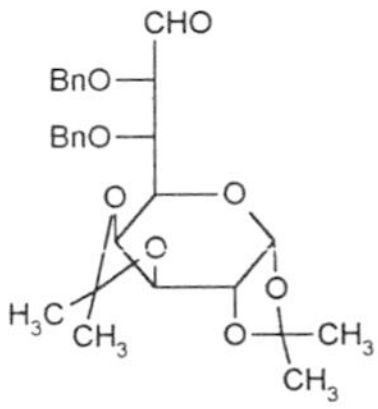	20	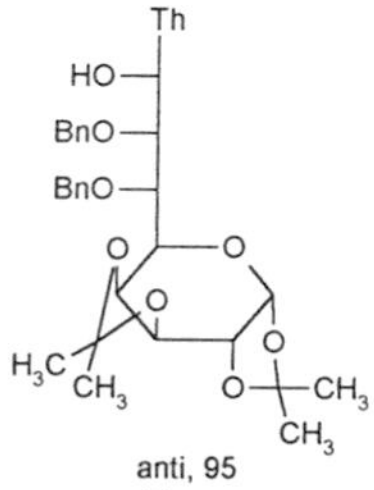 anti, 95	Oil	68
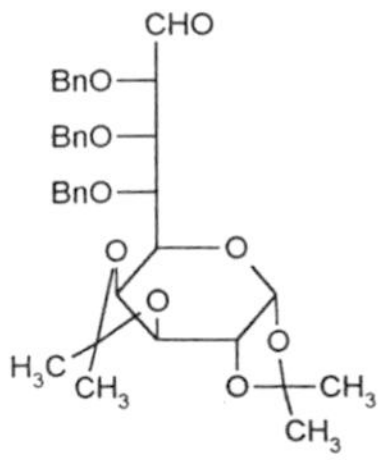	20	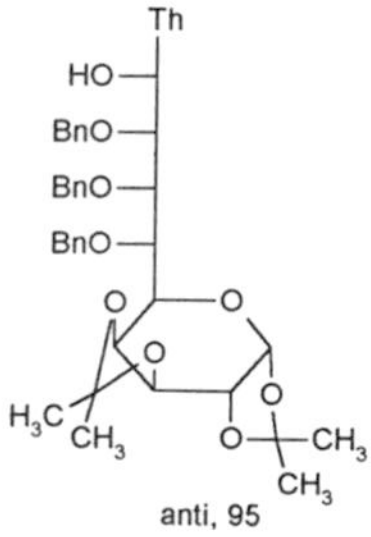 anti, 95	Oil	68

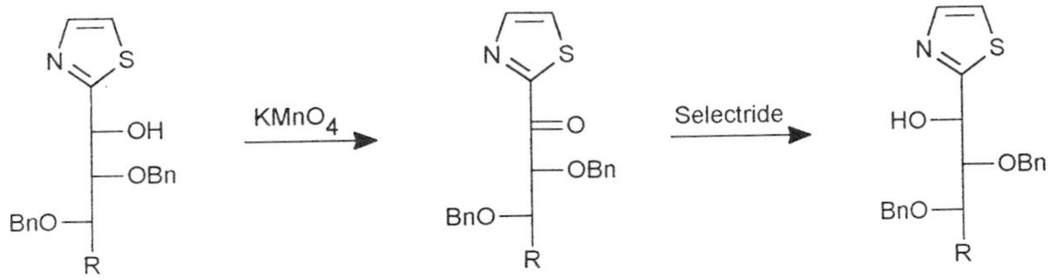

FIGURE 1.189

1-*C*-(2-furyl)-2,3-*O*-isopropylidene-D-glycerols (**191.3**), as shown in Figure 1.191.

This procedure has been successfully employed for uloses to produce furylcarbinols with a sugar chain. The diastereoisomeric alcohols can be readily separated by chromatography, and the configurational assignment is carried out by chiroptical methods. As reported by Zamojski *et al.*,[170] the *O*-benzoates of the (*R*)-series possess a negative CD band at ~230 nm and a positive band at 215–220 nm. The chain extension shown in Figure 1.191 was carried out in furan or in 2-methylfuran, as the solvents, and the results[170,171] are summarized in Table 1.31.

The chain extension with 2-methylfuran was also accomplished through the lithio analog, and in this case the *anti*-selectivity was found to be higher (95 : 5) than that of the chloroacetic acid–catalyzed transformations (93 : 7).

Chain extension of 2,3-O-isopropylidene-D-glyceraldehyde with the lithiated derivative of 2-methylfuran: preparation of (2R,3R)-1,2-O-isopropylidene-3-[2-(5-methylfuryl)]-1,2,3-propanetriol[172]   To a cooled (−30°C) and stirred solution of 2-methylfuran (15 ml, 166 mmol) in THF (160 ml) is added 1.6 M *n*-butyllithium in hexane (100 ml), and stirring is continued for additional 4 h by slowly raising the temperature to +10°C. Then anhydrous zinc bromide (36 g, 160 mmol) is added, and the mixture is stirred for 15 min and cooled to −40°C, followed by the dropwise addition of a solution of 2,3-*O*-isopropylidene-D-glyceraldehyde (20.8 g, 160 mmol) in THF (160 ml). It is stirred at this temperature for 4 h, and warmed to 0°C, and the reaction is quenched with saturated aqueous ammonium chloride and worked

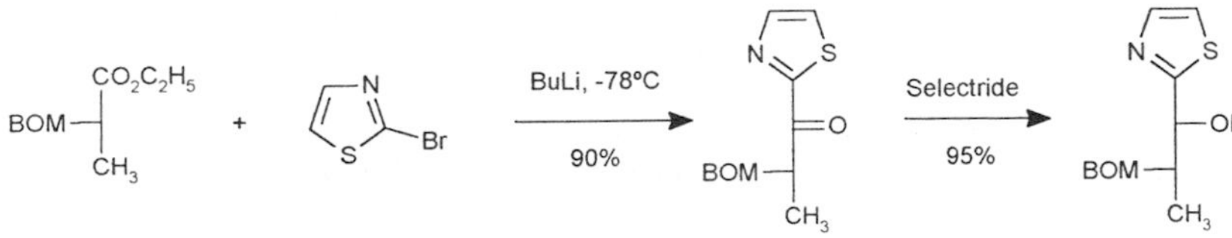

BOM = benzyloxymethyl

FIGURE 1.190

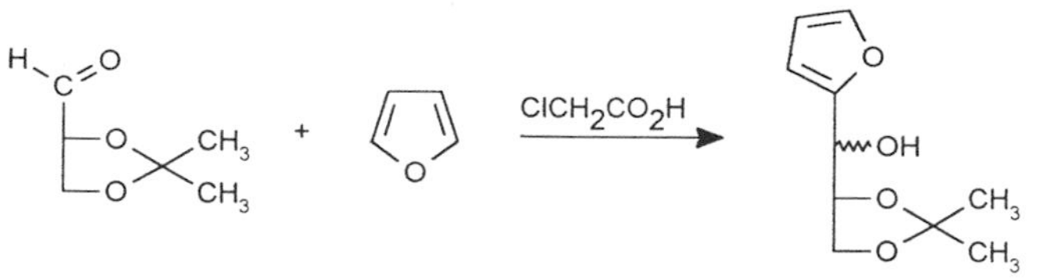

191.1 **191.2** **191.3**

FIGURE I.191

up in the usual manner. HPLC analysis shows a 95 : 5 *anti/syn* ratio (eluant: 97.5 : 2.5 heptane–ether). Recrystallization from hexane–ether gives 22.1 g (65%) of the pure title product with m.p. 63–64°C, $[\alpha]_D$ +29.5 (c = 1.07 in chloroform).

2,5-Dimethylfuran can also be reacted with 2,3-O-isopropylidene-D-glyceraldehyde at high pressure to furnish 22% of (1RS,2R)-1-C-(2-furylmethyl)-2,3-O-isopropylidene-glycerol.[173]

The addition of 2-(trimethylsilyloxy)furane to aldehydes results in a chain extension with a C_4 unit, corresponding to an α,β-unsaturated butyrolactone [2(5H)-butenolide]. The configuration of the new chiral center can be influenced by various catalysts,[174] and this type of chain extension has also been introduced[175] to the carbohydrate field for the production of D- and L-*hept-2-enono-1,4-lactones* with *arabino, ribo, xylo,* and *lyxo* configurations from 2,3-O-isopropylidene-D- and -L-glyceraldehyde, as shown in Figure 1.192. From the reaction mixture the predominant two products; the *arabino-* and *ribo*-lactones can be isolated in 56% and 13% yields, respectively.

Another alduloses, including 3-O-methyl-1,2-O-isopropylidene-α-D-*xylo*-pentodialdo-1,4-furanose, can also be homologated,[176] when the final products are derivatives of β-L-*ribo*-D-*gluco*-nonose. Two consecutive four-carbon homologations[177] of 2,3-O-isopropylidene-D-glyceraldehyde (**193.1**) lead to the penta-O-isopropylidene derivative (**193.9**) of D-*glycero*-D-*talo*-L-*talo*-undecose, as shown in Figure 1.193.

According to the results of Casiraghi *et al.,*[178] an optimized chain extension step with 2-(trimethylsilyloxy)-furan is as follows.

*6,7-O-Isopropylidene-2,3-dideoxy-D-*arabino- and D-ribo-*hept-2-eno-1,4-lactone*[178] A mixture of 2,3-O-isopropylidene-D-glyceraldehyde (10 mmol) and trimethylsilyloxyfuran (2.15 ml, 13 mmol) in dichloromethane (30 ml) is cooled to −80°C, and boron trifluoride etherate (1.23 ml, 10 mmol) is added under argon atmosphere. It is then stirred at this temperature for 6 h, saturated aqueous NaHCO$_3$ is added, the temperature is allowed to rise ambient temperature, and the mixture is extracted with dichloromethane. The organic layer is washed with aqueous NaHCO$_3$, dried over MgSO$_4$, and concentrated under reduced pressure. The residue is dissolved in methanol (10 ml), then citric acid (0.25 g) is added and the solution is stirred for 3 h. After dropwise addition of water (5 ml) the mixture is extracted with dichloromethane, the organic layer is dried, and concentrated, and the residue is purified by means of flash column chromatography (eluant: hexane–ethyl acetate) to obtain a 96 : 4 *arabino/ribo* mixture (90%). Physical data for the pure *arabino*-

TABLE 1.31 Conversion of aldehydo-Sugars with Furan and 2-Methylfuran

Educt	Product	Yield (%)	Diastereomeric ratio	Configuration of the major product
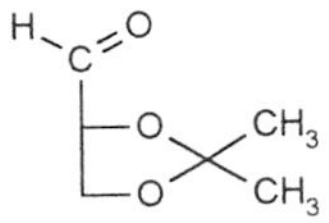	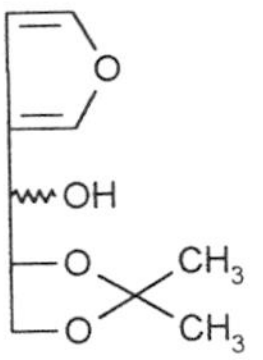	42	85:15	R
	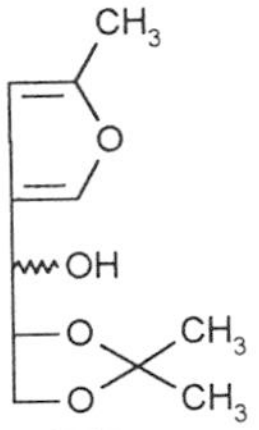	62	95:5	R
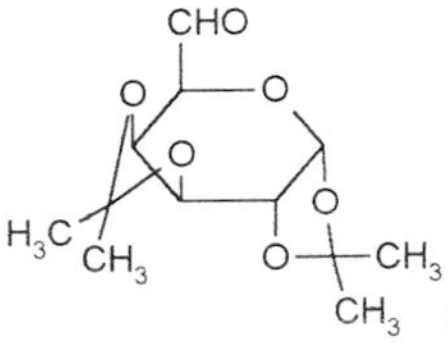	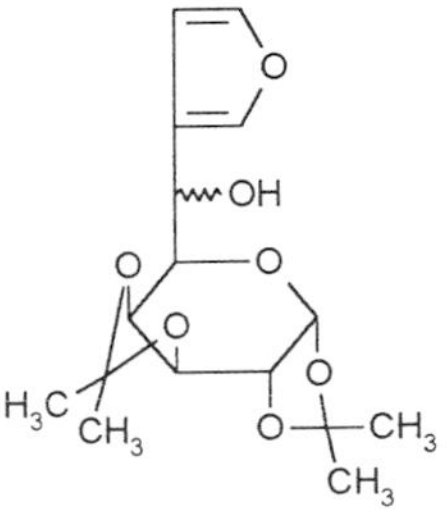	45	87:13	S
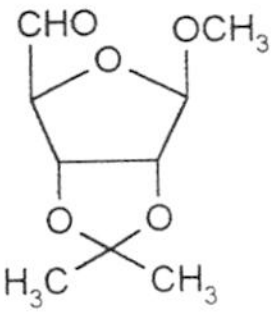	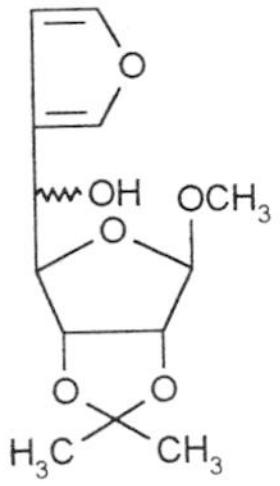	68	95:15	S
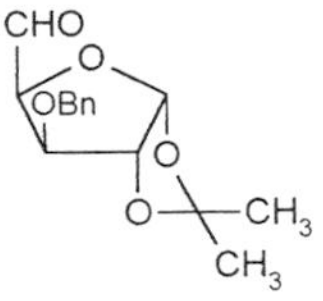	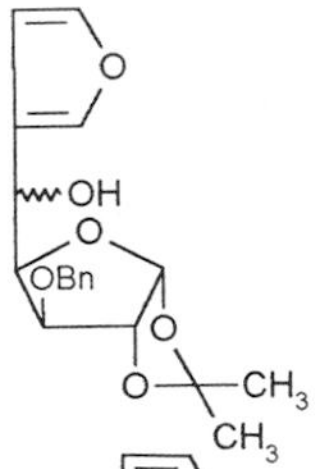	45	86:14	S
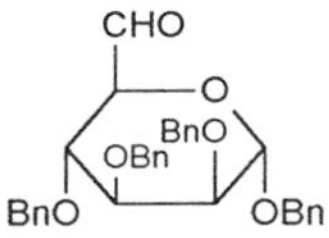	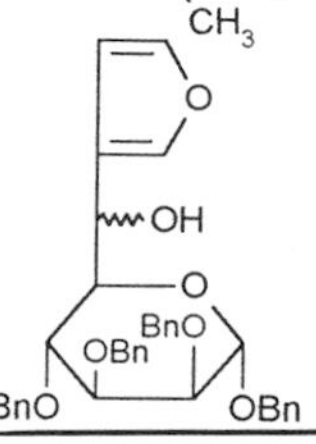	35	75:25	S

(continues)

TABLE 1.31   (*continued*)

Educt	Product	Yield (%)	Diastereomeric ratio	Configuration of the major product
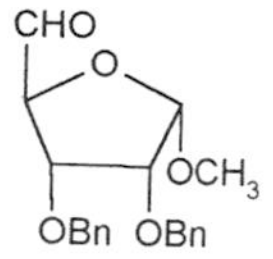	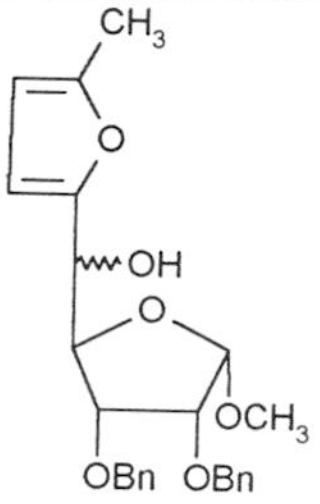	36	73:27	S
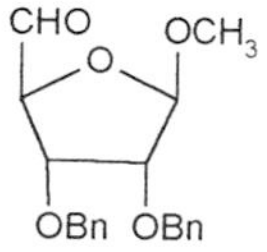	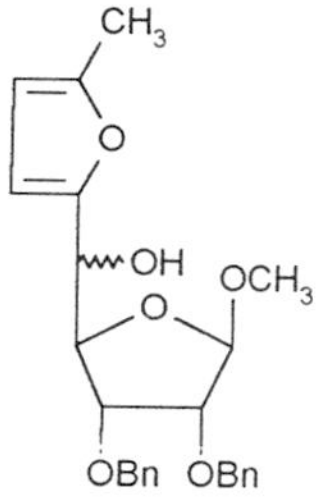	62	76:24	S
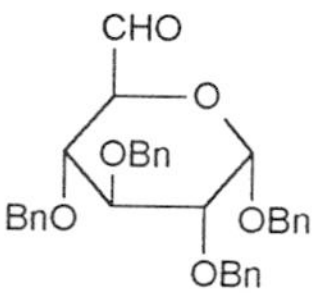	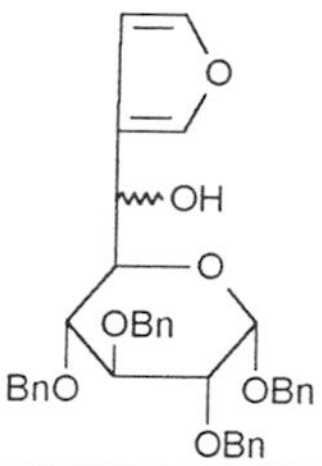	36	—	S

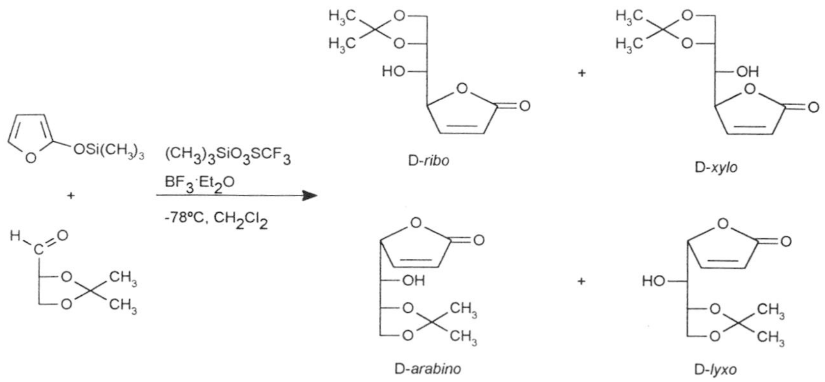

FIGURE 1.192

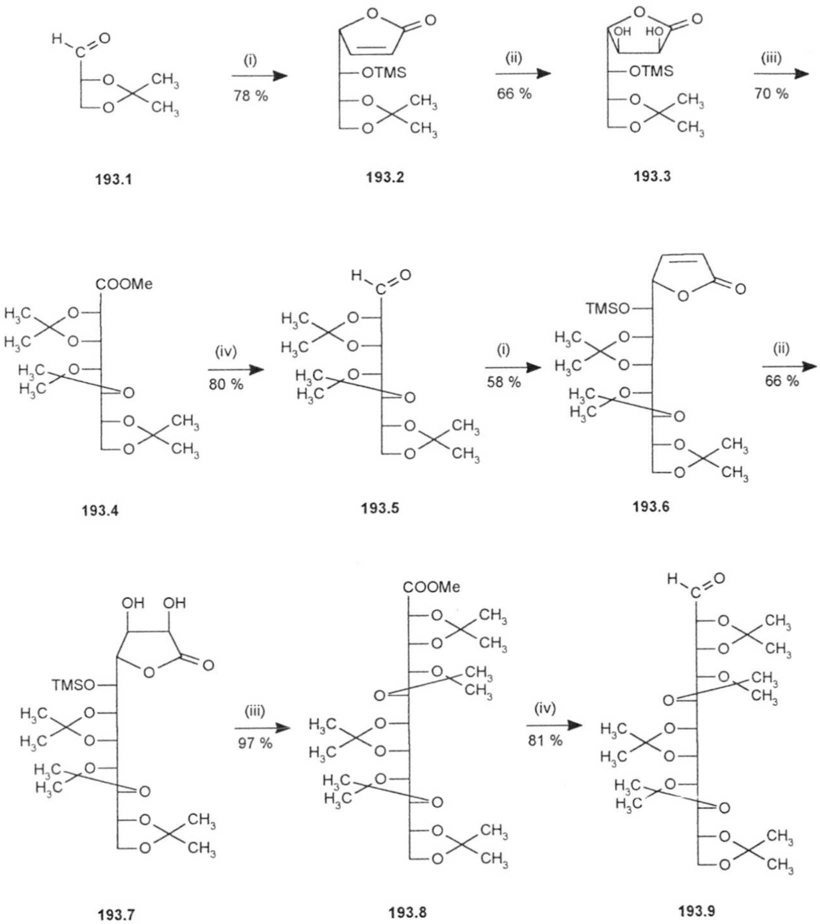
(i)
78 %
(ii)
66 %
(iii)
70 %
193.1
193.2
193.3
(iv)
80 %
(i)
58 %
(ii)
66 %
193.4
193.5
193.6
(iii)
97 %
(iv)
81 %
193.7
193.8
193.9

Reagents: (i) 2-(trimethylsilyloxy)furan (TMSOF), $BF_3 \cdot OEt_2$, -90°C, then Me_3SiCl, pyridine;

(ii) $KMnO_4$, DCH-18-crown-6, CH_2Cl_2, 15°C;

(iii) dimethoxypropane, TsOH, room temperature;

(iv) DIBAL, CH_2Cl_2, -90°C

FIGURE 1.193

lactone: m.p. 125°C, $[\alpha]_D^{20}$ +69.6 (c = 1 in chloroform) and for the pure *ribo*-analog: syrup, $[\alpha]_D^{20}$ −79.4 (c = 0.6 in chloroform).

The butenolide unit can be built into 3-(*tert*-butoxycarbonyl)-4-formyloxazolidine as well, and after the necessary transformations α-D-*glycero*-D-*talo*-heptopyranose and the corresponding uronic acid, *precursors to destomic acid* can be prepared.[179] The enantiomeric L-compounds can also be obtained[179] with this highly stereoselective and truly viable route.

Most recently 2-(*tert*-butyldimethylsilyloxy)thiophene (**194.1**) has been synthesized and coupled with 2,3-*O*-isopropylidene-D-glyceraldehyde (**194.2**) to afford[180] the products **194.3** and **194.4** shown in Figure 1.194.

Of the reagents used in saccharide chain extensions, certain *pyrrole derivatives,* especially, pyrrole-derived silyloxydienes, play significant role. In particular, *N*-(*tert*-butylcarbonyl)-2-(*tert*-butyldimethylsilyl)pyrrole (**195.1**, TBSOP), available[181] from pyrrole, has been found suitable for the chain extension of chiral substrates carrying aldehydo or imino groups, which is—in many cases—a key step in flexible methods aimed at constructing complex molecules bearing multiple contiguous chiral centers.[181–189] As shown in Figure 1.195, the sugars **195.2–195.4** are reacted with TBSOP (**195.1**) in the presence of suitable catalysts (SnCl$_4$, tritylperchlorate), and for a practical utilization of this important methodology, two prescriptions are given as follows.

4-Amino-8-O-benzyl-N-(tert-butoxycarbonyl)-2,3,4-trideoxy-6,7-O-isopropylidene-L-galacto-oct-2-enoic acid 1,4-lactam (195.6)[185] A mixture of 4-*O*-benzyl-2,3-*O*-isopropylidene-L-threose (**195.3**, 2.32 g, 11.27 mmol) and TBSOP (**195.1**, 3.35 g, 11.27 mmol) in dry ether (50 ml) is cooled to −80°C under argon. Then a 1 M/dm^3 solution of SnCl$_4$ in dichloromethane (16.9 ml, 16.9 mmol) is added via a cannula during 10 min, and the solution is stirred for 5 h. The reaction is quenched with saturated aqueous NaHCO$_3$, and the mixture is warmed to ambient temperature and extracted with ether (3 × 15 ml). The organic layer is dried (MgSO$_4$) and concentrated under reduced pressure to furnish the crude lactam, which is purified

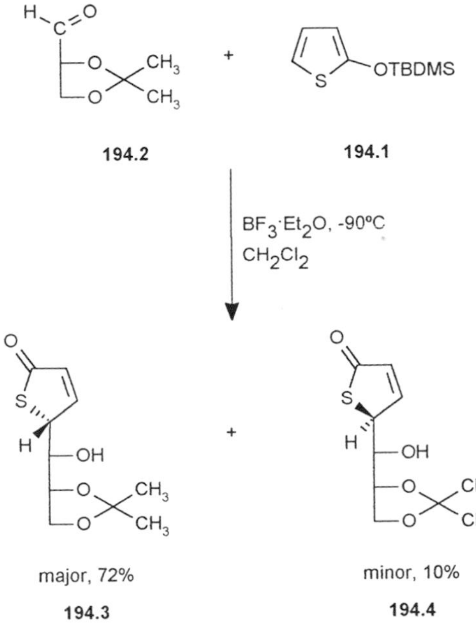

FIGURE 1.194

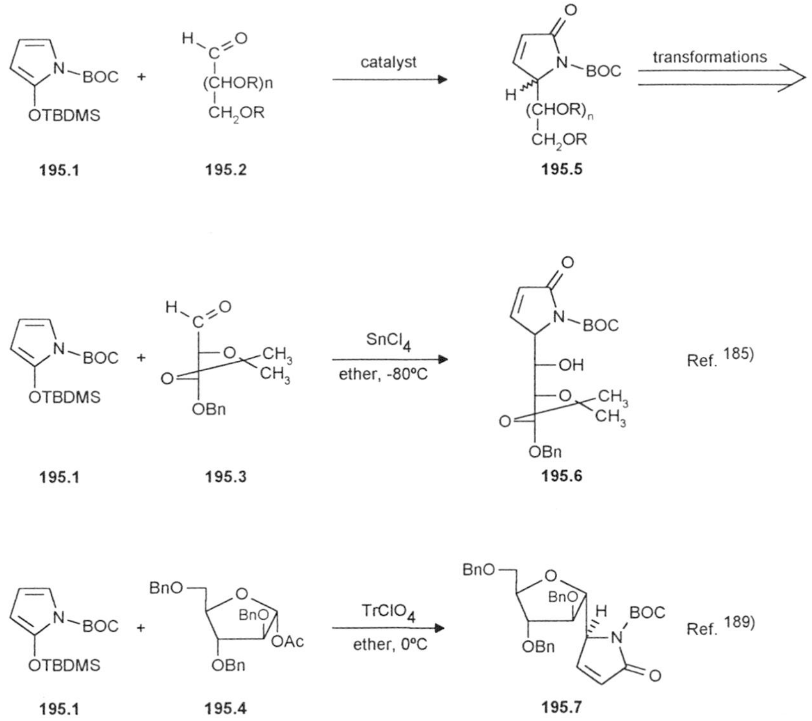

FIGURE 1.195

by flash column chromatography on silicagel (eluant: 65:35 ethyl acetate–hexane) to afford the pure lactam **195.6** (3.42 g, 80%), as a solid with m.p. 96–98°C, $[\alpha]_D^{20}$ +134.66 (c = 0.88 in chloroform).

6,7,9-Tri-O-benzyl-4-N-(tert-butylcarbonylamino)-5,8-anhydro-2,3,4-trideoxy-D-glycero-D-galacto-non-2-enono-1,4-lactone (195.7)[189]   To a solution of 1-O-acetyl-2,3,5-tri-O-benzyl-α-D-arabinose (**195.4,** 1.0 g, 2.16 mmol) in dry ether (10 ml) are added TBSOP (**195.1,** 770 mg, 2.59 mmol) and anhydrous tritylperchlorate (370 mg, 1.08 mmol) with stirring at 0°C. After 4 h, the temperature is allowed to rise to 20°C and, after additional 24 h, the reaction is quenched with saturated aqueous NaHCO$_3$ (15 ml). The mixture is extracted with ether (3 × 20 ml), the organic layer is washed with water, dried (MgSO$_4$), and concentrated. The pure product **195.7** (784 mg, 62%) is obtained by flash column chromatography on silicagel (eluant: 7:3 hexanes–ethyl acetate) as an oil, $[\alpha]_D^{22}$ −58.9 (c = 1.6 in chloroform).

1.2.7.3. The Reformatsky Reaction for the Chain Extension of Saccharides

This reaction, involving the zinc-mediated formation of β-hydroxycarboxylates from halogenoacetates and aldehydes/ketones[190] (Reformatsky-reaction), is employed in carbohydrate chemistry for the preparation of *nonbranched onic-acid esters*[191] (Fig. 1.196).

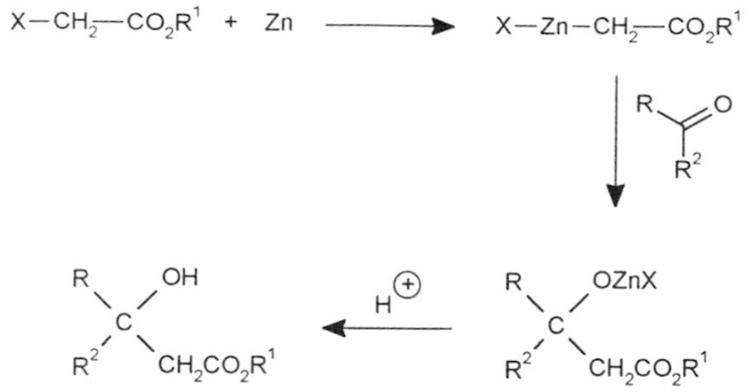

FIGURE 1.196

This Reformatsky method was applied for chain extensions with starting materials such as 3-*O*-benzyl-1,2-*O*-cyclohexylidene-α-D-xylofuranos-1,4-ulose,[192] 1,2-*O*-cyclohexylidene-α-D-xylofuranos-1,4-ulose,[193] 2,3:4,5-di-*O*-cyclohexylidene-*aldehydo*-L-arabinose,[193] and 2,3:5,6-di-*O*-isopropylidene-α-D-mannofuranose,[193] but the stereochemistry of the newly created chiral center was not determined (cf. Csuk and Glänzer[194]). Then the stereochemistry of a related Reformatsky reaction, carried out with 3-*O*-benzyl-1,2-*O*-isopropylidene-α-D-*xylo*-pentofuranos-1,4-ulose (**197.1**) and ethyl bromoacetate (**197.2**), was studied and the *anti*-configuration was assigned to the product **197.3**, suggesting[190] that the reaction proceeds under thermodynamic control (Fig. 1.197).

> *Ethyl 3-O-benzyl-1,2-O-isopropylidene-α-L-ido-heptonate (197.3)*[195] A suspension of freshly activated zinc (washed with 20% aqueous HCl, water, acetone, and ether and then dried; 655 mg, 10 mmol) in benzene (10 ml) is heated to reflux, and a mixture of the sugar **197.1** (2.0 g, 7.2 mmol), ethyl bromoacetate (1.6 ml, 14.4 mmol), and ether (3 ml) is added and the reaction mixture is kept under reflux for an additional 30 min. It is then hydrolyzed with 20% aqueous sulfuric acid and extracted with dichloromethane. The crude product obtained on usual workup is purified by means of column chromatography to yield 2.24 g (85%) of the pure syrupy heptonate **197.3** with $[\alpha]_D$ −22 (c = 2 in chloroform).

For the preparation of *2-deoxy-2,2-difluoro-D-ribose*, the Reformatsky chain extension was selected,[196] and thus 2,3-*O*-isopropylidene-D-

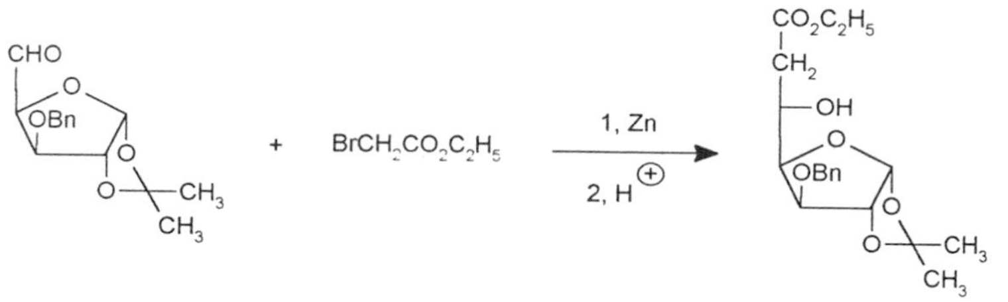

197.1   197.2   197.3

FIGURE 1.197

glyceraldehyde (**198.1**) was treated (Fig. 1.198) with the commercially available ethyl bromodifluoroacetate (**198.2**) to obtain a ~3:1 mixture of ethyl 2,2-difluoro-(3R)-hydroxy-3-(2,2-dimethyl-1,3-dioxolan-4-yl)propionate (**198.3**) and the corresponding (3S)-hydroxy isomer (**198.4**). Then the (3R)-hydroxy derivative **198.3** was transformed in three further steps[196] into *2-deoxy-2,2-difluoro-D-ribose*, and the *L-enantiomer* was also synthesized[197] according to this procedure.

> *Ethyl 2,2-difluoro-(3R)-hydroxy-3-(2,2-dimethyl-1,3-dioxolan-4-yl)propionate (**198.3**) and the corresponding (3S)-hydroxy isomer (**198.4**)*[196] To 24.9 g of activated zinc is added a small portion of a solution consisting of 55 g of 2,3-O-isopropylidene-D-glyceraldehyde (**198.1**) and 77.3 g of ethyl bromodifluoroacetate (**198.2**) in dry THF (129 ml) and dry ether (129 ml). The reaction mixture begins to reflux as soon as the first addition to the activated zinc is made. The remainder of the solution is added dropwise at a rate to maintain gentle reflux throughout the addition time of ~30 min. The mixture is stirred under a gentle reflux for an additonal 30 min, and then poured into 480 ml of 1 N hydrochloric acid and 480 g of ice, and the mixture is stirred until all the ice has melted. The aqueous mixture is extracted with ether (4 × 170 ml), the combined organic layer is washed with saturated aqueous NaCl and saturated aqueous NaHCO$_3$, dried over MgSO$_4$, and evaporated to obtain 104 g of a light-yellow syrup. This crude product is chromatographed on a 4-kg silicagel column (eluant: chloroform containing 0.5% of methanol) to isolate first 20 g of the minor (3S)-hydroxy isomer **198.4**, followed by the elution of 62 g (65%) of the (3R)-hydroxy sugar **198.3** in an essentially pure form.

When the reaction was performed in acetonitrile, 45% of a 1.8:1 mixture of the 3R- and 3S-isomers (**198.3** and **198.4**, respectively) was obtained by Japanese researchers.[198]

Reformatsky conditions were also applied in a novel synthesis[199] of *N*-acetylneuraminic acid. The key step of this procedure, shown in Figure 1.199, is the chain extension[199] of 2-acetamido-2-deoxy-3,4:5,6-di-*O*-isopropylidene-*aldehydo*-D-mannose (**199.1**) with *tert*-butyl 2-(bromomethyl)-prop-2-enoate (**199.2**). Of the various agents applied for the coupling of the two reaction partners, the highly reactive Zn/Ag couple on graphite was found to be more efficient than activated zinc, leading to the formation of a ~9:1 mixture of the two isomeric esters, **199.3** and **199.4**.

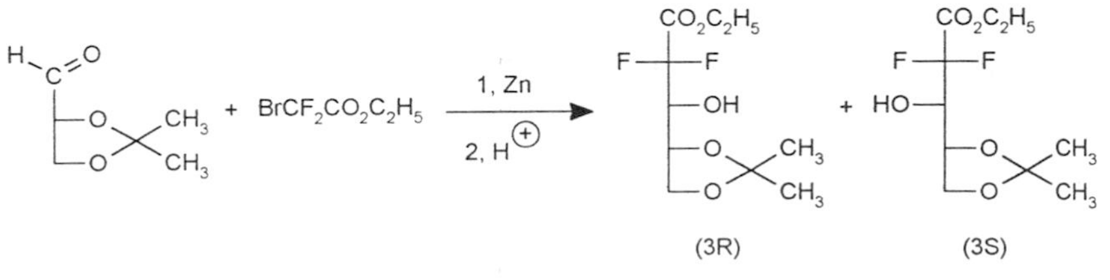

FIGURE 1.198

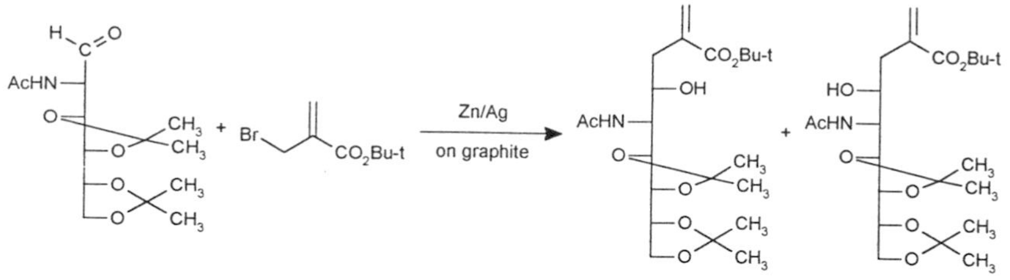

199.1   **199.2**   **199.3**   **199.4**

FIGURE 1.199

tert-*Butyl 5-acetamido-2,3,5-trideoxy-6,7:8,9-di-O-isopropylidene-2-methylidene-*
D-*glycero-*D-*galacto-nononate* (**199.3**) *and the corresponding* D-*glycero-*D-*talo-
isomer (**199.4**)*[199]   Graphite (2.5 g, 208.14 mmol) is heated under argon at 150°C
for 20 min, and under vigorous stirring, freshly cut clean potassium (0.98 g,
25.06 mmol) is added in several pieces over 5–10 min. Heating and stirring are
continued for 30 min, and the bronze-colored C_8K is allowed to cool to room
temperature and suspended in dry THF (100 ml). A mixture of anhydrous zinc
chloride (1.7 g, 12.47 mmol), and silver acetate (0.21 g, 1.26 mmol) is added in
three portions. After heating under reflux for 30 min, the mixture is cooled to
−78°C and a solution of the ester **199.2** (2.8 g, 12.66 mmol) and the sugar **199.1**
(3.0 g, 9.96 mmol) in dry THF (20 ml) is slowly added through a syringe. After
stirring for 30 min at −78°C, the temperature is allowed to warm to 0°C over 1 h,
the mixture is filtered through Celite, and the filtrate is evaporated to give an oil
(**199.3/199.4** = 88–91 : 8.8–11.1, HPLC, Zorbax Sil, 3 : 1 ethyl acetate–hexane,
1.5 ml/min). Column chromatography of this mixture on silicagel (eluant: 2 : 1
ethyl acetate–hexane) gives 3.7 g (83.7%) of **199.3**, m.p. 84–86°C, $[\alpha]_D^{20}$ +9.65
(c = 0.2 in chloroform) and 0.42 g (9.5%) of **199.4**, $[\alpha]_D^{20}$ +10.7 (c = 1.9 in chloroform).

For the preparation of 2,6-anhydro-hept-3-uloses (with D-*gluco* and
D-*manno* configuration) and 3,7-anhydro-oct-4-uloses from ulosyl bromide,[200] Reformatsky conditions were also applied when the reaction partner was formaldehyde or acetaldehyde. Starting from aldosuloses, *C-linked
disaccharides* can be obtained,[201] and in such reactions $CeCl_3$−NaI was
found to be a more efficient coupling agent than the Zn−Cu couple (see
Fig. 1.200).

Japanese authors reported successful Reformatsky reaction with
acylated sugars for the synthesis[202] of ethyl 3,6-anhydro-4,5,7-tri-O-
benzoyl-D-*ribo*-heptonate. The chain extension reaction of 2,3-O-
isopropylidene-D-glyceraldehyde with ethyl bromoacetate can be induced[203] with tin, indicating that other metals are also sufficient to perform
the Reformatsky reaction. Of these metals, indium is to be mentioned
here, because it has been successfully employed for the chain extension of
unprotected saccharides via their formyl groups.[204-208] Thus, indium−
mediated coupling[208] of lower monosaccharides with α-(bromomethyl)
acrylic acid gives the corresponding adducts in good yields, whose further
transformations allow the preparation of biologically important monosac-

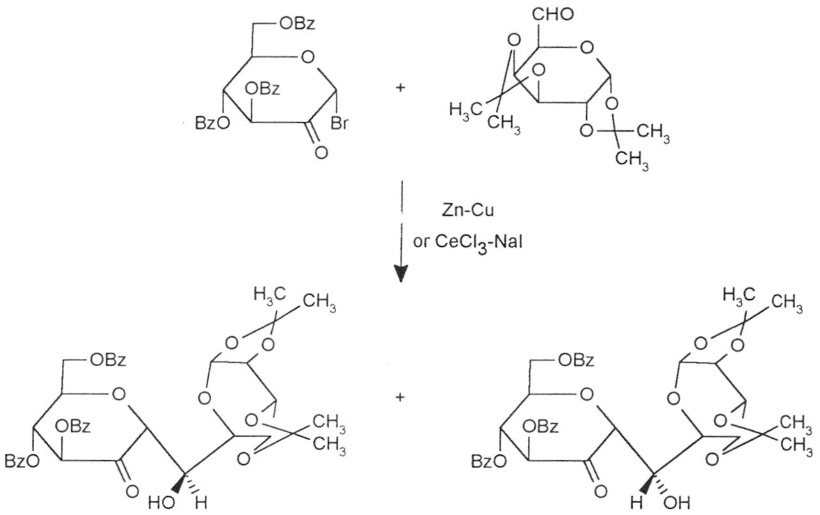

8 : 1
FIGURE I.200

charides, such as *Kdo* or *Neu5-Ac.* Precursors to these natural products can be obtained from *N*-acetyl-D-mannosamine (**201.1**) (Fig. 1.201).

5-*Acetamido-2,3,5-trideoxy-2-methylidene-*D-glycero-D-galacto-*nononic acid* (**201.2**, X = NHAc)[208] To a stirred mixture of *N*-acetyl-D-mannosamine (**201.1**, 957 mg, 4.0 mmol) and α-(bromomethyl)acrylic acid (3.96 g, 24 mmol) in ethanol (24 ml) and 0.1 N HCl (4 ml) is added indium powder (1.84 g, 16 mmol). The

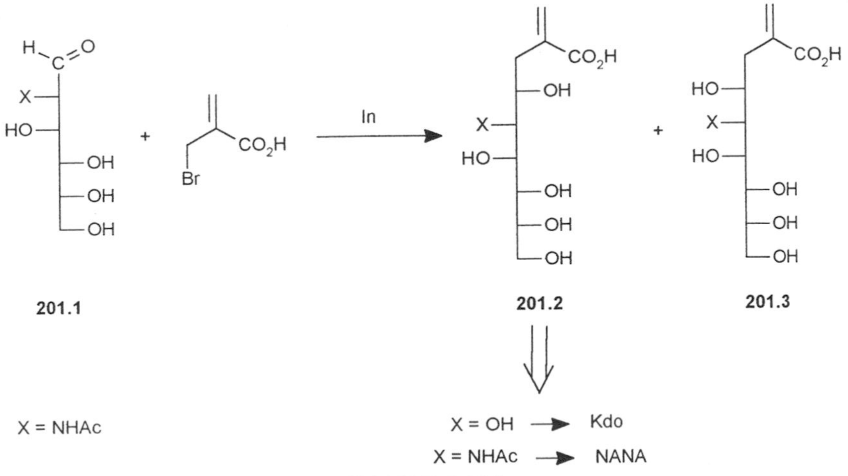

FIGURE I.201

reaction mixture is heated at 40°C with a sealed cap. After 12 h, the small indium clump is removed from the solution, extra indium powder (920 mg, 8 mmol) is added, and the mixture is heated for another 12 h. After being cooled to ambient temperature the mixture is filtered through a pad of Celite, it is rinsed with water, and the combined aqueous solution is deionized with Dowex 50 × 2–100 (H⁺) (5 g, dried weight), filtered, and evaporated to dryness below 30°C. Water (10 ml) is added, and the precipitate is filtered. The filtrate is lyophilized to give a colorless syrup that is chromatographed on Dowex 1 × 8–100 (formate form) anion-exchange resin by eluting with a 0–2 N formic acid gradient. The fractions (TLC: 7:3 2-propanol–water) with R_f = 0.44 (tailing) contain the desired product **201.2**. These are combined and lyophilized to afford 943 mg (77%) of the pure title product.

When lactones are treated with the derivatives of bromoacetic acid under Reformatsky conditions, the esters of ulosonic acids are produced. The reaction of 2,3:5,6-di-*O*-cyclohexylidene-D-mannonolactone with ethyl bromoacetate led to ethyl 4,5:7,8-di-*O*-cyclohexylidene-2-deoxy-D-manno-3-octulosonate, and simple derivatives of this compound (e.g., amide, methyl glycoside) are also available.[195,209] A very similar chain extension of 2,3:5,6-di-*O*-isopropylidene-D-gulonolactone (**202.1**), giving rise[210] to a single isomer **202.2** exclusively, is shown in Figure 1.202.

Ethyl 2-deoxy-4,5:7,8-di-O-isopropylidene-α-D-gulo-3-octulofuranosonate (**202.2**)[210]   A three-necked flask is heated in an oven and cooled in a nitrogen atmosphere. Then it is equipped with a KPG stirrer, a reflux condenser, and a dropping funnel. In the flask is placed activated zinc powder (2.7 g), and in the dropping funnel is placed a solution of 2,3:5,6-di-*O*-isopropylidene-D-gulono-1,4-lactone (**202.1**; 4 g, 15.5 mmol) and ethyl bromoacetate (7.2 g, 43 mmol) in 1,4-dioxane. A few milliliters of this solution is added to the zinc, and by the addition of a few crystals of iodine, the reaction is initiated. The mixture is stirred and warmed to 40–50°C, and the remainder of the preceding solution is added dropwise at this temperature when the color changes into green. Then the mixture is cooled to room temperature, and water (40 ml) is added and evaporated to dryness. The solid residue is rinsed with a solution of acetic acid in ether (5 × 30 ml of 10% acetic acid in ether), and the ethereal phase is separated, dried, and concentrated to a syrup that consists of (TLC, 9:1 chlorofom–methanol) a major product with R_f = 0.71 and three more slowly migrating by-products. The major product, **202.2** (2.69 g, 50%), is obtained by column chromatography (eluant: 9:1 chloroform–methanol) as a syrup that crystallizes from chloroform–hexanes in 4 weeks by storing in a deep-freezer, m.p. 39.5–40°C, $[\alpha]_D^{22}$ −12.7 (c = 1.04 in chloroform).

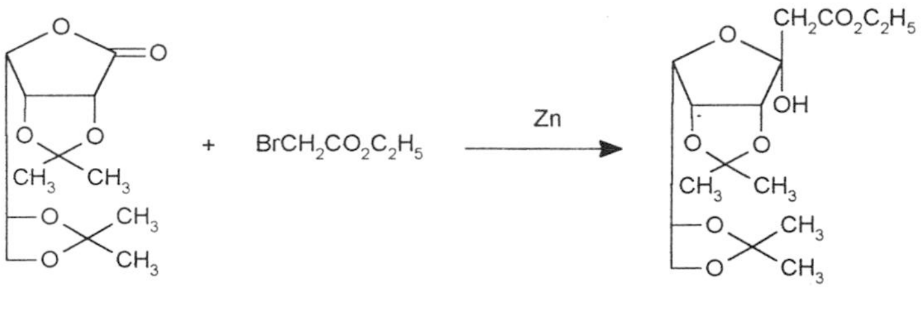

202.1   **202.2**

FIGURE I.202

The Reformatsky reaction of lactones can be performed under the reaction conditions[195] shown in Figure 1.199. An efficient general procedure for the condensation of furanoid and pyranoid aldonolactones with organozinc reagents derived from different haloalkanoates and the zinc/silver–graphite surface compound, and leading to chain-extended 3- or 4-ulofuranos- (or -pyranos)onates in high yields, is as follows.

> *General procedure for Reformatsky-type reactions*[194] Graphite (Fluka, 0.78 g, 65 mmol) and clean potassium (0.33 g, 8.44 mmol) are stirred at 150°C under argon as described on page 248 by Csuk et al.[199] To the resulting bronze-colored C_8K suspended in dry THF (20 ml), a mixture of anhydrous zinc chloride (0.55 g, 4.1 mmol) and silver acetate (0.06 g, 0.36 mmol) is added in several portions at room temperature with vigorous stirring. The addition of these salts causes the solution to boil. Refluxing is continued for an additional 20 min, the suspension is cooled to −40°C, and a solution of 3.3 mmol of the lactone and 4.3 mmol of the haloester in dry THF (5 ml) is slowly added. After stirring at this temperature for 20 min, the mixture is allowed to warm to 0°C, stirred further for 30 min, filtered through a pad of Celite, diluted with ethyl acetate (50 ml), and washed with icewater (5 ml) and brine (5 ml). The organic layer is dried (Na_2SO_4), the solvents are evaporated below 35°C, and the residue is subjected to column chromatography (eluant: 1:5 ethyl acetate–hexane) to afford the pure products.

The so-called Blaise reaction,[190,211] including an analogous transformation of nitriles (**203.1**) with alkyl bromoacetates (**203.2**) in the presence of zinc, gives rise to an ester (**203.3**) as the final product, *extended with two carbon atoms* in the chain (Fig. 1.203). Buchanan et al.[212] have applied this methodology for the chain extension of 2,3-O-isopropylidene-4-O-(methanesulfonyl)-D-erythrononitrile (**203.4**) to the unsaturated C_6-ester **203.5**.

> *Methyl (E/Z)-3-amino-2,3-dideoxy-4,5-O-isopropylidene-6-O-(methanesulfonyl)-D-erythro-hex-2-enonoate (203.5)*[212] To a hot suspension of activated zinc (6.24 g, 5 eq.) in THF (58 m) 0.1 ml portions of ethyl bromoacetate are added until a vigorous reaction starts. When the color of the mixture remains steadily green, a

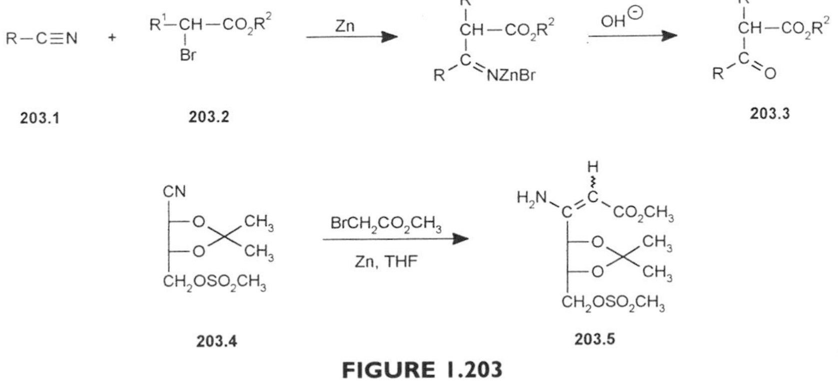

203.1   **203.2**   **203.3**

203.4   **203.5**

FIGURE 1.203

solution of the nitrile **203.4** (4.5 g) in THF (19 ml) is added dropwise over 5 min, followed by the dropwise addition of ethyl bromoacetate (7.36 ml, 4 eq) over 45 min. The mixture is warmed further for 10 min, cooled to ambient temperature, and diluted with THF (167.6 ml), and the reaction is quenched with 50% aqueous K_2CO_3 (27.8 ml). After vigorous stirring for 45 min, the mixture separates into two phases. The upper, organic layer is separated, the aqueous layer is extracted with THF (4 × 50 ml), and the combined organic layer is dried and concentrated, and the residue is chromatographed first on Florisil and then on Kieselgel (eluant: ether), to obtain first 0.135 g (2.2%) of the syrupy (*E*)-isomer, and then–eluted second–4.61 g (78%) of the pure major product **(Z)-203.5**, m.p. 97–98°C, $[\alpha]_D^{20}$ −156.6 (*c* = 1.66 in chloroform).

1.2.7.4. Preparation of Sugar Derivatives by Means of Chain Extension Based on Aldol-Condensation

This chain extension strategy utilizes the base-catalyzed transformation (Fig. 1.204) of aldehydes and ketones (**204.1**), containing an active methylene group at the α-position, and further conversion of the

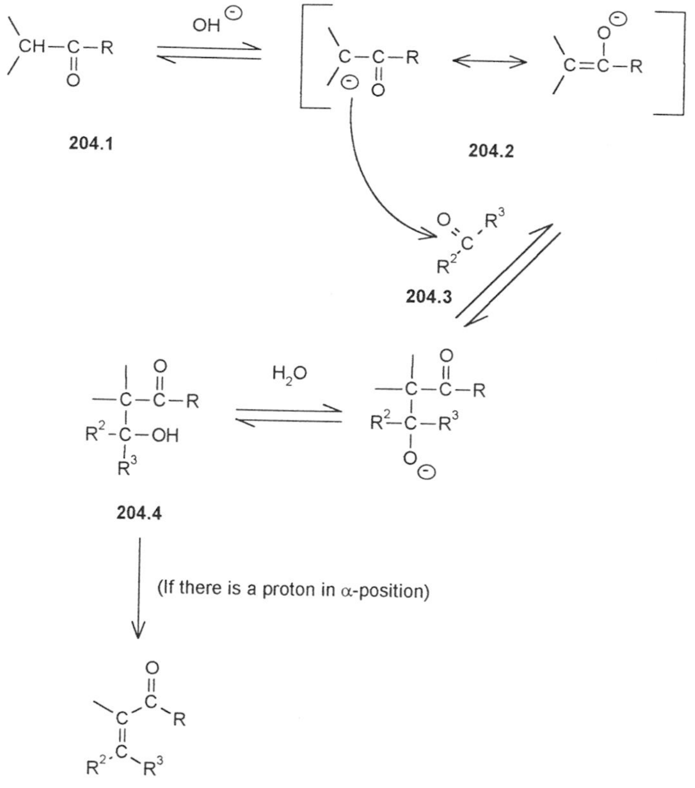

FIGURE I.204

β-hydroxyaldehydes (the so-called aldols; **204.4**) produced in the reaction, into α,β-unsaturated carbonyl compounds (**204.5**)—depending on the conditions (crotonization). Considering on the details of this process,[213] in the first step the enolate **204.2** is formed, whose condensation with the carbonyl compound **204.3** results in the aldol **204.4,** and the stereochemical outcome is determined by the chelate structure[214] of the transition state of the reaction. In this way, in the kinetically controlled process from the (Z), and (E)-enolates the *erythro-,* and the *threo-*isomers, respectively, are produced; however, bulky substituents may have a significant influence on the kinetically controlled aldolization. Under thermodynamic control the *threo-*isomers are the exclusive products—regardless of the steric arrangement of the enolate molecule.

The buildup of sugars molecules in Nature is based on analogous reactions: *The biosynthesis of saccharides follows the principle of aldol condensation.*[215] From a synthetic point of view it is very important that the aldol reaction of 2,3-O-isopropylidene-L-glyceraldehyde (**205.1**) with 1,3-dihydroxy-2-propanone (**205.2**) in the presence of anion-exchange resin (Fig. 1.205) leads (in 90% yield) to a mixture of hexuloses, from which the otherwise hardly available 2,3:4,5-di-O-isopropylidene-β-L-fructopyranose (**205.3**) was obtained on acetalization with acetone–sulfuric acid (Fig. 1.205). The additional acetals produced could be removed by mild acid hydrolysis, and the aldolization could also be carried out with the D,L-glyceraldehyde derivative, when removal of the D-enantiomeric product is accomplished by enzymatic degradation.

Preparation of 2,3:4,5-di-O-isopropylidene-β-L-fructopyranose (205.3)[216]   To a mixture of L-glyceraldehyde (480 mg) and 1,3-dihydroxypropanone (250 mg) in water (15 ml) freshly prepared Dowex 1 anion exchange-resin (HCO_3^- form) is

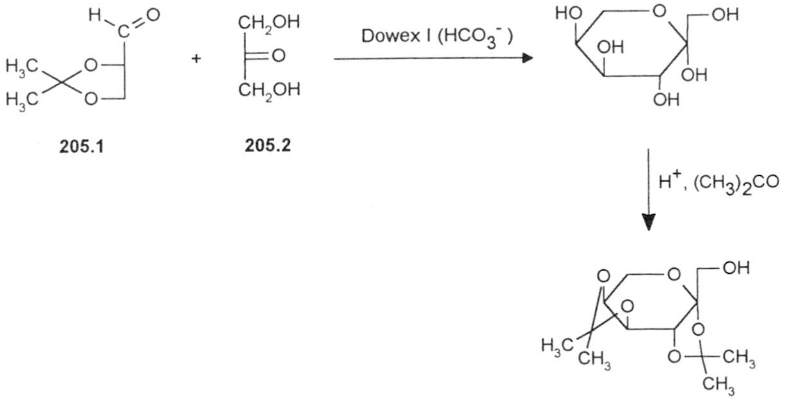

FIGURE 1.205

added, and is kept at ambient temperature for 15 min then treated with 50% aqueous acetic acid. The resin is filtered off, washed with water, and then eluted with aqueous acetic acid until no reducing sugar can be detected in the eluate. Evaporation of the eluate under reduced pressure gives a mixture of ketoses (665 mg, 91%), which is treated with 2.5% sulfuric acid in acetone (20 ml). After 4 h, solid NaHCO$_3$ is added until neutralization, when GC–MS examination shows that 60% of the product is present in the mixture. After filtration the filtrate is concentrated and the residue is taken up with 60% aqueous acetic acid (15 ml), kept at 55–60°C for 90 min, and then at ambient temperature overnight. The mixture is evaporated to dryness, and distributed between chloroform and water, the aqueous layer is extracted with chloroform, and the combined organic phase is dried over Na$_2$SO$_4$, filtered, and evaporated. The residue is taken up with petroleum ether (b.p. 40–60°C) and subjected to a slow evaporation to result in the separation of the crystalline title product **205.3** (517 mg, 49%), m.p. 96–97°C, $[\alpha]_D^{25}$ +23 (c = 2 in chloroform).

To determine the extent of asymmetric induction in related transformations, the aldol reaction of 2,3-*O*-isopropylidene-D-glyceraldehyde (**206.1**) and various ethers of lactaldehyde with different ketones, esters, and ketene acetals have been investigated,[217–220] since the products of such reactions are important starting materials in *syntheses of deoxysugars*. The following example describes the conversion of **206.1** with methyl acetate to give[217] an 85:15 mixture of the methyl trihydroxypentanoates **206.2** and **206.3** (Fig. 1.206).

*Methyl (3R,4R)- and (3S,4R)-2,4-O-isopropylidene-3,4,5-trihydroxypentanoate (**206.2** and **206.3**)*[217] To a mixture of diisopropylamine (0.55 ml, 3.9 mmol) in dry THF (10 ml), 2.6 ml of a 1.5 M solution of *n*-butyllithium in hexane (3.9 mmol) is added at 0°C; after 10 min the solution is cooled to −70°C, and 3.5 mmol of methyl acetate is added over 3 min. After stirring at −70°C for 2 h, 0.46 g (3.5 mmol) of the glyceraldehyde **206.1** is added, the reaction mixture is stirred further for 20 min, and then quenched with 10 ml of saturated aqueous NaHCO$_3$. It is allowed to warm to room temperature, extracted with ether, and the residue

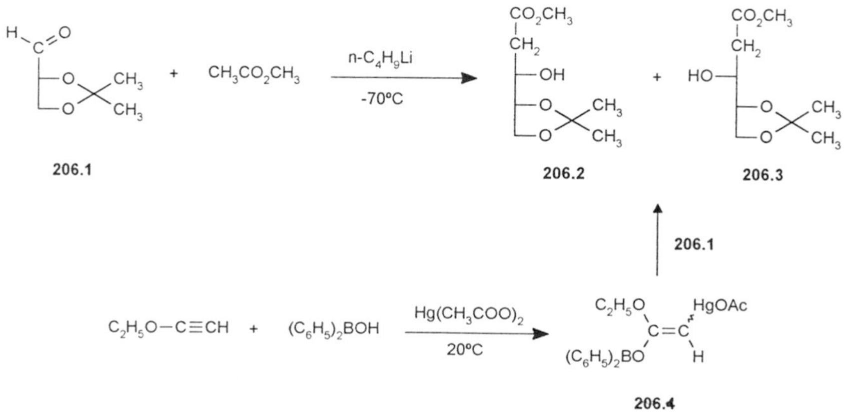

FIGURE I.206

obtained on evaporation is chromatographed (eluant: 2:3 ether–hexane) to give 74% of the title aldol mixture.

Besides *n*-butyllithium (as in this above procedure), diphenylborinic acid can also be used to generate enolates. Thus, for the preparation of *2-deoxy-D-ribose*, aldolization of 2,3-O-isopropylidene-D-glyceraldehyde (**206.1**) was also carried out (Fig. 1.206) with the adduct **206.4** (generated from ethoxyacetylene and diphenylborinic acid) to furnish,[221] again, the aldol mixture **206.2 + 206.3**. With the aim of the synthesis of *pederol*, a natural product,[222] the aldol reaction of (*S*)-3,4-dimethoxybutanal was carried out with enolsilanes.

The aldol condensation of 2,3-O-isopropylidene-D-glyceraldehyde has also been utilized for the preparation of pentose and octose derivatives.[223] The titanium tetrachloride–induced condensation of the glyceraldehyde **207.1** with the bicyclic silylenolether **207.2** afforded (1*S*,3*S*,4*S*,5*S*,6*S*)-3-exo-[(1'*S*,2'*R*)-1'-hydroxy-2',3'-(isopropylidenedioxy)-propyl]-5-*exo*,6-*exo*-(isopropylidenedioxy)-7-oxabicyclo[2.2.1]heptan-2-one (**207.3**) with a high *anti*-selectivity (Fig. 1.207), which was transformed in a few further synthetic steps into a separable mixture of partially protected D-*erythro*-D-*talo*-octose and D-*erythro*-D-*allo*-octose.[224] From the enantiomer of the enolether **207.2**, the *corresponding derivatives* of D-*threo*-L-*talo*-octose and D-*threo*-D-*allo*-octose have been prepared.[224]

An additional possibility for the derivatization into enolethers is the production of enolates from alkyl trihalogenoacatates and isopropylmagnesium chloride as shown in Figure 1.208. Addition of the resulting dihalogenomagnesium enolate **208.1** to 2,3-O-isopropylidene-D-glyceraldehyde (**208.2**) proceeds with good yield, but with a moderate stereoselectivity (*erythro*:*threo* ratio is ~7:3). Then the esters (**208.3** and **208.4**) of 2-dihalogenopentanoic acids can be converted[225] (in two additional steps) into the isomeric 3,5-diacetoxy-γ-valerolactones.

Methyl (3R,4R) and (3S,4R)-2,2-dichloro-4,5-O-isopropylidene-3,4,5-trihydroxy-pentanoates (208.3 and 208.4)[225]   To a cold (−78°C) solution of isopropylmagne-

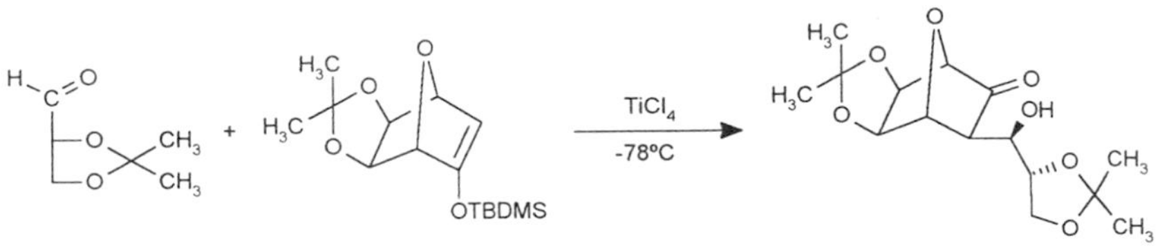

207.1   207.2   207.3

Yield: 55%, m.p. 131-132°C
$[\alpha]_D^{25}$ = -110.2 (c = 0.62, CH_2Cl_2)

FIGURE I.207

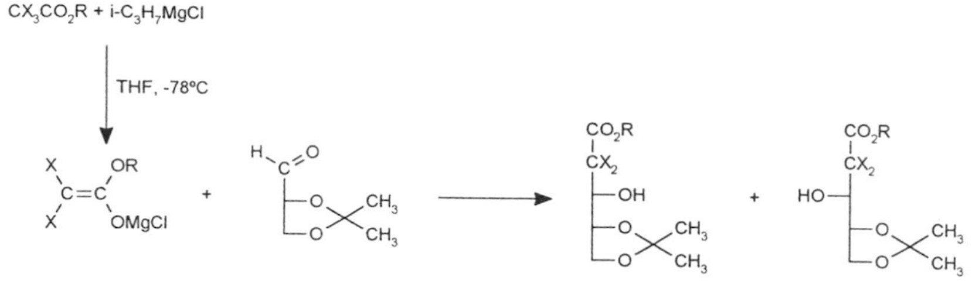

$CX_3CO_2R + i\text{-}C_3H_7MgCl$

THF, -78°C

208.1   **208.2**   **208.3**; X = Cl   **208.4**; X = Cl

(3R, 4R)   (3S, 4R)
erythro   threo

FIGURE 1.208

sium chloride in THF (1 M, 18 ml) methyl trichloroacetate (19.8 mmol, 1.1 eq) in THF is added, and after storing for 1 h at this temperature, a solution of 2,3-O-isopropylidene-D-glyceraldehyde (**208.2**, 1.3 g) in THF (10 ml) is added dropwise over a 1-h period. The mixture is kept at −78°C for 20 min and then allowed to warm to −20°C, and hydrolyzed with an acetate buffer. The product is extracted with ethyl acetate (3 × 100 ml), and the combined extract is washed with saturated NaHCO₃ and water. After drying (Na₂SO₄) and evaporating to dryness, the residue is chromatographed (eluant: 1:4 ethyl acetate–hexane) to isolate first 1.2 g (44%) of the (3R,4R)-product **208.3**, m.p. 100°C (from hexane), $[\alpha]_D^{25}$ +3.6 (c = 1.39 in ethanol), and then 0.545 g (20%) of the (3S,4R)-isomer **208.4**, as a syrup, $[\alpha]_D^{25}$ −10.6 (c = 1.39, in ethanol).

The additional two stereoisomeric isopropyl esters of 2,2-dichloro-4,5-O-isopropylidene-3,4,5-trihydroxypentanoic acid were synthesized on an essentially similar way.[225]

Aldolization of D-threose (**209.1**) with ethyl glyoxylate (**209.2**) allowed investigators to obtain *ascorbic acid* (**209.3**) in a rather simple way[226] (Fig. 1.209).

Similar aldol condensation of certain protected derivatives of D-ribose, D-glucose, and D-galactose with acetone, as the reaction partner, leads[227] to complex mixtures of various unsaturated saccharides. When such a reaction of 2,3-O-isopropylidene-D-ribofuranose (**210.1**) was conducted in the presence of potassium carbonate, the final product was 4,7-anhydro-1,3-dideoxy-5,6-O-isopropylidene-D-*altro*-2-octulose (**210.2**), but the corres-

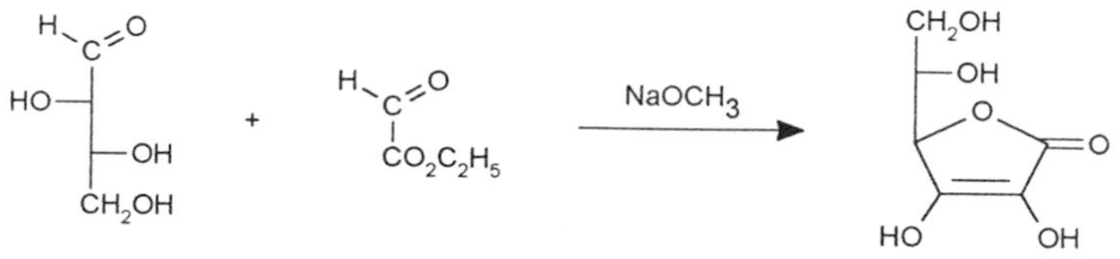

209.1   **209.2**   **209.3**

FIGURE 1.209

ponding D-*allo* isomer (**210.3**) was also detected (Fig. 1.210). The major product was isolated and characterized in form of the corresponding 8-*O*-benzoate **210.4**.

> *4,7-Anhydro-8-O-benzoyl-1,2-dideoxy-5,6-O-isopropylidene-D-altro-2-octulose (210.4)*[227] A mixture of the sugar **210.1** (0.19 g, 1 mmol), acetone (40 ml), water (5 ml), and potassium carbonate (0.196 g, 1.4 mmol) is heated under reflux for 12 h and then evaporated to dryness. The residue is taken up with water and extracted with chloroform, and the dried (Na_2SO_4) organic solution is concentrated to a syrup. Flash column chromatography of the residue (eluant: 2:1 hexane–ethyl acetate) leads to a homogeneous syrup (0.17 g, 75%), which is treated with 2 ml of benzoyl chloride in pyridine (15 ml). After 3 h the mixture is evaporated, the residue is dissolved in chloroform (50 ml), and the solution is washed with 1 N hydrochloric acid (10 ml) and water (2 × 10 ml) and then dried (Na_2SO_4). The syrupy residue is purified by means of preparative layer chromatography (developing system: 3:1 hexane–ethyl acetate) to furnish 0.23 g (69%) of pure **210.4**, $[\alpha]_D$ +8 (c = 0.5 in chloroform).

When either 2,3,5-tri-*O*-benzyl-D-ribofuranose or 2,3,4,6-tetra-*O*-benzyl-D-gluco- and D-galactopyranose is subjected to analogous reaction conditions,[227] mainly elimination products, such as (3*E*,5*Z*,7*S*)-5,8-dibenzyl-oxy-7-hydroxy-octa-3,5-dien-2-one or (3*E*,5*Z*,7*S*,8*R*)- and (3*E*,5*Z*,7*R*,8*R*)-5,7,9-tribenzyloxy-8-hydroxy-nona-3,5-dien-2-one, respectively, are produced.

The aldol reaction of protected 1-*O*-acetyl-ribofuranose derivatives with silylenolethers readily proceeds[228,229] in the presence of tin tetrachloride or tritylperchlorate catalysts, and with the benzyl protecting group (**211.1**), a product (**211.2**) with *altro*-configuration is obtained (Fig. 1.211).

According to the studies of Dondoni *et al.*,[230–232] 2-acetylthiazole—as

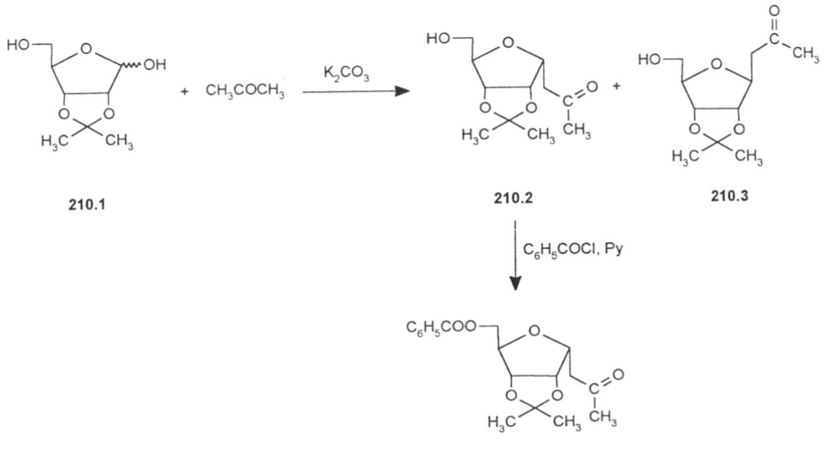

FIGURE I.210

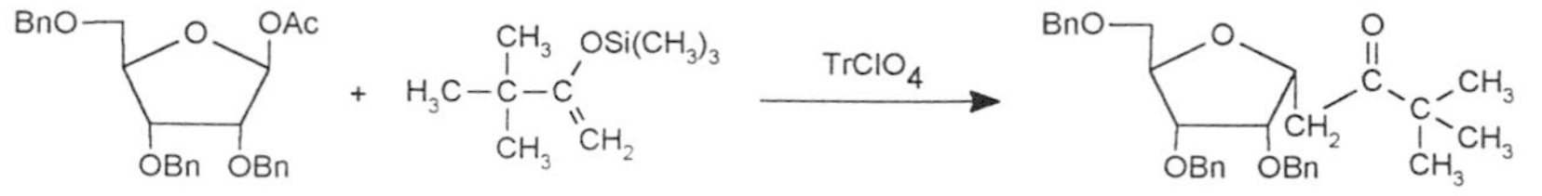

211.1   **211.2**

FIGURE 1.211

a reagent for the pyruvic acid β-anion synthon–is *extremely useful* for the chain extension of *aldehydo*-sugars with a three-carbon unit via *anti*-selective aldol condensation of its lithium enolate (Fig. 1.212). The related chain extension of saccharide derivatives is summarized in Table 1.32.[232] The diastereoisomeric ratio of the products was determined before chromatographic purification by means of integration of the signals in the region of 8.0–7.0 ppm (H-4 and H-5 thiazole protons) of the corresponding ^{1}H-NMR spectrum.

> *General procedure for the aldol condensation of* aldehydo-*sugars with 2-acetyl-thiazole*[232] To a well-stirred solution of *tert*-butanol (0.74 g, 10 mmol) in dry THF (15 ml) is added dropwise butyllithium (10.24 mmol, 6.4 ml of a 1.6 M solution in hexane) at room temperature. Stirring is continued for 30 min, the mixture is cooled to $-50°$C, and a solution of the *aldehydo*-sugar (10 mmol) and 2-acetylthiazole (1.3 g, 10.24 mmol) in dry THF (40 ml) is added dropwise. After 2 h saturated aqueous NH$_4$Cl (40 ml) is added, and the mixture is stirred for an additional 10 min at $-50°$C and then is allowed to warm to room temperature. Water (20 ml) is added, the two layers are separated, the aqueous layer is washed with ether (4 × 25 ml), the combined organic layer is dried (Na$_2$SO$_4$), and the solvent is evaporated under reduced pressure. The residue is purified by column chromatography on silicagel (eluant: 1 : 1 ether–hexane) to give the aldol derivatives shown in Table 1.32.

Condensation of the enolate **213.2**—derived from 3-*O*-benzyl-1,2-*O*-isopropylidene-5-deoxy-α-D-*xylo*-hexodialdo-1,4-furanose, **(213.1)** by treatment with bis-(trimethylsilyl)-lithium amide—with methyl 2,3,4-tri-*O*-benzyl-α-D-*gluco*-pentodialdo-1,5-pyranose (**213.3**) furnished a 6:1 mixture of the two *erythro*-aldols **213.4** and **213.5** in a moderate (43%) yield[233] (Fig. 1.213).

3-*Deoxy*-D-manno-2-*octulosonic acid* (**214.1,** *Kdo*),[234] a common ketoside component of the cell-wall lipopolysaccharides of gram-negative bacte-

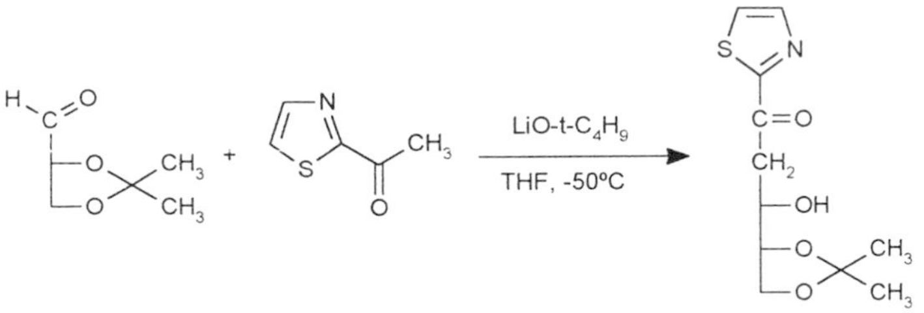

FIGURE 1.212

TABLE 1.32 Aldol Condensation of Saccharides Using the Lithium Enolate of 2-Acetylthiazole[232]

Educt	Aldol[a]	Yield (%)	Diastereoselectivity[b]
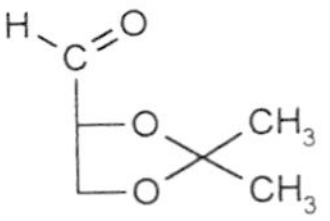	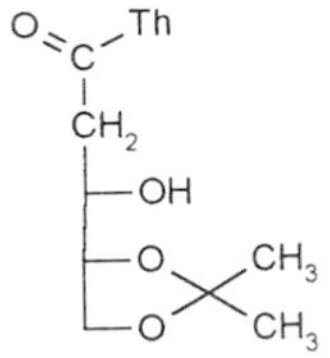	58	90
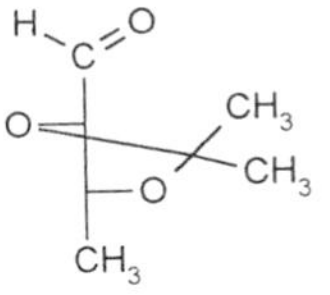	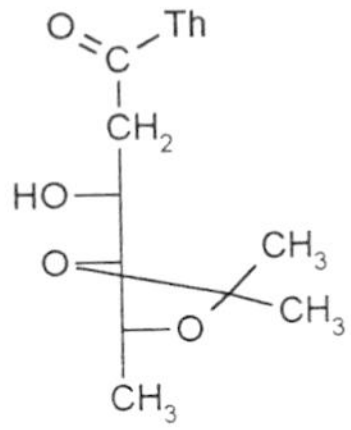	60	—
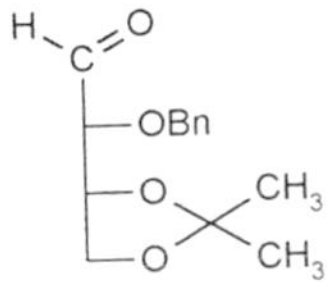	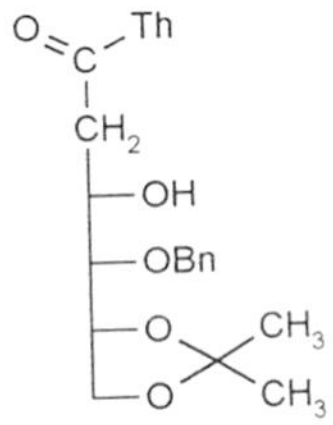	51	90
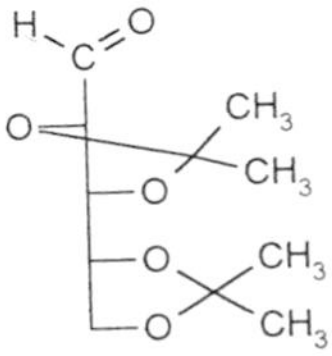	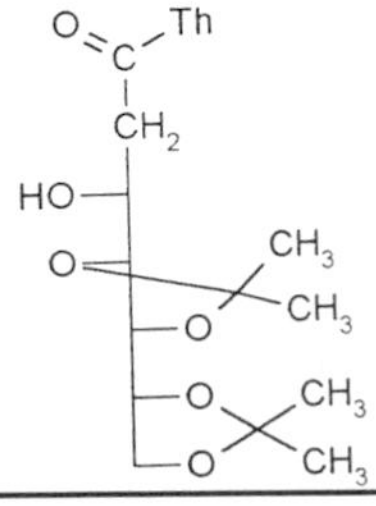	54	90

[a]Th = thiazole-2-yl.
[b]From the integration of the ^{1}H-NMR spectra.

ria, can also be most conveniently synthesized by an aldol condensation, followed by decarboxylation as shown schematically in Figure 1.214.

According to this (Fig. 1.214) mechanism, *Kdo* is obtained in 30% yield, as the highest, by the condensation of D-arabinose with oxaloacetic acid under the previously reported conditions.[235-237] In a review paper Unger[234] reported an improved methodology, and still another aldolization procedure[238] led to the ammonium salt of Kdo, as described below.

Preparation of Kdo by the aldol reaction of D-arabinose[238] To a solution of sodium carbonate (8.2 g, 77.36 mmol) and D-arabinose (15.53 g, 103.5 mmol) in

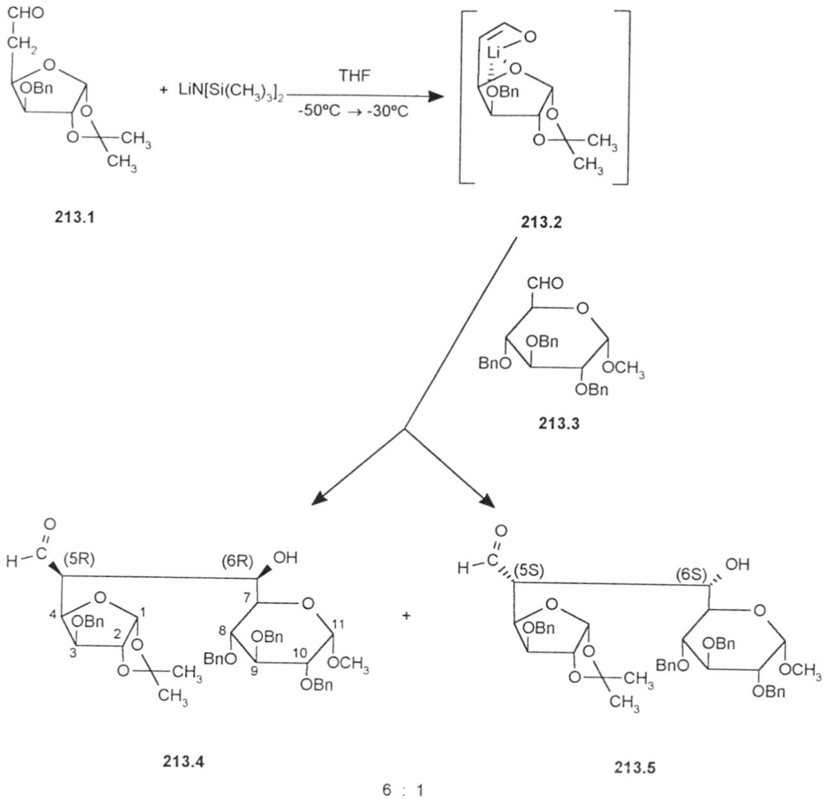

FIGURE I.213

water (40 ml), oxaloacetic acid (5 g, 37.86 mmol) is added slowly, the pH is adjusted to 11 with 10 N NaOH, and the mixture is stirred for 90 min. It is then acidified (pH = 1–2) with Amberlite IR-120 (H$^+$) ion exchange resin, filtered, and neutralized with ammonium hydroxide. The product is chromatographed on an Amberlite CG-400 column (HCO$_3^-$ form, 60 × 3.5 cm), washed with 3 liters of water, and eluted with 0.5 M ammonium hydrogencarbonate solution (4 liters). The eluate is concentrated to 50 ml under reduced pressure and freeze-dried. Following crystallization, the residue gives 3.60 g (37%) of Kdo, m.p. 118–122°C, [α]$_D^{25}$ +32 (c = 2.0 in water).

In a novel study[239] the final step of the ulosonic acid synthesis was investigated, and it was established that the decarboxylation can be facilitated with 1 mol% of NiCl$_2$ (with respect to oxaloacetic acid) and thereby the yield can be increased up to 66%. The reaction of D-mannose with oxaloacetic acid (Fig. 1.215) has also been studied,[239] and after optimization, the overall yield of the produced ammonium salt of 3-deoxy-D-*glycero*-β-D-*galacto*-non-2-ulosonic acid (**215.1**), together with the corresponding D-*talo*-epimer **215.2**, is ~70%, and it is important to keep the pH between 5

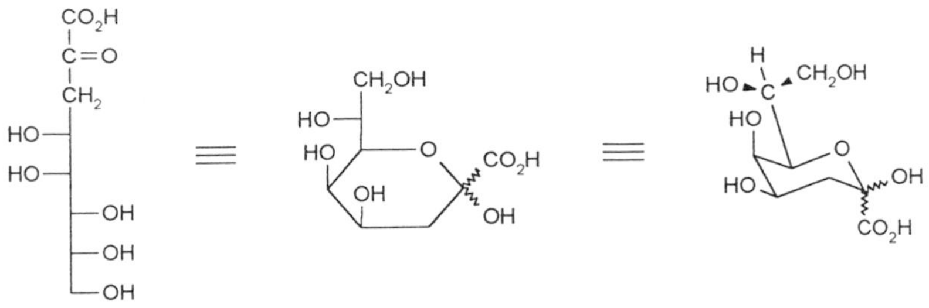

214.1

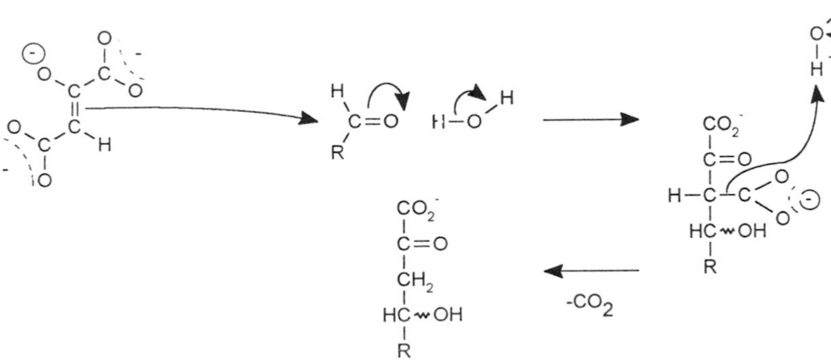

R= sugar portion

FIGURE 1.214

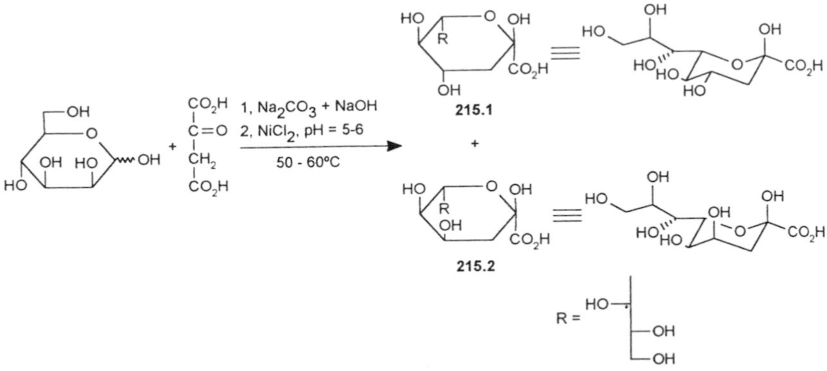

215.1 : 215.2 = 42 : 12

FIGURE 1.215

and 6. If no nickel chloride is added to the reaction mixture, the β-D-galacto isomer (215.1) can be obtained[240] with 39% yield, as follows.

> *Preparation of the ammonium salt of 3-deoxy-D-glycero-β-D-galacto-non-2-ulosonic acid (215.1)*[240]   To a solution of D-mannose (27.03 g, 150.03 mmol) and Na$_2$CO$_3$ (6.36 g, 60 mmol) in water (32 ml) oxaloacetic acid (6.61 g, 50 ml) is added slowly, the pH is adjusted to 10, and the mixture is stirred for 2 h and then acidified with Dowex 50 (H$^+$) to pH = 1–2. After filtration, the filtrate is neutralized with ammonia, and the product is purified on a Dowex 1 column (in HCO$_2^-$ form), which is washed first with water (2 liters) and then eluted with a 0.3 M solution of formic acid. The eluate is evaporated under diminished pressure, treated with ammonia, and freeze-dried to obtain 5.6 g (39%) of the amorphous product **215.1**, $[\alpha]_D^{20}$ −41 (in water).

An additional aldol reaction, described by Szabó[241] and involving the condensation of 2-O-benzyl-4-O-formyl-D-arabinose (216.1) with oxaloacetic acid, allows the isolation of the two isomeric oct-2-ulosonates, **216.2** and **216.3,** as shown in Figure 1.216.

> *Methyl 5-O-benzyl-3-deoxy-D-manno- (216.2) and -D-gluco-oct-2-ulosonate (216.3)*[241]   The pH of a cooled solution of oxaloacetic acid (13.2 g, 0.1 mol) in 2 M aqueous sodium tetraborate (100 ml) is rapidly adjusted to 1.5 with 5 M aqueous NaOH, and 2-O-benzyl-4-O-formyl-D-arabinose (216.1, 5.36 g, 0.02 mol), followed by a solution of nickel chloride (1.2 g) in water (2 ml) is added. The reaction mixture is kept at room temperature for 18 h (the pH of the solution is periodically adjusted to 11.5 with 5 M aqueous NaOH during the first 5 h), at which time the yield of the 3-deoxyulosonates is usually more than 50% (estimated by the thiobarbiturate reaction on 5 μl of the reaction mixture). The reaction mixture is diluted (250 ml) with water and its pH brought to 4 with Amberlite IR-120 (H$^+$) resin. The filtered solution is diluted (500 ml) with a 1 : 4 mixture of 1 M aqueous pyridinium acetate (pH 5)–ethanol, which causes rapid decarboxylation of the excess of oxaloacetic acid. The solution is stirred under vacuum until evolution of gas ceases (~30 min), then passed through a column (3.2 × 28 cm) of Lewatit MP 5080 resin (OH$^-$) (60–80 mesh, Merck) equilibrated with 0.25 M aqueous pyridinium acetate (pH 5)–ethanol (1 : 1 v/v). Elution is effected using a gradient resulting from a constant volume (1 liter) mixing chamber containing 0.25 M aqueous pyridinium acetate (pH 5)–ethanol (1 : 1 v/v) and a reserve chamber (1.2 liters) containing 0.5 M aqueous pyridinium acetate (pH 5)–ethanol (1 : 1 v/v). Fractions containing 3-deoxyulosonic acids (thiobarbiturate test) are combined and concentrated to dryness. After drying (over KOH pellets), the residue is dissolved in water and passed through a column (1.4 × 17 cm) of Amberlite IR-120 (H$^+$) resin. The neutralized eluant (1 M aqueous

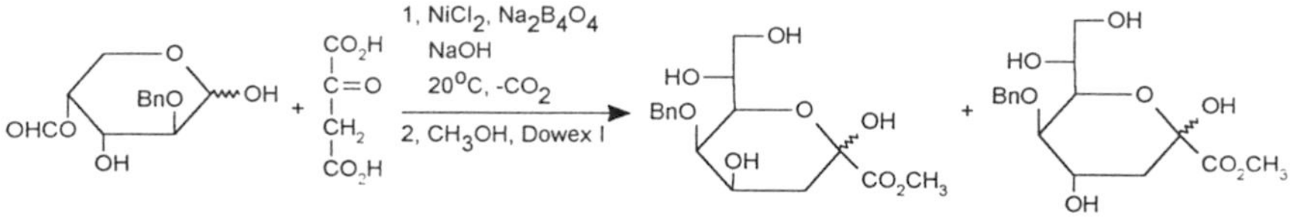

216.1   **216.2**   **216.3**

(D-manno)   (D-gluco)

FIGURE I.216

ammonium hydroxide) is concentrated to give a syrup that is dissolved in ethanol (20 ml), and any insoluble material is removed by centrifugation. The crude ammonium salts (4 g) are precipitated by addition of ether [paper electrophoresis in 0.1 M pyridinium acetate buffer pH 3.5 showed, besides **216.2** and **216.3** ($R_{\text{picric acid}}$ = 0.7), two major impurities (silver nitrate–sodium hydroxide) having $R_{\text{picric acid}}$ = 1.13 and 1.5], and are recovered by centrifugation, suspended in methanol, and stirred overnight at room temperature with dry IR-120 resin (H^+, 25 ml). The filtered solution is concentrated to give a yellow syrup (3.5 g) that contains two major compounds (TLC in 1 : 1 chloroform–methanol) with the major, R_f = 0.23 giving, after degradation,[242] 3-deoxy-glucitol, a product derived from 3-deoxy-D-*manno*-oct-2-ulosonic acid (**216.2**), the other (R_f = 0.27) giving 3-deoxy-galactitol, the degradation product of the D-*gluco*-isomer **216.3**. The two isomers are separated on a Lobar C (Merck) column (eluant: 9 : 1 chloroform–methanol), to obtain 1.1 g of the pure D-*manno* compound **216.2**, m.p. 126–127°C (after two recrystallizations from chloroform), $[\alpha]_D^{20}$ +47.4 (c = 1.15 in methanol).

Various representatives of *sialic acid analogs* can also be synthesized chemically by the aldol condensation methodology instead of the formerly applied enzymatic methods.[243] The synthesis of sialic acid derivatives (also known as *N-acetylneuraminic acid* analogs), playing important roles in many biological and immunologic processes, is still a great challenge for synthetic carbohydrate chemists. The first successful synthesis of *N*-acetyl-neuraminic acid (**217.6**, 5-acetamido-3,5-dideoxy-D-*glycero*-D-*galacto*-2-nonulopyranosonic-1-acid) was carried out by the aldol condensation of 2-acetamido-2-deoxy-D-glucose with pyruvic acid[244] or oxaloacetic acid.[245]

Kuhn and Baschang[246] have elaborated imporved procedures (Fig. 1.217) starting with 2-acetamido-2-deoxy-D-mannose (**217.1**) or 2-acet-amido-4,6-*O*-benzylidene-2-deoxy-D-glucose (**217.2**) and di-*tert*-butyl oxaloacetate (**217.3**). The application of the easily available glucose derivative **217.2** can be attributed to a facile epimerization[247] under the alkaline conditions employed.

Earlier studies showed that the reaction of aliphatic aldehydes with diethyl oxaloacetate leads[248] to carbethoxylactones, which are transformed into α-keto-γ-lactones on the action of dilute mineral acids. This observation was applied for *N*-acetyl-D-mannosamine (**217.1**), and di-*tert*-butyl oxaloac-etate (**217.3**) was found to be a very useful reaction partner[250] to produce the carboxylactone **217.4** by loss of isobutylene. Then decarboxylation of this latter compound in hot water (90–100°C) gave rise to the desired γ-*lactone* (**217.5**) of *N*-acetylneuraminic acid together with a few by-products. In practice the condensation of 2-acetamido-4,6-*O*-benzylidene-2-deoxy-D-glucose (**217.2**) with the ester **217.3** in 1,4-dioxane–methanol is recommended, when no previous *gluco* → *manno* epimerization is necessitated, and the overall yield is ~30%. A detailed procedure for the execution of the synthesis is as follows.

Synthesis of N-*acetylneuraminic acid (217.6)*[250] *Preparation of the potassium salt of di-*tert-*butyl oxaloacetate* The potassium salt obtained[249] by the condensa-tion of 1 mol of di-*tert*-butyloxalate[251] and 1 mol of *tert*-butylacetate is quickly

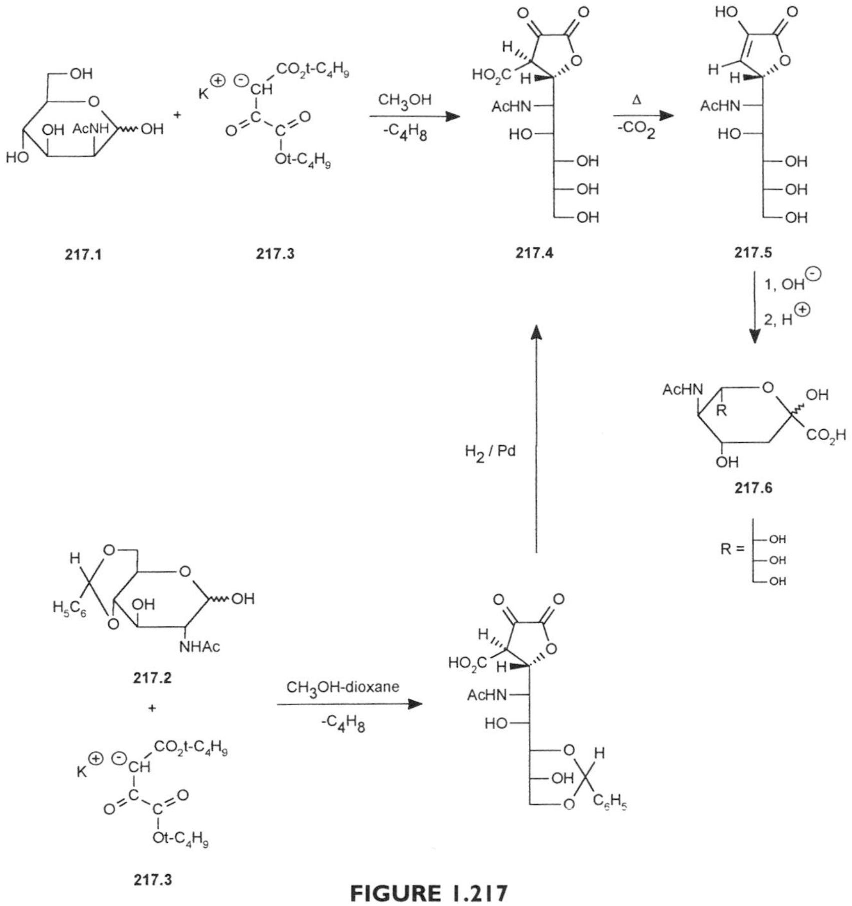

FIGURE 1.217

filtered off on a preheated glass filter and then washed with warm *tert*-butanol and ether. The yield is 85–90%.

A. From 2-acetamido-4,6-*O*-benzylidene-2-deoxy-D-glucose (**217.2**) First, 20 g of the sugar **217.2** and 20 g of the potassium salt of di-*tert*-butyl oxaloacetate (**217.3**) are shaken in a mixture of 1,4-dioxane (250 ml, freshly distilled from sodium) and methanol (250 ml). After shaking for 6–8 days at 20°C, a clear solution is obtained and the mixture is kept at ambient temperature for 3–6 days. It is then treated with Amberlite IR-120 resin (H⁺ form, ~30 ml, previously washed with methanol) until pH 6, concentrated to a syrup, taken up with methanol (some of the educt may crystallize during operation; this is filtered off), and deionized by elution from an Amberlite IR-120 (H⁺) column. Elution is continued until a negative Ehrlich-probe, the eluate is concentrated to 400 ml, and water (50 ml) is added and hydrogenated over Pd [prepared from 3 g of Pd(OH)₂]. The theoretical volume of hydrogen (2 mol/mol of the benzylidene sugar) is consumed until 3–5 days, methanol and toluene are distilled off, and the residue is dissolved in water (300 ml) and ether is added. The ethereal layer is separated, and the aqueous phase is extracted three times with ether and concentrated to a syrup by codistillation with 1-propanol. The residue is dissolved in 1-propanol and kept at 4°C to result in the crystallization of ~1.4 g of the educt. The solvent is distilled off, and the residue is taken up with water (200 ml) and heated on a 100°C steam bath until no more evolution of carbon dioxide is observed (~15 min). The red solution is cooled down quickly to ambient temperature, decolorized with charcoal and treated with 2 N NaOH until pH 9. The mixture is refrigerated for 24 h at this pH (which is checked and adjusted with 2 N NaOH if necessary), then applied onto the top of a Dowex 1 (HCOO⁻) column with a 20-drops/min rate and washed with water until no reducing materials can be detected (*m*-dinitrobenzene/NaOH reaction; Fehling probe). The acids are eluted from the column with 1 N formic acid (~4–5 liters) when the eluate gives a slightly positive Ehrlich reaction, evaporated to dryness, taken up with water, and slowly passed through a 4 × 3-cm charcoal column. Concentration of the eluate gives 7.2 g of crystalline *N*-acetylneuraminic acid contaminated with small amounts of the epimers. For crystallization the crude product is dissolved in warm water (15 ml), and 150 ml of glacial acetic acid is added. After filtration of the first crop of the crystals, the filtrate is concentrated, and this procedure is repeated several times to furnish 6.0 g (30% calculated for the used benzylidene sugar **217.2;** and 34% of the converted **217.2**) of the pure lactone pure **217.5,** m.p. 181–183°C, $[\alpha]_D^{20}$ −32.1 (*c* = 1.3 in water).

B. From 2-acetamido-2-deoxy-D-mannose (**217.1**) A mixture of anhydrous 2-acetamido-2-deoxy-D-mannose (8.35 g) and the potassium salt of di-*tert*-butyl oxaloacetate (15 g) in dry methanol (500 ml) is shaken until a clear solution is formed (1 h) and then kept at room temperature. After 24 h, 2-acetamido-2-deoxy-D-glucose is crystallized, and the mixture is shaken for additional 7 days, when the color turns red. The 2-acetamido sugar is filtered off, washed with methanol, and treated with dry Amberlite IR-120 resin (H⁺). The methanolic solution is poured onto a column filled with Amberlite IR-120 (H⁺) resin and eluted with methanol until no Ehrlich reaction is observed. The solution is concentrated under reduced pressure, the syrupy residue is taken up with ether/water, the aqueous layer is washed with ether, and the ethereal phase is reextracted once with water. The aqueous layer is concentrated and after addition of 1-propanol evaporated to dryness three times and taken up, again, in 1-propanol to allow 2-acetamido-2-deoxy-D-glucose to crystallize. This way, 4.0 g (48%) of 2-acetamido-2-deoxy-D-glucose can be recovered. Following evaporation of 1-propanol and drying over P_2O_5, 7.0 g (47.5%) of yellow glassy lactone (**217.4**) is obtained and is contaminated with traces of the 2-acetamido sugar. After chromatography on cellulose powder (eluant: *n*-butanol saturated with water), the specific optical rotation value is $[\alpha]_D$ −6 (*c* = 2.5 in water). The lactone **217.4** (6.3 g) is dissolved in water (70 ml) and heated on a steam bath until evolution of carbon dioxide has finished (~15 min). The red solution is quickly cooled to room temperature, the pH is adjusted to 9 with 2 N NaOH, and this pH is maintained for 24 h by addition of the base. It is then applied onto the top of a Dowex 1 (HCOO⁻) column (16 × 2.5 cm), washed with water until no color reaction with the Ehrlich reagent is observed and is then eluted with 1 N formic acid. After evaporation the residual crystalline substance contains small traces of the epimers. Yield: 3.6 g (66% for the converted saccharide and 34% for the applied amount of the saccharide). Following the decolorization procedure, described in method A, 2.30 g (42% and 22%, respectively, as above) of *N*-acetylneuraminic acid (**217.6**) is obtained, m.p. 182°C, $[\alpha]_D^{23}$ −32.4 (*c* = 0.9 in water).

This procedure, which serves for the synthesis of N-*acetylneuraminic acid,* has been extended[252] for the preparation of additional functionalized derivatives as well. As an example, the next procedure describes the method for obtaining N-*benzyloxycarbonyl-neuraminic acid.*

N-*Benzyloxycarbonylneuraminic acid*[252]   A mixture of 2-benzyloxycarbonyl-4,6-O-benzylidene-2-deoxy-D-glucosamine (60 g, 0.15 mol), the potassium salt of di-*tert*-butyl oxaloacetate (56 g, 0.2 mol), 1,4-dioxane (1 liter, dried over Na), and methanol (1.4 liters) is shaken for 2 weeks. It is then filtered, the filter cake is washed with 1:1 1,4-dioxane–methanol, and the pH of the combined filtrate and washings is adjusted to 6 with 100–120 ml of Amberlite IR-120 (H$^+$) resin and concentrated. The residual syrup is dissolved in methanol (4 liters), the starting material (precipitated on cooling) is filtered off and deionized with Amberlite IR-120 (H$^+$) resin. Elution is carried out with dry methanol, the eluate giving positive Bial test[253] is concentrated, water (500 ml) is added, and the mixture is subjected to steam distillation for 45 min. The reddish-brown solution is cooled quickly to ambient temperature and its pH is adjusted to 9 with 2 N NaOH, and it is refrigerated while the pH is being adjusted to the same value (with ~90 ml of 2 N NaOH). The solution is then poured onto the top of a column filled with Dowex 1 × 8 (HCOO$^-$ form) and eluted with water until the eluate gives a negative Fehling probe. The contaminants (together with some products) is eluted in a cold room with a formic acid graduent (2 liters of water and 1 liter of 2 N formic acid) with the aid of a constant volume mixer.[254] The product is eluted from the column with 1.5 N formic acid until the eluate gives a Bial-positive reaction.[254] The first (reddish-brown) fractions are separated form the main fractions and freeze-dried. The product is crystallized from a saturated aqueous solution (40°C) by the addition of ~10 parts of acetic acid. The residue obtained from the mother liquor on evaporation is crystallized from 1:10 water–acetic acid and dried over P_2O_5 in a desiccator to obtain the pure product with 20% yield, m.p. 191–193°C (dec.), $[\alpha]_D^{24}$ −30.4 (c = 2 in water).

A functionalized derivative, 2-acetamido-3-O-benzyl-4,6-O-benzylidene-2-deoxy-D-mannopyranose (**218.1**), of the preceding starting sugar is readily available from *N*-acetylmannosamine in four steps. Condensation of **218.1** with the oxaloacetate *K*-salt **218.2** gives the lactone **218.3,** which—on methylation and subsequent hydrogenolysis and alkaline treatment—gives rise (Fig. 1.218) to the *8-O-methyl ether of* N-*acetylneuraminic acid* (**218.4**), as reported by Khorlin and Privalova.[255]

6-O-*Benzyl-7,9-O-benzylidene-N-acetylneuraminic acid* γ-*lactone (218.3)*[255]   A suspension of the benzylidene sugar **218.1** (0.2 g) and the oxaloacetate *K*-salt **218.2** (0.15 g) in 1:1 methanol–1,4-dioxane (10 ml) is stirred for 5 days, filtered, deionized (Amberlite IR-120, H$^+$), and evaporated to dryness. The residue is washed with ether several times, dissolved in 1,4-dioxane (10 ml), and heated at 100°C for 15–20 min until no gas evolution is observed to furnish, on evaporation of the decolorized (charcoal) reaction mixture, 0.115 g (48%) of the lactone **218.3**.

Analogous chain extension of the 3-thio-mannosamine derivative **219.1** leads[256] (with 40% overall yield) to the products with D-*allo* (**219.2**) and D-*gluco* (**219.3**) configurations (see Fig. 1.219).

Aldolization of a furanoid 2-acetamido-2,3-dideoxy-3-thio-D-mannose derivative (**220.1**) with oxaloacetic acid at pH 7.5–8.0 proceeds with higher

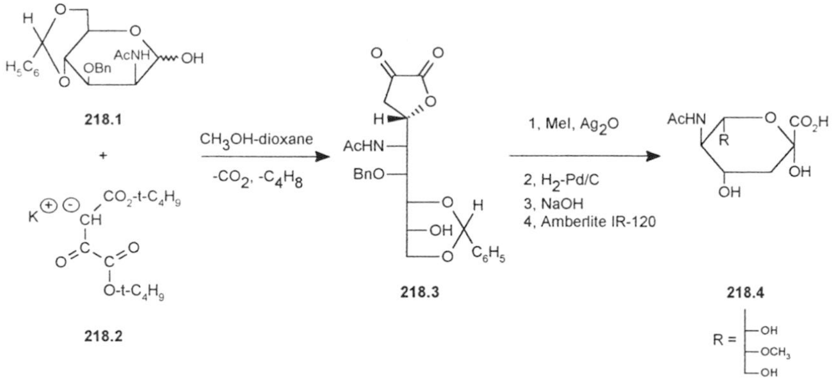

FIGURE 1.218

yield, and the final product, N-*acetyl-6-thioneuraminic acid* (**220.2**), can be obtained[256] (with 24% yield) on the synthetic route shown in Figure 1.220.

Related procedures, developed by Mack and Brossmer[257] served for the synthesis of further epimers of *N*-acetylneuraminic acid, such as *6-epi-* and *4,6-bis-epineuraminic acid.*

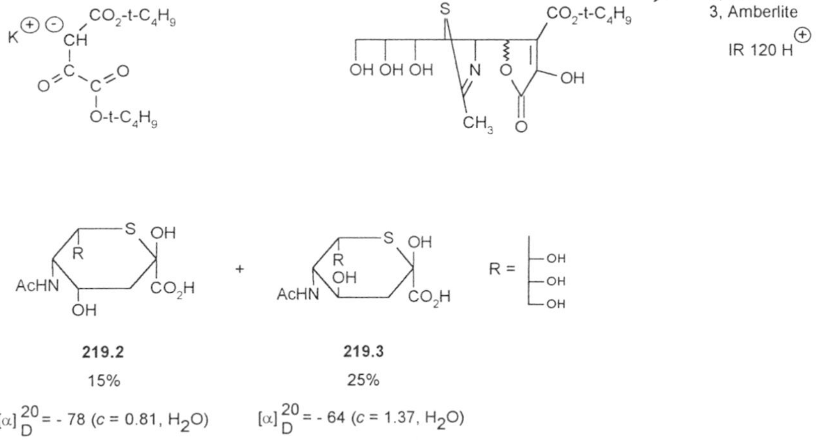

FIGURE 1.219

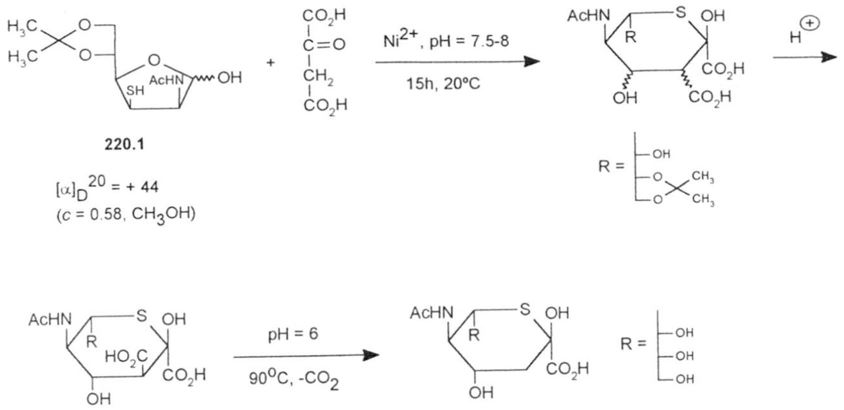

220.1

$[\alpha]_D^{20} = +44$ ($c = 0.58$, CH_3OH)

$[\alpha]_D^{20} = -109.5$ ($c = 0.85$, H_2O)

220.2

$[\alpha]_D^{20} = -82.5$ ($c = 1.0$, H_2O)

FIGURE 1.220

A well-established procedure for the preparation of *N*-acetylneuraminic acid by means of aldolization is based on the utilization of the stabilizing effect of the tetraborate ion in the base-catalyzed epimerization of 2-acylamino-2-deoxyaldoses.[258] For example, in the presence of sodium tetraborate the condensation of 2-acetamido-2-deoxy-D-mannose with oxaloacetic acid gave[258] 21% of N-*acetylneuraminic acid,* and in this work no emphasis was placed on the isolation of the additional products of the reaction.

N-*Acetylneuraminic acid*[258] To a solution of oxaloacetic acid (390 g) in water (2.6 liters), 10 N NaOH is added at 20°C until the pH is ~10 (cooling is necessary). Then sodium tetraborate (230 g) and 2-acetamido-2-deoxy-D-mannose monohydrate (650 g) are added, the pH is adjusted, again, to 10, and this pH value is maintained during the reaction. After 3- and 4.5-h reaction time additional amounts of oxaloacetic acid (95–95 g) are added, the pH is adjusted to 10, and after 46 h the reaction mixture is neutralized with acetic acid (pH 6) and the solution is successively eluted from a Zeokarb 225 (H^+ form, 45 × 17 cm) and a De-Acidite FF ($HCOO^-$ form, 45 × 15 cm) column. The latter resin is washed with water (200 liters) and eluted with 250 liters of 0.3 N formic acid. The fractions giving a positive sialic acid probe are collected and evaporated at 25°C with frequent addition of water. The resulting syrup (490 g) is dissolved in a 6:4:3 mixture of butanol–pyridine–water (some pyridine is added for complete dissolution) and applied onto a column of cellulose (33 kg, 52 × 45 cm) and eluted with the same solvent system. Paper chromatographic examination of the eluate shows three minor components besides the major product; *N*-acetylneuraminic acid. The fractions containing the product are evaporated with frequent addition of water, and recrystallization of the residue from 80% aqueous acetic acid gives 181 g (21.6%) of *N*-acetylneuraminic acid with m.p. 183°C (dec.) and $[\alpha]_D^{25}$ −34 (c = 1 in water).

Shiba[259] replaced the quite expensive N-acetyl-D-mannosamine with D-glucose, as the starting material, in a novel aldol-condensation procedure carried out in a sodium borate buffer. The major product of this method is 3-deoxy-D-*glycero*-D-*gulo*-2-nonulopyranosonic acid, a target to be functionalized into N-acetylneuraminic acid. The nitrogen function is introduced by a triflate → azide replacement. A furanoid minor product of this aldolization procedure has been applied for obtaining[260] a *structural isomer* of N-acetylneuraminic acid carrying the N-acetyl group at position C-6.

The stereochemical analysis[261] of the kinetically controlled aldol condensation (Fig. 1.221) of the simple chiral aminoaldehydes 2-acetamido-2-deoxy-D- (**221.1**) and -L-glyceraldehyde with di-*tert*-butyl oxaloacetate (**221.2**) revealed that the product is a 1 : 3 mixture of *tert*-butyl 5-acetamido-3-(*tert*-butoxycarbonyl)-3,5-dideoxy-D- (**221.3**) (and L-) -*xylo*-hexulopyranosonate and the corresponding D- (and L-) -*arabino* (**221.4**) derivative.

Tert-*butyl 5-acetamido-3-(*tert-butoxycarbonyl)-3,5-dideoxy-D-*arabino- *(221.4) and -D-*xylo-*hexulopyranosonate (221.3)*[261] The pH of a solution of 2-acetamido-2-deoxy-D-glyceraldehyde (**221.1**, 264 mg, 2.02 mmol) and di-*tert*-butyloxaloacetate (264 mg, 2.02 mol) in dry methanol (2 ml) is adjusted to ~12 by the addition of 0.5 N sodium methoxide in methanol (~2.1 ml). After standing for 1 h, the mixture is neutralized with Dowex 50 W (H$^+$) resin, the resin is filtered off and washed with ethanol, and the combined filtrate and washing is concentrated under reduced pressure (bath temperature 30°C). The resulting syrup contains two products and a significant amount of the starting material (TLC: 6 : 1 benzene–methanol). Column chromatography of this syrup on silicagel (12 g, eluant: 6 : 1 benzene–methanol) followed by another chromatographic purification on silicagel (12 g, eluant: 1 : 1 hexane–acetone) allows the isolation of a mixture of the two title condensation products, which are separated by silicagel chromatography (25 g) by eluting with a 15 : 1 mixture of chloroform–methanol. The less polar *arabino* isomer **221.4** (35 mg, 9%) is obtained as homogeneous colorless crystals. Twice recrystallizations from diisopropyl ether furnishes an analytic sample with m.p. 134–134.5°C, $[\alpha]_D^{27}$ −26 (c = 0.46 in chloroform). Further elution with 9 : 1 chloroform–methanol gives a substance (129 mg, 32%) with m.p. 169–170°C, which on treatment with acetone yields 27 mg (7%) of the *racemic* D,L-*xylo*-compound (**221.3**), m.p. 169–170°C, $[\alpha]_D^{27}$ ±0 (Me$_2$SO). Evaporation of the mother liquor of the crystallization of the racemate gives a syrup that crystallizes spontaneously, m.p. 85–87°C, $[\alpha]_D^{27}$ +24 (c = 0.52 in Me$_2$SO).

The copper complex of the simplest amino acid, glycin (**222.1**), has also been useful for aldol condensation with *aldehydo*-sugars,[262] as shown in

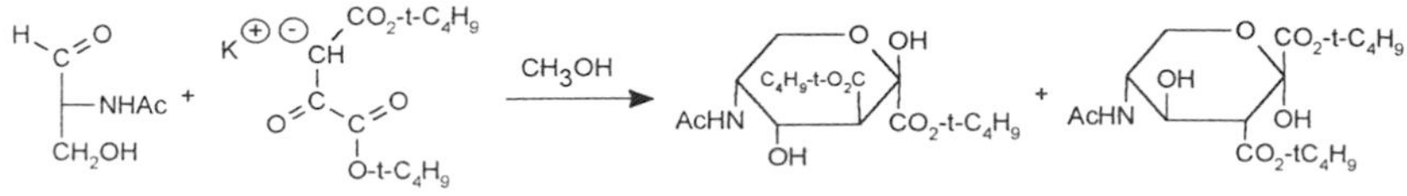

221.1   221.2   221.3   221.4

FIGURE 1.221

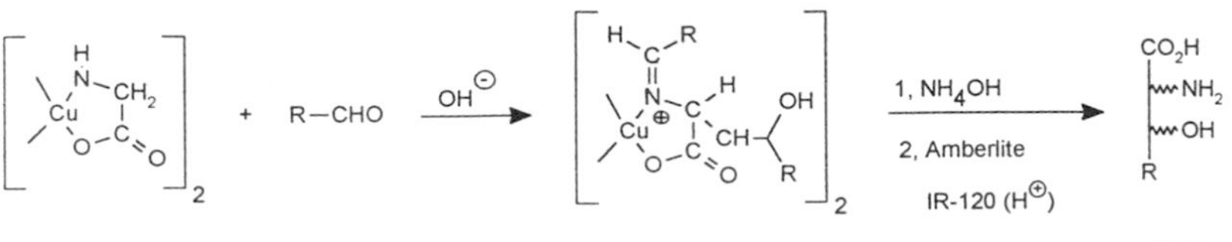

FIGURE I.222

Figure 1.222. Thus, related reaction of [bis-glycinato copper(II)] with 2,3-*O*-isopropylidene-D-glyceraldehyde and 2,4-*O*-ethylidene-*aldehydo*-D-erythrose furnished the two amino acids (**222.2**) 2-amino-2-deoxy-4,5-*O*-isopropylidene-D-xylonic acid and 2-amino-2-deoxy-4,6-*O*-ethylidene-D-gluconic acid with 31% and 22% yields, respectively, both ascended with two carbon atoms.

As this procedure requires two aldehyde molecules, it was modified so that an *N*-protected glycin complex, *N*-pyruvylidene-glycinatoaquocopper (II), was used as the C—C—N unit (Fig. 1.223). This modification resulted in a faster reaction to lead to the aminodeoxyaldonic acids in an hour and with good yields, which were then isolated and purified by means of ion-exchange technology. The formation of each of the possible isomers were detected, but not isolated; thus stereochemical data were not reported even for some of the major products. In the case of 2-amino-2-deoxyxylonic and -gluconic acid, those epimers are the prodominant ones in which the amino group is *trans* to the neighboring hydroxyl function (cf. the preparation of 2-amino-2-deoxyaldoses from aminonitriles[263]).

The condensation of *N*-pyruvylidene-glycinatoaquocopper(II) has been carried out[264,265] with 2,3-*O*-isopropylidene-D- and -L-glyceraldehyde, 2,4-*O*-ethylidene-*aldehydo*-D-erythrose and with 2,3:4,5-di-*O*-isopropylidene-*aldehydo*-D-arabinose at pH 9.5, and the yield of the resulting amino acids are in the range of 40–80%. The yields may somewhat vary by changing the individual isolation process.[265] The following procedure describes

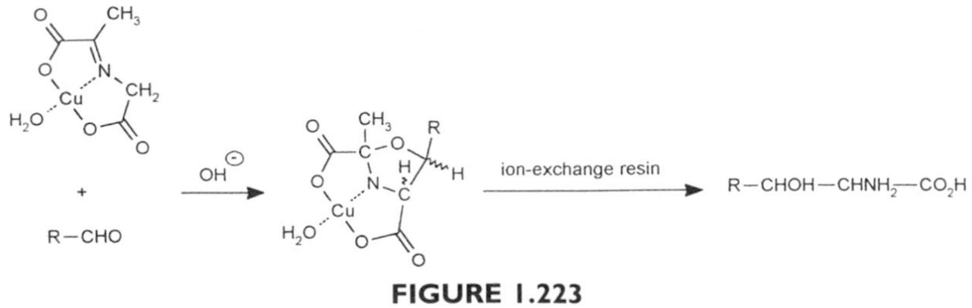

FIGURE I.223

the preparation of 2-amino-2-deoxy-4,5-*O*-isopropylidene-L-lyxonic acid (**224.3**) according to such a methodology (Fig. 1.224).

Synthesis of 2-amino-2-deoxy-4,5-O-isopropylidene-L-xylonic acid (**224.3**)[264]
To a solution of 4,5-*O*-isopropylidene-L-arabinose dibenzyl dithioacetal (4.2 g, 10 mmol) in benzene (80 ml) lead tetraacetate (4.7 g, 11 mmol) is added, and the mixture is stirred for ~30 min. The precipitate thus produced is filtered off, and the filtrate is concentrated under reduced pressure to a syrup (bath temperature ≤40°C). This is dissolved in methanol (20 ml), diluted with water (20 ml), and concentrated, again, to ~20 ml (bath temperature ≤40°C). To the solution of 2,3-*O*-isopropylidene-L-glyceraldehyde (**224.1**) obtained this way, a solution of N-pyruvylidene-glycinatoaquacopper(II) (**224.2**, 2.3 g, 9 mmol) in water (30 ml) is added and the pH is adjusted to 9.5 with 2 N NaOH. After stirring for 1 h at this pH, 2 N HCl added to reach pH 4.5, and the mixture is treated with H$_2$S. The precipitate is filtered off, and the filtrate is applied onto a 2.5 × 9 cm Amberlite IR-45 (OH⁻) column, which is washed with water (100 ml), and the eluate is concentrated to 50 ml and poured to an Amberlite IR-120B (NH$_4^+$ form) column. The column is washed with 100 ml of water, the effluent is concentrated to 50 ml and washed with dichloromethane (3 × 10 ml), and the aqueous phase is evaporated to a 10-ml volume. Addition of a small volume (a few milliliters) of ethanol gives a yellow product that is crystallized from ethanol to afford the pure amino acid **224.3** (0.65 g, 36%), m.p. 198°C (dec.), $[\alpha]_D^{20}$ −0.2 (*c* = 1 in water).

For the synthesis of *herbicidin* and its analogs, containing an undecose moiety, Vogel[266] examined the cross-aldol condensation of ketones with *aldehydo*-sugars. It was established that cross-aldolization (Fig. 1.225) of 3-*O*-(*tert*-butyldimethylsilyl)-5-deoxy-1,2-*O*-isopropylidene-α-D-*xylo*-hexodialdo-1,4-furanose (**225.1**) with the lithium enolate of (±)-6-*endo*-chloro-5-*endo*-(methoxymethoxy)-7-oxabicyclo[2.2.1]heptan-2-one (**225.2**) is highly *exo*-selective, furnishing a separable mixture of two major diastereoisomeric aldols **225.3** and **225.4** (Zimmerman–Traxler model is obeyed). The experimental conditions employed for this transformation are as follows.

(6R)-3-O-(tert-Butyldimethylsilyl)-6-C-[(1′R,3′S,4′R,5′S,6′S)-6′-endo-chloro-5′-endo-(methoxymethoxy)-2′-oxo-7′-oxabicyclo-[2.2.1]hept-3′-exo-yl]-5-deoxy-1,2-O-isopropylidene-α-D-xylo-hexofuranose {(−)-**225.3**} *and the corresponding (1′S,3′R,4′S,5′R,6′R) isomer* {(+)-**225.4**}[266] In this procedure, 1.6 M *n*-butyllithium in hexane (5.6 ml, 8.96 mmol) is added dropwise to a stirred solution of (Me$_3$Si)$_2$NH (2.2 ml, 10.5 mmol) in dry THF (47 ml), cooled to −10°C (three-necked flask dried

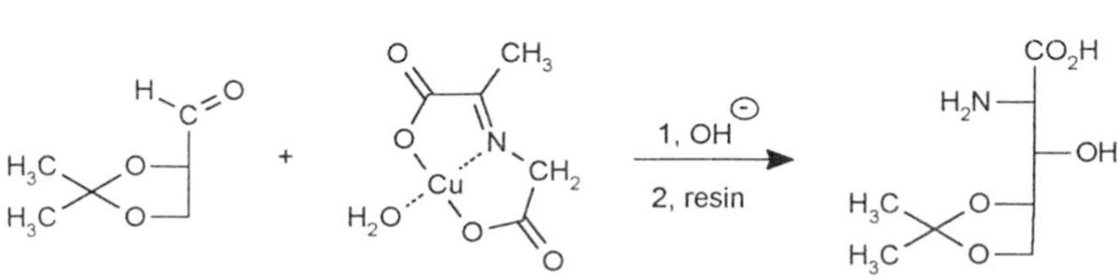

224.1   **224.2**   **224.3**

FIGURE 1.224

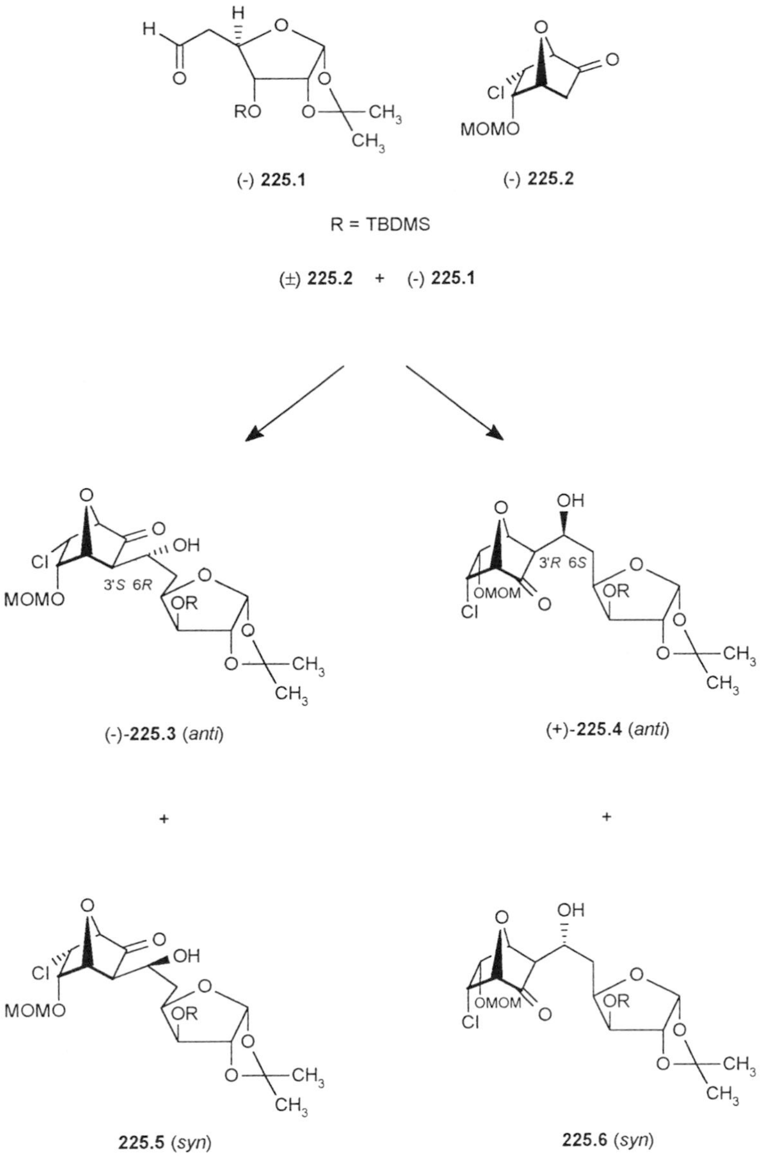

(-) 225.1   (-) 225.2

R = TBDMS

(±) 225.2 + (-) 225.1

(-)-225.3 (anti)   (+)-225.4 (anti)

+   +

225.5 (syn)   225.6 (syn)

FIGURE 1.225

in a flame) under an argon atmosphere. After stirring at −10°C for 10 min, a solution of **225.2** (1.55 g, 7.5 mmol) in dry THF (31 ml) is added slowly with stirring at −10°C. After stirring at this temperature for 1 h, the mixture is cooled to −65°C and the sugar **225.1** (2.85 g, 9 mmol) dissolved in dry THF (17 ml) is added slowly. Stirring is continued at −65°C for 3 h, and the mixture is poured into a mixture of dichloromethane (200 ml), a saturated aqueous solution of ammonium chloride

(200 ml), and ice (100 g). The aqueous layer is extracted with dichloromethane (170 ml, three times), and the combined organic layer is dried (MgSO$_4$) and concentrated. Fast column chromatography (500 g of silicagel, eluant: 1:2 ethyl acetate–petroleum ether) of the residue gives first 1.57 g of a 1:7.5 mixture of the starting heptan-2-one **225.2** (R_f = 0.35, vanillin) and the aldol **(+)-225.4** (R_f = 0.39). Crystallization from ether (5 ml) and petroleum ether (20 ml) yields 1.23 g (32.5%) of pure **(+)-225.4**, as colorless needles m.p. 91.5–93°C. A second fraction contains 1.76 g (45%) of a 16:1 mixture of **(−)-225.3** and **225.6**. Crystallization from ether (1 ml) and petroleum ether (15 ml) at −18°C affords 1.43 g (36%) of pure **(−)-225.3**, as colorless crystals with m.p. 102.5–104°C. Concentration of the mother liquors leads to a 2:1 mixture of **(−)-225.3** and **225.6**.

Cyclopentadienyl–carbonyl–triphenylphosphine–acetyliron, also called simply "acetyliron" [(η^5-C$_5$H$_5$)Fe(CO)(PPh$_3$)COCH$_3$)], is a practical reagent in carbohydrate chemistry enabling the ascending synthesis of several monosaccharides by aldol condensation with *aldehydo*-sugars. The reaction of the enantiomeric forms of acetyliron with (optically active) sugar aldehydes ("matched" and "mismatched" pairs) also permits one to draw conclusions regarding the stereochemistry of the transition state of this transformation. The stereochemical outcome of the chain extension[267,268] with acetyliron **(226.1)** shown in Figure 1.226 is strongly dependent on the counterion employed. Thus, high stereocontrol was achieved with tin(II), zirconium(IV), and diethylaluminum(I). Matched pairs, particularly with pentose- and hexose-derived aldehydes, furnished the corresponding aldol product with high stereoselectivities. Figure 1.226 presents the scheme of the foregoing transformation, and the sugars applied so far for these reactions are also illustrated. Decomplexation, involved in the reaction sequence, can be effected with NBS in methanol to provide the *deoxyaldonic acids* extended with two carbon atoms with the aid of this quite effective methodology.

Of the results of the detailed stereochemical investigations of the preceding process, those obtained with the chain extension of 2,3-*O*-isopropylidene-β-D-*ribo*-pentodialdo-1,4-furanose are summarized in Table 1.33, according to the work of Polish chemists.[268]

A procedure, described by Zamojski *et al.*,[268] and suggested for the preparation of deoxyheptoses, is presented here, as an example for obtaining the heptofuranoside uronates **227.3** and **227.4** (see Fig. 1.227).

Preparation of [(η^5-C$_5$H$_5$)Fe(CO)COCH$_2$CH(OH)C$_8$H$_{13}$O$_4$] (227.2)[268] A solution of the acetyliron complex[269] **(226.1**, 6.81 g, 15 mmol) in THF (50 ml) is cooled to −78°C, and *n*-butyllithium (11.2 ml, 18.0 mmol) is added. After 15 min a solution of methyl 2,3-*O*-isopropylidene-α-D-*lyxo*-pentodialdo-1,4-furanoside (**227.1**, 3.64 g, 18.0 mmol) in THF (10 ml) is added and the mixture is stirred at −78°C for 45 min. Methanol (15 ml) is added to the mixture, which is then allowed to attain room temperature. The solution is filtered through silicagel and concentrated to dryness. The resulting mixture (8.6 g) of the starting complex and the diastereoisomeric mixture **227.2** are used for the next step without further purification. An analytic sample was separated by preparative HPLC (8:3 hexane–ethyl acetate) to give the starting complex (40 mg, 40%), and **227.2** (86.6 mg, 60%).

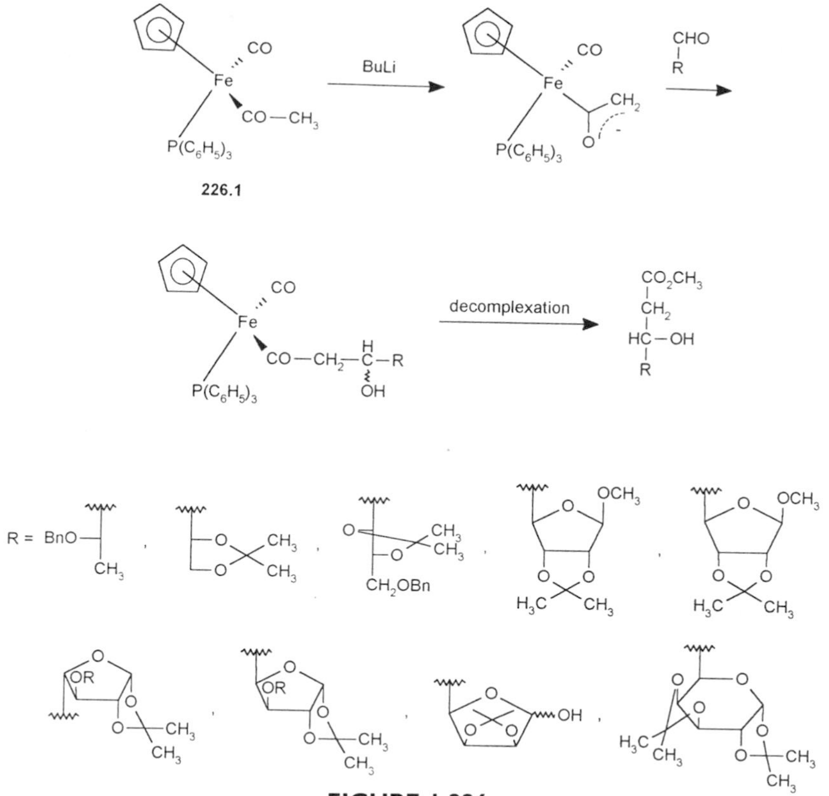

226.1

FIGURE 1.226

1.2.7.5. Chain Extension of Unsaturated Sugars to Nonbranched Derivatives

1.2.7.5.1. Chain Extension of Glycals and Hydroxyglycals with Alkenes

The Lewis acid–catalyzed reaction of alkenes with electrophiles gives rise to carbon–carbon coupled products, and this method has been utilized for the ascending syntheses of carbohydrates starting with unsaturated sugars (see Refs. 119 and 120; several additional examples can be find in the review papers[270,271] on C-glycosidic compounds). The outcome of such reactions, in general, specifically, the formation of hex-2-enopyranosyl-hydrocarbons, is shown in Figure 1.228, illustrating that the product from the glycal **228.1** is produced either by a fast S_N2'-substitution, or via an oxocarbenium ion.[272]

Table 1.34 summarizes the reaction conditions and isolation procedures reported in the literature[273] for obtaining chain-ascended products by the reaction of glycals, and a general procedure is as follows.

TABLE 1.33 Reactions with Methyl 2,3-O-isopropylidene-β-D-*ribo*-pentodialdo-1,4-furanoside (1)

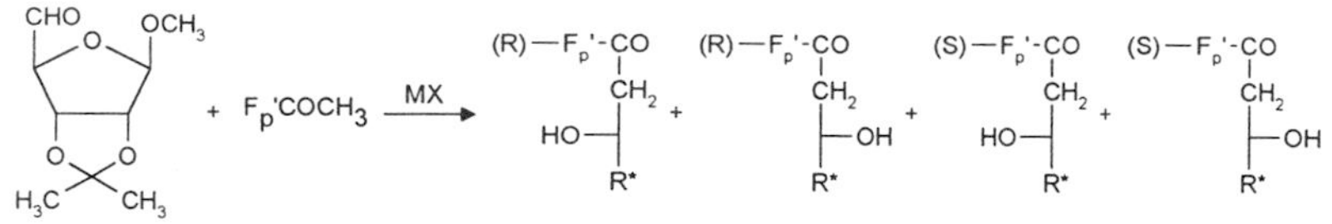

$RRR = R_{Fe}R_{\beta-C}S_{\gamma-C}$ (first letter denotes configuration at the iron atom; the second, at the β-carbon atom; and the third, at the γ-carbon atom).

	Entry	MX	Yield %	(RRR)	(RSR)	(SRR)	(SSR)
R	1	BuLi	50	85	15	—	—
	2	(iPro)$_3$TiCl	64	73	27	—	—
	3	ZrCl$_4$	63	79	21	—	—
	4	Et$_2$AlCl^a	55	50	50	—	—
	5	Et$_3$Al	46	94	6	—	—
	6	SnCl$_2^b$	14	95	5	—	—
	7	CeCl$_3$	56	84	16	—	—
	8	NiCl$_2$	59	84	16	—	—
	9	LaCl$_3$	52	87	13	—	—
	10	Cp$_2$TiCl$_2$	39	86	14	—	—
	11	MgBr$_2$	12	83	17	—	—
S	12	BuLi	50	—	—	70	30
	13	(iPro)$_3$TiCl	68	—	—	83	17
	14	ZrCl$_4$	65	—	—	76	24
	15	Et$_2$AlCl^b	75	—	—	97	3
	16	Et$_3$Al	25	—	—	71	29
	17	SnCl$_2^a$	6.5	—	—	66	34
	18	CeCl$_3$	54	—	—	71	29
	19	NiCl$_2$	57	—	—	71	29
	20	LaCl$_3$	48	—	—	73	27
	21	Cp$_2$TiCl$_2$	41	—	—	76	24
	22	MgBr$_2$	12	—	—	73	27

^{a}Mismatched pair.
^{b}Matched pair.

Procedure for the condensation of olefins with peracetylated glycals (see also Table 1.34)[274] Procedure A A round-bottomed flask equipped with a magnetic stirring bar is filled successively with the glycal, dichloromethane (1.5–3 ml/molar eq), and alkene (1.2 molar eq); then the mixture is cooled to the indicated temperature. Lewis acid (1.5 molar eq) is added and the progress of the reaction is monitored by TLC. When all the starting material has disappeared, the reaction mixture is poured into a 1:1 mixture of ether and saturated aqueous disodium hydrogen phosphate (10 ml/mol). The aqueous layer is extracted twice with ether (5 ml/mol), and the organic phase is washed sucessively with aqueous NaHCO$_3$ (5 ml/mol) and water (5 ml/mol), and dried over MgSO$_4$. Concentration under reduced pressure then flash column chromatography of the residue with the eluant indicated furnished the pure C-glycosidic compound.

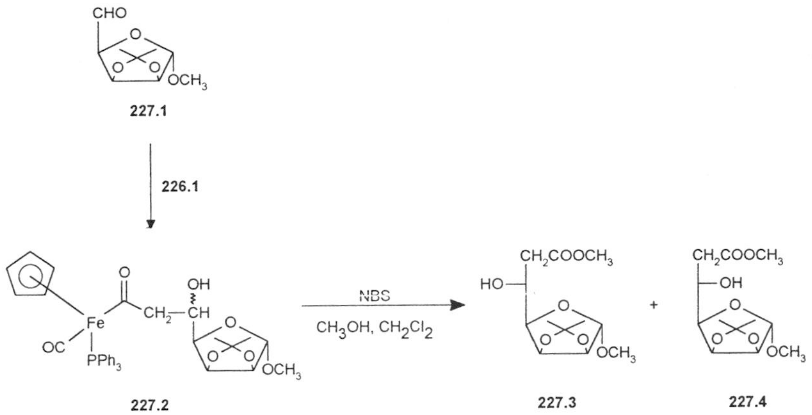

FIGURE 1.227

Procedure B A round-bottomed flask equipped with a magnetic stirring bar is filled sucessively with the glycal, acetonitrile (1.5–3 ml/molar eq) and alkene (1.2 molar eq); then the reaction mixture is cooled to −20°C and boron trifluoride–diethyl ether (1.5 molar eq) is added. The cooling bath is removed, and the progress of the reaction is monitored by TLC. When all the starting material has disappeared, the reaction mixture is poured into a 1 : 1 mixture of ether and saturated aqueous sodium hydrogencarbonate. Workup as described in procedure A gives the pure C-glycosidic compound.

It has been reported[275] that the reaction of hydroxy- and cyanoglycals with functionalized alkenes, such as enol ethers or ketene acetals, gives chain-extended products. For example, Figure 1.229 illustrates a related conversion of 3,5-bis-(benzoyloxy)-2-(benzyloxymethyl)-2,3-dihydro-4H-pyran-4-one (**229.1**) with the trimethylsilylenol ether of acetophenone (**229.2**).

(2,4,6-Tri-O-benzoyl-β-D-ribo-hexopyranos-3-ulosyl)-acetophenone (**229.3**)[275] Zinc chloride (0.7 g, 5 mmol) and freshly desiccated molecular sieves (4A, 0.5 g) are added to a solution of the glycal **229.1** (1.2 g, 2.5 mmol) in dichloromethane (50 ml) followed by the addition of the enol ether **229.2** (1.45 g, 3 molar eq). After stirring for 20 h at ambient temperature, the mixture is filtered through silicagel, which is thoroughly washed with dichloromethane, and the combined filtrate is washed with 1 N HCl (10 ml), saturated aqueous NaHCO$_3$ (2 × 20 ml) and water and then dried (Na$_2$SO$_4$). Evaporation of the solvent gives a syrup that is purified by elution from a silicagel column (2 × 20 cm) with 4 : 1 carbon tetrachloride–ethyl acetate. The syrup obtained on evaporation of the major fraction crystallizes on trituration with ether to give 1.1 g (73%) of pure **229.3** in two crops, m.p. 194–194.5°C, [α]$_D^{20}$ +67 (c = 0.9 in chloroform).

The products arising from analogous ascending syntheses are shown in Table 1.35.[276–282]

When the preceding reaction is performed with peracylated saccharides instead of glycals, undecitol derivatives are obtained in moderate yields after tedious chromatographic separation. Conversion[283] of the D-ribose derivative **230.1** with 1-hexene in the presence of various catalysts is shown in Figure 1.230.

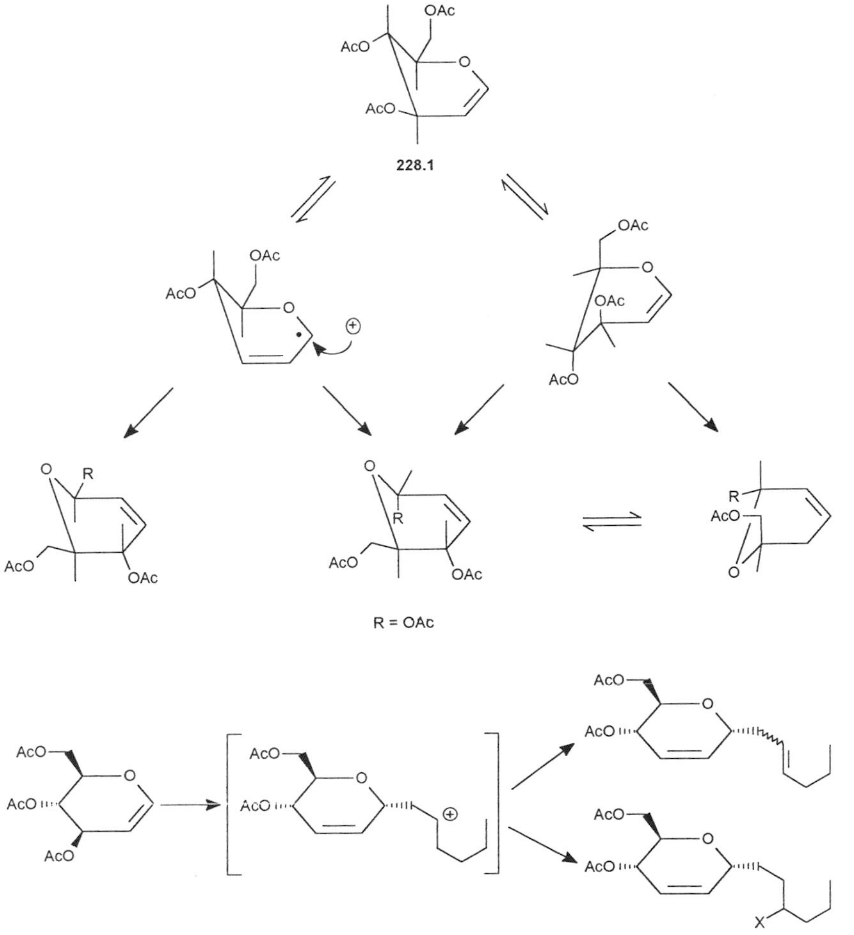

Mechanism of the addition of olefins

FIGURE I.228

Isobe has reported[284] that the chain elongation of glycals also proceeds with suitable acetylenic compounds; in Lewis acid–catalyzed reactions, tri-O-acetyl-D-glucal and tetraacetyl-2-hydroxy-D-glucal can be readily coupled with trimethysilyl-acetylene derivatives (Fig. 1.231).

1.2.7.5.2. Chain Extension by Hydroformylation of Glycals (Oxo Reaction)

Hydroformylation of olefines proceeds as shown in Figure 1.232, and the reaction can be completed under laboratory conditions in a shaking auto-clave.[285] The reactivity of olefins decreases in the order:

TABLE 1.34   Reaction of 1,1-Disubstituted Olefins with Glycals

Glycal	Olefin	Lewis acid	Procedure ($T(°C)$, time chromatography)	C-Glycoside [yield (%) (α/β) ratio]
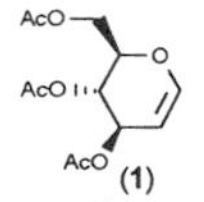 (1)	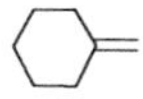 (5)	SnBr$_4$	A room temp., 5 min hexane - AcOEt (8 : 2)	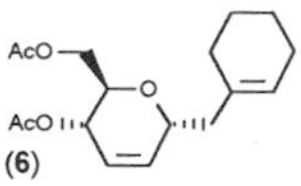 (6) 94% (100 / 0)
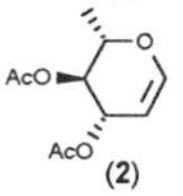 (2)	(5)	BF$_3$·Et$_2$O	A -25°C, 10 min hexane - AcOEt (98 : 2)	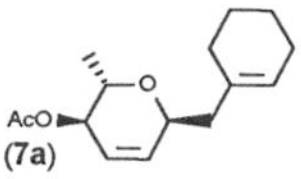 (7a) + (7b) 90% (87 / 15)
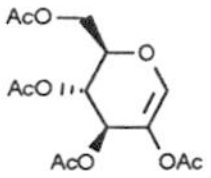 (3)	(5)	SnBr$_4$	B room temp., 30 min pentane - Et$_2$O (6 : 4)	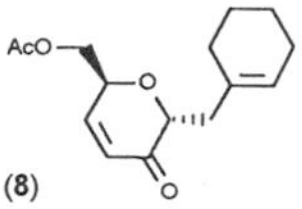 (8) 70% (100 / 0)
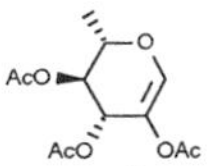 (4)	(5)	BF$_3$·Et$_2$O	C 0°C, 45 min hexane - AcOEt (96 : 4)	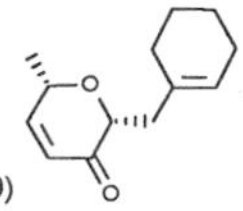 (9) 50% (100 / 0)
(1)	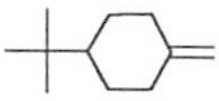 (10)	SnBr$_4$	A room temp., 5 min pentane - Et$_2$O (4 : 1)	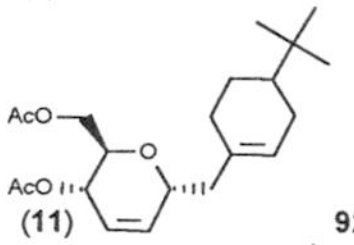 (11) 92% (100 / 0)
(2)	(10)	EtAlCl$_2$	A -20°C, 5 min pentane - Et$_2$O (19 : 1)	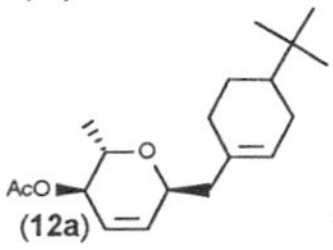 (12a) + (12b) 93% (88 / 12)
(1)	(13)	EtAlCl$_2$	A -20°C, 5 min pentane - Et$_2$O (5 : 1)	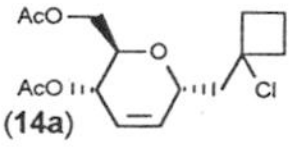 (14a) + (14b) 80% (91 / 9)
(2)	(13)	EtAlCl$_2$	A -20°C, 5 min pentane - Et$_2$O (5 : 1)	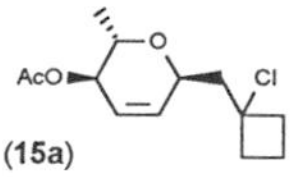 (15a) + (15b) 90% (86 / 14)
(3)	(13)	EtAlCl$_2$	B -20°C to room temp., 1h hexane - AcOEt (85 : 15)	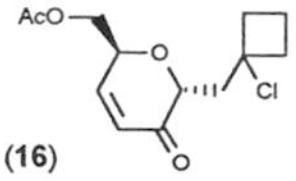 (16) 50% (100 / 0)
(4)	(13)	EtAlCl$_2$	B -20°C to room temp., 1h hexane - AcOEt (9 : 5)	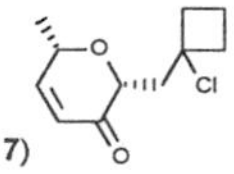 (17) 68% (100 / 0)

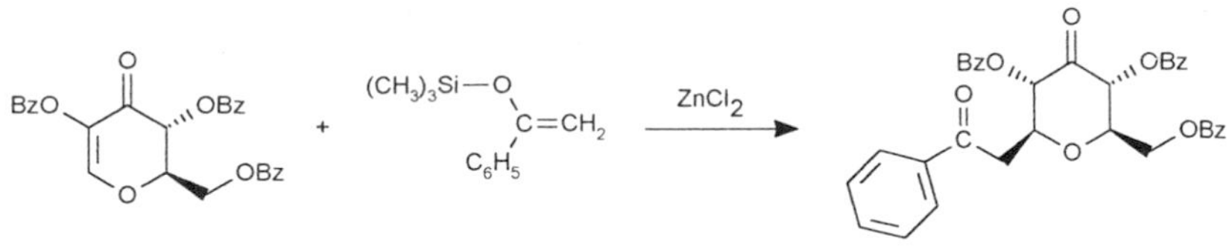
ZnCl2

229.1 229.2 229.3

FIGURE 1.229

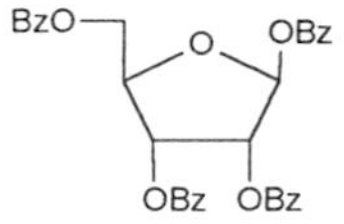

230.1

1-hexene
TMS-triflate
1-hexene
SnCl4

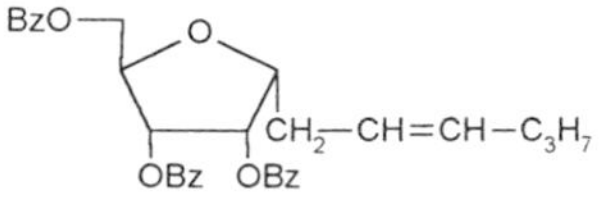

230.2

7,10-anhydro-1,2,3,4,5,6,-hexadeoxy-8,9,11-tri-O-benzoyl-D-*allo*-undec-4-enitol

+

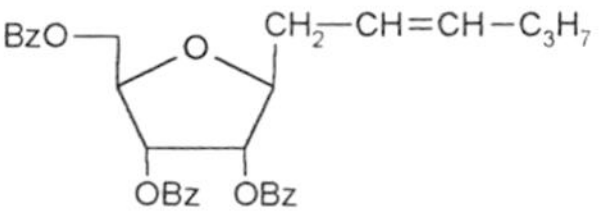

230.3

7,10-anhydro-1,2,3,4,5,6,-hexadeoxy-8,9,11-tri-O-benzoyl-D-*altro*-undec-4-enitol

230.2 + 230.3

+

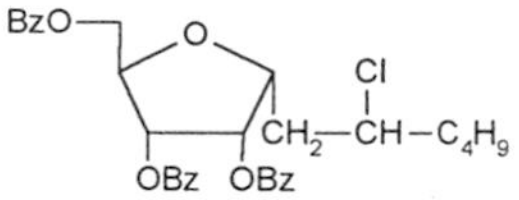

230.4

7,10-anhydro-5-chloro-1,2,3,4,5,6-hexadeoxy-8,9,11-tri-O-benzoyl-D-*allo*-undecitol

+

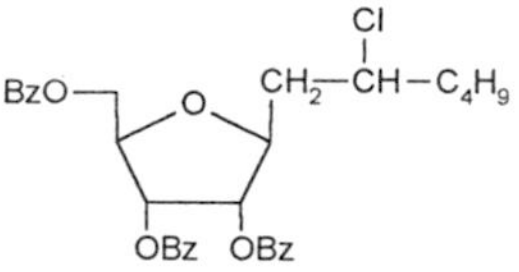

230.5

7,10-anhydro-5-chloro-1,2,3,4,5,6-hexadeoxy-8,9,11-tri-O-benzoyl-D-*altro*-undecitol

FIGURE 1.230

TABLE I.35 Chain Elongation Products from the Boron Trifluoride Etherate-Catalyzed Reaction between Glycals and Alkenes or Nitriles

Educt	Alkene	Isolated product(s) and its physical parameters
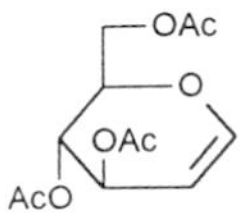	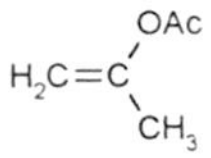	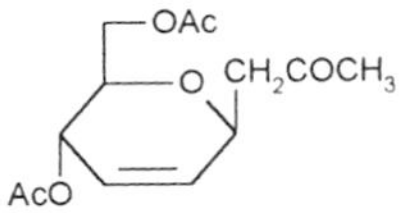 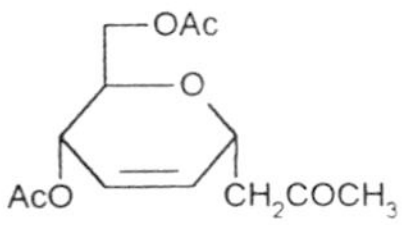 $[\alpha]^{20}_{D}$ = +65 (c = 1, $CHCl_3$) 5% ; $[\alpha]^{20}_{D}$ = +110 (c = 1, $CHCl_3$) 80% (4',6'-di-O-acetyl-2',3'-dideoxy-β- and α-D-*erythro*-hex-2-enopyranosyl)propan-2-one[276]
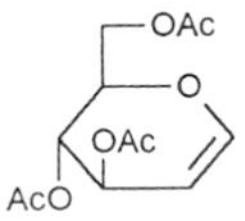	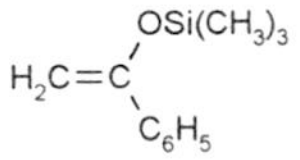	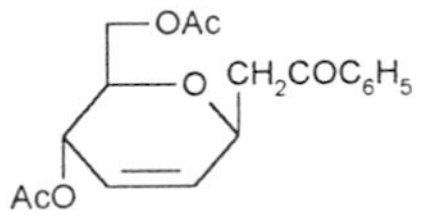 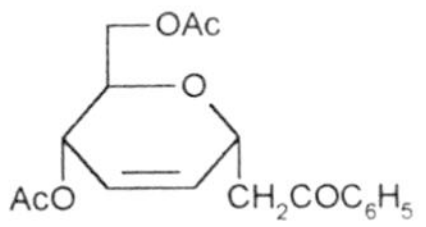 $[\alpha]^{20}_{D}$ = +42 (c = 1, CH_2Cl_2) ; $[\alpha]^{20}_{D}$ = +160 (c = 1, CH_2Cl_2) 94% (4',6'-di-O-acetyl-2',3'-dideoxy-β- and α-D-*erythro*-hex-2-enopyranosyl)-acetophenone[276]
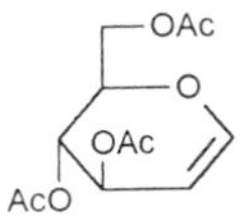	$H_2C{=}CH{-}OAc$	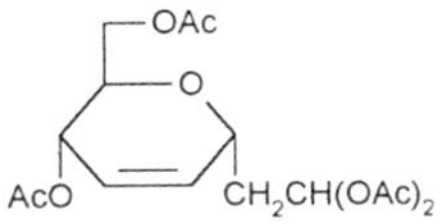 $[\alpha]^{20}_{D}$ = +44 (c = 1, CH_2Cl_2) 85% (4',6'-di-O-acetyl-2',3'-dideoxy-α-D-*erythro*-hex-2-enopyranosyl)-1,1-diacetoxyethane[276]
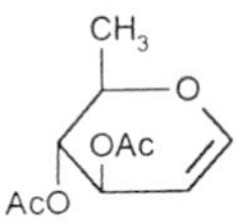	$H_2C{=}CH{-}OAc$	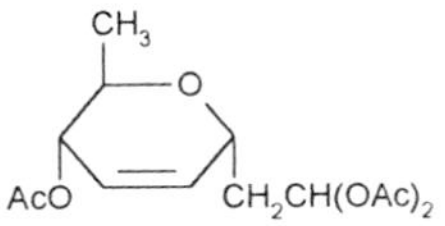 (no data) (4'-acetoxy-2',3',6'-trideoxy-α-D-*threo*-hex-2'-enopyranosyl)-1,1-diacetoxyethane[277]
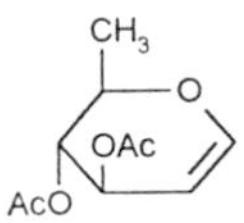	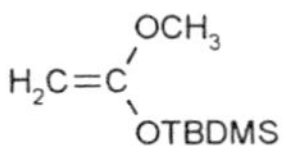	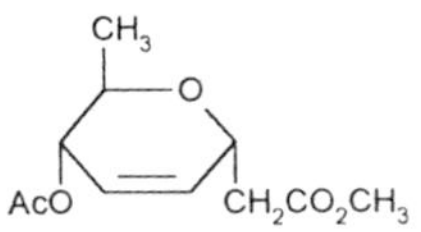 (no data) (4'-acetoxy-2',3',6'-trideoxy-α-D-*threo*-hex-2'-enopyranosyl)-acetic acid methylester[278]

(*continues*)

TABLE 1.35 *(continued)*

Educt	Alkene	Isolated product(s) and its physical parameters	
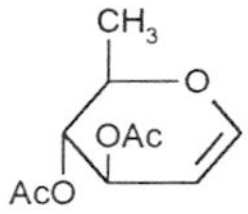	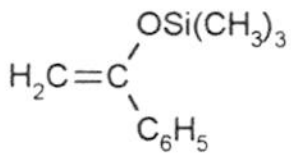	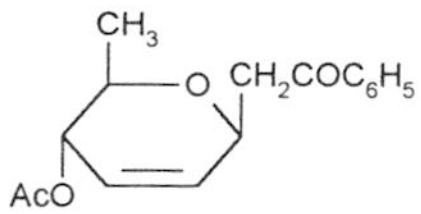	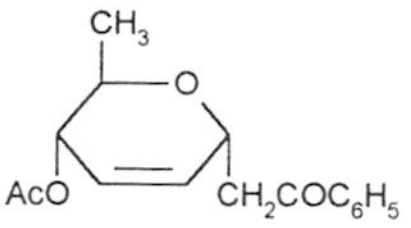
		$[\alpha]_D^{20}$ = -105 (*c* = 0.60, $CHCl_3$)	—
		1 : 1	
		β- and α-(4'-acetoxy-2',3',6'-trideoxy-D-*threo*-hex-2-enopyranosyl)acetophenone[277]	
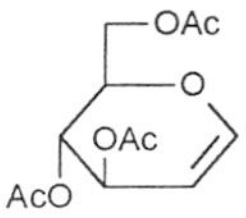	$(CH_3)_3SiCN$ or NaCN	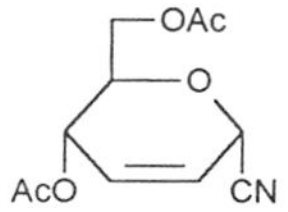	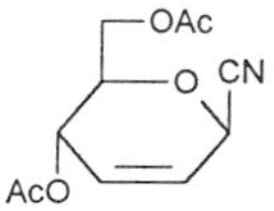
		$[\alpha]_D^{20}$ = -14.6 (c = 1, $CHCl_3$)	$[\alpha]_D^{20}$ = +197.5 (c = 1, $CHCl_3$)
		m.p. 90-91°C	m.p. — Lit.[279)]
	$(C_2H_5)AlCN$	79%	90%
		$[\alpha]_D^{20}$ = -16 (*c* = 1, CH_2Cl_2)	$[\alpha]_D^{20}$ = -13.0 (*c* = 1.2, $CHCl_3$)
		m.p. 91°C	m.p. 90-91°C
		Lit.[280)]	Lit.[281)]
		4,6-di-O-acetyl-2,3-dideoxy-α- and β-D-*erythro*-hex-2-enopyranosyl) cyanide (cf. Lit.[282])	
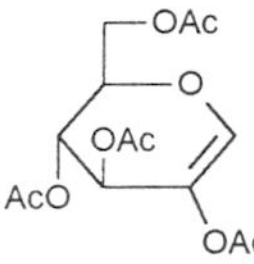	$(CH_3)_3SiCN$	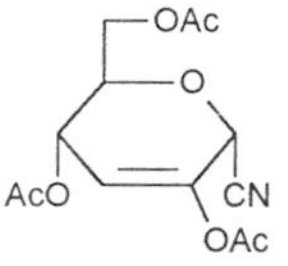	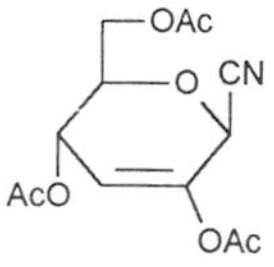
		$[\alpha]_D$ = +2 (*c* = 1, $CHCl_3$)	$[\alpha]_D$ = +66 (*c* = 1, $CHCl_3$) Lit.[279)]
		m.p. 71-72°C	m.p. —
		$[\alpha]_D$ = +18 (*c* = 1, CH_2Cl_2)	$[\alpha]_D$ = +150 (*c* = 1, $CHCl_3$) Lit.[280)]
		syrup	
		2,4,6-tri-O-acetyl-3-deoxy-α– and β-*erythro*-hex-2-enopyranosyl cyanide	
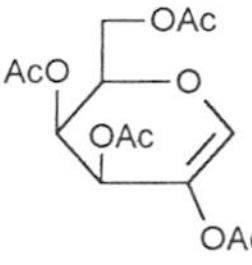	$(CH_3)_3SiCN$	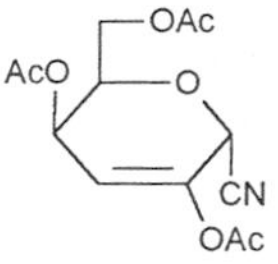	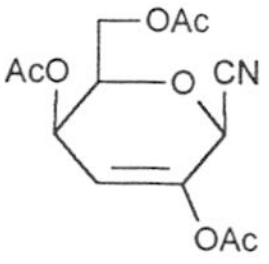
		$[\alpha]_D$ = -210 (*c* = 1.0, CH_2Cl_2)	$[\alpha]_D$ = -85 (*c* = 1.0, CH_2Cl_2)
		m.p. 86°C	m.p. 84°C Lit.[280)]
		2,4,6-tri-O-acetyl-3-deoxy-α– and β-*threo*-hex-2-enopyranosyl cyanide	

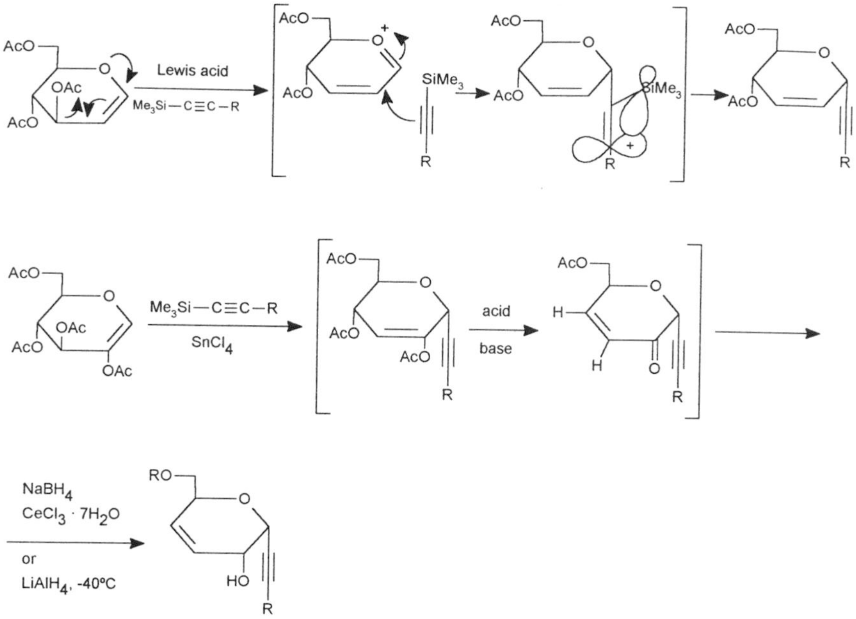

FIGURE 1.231

*Terminal olefin > open-chain olefin with an inside
double bond > branched-chain olefin*

This ascending approach was tried with glycals, and the reaction conditions were selected so that the intermediary anhydroaldose would be reduced to the corresponding alcohol.

Hydroformylation of 3,4-di-*O*-acetyl-D-xylal and subsequent deacetylation gives rise[286] to a mixture of 1,5-anhydro-4-deoxy-D-*arabino*- and -L-*xylo*-hexitol. Analogous conversion of 3,4,6-tri-*O*-acetyl-D-glucal and -galactal afforded ~1:1 mixtures of 2,6-anhydro-3-deoxy-D-*manno*- and -*gluco*-heptitols and 2,6-anhydro-3-deoxy-D-*galacto*- and -*talo*-heptitols, respectively. A detailed procedure for the preparation of these compounds has been reported.[287]

Of the hydroformylation products of 2,3,4,6-tetra-*O*-acetyl-D-*arabino*-hex-1-eno-pyranose, only 2,6-anhydro-D-*glycero*-D-*gulo*-heptitol could be

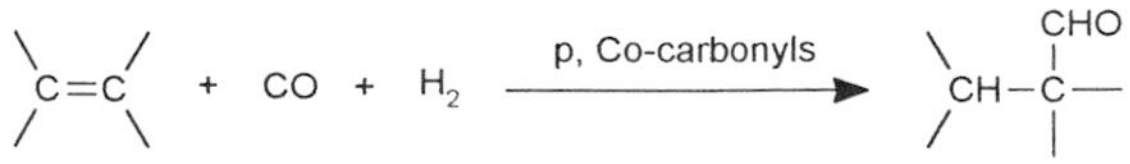

FIGURE 1.232

isolated in pure form (i.e., free from epimeric substances),[288] and hydroformylation of a 5,6-anhydro sugar derivative has also been described.[289]

1.2.7.5.3. Ascending Syntheses by Claisen Rearrangement of Glycals

The structural features of glycals allows a facile conversion into alkylvinyl ethers, whose rearrangement into γ,δ-unsaturated carbonyl compounds is also known as the *aliphatic Claisen rearrangement.* Thus, thermal [3,3]-sigmatropic rearrangement of a selectively protected glycalvinyl ether (**233.1**) leads[290,291] to the "C-glycosidic compound" **233.2** (see Fig. 1.233).

Studies on this transformation have revealed that for a single rearrangement, there is no need to distinguish between the hydroxyl groups of the glycal molecule with different protecting groups; mono–Claisen rearrangement of a glycal–poly(keteneacetal) sufficiently proceeds by the assistance of the ring-oxygen atom, considered as a vinylogous anomeric effect.[292] 3,4-Di-*O*-acetyl-1,5-anhydro-2,3-dideoxy-L-*erythro*-pent-1-enitol (di-*O*-acetyl-L-arabinal, **234.1**) can be converted, with quantitative yield, into the bis-acetal **234.2,** whose thermal rearrangement and subsequent removal of the silyl protecting groups gives rise[292] to methyl (2*R-cis*)-5-acetoxy-5,6-dihydro-2*H*-pyran-2-acetate (**234.3**), and the product (**234.4**) of a double rearrangement can be detected in a negligible quantity (Fig. 1.234).

cis-*[(3,4-Dihydro-2*H-*pyran-3,4-diyl)bis(oxyethenylideneoxy)]bis[(1,1-dimethylethyl)dimethylsilane] (234.2)*[292] A stirred solution of diisopropylamine (925 μl, 6.6 mmol) in oxolane (4 ml) is cooled to 0°C and treated with butyllithium (3.7 ml, 6.3 mmol, 1.7 M in hexane) over several minutes. After stirring for 10 min, the solution is cooled to −78°C and the glycal **234.1** (600 mg, 3.0 mmol) in oxolane (4 ml) is added dropwise over 2–3 min. After 15 min, *tert*-butylchlorodimethylsilane (995 mg, 6.6 mmol) in HMPA (4 ml) is added, and the resulting solution is stirred for an additional 1.5 h and poured into cold water–pentane. The pentane extract is washed with cold water and aqueous NaCl solution and dried (MgSO₄). Evaporation under reduced pressure gives 1.28 g (100%) of **234.2,** as a yellow viscous liquid.

Methyl (2R-cis)-5-acetoxy-5,6-dihydro-2H-pyran-acetate (234.3)[292] The ketene-silyl acetal **234.2** (531 mg, 1.24 mmol) is dissolved in chloroform (3 ml) and stirred at 60°C for 6 h. Following concentration, the residue is dissolved in HMPA (2 ml) and stirred for 12 h with water (130 μl, 7.4 mmol), KF (432 mg, 7.4 mmol), and KHCO₃ (745 mg, 7.4 mmol). Methyl iodide (1.23 ml) is added, and the mixture

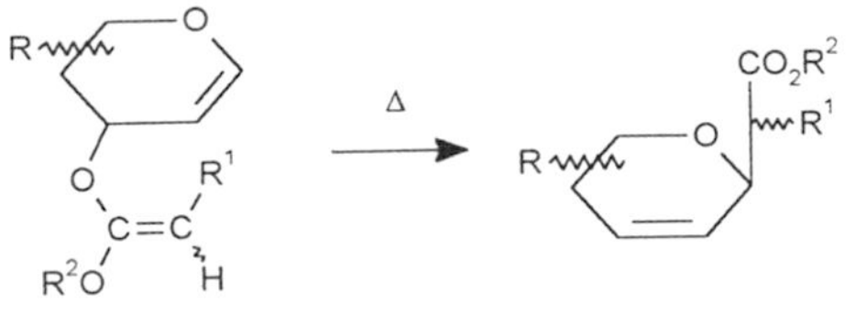

233.1   233.2

FIGURE 1.233

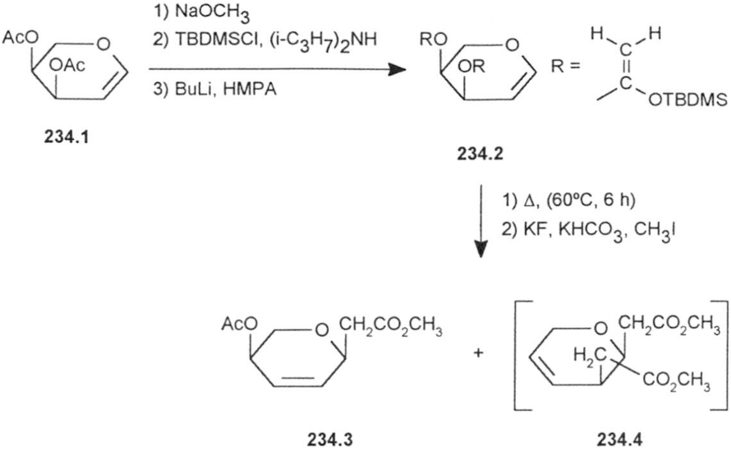

FIGURE 1.234

is stirred for an additional 12 h. Extraction with water, followed by chromatography (eluant: 1:3 ethyl acetate–hexane) affords 130 mg (49%) of pure **234.3** as a syrup, $[\alpha]_D^{25}$ −146 (c = 0.92 in chloroform).

By using similar procedures, several glycalketenesilylacetals have been transformed into the corresponding *C-glycosidic compounds* and these products are summarized in Table 1.36.

The Claisen rearrangement (Fig. 1.235) of 4,6-*O*-benzylidene-D-allal (**235.1**) requires more vigorous conditions; conversion of its 3-*O*-vinyl ether (**235.2**) into the hex-2′-acetaldehyde (**235.3**) proceeds sufficiently only in hot benzonitrile, with *N,N*-dimethylacetamide dimethylacetal the thermal rearrangement **235.1 → 235.4** is conducted[281] at the boiling point of xylene, and the corresponding silylketeneacetal can be transformed[293] into the hex-2′-enopyranosyl acetate **235.5** by heating in toluene at 100°C for a day. Two representative procedures are given as follows.

2-(4′,6′-Benzylidene-2′,3′-dideoxy-α-D-erythro-hex-2′-enopyranosyl)-acetaldehyde (235.3)[281]　A solution of the 3-*O*-vinyl ether **235.2** (0.3 g) in benzonitrile (10 ml) is hetaed under reflux for 1 h, and the solvent is removed by distillation under reduced pressure (oil rotary pump) to give 0.23 g (75%) of the syrupy **235.3**, $[\alpha]_D^{20}$ +96.5 (c = 0.65 in methanol).

N,N-Dimethyl-(4,6-O-benzylidene-2′,3′-dideoxy-α-D-erythro-hex-2′-enopyranosyl)-acetamide (235.4)[281]　A mixture of 2.34 g (20 mmol) of 4,6-*O*-benzylidene-D-allal (**235.1**), *N,N*-dimethylacetamide dimethylacetal (3.0 g, 20 mmol), and xylene (200 ml) is heated at reflux temperature in a dry argon atmosphere for 2 h. After concentration of the mixture, the residual crystalline product (3 g, 85%) is recrystallized from petroleum ether to obtain pure **235.4**, m.p. 108.5–109°C, $[\alpha]_D^{20}$ +56 (c = 0.85 in methanol).

When rearrangement of the 3-*O*-vinyl ether **235.2** was carried out in a solvent with higher boiling point (e.g., nitrobenzene), thermal fragmenta-

TABLE I.36 Transformation of Several Glycalketenesilylacetals into "C-Glycosides"

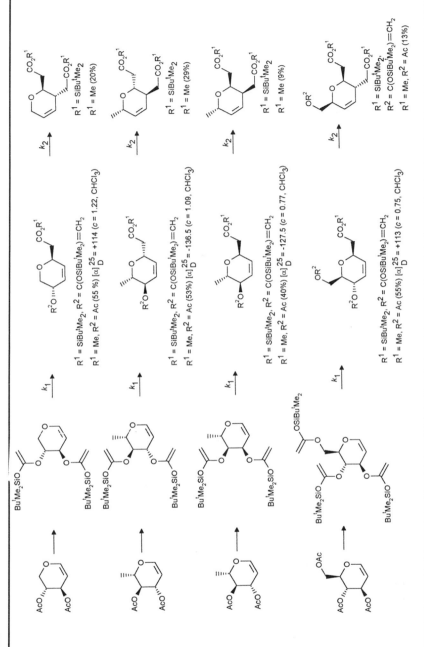

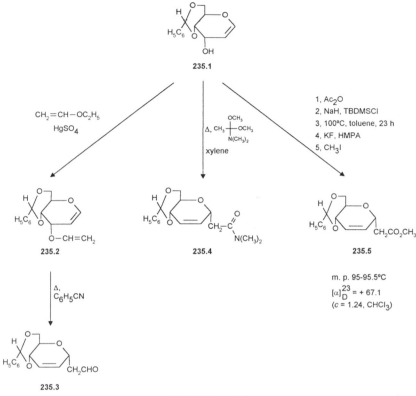

FIGURE 1.235

tion into 6,8-*O*-benzylidene-2,3,4,5-tetradeoxy-*aldehydo*-D-*erythro*-octa-2(*E*),4(*Z*)-dienose occurred.

1.2.7.6. Ascending Synthesis with *aldehydo*-Saccharides

A few methods with somewhat lesser practical utility are discussed in this section. For the chain extension of acetals and aldehydes, treatment with vinyl ethers has been reported by Zhdanov *et al.*[294] Thus, the reaction of 2,3,4,5,6-penta-*O*-acetyl-*aldehydo*-D-galactose and 1-ethoxybutadiene gave rise to 2,3-dehydro-2,3,4-trideoxy-6,7,8,9,10-penta-*O*-acetyl-D-*galacto*-decopyranoside, and in the case of hepta-*O*-acetyl aldoses (**236.1**), including D-mannose, D-galactose, and D-glucose, unseparated mixtures of the epimeric octoses (**236.2**) were obtained, as shown in Figure 1.236.

The chain extension of the *aldehydo*-nonose derivative **237.1** with a β-iodoenol (such as **237.2** or **237.3**), shown in Figure 1.237, is a contribution[295] from the Kishi group to the modern ascending methods in the carbohydrate field. Interestingly, this chromium(II)-mediated coupling[296] of the two reaction partners proceeds only in the presence of a catalytic amount

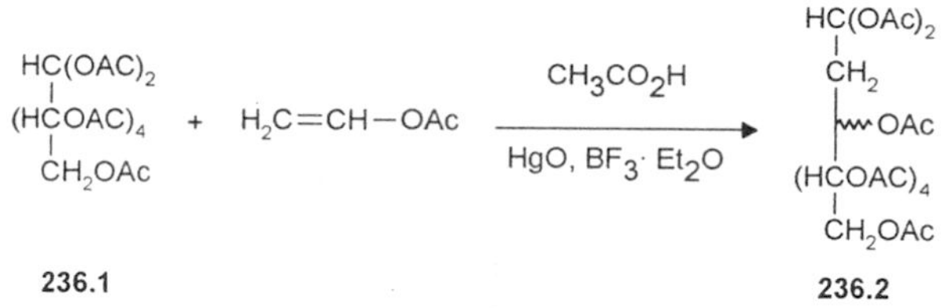

FIGURE I.236

of $NiCl_2$, and related coupling of a dozen of higher-carbon *aldehydo*-sugars were carried out (see the original paper) in an attempt to synthesize structural fragment of *palytoxin*. With the aid of this procedure, it is now possible to achieve chain extension by using $CrCl_2$ *from any source* with excellent reproducibility.

A nucleophilic trifluoromethylation reaction using trifluoromethyl trimethylsilane to an acyclic sugar aldehyde has been employed[297] for the preparation of the C-6 trifluoromethyl derivatives *of L-fucose* and *6-deoxy-D-altrose*.

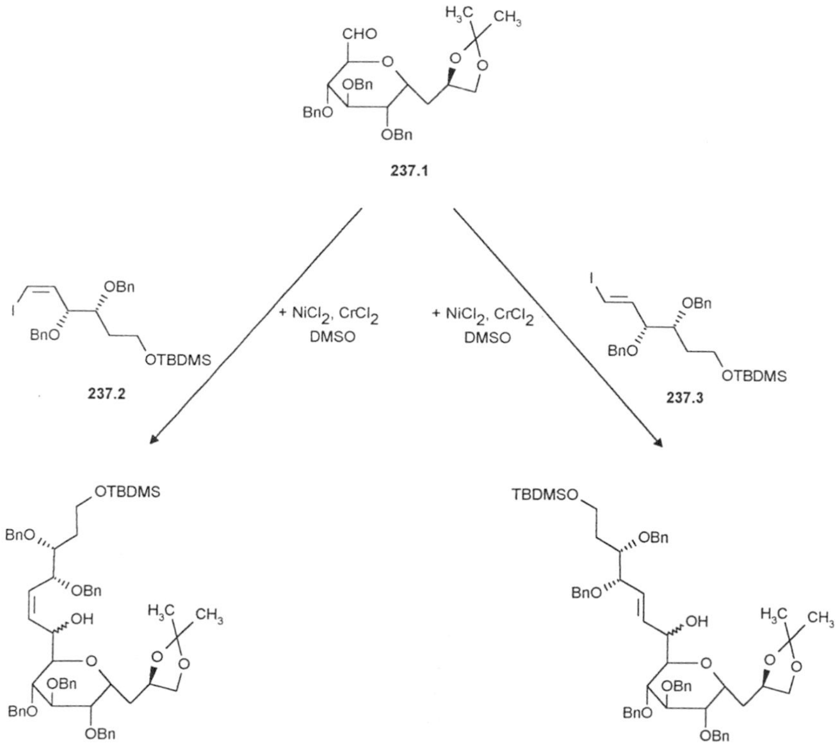

FIGURE I.237

The *anti*-selective reaction of the aldehydo function of a saccharide with prop-2-ynyl bromide in the presence of zinc to introduce a three-carbon unit has been used by Wu.[298,299] A typical procedure[299] for the conversion of the common *aldehydo*-sugars into ynoles is as follows.

Typical procedure for the reaction of aldehydo-*sugars with prop-2-ynyl bromide*[299] A well-stirred solution of the aldehyde (1 mmol) and propargyl bromide (2 mmol) in 1:1 DMF–ether (4 ml) is slowly treated with activated zinc dust (3 mmol, previously washed with 2% HCl and water and dried in vacuum) at room temperature. After 2–5 min the exothermic reaction brings itself to reflux. The reaction mixture is stirred for 5–10 h at room temperature until TLC indicates that the reaction is complete. The usual aqueous workup and column chromatography on silicagel give the required product.

Allylindium reagents have also been employed[204–208,300] for ascending syntheses starting from *aldehydo*-saccharides, and these recations were catalyzed with Yb(OTf)$_3$.

The propargylation reactions of α-alkoxyaldehydes are summarized[299] in Table 1.37, where the yields, the major products, and the *anti/syn* selectivities are also indicated.

For further examples of this efficient technique for assembling *various deoxysugars* by utilizing *in situ*–generated indium reagents in aqueous systems (via elongation of D-arabinose, its 2,3:4,5-di-*O*-isopropylidene derivative, or D-mannose), see the published procedures.[301–306]

Approaches to the chiral synthesis of *hydroxyanthraquinones,* such as the antibiotics *daunomycin* and *adriamycin,* brought reinvestigation of the reaction of *leuko*-chinizarin with aldehydes (the so-called Marschalk reaction). Thus, when the simple aldehydes are replaced with *aldehydo*-sugars, an ascending reaction proceeds under basic conditions to allow one to assemble[307–309] a polyhydroxyalkyl anthraquinone moiety from a suitably protected sugar chain. In Figure 1.238 application of a related chain extension methodology to 2,3:4,5-di-*O*-isopropylidene-*aldehydo*-D-arabinose[307] (**238.1**), and to 3-*O*-benzyl-[308] and 3-*O*-(p-chlorobenzyl)-1,2-*O*-isopropylidene-α-D-*xylo*-pentodialdo-1,4-furanose[309] (**238.2 and 238.3,** respectively) are indicated. An experimental procedure[307] is presented below for the conversion of the *aldehydo*-sugar **238.1.**

*1,4-Dihydroxy-2-(1-hydroxy-2,3:4,5-di-O-isopropylidene-D-arabinitol-1-yl)-9,10-anthraquinone (**238.4**)*[307] The sugar **238.1** (43 g, 0.187 mol) in methanol (50 ml) is added to a cooled (0°C) solution of *leuko*-quinizarin (45 g, 0.186 mol) in THF (960 ml) and methanol (780 ml). Then a solution of NaOH (32 g) in water (150 ml) is added, and the mixture is maintained at 0°C for 25 min under nitrogen. The brown solution is aerated for 2 h, and the resultant purple solution is added dropwise with rapid stirring to a mixture of hydrochloric acid (100 ml, 36% w/w), water (200 ml) and crushed ice (200 g). The resulting orange–red precipitate is filtered off, washed with water, and air-dried to give an orange–red solid (78.4 g). A solution of this crude product (30 g) in 4:1 toluene–ethyl acetate is applied to a silicagel

TABLE 1.37   Propargylation of α-Alkoxaldehydes

Aldehyde	Yield (%)[a]	Major product	Anti:syn
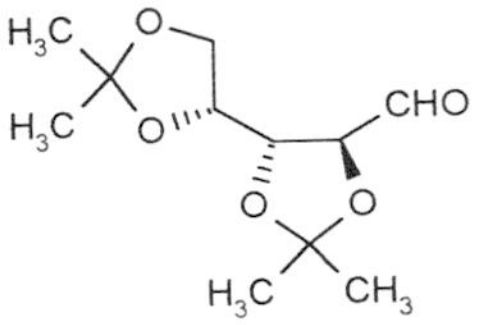	86	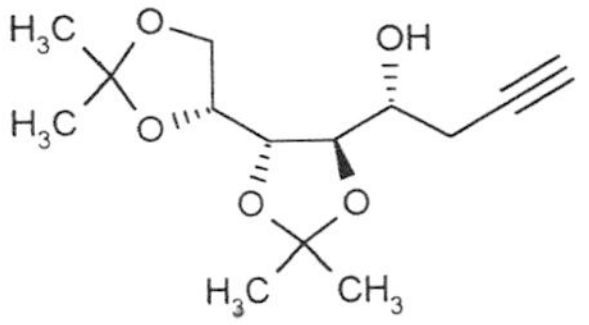	12
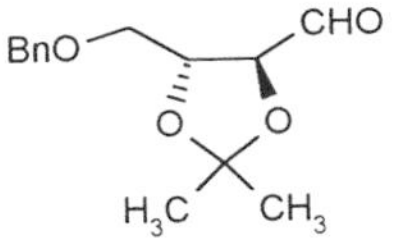	91[b]	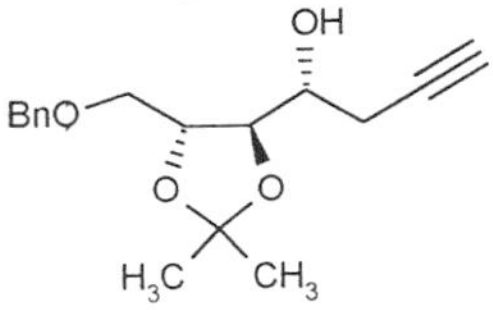	30
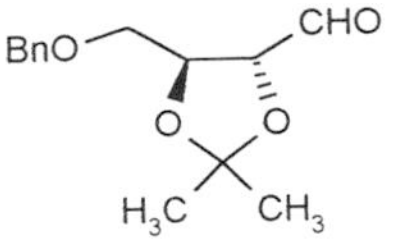	81[b]	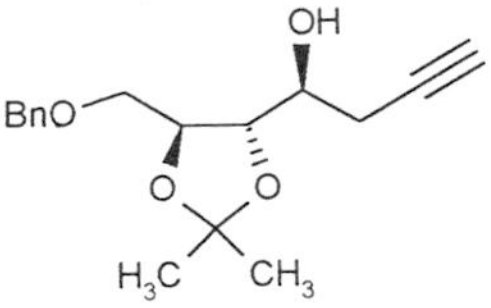	30
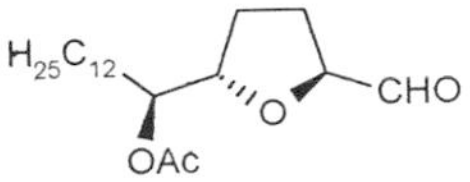	65[b]	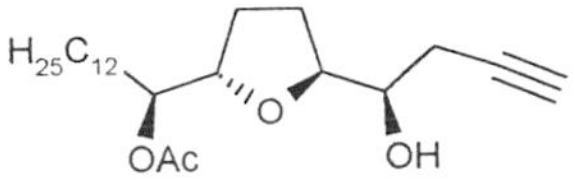	8.3
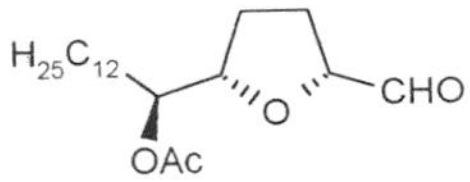	64[b]	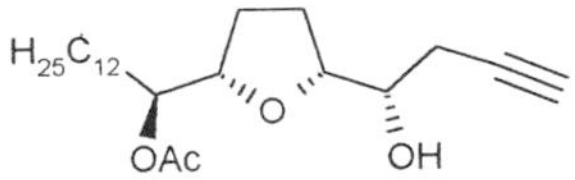	9.8
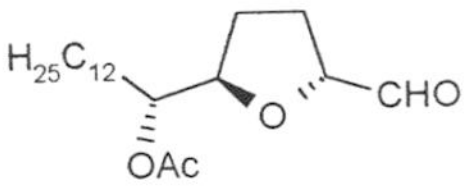	62[b]	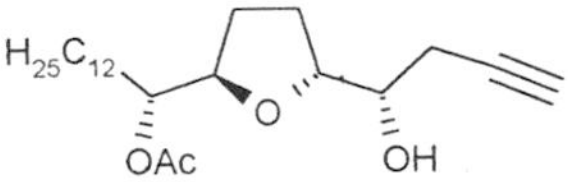	9.6
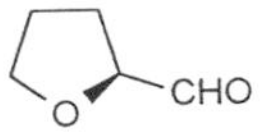	63[b]	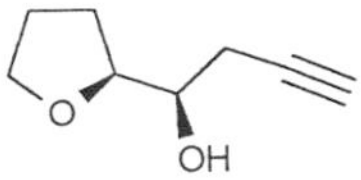	7.3[c]
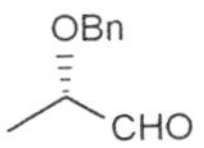	79[b]	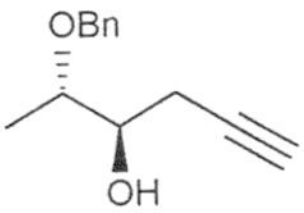	2.6[c]
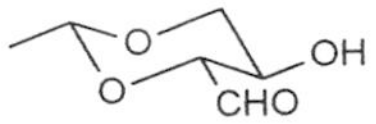	74	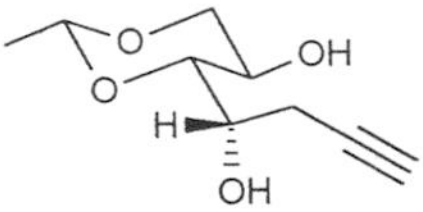	3.3
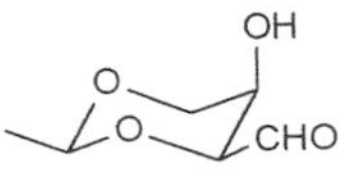	89	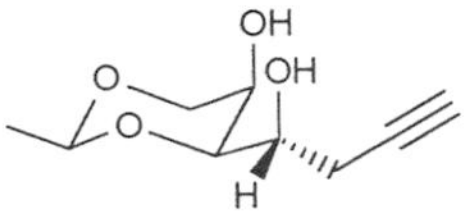	11.7
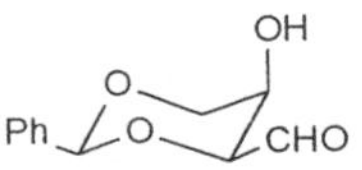	92	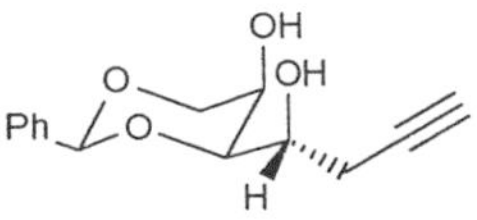	10.5

[a]Isolated yield.
[b]For two steps, from the alcohol.
[c]Determined by NMR.

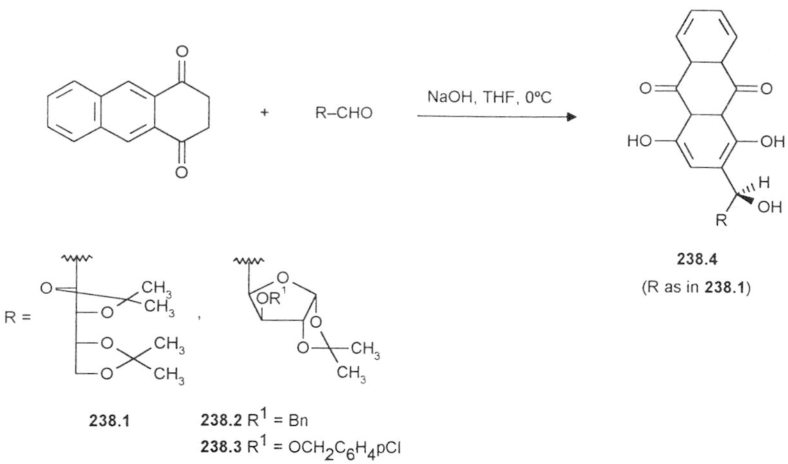

238.4
(R as in **238.1**)

R =

238.1   **238.2** R^1 = Bn
             238.3 R^1 = OCH$_2$C$_6$H$_4$pCl

FIGURE 1.238

column (10 × 60 cm) and eluted with the same solvent to afford 18.7 g (56%) of the anthraquinone **238.4,** as orange–red laths, m.p. 167°C (from ethanol).

The reaction of *aldehydo*-sugars with thioether sulfoxides and sulfones, resulting in a diastereoisomeric mixture of a functionalized derivative of an aldose elongated by one carbon atom, offers a further possibility for chain extension, as illustrated by the examples collected in Table 1.38[310–315].

As an extension of this strategy, in special cases both the aldehyde and the functionalized sulfur compound may carry sugar chains. On this basis, Schmidt and his coworkers[316–319] have developed an efficient ascending procedure in which the sulfur compounds are glycals, substituted with a sulfoxy group, which are reacted with *aldehydo*-sugars substituted with base-stable protecting groups (Fig. 1.239).

Thus, 3,4,6-tri-*O*-benzyl-D-glucal (**239.1**) is first transformed (with phenylsulfenyl chloride and DBU) into the phenylsulfenyl-glucal **239.2,** and this is converted into the diastereoisomeric sulfoxides **239.3.** The phenylsulfinyl group at C-2 of glycals permits clean 1-*C*-lithiation and subsequent reaction with various electrophiles: reductive removal of the phenylsulfinyl substituent in the product and formal water-addition to the double bond lead to highly functionalized *C*-glycosidic compounds of the *gluco* and *galacto* series.[316–319]

As the phenylsulfinyl-D-glucal derivative **239.3** is produced in form of a mixture of diastereoisomers, each of the four diastereoisomeric products are detected in the coupling reaction with aldehydes. However, on the basis of the observed ratio of the isomers, a stereocontrol by the chiral aldehyde is in effect to afford the *erythro*-isomer (with *S*-configuration, such as **239.5**) as the major product. Following the chain extension, products in the *nonitol*

TABLE 1.38 The Chain-Elongation Products of *aldehydo*-Sugars and Thioether Derivatives

Educt	Reagent	Product(s)	Yield (%)	Ref.
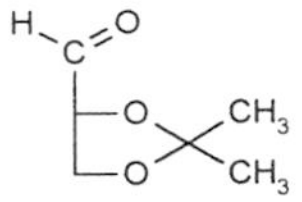	$C_6H_5SCH_2OCH_3$ + BuLi	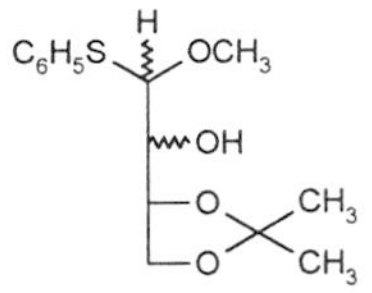	70	310
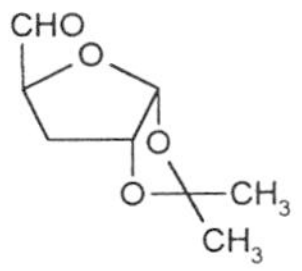	$C_6H_5SCH_2OCH_3$ + BuLi	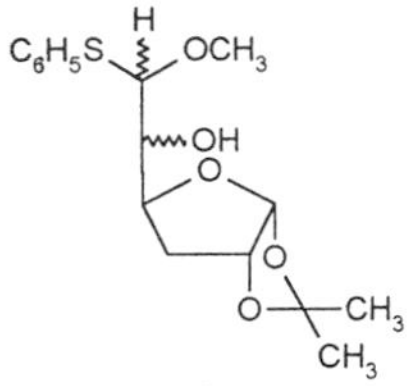	65	310
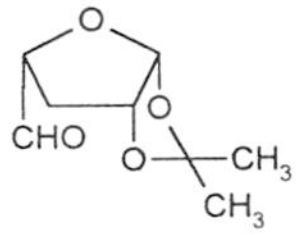	$C_6H_5SCH_2OCH_3$ + BuLi	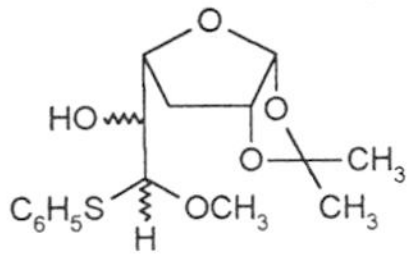	—	310
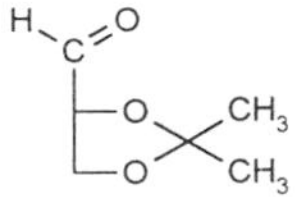	$C_6H_5SCH_2S(O)C_2H_5$	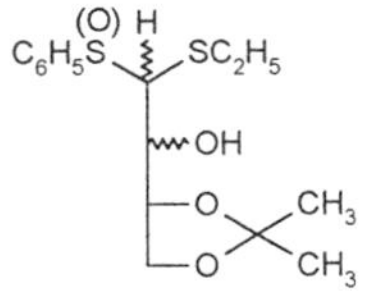	—	311
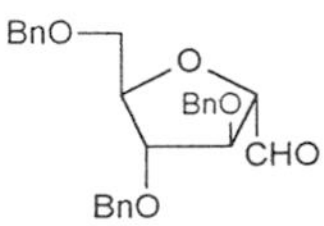	$C_6H_5SCH_2S(O)C_2H_5$	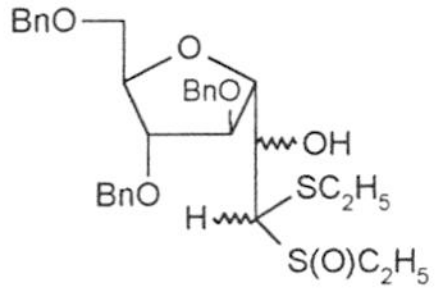	—	312
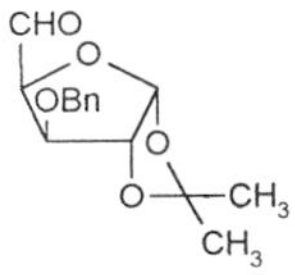	$LiCH_2SO_2C_6H_5$	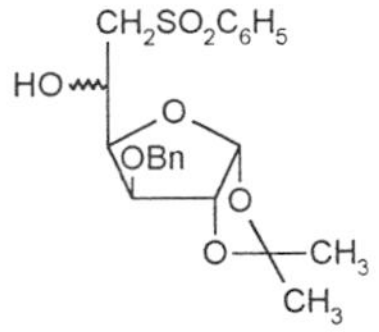	80–92	313
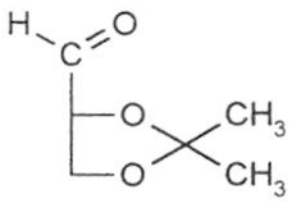	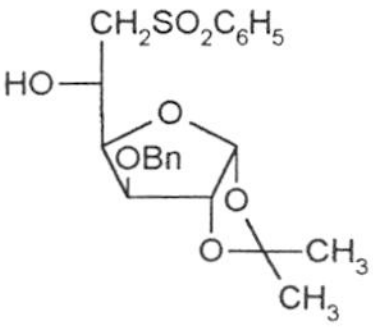	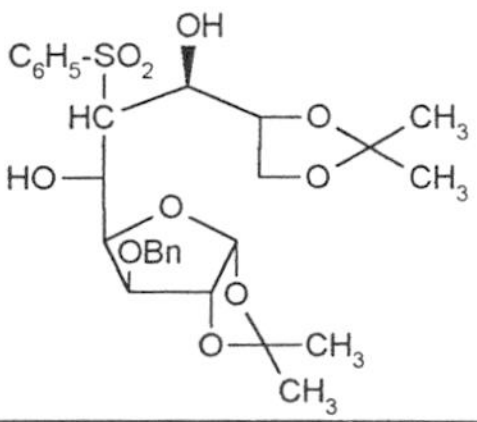	67	313

(*continues*)

TABLE I.38 (continued)

Educt	Reagent	Product(s)	Yield (%)	Ref.
(furanose) CN, BnO, O–C(CH$_3$)$_2$	CH$_3$S(O)CH$_2$SCH$_3$ + KH	CH$_3$S–C(SOCH$_3$)=C(...), H$_2$N-substituted enol furanoside, O–C(CH$_3$)$_2$	43	314
		H$_2$N–C(=O)– enone furanoside, O–C(CH$_3$)$_2$	56	
(bicyclic dioxolane) CHO, H$_3$C CH$_3$, O–C(CH$_3$)$_2$	C$_6$H$_5$SO$_2$CH$_2$S(O)–C$_6$H$_4$-pCl + piperidine	C$_6$H$_5$SO$_2$– vinyl sulfone with –OH, bicyclic acetonide (two diastereomers, one with OH, one with HO)	73	315

and *undecitol* series with L-*gulo*-D-*arabino* and D-*manno*-D-*gulo* configurations can be obtained in a few steps.[316]

1,5-Anhydro-3,4,6-tri-O-benzyl-2-phenylthio-D-arabino-hex-1-enitol (**239.2**)[316]
To a solution of 3,4,6-tri-O-benzyl-D-glucal (**239.1**, 10.0 g, 24.2 mmol) in dry carbon tetrachloride (100 ml), phenylsulfenyl chloride (7.1 g, 48.4 mmol) is added dropwise and the mixture is stirred, under protection from moisture, for 4–8 h. When all the starting material has reacted, the solution is concentrated to its half-volume, DBU (7.0 ml, 33 mmol) is added slowly and the mixture is stirred at 50°C for 2 h. When the reaction is complete, it is diluted with an equal volume of chloroform, washed with aqueous NH$_4$Cl, and the organic phase is concentrated and then purified by flash column chromatography (eluant: 9:1 petroleum ether–ethyl acetate) to obtain 8.9 g (70%) of **239.2** as a yellow syrup, [α]$_D^{20}$ +24.3 (c = 1 in chloroform).

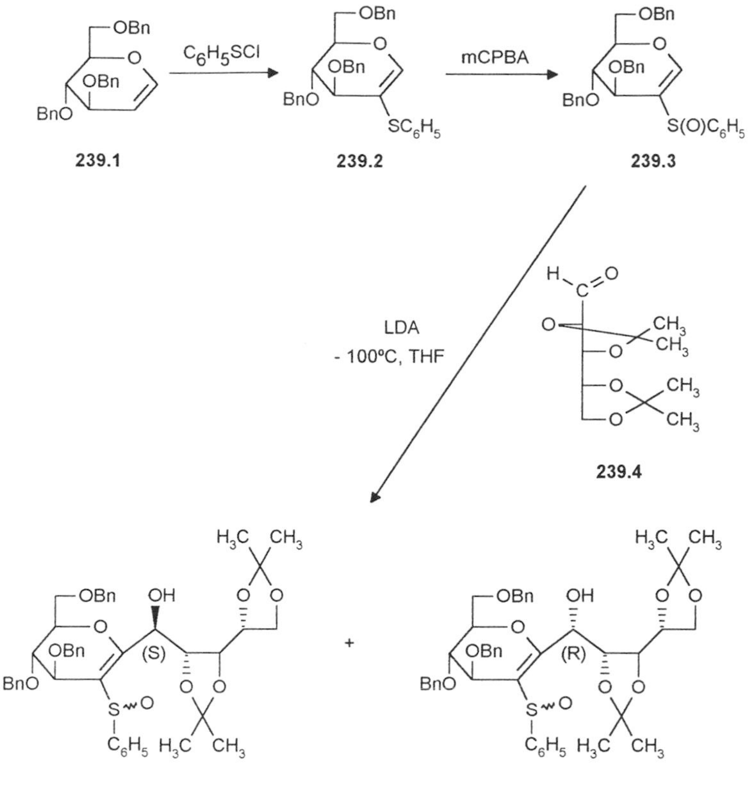

FIGURE I.239

1,5-Anhydro-3,4,6-tri-O-O-benzyl-1,2-dideoxy-2-phenylsulfinyl-D-arabino-hex-1-enitol (239.3)[316] In this procedure 7.5 g of compound **239.2** is dissolved in dry dichloromethane (150 ml) and treated by the dropwise addition of a solution of 3-chloroperoxybenzoic acid (3.1 g, 15.3 mmol) in dichloromethane (15 ml), followed by stirring for 30 min. When the transformation is complete, the mixture is poured into aqueous NaHCO₃, and the organic layer is washed with water, concentrated, and subjected to flash column chromatography (eluant: 6:4 petroleum ether–ethyl acetate to furnish 7.3 g (90%) of **239.3** as a 1:1 diastereoisomeric mixture. Low-pressure chromatography with the same eluant permits the separation of the isomers to a faster- and a slower-moving compound, and the latter can be crystallized from hexane–ethyl acetate;

Faster-moving isomer (FM): $[\alpha]_D^{20}$ +59.9 (c = 2.7 in chloroform)
Slower-moving isomer (SM): $[\alpha]_D^{20}$ +40.9 (c = 1.1 in chloroform).

The respective sulfoxides have also been prepared in the D-*galacto* series and the chirality of the sulfur atom has been determined, and it has been shown that the slower-moving isomer possesses (*R*)-configuration.[318]

Preuss and Schmidt[316] have performed the preceding ascending synthesis by employing 2,3:4,5-O-isopropylidene-D-arabinose (**239.4**) as the aldehyde partner (Fig. 1.239).

> *2,6-Anhydro-1,3,4-tri-O-benzyl-5-deoxy-8,9:10,11-di-O-isopropylidene-5-phenyl-sulfinyl-D-manno-D-arabino-undec-5-enitol [(S)-239.5] and the corresponding L-gulo-D-arabino-isomer [(R)-239.6][316]* A solution of the **FM** isomer of **239.3** (500 mg, 0.88 mmol) in THF (5 ml) is lithiated with 1.1 eq of lithium diisopropylamide (prepared from *tert*-butyllithium and diisopropylamine in ~25 ml of THF) for 30 min at $-100°C$ under N_2, followed by the addition of 1.1 eq of HMPA. The mixture is stirred at $-100°C$ for 30 min, and then a solution of the freshly distilled sugar **239.4** (1.1 eq) in THF is added. Stirring is continued at the same temperature for 3 h, the cold mixture is poured into aqueous ammonium chloride, 30 ml of ether is added and extracted with aqueous NaCl. The organic layer is dried (MgSO$_4$), and concentrated, and the residue is subjected to flash column chromatography (eluant: 1:1 petroleum ether–ethyl acetate) to give the pure **(S)-239.5** {$[\alpha]_D^{20}$ -18.7 ($c = 2.6$ in chloroform)} and **(R)-239.6** {$[\alpha]_D^{20}$ -5.1 ($c = 1.96$ in chloroform)} in a ratio of 4:1 with an 85% overall yield. By conducting the same reaction with the **SM**-isomer of **239.3**, the isomers [(R)-**FM**: **239.6**] {$[\alpha]_D^{20}$ $+24.3$ ($c = 0.3$ in chloroform)} and [(S)-**SM**: **239.5**] {$[\alpha]_D^{20}$ $+56.6$ ($c = 2$ in chloroform)} as syrupy substances are obtained in a ratio of 1.0:2.6 with an overall yield of 65%.

The (R)-, as well as the (S)-isomer (**240.1**), of 1,5-anhydro-3,4,6-tri-O-benzyl-2-deoxy-2-phenylsulfinyl-D-$lyxo$-hex-1-enitol has been applied[317,318] for the synthesis of a hydroxymethylene-bridged Gal-β-(1→3)Gal C-disaccharide (**240.2**), as shown in Figure 1.240.

Addition of electrophiles, including aldehydes, to C-1-lithiated glycals (**241.1**) offers an additional possibility[320] for chain extension into C-glycosidic compounds (**241.2**) (see Fig. 1.241).

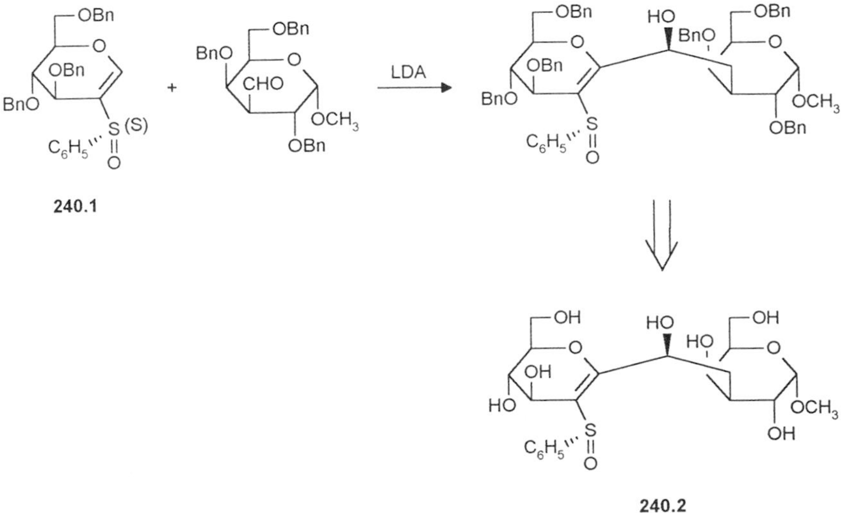

FIGURE I.240

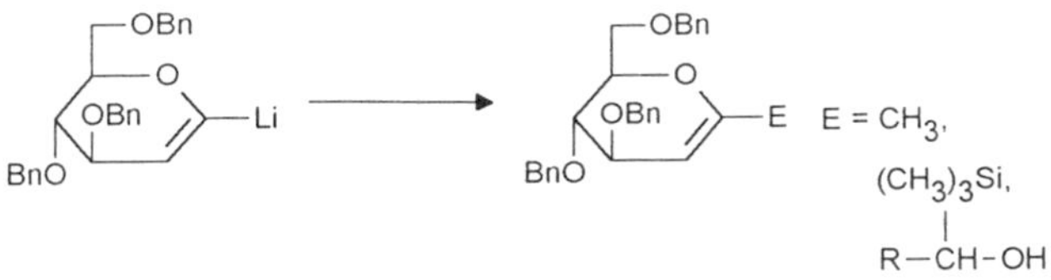

241.1   241.2

FIGURE 1.241

Another ascending synthesis (Fig. 1.242), based on the reaction of 2,3-O-isopropylidene-D-glyceraldehyde (**242.1**) with the anion **242.2**, leads to a 2.6 : 1 mixture of the $(2R,3S,4R)$- (**242.3**) and $(2S,3R,4R)$-2,3-anhydro-4,5-O-isopropylidenedioxypentanoic acids (**242.4**), which can be separated in the form of their methyl esters.[241] These sugars have been employed—via 2-amino-2-deoxy-D-altrofuranose intermediates—for the preparation of chiral β-lactams.[322]

The following two name reactions show that aldehydo-sugars readily undergo the Erlenmeyer–Plöchl "azlactone synthesis" and the Darzens condensation.

By means of the "azlactone synthesis" Zhdanov et al.[323] converted 2,3:4,5-di-O-isopropylidene-aldehydo-L-arabinose (**243.1**) into 3-deoxy-L-arabino-heptulono-1,4-lactone (**243.2**) as shown in Figure 1.243.

Darzens condensation involves the reaction of a dihaloacetate anion with a carbonyl compound to furnish an α-haloglycidate. When Coutrot[324] performed related condensation (Fig. 1.244) of 1,2:3,4-di-O-isopropylidene-α-D-galacto-hexodialdo-1,5-pyranose (**244.1**) as the aldehyde, with the isopropyl dihaloacetates **244.2**, a mixture of isopropyl 7-chloro-(bromo)-6,7-anhydro-1,2:3,4-di-O-isopropylidene-D-glycero- (**244.3**) and -L-glycero-octonates (**244.4**) were produced with good yields (X = Cl: 92%; X = Br: 82%). Treatment of these latters with MgI_2 followed by reduction with $NaHSO_3$ resulted in the isopropyl 6-deoxy-7-diulosonate derivative **244.5**.

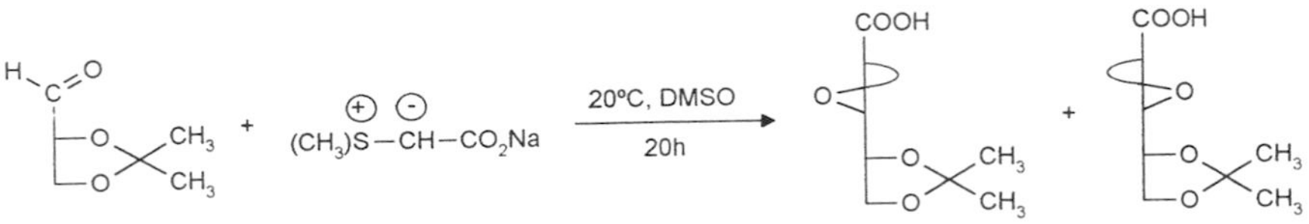

242.1   242.2   242.3   242.4

                                         $(2R,3S,4R)$ $(2S,3R,4R)$

                                                   78%

FIGURE 1.242

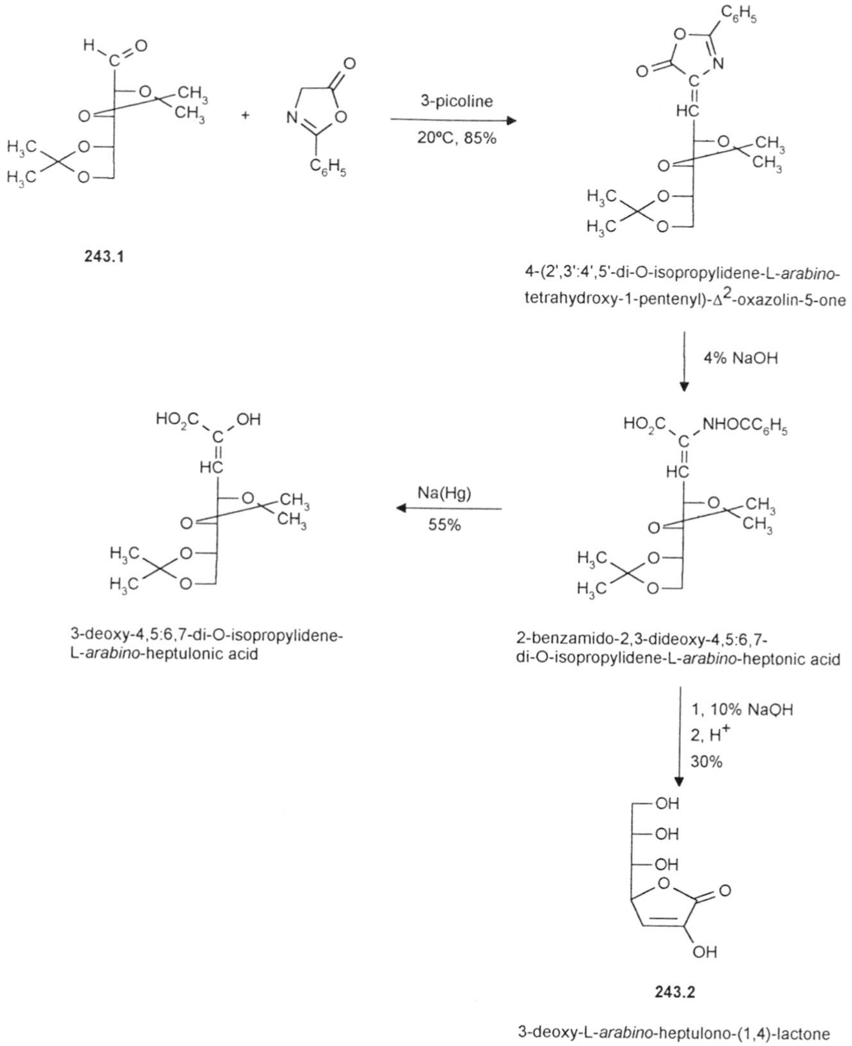

3-picoline
20°C, 85%
243.1
4-(2',3':4',5'-di-O-isopropylidene-L-*arabino*-tetrahydroxy-1-pentenyl)-Δ2-oxazolin-5-one
4% NaOH
Na(Hg)
55%
3-deoxy-4,5:6,7-di-O-isopropylidene-L-*arabino*-heptulonic acid
2-benzamido-2,3-dideoxy-4,5:6,7-di-O-isopropylidene-L-*arabino*-heptonic acid
1, 10% NaOH
2, H+
30%
243.2
3-deoxy-L-*arabino*-heptulono-(1,4)-lactone

FIGURE 1.243

This well-established ascending synthesis offers a rational, convenient route[325] to *Kdo* (**245.6**), which is shown in Figure 1.245. Experimental details for the two key steps of this procedure are given as follows.

*Darzens condensation of 4-(*tert*-butyldimethysilyl)-2,3:5,6-di-O-isopropylidene-*aldehydo-*D-mannose (**245.1**)*[325] In a typical procedure, a solution of aldose **245.1** (4.25 mmol) and isopropyl dihalogenoacetate **245.2** [X = Cl or Br] (18.5 mmol) in ether (10 ml) is added dropwise at 0°C to a solution of potassium isopropoxide (18.5 mmol) in 4:1 2-propanol–ether (50 ml). After stirring for 1.5 h at 0°C, the mixture is neutralized with a saturated HCl/ether solution. The potassium halide suspension is centrifugated and separated. The organic layer is concentrated under

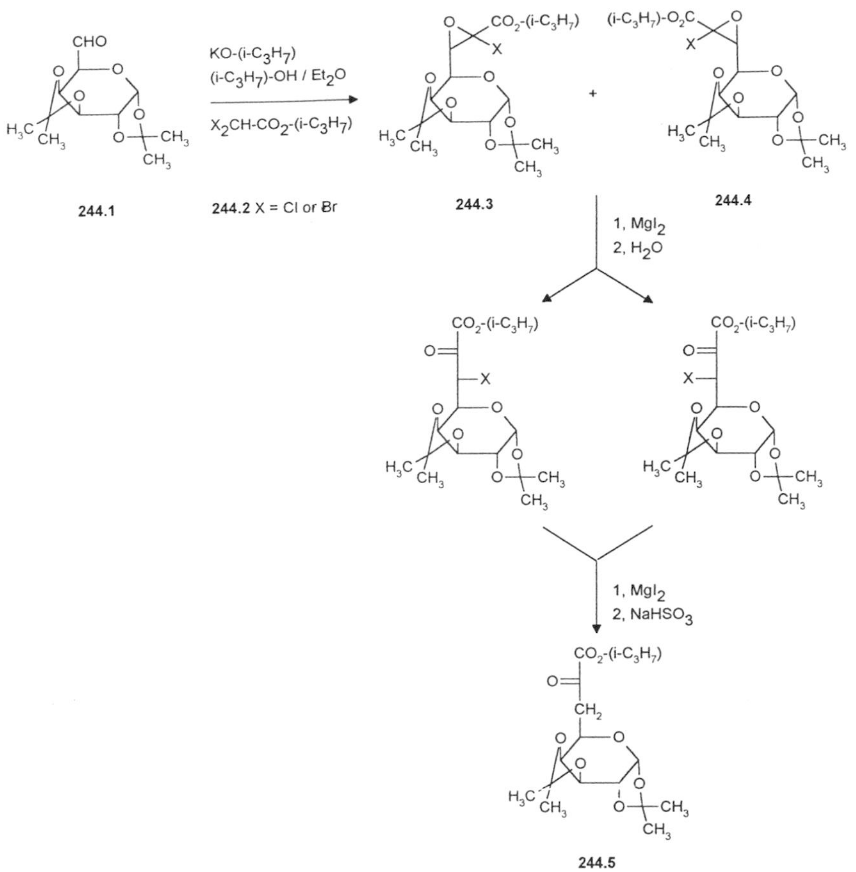

FIGURE I.244

reduced pressure to give diastereoisomeric mixtures of the α-halogenoglycidic esters
245.3 and **245.4** (**245.3a** : **245.4a** = 75 : 25; **245.3b** : **245.4b** = 63 : 37) in high yields
(92% and 85%, respectively). The next step of the procedure is epoxide cleavage
and reductive removal of the halogen atom, in which the reaction conditions are
crucial and require an exact temperature control. In a typical experiment, MgI_2
(786 mmol) in 3 ml of ether is added dropwise, at −60°C with stirring, to the
diastereoisomeric mixture of α-chloroglycidic esters **245.3** and **245.4** (393 mmol) at
the concentration of 0.02 M in a 4 : 2 mixture of ether–toluene. The reaction mixture
is allowed to warm to −30°C, and after stirring at this temperature for 90 min, it
is treated with a freshly prepared concentrated aqueous $NaHSO_3$ solution (5 ml)
and allowed to warm to ambient temperature. After 45 min of stirring, the usual
workup gives the ulosonate **245.5** (314 mmol), a target to transform Kdo (**245.6**)
on removal of the protecting groups.

1.2.7.7. Chain Extension of Aldonic Acids and Aldonolactones

Formal replacement of the lactone–carbonyl group with a methylene function can be effected with metallorganic compounds, of which

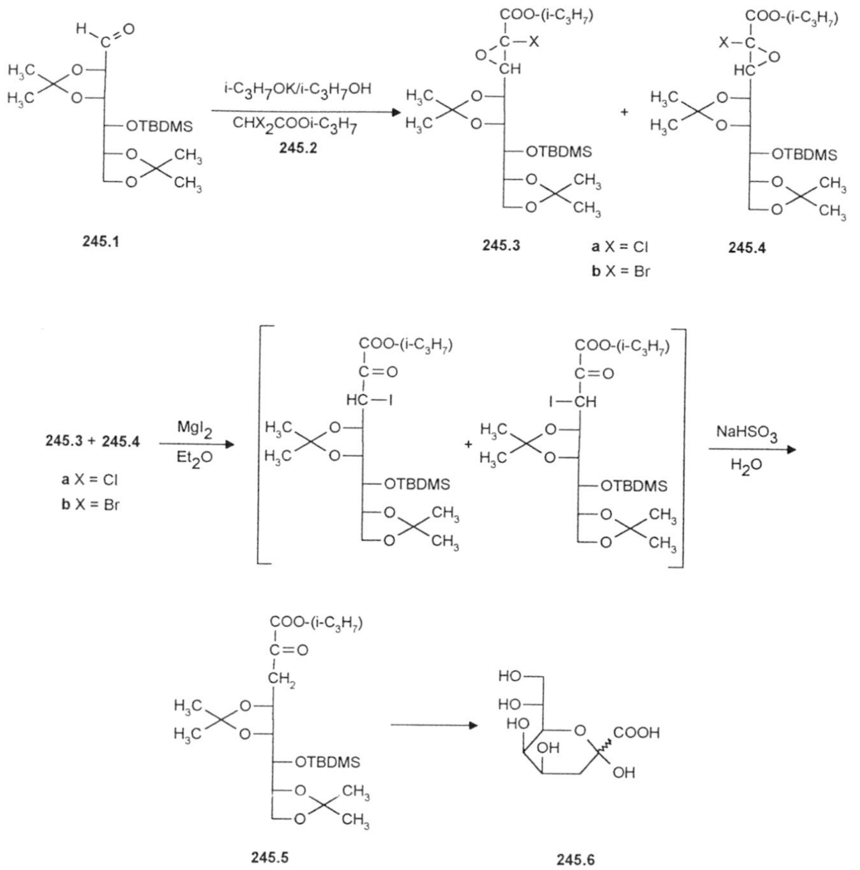

FIGURE I.245

the first to be applied was the carbenoid type compound: μ-chloro-bis[(η_5-cyclopentadienyl)dimethylaluminum]-μ-methylenetitanium (**246.1**), the so-called Tebbe reagent.[326] Treatment of lactones (**246.2**) with the Tebbe reagent leads to an exocyclic olefin extended by one carbon atom (**246.3**) via the reaction sequence shown in Figure 1.246.

The reagent formed from a special trimethylaluminum and titanocene dichloride reacts with the lactone (or with a C=O group) in the form of $Cp_2Ti=CH_2$ to produce the olefin **246.3** and Cp_2TiO. The procedure has been applied[327–329] for the sugar-lactones collected in Table 1.39. In a few cases formation of by-products (not listed in the table) was also reported.

General procedure for ascending syntheses of sugar ketones, esters and lactones with the Tebbe-reagent[329]   Trimethylaluminum in toluene (10.2 ml, 20 mmol) at 20°C is treated with titanocene dichloride (2.48 g, 10 mmol) for 72 h. This solution of the complex **246.1** (which can be stored at 0°C for at least 3 months) is used

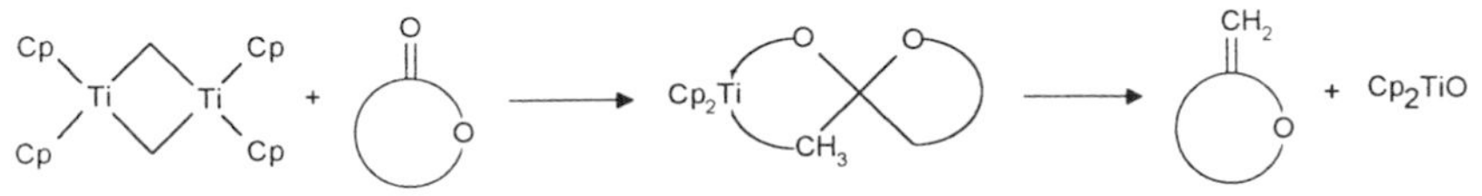

246.1   246.2   246.3

Tebbe-reagent

Cp = cyclopentadienyl

FIGURE I.246

without further purification, as follows. The carbohydrate derivative (1 mmol) in a mixture of toluene (3 ml), tetrahydrofuran (1 ml), and pyridine (5 μl) is stirred with the preceding solution of the complex (2.14 ml) at $-40°C$ for 30 min, and then it is allowed to reach ambient temperature during 1.5 h. The progress of the transformation is monitored by TLC. After cooling to $-10°C$, 15% aqueous NaOH (0.1 ml), ether (15 ml), and sodium sulfate (1 g) are added sequentially. The mixture is filtered through a pad of Celite and then eluted from a short column of silicagel with eluants that usually contain $\sim$0.3% of triethylamine. Evaporation of the solvents leaves the products shown in Table 1.39[330,331]

The Tebbe reagent can also be employed for the chain elongation of sugars containing an aldehydo group: Ikemoto and Schreiber[332] prepared ethyl 8,9-dideoxy-2,3,6,7-tetrakis-O-[(1,1-dimethylethyl)dimethylsilyl]-4,5-bis-O-(phenylmethyl)-D-*threo*-L-*galacto*-non-8-enonate, a key intermediate in the synthesis of *(-)-hikizimycin* from the corresponding uronate with 82% yield.

Dicyclopentadienyl-dimethyltitanium, $Cp_2Ti(CH_3)_2$, has been introduced[333] as an alternative to the titanocene methylidene complex for methylenation of aldonolactones. The reagent is reasonably stable and can be prepared in large quantities, exposed to air during handling, and stored at $-20°C$ for extended periods.

Procedures for the preparation of the $Cp_2Ti(CH_3)_2$ complex and its application in carbohydrate ascending syntheses are given, as follows, according to the work of Csuk and Glänzer.[333]

Dicyclopentadienyl-dimethyltitanium [$Cp_2Ti(CH_3)_2$][333]   To a cold (10°C) solution of titanocene dichloride (10 g, 40.16 mmol) in dry ether (200 ml) is carefully added a solution of methyllithium (60 ml, 96 mmol, 1.6 M in ether) under argon in the dark. After completion of the addition, the mixture is allowed to warm to ambient temperature, stirred for another 10 min, and then cooled to $0 - 5°C$, and at this temperature icewater (15 ml) is added dropwise to decompose the excess of methyllithium. The layers are separated, the aqueous phase is extracted with ether (2 × 50 ml), the combined organic layer is dried (Na_2SO_4), and the solvent is evaporated in the dark at 20°C to yield the title complex (7.1 g, 85%) as orange needles, dec.p. 93–96°C.

General procedure for the methyleneation of aldonolactones[333]   A toluene solution (5 ml/mmol of lactone) and the $Cp_2Ti(CH_3)_2$ complex (2.1 mmol/mmol lactone) is stirred in the dark for 48 h at 65–70°C under argon until TLC (3 : 1 hexane–ethyl

TABLE 1.39 (Sugar)Olefins from Chain Elongation of Aldonic Acid Lactones with the Tebbe Reagent

Educt	Product	Yield	$[\alpha]_D$	Ref.
		R = TBDMS		
		85%	−111 (CHCl$_3$)	327
		6%	−107 (CH$_2$Cl$_2$)	329
		R = CH$_3$		
		7%	−525 (CH$_2$Cl$_2$)	329
		70%	—	328
		R = Bn		
		82%	+60 (CH$_2$Cl$_2$)	328
		88%	+52 (CH$_2$Cl$_2$)	329
		91%		330
		R = (CH$_3$)$_3$Si		
		54%	+508 (CH$_2$Cl$_2$)	328
		R = (C$_2$H$_5$)$_3$Si		
		85%	—	328
		R = CH$_3$		
		95%	+67 (—)	329
		67.7%	−13.6 (CH$_2$Cl$_2$)	328

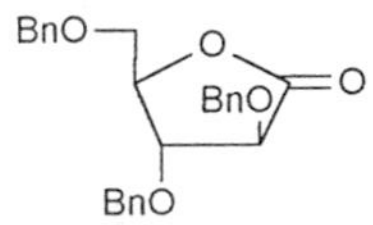

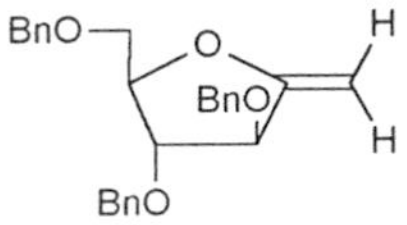

330

78%

—

329
329

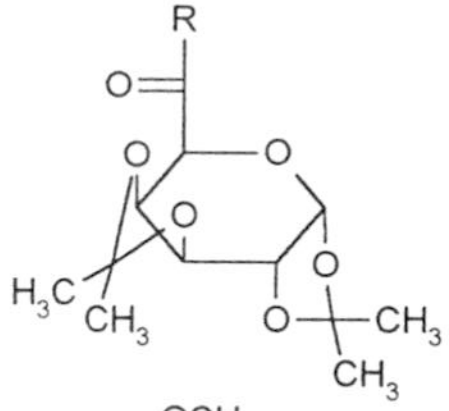

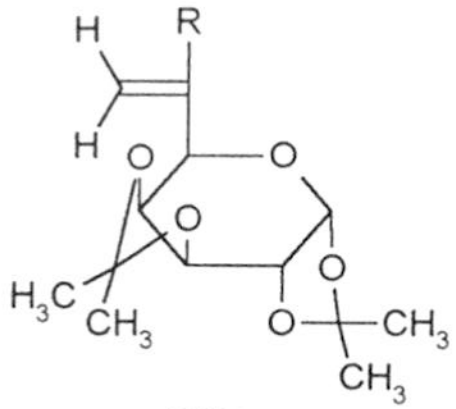

R = H
35%
R = OCH₃
86%

−190.5 (CH₂Cl₂)

−79 (CH₂Cl₂)

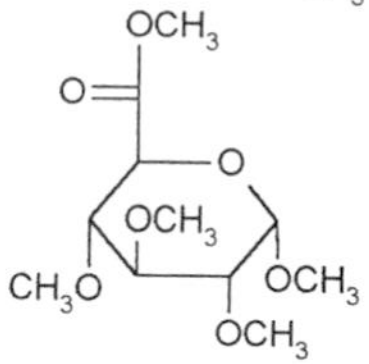

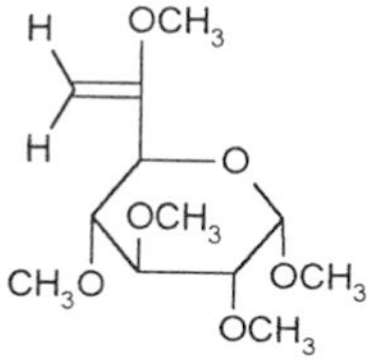

329

86%

+123 (CH₂Cl₂)

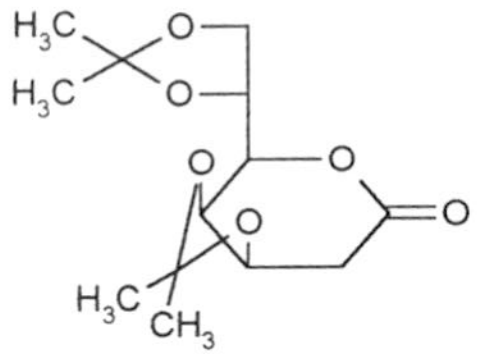

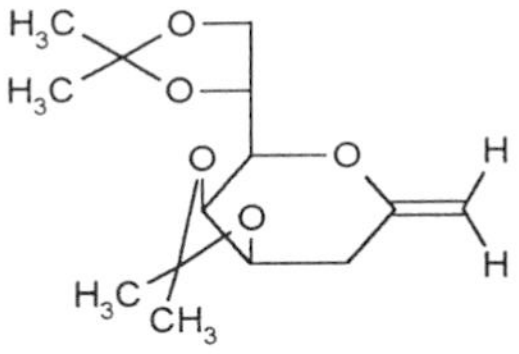

331

82%

—

(continues)

TABLE 1.39 (continued)

Educt	Product	Yield	$[\alpha]_D$	Ref.
		R = SEM 79%	—	331
		R = pivaloyl 80%	−13 (c = 0.5, CHCl$_3$)	
		R = SEM 67%	+34 (c = 1, CHCl$_3$)	331
		R = pivaloyl 81%	+5.5 (c = 0.55, CHCl$_3$)	

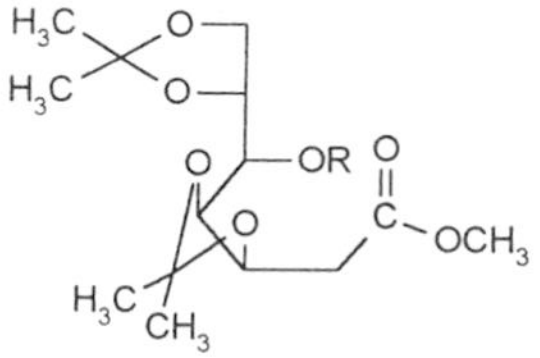

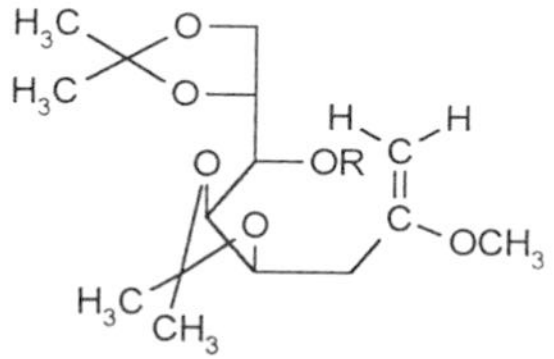

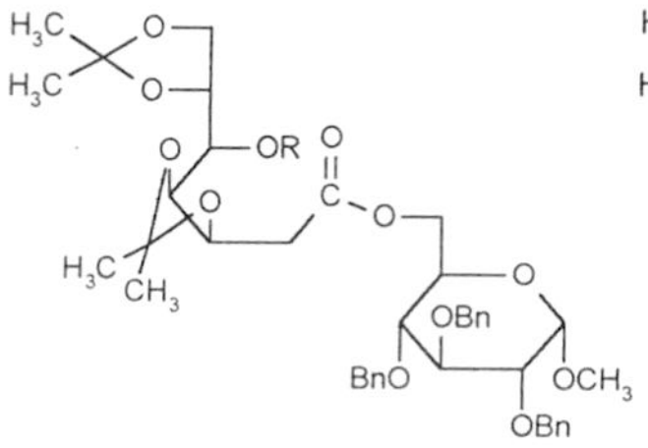

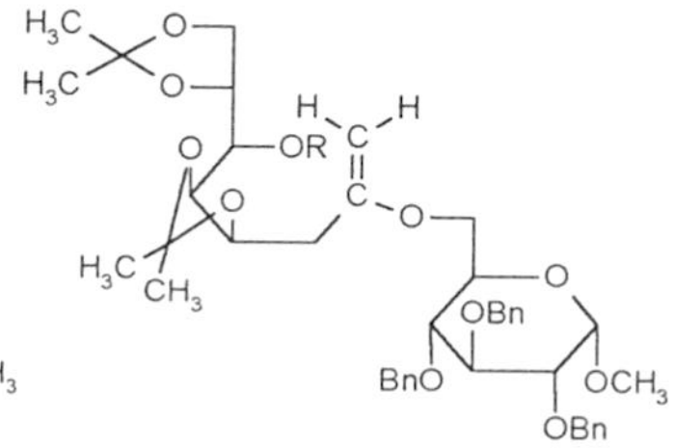

acetate) shows disappearance of the starting material. The brownish reaction mixture is concentrated, and the residual syrup (taken up with a minimum volume of toluene) is subjected to column chromatography on silicagel [column and eluant containing 1% of triethylamine; gradient: 20:1–5:1 (v/v) hexane–ethyl acetate] to afford the methylenated products.

A further possibility for the chain extension of lactones involves[334–336] addition of [(methoxymethoxy)methyl]lithium, generated *in situ* by tin–lithium exchange of the corresponding stannane derivative to perbenzylated lactones. According to the results of van Boom *et al.*,[335] details for the preparation of a protected α-D-*galacto*-heptulopyranose are as follows:

3,4,5,7-Tetra-O-benzyl-1-O-methoxymethyl-α-D-galacto-heptulopyranose[335]
To a solution of Bu₃SnCH₂OCH₂OCH₃ (2.19 g, 6.0 mmol), dried by evaporation with toluene (3 × 5 ml), in THF (15 ml) is added n-butyllitium (1.6 M in hexane, 3.7 ml, 5.9 mmol) under nitrogen with stirring while the temperature is maintained below −75°C. After 5 min, a solution of 2,3,4,6-tetra-O-benzyl-D-galactono-1,5-lactone (1.07 g, 2.0 mmol), previously dried by evaporation with toluene (3 × 5 ml) in THF (5 ml), is added via a syringe. After 15 min TLC analysis shows complete disappearance of the starting lactone. The reaction mixture is quenched with a 10% aqueous NH₄Cl solution and extracted with ether. The organic layer is washed with water, dried (MgSO₄), and concentrated under reduced pressure. The crude product is purified by column chromatography [eluant: 0:1–1:2 (v/v) ether–petroleum ether] to afford the title product as a colorless syrup (1.09 g, 89%), R_f = 0.45 in 2:1 ether–petroleum ether.

The heptulopyranose with L-*fuco*-configuration was synthesized in an essentially similar way.[335]

If a saccharide derivative is selected as the reagent for the above ascending procedure, then the chain can be extended with a longer unit. For example, *ketosides,* readily convertible to C-disaccharides can be synthesized. Thus, the reaction of 1,6-anhydro-2,3-di-O-benzyl-4-deoxy-4-C-(lithiomethyl)-β-D-galactopyranose (**247.1;** X = Li), obtained from the corresponding iodomethyl derivative (**247.1;** X = I), with 2,3,4,6-tetra-O-benzyl-D-gluconolactone (**247.2**) (or with the respective galactonolactone) gave[337] 1,6-anhydro-2,3-di-O-benzyl-4-deoxy-4-C-(3,4,5,7-tetra-O-benzyl-1-deoxy-α-D-*gluco*-2-heptulopyranos-1-yl)-β-D-galactopyranose (**247.3**), as shown in Figure 1.247.

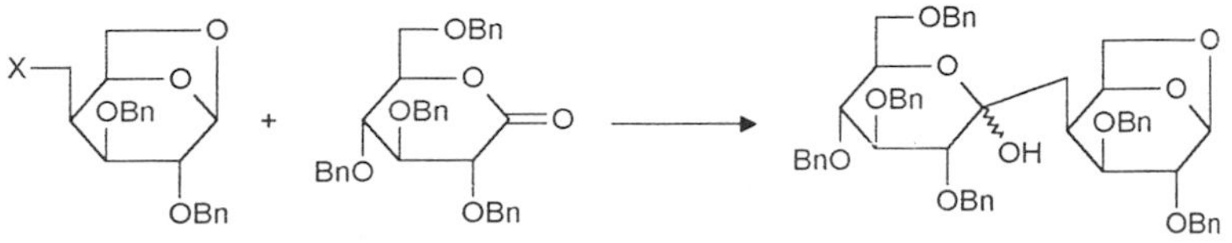

247.1   247.2   247.3

X = Li, I

FIGURE I.247

Schmidt *et al.*[338] employed a similar procedure (Fig. 1.248) to obtain the undeculose **248.4,** but difficulties emerged on attempted removal of the anomeric hydroxyl group with $BF_3 \times Et_2O$ (compare the effect[337,339] of Et_3SiH for removal of anomeric hydroxyl groups and the effect of $BF_3 \times Et_2O$ on ketosides[340]).

1,6-Anhydro-2,3-di-O-benzyl-4-deoxy-4-C-(3,4,5,7-tetra-O-benzyl-1-deoxy-α-D-gluco-2-heptopyranos-1-yl)-β-D-galactopyranose (248.4)[338]   To a solution of the iodosugar **248.1** (300 mg, 0.64 mmol) in dry THF (20 ml) is added a 1.6 M solution of *n*-butyllithium (0.52 ml, 0.83 mmol in hexane) at −90°C under nitrogen atmosphere to produce the lithium derivative **248.2**. The mixture is stirred for 30 min, and then a solution of 2,3,4,6-tetra-*O*-benzyl-D-gluconolactone (**248.3**) (410 mg, 0.76 mmol) in dry THF (5 ml) is added slowly at the same temperature. After 45 min the temperature is raised to −50°C and the solution is poured into a saturated aqueous ammonium chloride solution. The mixture is extracted with ether, the extract is dried (MgSO₄), the solvent is evaporated, and the residue is purified by means of flash column chromatography on a silicagel column (eluant: 3 : 1 petroleum ether–ethyl acetate) to furnish 300 mg (53%) of the product **248.4** as a colorless syrup, $R_f = 0.37$, $[\alpha]_D^{20}$ −16.5 ($c = 1$ in ethyl acetate).

Aldosulosonic acids are also available by the chain extension of aldonolactones with various silicon compounds, such as 2-trimethylsilylpropionic acid, methyl trimethylsilyl acetate, alkyl trimethylsilylacrylates and trimethylsilyl acetonitrile.[341] The chain-extended trimethylsilylglycosides thus produced are desilylated with tetrabutylammonium fluoride to obtain the *C-glycosidic substances* indicated in Table 1.40 with high yields.

Ascending syntheses of lactones with acetylenic compounds, aimed at the production[342–346] of certain *oligosaccharide analogs of polysaccharides,* have attracted considerable interest. As a related example, Figure 1.249 shows the incorporation of a silylated acetylenic moiety to 2,3,4,6-tetra-*O*-benzyl-D-gluconolactone (**249.1**) by treatment with the silylethin **249.2** to afford **249.3,** which serves as a model compound for the selection of a suitable protecting group strategy[346] in syntheses of polysaccharide analogs.

With {[dimethyl(oxy)propyl]dimethylsilyl}acetylenes (DOPSA), the ascending synthesis is to be carried out as follows.

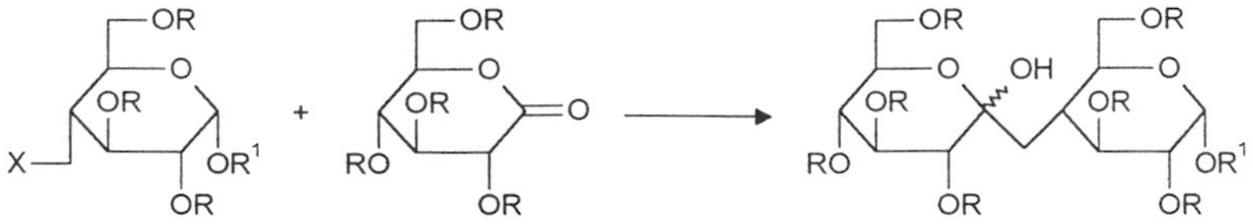

248.1 X = I
248.2 X = Li

248.3

248.4

R = Bn, R¹ = CH₃, Bn

FIGURE 1.248

General procedure for the preparation of the hemikatals **249.3**[346]   A solution of the selected DOPSA (**249.2**, 0.22 mmol) in dry THF (1 ml) is treated with 1.5 M *n*-butyllithium in hexane (0.14 ml, 0.21 mmol) at −76°C. The resulting solution is injected, at −76°C, into a solution of the sugar **249.1** (92 mg, 0.17 mmol) in THF (2 ml), and the mixture is stirred at this temperature for 10 min to 2 h and quenched with 0.1 N aqueous HCl. The usual workup, followed by fast column chromatography (eluant: 92 : 8 → 85 : 15 hexane–ethyl acetate), gives the syrupy product **249.3** (72%).

Several procedures have been elaborated for the chain extension of protected lactones with heteroaryllithium compounds[347] and acetalde-hyde,[348] as well as for their difluoromethylenation[349,350] and conversion into phosphonic acid analogs.[351]

An efficient procedure for the chain elongation of aldonolactones carrying base-stable protecting groups involves[352] the reaction with *in situ*–generated tris(methylthio)methyllithium (**250.1**) to give an intermediary trithioester, which is readily convertible, with mercuric chloride–mercuric oxide in methanol into the methyl ulosonate **250.2,** as shown in Figure 1.250, and the products synthesized using this procedure are summarized in Table 1.41.

An interesting ascending synthesis of lactones with *p*-tolylsulfonyl-methyl cyanide {isocyano[(tol-4-yl)sulfonyl]methane} has been described by South African chemists,[353] and the procedure has been adapted to aldonolactones by French authors[354] (Fig. 1.251).

An efficient protocol for incorporating a formyl group at the anomeric position of sugars starting from the corresponding lactone has been developed by Dondoni and Scherrmann.[355] The strategy involves the addition of 2-lithiothiazole to the sugar lactone, followed by the silane reduction of the resulting acetylated ketol and unmasking of the formyl group from the thiazole moiety. This ascending procedure has been executed with both pyranose and furanose lactones to afford the corresponding α- or β-ketol—depending on the workup conditions. The experimental procedure below describes the conversion of 2,3,4,6-tetra-*O*-benzyl-D-gluconolactone.

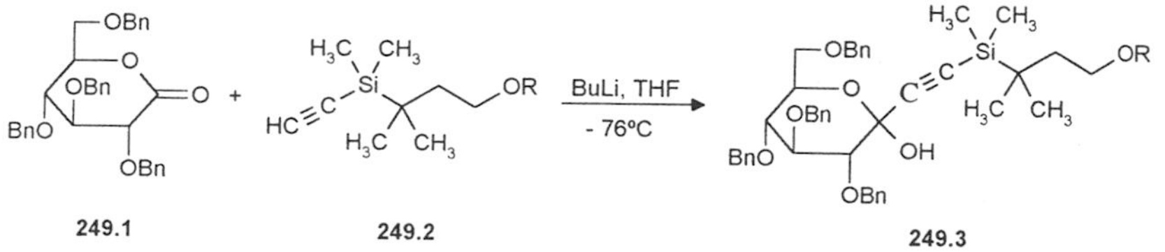

249.1   249.2   249.3

R = CH₃OCH₂-,
4-CH₃O-C₆H₄CH₂-,
tetrahydropyranyl-

FIGURE I.249

TABLE 1.40 Preparation of Ulosonic Derivatives via Reaction between Protected Aldonic Acid Lactones and Silicon Reagents

Educt	Si reagent	Product	$[\alpha]_D$
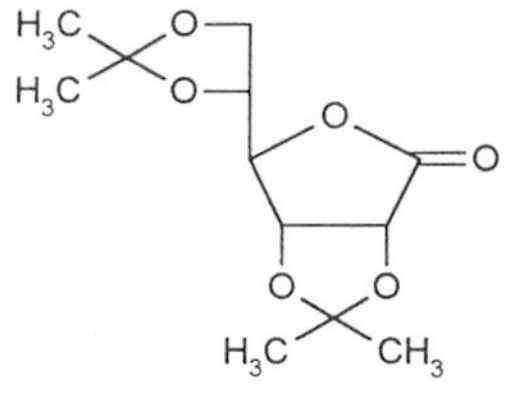	$(CH_3)_3SiCH_2CO_2C_2H_5$	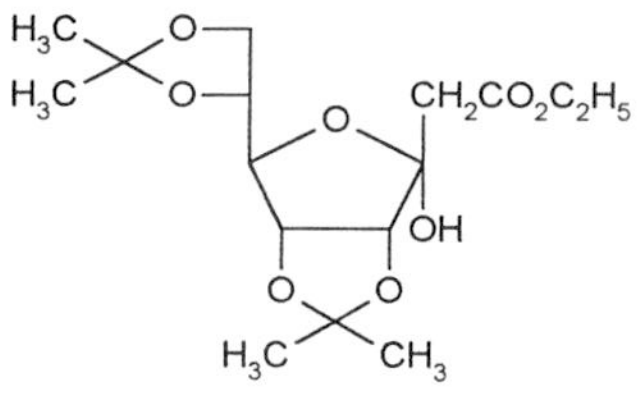	$+5.7$ ($c = 2.5$, CHCl$_3$)
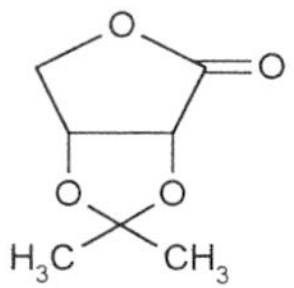	$(CH_3)_3SiCH_2CO_2C_2H_5$	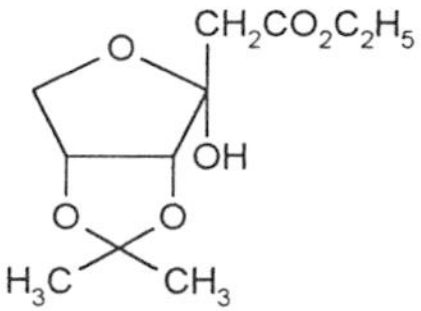	-56.1 ($c = 3.0$, CHCl$_3$)
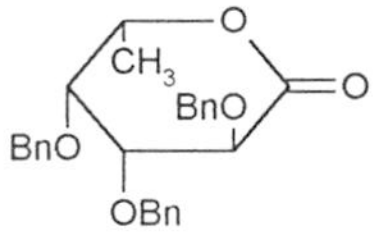	$(CH_3)_3SiCH_2CO_2C_2H_5$	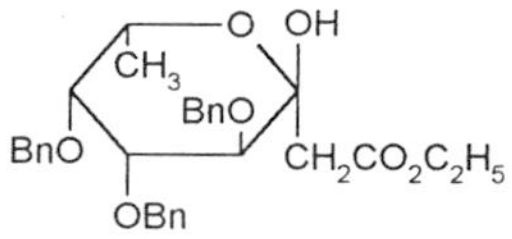	—
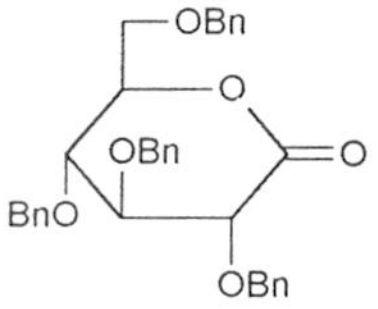	$(CH_3)_3SiCH_2CO_2C_2H_5$	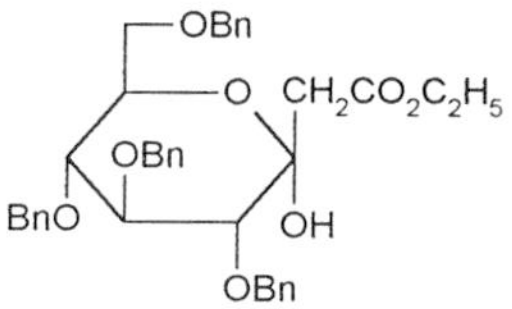	-5.4 ($c = 1.0$, CHCl$_3$)

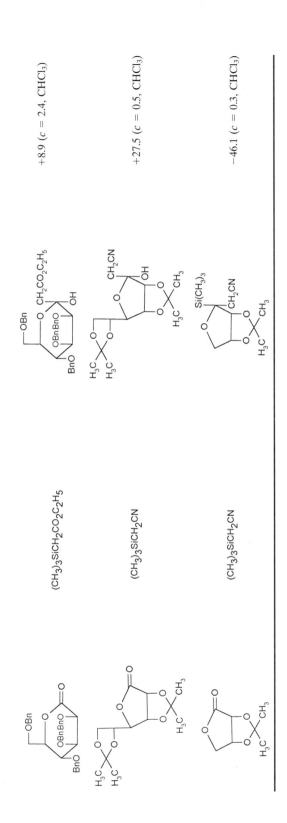

+8.9 (c = 2.4, CHCl₃)

+27.5 (c = 0.5, CHCl₃)

−46.1 (c = 0.3, CHCl₃)

2,3,4,6-Tetra-O-benzyl-1-(2-thiazolyl)-α-D-glucopyranose[355] To a cooled (−78°C) and stirred solution of *n*-butyllithium (7.6 ml, 12.1 mmol of a 1.6 M solution in hexane) in dry ether (17 ml) is added dropwise a solution of freshly distilled 2-bromothiazole (1.8 g, 11.1 mmol) in ether (4.3 ml) over a 30-min period. After stirring of the yellow solution at −78°C for 20 min, a solution of 2,3,4,6-tetra-*O*-benzyl-D-gluconolactone (5.0 g, 9.29 mmol) in dry THF (17 ml) is added slowly over 25 min. After an additional 20 min the mixture is allowed to warm to −65°C in 30 min and poured into 200 ml of a 1 M phosphate buffer (pH 7). The layers are separated, and the aqueous phase is extracted with dichloromethane (2 × 100 ml). The combined organic layer is dried (Na₂SO₄), and concentrated. Flash column chromatography (eluant: 5:2 petroleum ether–ethyl acetate) of the residue gives 4.60 g (80%) of the title product, m.p. 96–97°C (from ethyl acetate–hexane), [α]_D +10.8.

This procedure employed the C-2 carbon atom of the thiazole ring for the one-carbon chain extension, and Vasella[356] applied imidazole for a similar purpose. Experimental details of this latter ascending methodology in which the effective reagent is 1-lithio-imidazole, generated from 1-[(dimethylamino)methyl]-1*H*-imidazole with *n*-butyllithium, and the educt is 2,3,4,6-tetra-*O*-benzyl-D-gluconolactone are given as follows.

2,3,4,6-Tetra-O-benzyl-1-C-(1H-imidazol-2-yl)-α-D-glucopyranose[356] A cold (−78°C) solution of 1-[(dimethylamino)methyl]-1*H*-imidazole (764 mg, 6.87 mmol) in dry THF (40 ml) is treated dropwise with *n*-butyllithium (1.6 M in hexane, 4.24 ml) and stirred at the same temperature for 1 h. Then a solution of 2,3,4,6-tetra-*O*-benzyl-D-gluconolactone (3.32 g, 6.15 mmol) in THF (30 ml) is added dropwise over a period of 35 min at −78°C. The yellow solution is then stirred at the same temperature for 5 h and neutralized with a saturated aqueous solutiuon of ammonium chloride. The usual workup gives 3.8 g of a white foam, which is crystallized from 15:85 chloroform–ether to afford 2.52 g (67.5%) of the product as white, slightly hygroscopic crystals, m.p. 141°C, [α]_D^{25} +31.3 (*c* = 0.93 in chloroform), *R*_f = 0.39 (in 4:1 ethyl acetate–hexane).

Chloromethyltrimethylsilane has also been utilized in certain ascending syntheses carried out with aldonolactones. When the reagent is treated with *tert*-butyllithium or with *sec*-butyllithium in the presence of *N,N,N',N'*-tetramethylenediamine, trimethylsilyllithium and chloro(trimethylsilyl)-methyllithium, respectively, are produced, which have been introduced by Csuk and Glänzer[357] to the carbohydrate field for obtaining methyl ketones and chloromethyl ketones, respectively, from saccharide–lactones. Experimental details for this procedure are reported as follows.

General procedure for the reaction of lactones with chloro(trimethylsilyl)methyllithium[357] To a solution of chloromethyltrimethylsilane (0.18 ml, 2 mmol) in dry

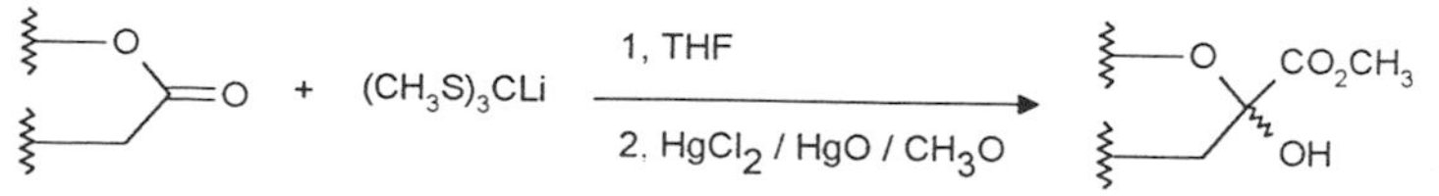

250.1   **250.2**

FIGURE I.250

TABLE 1.41   Conversion of Aldonolactones to Methyl 2-Ulosonates

Lactone	Methyl 2-ulosonate	Yield (%)
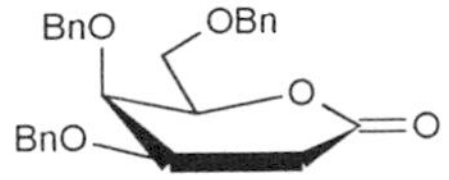	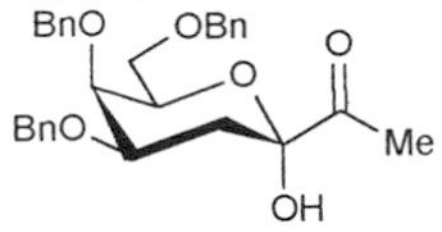	40
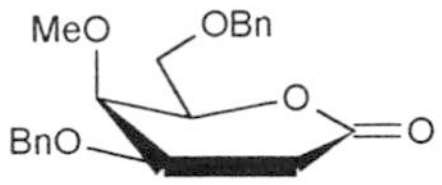	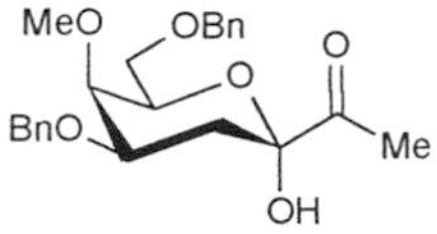	33
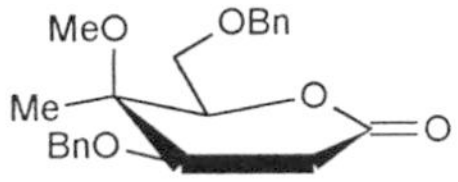	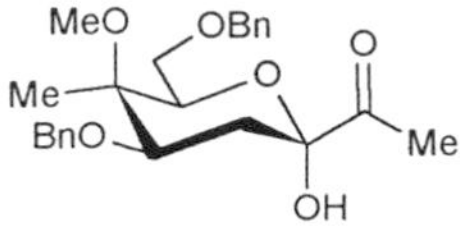	42
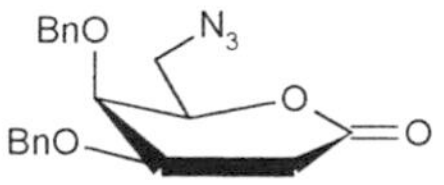	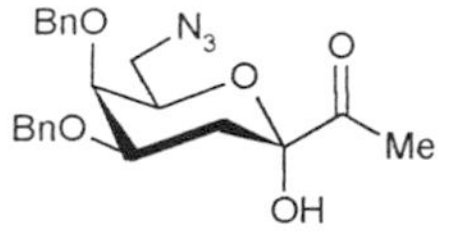	40
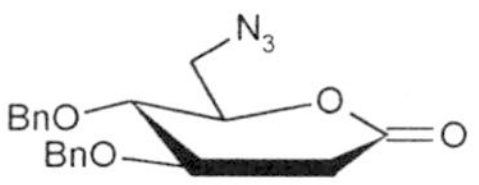	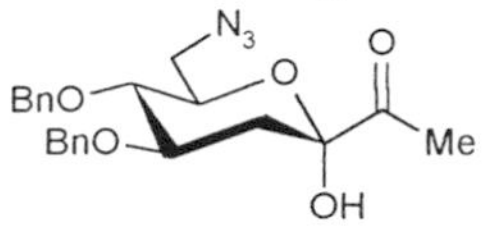	42
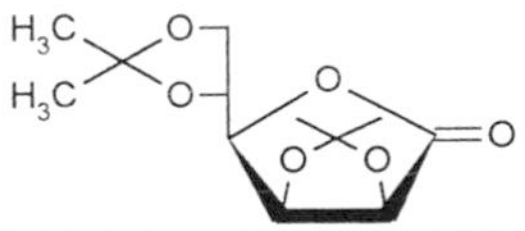	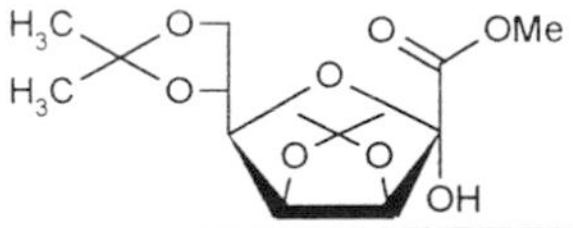	49

THF (10 ml) at −70°C under argon is slowly added a solution of *sec*-butyllithium (1.6 ml, 1.4 M in 92:8 cyclohexane–isopentane) via a syringe. The mixture is stirred for 5 min, N,N,N',N'-tetramethylenediamine (0.33 ml, 2.2 mmol) is added and stirring at −60°C is continued for 30 min. Then a solution (1 mmol/ml) of the lactone (1 mmol) in dry THF is added, and the mixture is stirred at the given temperature until complete disappearance of the lactone (TLC in 3:1 hexane–ethyl acetate). The mixture is poured with stirring into ice-cold saturated aqueous ammonium chloride (10 ml) and extracted with ethyl acetate (5 × 20 ml). The combined extract is washed with cold water and brine (5 ml each) and dried (MgSO₄), the solvent is evaporated, and toluene (2 × 20 ml) is evaporated from the residue. The resulting syrup is subjected to either flash column or column chromatography (eluant: 3:1 hexane–ethyl acetate) to afford the product.

The preparation of the simple homologs of free carboxylic acids has been discussed in Section 1.2.4.1. Steglich *et al.*[358-360] reported an interesting ascending synthesis of *glyconic acids* and *glycuronic acids*. This strategy is based, essentially, on the production of an allyl N-acyl-C-phenylglycinate **252.1** from the corresponding acid (glyconic acid or glycuronic acid), C-phenylglycine, and an allylic alcohol, and subsequent cyclization into

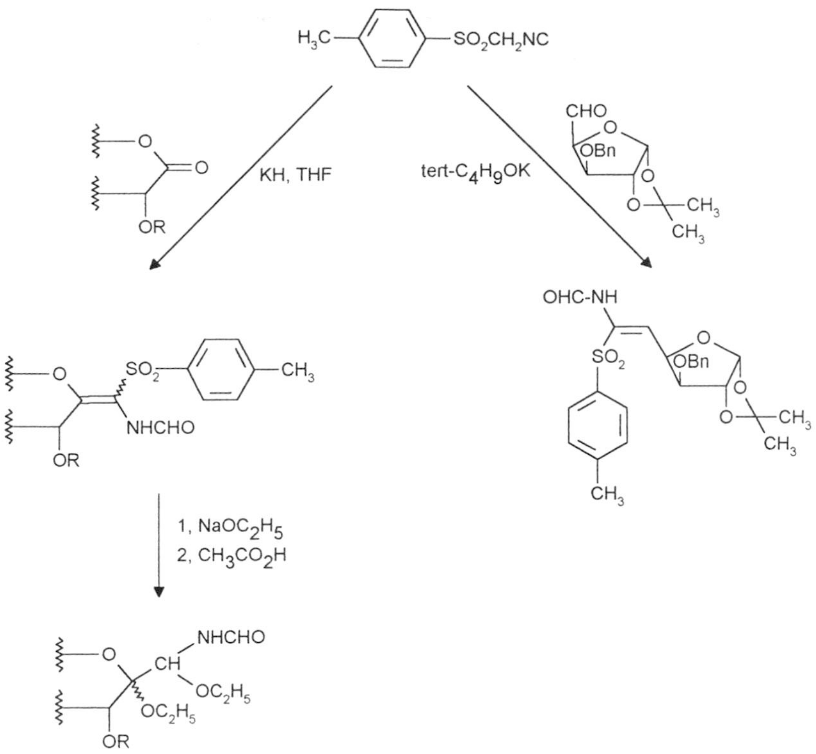

FIGURE 1.251

(allyloxo)-oxazole with triphenylphosphine in the presence of hexachloro-ethane and triethylamine. The product is then stabilized under the applied reaction conditions in the form of a 5(2H)-oxazolone (**252.2**) by a double [3.3]-sigmatropic rearrangement (Fig. 1.252). The latter oxazolone can be readily split with chromium(II)acetate in DMF into a β,γ-unsaturated ketone (**252.3**), and then the chain-extended ketoses (**252.4**) are obtained by removal of the protecting ester groups (generally acetyl) on Zemplén transesterification.

Three procedures have been elaborated[358] for obtaining the allyl esters (**252.1**) and are shown in Figure 1.253. In method A glyconic chlorides (**253.1**) are reacted with trimethylsilyl N-trimethylsilyl-C-phenylglycinate (**253.2**), and the desired allyl esters (**253.5**) are obtained from the resulting N-acyl-C-phenylglycines (**253.3**) by alkylative esterification with the allyl-bromides **252.4** in the presence of dicyclohexylamine and DCC. Method B involves transformation of the peracetylated glyconic chloride **253.1** into the active ester **253.7** with 2-oxo-4,6-diphenylthieno[3,4-d]-1,3-dioxol-5,5-dioxide (**253.6**) followed by base-catalyzed coupling with the hydrobromide

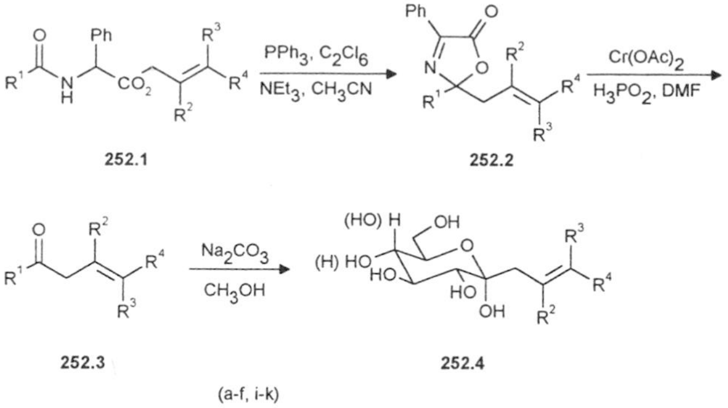

252.1   **252.2**

252.3   **252.4**

(a-f, i-k)

	R^1	R^2	R^3	R^4		R^1	R^2	R^3	R^4
a	PAGlP[a]	H	CH$_3$	CH$_3$	h	PAGlP[a]	H	H	(E)-CH=CHCH$_3$
b	PAGlP[a]	Geranyl[b]			i	PAGlP[a]	H	H	Ph
c	PAGlP[a]	Farnesyl[b]			j	PAGlP[a]	H	Cl/CH$_3$	Cl/CH$_3$[c]
d	PAGlP[a]	Geranylgeranyl[b]			k	PAGaP[d]	Geranylgeranyl[b]		
e	PAGlP[a]	Farnesylgeranyl[b]			l	MTAA[e]	H	CH$_3$	CH$_3$
f	PAGlP[a]	Solanesyl[b]			m	MTAA[e]	H	H	Ph
g	PAGlP[a]	H	H	CH=CH$_2$	n	MTAA[e]	CO$_2$CH$_3$	Ph	H

[a]PAGlP = 1,2,3,4,5-pentaacetoxy-D-gluco-pentyl,
[b]The name of the alkyl component CH$_2$C(R^2)=CR^{3}R^4,
[c](E/Z) mixture,
[d]PAGaP = 1,2,3,4,5-pentaacetoxy-D-galacto-pentyl,
[e]MTAA = (5S)-methyl-2,3,4-tri-O-acetyl-α-L-arabinopyranosid-5-yl.

FIGURE 1.252

of C-phenylglycine allyl esters (**253.9**) into the target allyl esters **253.5**. The C-phenylglycine ester salts **253.9** are prepared from the C-phenylglycine derivatives **253.8** by treatment with the allylbromides **253.4**. The glyconic acids can also be coupled with the amine-hydrobromides **253.9** in the presence of DCC (method C) and the products **253.5** are isolated and purified by means of chromatographic techniques.

Table 1.42 gives an account on the glyconic esters **253.5** prepared[358] with the preceding three procedures. Besides these open-chain compounds, several cyclic pyranosyl derivatives have also been synthesized[358-360] according to this methodology.

Experimental details for executing the three procedures discussed in the preceding paragraphs are as follows.

Preparation of N-glyconyl-D,L-2-phenylglycine allyl esters (**253.5**) *Method A* (alkylative esterification). A mixture of 20 mmol of the N-glyconyl-D,L-2-phenylglycine **253.3**, dicyclohexylamine (4.0 g, 22 mmol), and the allyl bromide **253.4** (20 mmol) in THF (100 ml) is kept under reflux for 15 h. After cooling to 0°C, the precipitated dicyclohexyl ammonium bromide is filtered off and the filtrate

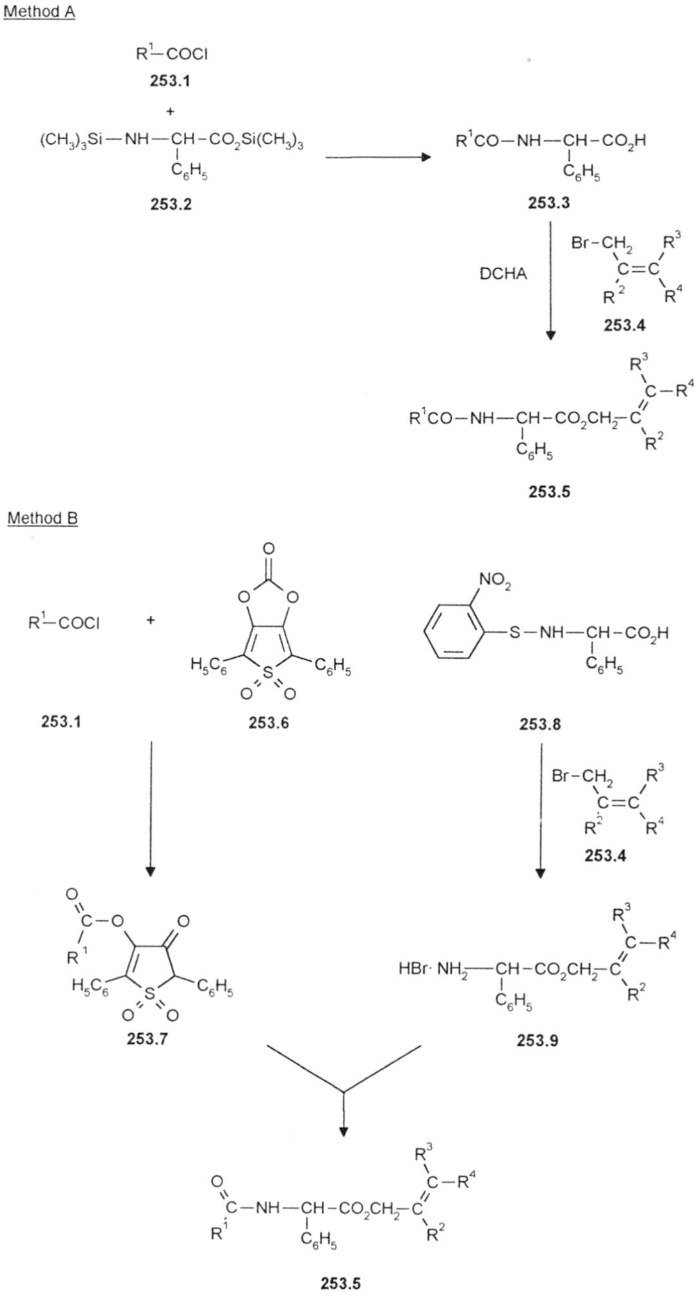

Method A

$R^1\text{—COCl}$

253.1

+

$(CH_3)_3Si\text{—NH—CH—CO}_2Si(CH_3)_3$
$\qquad\qquad\quad |$
$\qquad\qquad\quad C_6H_5$

253.2

$\longrightarrow$

$R^1CO\text{—NH—CH—CO}_2H$
$\qquad\qquad\quad |$
$\qquad\qquad\quad C_6H_5$

253.3

$\Big\downarrow$ DCHA

$\text{Br—CH}_2 \quad R^3$
$\qquad\quad C=C$
$\qquad R^2 \quad\quad R^4$

253.4

$R^1CO\text{—NH—CH—CO}_2CH_2\text{—C}$
$\qquad\qquad\quad | \qquad\qquad\qquad$
$\qquad\qquad\quad C_6H_5$

$\qquad\qquad\qquad\qquad R^3$
$\qquad\qquad\qquad\qquad C\text{—R}^4$
$\qquad\qquad\qquad\qquad R^2$

253.5

Method B

$R^1\text{—COCl}$ +

253.1

253.6

NO_2

—S—NH—CH—CO_2H
$\qquad\qquad\quad |$
$\qquad\qquad\quad C_6H_5$

253.8

$\Big\downarrow$

$\text{Br—CH}_2 \quad R^3$
$\qquad\quad C=C$
$\qquad R^2 \quad\quad R^4$

253.4

253.7

$\Big\downarrow$

$\text{HBr· NH}_2\text{—CH—CO}_2CH_2\text{—C}$
$\qquad\qquad\quad | \qquad\qquad\qquad$
$\qquad\qquad\quad C_6H_5$

$\qquad\qquad\qquad\qquad R^3$
$\qquad\qquad\qquad\qquad C\text{—R}^4$
$\qquad\qquad\qquad\qquad R^2$

253.9

$\searrow \qquad \swarrow$

$\Big\downarrow$

$\qquad\qquad O$
$\qquad\qquad ||$
$\qquad\quad C\text{—NH—CH—CO}_2CH_2\text{—C}$
$\quad R^1 \qquad\quad | \qquad\qquad\qquad$
$\qquad\qquad\quad C_6H_5$

$\qquad\qquad\qquad R^3$
$\qquad\qquad\qquad C\text{—R}^4$
$\qquad\qquad\qquad R^2$

253.5

FIGURE 1.253

TABLE I.42 N-Glyconoyl-D,L-2-Phenylglycin Allylesters

Entry	Compound	Yields (%)	Method
1	*N*-(2,3,4,5,6-Penta-*O*-acetyl-D-gluconoyl)-D,L-2-phenylglycin-3-methyl-2-butenylester	92	B
2	*N*-(2,3,4,5,6-Penta-*O*-acetyl-D-gluconoyl)-D,L-2-phenylglycin-geranylester	74	C
3	*N*-(2,3,4,5,6-Penta-*O*-acetyl-D-gluconoyl)-D,L-2-phenylglycin-farnesylester	89.5	B
4	*N*-(2,3,4,5,6-Penta-*O*-acetyl-D-gluconoyl)-D,L-2-phenylglycin-geranylgeranylester	83	A
5	*N*-(2,3,4,5,6-Penta-*O*-acetyl-D-gluconoyl)-D,L-2-phenylglycin-farnesylgeranylester	78	A
6	*N*-(2,3,4,5,6-Penta-*O*-acetyl-D-gluconoyl)-D,L-2-phenylglycin-solanesylester	61	A
7	(*E*)-*N*-(2,3,4,5,6-Penta-*O*-acetyl-D-gluconoyl)-D,L-2-phenylglycin-2,4-pentadienylester	73.5	A
8	(*E,E*)-*N*-(2,3,4,5,6-Penta-*O*-acetyl-D-gluconoyl)-D,L-2-phenylglycin-2,4-hexadienylester	84.5	A
9	(*E*)-*N*-(2,3,4,5,6-Penta-*O*-acetyl-D-gluconoyl)-D,L-2-phenylglycin-cinnamylester	92	B
10	*N*-(2,3,4,5,6-Penta-*O*-acetyl-D-gluconoyl)-D,L-2-phenylglycin-3-chlor-2-butenylester	92.5	A
11	*N*-(2,3,4,5,6-Penta-*O*-acetyl-D-galactonoyl)-D,L-2-phenylglycin-geranylgeranylester	86	A
12	*N*-(Methyl-2,3,4-tri-*O*-acetyl-β-D-galactopyranosiduronyl)-D,L-2-phenylglycin-3-methyl-2-butenylester	91	B
13	(*E*)-*N*-(Methyl-2,3,4-tri-*O*-acetyl-β-D-galactopyranosiduronyl)-D,L-2-phenylglycin-cinnamylester	86	B
14	(*E*)-*N*-(Methyl-2,3,4-tri-*O*-acetyl-β-D-galactopyranosiduronyl)-D,L-2-phenylglycin-2-(methoxycarbonyl)cinnamylester	96	B

is evaporated. Purification of the product is caried out by silicagel chromatography with 10:1, 20:1 and 30:1 carbon tetrachloride–acetone and 50:1 and 100:1 dichloromethane–acetone mixtures, as the eluants.

Method B (Acylation with active ester.) To a mixture of the active ester **253.7** (20 mmol) and the amino acid hydrobromide salt **253.9** (20 mmol) in dry dichloromethane (150 ml), triethylamine (4.5 g, 44 mmol) is added with external cooling on a water bath. The mixture is stirred at 25°C until the cherry-red color turns yellow (30 min to 10 h). The organic phase is washed with 20% aqueous citric acid and then with aqueous NaHCO$_3$ until the aqueous layer remains colorless. It is washed once again with aqueous citric acid and then with water, dried (MgSO$_4$), and concentrated under reduced pressure. The products are generally pure (NMR examination), but can be recrystallized or chromatographed (eluants: 10:1 carbon tetrachloride–acetone and 50:1 dichloromethane–acetone).

Method C (Coupling with DCC.) To a solution of the sugar-derived acid (20 mmol) in dry THF 4.55 g of DCC (22 mmol) is added and the mixture is stirred at 0°C for 1 h and then at 20°C for 1 h, followed by the dropwise addition of a solution of the D,L-2-phenylglycine allyl ester salt **253.9** (20 mmol) in THF (20 ml) and triethylamine (2.02 g, 20 mmol). The mixture is stirred at 20°C for 2 h and cooled to 0°C, the precipitated dicyclohexylurea is filtered off, and the filtrate is evaporated. The residue is dissolved in ethyl acetate and washed twice with saturated aqueous NaHCO$_3$ and 20% aqueous citric acid. The organic layer is dried (MgSO$_4$) and concentrated, and the residue is subjected to column chromatography (eluant: 40:1 dichloromethane–acetone).

Conversion of the prepared allyl *N*-glyconyl-*C*-phenylglycinates **253.5** into the corresponding 5(2*H*)-oxazolones **252.2** is carried out by simultaneous treatment with triphenylphosphine, hexachloroethane, and triethylamine in acetonitrile at 100°C for 1 h as shown in Figure 1.252, and the syrupy products are isolated by means of chromatography.

General procedure for the preparation of the 2-allyl-4-phenyl-5(2H)-oxazolones **252.2**[358]   In a pressure vessel are placed triphenylphosphine (5.26 g, 20 mmol), the allyl *N*-glyconyl-D,L-2-phenylglycinate **252.1** (10 mmol), and triethylamine (4.05 g, 40 mmol), and then hexachloroethane (4.74 g, 20 mmol) is added in one portion, and the vessel is closed and quickly heated to 95–100°C, and kept at this temperature for 1 h. After cooling the solvent is evaporated *in vacuo,* the residue is taken up in ether or THF (according to the solubility), and triethylamine hydrochloride, precipitated, is filtered off. The filtrate is concentrated under reduced pressure, and the residue is freed from triphenylphosphine oxide by column chromatography on a 6 × 10 cm filtering column (eluants: 60:1, 50:1, and 30:1 carbon tetrachloride–acetone and dichloromethane) to obtain the pure products as syrups or foams.

The yields of the previously synthesized[358] 2-allyl-4-phenyl-5(2*H*)-oxazolones are summarized in Table 1.43.

The prepared 5(2*H*)-oxazolones are cleaved, under mild conditions, into the β,γ-unsaturated ketones **252.3** with chromium(II)acetate. Then subsequent deacetylation gives rise to the chain-extended ketoses **252.4,** as described in the following general procedure.

General procedure for the preparation of ketopyranosides[358]   A mixture of the 5(2*H*)-oxazolone **252.2** (5 mmol) hypophosphorous acid (50% solution, 5.28 ml, 50 mmol, previously freed of oxygen), oxygen-free DMF (50 ml), and

TABLE 1.43 **2-Allyl-4-phenyl-5(2*H*)oxazolones**[358]

Entry	Compound	Yields (%)
1	2-(3-Methyl-2-butenyl)-2-(1,2,3,4,5-pentaacetoxy-D-*gluco*-pentyl)-4-phenyl-...	86
2	2-Geranyl-2-(1,2,3,4,5-pentaacetoxy-D-*gluco*-pentyl)-4-phenyl-...	81
3	2-Farnesyl-2-(1,2,3,4,5-pentaacetoxy-D-*gluco*-pentyl)-4-phenyl-...	72
4	2-Geranylgeranyl-2-(1,2,3,4,5-pentaacetoxy-D-*gluco*-pentyl)-4-phenyl-...	81
5	2-Farnesylgeranyl-2-(1,2,3,4,5-pentaacetoxy-D-*gluco*-pentyl)-4-phenyl-...	80
6	2-(1,2,3,4,5-Pentaacetoxy-D-*gluco*-pentyl)-4-phenyl-2-solanesyl-...	67
7[a]	(*E*)-2-(1,2,3,4,5-Pentaacetoxy-D-*gluco*-pentyl)-2-(2,4-pentadienyl)-4-phenyl-...	70.5
8[b]	(*E,E*)-2-(2,4-Hexadienyl)-2-(1,2,3,4,5-pentaacetoxy-D-*gluco*-pentyl)-4-phenyl-...	69.5
9	(*E*)-2-Cinnamyl-2-(1,2,3,4,5-pentaacetoxy-D-*gluco*-pentyl)-4-phenyl-...	76
10[c]	2-(3-Chlor-2-butenyl)-2-(1,2,3,4,5-pentaacetoxy-D-*gluco*-pentyl)-4-phenyl-...	73.5
11	2-Geranylgeranyl-2-(1,2,3,4,5-pentaacetoxy-D-*galacto*-pentyl)-4-phenyl-...	83
12	2-(3-Methyl-2-butenyl)-2-[(5*S*)-methyl-2,3,4-tri-*O*-acetyl-α-L-arabinopyranosid-5-yl]-4-phenyl-...	91
13	(*E*)-2-Cinnamyl-2-[(5*S*)-methyl-2,3,4-tri-*O*-acetyl-α-L-arabinopyranosid-5-yl]-4-phenyl-...	86
14	(*E*)-2-(2-Methoxycarbonyl)cinnamyl-2-[(5*S*)-methyl-2,3,4-tri-*O*-acetyl-α-L-arabinopyranosid-5-yl]-4-phenyl-...	85

[a]Contains 15–20% of the *Z*-compound.
[b]Contains 15–20% of the (*Z,E*)-compound.
[c](*E,Z*)-mixture.

chromium(II)acetate (4.25 g, 25 mmol; on larger-scale reactions gradual addition is required at 25°C) is stirred at 25°C for 10–30 min, and the progress of the reaction is monitored by TLC (the color change—red to green—does not necessarily mean completion of the reaction). Then, with external cooling on a water bath, 1 N HCl (50 ml) is added, and the precipitate is filtered off, and is thoroughly washed with a 1:1 DMF–ether mixture. The aqueous layer is extracted with ether (4 × 40 ml) and the combined organic phase is washed with 1 N HCl and water, dried (MgSO₄), and concentrated under reduced pressure to obtain the acetylated ketoses **252.3** (usually pure as checked by ¹H-NMR investigation). If removal of the precipitate by filtration is difficult, the mixture can be diluted with 250 ml of water, and filtration is neglected during workup. For further conversion the crude products are employed. The ketoses can be stored at 25°C for only a few days, but they are stable for several months at −20°C. The crude product **252.3** is dissolved in aqueous methanol (60 ml), Na₂CO₃ (5.3 g, 50 mmol) is added, and the mixture is stirred at 25°C until complete removal of the protecting groups (~5 h, TLC monitoring in 2:1:1 dichloromethane–acetone–*n*-butanol). Following filtration, the filtrate is stirred with a weak acidic ion-exchange resin (Amberlite IRC-50) for 10 min, filtered, and

TABLE 1.44   Chain-Extended Ketopyranosides[358,360]

Synthesized compound	Yield (%)	Optical rotation
(3-Methyl-2-butenyl) (2,3,4-tri-O-acetyl-β-L-lyxopyranosyl) ketone	95	+45.5 ($CHCl_3$)
(/E/-Methylcinnamyl) (2,3,4-tri-O-acetyl-β-L-lyxopyranosyl) ketone	78	+25.7 ($CHCl_3$)
(/E/-Cinnamyl) (2,3,4-tri-O-acetyl-β-L-lyxopyranosyl) ketone	82	+41.5 ($CHCl_3$)
1-C-(3-Methyl-2-butenyl)-α-D-glucose	70	+65.7 (CH_3OH)
1-C-Geranyl-α-D-glucose	67	+46.5 (CH_3OH)
1-C-Farnesyl-α-D-glucose	72	+40.4 (CH_3OH)
1-C-Geranylgeranyl-α-D-glucose	64	+31.2 (CH_3OH)
1-C-Farnesylgeranyl-α-D-glucose	65	+22.5 (CH_3OH)
1-C-Solanesyl-α-D-glucose	60	+8.3 (CH_3OH)
(E)-1-C-Cinnamyl-α-D-glucose	65.5	+28.5 (CH_3OH)
1-C-(3-Chloro-2-butenyl)-α-D-glucose	49.5	+58.6 (CH_6OH)
1-C-Geranylgeranyl-α-D-galactose	71	+14.1 (CH_3OH)

concentrated to furnish the foamy, syrupy product **252.4** (pure as checked by ^1H NMR). For further purification, column chromatography (resulting in ~20% loss of the material) with the following eluant systems can be applied: 20:1 to 10:1 dichloromethane–methanol or 1:1 dichloromethane–acetone. As an alternative, reversed–phase chromatography (on RP-8) is also suggested (eluant: 1:1 water–methanol). The longer-chain pyranosides usually cannot be completely freed of the contaminants.

Table 1.44 summarizes the data related to the spectroscopically pure (^1H-NMR) chain-extended ketopyranosides.

Tolstikov et al.[361,362] reported a special case of saccharide chain extension in which glyconoyl chlorides (**254.1**) are condensed with the heteroaryl-methyldiethylalanes **254.2** [e.g., diethyl-2-picolylalane, 2-(4,6-dimethyl)-pyrimidylmethyldiethylalane], giving rise to 1-C-heteroaryl ketosides (**254.3**), as shown in Figure 1.254.

1.2.7.8. Anhydroaldononitriles: The C-1 Chain-Extended Products of Cyclic Aldose Derivatives

Anhydroaldononitriles, widely used for the synthesis of *nucleosides* and *antibiotics,* as well as enzyme inhibitory substances, are most frequently prepared by means of one-carbon chain extension of cyclic aldose derivatives. The most important methods for the production of anhydroaldononitriles are briefly summarized[363] as follows:

> *A. Transformation of a glycosyl halide*
> 1. With sodium cyanide in various solvents
> 2. With mercuric(II) cyanide in acetonitrile or on melting

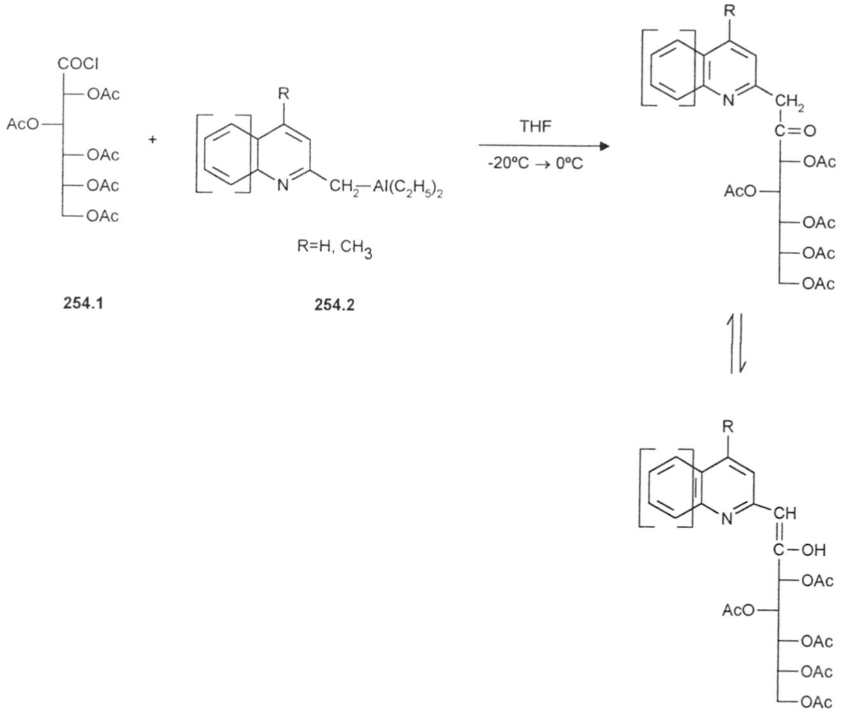

FIGURE 1.254

B. *Reaction of acylated, benzylated, or isopropylidenated sugars with trimethylsilyl cyanide*
   1. With Lewis acid catalysis
   2. From fluorosugars with diethylaluminium cyanide
   3. Ring opening of epoxides
C. *By the transformation of another functional groups*
   1. Reaction of anhydro-1-deoxy-1-nitroalditols with PCl$_3$ in pyridine
   2. Dehydration of anhydroaldonoamides with chloromethylene-dimethylformimidium chloride
D. *Isomerization of the 1,2-O-(1-cyanoethylidene) derivatives of aldoses*

Of these methodologies, the most frequently used one is method A,[364–369] which, as mentioned above, is based on the conversion of a glycosyl halide (preferably chloride or bromide) with mercuric(II)cyanide by fusing, or reacting in an appropriate solvent, such as acetonitrile or nitromethane.

It is well known that pyranosyl halides react with nucleophiles with neighboring-group participation, and thus it does not matter whether the starting halide is of α- or β-configuration and the formation of an intermediary *acetoxonium (dioxocarbenium) ion* (**255.2**) is postulated on cleavege of the halide ion, which is more stable than the reactive *oxocarbenium ion*[370] (**255.1**) (Fig. 1.255). For steric reasons, nucleophilic ring opening of the acetoxonium ion with cyanide results in the β-cyanide **255.3** (anhydroaldonitrile), and thus anchimeric assistance can be utilized for the stereoselective synthesis of the β-cyanide. However, competition by the reaction of the oxocarbenium ion **255.1** gives the α-cyanide (**255.4**) in a smaller quantity.

It has been shown[371,372] that in the presence of Lewis acids trimethylsilyl cyanide is a useful reagent for incorporation of a cyano group to position C-1 of furanoid and pyranoid 1-O-acyl-sugars.

Disadvantages of both of the two preceding methods are that the reagents are highly toxic, and that the reactions produce cyanide-containing heavy-metal waste materials. In addition, the C-2 acyl substituent, neighboring to the anomeric center, directs a 1,2-*trans*-stereoselectivity by anchimeric assistance, and thus the configuration of C-2 predominantly determines the anomeric configuration of the cyanide produced in the reaction; the other epimeric nitrile appears as the by-product.

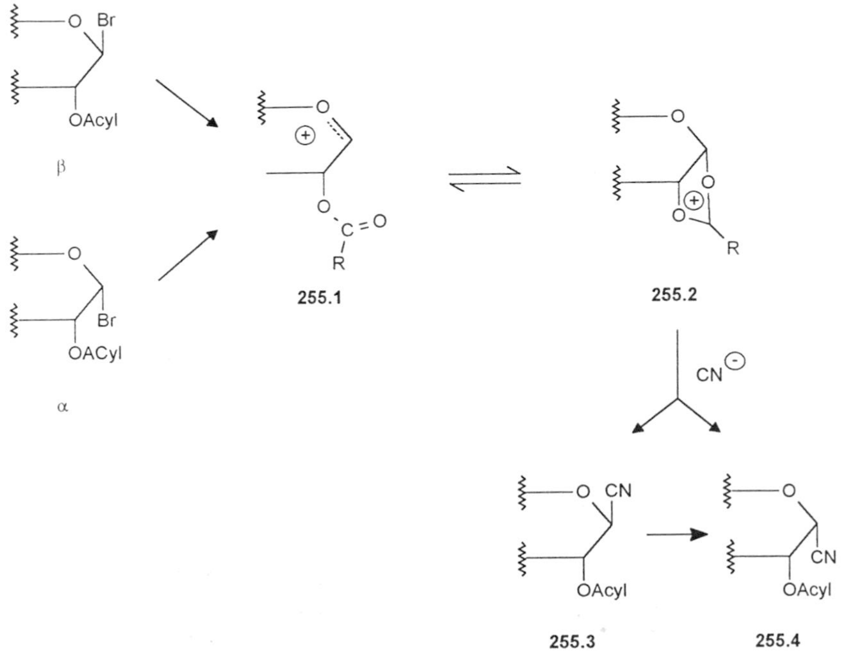

FIGURE 1.255

When employing method A, 1,2-O-(1-cyanoalkylidene)-derivatives may also be formed, sometimes as the major products,[373] so chromatographic separation is necessary in almost each case.

A novel procedure of Wehrli and Schaer[374] for the synthesis and conversion of anhydro-1-deoxy-1-nitroalditols into the corresponding cyanides by reduction of the nitromethyl function of a suitable educt with PCl_3 in pyridine, allows the preparation of 1,2-cis-cyanides as well, which are not available by either method A, B, or C.

Still other reports[375] describe the rearrangement of 1,2-O-(1-cyanoethylidene)acetals, produced in kinetically controlled cyanide-displacement reactions, into anhydroaldononitriles on treatment with hard Lewis acids such as boron trifluoride etherate (see Lay et al.[376]) (Fig. 1.256).

An advantage of method B-2 is that a base-stable protecting group (e.g., isopropylidene) is also compatible with the applied conditions. At the same time, besides the target anhydroaldononitriles (**257.1** and **257.2**), the two epimeric isonitriles (**257.3** and **257.4**) may also be produced[377] (Fig. 1.257).

Although Italian authors[376] have reported that spiro-epoxides can be stereoselectively split with tetrabutylammonium cyanide, method B-3 appears to be still incompletely elaborated.

Table 1.45 lists data[378–398] for previously synthesized, O-substituted anhydroaldononitriles.

The following procedures represent easily reproducible methods for practical execution of the three methods (A–C) discussed above.

Method A-2: preparation of 3,4,5-Tri-O-acetyl-2,6-anhydro-D-glucononitrile[367]
To a stirred mixture of powdered mercuric cyanide (12.6 g, 0.05 mol) in dry acetoni-

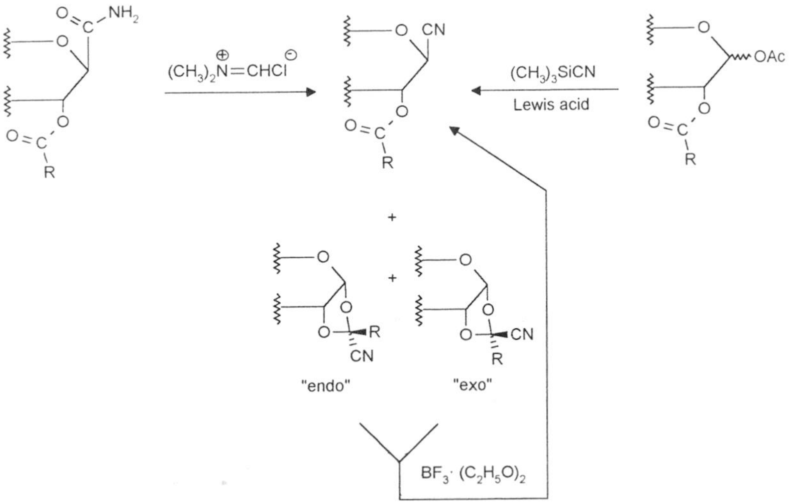

FIGURE 1.256

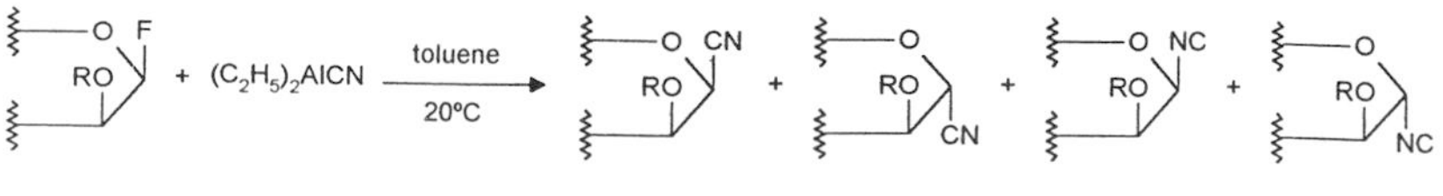

257.1 257.2 257.3 257.4

FIGURE I.257

trile (150 ml) 2,3,4-tri-O-acetyl-α-D-xylopyranosyl bromide (33.9 g, 0.1 mol) is added. After the exothermal reaction is finished (~1.5 h), the mixture is evaporated to dryness, the residue is taken up with chloroform, the insoluble mercuric salts are filtered off, and the filtrate is washed with 1 N aqueous potassium bromide (3 × 50 ml) and dried (Na_2SO_4). The residual syrup obtained on evaporation is treated with methanol (40 ml) and maintained at 0°C. The precipitated crystalline material (12.97 g, 47%) is recrystallized first from 12 parts of carbon tetrachloride and then from 5 parts of benzene to obtain the pure product with m.p. 128–133°C (shrinking), $[\alpha]_D^{21}$ −57.9 (c = 2.4 in chloroform).

Method B-1: preparation of 2,3-Anhydro-3,4,6-tri-O-benzoyl-β-D-allononitrile[399] A stirred solution of 1-O-acetyl-2,3,5-tri-O-benzoyl-β-D-ribofuranose (40.3 g, 80 mmol), 1,2-dichloroethane (100 ml), and cyanotrimethylsilane (15.84 g, 160 mmol) is treated in one portion via a syringe with anhydrous stannic chloride (20.8 g, 9.33 ml, 80 mmol). The darkening solution is stirred for 2 min, then poured into saturated aqueous $NaHCO_3$ (800 ml), and stirred for 5 min (pH 7). Chloroform (1 liter) is added and the resulting emulsion is filtered through Celite. The organic layer is separated, dried ($MgSO_4$), and evaporated under reduced pressure (15 torr, 40°C) to a light-orange syrup, which is crystallized from ethanol (by decolorizing with charcoal) to furnish the title product (30 g from two crops, 80%) as long white needles, m.p. 77–78°C after drying at 0.5 torr, 60°C for 2 h, $[\alpha]_D^{25}$ +24.4 (c = 0.5 in chloroform).

In methanolic ammonia the tribenzoate, produced in method B-1 can be easily converted into the respective 6-O-benzoate.[400]

5-O-Benzoyl-D-ribofuranosyl cyanide[400] A solution of 2,3,5-tri-O-benzoyl-D-ribofuranosyl cyanide (3.5 g, 7.4 mmol) in methanolic ammonia (150 ml, saturated at 5°C) is allowed to stand at 5°C for 3 h and evaporated to dryness under reduced pressure. The residue is triturated with ligroin (2 × 75 ml) and then with benzene (3 × 100 ml), followed by chloroform (100 ml). The combined organic extract is evaporated to dryness to give the crude product, which is purified by high-pressure column chromatography (eluant: 1 : 1 benzene–ethyl acetate). The pure product is isolated as a light–sensitive solid: yield 710 mg (36%), m.p. 118°C.

Method C-1: general procedure for the reduction of anhydroalditols with phosphorous trichloride[383] 1 Mmol of the acetylated anhydroalditol is dissolved in pyridine (3 ml), cooled to 0°C, and phosphorous(III)chloride (1.1 mmol) is added. The mixture is allowed to slowly warm up to ambient temperature, the progress of the reaction is monitored by TLC, and when no starting material is present the reaction is quenched by pouring into cold 1 N HCl. After stirring for 30 min, the mixture is extracted with chloroform, the organic phase is dried and concentrated.

Method C-2: general procedure for the dehydration of anhydroaldonoamides with methylenedimethylformamidium chloride[401] To a stirred solution of N,N-dimethyl-

TABLE 1.45   Physical Data for Synthesized O-Substituted Anhydroaldononitriles

Name, formula	Method	Yield (%)	$[\alpha]_D$ (CHCl₃)	M.p. (°C)	Ref(s).
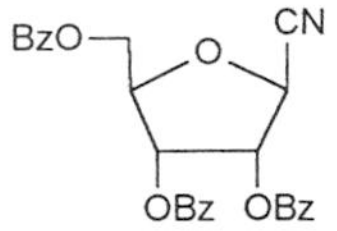 2,5-anhydro-3,4,6-tri-O-benzoyl-D-allononitrile	A-2	88	+23.8	78.5–80	378
	B-1	86	+24	78–80	371
	B-1	45	—	—	372
	B-1	38	—	—	379
	B-1	43	+23.8	80–81	380
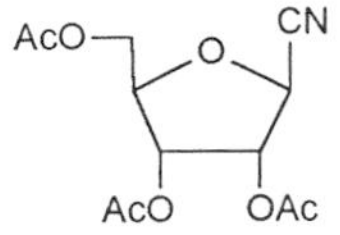 3,4,6-tri-O-acetyl-2,5-anhydro-D-allononitrile	B-1	59	+6	Syrup	371
	B-1	64	—	Syrup	372
	B-1	98	—	Oil	381
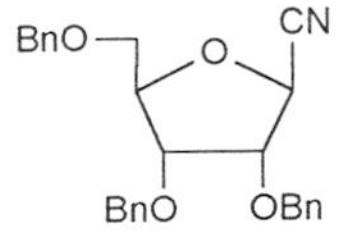 2,5-anhydro-3,4,6-tri-O-benzyl-D-allononitrile	B-1	40	+12	Syrup	371
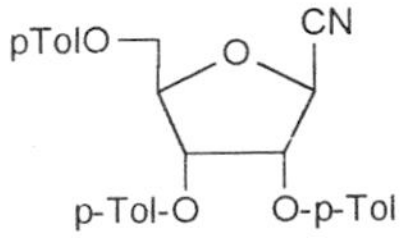 2,5-anhydro-3,4,6-tri-O-(p-tolyl)-D-allononitrile	A-2	60	+30	95–100	382
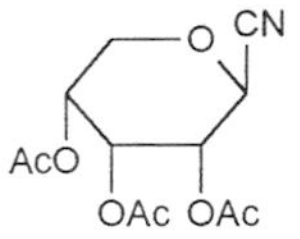 3,4,5-tri-O-acetyl-2,6-anhydro-D-allononitrile	C-1	72	−26.8	Oil	383
	B-1	78	−18	Syrup	371
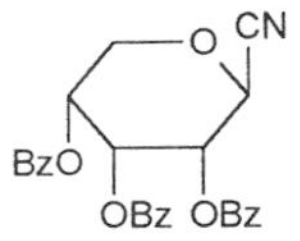 2,6-anhydro-3,4,5-tri-O-benzoyl-D-allononitrile	A-2	71	−76.4	170–171	384
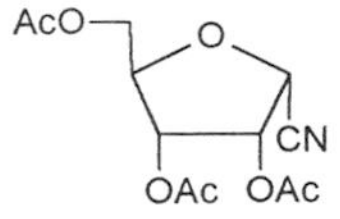 3,4,6-tri-O-acetyl-2,5-anhydro-D-altrononitrile	D-1	35	—	—	372
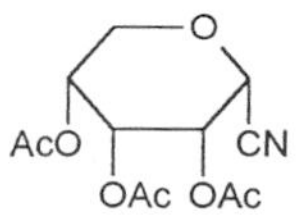 3,4,5-tri-O-acetyl-2,6-anhydro-D-altrononitrile	C-1	74	+93.8	72–73	383

(*continues*)

TABLE I.45 *(continued)*

Name, formula	Method	Yield (%)	$[\alpha]_D$ (CHCl$_3$)	M.p. (°C)	Ref(s).
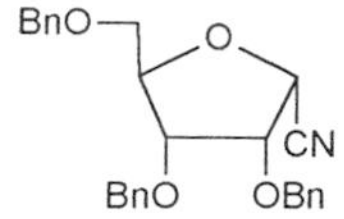 2,5-anhydro-3,4,6-tri-O-benzyl-D-altrononitrile	B-1	45	+70	Syrup	371 (cf. 202)
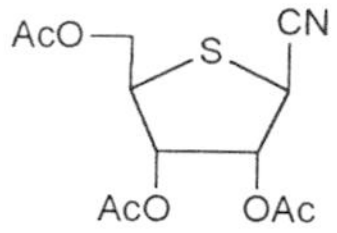 3,4,6-tri-O-acetyl-2,5-anhydro-5-thio-D-allononitrile	B-1	79.8	+136.6	Oil	385
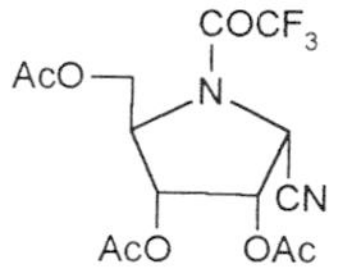 3,4,6-tri-O-acetyl-2,5-epimino-5-trifluoracetamido-D-altrononitrile	B-1	—	—	—	386
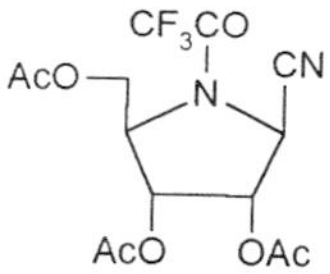 3,4,6-tri-O-acetyl-2,5-epimino-5-trifluoracetamido-D-allononitrile	B-1	52	+16.3	Oil	386
  2,5-anhydro-3,4,6-tri-O-benzoyl-D-gulononitrile	B-1 B-1	90 35	— +54.1	106–107 98	385 380
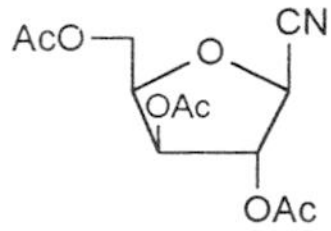 3,4,6-tri-O-acetyl-2,5-anhydro-D-gulononitrile	C-1	47	−10.6	Syrup	383
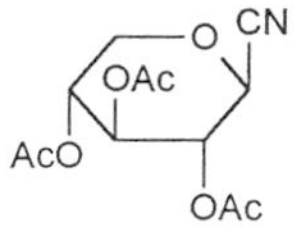 3,4,5-tri-O-acetyl-2,6-anhydro-D-gulononitrile	C-1 A-2	72 47	−57.9 −57.9	132–133 128–133	383 367

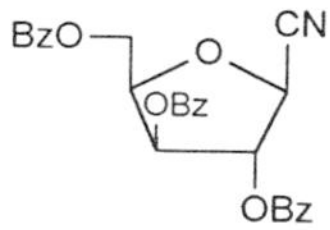

(continues)

TABLE I.45 (continued)

Name, formula	Method	Yield (%)	$[\alpha]_D$ (CHCl₃)	M.p. (°C)	Ref(s).
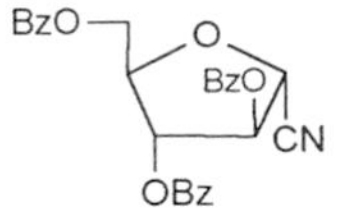 2,5-anhydro-3,4,6-tri-O-benzoyl-D-mannononitrile	A-2	57	−23.89 (acetone)	80	387
	A-2	86	−104 (acetone)	69–70	380
	B-1	48	−21.6	73–74	380
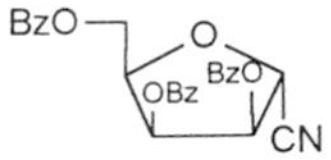 2,5-anhydro-3,4,6-tri-O-benzoyl-D-talononitrile	B-1	41	+33	104–105	380
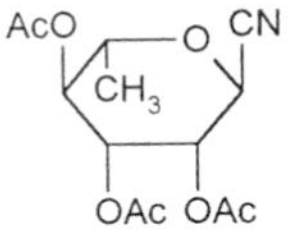 3,4,5-tri-O-acetyl-2,6-anhydro-7-deoxy-L-*glycero*-L-*talo*-heptononitrile	A-2	5	—	87	388
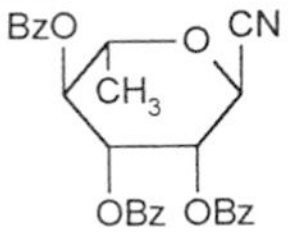 3,4,5-tri-O-benzoyl-2,6-anhydro-7-deoxy-L-*glycero*-L-*talo*-heptononitrile	A-1	58	+177	80	389
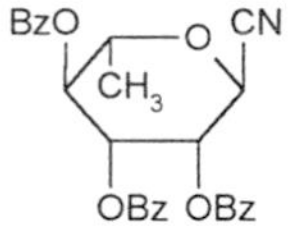 2,6-anhydro-3,4,5-tri-O-benzoyl-7-deoxy-L-*glycero*-L-*galacto*-heptononitrile	A-1	13	+219	85	389
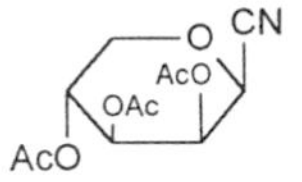 3,4,5-tri-O-acetyl-2,6-anhydro-D-galactononitrile	C-1	75	−125.2	Syrup	383
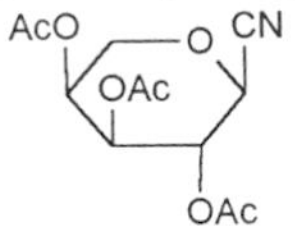 3,4,5-tri-O-acetyl-2,6-anhydro-L-mannononitrile	C-1	69	+6.5	131	383
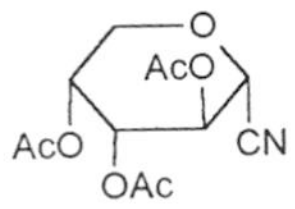 3,4,5-tri-O-acetyl-2,6-anhydro-D-mannononitrile	B-1	67	−5	137–139	371

(*continues*)

TABLE 1.45   (*continued*)

Name, formula	Method	Yield (%)	$[\alpha]_D$ (CHCl₃)	M.p. (°C)	Ref(s).
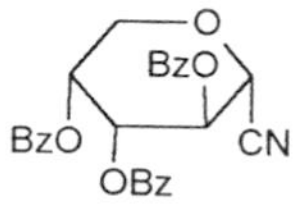 2,6-anhydro-3,4,5-tri-O-benzoyl-D-mannononitrile	B-1	84	−159	184–185	371
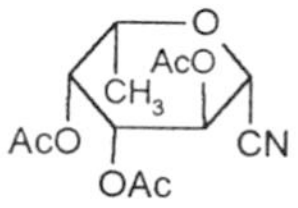 3,4,5-tri-O-acetyl-2,6-anhydro-7-deoxy-L-*glycero*-D-*manno*-heptononitrile	A-2	71	−33.1	124–125	369
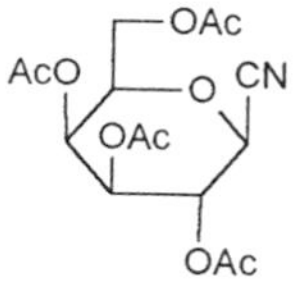 3,4,5,7-tetra-O-acetyl-2,6-anhydro-D-*glycero*-L-*manno*-heptononitrile	C-1	78	+32.1	167–168	383
	A-2	25	+37.2	168–169	390
	A-2	79	+35.2	169–170	369
	B-1	71	+35.0	168–169	371
	A-2	—	+37.2	168–169	366
	D	67	—	169–171	375
	B-1	67	—	170–171	375
		(from β-penta-O-acetate)			
	B-1	77	—	170–171	375
		(from α-penta-O-acetate)			
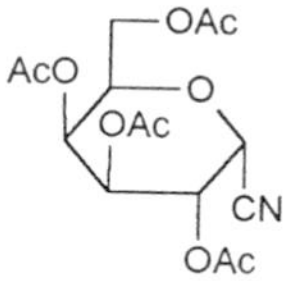 3,4,5,7-tetra-O-acetyl-2,6-anhydro-D-*glycero*-L-*gluco*-heptononitrile	D	1.9	+131	93–94	375
	A-2	2.9	—	93–94	375
	C-2	87	+120	97	391
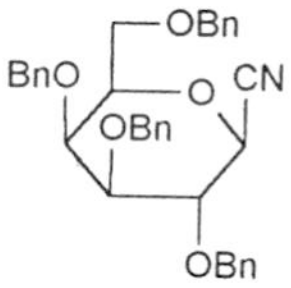 2,6-anhydro-3,4,5,7-tetra-O-benzyl-D-*glycero*-L-*manno*-heptononitrile	B-1	40	+12.7	85–86	392
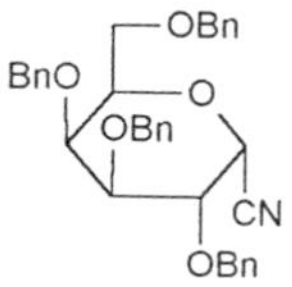 2,6-anhydro-3,4,5,7-tetra-O-benzyl-D-*glycero*-L-*gluco*-heptononitrile	B-1	40	+29.6	84–85	392

(*continues*)

TABLE I.45   (continued)

Name, formula	Method	Yield (%)	$[\alpha]_D$ (CHCl₃)	M.p. (°C)	Ref(s).
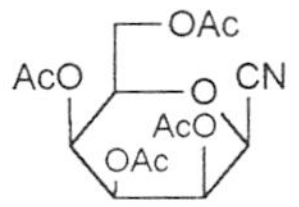 3,4,5,7-tetra-O-acetyl-2,6-anhydro-D-glycero-L-altro-heptononitrile	C-2	81	−2	118	391
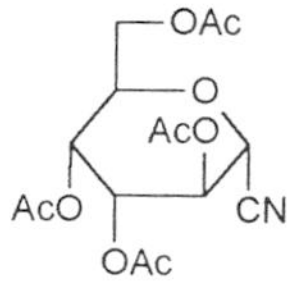 3,4,5,7-tetra-O-acetyl-2,6-anhydro-D-glycero-D-manno-heptononitrile	B-1	62	+43.1	46–47	383
 3,4,5,7-tetra-O-acetyl-2,6-anhydro-D-glycero-L-gulo-heptononitrile	A-1 B-1 D A-2 B-1 A-2 C-1 B-1	30 35 6.5 30 18 18 73 45	— +38.1 — — — +10.1 +9.4 +9.4	— — 112–114 114–115 113–115 114–115 113–114 113–114	368,393 372 376 375 375 378 383 383
 3,4,5,7-tetra-O-acetyl-2,6-anhydro-D-glycero-L-ido-heptononitrile	A-2 B-1 C-2	0.9–2.5 43 67	+125.5 +119.1 +76	111–112 — 112	375 372 391
 2,6-anhydro-3,4,5,7-tetra-O-benzyl-D-glycero-D-gulo-heptononitrile	B-1 B-1	40 38	+29 +24.5	76–78 85.5–86.5	392 394[a]
 2,6-anhydro-3,4,5,7-tetra-O-benzyl-D-glycero-D-ido-heptononitrile	B-1 B-2 D B-1	50 — — 45	+37 +31.5 +36.3 +28.7	Syrup Syrup Syrup Oil	392 395 396 394[a]

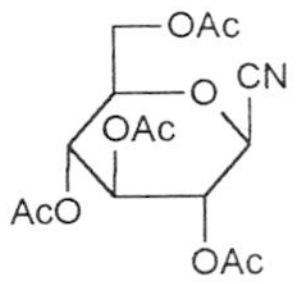

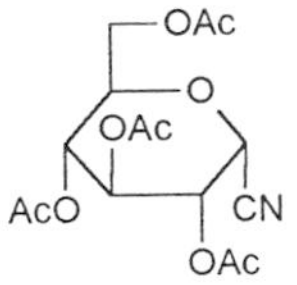

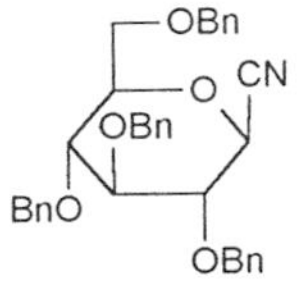

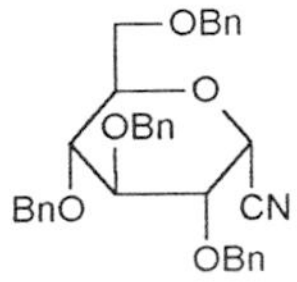

(continues)

TABLE I.45 (continued)

Name, formula	Method	Yield (%)	$[\alpha]_D$ (CHCl$_3$)	M.p. (°C)	Ref(s).
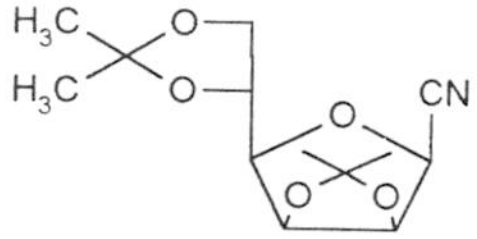 2,6-anhydro-3,4:5,7-di-O-isopropylidene-D-*glycero*-D-*galacto*-heptononitrile	E	—	−36.4	Oil	377
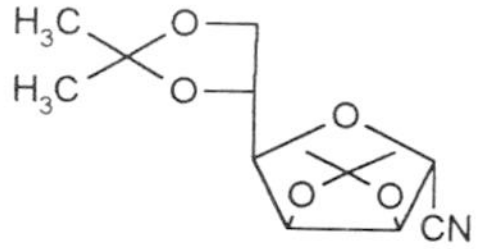 2,5-anhydro-3,4:6,7-di-O-isopropylidene-D-*glycero*-D-*talo*-heptononitrile	E	7	—	—	377
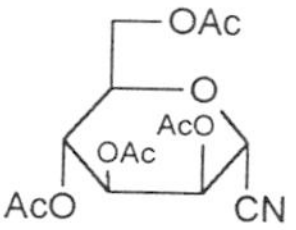 3,4,5,7-tetra-O-acetyl-2,6-anhydro-D-*glycero*-D-*talo*-heptononitrile	B-1	51	+27.8	91.5–92.5	385
	B-1	56	—	57–59	375
	D	33	—	58–60	375
	A-2	49	—	57–60	375
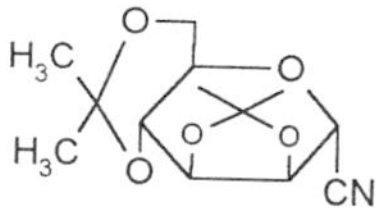 2,6-anhydro-3,4:5,7-di-O-isopropylidene-D-*glycero*-D-*talo*-heptononitrile	B-2	7	−55.2	148–149	377
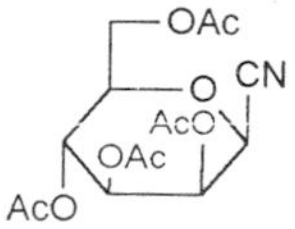 3,4,5,7-tetra-O-acetyl-2,6-anhydro-D-*glycero*-D-*galacto*-heptononitrile	A-2	15.7	—	143–144	387
	C-2	75	−28	149–150	391
	D	3.8	—	142–144	375
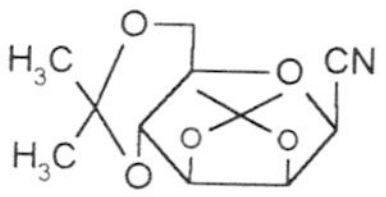 2,6-anhydro-3,4:5,7-di-O-isopropylidene-D-*glycero*-D-*galacto*-heptononitrile	D	—	—	—	Cf. 377
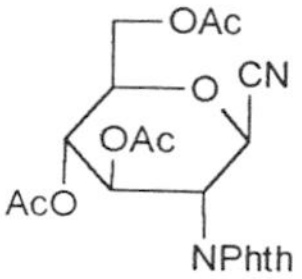 3,4,5,7-tetra-O-acetyl-2,6-anhydro-D-*glycero*-D-*galacto*-heptononitrile	B-1	68	—	176–178	375,387
	C-2	12	+78	178	391

(continues)

TABLE I.45   (*continued*)

Name, formula	Method	Yield (%)	$[\alpha]_D$ (CHCl$_3$)	M.p. (°C)	Ref(s).
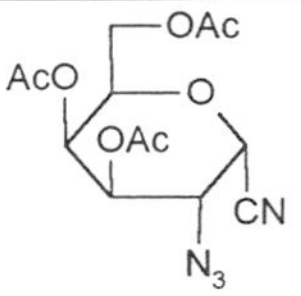 4,5,7-tri-O-acetyl-2,6-anhydro-3-azido-3-deoxy-D-*glycero*-L-*manno*-heptononitrile	A-2	18.5	+83.1	107–108	397
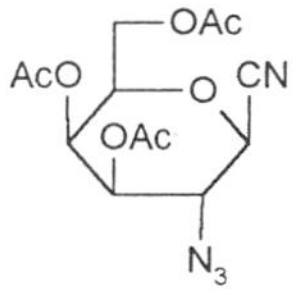 4,5,7-tri-O-acetyl-2,6-anhydro-3-azido-3-deoxy-D-*glycero*-L-*gluco*-heptononitrile	A-2	9.6	+3.8	128.5–129.5	397
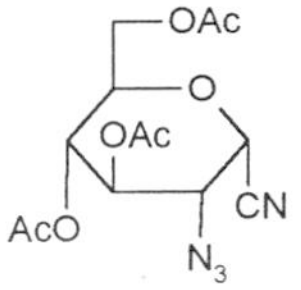 4,5,7-tri-O-acetyl-2,6-anhydro-3-azido-3-deoxy-D-*glycero*-D-*ido*-heptononitrile	A-2	18.5	+85.3	Oil	397
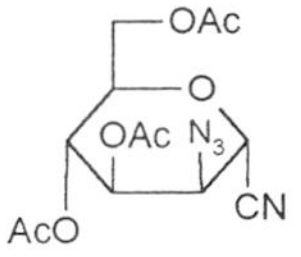 4,5,7-tri-O-acetyl-2,6-anhydro-3-azido-3-deoxy-D-*glycero*-D-*galacto*-heptononitrile	A-2	28	+67.9	Oil	397
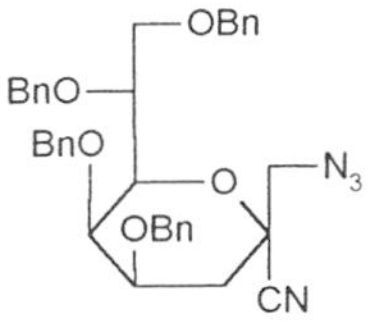 1-azido-4,5,7,8-tetra-O-benzyl-1,3-dideoxy-α-D-manno-2-octulopyranonitrile	B-1	81	+10.2	Syrup	398

[a]The authors gave the configuration of the two compounds transposed.

formamide (0.19 ml, 2.4 mmol) in dry acetonitrile (5 ml) is added oxalyl chloride (0.2 ml, 2.3 mmol) at 0°C (white precipitate appears), followed by the addition of a solution of 3,4,5,7-tetra-*O*-acetyl-2,6-anhydro-D-heptonamide (0.75 g, 2 mmol) in acetonitrile (2 ml). The reaction mixture becomes homogeneous on complete addition of the solution of the sugar. Dry pyridine (0.36 ml, 4.4 mmol) is added, and stirring is continued for 15 min. The mixture is then diluted with dichloromethane

(60 ml), washed with saturated brine containing 1% of HCl (2 × 20 ml), dried (MgSO$_4$), and evaporated, to yield a colorless syrup, which is chromatographed on a Silicagel 60 column (Merck, 230–400 mesh) with 2 : 1 light petroleum–ethyl acetate.

In the procedure described by Mio et al.,[402] (see also Witczak[403] and Mukaiyama *et al.*[404]) which employs method B-1, chain extension of 5-*O*-benzyl-1,2:3,4-di-*O*-isopropylidene-D-psicofuranose (**258.1**) is carried out with trimethysilyl cyanide (Fig. 1.258), and both of the epimeric aldononitriles (**258.2** and **258.3**) could be isolated.

> *C-Glycosylation of 5-O-benzyl-1,2:3,4-di-O-isopropylidene-D-psicofuranose (258.1) with trimethylsilyl cyanide,*[402] *using trimethysilyl triflate as a Lewis acid*   To a −20°C solution of the sugar **258.1** (3.99 g, 11.4 mmol) in dichloromethane (50 ml) are added trimethylsilyl cyanide (4.6 ml, 34 mmol) and trimethylsilyl triflate (3.3 ml, 17 mmol). The resulting solution is stirred for 2 h at −20°C, and then it is poured into saturated aqueous ammonium chloride. The aqueous layer is extracted with ether, and the combined organic phase is dried over Na$_2$SO$_4$, filtered and concentrated to a colorless syrup, which is chromatographed on silicagel (eluant: 1 : 3 to 1 : 1 ethyl acetate–hexane) to give a 4 : 1 mixture of the α- and β-aldononitriles **258.2** and **258.3** (2.9 g, 81%), along with 0.4 g (16%) of 5-benzyloxymethyl-2-formylfuran. For **258.3**: [α]$_D^{25}$ −29.7 (*c* = 1.72 in chloroform).

In another ascending syntheses with trimethylsilyl cyanide, various additional catalysts have been employed[405–407] and diastereocontrolled alkylation of 4-cyanofuranose sugars have also been reported.[408]

Related chain extension of unsaturated sugars, such as glycals and hydroxyglycals, has emerged as an important tool for obtaining anhydroal-

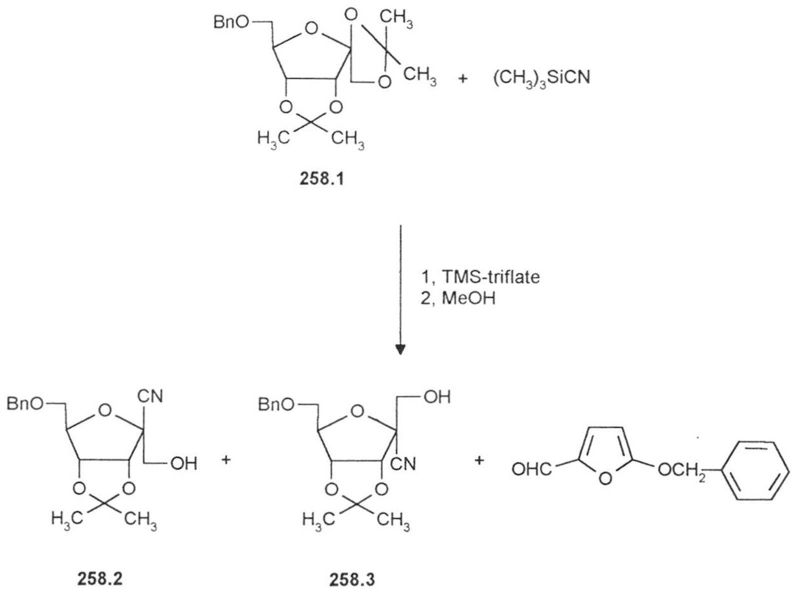

258.1

1, TMS-triflate
2, MeOH

258.2   **258.3**

FIGURE 1.258

dononitriles. Reaction of 3,4,6-tri-*O*-acetyl-D-glucal (**259.1**) and 3,4,6-tri-*O*-acetyl-D-galactal (**259.2**) with trimethylsilyl cyanide in solvents such as nitromethane or methylene chloride and in the presence of boron trifluoride etherate afforded[409,410] two 2,3-unsaturated pyranosyl cyanide α- and β anomers (**259.3** and **259.4,** respectively) in good to excellent yields (Fig. 1.259). As in other reactions of glycals with nucleophiles, the attachment of the cyano group to the anomeric position of the glycal occurred, together with the elimination of the 3-acetoxy group and migration of the 1,2-double bond to the 2,3-position. The following two procedures, reported by de las Heras[409] and Grynkiewicz[410] for the chain extension of the glucal **259.1** using this methodology, are presented.

Reaction of 3,4,6-tri-O-acetyl-D-glucal (259.1) with trimethylsilyl cyanide.

Procedure A[409] To a solution of **259.1** (1 g, 3.67 mmol) in dry nitromethane (15 ml), trimethylsilyl cyanide (1 ml) is added dropwise, the mixture is stirred for 15 min at room temperature, and then boron trifluoride etherate (4 drops) is added. Stirring is continued until the sugar disappears. Following the usual workup, the residue is purified by repeated chromatography on preparative TCL plates (eluant: 1 : 4 ethyl acetate–hexane) to furnish two compounds. From the faster-moving band, 0.5 g (57%) of 4,6-di-*O*-acetyl-2,3-dideoxy-α-D-*erythro*-hex-2-enopyranosyl cyanide (**259.3**) is isolated as a white solid, m.p. 90–91°C (from water), $[\alpha]_D$ −14.6 ($c = 1$ in chloroform). The slower-running band afforded 0.368 g (42%) of the β-cyanide **259.4** as a syrup, which decomposed on standing, $[\alpha]_D$ +197.5 ($c = 1$ in chloroform).

Procedure B[410] To a stirred mixture of the glucal **259.1** (300 mg, 1.1 mmol) and trimethylsilyl cyanide (120 mg, 1.2 mmol) in dichloromethane (5 ml) 1 drop of boron trifluoride etherate is added at room temperature. After 5 min the starting material is absent (TLC in 1 : 1 ethyl acetate–hexane). The mixture is diluted with ether (30 ml), successively washed with aqueous NaHCO₃ (5 ml) and water (10 ml), dried (MgSO₄), and filtered through a 1-cm layer of silicagel. Evaporation of

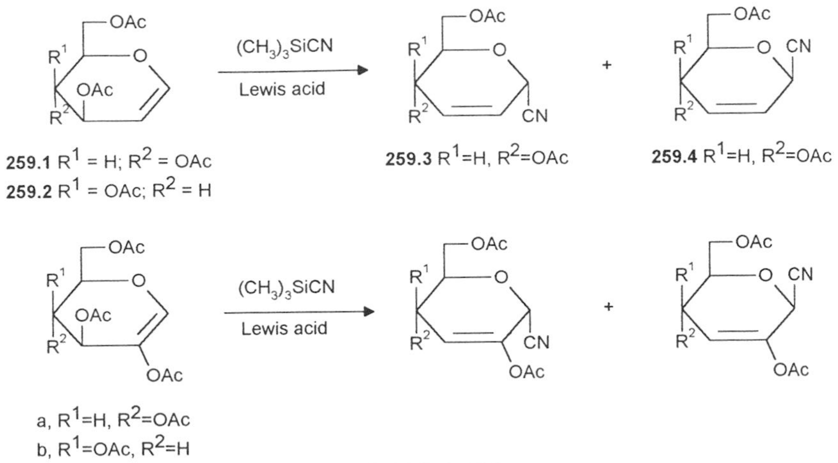

259.1 R¹ = H; R² = OAc
259.2 R¹ = OAc; R² = H

259.3 R¹=H, R²=OAc

259.4 R¹=H, R²=OAc

a, R¹=H, R²=OAc
b, R¹=OAc, R²=H

FIGURE I.259

the filtrate gives 208 mg (79%) of the α-cyanide **259.3**, $[\alpha]_D$ −16 (c = 1 in dichloromethane).

It has been reported[411,412] that cyanides (**260.1**) can be coupled with acetylene compounds (**260.2**) in the presence of π-(cyclopentadienyl)cobalt-1,5-cyclooctadiene [CpCo(COD)] in an interesting ascending procedure resulting in *cyclic products,* such as **260.3** (Fig. 1.260). It is important to emphasize that in the case of optically active nitriles, the product remains optically active[411] under the quite vigorous conditions (8 atm, 140°C). Therefore, it was very interesting to examine this reaction of the simplest chiral cyanosugar, 2,3-O-isopropylidene-D-glyceronitrile (**260.5**) derived from D-glyceraldehyde. It was found[411] that the conversion proceeded with 98% enantiomeric excess, and furnished 81% of the pyridyl–dioxolane **260.6**.

(S)-4-(2-Pyridyl)-2,2-dimethyl-1,3-dioxolane (260.6)[411] π-(Cyclopentadienyl)-cobalt-1,5-cyclooctadiene (250 mg) is placed in a stainless-steel autoclave (200 ml), and the autoclave is rocked and the air is removed (0.1 atm). A solution of (S)-4-cyano-2,2-dimethyl-1,3-dioxolane (**260.5**; 4.7 g, 37 mmol) in toluene (30 ml) is introduced by suction. The reaction vessel is pressurized with acetylene up to 14 atm and then rocked and heated at 120°C. After 24 h the autoclave is cooled and the residual gas released. The reaction mixture is filtered, the solvent is evaporated, and the residue is purified by chromatography on silicagel (eluant: 7 : 3 petroleum ether–ethyl acetate) to give the pure title compound **260.6** (5.6 g, 85%), b.p. 70°C (0.3 mmHg), $[\alpha]_D^{25}$ +93.6 (c = 2.9 in chloroform).

Preparation of the catalyst π-(cyclopentadienyl)cobalt-1,5-cyclooctadiene [CpCo-(COD)][412] Cyclopentadiene (7.35 g, 111.35 mmol) and 1,5-cyclooctadiene (29.2 g, 270.3 mmol) are added to a 1.0 M solution of triethylaluminium in hexane (400 ml). The mixture is vigorously stirred under argon at 0 to −10°C and cobalt(III)-acetylacetonate (38.5 g, 108.1 mmol) is added in small portions (over ∼2 h). A vigorous gas evolution occurs. After the additon of the cobalt salt, the mixture is allowed to warm to room temperature over 2 h and then filtered through a glass frit, and the filtrate is cooled to −50°C. The orange–brown product crystallized out

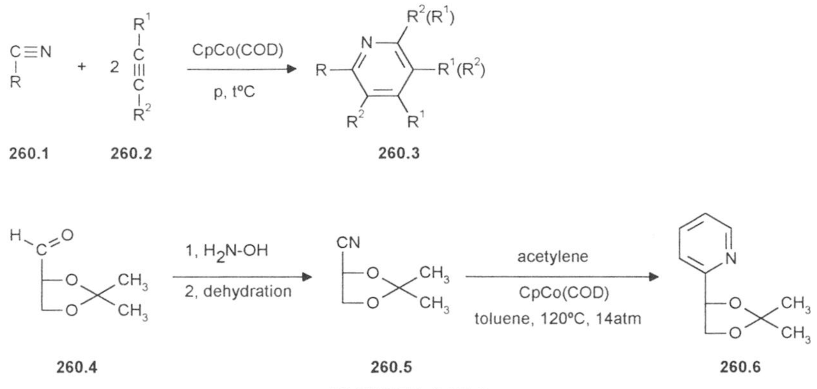

FIGURE 1.260

in 10 h, the supernatant liquid is removed, and the crystals are washed with pentane (2 × 50 ml) at −50°C and dried *in vacuo* to give 19.2 g (77%) of [CpCo(COD)].

A thermal conversion of isonitriles into nitriles can also be effected,[377,396,402] but under the conditions applied, ring closure to 1,6-anhydro derivatives may also occur, such as in the case of 2,3,4,6-tetra-*O*-benzyl-α-D-glucopyranosyl isonitrile.[396]

1.2.7.9. Chain Extension of Saccharides Starting with Acetylene Derivatives

The synthesis of the acetylene derivatives of sugars has become an extensively studied field (see Sections 1.2.7.1.1, 1.2.7.7 and 1.2.7.10), allowing the preparation *higher-carbon sugars* with the well-known coupling reactions of acetylene chemistry. As a suitable acetylene–sugar 3,6-di-*O*-acetyl-4,5:7,8-di-*O*-isopropylidene-1-octyn-D-*glycero*-D-*galacto*-3,4,5,6,7,8-hexaol (**261.1**) (see Fig. 1.261) can be transformed into the polyhydroxylated C_{16}-diyne **261.2** by oxidative dimerization with copper(I)chloride. Reduction of **261.2** with $LiAlH_4$ gives the dimeric alkene **261.3**, to be converted into the saturated alcohol; (2*R*,3*R*,4*R*,5*R*,6*S*,11*S*,12*R*,13*R*,14*R*,15*R*)-1,2,3,4,5,6,11,12,13,14,15,16-dodecahydroxyhexadecane (**261.4**) on catalytic hydrogenation and Zemplén *O*-deacylation with 91% yield.[413]

> *Oxidative dimerization*[413] *of the acetylene–sugar **261.1*** Air is bubbled through a stirred mixture of the octyne **261.1** and 1 g of freshly prepared cuprous chloride in 10 ml of pyridine and 80 ml of methanol. After air is passed through the solution for 3 h at 30–35°C, 100 ml of saturated aqueous ammonium chloride is added. The mixture is extracted with ether, and the organic phase is washed with dilute aqueous sodium carbonate and dried ($MgSO_4$). The solvent is removed by evaporation, and the residue is crystallized from benzene–petroleum ether (b.p. 30–60°C) to give 9.3 g (93%) diyne **261.2**, m.p. 147°C.

By applying an essentially similar strategy, Horton[414] synthesized 1,4-bis(1,2:3,4-di-*O*-isopropylidene-D-*glycero*-D-*galacto*-hexopyranos-6-yl)-1,3-butadiyne (**262.2**) from the acetylenic sugar **262.1** (see Fig. 1.262). Reduction of the product then gave the corresponding *trans,trans*-1,3-butadiene. Tronchet and Bonen[415] reported on the coupling of another saccharide acetylene derivatives, including 6-bromo-5,6-dideoxy-1,2-*O*-isopropylidene-3-*O*-methyl-α-D-*xylo*-hex-5-yno-1,4-furanose with copper(I) chloride, as a very useful reagent.

With the goal of synthesizing a *6-deoxypentadecose*, Polish authors[416] have described the formation of diastereoisomeric alkynols (**263.2** and **263.3**) in the condensation reaction of 6-*O*-benzyl-7,8-dideoxy-1,2:3,4-di-*O*-isopropylidene-D-*glycero*-α-D-*galacto*-oct-7-ynopyranose (**263.1**) with methyl 2,3,4-tri-*O*-benzyl-6-deoxy-β-D-*galacto*-heptodialdo-1,5-pyranose (**262.4**) in the presence of lithium diisopropylamide (Fig. 1.263).

> *Preparation of the (1S)- and (1R)-isomers (**263.2** and **263.3**) of 3-(6-O-benzyl-1,2:3,4-di-O-isopropylidene-α-D-galactopyranos-6-yl)-1-hydroxy-1-(methyl 2,3,4-tri-*

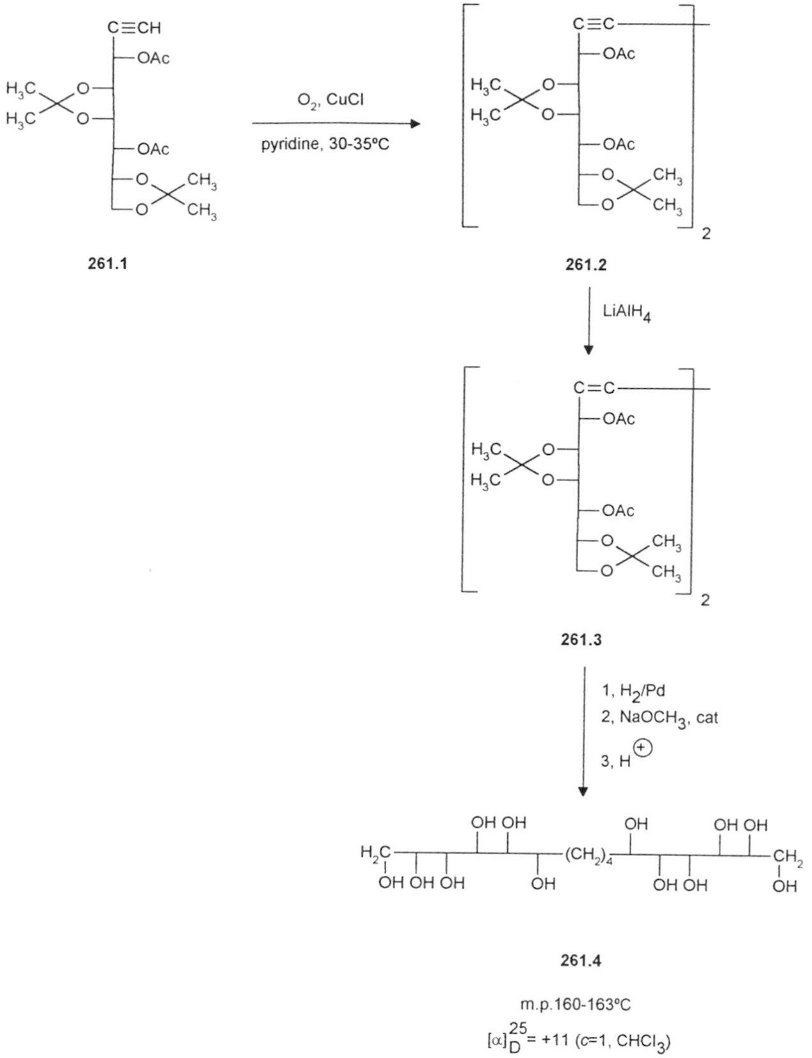

FIGURE I.261

O-benzyl-6-deoxy-β-D-galactopyranosid-6-yl)-propyne[416]   To 2 mmol of lithium di-isopropylamide (generated from 0.28 ml of diisopropylamine and 1.26 ml of 1.6 M butyllithium in 2 ml of THF at 0°C for 15 min) is added a solution of the acetylenic sugar **263.1** (750 mg, 2 mmol) in tetrahydrofuran (3 ml). After stirring (45 min) at 0°C, the mixture becomes reddish, a solution of **263.4** (700 mg, 1.49 mmol) in THF (5 ml) is added slowly, and the mixture is stirred at 0°C for 15 min. TLC (9:1 toluene–acetone) shows the disappearance of the starting sugars and the formation of a more polar product, which is isolated by column chromatography (95:5 toluene–acetone). The product (610 mg, 48%) contains the diastereoisomeric alcohols **263.2** and **263.3** in a ~2:1 ratio, which can be differentiated by means of TLC (2:1 light petroleum–ethyl acetate, two developments). Column chromatography (eluant:

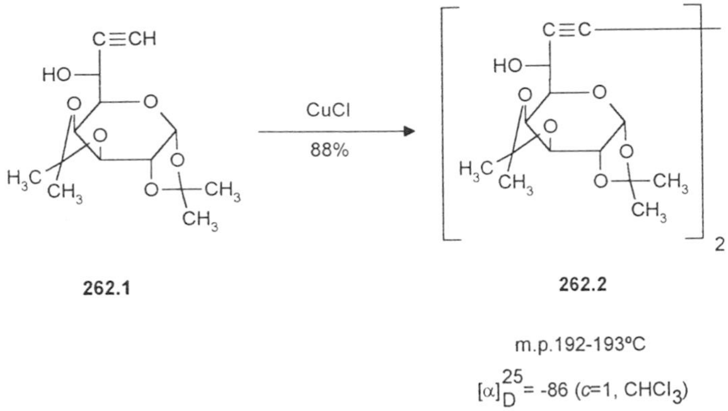

CuCl
88%
m.p.192-193°C
[α]$^{25}_{D}$ = -86 (c=1, CHCl$_3$)

262.1

262.2

FIGURE 1.262

85:15 light petroleum–ethyl acetate) gave, first, the (1*S*)-isomer **263.2** (106 mg), as a syrup, $[\alpha]_D$ −36 (c = 4.3 in chloroform). Eluted second is **263.2** contaminated with the (1*R*)-isomer **263.3** (308 mg). Eluted third is the pure (1*R*)-diastereoisomer **263.3** (150 mg), isolated as a syrup, $[\alpha]_D$ −34 (c = 1.7 in chloroform).

The "cross-coupling" of two diversely substituted acetylenic sugars (Fig. 1.264) has been worked out by the Vasella group[346] by conducting the reaction under optimum conditions to facilitate preferential cross-coupling, and to reduce the formation of homodimers from the starting acetylene derivatives. The following procedure demonstrates the effectiveness of the coupling agent in related condensations.

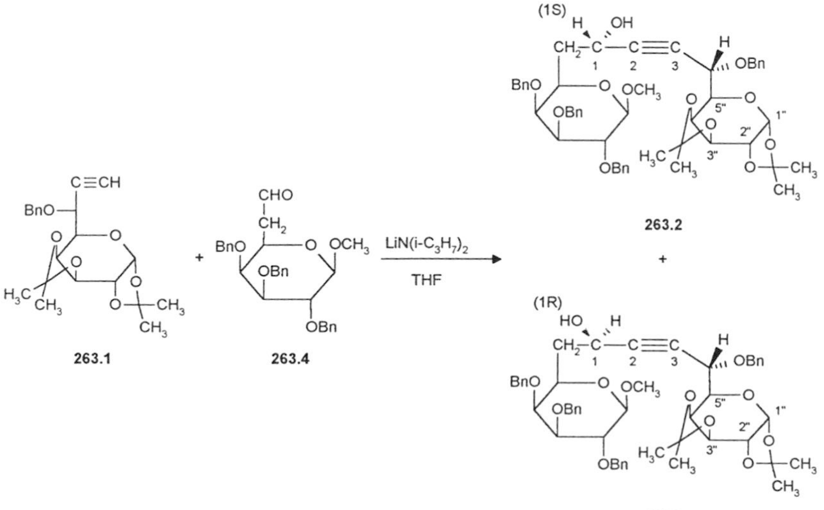

LiN(i-C$_3$H$_7$)$_2$
THF

263.1 263.4 263.2 263.3

FIGURE 1.263

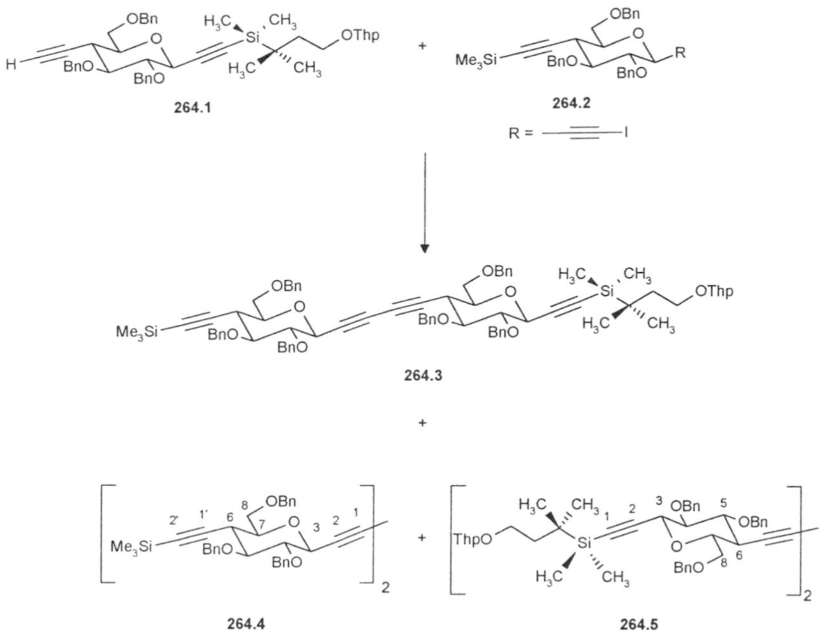

FIGURE I.264

Cross-coupling[346] *of 3,7-anhydro-4,5,8-tri-O-benzyl-1,1,2,2-tetradehydro-1,2,6-trideoxy-1-C-{[1,1-dimethyl-3-(tetrahydro-2H-pyran-2-yloxy)propyl]dimethylsilyl}-6-C-ethynyl-D-glycero-D-gulo-octitol* (**264.1**) *with 3,7-anhydro-4,5,8-tri-O-benzyl-1,1,2,2-tetrahydro-1,2,6-trideoxy-1-iodo-6-C-[(trimethylsilyl)ethynyl]-D-glycero-D-gulo-octitol* (**264.2**) At room temperature a mixture of [Pd$_2$(dba)$_3$] (dba = dibenzylideneacetone, 1.38 mg, 3.0 μmol), CuI (0.48 mg, 2.5 μmol), and tri(fur-2-yl)phosphine (1.39 mg, 6.0 μmol) is treated with a solution of **264.1** (87 mg, 0.125 mmol) and **264.2** (83 mg, 0.125 mmol) in Me$_2$SO (2.5 ml; distilled and degassed). The resulting brown solution is stirred for 5 min, treated with 1,2,6,6-pentamethylpiperidine (64 μl, 0.354 mmol), stirred for 3 h, diluted with ether, treated with 0.1 N aqueous HCl (3 ml) and worked up in the usual manner. Fast column chromatography (eluant: 92:8 → 9:1 hexane–ethyl acetate) of the crude product gives 117 mg (76%) of the cross-coupled D-*glycero*-D-*gulo*-octitol **264.3**, as a syrup, $R_f = 0.34$ (97:3 benzene–THF), together with the two homodimers **264.4** (syrup), $R_f = 0.64$ (97:3 benzene–THF), [α]$_D^{25}$ −74.6 (c = 0.77 in chloroform) and **264.5** (syrup), $R_f = 0.26$ (97:3 benzene–THF).

1.2.7.10. Chain Extension of Halogenide Compounds

For obtaining nonbranched, chain-extended saccharides with related ascending syntheses two types of halosugars are applied: aldosyl halides and terminal halosugars (see Section 1.2.7.1). Some examples for the application of the latter starting materials were discussed in Sections 1.2.2 and

1.2.6.1.1. In addition, 6-deoxy-6-iodohexopyranosides, such as the galactose derivative **265.1,** were subjected[417] to transformation into the corresponding Grignard compounds (Fig. 1.265), but these transformations resulted, mostly, in dimerization (e.g., **265.2**) together with the production of the 6-deoxysugar (e.g., **265.3**).

Formation of the dimeric product **265.2** has been also observed in other cases; the yield of this compound is as high as 31% even in short reaction times.[418] The same reaction of 2,2-dimethyl-4-(iodomethyl)-1,3-dioxolane gives rise to 70% of the dideoxyhexitol; 1,2:5,6-di-O-isopropylidene-hexane-1,2,5,6-tetraol.

A modern reagent, magnesium–graphite, introduced to the carbohydrate field by Csuk *et al.*,[419,420] also induces the preceding Wurtz-type reaction, allowing—for example—the simple preparation[420] of bis(methyl 6-deoxy-2,3,4-tri-O-methyl-α-D-glucopyranosid-6-yl) from the corresponding 6-deoxy-6-iodo derivative.

> *Preparation of bis(methyl 6-deoxy-2,3,4-tri-O-methyl-α-D-glucopyranoside-6-yl)*[420] A solution of methyl 6-deoxy-6-iodo-2,3,4-tri-O-methyl-α-D-glucopyranoside (1.04 g, 3 mmol) in dry THF (20 ml) is added dropwise to a suspension of magnesium–graphite (7.65 mmol) in THF (25 ml) at ambient temperature under argon, and the mixture is kept under reflux for 3 h. After cooling, filtration, washing of insolubles with THF (50 ml), and evaporation, the residue is subjected to column chromatography (eluant: 3 : 1 toluene–ethyl acetate) to give the title product (0.45 g, 68%), m.p. 86–87°C, $[\alpha]_D^{20}$ +158 (c = 1.1 in chloroform) and 50 mg (8%) of methyl 6-deoxy-2,3,4-tri-O-methyl-α-D-glucopyranoside.

The reaction of alanes with acyl chlorides[361,362] has been discussed in Section 1.2.7.7. A report[421] in this field describes the utilization of hexenyl-diisobutylalanes for the chain extension of 2,3,4,6-tetra-O-benzyl-α,β-D-glucopyranosyl fluoride.

The conversion of glycosyl bromides with acetylenic stannanes was first reported by Williams,[422] and this procedure was also employed by Veyriéres.[423] When glycosyl halides were treated with 2 eq of tri-n-butyltin acetylides in the presence of $ZnCl_2$ (2 eq) in carbon tetrachloride at room temperature, the corresponding alkynes were formed, and this reaction

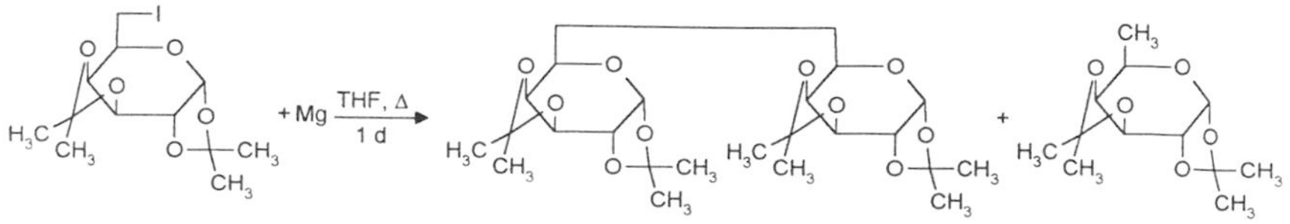

265.1   **265.2**   **265.3**

6,7-dideoxy-1,2:3,4:9,10:11,12-tetra-O-isopropylidene-α-L-*galacto*-
α-D-*galacto*-dodeca-1,12-dialdo-1,5:8,12-dipyranose
m.p. 107-109°C, $[\alpha]_D^{25}$ = -77 (c = 1, $CHCl_3$)

FIGURE I.265

proceeded with net retention of stereochemistry. It was found that the solvent is crucial for this reaction, no reaction was observed in aprotic solvents such as toluene or THF, and carbon tetrachloride was found to be best for such couplings. A general procedure for the reaction shown in Figure 1.266 is as follows.

> *General procedure for the preparation of the C-acetylene derivatives of D-glucose and D-ribose*[422]   To a stirred solution of 1-O-(p-nitrobenzoyl)-2,3,4,6-tetra-O-ben-zyl-α-D-glucopyranose (1 eq) or 1-O-(p-nitrobenzoyl)-2,3,5-tri-O-benzyl-β-D-ribo-furanose (1 eq) in dry dichloromethane is bubbled anhydrous HBr for 3–5 min at room temperature. The precipitated p-nitrobenzoic acid is removed by filtration, and the filtrate is evaporated to dryness to afford a syrup, which is directly used for the next reaction without purification. The syrup is dissolved in dry carbon tetrachloride, the solution is heated to reflux, to which the corresponding tri-n-butyltin acetylide (1.05 eq) and a solution of ZnCl$_2$ in THF (0.5 eq) were added. The resulting mixture is allowed to reflux for 20–30 min, cooled, evaporated, and separated on preparative TLC (eluant: 3 : 1 hexane–ethyl acetate).

According to Veyriéres,[423] the yield of the coupling reaction is higher in the presence of AgBF$_4$; the ZnCl$_2$-catalyzed reaction proceeded with 40% yield, whereas application of AgBF$_4$ resulted in 85% (α : β ratio = 9 : 1).

> *Coupling of 6-O-acetyl-2,3,4-tri-O-benzyl-α-D-glucopyranosyl chloride with 1-tributylstannyloct-1-yne*[423]   A solution of the glucosyl chloride and the stannane (5 eq; this large excess of stannane is required to obtain a clean and total conversion) in dry 1,2-dichloroethane is stirred for 30 min at room temperature under argon in the presence of activated powdered 3Å molecular sieves, then cooled at −30°C. Dry AgBF$_4$ (2 eq) is added and the mixture is gently warmed up to 0°C and then left overnight at this temperature. After the usual workup, the crude product is deacetylated (in 10 : 4 : 1 methanol–water–triethylamine; overnight at room temperature). TLC (in 7 : 3 hexane–ethyl acetate) allowed good resolution between traces of the β anomer (R_f = 0.49) and the major product **266.1** (α anomer). Tributylstannyl-oct-1-yne is prepared by treatment of oct-1-yne with n-butyllithium in THF followed by reaction with Bu$_3$SnCl for 1 h under reflux.

Recently glycosyl fluorides have become popular starting materials for the preparation[424] of *aryl-C-glycosidic compounds.* In Figure 1.267 the Cp$_2$HfCl$_2$/AgClO$_4$–mediated coupling of the fluorosugar **267.1** with the phenol **267.2** is shown to give rise to a single regioisomer (**267.3**), and no formation of *O*-glycoside is observed. Related *C*-glycosidic compounds can be derived with rather poor yields from deoxysugars, except when diaryl

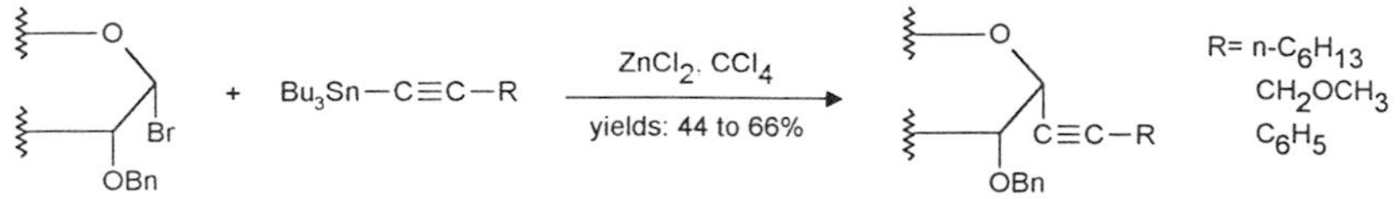

266.1

FIGURE 1.266

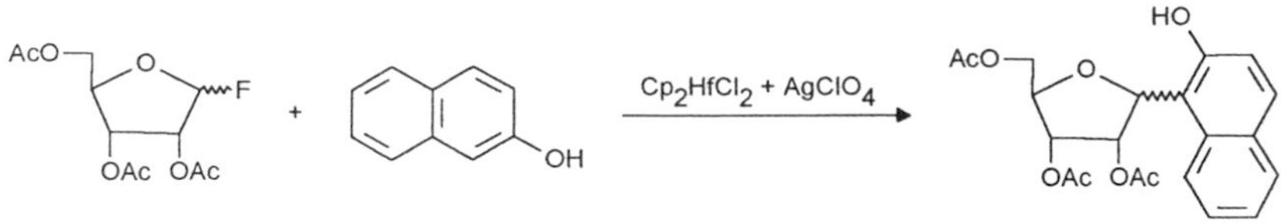

FIGURE I.267

cadmium and 3,5-di-O-(p-toluenesulfonyl)-α-D-*erythro*-pentofuranosyl chloride are applied, as suggested by Kool.[425]

For the formation of transition-metal anomeric complexes[426,427] anomeric halosugars serve, again, as the starting materials. DeShong et al.[427] have employed manganase chemistry for carbon–carbon bond formation at the anomeric center (Fig. 1.268): glycosyl bromides were treated with sodium pentacarbonyl manganate [NaMn(CO)₅] to give the anomeric pentacarbonylmanganese complexes, which were then induced to undergo migratory insertion to furnish the acylmanganese complexes. Cleavage of these latters with alkoxide or thiolate produced the ester derivatives. Alternatively, the manganese complex underwent high-pressure–induced sequential insertion of CO and methyl acrylate to afford manganacycles. Subsequent photodemetalation resulted in the formation of C-glycosyl compounds. The stereoselectivity and the yield of the condensation of sodium pentacarbonylmanganate(I) with glycosyl halides can be influenced by the addition of bromide salts to the reaction mixtures.

Because of the captodative character of the anomeric center, glycosyl halides are known to readily participate in radical reactions to result in the extension of the carbon chain, and addition of anomeric radicals to alkenes is one of the most interesting methods for the *synthesis of* C-*glycosidic compounds.*[428,429] An easy formation of a radical at the anomeric center is due to its captodative character–generated by the presence of both an electron acceptor and an electron-donating group (the ring oxygen and the halogen atom, respectively). The nucleophilic radical readily reacts with the alkene, carrying an electron-donating function (acrylates or acrylonitrile), to result in a chain-extended product. However, no simple rule for the stereochemical outcome of such ascending procedures can be drawn because of the differences in the stability of the anomeric radicals.

In the ascending syntheses based on radical reactions, generation of the radicals is effected by various methods; those most frequently employed are photochemical reactions, thermal transformations with azobisisobutyronitrile, or degradation of certain complexes. The resulting radicals then give C-glycosidic compounds with electron-deficient olefins as shown schematically in Figure 1.269.

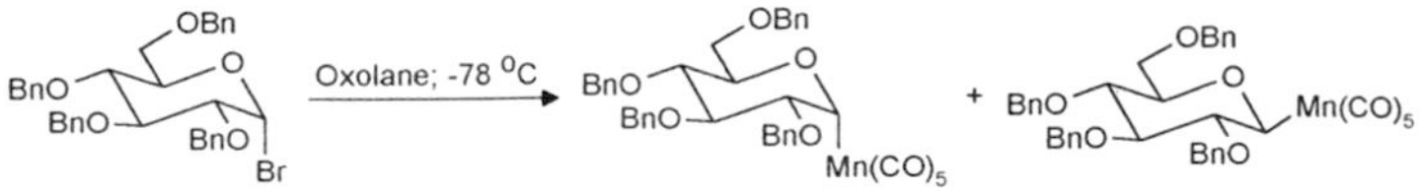

Reaction of NaMn(CO)$_5$ with compound **268.1**

Conditions	Yield (%)	**268.2** : **268.3** ratio
NaMn(CO)$_5$	75	0 : 100
NaMn(CO)$_5$, 3 eq Bu$_4$N$^+$Br$^-$	50	3 : 2
NaMn(CO)$_5$, 3 eq KBr	90	0 : 100

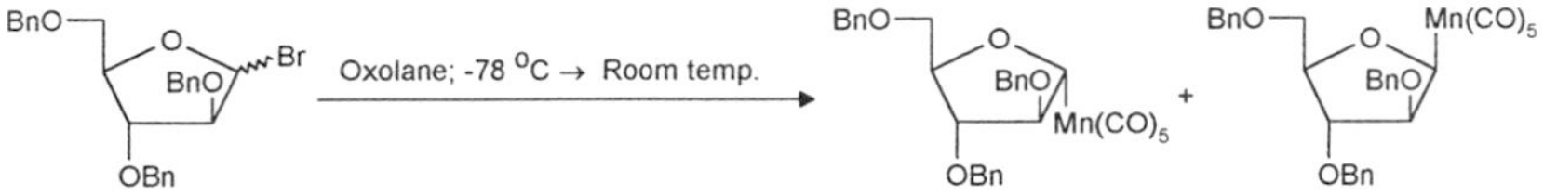

Reaction of NaMn(CO)$_5$ with compound **268.4**

Conditions	Yield (%)	**268.5** : **268.6** ratio
NaMn(CO)$_5$	70	2 : 1
NaMn(CO)$_5$, 3 eq Bu$_4$N$^+$Br$^-$	55	> 98 : 2
NaMn(CO)$_5$, 3 eq KBr	90	2 : 1

FIGURE 1.268a

Many procedures of this kind have been reported during the past decades, and because of severe space limits, only those that provide methodologically well-established results are discussed in the present section.

As reported by Keck *et al.*,[430,431] thermal formation of radicals can be induced when allyl-tri-*n*-butylstannane (**270.2**) and 2,2′-azobisisobutyronitrile (AIBN) are used, to prepare (Fig. 1.270) anhydrononitol derivatives, such as **270.3**, available from 2,3,4,6-tetra-*O*-acetyl-α-D-glucopyranosyl bromide (**270.1**) (see Section 1.2.7.1.3).

A similar radical conversion of 2,3:4,5-di-*O*-isopropylidene-D-mannofuranosyl chloride has also been reported,[431] and terminal 6-bromosugars, such as **271.1**, also readily undergo analogous radical substitution to furnish **271.2** (Fig. 1.271).

Tributyltin hydride and unsaturated compounds, such as acrylonitrile, methyl vinylketone, ethylenecarbonate, and fumarodinitrile, can also be employed for related radical reactions. In these cases "higher adducts" are also produced[376,432,433] in addition to the monoaddition products, and anhydroalditols, as by-products, often appear. For example, Figure 1.271 shows the formation[434] of the two nonononitriles **271.4** and **271.5** from 2,3,4,6-tetra-*O*-acetyl-α-D-glucopyranosyl bromide (**271.3**).

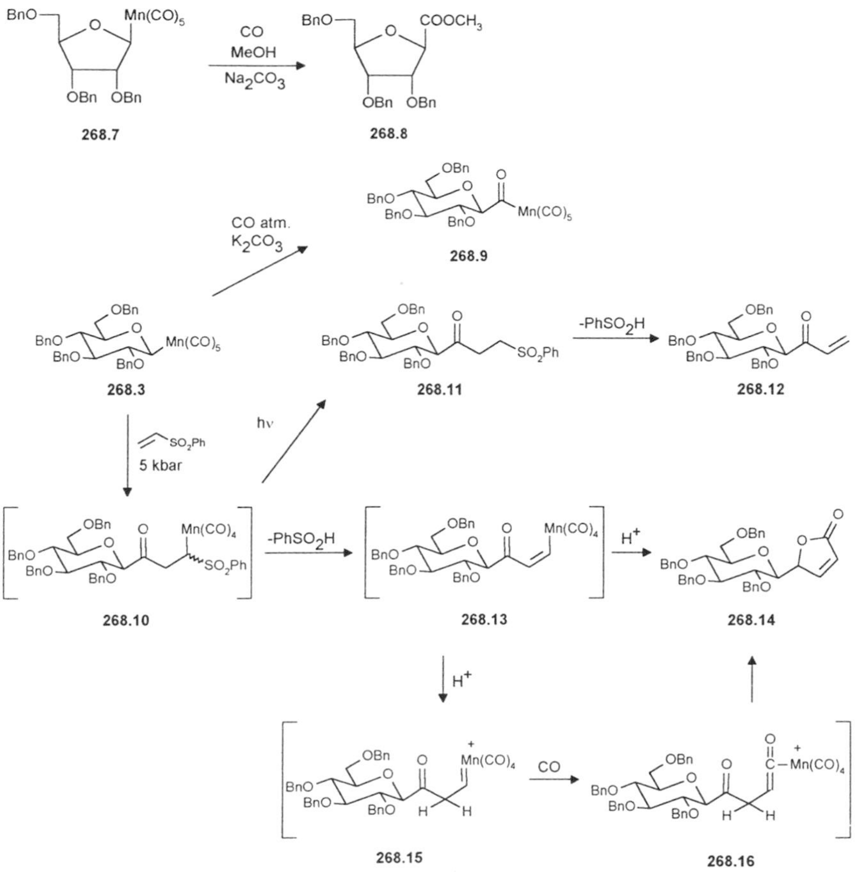

FIGURE 1.268b

5,6,7,9-Tetra-O-acetyl-4,8-anhydro-2,3-dideoxy-D-glycero-D-ido-nonononitrile (271.4) and the corresponding D-glycero-D-gulo-isomer (271.5)[434] (Photolytic initiation.) To a solution of the bromide **271.3** (20.6 g, 50 mmol) in dry ether (100 ml) at reflux is added, under nitrogen, acrylonitrile (13.5 g, 250 mmol) and tributyltin hydride (16 g, 55 mmol). After a 4-h irradiation with a sun lamp or a high-pressure mercury lamp, the precipitate is filtered off, further acrylonitrile (6.6 g, 120 mmol) and tributyltin hydride (5.8 g, 20 mmol) are added, and the filtrate is again irradiated. When the starting bromide **(271.3)** has completely reacted, the cold mixture is filtered and the combined precipitates give 8.6 g (45%) of **271.4** after crystallization from ether. The filtrates are evaporated, the residue is dissolved in acetonitrile (50 ml), and the solution is extracted with pentane (3 × 50 ml). The acetonitrile solution is evaporated, and the resulting syrup is flash-chromatographed on silicagel (eluant: 1 : 1 ethyl acetate–hexane). The first fraction contained tetra-O-acetyl-1,5-anhydro-D-glucitol (3.5 g, 21%); the second, pure **271.5** (950 mg, 5%), and the third, an additional crop of **271.4** (2.5 g, 13%). The **271.4** : **271.5** ratio for the mixture before workup was 93 : 7 [gas–liquid partition chromatography (GLPC)]. In a synthesis with **271.3** (2 g) in boiling oxolane (50 ml) 1.4 g (75%) of **271.4** was isolated by flash column chromatography. Physical data for **271.4**: colorless crystals (from

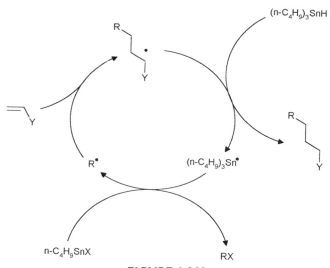

FIGURE I.269

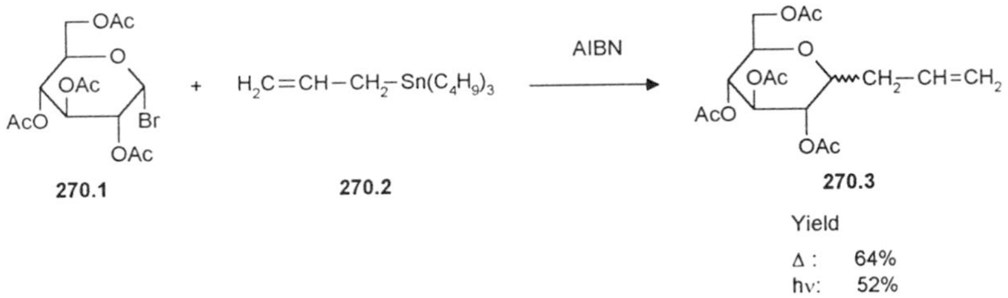

FIGURE I.270

FIGURE I.271

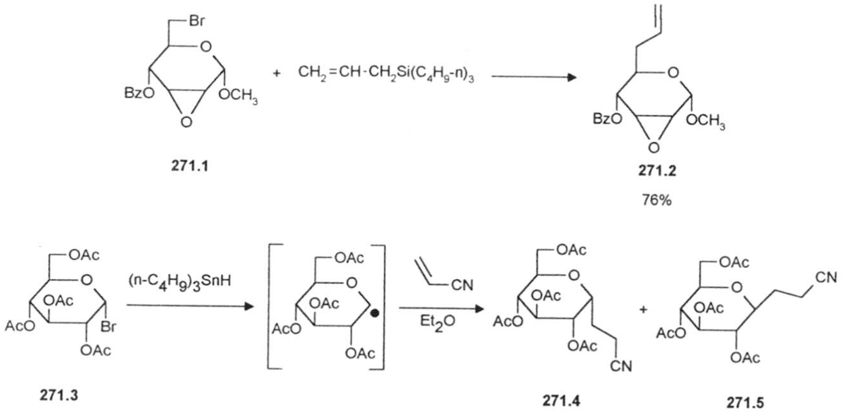

ether), m.p. 121–123°C, $[\alpha]_D^{20}$ +66.2 (c = 0.7 in chloroform). For **271.5**: colorless crystals, m.p. 117–119°C, $[\alpha]_D^{25}$ −19.6 (c = 1 in chloroform).

When studying radical ascending syntheses with tributyltin hydride and acrylonitrile, Giese[434] carefully examined the stereoselectivity of the reactions of hexopyranosyl and pentopyranosyl bromides. The major product obtained from 2,3,4-tri-O-acetyl-α-D-lyxopyranosyl bromide was 5,6,7-tri-O-acetyl-4,8-anhydro-2,3-dideoxy-D-*talo*-octononitrile, containing the substituent introduced in *equatorial* position, and not the corresponding D-*galacto*-epimer. An interesting observation was that in the absence of competing intramolecular or intermolecular radical reactions, the glycosyl radicals dimerize to yield carbohydrate dimers. An example of such a transformation is taken from the results of Giese *et al.*,[435] who applied 3,4,6-tri-O-acetyl-2-O-methyl-α-D-glucopyranosyl bromide (**272.1**), in which the hydroxyl function at C-2 is methylated to prevent acetoxy migrations that may occur in acylated glycosyl radicals. In the reaction induced by hexamethylditin (Fig. 1.272), a three-component product mixture was isolated, and from the structures of the separated products (**272.2–272.4**), the conformation of the intermediary radicals was concluded.

Dimerization of 3,4,5-tri-O-acetyl-2-O-methyl-α-D-glucopyranosyl bromide (272.1)[435]   A solution of the bromide **272.1** (1.53 g, 4 mmol) and 1.31 g (4 mmol) of hexamethylditin in benzene (10 ml) is irradiated with a Philips HPK 125 W mercury lamp at 50°C. After 12 h the solvent is distilled off and the residue flash-chromatographed on silicagel (eluant: 1:1 ether–pentane) to afford 95 mg (8%) of **272.2,** 194 mg (16%) of **272.3** and 99 mg (8%) of **272.4.** Physical data: (1)   1,3,4,9,10,12-hexa-O-acetyl-2,6:7,11-dianhydro-5,8-di-O-methyl-D-*erythro*-L-*galacto*-L-*gulo*-dodecitol (**272.2**); m.p. 165–166°C (from ether), $[\alpha]_D^{20}$ +4 (c = 0.84 in dichloromethane); (2) 1,3,4,9,10,12-hexa-O-acetyl-2,6:7,11-dianhydro-5,8-di-O-methyl-D-*erythro*-L-*gulo*-L-*gulo*-dodecitol (**272.3**): m.p. 178–180°C (from ether),

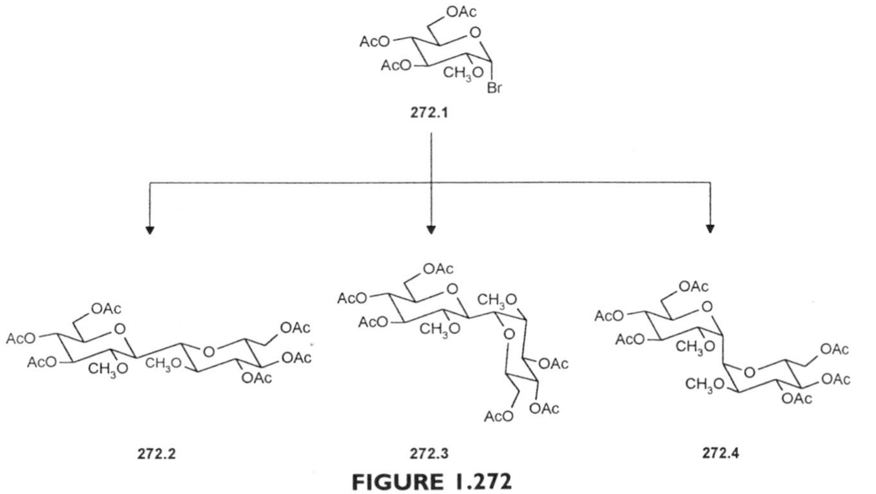

FIGURE I.272

$[\alpha]_D^{20}$ +62 (c = 1.05 in dichloromethane); (3) 1,3,4,9,10,12-hexa-O-acetyl-2,6:7,11-dianhydro-5,8-di-O-methyl-D-*erythro*-L-*ido*-L-*gulo*-dodecitol (**272.4**): colorless oil, $[\alpha]_D^{20}$ +53 (c = 0.69 in dichloromethane).

The scope and effectiveness of the radical chain extensions are supported by novel results dealing with the synthesis of the C-*glycosyl analogs of O-glycosyl-serine*. In these experiments the reaction partner of the glycosyl halides are C-methylenemalonester,[436] or more preferably, a suitable dehydroalanine derivative.[437] From the three glycosyl halides (acetobromo-D-galactose, acetobromo-D-glucose, and acetobromo-D-lactose; **273.1, 273.2,** and **273.3,** respectively) shown in Figure 1.273 only the α-anomeric C-glycosyl amino acids (**273.10–273.20**) are produced in the tributyltin-mediated reaction with the dehydroalanine derivatives **273.4–273.9**, with a predominance of the (S)-configuration of the newly developed asymmetric center.

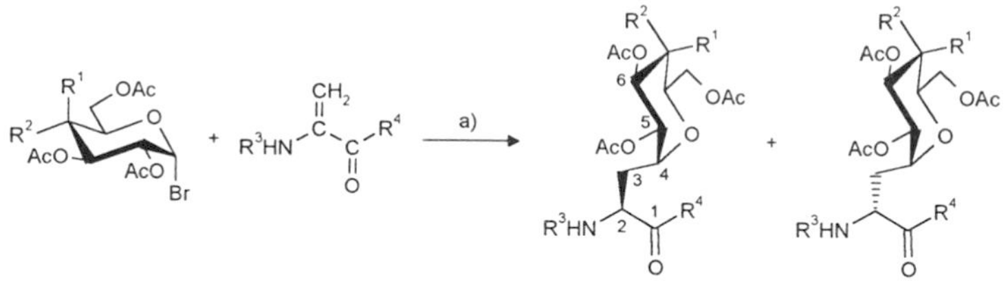

273.1-3   **273.4-9**   **(S)-273.10—20**   **(R)-273.10—20**

Synthesis of C-glycosides **273.10-20** *via* radical addition of glycosylbromides on dehydroalanine derivatives. (S) and (R) refers to the configuration at C-2. **273.1**: R^1 = OAc, R^2 = H; **273.2**: R^1 = H, R^2 = OAc; **273.3**: R^1 = H, R^2 = O-(2,3,4,6-Tetra-O-acetyl-β-D-galactopyranosyl); **273.4**: R^3 = Fmoc, R^4 = OBzl; **273.5**: R^3 = Z, R^4 = OBzl; **273.6**: R^3 = Boc, R^4 = OBzl; **273.7**: R^3 = Fmoc, R^4 = Ph-OBzl; **273.8**: R^3 = Fmoc, R^4 = D-Ph-OBzl; **273.9**: R^3 = Fmoc-Pro, R^4 = AlaOBzl; a): Bu$_3$SnH, AIBN, dry toluene, 50–65 °C

Bromide	Dehydroalanine derivative	Product^a		Yield (%)	S : R
273.1	Fmoc-ΔAla-OBzl	273.4 Fmoc-Ala(TA-gal)-OBzl	(S)-**10**/(R)-**10**	65 %	2.5 : 1
273.1	Z-ΔAla-OBzl	273.5 Z-Ala(TA-gal)-OBzl	(S)-**11**/(R)-**11**	60 %	2.4 : 1
273.1	Boc-ΔAla-OBzl	273.6 Boc-Ala(TA-gal)-OBzl	(S)-**12**/(R)-**12**	61 %	3.8 : 1
273.2	Fmoc-ΔAla-OBzl	273.4 Fmoc-Ala(TA-glc)-OBzl	(S)-**13**/(R)-**13**	73 %	2.6 : 1
273.2	Z-ΔAla-OBzl	273.5 Z-Ala(TA-glc)-OBzl	(S)-**14**/(R)-**14**	55 %	2.3 : 1
273.2	Boc-ΔAla-OBzl	273.6 Boc-Ala(TA-glc)-OBzl	(S)-**15**/(R)-**15**	65 %	3.8 : 1
273.3	Fmoc-ΔAla-OBzl	273.4 Fmoc-Ala(HA-lac)-OBzl	(S)-**16**/(R)-**16**	55 %	1.9 : 1
273.3	Z-ΔAla-OBzl	273.5 Z-Ala(HA-lac)-OBzl	(S)-**17**/(R)-**17**	13 %	3.2 : 1
273.1	Fmoc-ΔAla-Ph-OBzl	273.7 Fmoc-Ala(TA-gal)-Ph-OBzl	(S)-**18**/(R)-**18**	45 %	1.6 : 1
273.1	Fmoc-ΔAla-D-Ph-OBzl	273.8 Fmoc-Ala(TA-gal)-D-Phe-OBzl	(S)-**19**/(R)-**19**	23 %	≥2.0 : 1
273.1	Z-Pro-ΔAla-OBzl	273.9 Z-Pro-Ala(TA-gal)-Ala-OBzl	(S)-**20**/(R)-**20**	40 %	1.0 : 1

^{a} (S) and (R) refers to the configuration of C-2 in the glycosylated amino acids.

FIGURE I.273

A novel application of the highly nucleophilic glycosyl radicals is associated with the chemical synthesis of biologically important target molecules. Syntheses of *Kdo* with radical reactions have been performed by Giese[436,438] and Branchaud[439] and their colleagues. The ascending step of one of the methods leading to Kdo (Fig. 1.274) involves the carbon–carbon coupling of (5*S*)-1,2,3,4-tetra-*O*-acetyl-5-bromo-α-D-lyxopyranose (**274.1**) with *tert*-butyl (2-tributylstannylmethyl)propenoate (**274.2**). Details for the preparation of the starting bromosugar, as well as of the key step in the procedure (both radical reactions), are given according to the work of Giese and Linker.[438]

(5S)-1,2,3,4-Tetra-O-acetyl-5-bromo-α-D-lyxopyranose (274.1)[438]   A mixture of 1,2,3,4-tetra-*O*-acetyl-α-D-lyxopyranose (2.39 g, 7.5 mmol) and freshly recrystallized NBS (6.68 g, 37.5 mmol) in dry carbon tetrachloride is irradiated with an OSRAM Power Star HQI-T lamp (400 W) and allowed to heat under reflux. After 1 h the dark-red mixture is cooled to ambient temperature and filtered, and the solid is washed with carbon tetrachloride (2 × 30 ml). The filtrate is concentrated *in vacuo* and immediately purified by flash column chromatography (silicagel, 3 : 1 pentane–ethyl acetate) to afford pure **274.1** (1.05 g, 35%) as a white solid, m.p. 123–125°C.

tert-Butyl   1,2,3,4-tetra-O-acetyl-6,7-dideoxy-7-methylene-α-D-manno-octopyra-nuronate (274.3)[438]   In an argon-flushed flask a solution of the bromide **274.1** (500 mg, 1.26 mmol) and the stannane **274.2** (1.63 g, 3.78 mmol) in dry benzene (15 ml) is heated under reflux. At this temperature a solution of AIBN (40 mg, 0.24 mmol) in dry benzene (2 ml) is added dropwise over 1.5 h, and stirring is continued at 80°C for 30 min. After cooling to room temperature, the solvent is evaporated at reduced pressure and the residue is dissolved in acetonitrile (30 ml). This solution is washed with pentane (4 × 10 ml). The solvent of the CH₃CN layer is evaporated under reduced pressure, and the crude product is purified by flash-column chromatography (silicagel, eluant: 4 : 1 pentane–ethyl acetate) to afford a 3 : 1 mixture (395 mg, 68%) of the title product **274.3** and the diastereoisomeric **274.4** as a yellow syrup. This is separated into two fractions by HPLC (eluant: 70 : 30 hexane–*tert*-butyl methyl ether in 20 min to 60 : 40, 16 ml/min). Eluted first is pure **274.3** (240 mg, 41%), and the following fraction contains a 2 : 1 mixture of **274.3** and **274.4** (155 mg, 27%).

An additional *radical synthesis*[440] of *Kdo* is based on the fact that alkylcobaloxime complexes can act as radical precursors because irradiation

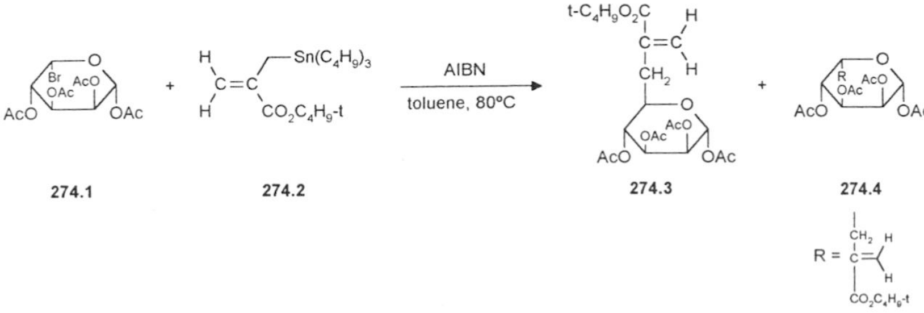

FIGURE I.274

cleaves the cobalt–carbon bond homolytically (Fig. 1.275). The α-glycosyl cobaloximes (**275.1**), obtained under reductive conditions, can be isomerized into the β-derivatives (**275.2**), and these isomerization reactions occur via radicals which can be trapped by alkenes (**275.3**) or other compounds. Such reactions then give rise to addition and/or substitution products[440] (**275.4** and **275.5**).

In the *Kdo synthesis* reported by Branchaud[439] $NaCo^I(dmg)_2py$ is applied, and the strategic reaction is a $C-C$ bond construction at C-6 of D-mannose *via* photochemically induced radical cross-coupling of an alkylcobaloxime derivative of D-mannose (**276.1**) with α-ethoxyacrylonitrile (**276.2**) without protection of the saccharide hydroxyl groups, as shown in Figure 1.276.

Bis-(dimethylglyoximato)(pyridine)(benzyl 6-deoxy-α-D-mannopyranosid-6-yl)-cobalt (276.1) In a 25-ml round-bottomed flask equipped with a magnetic stirring bar and a rubber septum, a suspension of $CoCl_6 \times H_2O$ (238 mg, 1 mmol) and $dmgH_2$ (239 mg, 2.06 mmol) in methanol (5 ml) is deoxygenated by bubbling nitrogen through a syringe needle for 5 min. It is then treated with 50% aqueous NaOH (167 mg, 2.09 mmol) and pyridine (82 μl, 80 mg, 1 mmol). The dark-brown suspension is deoxygenated for an additional 5 min, and sodium borohydride (39 mg, 1 mmol) is added. The resulting dark-blue mixture is stirred for 5 min, and then a deoxygenated solution of benzyl 6-deoxy-6-iodo-α-D-mannopyranoside (285 mg, 0.78 mmol) in 3 ml of deoxygenated methanol is added via cannula, and the cannula is rinsed into the reaction mixture with an additional 2 ml of deoxygenated methanol. The mixture is reduced, again, with sodium borohydride (30 mg) and then stirred for 3 h; then the septum cap is removed, the mixture is diluted with acetone (10 ml), and a few grams of silicagel are added. The solvents are removed under diminished pressure to leave a free-flowing powder, which is placed on the top of 2 cm of silicagel in a fritted-glass funnel and filtered with 4:1 ethyl acetate–acetone. The filtrate is evaporated to leave the title product **276.1** as a glassy orange solid (0.44 g, 94%).

General information on photolyses is as follows. All photolyses were conducted with a 20-mmol $RCo(dmgH)_2py$ concentration and an alkene concentration of 400 mmol in 95% ethanol. Photolyses were performed in Pyrex tubes fitted with rubber septa and equipped with magnetic stirring bars. The reaction mixtures were deoxygenated by bubbling argon gas through the mixtures for 1 min/ml of the mixture, and were maintained under a positive pressure of argon by means of syringe needles inserted through the septa. The argon gas was deoxygenated by passage through a heated column of BASF catalyst R3-11 in the black (reduced) form. The light sources were 300 W Sylvania incandescent floodlamps mounted in ceramic sockets and positioned 5 cm from a 800-ml beaker of water containing an immersed coil of copper tubing (10 cm diameter, 4 turns). The water bath was stirred magnetically and tap water flowing through the copper coil was used to maintain the temperature of the bath at 15–20°C. The entire apparatus wrapped in aluminum foil, and a stream of air was directed over the lightbulb from the back to cool the bulb. The reactions were monitored by TLC by removing a 1-drop sample of the anaerobic reaction mixture with a long syringe needle.

Preparation of benzyl 6,7-dideoxy-8-ethyl-α-D-manno-non-7-enopyranosiduro-nonitrile (276.3)[439] A solution of **276.1** (0.444 g, 0.71 mmol) and α-ethoxyacryloni-

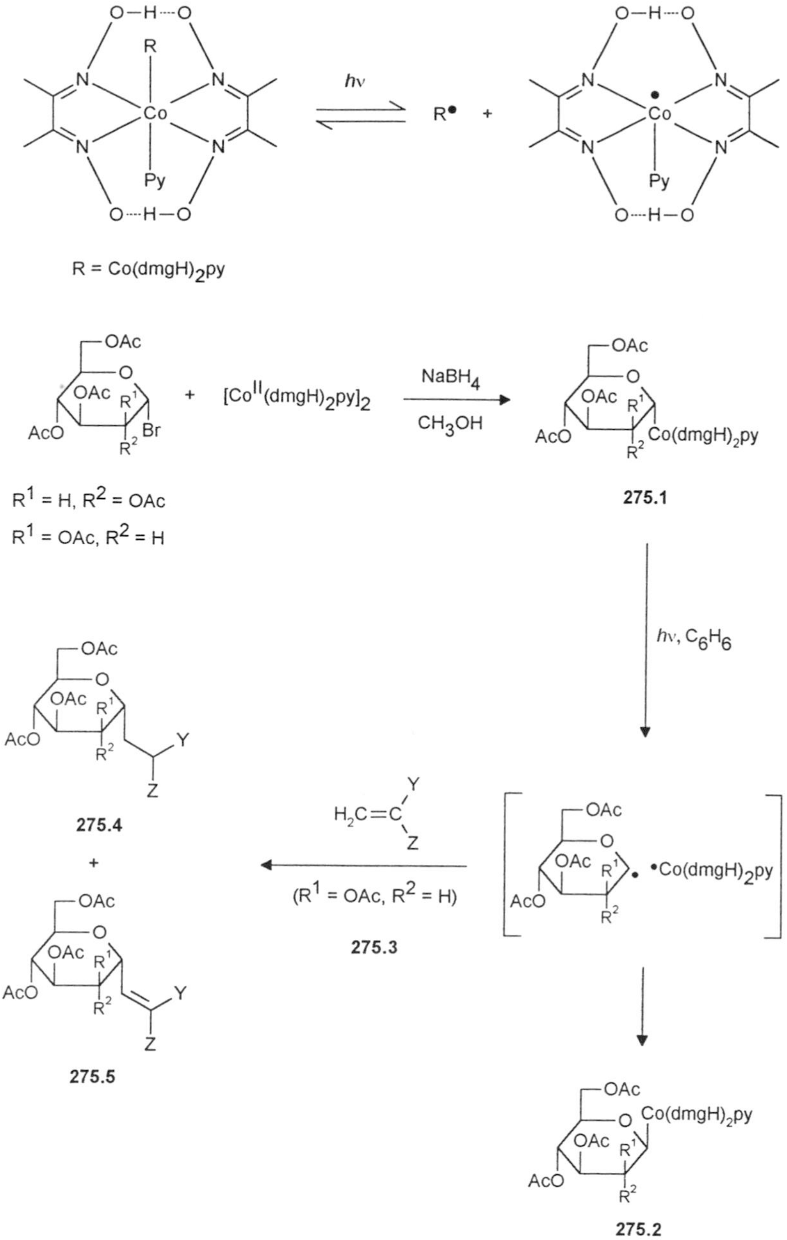

R = Co(dmgH)$_2$py

R^1 = H, R^2 = OAc
R^1 = OAc, R^2 = H

275.1

275.4

275.3

275.5

275.2

FIGURE 1.275

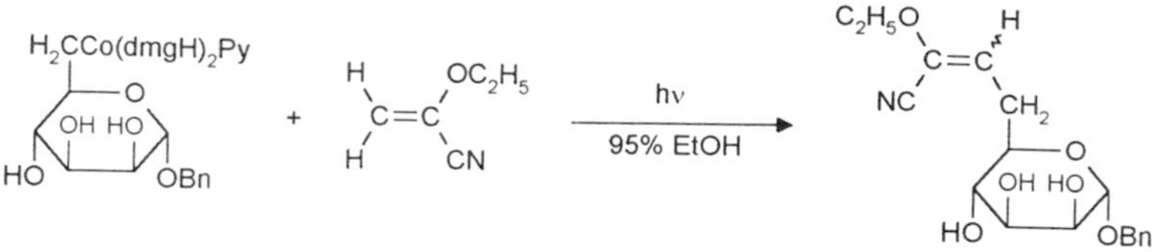

276.1 **276.2** **276.3**

FIGURE 1.276

trile (1.36 g, 14 mmol) in 95% ethanol (35 ml) is deoxygenated by bubbling argon through the solution for 30 min, and then photolyzed for 74 h. The reaction mixture is rinsed into a round-bottomed flask with acetone, and a few grams of silicagel is added. The solvents are evaporated under reduced pressure, and the resulting powder is placed on top of a 3-cm pad of silicagel in a fritted-glass funnel, and suction-filtered with ethyl acetate. The filtrate is evaporated, and the residue is purified by means of preparative TLC (eluant: 3:2 hexane–*n*-butanol) to give **276.3** (0.2 g, 81%), as a syrupy unseparable mixture of isomers.

Thoma and Giese[441] have also applied cyclopentadienyl dicarbonyl iron[442] [CpFe(CO)$_2$] for generating saccharide radicals and have synthesized[443] methylene-bridged *C*-disaccharides.

An efficient single-electron-transfer system (SmI$_2$–THF–HMPA) permits a SmI$_2$-mediated coupling[444] of the halide and the carbonyl compound (ketone or aldehyde) in the so-called Barbier reaction. In both of the two proposed reaction mechanisms[445] the halide is supposedly reduced by SmI$_2$, and the subsequent steps are as summarized in Figure 1.277.

Sinay has postulated[446] that the reactive transient intermediate in this reaction is a chiral anomeric organosamarium(III) species. The process can also be readily executed with glycosyl sulfones, but the stereochemical outcome is different from that observed for glycosyl halides. Experimental details on the reductive samariation of 3,4,6-tri-*O*-benzyl-2-deoxy-α-D-*arabino*-hexopyranosyl chloride (**277.1**) are as follows.

Preparation of 1-(3,4,6-tri-O-benzyl-2-deoxy-α- and β-D-arabino-hexopyranosyl) cyclopentanol (277.2 and 277.3)   A solution of 3,4,6-tri-*O*-benzyl-α-D-*arabino*-hexopyranosyl chloride (**277.1**, 500 mg, 1.1 mmol) and cyclopentanone (2 eq, 195 µl) in dry THF is added dropwise at room temperature under argon to a mixture of a 0.1 M solution of samarium diiodide in THF (3 eq, 33 ml) and HMPA (5% vol, 1.65 ml). The solution is stirred until turning brown–yellow and the progress of the reaction is monitored by TLC (2:1 cyclohexane–ethyl acetate). Following dropwise addition of saturated aqueous ammonium chloride, the reaction mixture is extracted twice with ether. The organic layer is dried (MgSO$_4$), concentrated and purified by means of flash column chromatography (eluant: 5:1 cyclohexane–ethyl acetate) to furnish, successively, 1,5-anhydro-3,4,6-tri-*O*-benzyl-2-deoxy-D-*arabino*-hexitol (4.1 mg, 1%) and the target α-anomeric sugar **277.2** (385 mg, 70%), [α]$_D$ −5.4 (*c* = 1.07 in chloroform). The next product to be eluted is the respective β-anomer **277.3** (95 mg, 17%), [α]$_D$ +27 (*c* = 1.07 in chloroform).

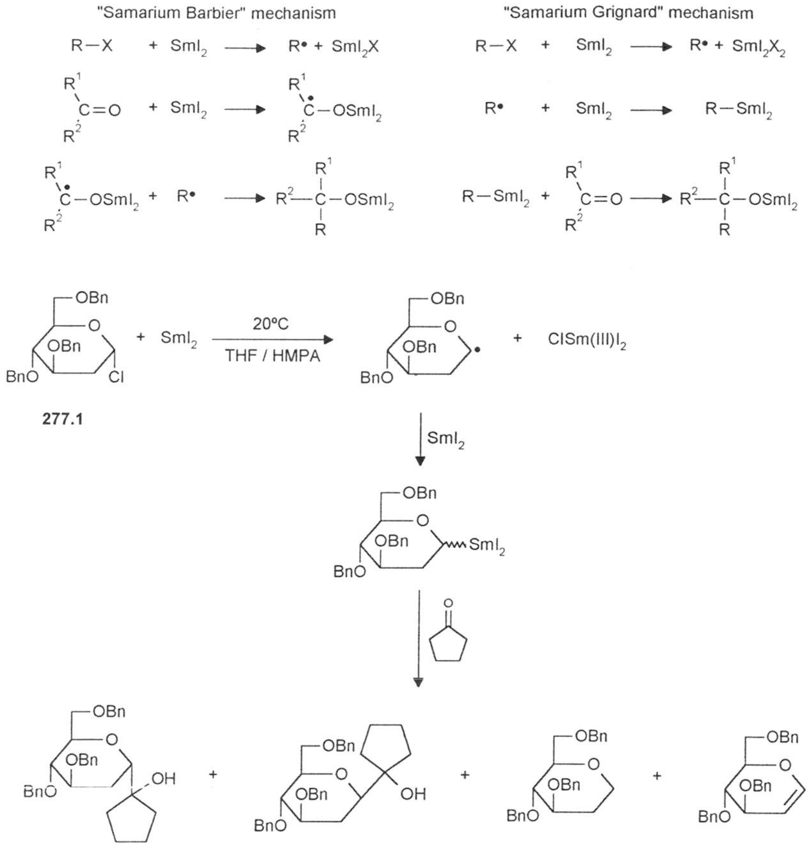
"Samarium Barbier" mechanism
"Samarium Grignard" mechanism
20°C
THF / HMPA
277.1
277.2
277.3

FIGURE 1.277

1.2.7.11. Ascending Syntheses with Sulfonic Acid Esters

Growing interest has been devoted to saccharide sulfonic acid esters in ascending procedures, and this is clearly because of the widespread application of trifluoromethanesulfonate esters (triflates).[447] For the chain extension of primary triflates, Berkowitz[448] worked out a method and observed that treatment of methyl 4-*O*-benzyl-2,3-di-*O*-methoxymethyl-6-*O*-trifluoromethanesulfonyl-α-D-glucopyranoside or 3-*O*-benzyl-1,2-*O*-isopropylidene-5-*O*-trifluoromethanesulfonyl-α-D-ribofuranoside with a variety of functionalized *C*-nucleophiles in THF/HMPA leads to the corresponding chain-extended sugars in good yields. A scheme for these transformations, reported by American chemists,[448] is shown in Figure 1.278 with the note that Fleet *et al.*[449] previously described the successful

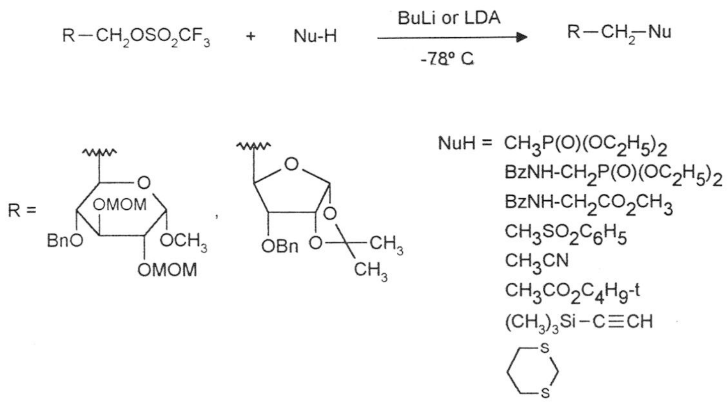

$$R-CH_2OSO_2CF_3 \quad + \quad Nu-H \xrightarrow[-78°\ C]{BuLi\ or\ LDA} \quad R-CH_2-Nu$$

NuH = $CH_3P(O)(OC_2H_5)_2$
$BzNH-CH_2P(O)(OC_2H_5)_2$
$BzNH-CH_2CO_2CH_3$
$CH_3SO_2C_6H_5$
CH_3CN
$CH_3CO_2C_4H_9\text{-}t$
$(CH_3)_3Si-C{\equiv}CH$

FIGURE I.278

chain extension of 4,5-anhydro-1-azido-1-deoxy-2,3-*O*-isopropylidene-6-*O*-trifluoromethanesulfonyl-D-talitol with *tert*-butyl lithioacetate.

The next experimental procedure, where the *C*-nucleophile employed is acetonitrile, can be generally applied[448] for related chain extensions.

> *Typical triflate displacement procedure*[448] All solutions were deoxygenated by freezing (liquid nitrogen) and being subjected to five cycles of evacuation and purging with argon. To a solution of disopropylamine (216 μl, 1.55 mmol) and HMPA (268 μl, 1.55 mmol) in THF (2 ml) at −78°C is added *n*-butyllithium (97 μl of a 1.6 M solution in hexane, 1.55 mmol). The reaction mixture is stirred at 0°C for 30 min, cooled to −78°C, and a cooled (−78°C) solution of dry acetonitrile (82 ml, 1.55 mmol) in THF (1 ml) and then, 2 min later, a cooled (−78°C) solution of 3-*O*-benzyl-1,2-*O*-isopropylidene-5-*O*-trifluoromethanesulfonyl-α-D-ribofurano-side (180 mg, 0.436 mmol) in THF (2 ml) are added via a cannula. After 10 min at −78°C, the reaction is quenched [NH_4Cl (aqueous 3 ml/Et_2O (3 ml)], the aqueous layer is extracted with ethyl acetate (2 × 15 ml) and the combined extracts dried ($MgSO_4$). Flash column chromatography (eluant: 30% ethyl acetate in hexane) gives 110 mg (83%) of pure 3,6-anhydro-4-*O*-benzyl-5,6-*O*-isopropylidene-L-*ribo*-hepto-nonitrile.

In an additional procedure, reported by Bartlett,[450] the primary tosylate **279.1** is transformed to the acetylene–sugar **279.2,** which is then subjected to a further one-carbon chain extension with formaldehyde to result in the dec-8-yno-1,4-furanose **279.3** (Fig. 1.279).

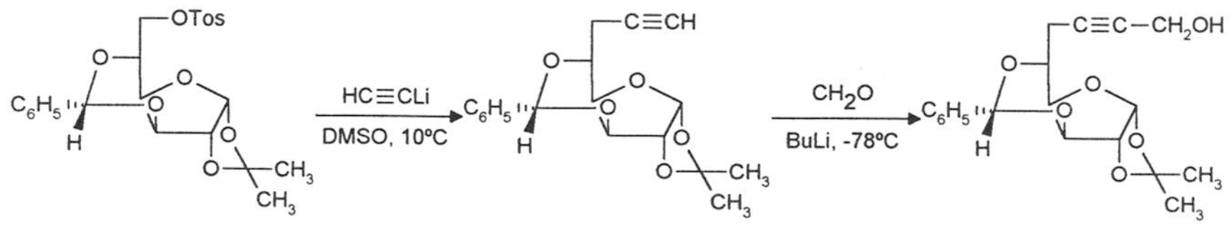

279.1   **279.2**   **279.3**

FIGURE I.279

3,5-O-(R)-Benzylidene-6,7,8,9-tetradeoxy-1,2-O-isopropylidene-α-D-gluco-non-8-yno-1,4-furanose (279.2)[450] To a dry round-bottomed flask are placed 1.92 g (18.8 mmol) of lithium acetylide–ethylenediamine complex and 9 ml of dry Me$_2$SO under inert atmosphere. The slurry is stirred for 15 min at room temperature, then cooled to 10°C, and the tosylate **279.1** (4.47 g, 9.38 mmol), in 14 ml of Me$_2$SO, is added dropwise over 5 min. After stirring at 10°C for 30, min the reaction mixture is partitioned between water and 50 ml of dichloromethane. The organic layer is washed with 1 N HCl and saturated aqueous NaHCO$_3$ (150 ml each) and worked up to afford a yellow syrup. Chromatography of the crude product (eluant: 1:5 ethyl acetate–hexane) furnished 2.96 g (96%) of pure **279.2**, as a clear slightly yellow syrup, $[\alpha]_D^{24}$ +96 (c = 1 in chloroform).

3,5-O-(R)-Benzylidene-6,7,8,9-tetradeoxy-1,2-O-isopropylidene-α-D-gluco-dec-8-yno-1,4-furanose (279.3)[450] An oven-dried, three-necked round-bottomed flask is charged with a solution of the acetylene sugar **279.2** (1.36 g, 4.12 mmol) in dry THF (5.5 ml), and *n*-butyllithium (3.64 ml, 1.70 M solution in hexane) is added at −78°C over 3 min under inert atmosphere. The reaction mixture is stirred for 15 min before the addition of formaldehyde. The formaldehyde gas inlet consists of a Pasteur pipette connected to a T-tube on a one-necked 50-ml round-bottomed flask in which 1.86 g (61.8 mmol) of dry paraformaldehyde is placed. The paraformaldehyde is cracked using a heat gun and bubbled into the brown acetylide solution at −78°C with the aid of a stream of nitrogen gas. The reaction mixture is quenched after 10 min with saturated aqueous NH$_4$Cl, concentrated, partitioned between chloroform (150 ml) and water (200 ml), and worked up. The crude product (1.65 g) is purified by chromatography (eluant: 1:3 ethyl acetate–hexane) to furnish 199 mg (15%) of recovered starting sugar **279.2** and 1.14 g (77%) of the title propargyl alcohol **279.3** as a pale-yellow syrup, $[\alpha]_D^{24}$ +52 (c = 0.5 in chloroform).

In simple cases the conventional tosyl esters can also be employed (see Section 1.2.2), and for enhancing the effectiveness of the chain extension, bromide ions are added to the reaction mixture, such as in the conversion of 3,4-di-*O*-acetyl-6-*O*-(*p*-tolylsulfonyl)-D-glucal with sodium cyanide.[451]

3,4-Di-O-acetyl-6-cyano-6-deoxy-D-glucal[451] A mixture of 3,4-di-*O*-acetyl-6-*O*-(p-tolylsulfonyl)-D-glucal (0.324 g, 0.842 mmol), powdered sodium cyanide (0.109 g, 2.6 eq) and tetrabutyammonium bromide (0.545 g, 2.0 eq) in acetonitrile (3 ml) is refluxed at 83°C (bath temperature) for 24 h. After cooling, the mixture is poured onto ice water (50 ml) and extracted with ether (3 × 50 ml). The combined organic layer is washed with water and brine, and then dried over MgSO$_4$. Evaporation of the solvent and purification of the residual red–orange syrup (120 mg, 60%) by chromatography (eluant: 10% ethyl acetate in pentane) gives 40% of the pure title product, R_f = 0.61 in 7:3 toluene–ethyl acetate.

Intramolecular alkylation involving a *p*-toluenesulfonate function is employed for the construction of certain *constituents of octosylic acids*. The ascending step of one of the related procedures[452] is shown in Figure 1.280.

3,7-Anhydro-7-bis-(C-ethoxycarbonyl)-6-deoxy-1,2-O-isopropylidene-α-D-alloheptose (280.2) and 5,6-anhydro-3-O-bis-(ethoxycarbonyl)methyl-1,2-O-isopropylidene-α-D-allofuranose (280.3)[452] A solution of 3-*O*-bis(ethoxycarbonyl)-methyl-1,2-*O*-isopropylidene-6-*O*-(*p*-toluenesulfonyl)-α-D-allofuranose (**280.1**, 0.7 g, 1.3 mmol) in dry THF (20 ml) is cooled to −15°C, and sodium hydride (34 mg, 1.4 mmol) is added. After stirring for 24 h the mixture is cooled, again, to −15°C

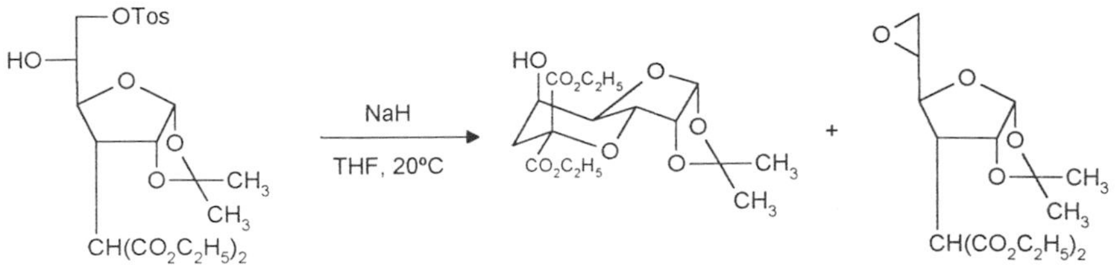

280.1   **280.2**   **280.3**

FIGURE I.280

and quenched by the addition of ethanol and acetic acid (1ml each). The mixture is evaporated, and the residue is taken up with ethyl acetate and purified by means of column chromatography (eluant: 4 : 1 → 1 : 1 benzene–ethyl acetate). Eluted first is the 3,7-anhydro drivative **280.2**, followed by the less polar epoxide **280.3**.

Intramolecular ring closure of a methanesulfonic ester derivative (the so-called Williams reaction) has been employed in a total synthesis[453] of *octosylic acid A* from a nucleoside, as shown in Figure 1.281.

Saccharide sulfonic esters are also used as educts in oxidatively induced carbonyl-insertion reactions (ligandum-transfer reaction).[454] First, the substitution product is derived from the sulphonate with sodium dicarbonylpentahaptocyclopentadienyliron {Na^+ [$FeCp(CO)_2$]$^-$}, followed by treatment with an alcohol and an oxidizing agent to result in the oxidative incorporation: the produced [$R–FeCp(CO)_2$]$^+$ transforms into the cationic acyliron complex [$R–CO–FeCp(CO)$]$^+$, a reactive species to split into an ester on the attack of the alcohol.

In the carbohydrate field this methodology has been employed by Baer *et al.*[455,456] to synthesize *uronates* from sulfonate esters. The oxidative insertion was effected with copper(I) chloride or with bromine, but other halogen derivatives were found to be useful as well, and the uronates prepared[455,456] using this method are summarized in Table 1.46.

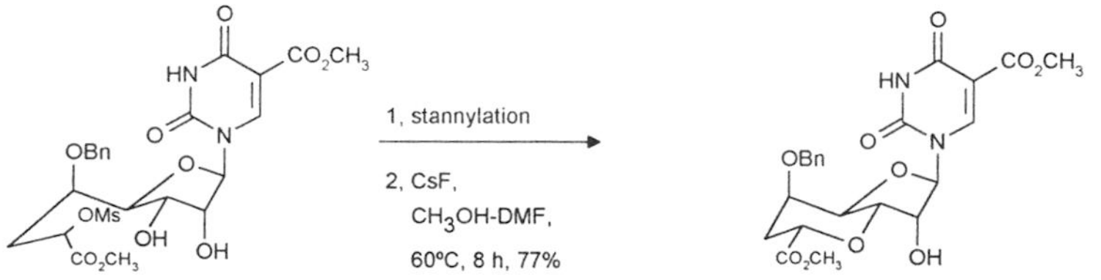

Methyl 3,7-anhydro-1,6-dideoxy-1-[5-(methoxycarbonyl)-
3,4-dihydro-2,4-dioxo-1(2H)-pyrimydinyl]-5-O-benzyl-
D-*glycero*-β-D-*allo*-octofuronuronate

FIGURE I.281

TABLE 1.46 Chain Elongation with Oxidative Insertion of Uronic Acids Starting from 6-O-Tosyl- and 6-Halogeno-6-deoxyhexoses

Educt	Product	Yield (%)	M.p. (°C)	$[\alpha]_D$ (CHCl$_3$)
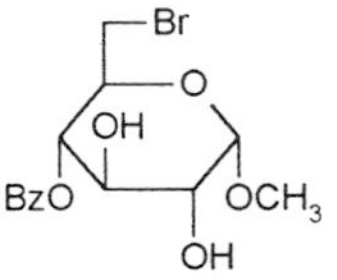	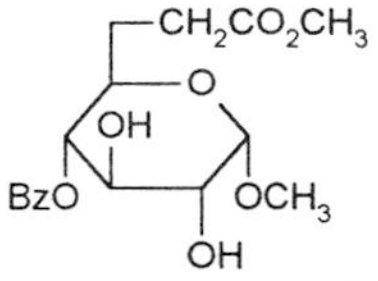	70	154–155.5	+124.9 (c = 3.5)
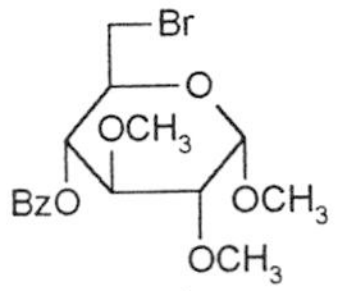	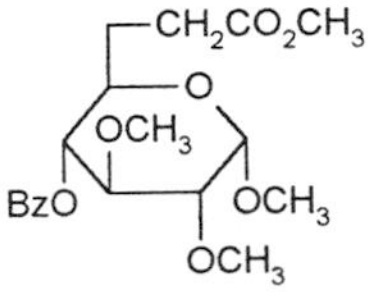	85	—	+62.1 (c = 0.7)
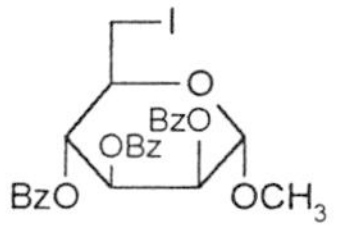	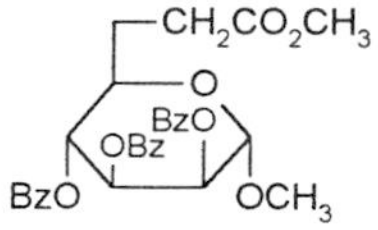	75	136.5–138	−135.6 (c = 0.7)
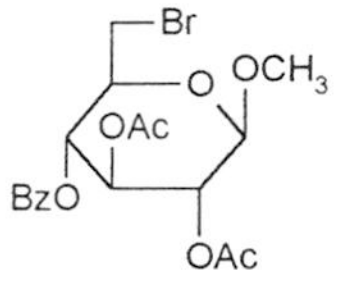	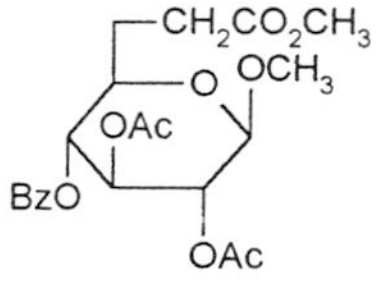	71	131.5	−69 (c = 0.75)
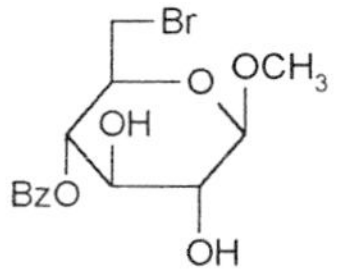	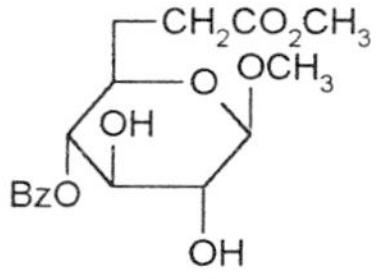	80	—	−13.2 (c = 1.5)
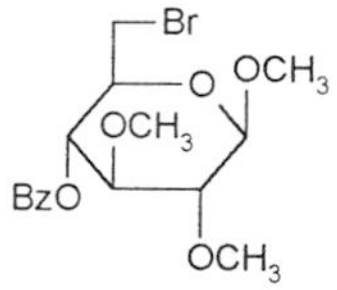	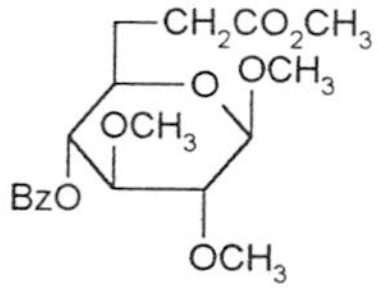	90	—	−48.9 (c = 1.5)
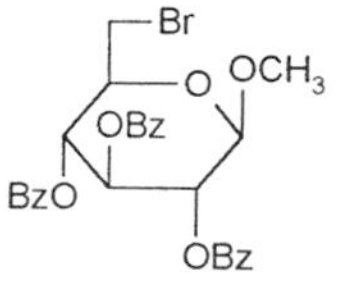	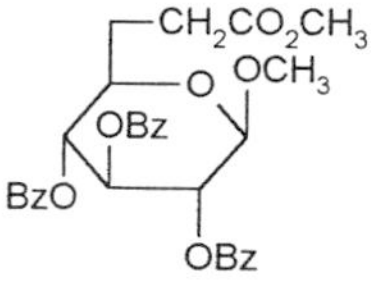	79	—	+37.5 (c = 1.6)
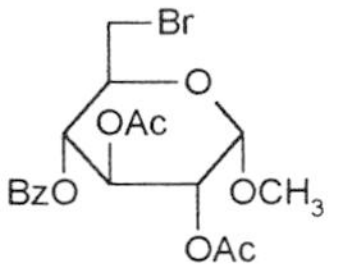	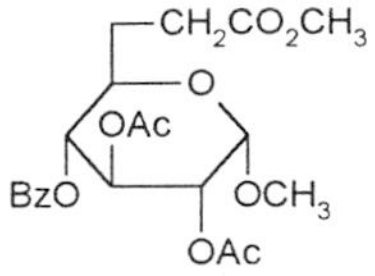	88	99–101	+56.3 (c = 0.9)
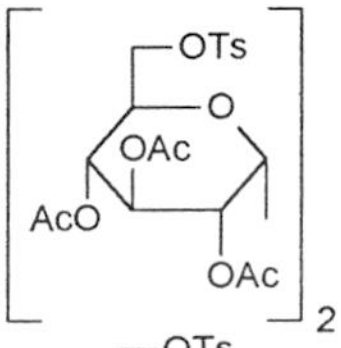	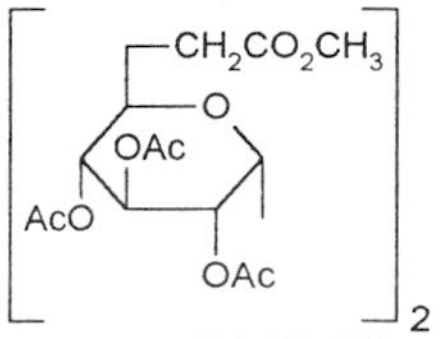	86	75–95	+112 (c = 0.5)
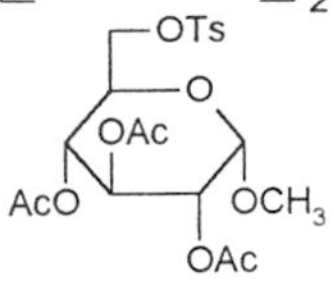	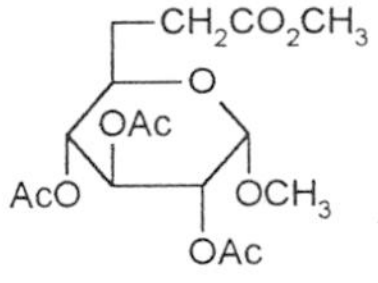	46	167–168	−12 (c = 0.7)

Experimental details on this "ironcarbonyl" method are given by the example of the chain extension[456] of 6,6'-di-*O*-tosyl-α,α-trehalose hexaacetate.

> *Methyl [(methyl 2,3,4-tri-O-acetyl-6-deoxy-α-D-gluco-heptopyranosyluronate)-2,3,4-tri-O-acetyl-6-deoxy-α-D-gluco-heptopyranoside]uronate*[456] A solution of sodium dicarbonyl-η^5-cyclopentadienyliron (NaFp) [prepared from 1.065 g of Fe(CO)$_2$Cp dimer and sodium amalgam from 6 ml of Hg and 1.5 g of Na] in oxolane (200 ml) is added under anhydrous conditions to 6,6'-di-*O*-tosyl-α,α-trehalose hexaacetate (2.025 g, 2.25 mmol) under nitrogen. The sugar dissolved on stirring and, after 1.5 h, is completely consumed (TLC in 2 : 1 ethyl acetate–hexane) and a strong, faster-moving yellow spot is seen prior to spraying (sulfuric acid). A stream of CO is passed through the solution at 0°C, and absolute methanol (350 ml) is added, followed by bromine (2.1 ml). TLC reveals the reaction to be complete after 0.5 h; the yellow spot (visible without spraying) is replaced by a strong spot (R_f = 0.6) of the title product, accompanied by faster- and slower-moving spots of by-products (visible after spraying and heating). The reaction mixture is concentrated to a small volume, diluted with ethyl acetate; washed sequentially with aqueous Na$_2$S$_2$O$_3$, aqueous NaHCO$_3$, and water; dried (MgSO$_4$), and concentrated. The resulting brown syrup is dissolved in ether and precipitated with light petroleum (b.p. 35–60°C). The supernatant solvent is decanted and column chromatography (eluant: 1 : 1 ethyl acetate–hexane) of the syrupy precipitate gives the pure title compound (620 mg, 42%), m.p. 135–137°C, [α]$_D$ +146 (*c* = 0.6 in chloroform).

As shown by the data in Table 1.46, the free uronic acid can be obtained when the oxidative-insertion process is performed in an aqueous medium.[455,456]

1.2.7.12. Ascending Syntheses with Nitrogen-Containing Saccharides

Peseke[457] has demonstrated that monosaccharides carrying a nitromethyl group are suitable materials for chain extension. Thus, as shown in Figure 1.282, the reaction of methyl 2,3,4-tri-*O*-acetyl-6-deoxy-6-nitro-α-D-glucopyranoside (**282.1a**) and 3,4,5,7-tetra-*O*-acetyl-2,6-anhydro-1-deoxy-

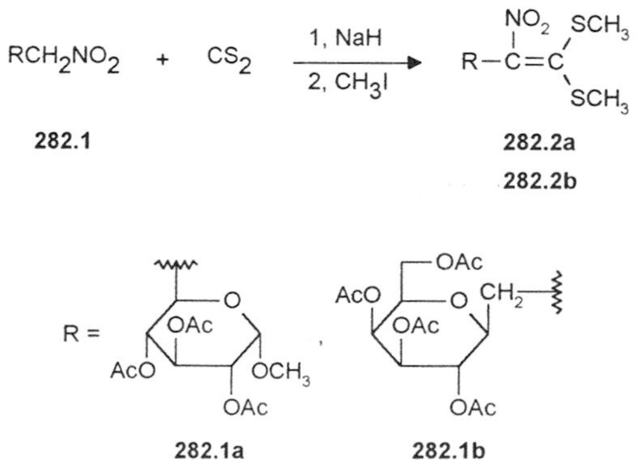

FIGURE 1.282

1-nitro-D-*glycero*-D-*manno*-heptitol (**282.1b**) with carbon disulfide, methyl iodide, and sodium hydride gave methyl 2,3,4-tri-*O*-acetyl-6,7-dideoxy-7,7-bis(methylthio)-6-nitro-α-D-*gluco*-hept-6-enopyranoside (**282.2a**) and 4,5,6,8-tetra-*O*-acetyl-3,7-anhydro-2-deoxy-2-nitro-D-*glycero*-L-*manno*-oct-1-enose dimethyl dithioacetal (**282.2b**), respectively. The simple experimental procedure[457] for deriving the chain-extended 6-nitrosugar **282.2a** is as follows.

> *Methyl 2,3,4-tri-O-acetyl-6,7-dideoxy-7,7-bis-(methylthio)-6-nitro-α-D-gluco-hept-6-eno-pyranoside (282.2a)*[457] To a well-stirred suspension of sodium hydride (0.48 g, 20 mmol) in THF (50 ml), under argon, is added the methyl glycoside **282.1a** (3.5 g, 10 mmol). The mixture is stirred for 2 h, carbon disulfide (1.2 ml, 20 mmol) and methyl iodide (3 ml, 48 mmol) are added dropwise with stirring, and this mixture is then boiled under reflux for 1h. After being poured onto crushed ice (500 g) and extraction with chloroform (3 × 100 ml), the combined extract is washed with water (3 × 100 ml), dried (MgSO₄), and concentrated under reduced pressure. The residue is crystallized from ethanol to give 2.26 g (50%) of **282a** as yellow crystals, m.p. 140–141°C, $[\alpha]_D^{18}$ −29 (c = 1.0 in chloroform).

The key intermediate of a synthesis of N-*acetylneuraminic acid* (and its *C-4-epi- derivative*) described by Baumberger and Vasella,[458] is a 4,6-*O*-acetal (**283.1**) of 1,2-di-deoxy-1-nitro-D-mannopyranose, and the key step is its DBU-catalyzed Michael addition to *tert*-butyl 2-(bromomethyl)prop-2-enoate (**283.2**) as shown in Figure 1.283. Then careful hydrolysis of the nitro group, followed by reduction, ozonolysis, and acetal cleavage led to N-acetylneuraminic acid and its C-4 epimer. The preparation of the *tert*-

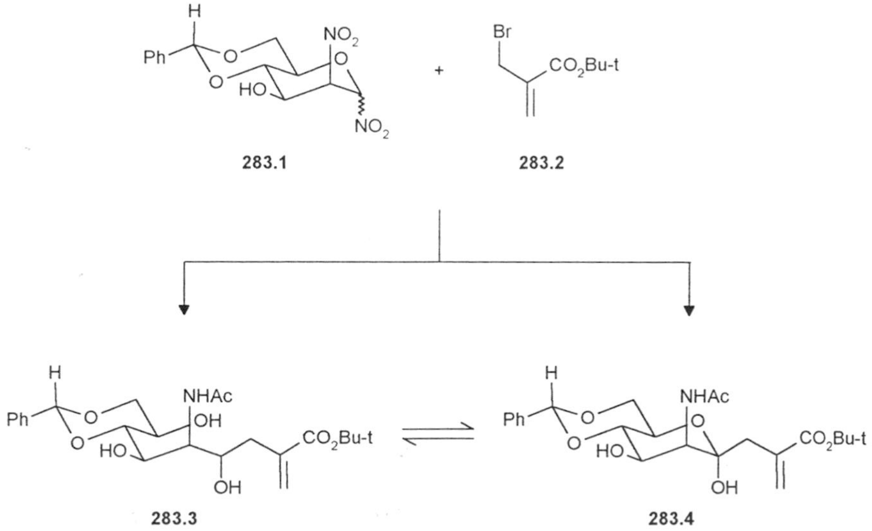

FIGURE I.283

butyl nonulosonates **283.3** and **283.4** was carried out using the following procedure.[458]

tert-*Butyl 5-acetamido-7,9-O-benzylidene-2,3,5-trideoxy-2-methylidene-D-manno-4-non-*
ulosonate (**283.3**) *and* tert-*butyl 5-acetamido-7,9-O-benzylidene-2,3,5-trideoxy-*
2-methylidene-D-manno-*4-nonulopyranosonate* (**283.4**)[458] To a stirred, cold (0°C)
solution of 2-acetamido-4,6-O-benzylidene-1,2-dideoxy-1-nitro-D-mannopyranose
(**283.1**, 8.4 g, 24.8 mmol) and *tert*-butyl 2-(bromomethyl)prop-2-enoate (**283.2**,
8.4 g, 37.2 mmol) in THF (75 ml) is added, dropwise, a solution of DBU (8.4 g,
49.6 mmol) in 25 ml of THF over a period of 4 h. Stirring is continued at the same
temperature for 20 h, then the precipitate is filtered off and the filtrate is diluted
with 200 ml of ethyl acetate. The usual workup, involving extraction with water
and brine, yields the crude product (13.1 g), which is taken up in a mixture of THF
(80 ml) and 20 ml of a pH-6.6 phosphate buffer, and then treated with urea (1.95 g,
27.3 mmol). The resulting mixture is stirred at room temperature for 3 days,
diluted with ethyl acetate (100 ml), and washed with 5% aqueous NaHCO₃, water,
and brine to give a yellow syrup, which is dissolved in a 1:1 ethyl acetate–ether
mixture. Addition of hexane gives a precipitate, which is filtered off and crystallized
from ethyl acetate–ether–hexane affording slightly yellow crystals of **283.3** and
283.4 (2.2 g). Fast column chromatography of the combined mother liquor on
silicagel (500 g; eluant: 97:3 dichloromethane–methanol) gives an additional crop
(5.0 g, 64%) of **283.3** and **283.4**, m.p. 143–144°C, $[\alpha]_D^{25}$ +20.5 (c = 1.0 in Me₂SO).

Further chain extensions with Michael addition were carried out between 1-deoxy-2,3-O-isopropylidene-1-nitro-5-O-pivaloyl-β-D-ribofuranose
(**284.1**) and acrylonitrile or methyl propynoate. In both cases the β-anomeric
nitroaldoses (**284.2** and **284.4**) predominated in the anomeric mixtures produced in the reaction (Fig. 1.284), indicating a preferred *endo*-attack on the
nitronate anion derived from the educt,[459] and this was also substantiated by
AM1 calculations. The ascending step with methyl propynoate could be
executed under exceptionally mild conditions (at −30°C) as described in
the following experimental procedure.[459]

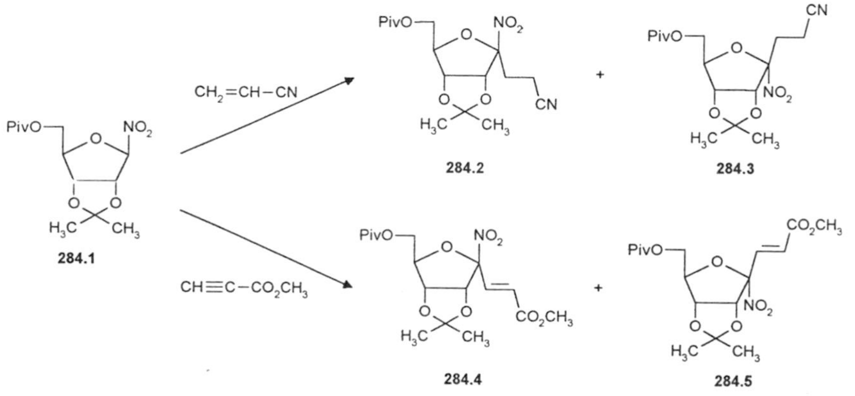

FIGURE 1.284

*Methyl (E)-2,3,5-trideoxy-5,6-O-isopropylidene-4-nitro-8-O-pivaloyl-β- and α-D-oct-2-en-4-ulofuranosonate (**284.4** and **284.5**)*[459]   A solution of the 1-nitrosugar **284.1** (6 g, 19.78 mmol) in dichloromethane (20 ml) is treated at −30°C with triethylamine (8.28 ml, 59.4 mmol). Then a solution of methyl propynoate (1.82 ml, 21.78 mmol) in dichloromethane (20 ml) is added dropwise over 30 min. The reaction mixture is stirred for 30 min at −30°C, allowed to warm to room temperature, and worked up. Chromatographic purification (eluant: 1:3 ether–hexane) gives 3.67 g (48%) of **284.4**, as a syrup, $[\alpha]_D$ −128 (c = 0.1 in chloroform), R_f = 0.46 (1:1 ether–hexane), and 1.83 g (24%) of **284.5**, m.p. 69–70°C, $[\alpha]_D$ −33 (c = 0.63 in chloroform), R_f = 0.39 (1:1 ether–hexane).

As reported by the Vasella group, glycosylidene carbenes—available from diaziridines[460–465] via diazirines (also called 1-deoxyhydrazi- and 1-azi-1-deoxyglycoses)—are versatile nitrogen-containing saccharide derivatives[461] for syntheses, including chain extensions.

Diazirines are prepared from aldonhydroximolactones (**285.2**) available from aldose oximes (**285.1**) by dehydrogenation[460] (Fig. 1.285). On thermolysis, diazirines (**285.3**) are transformed into glycosylcarbenes (**285.4**). The first representative reactions of these reactive species (among others, with hydroquinone monomethyl ether) have shown[462] that formation of an O-glycoside is expectedly preferential. Thus, from 1-azi-2,3,4,6-tetra-O-benzyl-1-deoxy-D-glucopyranoside, 69% of 4′-methoxyphenyl 2,3,4,6-tetra-O-benzyl-α,β-D-glucopyranoside was produced[462] together with 16% of a mixture of (1S)- and (1R)-1,5-anhydro-2,3,4,6-tetra-O-benzyl-1-C-(2′-hydroxy-5′-methoxyphenyl)-D-glucitol.

Glycosylidene carbenes are expected to be ambiphilic–nucleophilic, and to form spirocyclopropanes by cycloaddition to acceptor-substituted alkenes. Descotes and Praly have shown[463] that photolysis of O-acetylated glycopyranosylidene-1,1-diazides (**286.1**) in the presence of acrylonitrile

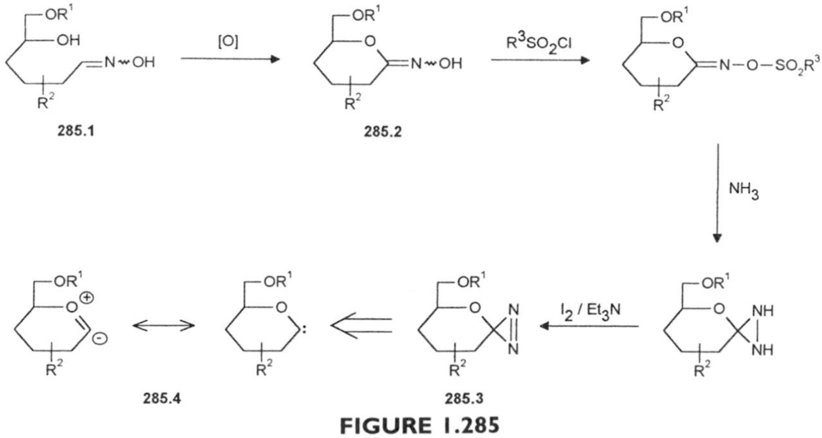

FIGURE 1.285

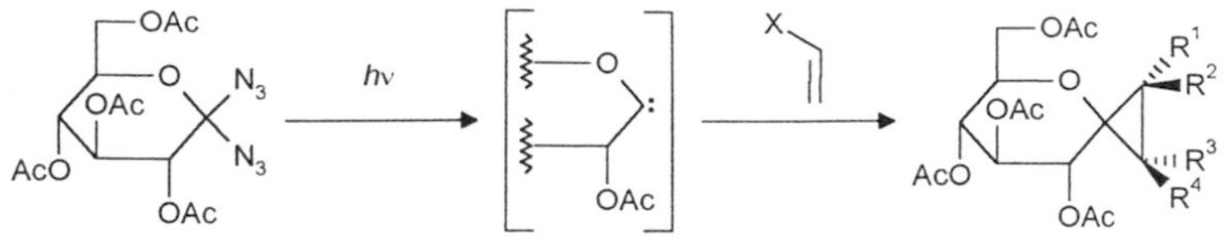

286.1   **286.2**

X = electron acceptor

FIGURE I.286

leads to a mixture of the diastereoisomeric spirocyclopropanes **286.2** (Fig. 1.286).

Mixtures of isomeric spirocyclopropanes can also be obtained[464] in good yields by thermolysis of *O*-benzylated glycosylidene–diaziridines in the presence of *N*-phenylmaleimide, acrylonitrile, dimethyl fumarate, or dimethyl maleate (Fig. 1.287). Preparation of the glycosylidene–carbene from 1-hydrazi-2,3,4,6-tetra-*O*-benzyl-1-deoxy-D-glucopyranose, and its chain extension with acrylonitrile are given[460] in the following procedures.

1-Azi-2,3,4,6-tetra-O-benzyl-1-deoxy-D-glucopyranose *(287.1)*[460] Powdered 1-hydrazi-2,3,4,6-tetra-*O*-benzyl-1-deoxy-D-glucopyranose (500 mg, 0.9 mmol) is dissolved at room temperature in methanol (25 ml), and triethylamine (2 ml, 14.3 mmol) is added. The solution is cooled to −45°C, and under efficient stirring a solution of iodine (230 mg, 0.9 mmol) in methanol (4.5 ml) is added dropwise (0.5 ml/min). After addition of about two-thirds of the iodine solution, **287.1** starts to precipitate. Following complete addition, the crystalline product is filtered off under nitrogen and washed with cold (−40°C) methanol and then three times with hexane (at ambient temperature) to yield 458 mg (92%) of **287.1**.

Cyclopropanation of 287.1 with acrylonitrile[460] Acrylonitrile (3 ml, 78.5 mmol) is stirred under nitrogen in the presence of 0.5 g of 4Å molecular sieves at room

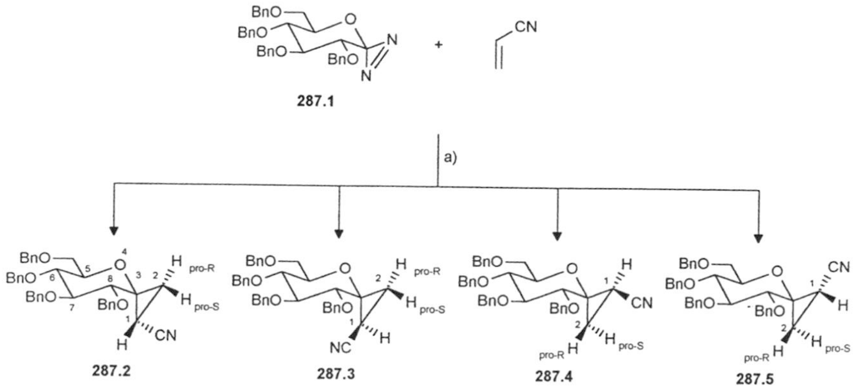

287.1

a)

287.2   **287.3**   **287.4**   **287.5**

a) R.t., 12 h, **287.2**: 36%; **287.3**: 22%; **287.4**: 8%; **287.5**: 4%

FIGURE I.287

temperature for 30 min. Then, 690 mg (1.25 mmol) of **287.1** is quickly added, and the mixture is stirred at room temperature for 12 h, diluted with dichloromethane (5 ml), and filtered through Celite. The Celite is washed several times with dichloromethane, the combined filtrate is evaporated, and the residue is subjected to fast column chromatography (eluant: 4:1 pentane–ether) to give 506 mg (70%) of a mixture of products which were separated by a second chromatography (eluant: 10:1 → 4:1 pentane–ether) to give the diastereoisomeric 6,7,8-tris-(benzyloxy)-5-[(benzyloxy)methyl]-4-oxaspiro[2.5]octane-1-carbonitriles **287.2–287.5,** as colorless syrups, with the following physical data (TLC in 1:1 pentane–ether).

287.2: (1*R*,3*R*,5*R*,6*R*,7*S*,8*R*), 36%, $[\alpha]_D^{25}$ +108.7 (c = 2.4 in chloroform), R_f = 0.86
287.3: (1*S*,3*R*,5*R*,6*R*,7*S*,8*R*), 22%, $[\alpha]_D^{25}$ −2.5 (c = 2.0 in chloroform), R_f = 0.65
287.4: (1*R*,3*S*,5*R*,6*R*,7*S*,8*R*), 8%, $[\alpha]_D^{25}$ +50.2 (c = 0.77 in chloroform), R_f = 0.76
287.5: (1*S*,3*S*,5R,6*R*,7*S*,8*R*), 4%, R_f = 0.84

Formally, the *highest carbon chain extension* of saccharides has been performed by the Vasella group[466,467] with the reaction of glycosyl–carbenes with buckminsterfullerene (C_{60}) to provide spherical (and not open-chain) products (Fig. 1.288). When preparing such fullerenes, investigators had to focus special attention on the removal of the protecting groups of the saccharide; the first experiments failed with benzyl functions.[466] Acetal

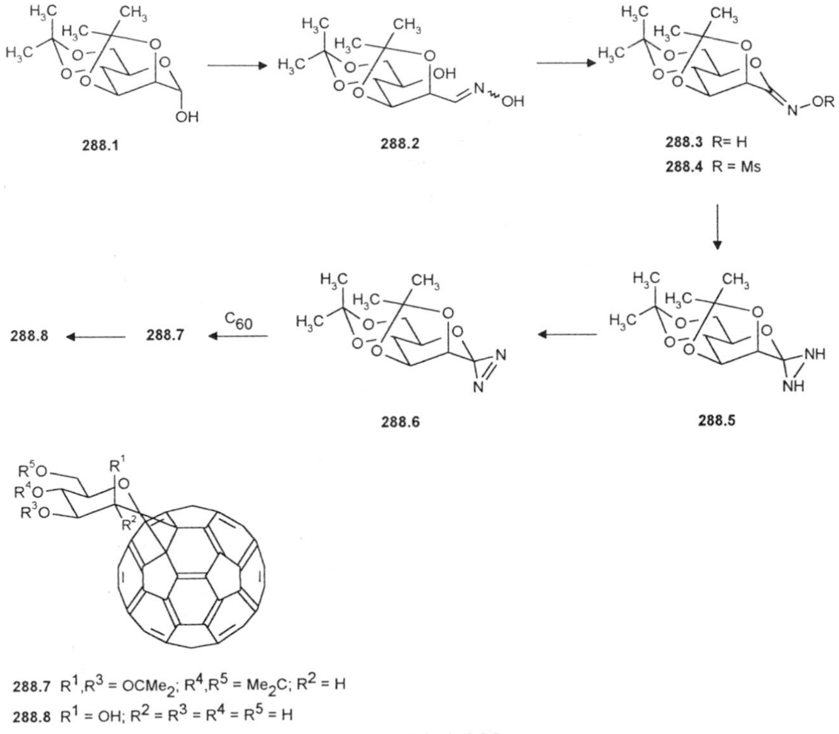
288.1
288.2
288.3 R= H
288.4 R = Ms
288.5
288.6
C_{60}
288.7
288.8
288.7 R1,R3 = OCMe2; R4,R5 = Me2C; R2 = H
288.8 R1 = OH; R2 = R3 = R4 = R5 = H

FIGURE 1.288

protecting groups could be readily removed from the coupled products (such as **288.7**), opening a new perspective on the synthesis of "building blocks of supramolecular assemblies and new materials."[467]

In the following series of procedures[466] the five-step synthesis of the diazirine **288.6** from 2,3:4,6-di-*O*-isopropylidene-α-D-mannopyranose (**288.1**) is described, together with the experimental details of the ascending step and subsequent deprotection.

Preparation of (E)- and (Z)-2,3:4,6-di-O-isopropylidene-D-mannose oxime (288.2)[466] A solution of **288.1** (4 g, 15.4 mmol) in ethanol (76 ml) is added to a suspension of sodium (1.42 g, 62.2 mmol) and hydroxylamine hydrochloride (8.33 g, 119.8 mmol) in boiling ethanol (208 ml). After 50 min the solvent is evaporated, and the residue is taken up with dichloromethane (200 ml), washed with brine, dried (Na$_2$SO$_4$), and evaporated to give a ~2:3 mixture of the (*E*)- and (*Z*)- isomers of **288.2** (3.83 g, 90%), which is useful for the next step without purification. Fast column chromatography (eluant: 1:1 ethyl acetate–hexane) gives pure fractions of the (*E*)-isomer, R_f = 0.22.

*(Z)-2,3:4,6-Di-O-isopropylidene-D-*mannonhydroximo-1,5-lactone (**288.3**)[466] A solution of **288.2** (4 g, 14.5 mmol) and DBU (2.97 ml, 20 mmol) in dichloromethane (200 ml) is treated with *N*-chlorosuccinimide (2.66 g, 20 mmol) at −20°C. The mixture is stirred at this temperature for 20 min, allowed to warm to 0°C, diluted with dichloromethane (200 ml), and washed with saturated aqueous NaHCO$_3$. The organic layer is dried (Na$_2$SO$_4$), evaporated, and the residue is crystallized from ethyl acetate–hexane to afford 3.57 g (90%) of **288.3**, m.p. 171–173°C, $[\alpha]_D^{25}$ +25 (*c* = 0.41 in chloroform), R_f = 0.45 (in 1:1 ethyl acetate–hexane).

Preparation of the methanesulfonate (288.4) of 288.3[466] To a solution of the oxime **288.3** (3.57 g, 13.1 mmol) in dichloromethane (150 ml), triethylamine (2.79 ml, 20 mmol) and methanesulfonyl chloride (1.22 ml, 15.7 mmol) are added at 0°C, and the mixture is stirred for 15 min. It is then diluted with dichloromethane (50 ml), and washed with saturated aqueous NaHCO$_3$, the organic layer is dried (Na$_2$SO$_4$) and concentrated. Crystallization of the residue from ethyl acetate–hexane gives 3.87 g (87%) of the pure mesylate **288.4**, m.p. 130–132°C, $[\alpha]_D^{25}$ +31.4 (*c* = 1.49 in chloroform), R_f = 0.37 (in 1:1 ethyl acetate–hexane).

1,5-Anhydro-1-hydrazi-2,3:4,6-di-O-isopropylidene-D-mannitol (288.5)[466] Compound **288.4** (1 g, 2.85 mmol) is dissolved in a solution of ammonia in methanol (20 ml) at 0°C and stirred in a closed flask for 8 h at room temperature. The solvent is evaporated to afford 580 mg (75%) of the hydrazialditol **288.5**, suitable for the next step without purification, R_f = 0.37 (in 3:2 ethyl acetate–hexane containing 0.5% of triethylamine).

1,5-Anhydro-1,1-(1,2-dihydrofullerene[60]-1,2-diyl)-2,3:4,6-di-O-isopropylidene-D-mannitol (288.7)[466] A solution of **288.5** (294 mg, 1.08 mmol) and triethylamine (2 ml, 21.3 mmol) in dry ether (25 ml) under argon is treated dropwise with a solution of iodine (192 mg, 0.76 mmol) in ether (5 ml). The mixture is concentrated at −60°C, the residue is taken up in ether (20 ml), the insolubles are filtered off, and the filtrate (containing ~0.03 M of **288.6** in the ether solution) is used immediately for the next step (R_f = 0.8 in ether), as follows. A solution of buckminsterfullerene[60] (200 mg, 0.275 mmol) in toluene (200 ml) is treated with the preceding solution of **288.6** (~55 mmol) in ether. After stirring for 5 h at room temperature, the mixture is concentrated, and the residue submitted to column chromatography (eluant: toluene) to furnish 83 mg (31%) of the title product **288.7**, $R_f = 0.46$ (in 1:2 ether–hexane) and 82 mg (41%) of the starting fullerene.

The results of modern organic chemistry have led investigators[468,469] to prepare saccharide lactone–sulfonylhydrazine salts for conversion into glycosylidene–carbenes, suitable for the chain extensions discussed above. Figure 1.289 surveys the results of the procedures published to date.

An ascending procedure starting from sulfonylhydrazones and proceeding via an allylic diazene intermediate has also been reported[470] in the field

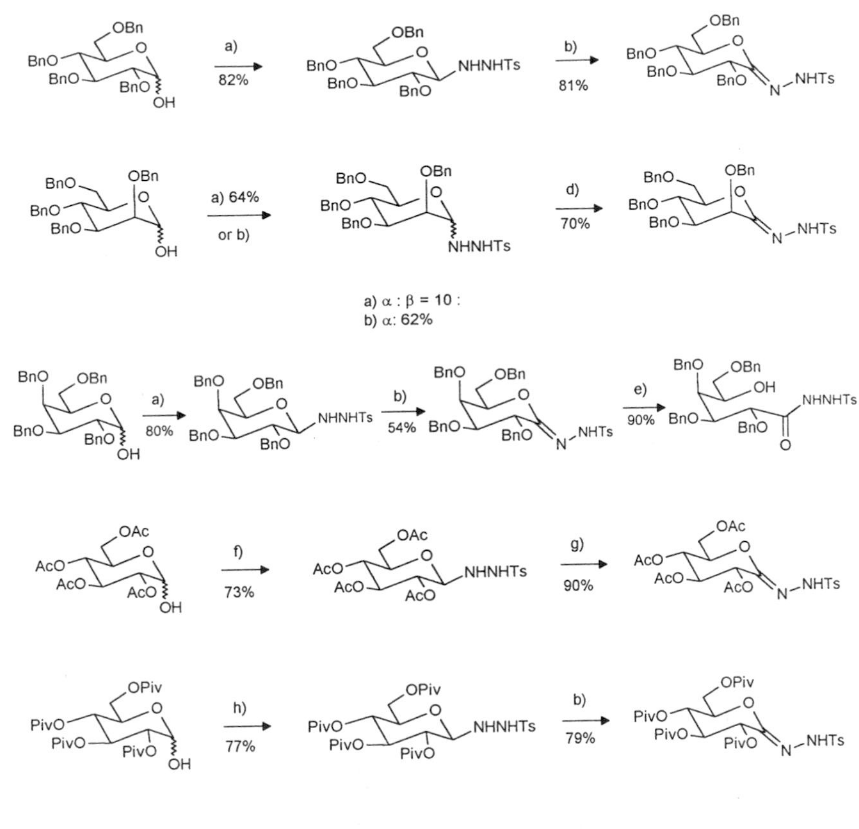

a) α : β = 10 :
b) α: 62%

Bn = PhCH$_2$, Ts = 4-MeC$_6$H$_4$SO$_2$, Piv = (t-Bu)CO

a) 1 equiv. of TsNHNH$_2$, 0.05 equiv. of AcOH, toluene, reflux; b) 1.1 equiv. of NBS, 1.2 equiv. of DBU, r.t.;

c) 1 equiv. of TsNHNH$_2$, 0.05 equiv. of AcOH, MeCN, reflux; d) CrO$_3$·2C$_5$H$_5$N, CH$_2$Cl$_2$, 0°C

e) wet solvents; f) 1 equiv. of TsNHNH$_2$, MeCN, reflux; g) pyridinium dichromate, CH$_2$Cl$_2$, r.t.;

h) 1 equiv. of TsNHNH$_2$, toluene, reflux

FIGURE I.289

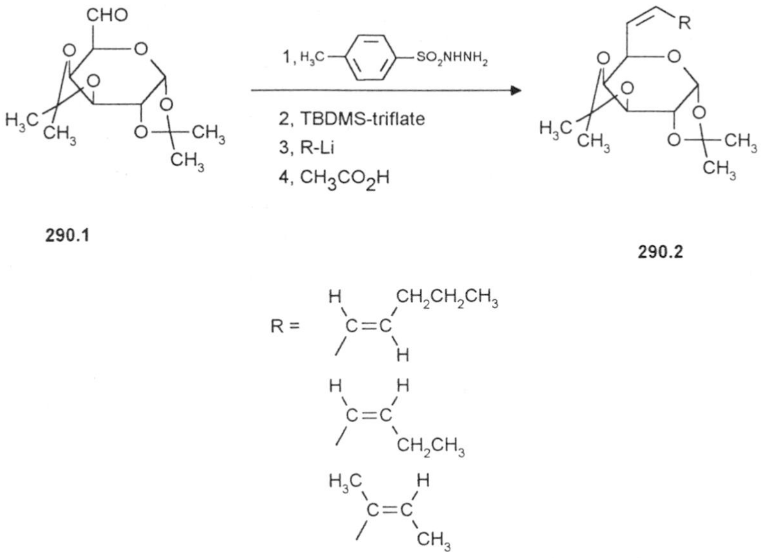

290.1

290.2

$$R =$$

FIGURE 1.290

of saccharides. The saccharide tosylhydrazone is converted into an *N-tert*-butyldimethylsilyltosylhydrazone, which is then transformed in the olefin-forming step with organolithium compounds. As an example, Figure 1.290 shows a related transformation of 1,2:3,4-di-*O*-isopropylidene-α-D-*galacto*-hexodialdo-1,5-pyranose (**290.1**) into the olefinic chain-extended product, **290.2**.

REFERENCES TO SECTION 1.2.7

1. E. L. Eliel and S. H. Wilen, *Stereochemistry of Organic Compounds.* Wiley, New York, 1993; M. T. Reetz, *Angew. Chem.* **96,** 542 (1984); *Angew. Chem., Int. Ed. Engl.* **23,** 556 (1984).
2. M. L. Wolfrom and S. Hanessian, *J. Org. Chem.* **27,** 1800 (1962).
3. G. J. McGarvey, M. Kimura, T. Oh, and J. M. Williams, *J. Carbohydr. Chem.* **3,** 125 (1984) and the literature cited therein; M. Braun and H. Mahler, *Angew. Chem.* **101,** 948 (1989); *Angew. Chem., Int. Ed. Engl.* **28,** 896 (1989).
4. J. Mulzer, A. Angermann, and W. Münch, *Justus Liebigs Ann. Chem.,* p. 825. (1986) cf. also M. S. Solomon and P. B. Hopkins, *Tetrahedron Lett.* **32,** 3297 (1991).
5. D. Horton, J. B. Hughes, and J. K. Thomson, *J. Org. Chem.* **33,** 728 (1968).
6. B. Mekki, G. Singh, and R. H. Wightman, *Tetrahedron Lett.* **32,** 5143 (1991).
7. K. S. Kim, Y. H. Ahn, S. B. Park, I. H. Cho, Y. H. Joo, and B. H. Youn, *J. Carbohydr. Chem.* **10,** 911 (1991).
8. B. Reitstoen, L. Kilaas, and T. Anthonsen, *Acta Chem. Scand., Ser. B* **B40,** 440 (1986).
9. J. S. Yadav and D. Rajagopal, *Tetrahedron Lett.* **31,** 5077 (1990).
10. G. A. Kraus and J. Shi, *J. Org. Chem.* **55,** 4922 (1990).

11. L. J. Liotta, J. Lee, and B. Ganem, *Tetrahedron* **47** 2433 (1991).
12. H. Hashimoto and M. Izumi, *Chem. Lett.* p. 25 (1992).
13. H. Ohle and C. Dambergis, *Justus Liebigs Ann. Chem.* **481**, 255 (1930).
14. H. Ohle and I. Blell, *Justus Liebigs Ann. Chem.* **492**, 1 (1931).
15. J. E. English, Jr., and P. H. Griswold, Jr., *J. Am. Chem. Soc.* **67**, 2039 (1945); **70**, 1390 (1948).
16. W. A. Bonner, *J. Am. Chem. Soc.* **73**, 3126 (1951).
17. W. A. Bonner, *Methods Carbohydr. Chem.* **2**, 465 (1963).
18. D. Horton, A. Liav, and S. E. Walker, *Carbohydr. Res.* **28**, 201 (1973).
19. J. G. Buchanan, A. D. Dunn, and A. R. Edgar, *J. Chem. Soc., Perkin Trans. 1*, p. 1191 (1975); p. 68 (1976); R. E. Dolle and K. C. Nicolaou, *Chem. Commun.*, p. 1016 (1985).
20. H. Ogura, H. Takahashi, and T. Itoh, *J. Org. Chem.* **37**, 72 (1972); H. Ogura and H. Takahashi, *Synth. Commun.* **3**, 135 (1973); T. K. M. Shing, H.-C. Tsui, Z.-H. Zhou, and T. C. W. Mak, *J. Chem. Soc., Perkin Trans. 1*, p. 887 (1992).
21. J. Gätzi and T. Reichstein, *Helv. Chim. Acta* **21**, 914 (1938).
22. T. D. Inch, *Carbohydr. Res.* **5**, 45 (1967).
23. H. C. Jarell and W. A. Szarek, *Can. J. Chem.* **57**, 924, (1979).
24. S. J. Danishefsky, W. H. Pearson, D. F. Harvey, C. J. Maring, and J. P. Springer, *J. Am. Chem. Soc.* **107**, 1256 (1985).
25. J. Mulzer, H. Dehmlow, J. Buschmann, and P. Luger, *J. Org. Chem.* **57**, 3194 (1992).
26. H. Redlich, W. Sudau, A. K. Szardenings, and R. Vollerthun, *Carbohydr. Res.* **226**, 57 (1992).
27. M. Gerspacher and H. Rapoport, *J. Org. Chem.* **56**, 3700 (1991).
28. J. Mulzer, C. Seilz, P. Luger, M. Weber, and W. Reutter, *Justus Liebigs Ann. Chem.*, p. 947 (1991).
29. M. Dasser, F. Chrétien, and Y. Chapleur, *J. Chem. Soc., Perkin Trans. 1*, p. 3091 (1990).
30. M. Carcano, F. Nicotra, L. Panza, and G. Russo, *J. Chem. Soc., Chem. Commun.*, p. 297 (1989); L. Lay, F. Nicotra, L. Panza, and A. Verani, *Gazz. Chim. Ital.* **122**, 345 (1992).
31. M. S. Feather and S. J. Eitelman, *J. Carbohydr. Chem.* **7**, 251 (1988).
32. N. Berg and O. Kjolberg, *Carbohydr. Res.* **57**, 65 (1977).
33. J. G. Buchanan, M. L. Quijano, and R. H. Wightman, *J. Chem. Soc., Perkin Trans. 1*, p. 1573 (1992).
34. M. Nagai, J. J. Gaudino, and C. S. Wilcox, *Synthesis*, p. 163 (1992).
35. G. Aslani-Shotorbani, J. G. Buchanan, A. R. Edgar, and P. K. Shahidi, *Carbohydr. Res.* **136**, 37 (1983).
36. J. G. Buchanan, A. R. Edgar, and M. J. Power, *J. Chem. Soc., Chem. Commun.*, p. 346 (1972).
37. D. Horton and F. O. Swanson, *Carbohydr. Res.* **14**, 159 (1970).
38. R. Hems, D. Horton, and M. Nakadate, *Carbohydr. Res.* **25**, 205 (1972); S. Jarosz, J. Glodek, and A. Zamojski, *ibid.* **163**, 289 (1987).
39. S. Czernecki, S. Horns, and J.-M. Valéry, *J. Org. Chem.* **60**, 650 (1995.); S. Czernecki, and J.-M. Valéry, *J. Carbohydr. Chem.* **7**, 151 (1988); **8**, 793 (1989).
40. W. S. Chilton, W. C. Lontz, R. B. Roy, and C. Yoda, *J. Org. Chem.* **36**, 3222 (1971).
41. T. Watanabe, S. Nishiyama, S. Yamamura, K. Kato, M. Nagai, and T. Takita, *Tetrahedron Lett.* **32**, 2399 (1991).
42. P. Smid, F. J. M. Schipper, H. J. G. Broxterman, G. J. P. G. Boons, G. A. van der Marel, and J. H. van Boom, *Recl. Trav. Chim. Pays-Bas*, **112**, 451 (1993); F. L. van Delft, M. de Kort, G. A. van der Marel, and J. H. van Boom, *J. Org. Chem.* **61**, 1883 (1996).
43. K. Dziewiszek and A. Zamojski, *Carbohydr. Res.* **150**, 163 (1986).
44. K. Tamao and N. Ishida, *Tetrahedron Lett.* **25**, 4245 (1984).
45. G. J. P. G. Boons, P. A. M. van der Klein, G. A. van der Marel, and J. H. van Boom, *Recl. Trav. Chim. Pays-Bas*, **107**, 507 (1988).

46. G. J. P. G. Boons, G. A. van der Marel, and J. H. van Boom, *Tetrahedron Lett.* **29**, 229 (1989).
47. A. Fürstner and H. Weidmann, *J. Org. Chem.* **55**, 1363 (1990)
48. G. J. P. G. Boons, M. Overhand, G. A. van der Marel, and J. H. van Boom, *Carbohydr. Res.* **192**, C1 (1989).
49. G. J. P. G. Boons, G. A. van der Marel, J. T. Poolman, and J. H. van Boom, *Recl. Trav. Chim. Pays-Bas,* **108**, 108 (1989).
50. P. J. Garegg, S. Oscarson, and M. Szőnyi, *Carbohydr. Res.* **205**, 125 (1990).
51. G. J. P. G. Boons, R. Steyger, M. Overhand, G. A. van der Marel, and J. H. van Boom, *J. Carbohydr. Chem.* **10**, 995 (1991).
52. B. I. Glänzer, Z. Györgydeák, B. Bernet, and A. Vasella, *Helv. Chim. Acta* **74**, 343 (1991).
53. J. Mulzer and H. Angermann, *Tetrahedron Lett.* **24**, 2843 (1983).
54. J.-P. Gesson, J.-C. Jacquesy, M. Mondon, and P. Petit, *Tetrahedron Lett.* **33**, 3637 (1992).
55. K. Suzuki, Y. Yuki, and T. Mukaiyama, *Chem. Lett.,* p. 1592 (1981); T. Mukaiyama, Y. Yuki, and K. Suzuki, *ibid.* p. 1169 (1982).
56. T. Mukaiyama, K. Suzuki, T. Yamad, and F. Tabusa, *Tetrahedron.* **46**, 265 (1990); S. F. Martin, H.-J. Chen, and V. M. Lynch, *J. Org. Chem.* **60**, 276 (1995).
57. S. F. Martin and P. W. Zinke, *J. Org. Chem.* **56**, 6600 (1991).
58. M. Yokoyama, T. Tanabe, A. Toyoshima, and H. Togo, *Synthesis,* p. 517 (1993).
59. F. L. Boyd, Jr., and D. C. Baker, *J. Carbohydr. Chem.* **5**, 257 (1986).
60. J. J. Gaudino, and C. S. Wilcox, *J. Am. Chem. Soc.* **112**, 4374 (1990).
61. I. Hoppe and U. Schöllkopf, *Justus Liebigs Ann. Chem.,* p. 1474 (1980).
62. G. B. Howarth, W. A. Szarek, and J. K. N. Jones, *J. Chem. Soc. C,* p. 2218 (1970); G. R. Woolard, E. B. Rathbone, W. A. Szarek, and J. K. N. Jones, *J. Chem. Soc., Perkin Trans. 1,* p. 950 (1976).
63. R. R. Schmidt and R. Betz, *Angew. Chem.* **96**, 420 (1984); *Angew. Chem., Int. Ed. Engl.* **23**, 430 (1984); A. Esswein, R. Betz, and R. R. Schmidt, *Helv. Chim. Acta* **72**, 213 (1989).
64. A. Ehnsen and R. R. Schmidt, *Justus Liebigs Ann. Chem.,* p. 69 (1989).
65. D. Lafont, M. Hoch, and R. R. Schmidt, *J. Carbohydr. Chem.* **5**, 601 (1986).
66. R. R. Schmidt, J. Kast, and H. Speer, *Synthesis,* p. 725 (1983).
67. G. A. Danilova, V. I. Melnikova, and K. K. Pivnitskii, *Zh. Org. Khim.* **26**, 2208 (1990).
68. H. Ina and C. Kibayashi, *Tetrahedron Lett.* **32**, 4147 (1991).
69. M. Tokoyama, A. Toyoshima, T. Akibo, and H. Togo, *Chem. Lett.,* p. 265 (1994).
70. K. Tatsuta, S. Miura, S. Ohta, and H. Gunji, *J. Antibiot.* **48**, 286 (1995); K. Tatsuta and S. Miura, *Tetrahedron Lett.* **36**, 6721 (1995).
71. S. Horito, M. Amano, and H. Hashimoto, *J. Carbohydr. Chem.* **8**, 68 (1989).
72. A. Dondoni, F. Junquera, F. L. Merchán, P. Merino, and J. Tejero, *Tetrahedron Lett.* **33**, 4221 (1992); A. Dondoni, S. Franco, F. L. Merchán, P. Merino, and J. Tejero, *Synlett,* p. 78 (1993); S. Franco, F. Junquera, and J. Tejero, *Synth. Commun.* **24**, 2537 (1994); F. L. Merchán, P. Merino, I. Rojo, J. Tejero, and A. Dondoni, *Tetrahedron: Asymmetry* **6**, 2145 (1995).
73. D. Seebach, *Synthesis* **1**, 17 (1969); D. Seebach, *Angew. Chem.* **81**, 690 (1969); *Angew. Chem., Int. Ed. Engl.* **8**, 639 (1969); H. Paulsen, *Pure Appl. Chem.* **49**, 1169 (1977).
74. P. C. Bulman Page, M. B. van Niel, and J. C. Prodger, *Tetrahedron* **45**, 7643 (1989); T. Nakata, T. Suenaga, T. Oishi, *Tetrahedron Lett.* **29**, 6525 (1989).
75. A.-M. Sepulchre, G. Lukács, G. Vass, and S. D. Gero, *Angew. Chem.* **84**, 111 (1972); *Angew. Chem., Int. Ed. Engl.* **11**, 149 (1972).
76. N. P. Peet, E. W. Huber, and R. A. Farr, *Tetrahedron* **47**, 7537 (1991).
77. W. O. Moss, R. H. Bradbury, N. J. Hales, and T. Gallagher, *J. Chem. Soc., Perkin Trans. 1,* p. 1901 (1992).
78. A. Gateau-Olesker, A. M. Sepulchre, G. Vass, and S. D. Gero, *Tetrahedron* **33**, 393 (1977).
79. A. M. Sepulchre, A. Gateau-Olesker, G. Lukács, G. Vass, and S. D. Gero, *Tetrahedron Lett.* **13**, 3945 (1972).

80. A. M. Sepulchre, G. Lukács, G. Vass, and S. D. Gero, *Bull. Soc. Chim. France*, p. 4000 (1979); G. E. Levitan, V. I. Kornilov, and Yu. A. Zhdanov, *Zh. Obshch. Khim.* **56**, 212 (1986).

81. H. Paulsen, K. Roden, V. Sinnwell, and W. Koebernick, *Angew. Chem.* **88**, 477 (1976); *Angew. Chem., Int. Ed. Engl.* **88**, 439 (1976).

82. H. Paulsen, M. Schüller, A. Heitmann, M. A. Nashed, and H. Redlich, *Justus Liebigs Ann. Chem.*, p. 675 (1986).

83. H. Redlich, B. Schneider, and W. Francke, *Tetrahedron Lett.* **21**, 3013 (1980).

84. Yu. A. Zhdanov, V. I. Kornilov, Yu. M. Miksiev, B. B. Paidak, and V. M. Stoianov, *Zh. Obshch. Khim.* **52**, 2355 (1982); B. B. Paidak, Yu. M. Miksiev, G. E. Levitan, V. I. Kornilov, and Yu. A. Zhdanov, *ibid.* **56**, 212 (1986); Yu. M. Miksiev, B. B. Paidak, V. I. Kornilov, and Yu. A. Zhdanov, *Bioorg. Khim.* **16**, 1118 (1990).

85. A. M. Sepulchre, G. Vass, and S. D. Gero, *Tetrahedron Lett.* **14**, 3619 (1973).

86. M. Imoto, S. Kusumoto, and T. Shiba, *Tetrahedron Lett.* **28**, 6235 (1987).

87. P. A. M. van der Klein, G. J. P. G. Boons, G. H. Veeneman, G. A. van der Marel, and J. H. van Boom, *Tetrahedron Lett.* **30**, 5477 (1989); B. Fössel, M. Stenzel, R. Baudouy, G. Condemine, J. Robert-Baudouy, and B. Fenet, *Bull. Soc. Chim. Fr.* **132**, 829 (1995).

88. H. Paulsen and H. Bünsch, *Chem. Ber.* **111**, 3484 (1978).

89. R. J. Ferrier and P. C. Tyler, *Carbohydr. Res.* **136**, 249 (1985).

90. M. E. L. Sanchez, V. Michelet, I. Besurier, and J. P. Genet, *Synlett*, p. 705 (1994).

91. H. Ogura, K. Furuhata, H. Takahashi, and Y. Iitaka, *Chem. Pharm. Bull.* **26**, 2782 (1978).

92. D. Horton and W. Priebe, *Carbohydr. Res.* **94**, 27 (1981).

93. H. Ogura and H. Takahashi, *J. Org. Chem.* **39**, 1347 (1974).

94. D. Horton and R. A. Markovs, *Carbohydr. Res.* **78**, 295 (1980).

95. B. T. Gröbel and D. Seebach, *Synthesis*, p. 357 (1977); M. Kitamura, M. Isobe, Y. Ichikawa, and T. Goto, *J. Am. Chem. Soc.* **106**, 3252 (1984); P. A. M. van der Klein, and J. H. van Boom, *Carbohydr. Res.* **224**, 193 (1992); S. Knapp, W.-C. Shieh, C. Jaramillo, R. V. Trilles, and S. R. Nandan, *J. Org. Chem.* **59**, 946 (1994).

96. P. Di Cesare and D. Horton, *Carbohydr. Res.* **107**, 47 (1982).

97. Y. Izumi and A. Tai, *Stereodifferentiating Reactions*. Academic Press, New York, 1977; J. D. Morrison and M. S. Mosher, *Asymmetric Organic Reactions*. Prentice Hall, Englewood Cliffs, N.J, 1971; N. T. Anh, *Top. Curr. Chem.* **88**, 145 (1980); J. D. Morrison, *Asymmetric Synthesis*, Vol. 2, Parts A and B. Academic Press, New York, 1983, 1984; D. A. Evans, J. V. Nelson, and T. R. Taber, *Top. Stereochem.* **13**, 1 (1983); R. Mead and T. L. Macdonald, *J. Org. Chem.* **50**, 422 (1985).

98. A. Hosomi, and H. Sakurai, *Tetrahedron Lett.* **17**, 1295 (1976); Y. Yamamoto and K. Maruyama, *Heterocycles* **18**, 357 (1982).

99. T. Tsunoda, M. Suzuki, and R. Noyori, *Tetrahedron Lett.* **21**, 71 (1980).

100. T. Sammakia and R. S. Smith, *J. Am. Chem. Soc.* **114**, 10998 (1992).

101. M. D. Lewis, J. K. Cha, and Y. Kishi, *J. Am. Chem. Soc.* **104**, 4976 (1982).

102. D. R. Williams and F. D. Klingler, *Tetrahedron Lett.* **23**, 869 (1987).

103. T. L. Cupps, D. S. Wise, and L. B. Townsend, *J. Org. Chem.* **47**, 5115 (1982).

104. T. Mukaiyama, S. Kobayashi, and S.-i. Shoda, *Chem. Lett.*, p. 1529 (1984).

105. S. J. Danishefsky, M. P. DeNinno, G. B. Phillips, R. E. Zelle, and P. A. Lartey, *Tetrahedron* **42**, 2809 (1986).

106. D. D. Dhavale, E. Tagliavini, C. Trombini, and A. Umani-Ronchi, *J. Org. Chem.* **54**, 4100 (1989).

107. D. Cabaret and M. Wakselman, *J. Carbohydr. Chem.* **10**, 55 (1991).

108. O. R. Martin, S. P. Rao, T.-F. Yang, and F. Fotia, *Synlett*, p. 702 (1991).

109. A. P. Kozikowski, K. L. Sorgi, B. C. Wang, and Z.-b. Xu, *Tetrahedron Lett.* **24**, 1563 (1983).

110. Y. Araki, N. Kobayashi, Y. Ishido, and J. Nagasawa, *Carbohydr. Res.* **171**, 125 (1987).

111. A. Giannis and K. Sandhoff, *Tetrahedron Lett.* **26**, 1479 (1985).

112. J. A. Bennek and G. R. Gray, *J. Org. Chem.* **52,** 892 (1987).
113. A. Hosomi, Y. Sakata, and H. Sakurai, *Tetrahedron Lett.* **25,** 2383 (1984).
114. D. Horton and T. Miyake, *Carbohydr. Res.* **184,** 221 (1988).
115. C. Bertozzi and M. Bednarski, *Carbohydr. Res.* **223,** 243 (1992).
116. C. Bertozzi and M. Bednarski, *Tetrahedron Lett.* **33,** 3109 (1992).
117. R. A. Veloo, M. J. Wanner, and G.-J. Koomen, *Tetrahedron* **48,** 5301 (1992).
118. M. L. Shulman, S. D. Shilyan, and A. Ya. Khorlin, *Carbohydr. Res.* **31,** 229 (1974); A. Hosomi, Y. Sakata, and H. Sakurai, *ibid.* **171,** 223 (1987).
119. S. Danishefsky and J. F. Kerwin, *J. Org. Chem.* **47,** 3803, 5428 (1992).
120. Y. Ichikawa, M. Isobe, M. Konobe, and T. Goto, *Carbohydr. Res.* **171,** 193 (1987); A. G. Tolstikhov, O. F. Prokopenko, A. V. Spirikhin, V. P. Sultanmuratova, V. N. Odinokov, and G. A. Tolstikov, *Zh. Org. Khim.* **26,** 879 (1991).
121. R. J. Ferrier and P. M. Petersen, *J. Chem. Soc., Perkin Trans. 1,* p. 2023 (1992).
122. M. De Gracia Garcia Martin and D. Horton, *Carbohydr. Res.* **191,** 223 (1989).
123. E. M. Acton, K. J. Ryan, and M. Tracy, *Tetrahedron Lett.* **25,** 5743 (1984).
124. J. Ornet, L. Miginiac, K. Jaworski, and B. Randrianoelina, *Organometallics* **4,** 333 (1985).
125. S. A. Babirad, Y. Wang, and Y. Kishi, *J. Org. Chem.* **52,** 1370 (1987); T. Haneda, P. G. Goekjian, S. H. Kim, and Y. Kishi, *ibid.* **57,** 490 (1992).
126. C. Bruckner, H. Holzinger, and H. U. Reissig, *J. Org. Chem.* **53,** 2450 (1988).
127. W. R. Robertz, C. R. Bertozzi, and M. D. Bednarski, *Tetrahedron Lett.* **33,** 737 (1992).
128. H. Sugimura and M. Uematsu, *Tetrahedron Lett.* **29,** 4953 (1988).
129. H. Sugimura and K. Osumi, *Tetrahedron Lett.* **30,** 1574 (1989).
130. H. Sugimura, *Tetrahedron Lett.* **31,** 5909 (1990).
131. H. Sugimura, K. Osumi, T. Yamazaki, and T. Yamaya, *Tetrahedron Lett.* **32,** 1809 (1991).
132. K. Osumi and H. Sugimura, *Tetrahedron Lett.* **36,** 5789 (1995).
133. K. J. Henry, Jr. P. A. Grieco, and C. T. Jagoe, *Tetrahedron Lett.* **33,** 1817 (1992).
134. S. Jarosz, *Carbohydr. Res.* **166,** 211 (1987).
135. S. Jarosz, *Tetrahedron Lett.* **29,** 1193 (1988).
136. S. Jarosz, and B. Fraser-Reid, *J. Org. Chem.* **54,** 4011 (1989).
137. S. Jarosz, *J. Carbohydr. Chem.* **12,** 1149 (1993).
138. P. Lesimple, J.-M. Beau, and P. Sinay, *Carbohydr. Res.* **171,** 289 (1987).
139. J. Prandi, C. Audin, and J.-M. Beau, *Tetrahedron Lett.* **32,** 769 (1991).
140. Y. Y. Belosludtsev, R. K. Bhatt, and J. R. Falck, *Tetrahedron Lett.* **36,** 5881 (1995); O. Frey, M. Hoffman, and H. Kessler, *Angew. Chem.* **107,** 2194 (1995); *Angew. Chem., Int. Ed. Engl.* **34,** 2026 (1995).
141. D. K. Hutchinson and P. L. Fuchs, *J. Am. Chem. Soc.* **109,** 4930 (1987).
142. E. Dubois and J.-M. Beau, *Carbohydr. Res.* **228,** 103 (1992).
143. S. Hanessian, M. Martin, and R. C. Desai, *J. Chem. Soc., Chem. Commun.,* p. 926 (1986).
144. K. Burgess and D. A. Chaplin, *Tetrahedron Lett.* **33,** 6077 (1992).
145. W. R. Roush, *ACS Symp. Ser.* **386,** 282 (1989).
146. R. W. Hoffmann, A. Endesfelder, and H.-J. Zeiss, *Carbohydr. Res.* **123,** 320 (1983).
147. W. R. Roush, A. E. Walts, and L. K. Hong, *J. Am. Chem. Soc.* **107,** 8186 (1985).
148. W. R. Roush, P. T. Grover, and X. Lin, *Tetrahedron Lett.* **31,** 7563 (1990).
149. W. R. Roush and P. T. Grover, *Tetrahedron Lett.* **31,** 7567 (1990).
150. W. R. Roush, M. J. Adam, A. E. Walts, and D. J. Harris, *J. Am. Chem. Soc.* **108,** 3422 (1986).
151. W. R. Roush, D. J. Harris, and B. M. Lesur, *Tetrahedron Lett.* **24,** 2227 (1983).
152. W. R. Roush and M. R. Michaelides, *Tetrahedron Lett.* **27,** 3353 (1986).
153. W. R. Roush and J. A. Straub, *Tetrahedron Lett.* **27,** 3349 (1986).
154. P. G. M. Wuts and S. S. Bigelow, *J. Org. Chem.* **48,** 3489 (1983).
155. R. W. Hoffmann, R. Metternich, and J. W. Lanz, *Justus Liebigs Ann. Chem.,* p. 881 (1987).
156. R. W. Hoffmann, B. Kemper, R. Metternich, and T. Lehmeier, *Justus Liebigs Ann. Chem.,* p 2246 (1985).

157. W. R. Roush, J. A. Straub, and M. S. Van Nieuwenhze, *J. Org. Chem.* **56**, 1636 (1991).
158. W. R. Roush, in *Comprehensive Organic Synthesis* (C. H. Heathcock, ed.), Vol. 2, p. 40. Pergamon Press, Oxford (1991).
159. W. R. Roush, X. Lin, and J. A. Straub, *J. Org. Chem.* **56**, 1649 (1991).
160. A. Dondoni, G. Fantin, M. Fogagnolo, A. Medici, and P. Pedrini, *J. Org. Chem.* **54**, 693 (1989).
161. A. Dondoni, G. Fantin, M. Fogagnolo, A. Medici, and P. Pedrini, *J. Org. Chem.* **53**, 1748 (1988); A. Dondoni, *Pure Appl. Chem.* **62**, 643 (1990).
162. A. Dondoni, J. Orduna, and P. Merino, *Synthesis*, p. 201 (1992).
163. A. Dondoni, G. Fantin, M. Fogagnolo, A. Medici, and P. Pedrini, *J. Org. Chem.* **54**, 702 (1989).
164. A. Dondoni, G. Fantin, M. Fogagnolo, and P. Pedrini, *Tetrahedron* **45**, 5141 (1989).
165. A. Dondoni and P. Merino, *Synthesis*, p. 196 (1992).
166. A. Dondoni, F. Merchán, P. Merino, T. Tejero, and V. Bertolasi, *J. Chem. Soc., Chem. Commun.*, p. 1731 (1994).
167. A. Dondoni, F. Franco, F. Junquera, F. Merchán, P. Merino, T. Tejero, and V. Bertolasi, *Chem. Eur. J.*, p. 505 (1995).
168. P. Nedenskov, N. Elming. J. T. Nielsen, and N. Clauson-Kaas, *Acta Chem. Scand.* **9**, 17 (1955); J. Jurczak and S. Pikul, *Tetrahedron Lett.* **26**, 3039 (1985).
169. K. Dziewiszek, M. Chmielewski, and A. Zamojski, *Carbohydr. Res.* **104**, C1 (1982).
170. J. Gawronski, D. Radocki, J. Jurczak, Z. Pakulski, J. Raczko, J. Ramza, and A. Zamojski, *J. Org. Chem.* **55**, 1118 (1990).
171. B. Grzeszczyk, K. Dziewiszek, S. Jarosz, and A. Zamojski, *Carbohydr. Res.* **145**, 145 (1985).
172. S. Pikul, J. Raczko, K. Ankner, and J. Jurczak, *J. Am. Chem. Soc.* **109**, 3981 (1987).
173. J. Jurczak and S. Pikul, *Tetrahedron Lett.* **25**, 3107 (1984).
174. C. W. Jefford, D. Jaggi, and J. Boukouvalas, *Tetrahedron Lett.* **28**, 4037 (1987) and the literature cited therein.
175. G. Casiraghi, L. Colombo, G. Rassu, and P. Spanu, *Tetrahedron Lett.* **30**, 5325 (1989).
176. G. Casiraghi, L. Colombo, G. Rassu, and P. Spanu, *J. Org. Chem.* **55**, 2565 (1990).
177. G. Casiraghi, L. Colombo, G. Rassu, and P. Spanu, *J. Org. Chem.* **56**, 2135 (1991).
178. G. Casiraghi, L. Colombo, G. Rassu, P. Spanu, G. Gasparri Fava, and M. Ferrari Belicchi, *Tetrahedron* **46**, 5807 (1990).
179. G. Casiraghi, L. Colombo, G. Rassu, and P. Spanu, *J. Chem. Soc., Chem. Commun.*, p. 603 (1991).
180. G. Rassu, P. Spanu, L. Pinna, F. Zanardi, and G. Casiraghi, *Tetrahedron Lett.* **36**, 1941 (1995).
181. G. Casiraghi, G. Rassu, P. Spanu, and L. Pinna, *J. Org. Chem.* **57**, 3760 (1992).
182. G. Rassu, G. Casiraghi, P. Spanu, L. Pinna, G. Gasparri Fava, M. Ferrari Belicchi, and G. Pelosi, *Tetrahedron: Asymmetry* **3**, 1035 (1992).
183. M. Cornia, G. Casiraghi, and L. Zetta, *J. Org. Chem.* **56**, 5466 (1991).
184. G. Casiraghi, P. Spanu, G. Rassu, L. Pinna, and F. Ulgheri, *J. Org. Chem.* **59**, 2906 (1994).
185. G. Casiraghi, F. Ulgheri, P. Spanu, G. Rassu, L. Pinna, G. Gasparri Fava, M. Ferrari Belicchi, and G. Pelosi, *J. Chem. Soc., Perkin Trans. 1*, p. 2991(1993).
186. G. Rassu, L. Pinna, F. Ulgheri, M. Cornia, F. Zanardi, and G. Casiraghi, *Tetrahedron* **49**, 6489 (1993).
187. G. Rassu, F. Zanardi, M. Cornia, and G. Casiraghi, *J. Chem. Soc., Perkin Trans. 1*, p. 2431 (1994).
188. G. Casiraghi, G. Rassu, P. Spanu, and L. Pinna, *Tetrahedron Lett.* **35**, 2423 (1994).
189. G. Rassu, F. Zanardi, L. Battistini, and G. Casiraghi, *Tetrahedron: Asymmetry* **6**, 371 (1995).
190. M W. Rathke and P. Weipert, in *Comprehensive Organic Synthesis* (C. H. Heathcock, ed.), Vol. 2. p. 277. Pergamon Press, Oxford, (1991).

191. A. Fürstner, *Synthesis,* p. 54 (1989).
192. Yu. A. Zhdanov, Yu. E. Alexeev, and H. A. Khourdanov, *Zh. Obsch. Khim.* **40,** 943 (1970).
193. Yu. A. Zhdanov, Yu. E. Alexeev, and H. A. Khourdanov, *Zh. Obsch. Khim.* **41,** 1836 (1971).
194. R. Csuk and B. I. Glänzer, *J. Carbohydr. Chem.* **9,** 797 (1990).
195. J.-P. Gesson, J.-C. Jacquesy, and M. Mondon, *Tetrahedron* **45,** 2627 (1989).
196. L. W. Hertel, J. S. Kroin, J. W. Misner, and J. M. Tustin, *J. Org. Chem.* **53,** 2406 (1988).
197. Y. Xiang, L. P. Kotra, C. K. Chu, and R. F. Schinazi, *Bioorg. Med. Chem. Lett.* **5,** 743 (1995).
198. O. Kitagawa, T. Takeuchi, and Y. Kobayashi, *Tetrahedron Lett.* **29,** 1803 (1988).
199. R. Csuk, M. Hugener, and A. Vasella, *Helv. Chim. Acta* **71,** 609, (1988).
200. F. W. Lichtenthaler, S. Schwidetzky, and K. Nakamura, *Tetrahedron Lett.* **31,** 71 (1990).
201. H. M. Binch, A. M. Griffin, S. Schwidetzky, M. V. J. Ramsay, T. Gallagher, and F. W. Lichtenthaler, *J. Chem. Soc., Chem. Commun.,* p. 967 (1995).
202. M. Hayashi, M. Sugiyama, T. Toba, and N. Oguni, *J. Chem. Soc., Chem. Commun.,* p. 767 (1990).
203. T. Harada and T. Mukaiyama, *Chem. Lett.,* p. 161 (1982).
204. W. Schmid and G. M. Whitesides, *J. Am. Chem. Soc.* **113,** 6674 (1991).
205. C.-J. Li and T. H. Chan, *Tetrahedron Lett.* **32,** 7017 (1991).
206. T. H. Chan and C.-J. Li, *J. Chem. Soc., Chem. Commun.,* p. 747 (1992).
207. D. M. Gordon and G. M. Whitesides, *J. Org. Chem.* **58,** 7937 (1993).
208. T. H. Chan and M. C. Lee, *J. Org. Chem.* **60,** 4228 (1995); C.-J. Li, *Tetrahedron* **52,** 5643 (1996).
209. Yu. A. Zhdanov, Yu. E. Alexeev, and H. A. Khourdanov, *Carbohydr. Res.* **14,** 422 (1970); Yu. A. Zhdanov, Yu. E. Alexeev, and H. A. Khourdanov, *Zh. Obshch. Khim.* **42,** 2776 (1972).
210. V. K. Srivastava and L. M. Lerner, *J. Org. Chem.* **44,** 3368 (1979).
211. J. March, *Advanced Organic Chemistry. Reactions, Mechanisms and Structures,* 4th ed. Wiley, New York, 1992.
212. J. C. Buchanan, V. J. Jigajinni, G. Singh, and R. H. Wightman, *J. Chem. Soc., Perkin Trans. 1,* p. 2377 (1987).
213. Z. G. Hajós, *Carbon-Carbon Bond Formation* (M. Augustine, ed.), Vol. 1. p. 1. Dekker, New York, 1979; *Houben-Weyl, Methoden der Organischen Chemie,* Vol. 4/2, p. 25 (1955); Vol. 7/1, p. 76 (1954).
214. P. A. Bartlett, *Tetrahedron* **36,** 3 (1980); S. Masamune, W. Choy, J. S. Petersen, and L. R. Sita, *Angew. Chem.* **97,** 1 (1985); *Angew. Chem., Int. Ed. Engl.* **24,** 1 (1985); M. Braun, *Angew. Chem.* **99,** 24 (1987); *Angew. Chem., Int. Ed. Engl.* **26,** 24 (1987).
215. J. C. Speck, Jr., *Adv. Carbohydr. Chem.* **13,** 63 (1958); L. Hough and J. K. N. Jones, *ibid.* **11,** 185 (1956); D. Müller, S. Pitsch, A. Kittaka, E. Wagner, C. E. Wintner, and A. Eschenmoser, *Helv. Chim. Acta* **73,** 1410 (1990).
216. S. Morgenlie, *Carbohydr. Res.* **107,** 137 (1982).
217. C. H. Heathcock, S. D. Young, J. P. Hagen, M. C. Pirrung, C. T. White, and D. Vanderveer, *J. Org. Chem.* **45,** 3846 (1980).
218. C. H. Heathcock, C. T. White, J. J. Morrison, and D. Vanderveer, *J. Org. Chem.* **46,** 1296 (1981).
219. G. A. Danilova, V. I. Melnikova, and K. K. Pivnitsky, *Tetrahedron Lett.* **27,** 2489 (1986).
220. M. Terada, J. H. Gu, D. C. Deka, K. Mikami, and T. Nakai, *Chem. Lett.,* p. 29 (1992).
221. M. Murakami and T. Mukaiyama, *Chem. Lett.,* p. 241 (1982).
222. T. M. Wilson, P. Kocienski, K. Jarowicki, K. Isaac, P. M. Hithcock, A. Faller, and S. F. Campbell, *Tetrahedron* **46,** 1767 (1990); cf. also T. Gallagher, M. Giles, R. S. Subramanian, and M. S. Hadley, *J. Chem. Soc., Chem. Commun.,* p. 166 (1992).

223. T. Honda, T. Hayakawa, H. Kondoh, A. Okuyama, and M. Tsubuki, *Chem. Lett.,* p. 1861 (1991).
224. S. Jeganathan and P. Vogel, *J. Org. Chem.* **56**, 1133 (1991).
225. B. Rague, Y. Chapleur, and B. Castro, *J. Chem. Soc., Perkin Trans. 1,* p. 2063 (1982).
226. B. Helferich and O. Peters, *Ber. Dtsch. Chem. Ges.* **70**, 465 (1937); T. C. Crawford and S. A. Crawford, *Adv. Carbohydr. Chem. Biochem.* **37**, 149 (1980).
227. A. Calvo-Mateo, M. J. Camarasa, A. Diaz-Ortiz, F. G. de las Heras, and A. Alemany, *J. Chem. Soc., Perkin Trans. 1,* p. 2861 (1988).
228. Y. S. Yokoyama, M. R. H. Elmoghayar, and I. Kuwajima, *Tetrahedron Lett.* **23**, 2673 (1982).
229. T. Mukaiyama, S. Kobayashi, and S. Shoda, *Chem. Lett.,* p. 1529 (1984).
230. A. Dondoni, G. Fantin, M. Fogagnolo, and P. Merino, *Tetrahedron Lett.* **31**, 4513 (1990).
231. A. Dondoni, G. Fantin, and M. Fogagnolo, *Tetrahedron Lett.* **30**, 6063 (1990).
232. A. Dondoni and P. Merino, *J. Org. Chem.* **56**, 5294 (1991).
233. S. Jarosz and B. Fraser-Reid, *Tetrahedron Lett.* **30**, 2359 (1989).
234. F. M. Unger, *Adv. Carbohydr. Chem. Biochem.* **38**, 323 (1981).
235. E. C. Hearh and M. A. Ghalambor, *Biochem. Biophys. Res. Commun.* **10**, 340 (1963).
236. M. A. Ghalambor, E. M. Levine, and E. C. Hearth, *J. Biol. Chem.* **241**, 3207 (1966).
237. C. S. Hershberger, M. Davis, and S. B. Binkley, *J. Biol. Chem.* **243**, 1585 (1968); C. S. Hershberger and S. B. Binkley, *ibid.,* p. 1578.
238. P. A. Mc Nicholas, M. Batley, and J. W. Redmond, *Carbohydr. Res.* **146**, 219 (1986).
239. R. Shirai and H. Ogura, *Tetrahedron Lett.* **30**, 2263 (1989).
240. M. Nakamura, K. Furuhata, and H. Ogura, *Chem. Pharm. Bull.* **36**, 4807 (1988).
241. D. Charon and L. Szabó, *J. Chem. Soc., Perkin Trans. 1,* p. 1971 (1980).
242. D. Charon and L. Szabó, *J. Chem. Soc., Perkin Trans. 1,* p. 1628 (1976).
243. R. Schauer, *Adv. Carbohydr. Chem. Biochem.* **40**, 131 (1982).
244. A. Gottschalk, *Nature (London)* **176**, 881 (1955).
245. J. W. Cornforth, M. E. Firth, and A. Gottschalk, *Biochem. J.* **68**, 57 (1958).
246. P. M. Corrall and J. W. Cornforth, *Biochim. Biophys. Acta* **39**, 161 (1960).
247. R. Kuhn and R. Brossmer, *Justus Liebigs Ann. Chem.* **616**, 221 (1958); D. G. Comb and S. Roseman, *J. Am. Chem. Soc.* **80**, 3166 (1958); C. T. Spivak and S. Roseman, *J. Am. Chem. Soc.* **81**, 2403 (1959); R. Kuhn and G. Baschang, *Justus Liebigs Ann. Chem.* **636**, 164 (1960); J. Yoshimura, H. Sakai, N. Oda, and H. Hashimoto, *Bull. Chem. Soc. Jpn.* **45**, 2027 (1972); cf. also: W. L. Salo, M. Hamri, and L. Hallcher, *Carbohydr. Res.* **50**, 287 (1976); L. Szilágyi, P. Herczegh, and Gy. Bujtás, *Z. Naturforsch. B: Anorg. Chem., Org. Chem.* **32B**, 296 (1977).
248. H. Gault, *Ann. Chim. (Paris)* **6**, 220, 322 (1951); R. Durand, *ibid.,* p. 246; R. Ritter, *ibid.* p. 247; L. Erichomotowicz, *ibid.* p. 276.
249. C. Heidelberger and R. B. Hurlbert, *J. Am. Chem. Soc.* **72**, 4704 (1950).
250. R. Kuhn and G. Baschang, *Justus Liebigs Ann. Chem.* **659**, 156 (1962).
251. H. J. Backer and J. D. H. Homan, *Recl. Trav. Chim. Pays-Bas,* **58**, 1048 (1939).
252. H. Wesemann and F. Zilliken, *Justus Liebigs Ann. Chem.* **695**, 209 (1966).
253. M. Bial, *Dtsch. Med. Wochenschr.* **29**, 477 (1903).
254. F. Zilliken and P. J. O'Brien, *Biochem. Prep.* **7**, 1 (1960).
255. A. Ya. Khorlin and I. M. Privalova, *Carbohydr. Res.* **13**, 373 (1970).
256. H. Mack and R. Brossmer, *Tetrahedron Lett.* **28**, 191 (1987).
257. H. Mack and R. Brossmer, *Tetrahedron Lett.* **33**, 1867 (1992).
258. M. J. How, M. D. A. Halford, M. Stacey, and E. Vickers, *Carbohydr. Res.* **11**, 313 (1969).
259. T. Yamamoto, T. Teshima, K. Inami, and T. Shiba, *Tetrahedron Lett.* **33**, 325 (1992).
260. T. Yamamoto, H. Kumazawa, K. Inami, T. Teshima, and T. Shiba, *Tetrahedron Lett.* **33**, 5791 (1992).
261. M. Miljkovic and P. Hagel, *Carbohydr. Res.* **141**, 213 (1985).

262. T. Ichikawa, T. Okamoto, S. Maeda, S. Ohdan, Y. Araki, and Y. Ishido, *Tetrahedron Lett.* **12**, 79 (1971); T. Ichikawa, S. Maeda, T. Okamoto, Y. Araki, and Y. Ishido, *Bull. Chem. Soc. Jpn.* **44**, 2779 (1971).

263. R. Kuhn, W. Bister, and H. Fischer, *Justus Liebigs Ann. Chem.* **617**, 109 (1958).

264. S. Ohdan, T. Okamoto, S. Maeda, T. Ichikawa, Y. Araki, and Y. Ishido, *Bull. Chem. Soc. Jpn.* **46**, 981 (1973).

265. S. Ohdan, T. Okamoto, Y. Araki, and Y. Ishido, *Bull. Chem. Soc. Jpn.* **47**, 1295 (1974).

266. F. Emery and P. Vogel, *J. Org. Chem.* **60**, 5843 (1995).

267. Z. Pakulski and A. Zamojski, *Tetrahedron* **51**, 871 (1995).

268. J. W. Krajewski, P. Gluziński, Z. Pakulski, A. Zamojski, A. Mishnev, and A. Kemme, *Carbohydr. Res.* **252**, 97 (1994).

269. M. Brookhart, J. R. Tucker, and G. R. Rusk, *J. Am. Chem. Soc.* **105**, 258 (1993).

270. S. Hanessian and A. G. Pernet, *Adv. Carbohydr. Chem. Biochem.* **33**, 111 (1976).

271. C. Jaramillo and S. Knapp, *Synthesis,* p. 1 (1994).

272. J. Herscovici, S. Delatre, and K. Antonakis, *J. Org. Chem.* **52**, 5691 (1987).

273. J. Herscovici, K. Muleka, L. Boumaiza, and K. Antonakis, *J. Chem. Soc., Perkin Trans. 1,* p. 1995 (1990).

274. J. Herscovici, L. Boumaiza, and K. Antonakis, *J. Org. Chem.* **57**, 2476 (1992).

275. F. W. Lichtenthaler, S. Nishiyama, and T. Weimer, *Justus Liebigs Ann. Chem.,* p. 1163 (1989).

276. G. Grynkiewicz and J. N. BeMiller, *J. Carbohydr. Chem.* **1**, 121 (1982).

277. N. Greenspon and K. Keinan, *J. Org. Chem.* **53**, 3723 (1988).

278. K. Okazaki, K. Nomura, and E. Yoshii, *J. Chem. Soc., Chem. Commun.,* p. 355 (1989).

279. F. G. de las Heras, A. San Felix, and P. Fernández-Resa, *Tetrahedron* **39**, 1617 (1983).

280. G. Grynkiewicz and J. N. BeMiller, *Carbohydr. Res.* **108**, 229 (1982).

281. D. B. Tulshian and B. Fraser-Reid, *J. Org. Chem.* **49**, 518 (1984).

282. D. S. Grierson, M. Bonin, and H.-P. Husson, *Tetrahedron Lett.* **25**, 4665 (1984).

283. T. L. Cupps, D. S. Wise, and L. B. Townsend, *Carbohydr. Res.* **115**, 59 (1983).

284. T. Tsukiyama and M. Isobe, *Tetrahedron Lett.* **33**, 7911 (1992).

285. J. Falbe, *New Syntheses with Carbon Monoxide.* Springer-Verlag, New York, 1980; H. Wender and P. Dino, *Organic Syntheses with Metal Carbonyls,* Vol. 2. Wiley, New York, 1977.

286. A. Rosenthal and D. Abson, *Can. J. Chem.* **42**, 1811 (1964).

287. A. Rosenthal and D. Read, *Methods Carbohydr. Chem.* **2**, 457 (1963); A. Camerman, J. Trotter, H. J. Koch, and A. Rosenthal, *Can. J. Chem.* **42**, 2630 (1964); A. Rosenthal and H. J. Koch, *Can. J. Chem.* **43**, 1375 (1965).

288. A. Rosenthal and D. Abson, *Carbohydr. Res.* **3**, 112 (1966).

289. A. Rosenthal and J. N. C. Whyte, *Can. J. Chem.* **46**, 2239 (1968).

290. S. J. Rhoads and N. R. Raulins, *Org. React. (N.Y.)* **22**, 1 (1975); G. B. Bennett, *Synthesis,* p. 589 (1977).

291. D. Felix, K. Geschwend-Steen, A. E. Wick, and A. Eschenmoser, *Helv. Chim. Acta* **52**, 1030 (1969); R. E. Ireland, R. C. Andersen, R. Badoud, B. J. Fitzsimmons, G. Mc Garvey, S. Thaisrivongs, and C. S. Wilcox, *J. Am. Chem. Soc.* **105**, 1988 (1983) and references cited therein.

292. D. P. Currran and Y.-G. Suh, *Carbohydr. Res.* **171**, 116 (1987).

293. R. E. Ireland, C. S. Wilcox, S. Thaisrivongs, and N. R. Vanier, *Can. J. Chem.* **57**, 1743 (1979).

294. Yu. A. Zhdanov, L. A. Uslova, and K. V. Gaponova, *Zh. Obshch. Khim.* **38**, 2618 (1968).

295. H. Jin, J.-I. Uenishi, W. J. Christ, and Y. Kishi, *J. Am. Chem. Soc.* **108**, 5644 (1986).

296. K. Takai, K. Kimura, T. Kuroda, T. Hiyama, and H. Nozaki, *Tetrahedron Lett.* **24**, 5281 (1983).

297. R. C. Bansal, B. Dean, S. Hakomori, and T. Toyokuni, *Chem. Commun.,* p. 796 (1991).

298. Y.-L. Li, X. H. Mao, and Y.-L. Wu, *J. Chem. Soc., Perkin Trans. 1*, p. 1559 (1995).
299. Y.-L. Wu, Z.-J. Yao, Y.-L. Li, J.-C. Li, Y. Xia, and Y.- L. Wu, *J. Org. Chem.* **60**, 3257 (1995).
300. R. Wang, C.-M. Lim, C.-H. Tan, B.-K. Lim, K.-Y. Sim, and T.-P. Loh, *Tetrahedron: Asymmetry* **6**, 1825 (1995).
301. R. H. Prenner, W. H. Binder, and W. Schmid, *Justus Liebigs Ann. Chem.*, p. 73 (1994).
302. Ph. Coutrot, C. Grison, and M. Tabyaoui, *Tetrahedron Lett.* **34**, 5089 (1993).
303. B. Giese and T. Linker, *Synthesis*, p. 46 (1992).
304. D. M. Gordon and G. M. Whitesides, *J. Org. Chem.* **58**, 7937 (1993).
305. J. Gao, R. Harter, D. M. Gordon, and G. M. Whitesides, *J. Org. Chem.* **59**, 3714 (1994).
306. G. Casiraghi, F. Zanardi, G. Rassu, and P. Spanu, *Chem. Rev.* **95**, 1677 (1995).
307. D. J. Mincher, G. Shaw, and E. DeClercq, *J. Chem. Soc., Perkin Trans. 1*, p. 613 (1983).
308. D. J. Mincher, G. Shaw, and E. DeClercq, *J. Chem. Soc., Perkin Trans. 1*, p. 1279 (1984).
309. S. Qureshi, G. Shaw, and G. E. Burgess, *J. Chem. Soc., Perkin Trans. 1*, p. 1557 (1985).
310. J. L. Mateo, *Tetrahedron* **45**, 1475 (1989).
311. J. A. Lopez-Sastro, A. Sanz Tejedor, J. F. Rodriguez Amo, J. Molina Molina, and I. Izquierdo Cubero, *An. Quím., Ser. C.* **82C**, 140 (1986).
312. J. A. Lopez-Sastro, C. Romero-Avila Garcia, J. Molina Molina, I. Izquierdo Cubero, and R. Sola Jabega, *An. Quím. Ser. C.* **84C**, 306 (1988).
313. K. S. Kim, J.-K. Shong, and S. B. Ha, *Tetrahedron Lett.* **29**, 2847 (1988).
314. A. J. Brink, O. G. de Villiers, and A. Jordaan, *S. Afr. J. Chem.* **31**, 59 (1978).
315. B. M. Trost and T. A. Grese, *J. Org. Chem.* **56**, 3189 (1991).
316. R. Preuss and R. R. Schmidt, *Justus Liebigs Ann. Chem.*, p. 429 (1989).
317. S. Maier, R. Preuss, and R. R. Schmidt, *Justus Liebigs Ann. Chem.*, p. 483 (1990).
318. R. R. Schmidt and A. Beyerbach, *Justus Liebigs Ann. Chem.*, p. 983 (1992).
319. H. Dietrich and R. R. Schmidt, *Justus Liebigs Ann. Chem.*, p. 975 (1994).
320. P. Lesimple, J.-M. Beau, G. Jaurand, and P. Sinay, *Tetrahedron Lett.* **27**, 6201 (1986).
321. J. Adams, L. Hoffman, Jr., and B. M. Trost, *J. Org. Chem.* **35**, 1600 (1970).
322. M. Shiozaki, N. Ishida, and S. Sato, *Bull. Chem. Soc. Jpn.* **62**, 3950 (1989).
323. Yu. A. Zhdanov, A. V. Kirjanov, and G. A. Korolchenko, *Zh. Obshch. Khim.* **49**, 2618 (1979).
324. P. Coutrot, C. Grison, M. Tabyaoui, S. Czernecki, and J.-M. Valéry, *J. Chem. Soc., Chem. Commun.*, p. 1515 (1988).
325. P. Coutrot, C. Grison, and M. Tabyaoui, *Tetrahedron Lett.* **34**, 5089 (1993).
326. F. N. Tebbe, G. W. Parshall, and G. S. Reddy, *J. Am. Chem. Soc.* **100**, 3611 (1977); S. H. Pine, R. Zahler, D. A. Evens, and R. H. Grubbs, *ibid.* **102**, 3270 (1980); K. A. Brown-Wesley, S. L. Buchwald, L. Cannizzo, L. Clawson, S. Ho, D. Meinhardt, J. R. Stille, D. Staus, and R. H. Grubbs, *Pure Appl. Chem.* **55**, 1733 (1983); L. F. Cannizzo and R. H. Grubbs, *J. Org. Chem.* **50**, 2386 (1985); M. Bottrill, P. D. Gavens, J. W. Kelland, and J. McMeeking in *Comprehensive Organometallic Chemistry* (G. Wilkinson, F. G. A. Stone, and E. W. Abel, eds.) Vol. 3, p. 271. Pergamon Press, Oxford, 1982.
327. C. S. Wilcox, G. W. Long, and H. Suh, *Tetrahedron Lett.* **25**, 395 (1984).
328. T. V. RajanBabu and G. S. Reddy, *J. Org. Chem.* **51**, 5458 (1986).
329. M. H. Ali, P. M. Collins, and W. G. Overend, *Carbohydr. Res.* **205**, 428 (1990).
330. F. Nicotra, L. Panza, and G. Russo, *Tetrahedron Lett.* **32**, 4035 (1991).
331. A. Haudrechy and P. Sinay, *J. Org. Chem.* **57**, 4142 (1992).
332. N. Ikemoto and S. L. Schreiber, *J. Am. Chem. Soc.* **114**, 2524 (1992).
333. R. Csuk and B. I. Glänzer, *Tetrahedron* **47**, 1655 (1991) and references cited therein.
334. B. M. Heskamp, D. Noort, G. A. van der Marel, and J. H. van Boom, *Synlett*, p. 713. (1992).
335. B. M. Heskamp, G. H. Veeneman, G. A. van der Marel, C. A. A. van Boeckel, and J. H. van Boom, *Tetrahedron* **51**, 5657 (1995); M. Shiozaki, *J. Org. Chem.* **56**, 528 (1991).
336. O. R. Martin and O. M. Saavedra, *Tetrahedron Lett.* **36**, 799 (1995).
337. R. Preuss and R. R. Schmidt, *J. Carbohydr. Chem.* **10**, 887 (1991).

338. R. Preuss, K.-H. Jung, and R. R. Schmidt, *Justus Liebigs Ann. Chem.*, p. 377 (1992).
339. E. Calzada, C. A. Clarke, C. Roussin-Bouchard, and R. H. Wightman, *J. Chem. Soc., Perkin Trans. 1*, p. 517 (1995); M. D. Lewis, J. K. Cha, and Y. Kishi, *J. Am. Chem. Soc.* **104**, 4976 (1982).
340. L. Lay, F. Nicotra, L. Panza, G. Russo, and E. Caneva, *J. Org. Chem.* **57**, 1304 (1992).
341. R. Csuk and B. Glänzer, *J. Carbohydr. Chem.* **9**, 809 (1990).
342. H. Ogura, H. Takahashi, and T. Itoh, *J. Org. Chem.* **37**, 72 (1972).
343. J.-M. Lancelin, P. H. A. Zollo, and P. Sinay, *Tetrahedron Lett.* **24**, 4833 (1983).
344. R. Tsang and B. Fraser-Reid, *J. Org. Chem.* **57**, 1065 (1992).
345. J. Alzeer and A. Vasella, *Helv. Chim. Acta* **78**, 177 (1995).
346. C. Cai and A. Vasella, *Helv. Chim. Acta* **78**, 732 (1995).
347. G. A. Kraus and M. T. Molina, *J. Org. Chem.* **53**, 752 (1988).
348. M. Shiozaki, Y. Kobayashi, T. Hata, and Y. Furukawa, *Tetrahedron* **47**, 2785 (1991).
349. P. Munier, A. Krusinski, D. Picq, and D. Anker, *Tetrahedron* **51**, 1229 (1995).
350. W. B. Motherwell, M. J. Tozer, and B. C. Ross, *J. Chem. Soc., Chem. Commun.*, p. 1437 (1989).
351. R. Csuk and P. Dörr, *J. Carbohydr. Chem.* **14**, 35 (1995).
352. J. E. Hengeveld, V. Grief, J. Tadanier, C.-M. Lee, D. Riley, and P. A. Lartey, *Tetrahedron Lett.* **25**, 4075 (1984).
353. R. H. Hall, K. Bischofsberger, A. J. Brink, O. G. de Villiers, and A. Jordan, *J. Chem. Soc., Perkin Trans. 1*, p. 1979 (1979).
354. A. Frankowski, D. Deredas, D. Le Nouen, T. Tschamber, and J. Streith, *Helv. Chim. Acta* **78**, 1837 (1995).
355. A. Dondoni and M.-C. Scherrmann, *J. Org. Chem.* **59**, 6404 (1994).
356. T. Granier and A. Vasella, *Helv. Chim. Acta* **78**, 1738 (1995).
357. B. I. Glänzer and R. Csuk, *Carbohydr. Res.* **220**, 79 (1991).
358. H. Wild, K. Mohrs, U. Niewöhner, and W. Steglich, *Justus Liebigs Ann. Chem.*, p. 1548 (1986).
359. U. Klein, K. Mohrs, H. Wild, and W. Steglich, *Justus Liebigs Ann. Chem.*, p. 485 (1987).
360. U. Klein and W. Steglich, *Justus Liebigs Ann. Chem.*, p. 247 (1989).
361. G. A. Tolstikhov, A. Yu. Spivak, I. V. Chresteleva, L. V. Spirikhin, and V. S. Sultanova, *Zh. Org. Khim.* **25**, 149 (1989).
362. G. A. Tolstikhov, I. V. Chresteleva, A. Yu. Spivak, A. Yu. Sklaev, and I. P. Baikova, *Zh. Org. Khim.* **27**, 1497 (1991).
363. Z. J. Witczak, in *Studies in Natural Products Chemistry* (A. Atta-ur-Rahman, ed.) Vol. 3. p. 209, Elsevier, Amsterdam, 1989.
364. B. Helferich and K. F. Wedemeyer, *Justus Liebigs Ann. Chem.* **563**, 139 (1949).
365. N. Constantzas and J. Kocourek, *Collect. Czech. Chem. Commun.* **24**, 1099 (1959).
366. B. Helferich and K. L. Bettin, *Chem. Ber.* **94**, 1159 (1961).
367. B. Helferich and W. Ost, *Chem. Ber.* **95**, 2612 (1962).
368. E.-F. Fuchs and J. Lehmann, *Chem. Ber.* **108**, 2254 (1975).
369. R. W. Myers and Y. C. Lee, *Carbohydr. Res.* **132**, 61 (1984).
370. K. Igarashi, *Adv. Carbohydr. Chem. Biochem.* **34**, 243 (1977).
371. F. G. de las Heras, and P. Fernandes-Resa, *J. Chem. Soc., Perkin Trans. 1*, p. 903 (1982); S. K. Maity, S. K. Dutta, A. K. Banerjee, B. Achari, and M. Singh, *Tetrahedron* **50**, 6965 (1994).
372. K. Utimoto and T. Horiie, *Tetrahedron Lett.* **23**, 237 (1982).
373. V. I. Betaneli, M. V. Ovchinnikov, L. V. Backinowsky, and N. K. Kochetkov, *Carbohydr. Res.* **76**, 252 (1979); M. M. Litvak, V. I. Betaneli, L. V. Backinowsky, and N. K. Kochetkov, *Bioorg. Khim.* **8**, 1133 (1982) and references cited therein.
374. P. A. Wehrli and B. Schaer, *J. Org. Chem.* **42**, 3956 (1977).
375. R. W. Myers and Y. C. Lee, *Carbohydr. Res.* **154**, 145 (1986).

376. L. G. Lay, F. Nicotra, L. Panza, and G. Russo, *Synlett*, p. 167 (1995).
377. K. N. Drew and P. H. Gross, *J. Org. Chem.* **56**, 509 (1991).
378. M. Bobek and J. Farkas, *Collect. Czech. Chem. Commun.* **34**, 247 (1969).
379. P. W. K. Woo, *J. Labelled Compd. Radiopharm.* **25**, 1149 (1988).
380. J. Farkas and I. Fric, *Collect. Czech. Chem. Commun.* **50**, 1291 (1985).
381. M. T. Reetz, I. Chatziliosifidis, H. Künzer, and H. Müller-Starke, *Tetrahedron* **39**, 961 (1983).
382. H. S. El Khadem and J. Kawai, *Carbohydr. Res.* **115**, 131 (1983).
383. P. Köll and A. Förtsch, *Carbohydr. Res.* **171**, 301 (1987); P. Köll, J. Kopf, D. Wess, and H. Brandenburg, *Justus Liebigs Ann. Chem.*, p. 685 (1988).
384. B. Coxon, *Tetrahedron* **22**, 2281 (1966).
385. G. D. Kini, C. R. Petrie, W. J. Hennen, N. K. Dalley, B. E. Wilson, and R. K. Robins, *Carbohydr. Res.* **159**, 81 (1987).
386. G. D. Kini, W. J. Hennen, and R. K. Robins, *J. Org. Chem.* **51**, 4436 (1986).
387. G. Barnathan, T. Huynh-Dinh, A. Kolb, and J. Igolen, *Eur. J. Med. Chem.* **11**, 67 (1976).
388. L. Birkofer and B. Hammes, *Justus Liebigs Ann. Chem.*, p. 731 (1973).
389. T. Huynh-Dinh, C. Gouyette, and J. Igolen, *Tetrahedron Lett.* **21**, 4499 (1980); P. Allard, T. Huynh-Dinh, C. Gouyette, J. Igolen, J.-C. Chermann, and F. Barré-Sinoussi, *J. Med. Chem.* **24**, 1291 (1981).
390. N. Constantzas and J. Kocourek, *Chem. Listy,* **52**, 1629 (1958); J. Kocourek, *Chem. Ber.* **94**, 3346 (1961); B. Coxon and H. G. Fletcher, Jr., *J. Amer. Chem. Soc.* **86**, 922 (1964).
391. G. Grynkiewicz and J. N. BeMiller, *Carbohydr. Res.* **112**, 324 (1983); G. Grynkiewicz and J. N. BeMiller, *Carbohydr. Res.* **124**, C30 (1983).
392. M.-T. García López, F. G. de las Heras, and A. San Félix, *J. Carbohydr. Chem.* **6**, 273 (1987).
393. B. Coxon and H. G. Fletcher, Jr., *J. Am. Chem. Soc.* **85**, 2637 (1963).
394. P. Allevi, M. Anastasia, P. Ciuffreda, and A. Scala, *J. Carbohydr. Chem.* **12**, 209 (1993).
395. Y. Araki, N. Kobayashi, K. Watanabe, and Y. Ishido, *J. Carbohydr. Chem.* **4**, 565 (1985).
396. P. Boullanger, D. Marmet, and G. Descotes, *Tetrahedron* **35**, 163 (1979).
397. J. N. BeMiller, V. J. Blazis, and R. W. Myers, *J. Carbohydr. Chem.* **9**, 39 (1990).
398. J. Tadanier, C.-M. Lee, H. Hengeveld, W. Rosenbrook, Jr. D. Whittern, and N. Wideburg, *Carbohydr. Res.* **201**, 209 (1990).
399. P. D. Cook and D. J. McNamara, *J. Heterocycl. Chem.* **23**, 155 (1986).
400. J. A. Montgomery and K. Hewson, *J. Heterocycl. Chem.* **7**, 443 (1970).
401. G. Grynkiewicz and J. N. BeMiller, *Carbohydr. Res.* **112**, 324 (1983).
402. H. Sano, S. Mio, J. Kitagawa, and S. Sugai, *Tetrahedron: Asymmetry* **5**, 2233 (1994).
403. Z. J. Witczak, *J. Carbohydr. Chem.* **3**, 359 (1984).
404. T. Mukaiyama, T. Shimpuku, T. Takashima, and S. Kobayashi, *Chem. Lett.*, p. 145 (1989).
405. T. Mukaiyama, S. Kobayashi, and S.-i. Shoda, *Chem. Lett.* p. 1529 (1984).
406. J.-H. Gu, M. Okamoto, M. Terada, K. Mikami, and T. Nakai, *Chem. Lett.*, p. 1169 (1992).
407. H. Togo, S. Ishigama, and M. Yokoyama, *Chem. Lett.*, p. 1673 (1992).
408. A. Cousson, G. Le Gouadec, C. Monneret, and J.-C. Florent, *J. Chem. Soc., Chem. Commun.*, p. 388 (1993).
409. F. G. de las Heras, A. San Félix, and P. Fernandes-Resa, *Tetrahedron* **39**, 1617 (1983).
410. G. Grynkiewicz and J. N. BeMiller, *Carbohydr. Res.* **108**, 229 (1982).
411. G. Chelucci, M. A. Cabras, and A. Saba, *Tetrahedron: Asymmetry* **5**, 1973 (1994).
412. G. Chelucci, *Tetrahedron: Asymmetry* **6**, 811 (1995).
413. R. B. Boy and W. S. Chilton, *J. Org. Chem.* **36**, 3242 (1971).
414. D. Horton and J.-H. Tsai, *Carbohydr. Res.* **75**, 151 (1979).
415. J. M. J. Tronchet and A. Bonen, *Helv. Chim. Acta* **60**, 892 (1977).
416. J. W. Krajewski, P. Gluzinski, S. Jarosz, A. Zamojski, A. Mishnyov, and A. Kemme, *Carbohydr. Res.* **144**, 183 (1985).

417. E. I. Stout, W. M. Doane, and V. C. Triṇkus, *Carbohydr. Res.* **50**, 282 (1976).
418. M. Ariatti and J. Zemlicka, *J. Org. Chem.* **46**, 4204 (1981).
419. R. Csuk, B. I. Glänzer, and A. Fürstner, *Adv. Organomet. Chem.* **28**, 85 (1988); A. Fürstner, R. Csuk, C. Rohrer, and H. Weidmann, *J. Chem. Soc., Perkin Trans. 1*, p. 1729 (1988).
420. A. Fürstner and H. Weidmann, *J. Org. Chem.* **54**, 2307 (1989).
421. A. S. Kende and Y. Fujii, *Tetrahedron Lett.* **32**, 2199 (1991); A. S. Kende, Y. Fujii, and J. S. Mendoza, *J. Am. Chem. Soc.* **112**, 9645 (1990); S. F. J. Macdonald, W. B. Huizinga, and T. C. MacKenzie, *J. Org. Chem.* **53**, 3371 (1988); G. H. Posner and S. R. Haines, *Tetrahedron Lett.* **26**, 1823 (1985); K. C. Nicolaou, R. E. Dolle, A. Chucholowski, and J. L. Randall, *J. Chem. Soc., Chem. Commun.*, p. 1154 (1984); D. T. Connor and M. J. von Strandtmann, *J. Org. Chem.* **43**, 4606 (1987); Y. Araki, K. Watanabe, F. Kuan, K. Itoh, N. Kobayashi, and Y. Ishido, *Carbohydr. Res.* **127**, C5 (1984).
422. D. Zhai, W. Zhai, and R. M. Williams, *J. Am. Chem. Soc.* **110**, 2501 (1988).
423. L. Jobron, C. Leteux, A. Veyriéres, and J.-M. Beau, *J. Carbohydr. Chem.* **1994**, 507.
424. T. Matsumoto, M. Katsuki, H. Jona, and K. Suzuki, *Tetrahedron Lett.* **30**, 6185 (1989); H. Matsumoto, K. Suzuki, and M. Katsuki, *Tetrahedron Lett.* **29**, 6909 (1988); H. Matsumoto, K. Suzuki, and M. Katsuki, *Tetrahedron Lett.* **30**, 833 (1989); T. Matsumoto, H. Maeta, K. Suzuki, and G. Tsuchihasi, *Tetrahedron Lett.* **29**, 3567 (1988); R. R. Schmidt and G. Effenberger, *Carbohydr. Res.* **171**, 59; T. Matsumoto, K. Katsuki, and K. Suzuki, *Tetrahedron Lett.* **29**, 6935 (1988); C. Jaramillo and S. Knapp, *Synthesis*, p. 1 (1994).
425. N. C. Chaudhuri and E. T. Kool, *Tetrahedron Lett.* **36**, 1795 (1995).
426. P. DeShong, G. A. Slough, and V. Elango, *Carbohydr. Res.* **171**, 342 (1987).
427. P. DeShong, G. A. Slough, D. R. Sidler, V. Elango, P. J. Rybczynski, L. J. Smith, T. A. Lessen, T. X. Lee, and G. B. Anderson, *ACS Symp. Ser.* **494**, 99 (1992).
428. B. Giese, *Radicals in Organic Synthesis: Formation of Carbon-Carbon Bonds*. Pergamon Press, Oxford, 1986.
429. G. Descotes, *J. Carbohydr. Chem.* **7**, 1 (1988).
430. G. E. Keck and J. B. Yates, *J. Am. Chem. Soc.* **104**, 5829 (1982).
431. G. E. Keck, E. J. Enholm, J. B. Yates, and M. R. Wiley, *Tetrahedron* **41**, 4079 (1985).
432. Y. Araki, T. Endo, M. Tanji, J. Nagasawa, and Y. Ishido, *Tetrahedron Lett.* **28**, 5853 (1987).
433. Y. Araki, T. Endo, M. Tanji, Y. Arai, and Y. Ishido, *Tetrahedron Lett.* **29**, 2325 (1988).
434. B. Giese, J. Dupuis, M. Leising, M. Nix, and H. J. Lindner, *Carbohydr. Res.* **171**, 329 (1987) and references cited therein.
435. B. Giese, B. Rückert, K. S. Gröninger, R. Muhn, and J. Lindner, *Justus Liebigs Ann. Chem.*, p. 997 (1988).
436. B. Giese, T. Linder, and R. Muhn, *Tetrahedron* **45**, 935 (1989).
437. H. Kessler, V. Wittmann, M. Köck, and M. Kottenhahn, *Angew. Chem.* **104**, 874 (1992); *Angew. Chem., Int. Ed. Engl.* **31**, 902 (1992).
438. B. Giese and T. Linker, *Synthesis*, p. 46 (1992).
439. B. P. Branchaud and M. S. Meier, *J. Org. Chem.* **54**, 1320 (1989).
440. A. Ghosez, T. Göbel, and B. Giese, *Chem. Ber.* **121**, 1807 (1988).
441. G. Thoma and B. Giese, *Tetrahedron Lett.* **30**, 2907 (1989).
442. S. P. Elvey and D. R. Mootoo, *J. Am. Chem. Soc.* **114**, 9685 (1992).
443. B. Giese, M. Hoch, C. Lamberth, and R. R. Schmidt, *Tetrahedron Lett.* **29**, 1375 (1988).
444. P. Girard, J. L. Namy, and H. B. Kagan, *J. Am. Chem. Soc.* **102**, 2693 (1980); H. B. Kagan, *Nouv. J. Chim.* **14**, 453 (1990); J. L. Namy, J. Collin, C. Bied, and H. B. Kagan, *Synlett*, p. 733 (1992); D. P. Curran, T. L. Fevig, C. P. Jasperse, and M. J. Totleben, *Synlett*, p. 943 (1992).
445. T. Benneche, *Synthesis*, p. 1 (1995).
446. P. de Pouilly, A. Chénédé, J.-M. Mallet, and P. Sinay, *Bull. Soc. Chim. Fr.* **130**, 256 (1993).
447. R. W. Binkley and D. G. Hehemann, *J. Org. Chem.* **43**, 3244 (1978).

448. Q. Shen, D. G. Sloss, and D. B. Berkowitz, *Synth. Commun.*, p. 1519 (1994).
449. N. M. Carpenter, G. W. J. Fleet, I. Cenci di Bello, B. Winchester, L. E. Fellows, and R. J. Nash, *Tetrahedron Lett.* **30,** 7261 (1989).
450. K. S. Akerfeldt and P. A. Bartlett, *J. Org. Chem.* **56,** 7133 (1991).
451. L. V. Dunkerton, K. T. Brady, F. Mohamed, and B. P. McKillican, *J. Carbohydr. Chem.* **7,** 49 (1988).
452. K. Anzai and T. Saita, *Bull. Chem. Soc. Jpn.* **50,** 169 (1977).
453. S. J. Danishefsky, R. Hungate, and G. Schulte, *J. Am. Chem. Soc.* **110,** 7434 (1988).
454. *Houben-Weyl, Methoden der Organischen Chemie,* Vol. E/18, p. 1004 (1986); F. L. Bowden and L. H. Wood *The Organic Chemistry of Iron.* (E. A. Koerner von Gustorf, F.-W. Grevels, and I. Fischler, eds.), Vol. 1, pp. 345-396. Academic Press, New York, 1978; W. P. Fehlhammer, H. Stolzberg in *Comprehensive Organometallic Chemistry* (G. Wilkinson, F. G. A. Stone, and E. W. Abel, eds.) Vol. 4. p. 513. Pergamon Press, Oxford, 1982.
455. H. H. Baer and H. R. Hanna, *Carbohydr. Res.* **102,** 169 (1982).
456. H. H. Baer, R. L. Breton, and Y. Shen, *Carbohydr. Res.* **200,** 377 (1990).
457. K. Peseke, H.-D. Ambrosi, and M. Michalik, *Carbohydr. Res.* **194,** 87 (1989).
458. F. Baumberger and A. Vasella, *Helv. Chim. Acta* **69,** 1205 (1986).
459. K. Mahmood, A. Vasella, and B. Bernet, *Helv. Chim. Acta* **74,** 1555 (1991).
460. K. Briner and A. Vasella, *Helv. Chim. Acta* **72,** 1371 (1989).
461. A. Vasella, *Pure Appl. Chem.* **63,** 507 (1991).
462. K. Briner and A. Vasella, *Helv. Chim. Acta* **73,** 1764 (1990).
463. J.-P. Praly, Z. El Kharraf, and G. Descotes, *Tetrahedron Lett.* **31,** 4441 (1990).
464. A. Vasella and C. A. A. Waldraff, *Helv. Chim. Acta* **74,** 585 (1991).
465. A. Vasella, K. Briner, N. Soudararajan, and M. S. Platz, *J. Org. Chem.* **56,** 4741 (1991).
466. P. Uhlmann, E. Harth, A. B. Naughton, and A. Vasella, *Helv. Chim. Acta* **77,** 2335 (1994).
467. U. Jonas, F. Cardullo, P. Belik, F. Diederich, A. Gügel, E. Harth, A. Herrman, L. Isaacs, K. Müllen, H. Ringsdorf, C. Thilgen, P. Uhlmann, A. Vasella, C. A. A. Waldraff, and M. Walter, *Chem. Eur. J.* **1,** 243 (1995).
468. S. E. Mangholz and A. Vasella, *Helv. Chim. Acta* **74,** 2100 (1991).
469. L. Somsák, J.-P. Praly, and G. Descotes, *Synlett,* p. 119 (1992).
470. A. G. Myers and P. J. Kukkola, *J. Am. Chem. Soc.* **112,** 8208 (1990).

2

DESCENDING SYNTHESES
OF MONOSACCHARIDES

Many of the reactions of saccharide derivatives lead to various degradation products by pathways involving splitting or fragmentation of the carbon skeleton. The descended substances produced in these reactions, often serve as invaluable materials for the production of other sugars and chiral building units for the synthesis of different types of organic compounds. This chapter briefly summarizes the descending syntheses that are considered the most important and useful for the reader.

2.1. DISULFONE DEGRADATION

α-Hydroxydiethylsulfonylalkanes can be readily split according to the patterns shown in Fig. 2.1, and thus the aldehyde component can be recovered.[1] The extension of this methodology to the carbohydrate field involves oxidation of the well-known[2] sugar–dithioacetals and mercaptols (**1.1;** aldose and ketose dialkyldithioacetals) into the corresponding sulfones (**1.2**), followed by descent, with a base, into an aldose with a *one-carbon-shorter* chain (**1.3**) and bis(dialkylsulfonyl)methane (**1.4**).

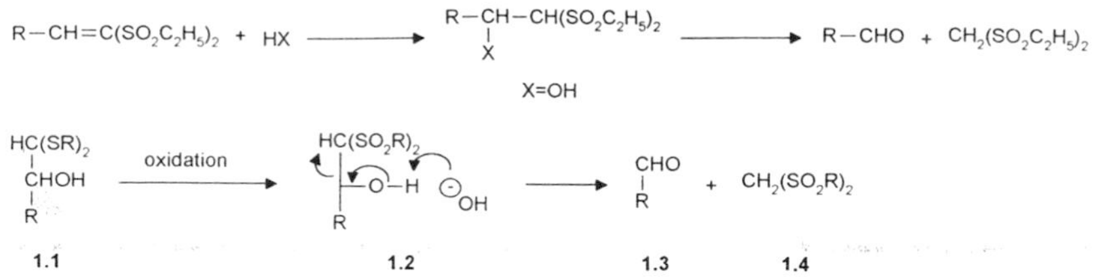

$X=OH$

FIGURE 2.1

This method has been employed for obtaining[3] D-*arabinose from D-mannose,* and the execution of this easily reproducible procedure (MacDonald degradation) has been reported[4] in detail. The MacDonald methodology permits descent of ketoses with two carbon atoms, and thus makes D-*erythrose easily available*[5,6] from D-fructose as shown in Figure 2.2.

Degradation of D-fructose according to the procedure of Bourne and Stephens[5]
To a solution of penta-O-acetyl-D-fructose diethyl dithioacetal (**2.1**, 0.75 g) in ice-cold ether (20 ml) an ethereal solution of monoperoxyphthalic acid[7] (30 ml) is added; the mixture is kept at 0°C for 1 h, and then at ambient temperature for 40 h. The solvent is distilled off at reduced pressure, the residue is extracted with chloroform, and the organic layer is washed with aqueous $NaHCO_3$ and water and then dried (Na_2SO_4). Following evaporation, the residue is recrystallized from ethanol to furnish 0.62 g of D-*arabino*-1,3,4,5,6-pentaacetoxy-bis(ethylsulfonyl)hexane (**2.2**) as orthogonal plates, m.p. 144–145°C, $[\alpha]_D^{17}$ +7.2 (c = 2.2 in chloroform). A solution of **2.2** (2.09 g) in methanol (200 ml) is saturated with ammonia gas at 0°C and then left at room temperature for 2 days. Following evaporation to a mass of crystals, acetamide is removed by sublimation at 13.3 kPa at 60°C. Recrystallization of the residue from dry methanol gives 0.4 g of 1,1-bis(acetamido)-1-deoxy-D-erythrose (**2.3**), m.p. 210–211°C, $[\alpha]_D^{19}$ +9.0 (c = 1.3 in

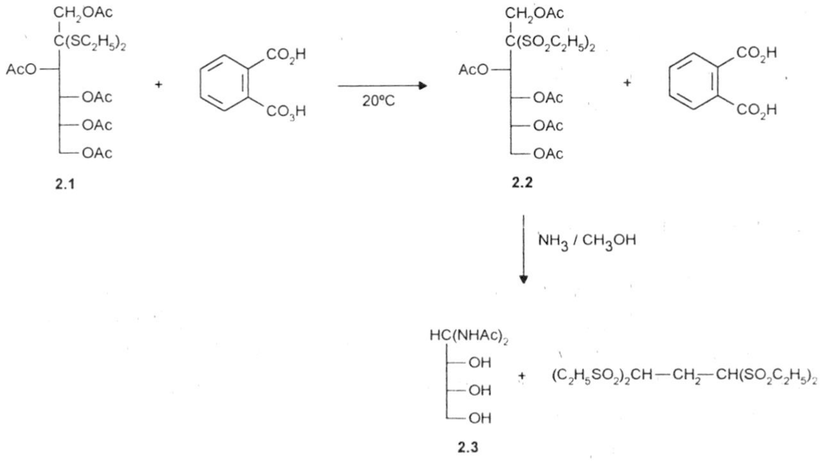

FIGURE 2.2

water). From the mother liquor 1,1,3,3-tetraethylsulfonylpropane (m.p. 158–159°C) was isolated.

Degradation of the 2,2-bis(benzylsulfonyl) analog of **2.2** with ammonia also leads[5] to the aminoerythritol **2.3**. Application of hydrazine instead of ammonia and subsequent reduction gives rise to D-*erythritol*, isolated[6] in form of its tetraacetate.

Descending synthesis of 1,1-(diethylsulfonyl)-D-*glycero*-D-*manno*-2,3,4,5,7-hexahydroxyheptane with ammonia to D-galactose proceeds[8] without side reactions, but in most cases the degradation is rather complex.

Depending on the reaction conditions, the preceding oxidation methods give rise to diastereoisomer sulfoxide mixtures, and sometimes result in the direct production of disulfones or the disulfones of aldos-1-enes.[3,5] The influence of oxidation conditions on product distribution has been investigated and reported[9–13] in detail. Of the possible oxidizing agents, those used most frequently are peroxyacetic acid, peroxypropionic acid, monoperoxyphthalic acid, or simply, hydrogen peroxide in acetic acid in the presence of ammonium molybdate catalyst.[9]

Preparation of D-galactose diethylsulfone[9]   To a suspension of D-galactose diethyl dithioacetal (1.45 g) in 30% hydrogen peroxide (5 ml) is added at 0°C a small, catalytic amount of ammonium molybdate; the mixture is shaken and then kept in an ice bath for 30 min. It is extracted with ether (5 ml) for the removal of hydrogen peroxide, and the aqueous layer is concentrated under diminished pressure (bath temperature 35°C) to a syrup, which is then treated with a small volume of methanol. The crude product is crystallized from 2-propanol to obtain 1.4 g (74%) of the title product, as cubes, m.p. 197°C, $[\alpha]_D^{20}$ −1.5 (c = 3.11 in water).

Other authors have reported[14,15] physical data different from those given above for D-galactose diethylsulfone [1-deoxy-1,1-bis(ethylsulfonyl)-D-galactitol or -glucitol].

D-Galactose diethylsulfone[15]   To a cooled (−20°C) solution of D-galactose diethyl dithioacetal (2 g) in DMF (20 ml) is added, dropwise, peroxypropionic acid (20% excess) over 1 h, in a rate such that the temperature does not exceed −10°C. The mixture is then kept at −10°C for 2 days, and the crystals separated are filtered off and washed with cold ether to give 0.75 g (32%) of the title product (which sometimes contains traces of the educt). After drying over Mg(ClO₄)₂ and NaOH the physical data are m.p. 151–152°C, $[\alpha]_D^{22}$ −17.0 (c = 1.5 in 5% acetic acid). On cooling at −10°C a further crop (1.3 g, 55%) of the product can be obtained from the combined mother liquor and washings; m.p. 149–150°C, which is contaminated with a cyclic product (see the following procedure).

Degradation of D-galactose diethylsulfone to D-lyxose[15]   The diethylsulfone (1 g) is dissolved in 0.28% aqueous ammonium hydroxide (5 ml), when the substance dissolves immediately and bis(ethylsulfonyl)methane precipitates. This is filterd off after 30 min and recrystallized to give 0.49 g (82%), m.p. 102–103°C. The filtrate, containing D-lyxose, is washed four times with chloroform, and the aqueous layer is concentrated. The resulting syrup is dissolved in methanol and seeded with D-lyxose. The separated crystals of the sugar are filtered off after storing at 0°C for 2 days, to furnish 0.36 g (80%), $[\alpha]_D^{20}$ −13.0 (equilibrium value, c = 4.0 in water).

With this simple procedure, D-*arabinose* has been readily prepared[15] from D-glucose and D-mannose.

Detailed studies have shown[16] that descending synthesis of the disulfone derivative to a one-carbon-atom shorter aldose does not proceed directly. Instead, first an intermediary 1,2-(dialkylsulfonyl)glycos-1-ene (**3.2**) is produced (Fig. 2.3) either simultaneously with the formation of the disulfone or on treatment of this latter with a base, which is then transformed, with dilute ammonia, into the chain-shortened aldose or anhydroaldose dialkylsulfone. Acylation may also cause-β-elimination of the disulfones, and degradation of the acylated 1,1-dialkylsulfonylglycos-1-enes thus produced proceed in an essentially similar way.

The transformation discussed in the preceding paragraphs is illustrated by the following procedure[10] (see also Hough and Taylor[17]).

> *1,1-Bis(ethylsulfonyl)-D-threo-pentos-en-(1)* (**3.2**)[10]   To a solution of D-lyxose- or D-lyxose diethyl dithioacetal (5.13 g, 0.02 mol) in acetone (40 ml), peroxypropionic acid (50%, 16 ml) is added dropwise; the mixture is kept at ambient temperature for 1 day and then concentrated at 30°C. The residual syrup solidifies into a crystal mass in a few hours; it is taken up with methanol, filtered, and recrystallized from methanol to give 5.6 g (92%) of **3.2**, m.p. 114°C, $[\alpha]_D^{20}$ +26.2 (c = 2.48 in methanol).

According to a slightly modified procedure of Kuhn and Baschang,[18] oxidation of D-xylose diethyl dithioacetal gives rise to a disulfone mixture, whose degradation leads to syrupy D-*threose* with 85–90% yield.

> *D-Xylose-1,1-diethylsulfone*[18]   D-Xylose diethyl dithioacetal (100 g) is dissoved in purified 1,4-dioxane (700 ml) by gentle heating, and to the cooled (20–25°C) and rapidly stirred solution peroxypropionic acid (4.15 eq) is added to obtain 90–99% of a disulfone mixture (m.p. 85–120°C), consisting of ~80% of the saturated and 20% of the unsaturated sulfone. After precipitation of the crude product from ethanol with ether, D-xylose-1,1-diethysulfone is obtained, m.p. 143–145°C, $[\alpha]_D^{20}$ −5 (c = 1.0 in methanol). The title unsaturated sulfone can be obtained by refluxing the major product in ethanol. After concentration of the reaction mixture, the resultant syrup is crystallized by scrubbing, m.p. 128–131°C, $[\alpha]_D^{23}$ +25.6 (c = 1.08 in methanol).

> *Degradation of D-xylose-1,1-diethylsulfone into D-threose*   The preceding disulfone mixture is washed well with a mixture of ether and petroleum ether and dried over KOH *in vacuo* for several days to remove the acid traces. Descending synthesis of the saturated disulfone proceeds in ~12 h at room temperature without a recognizable change of color. A complete degradation of the unsaturated analog requires

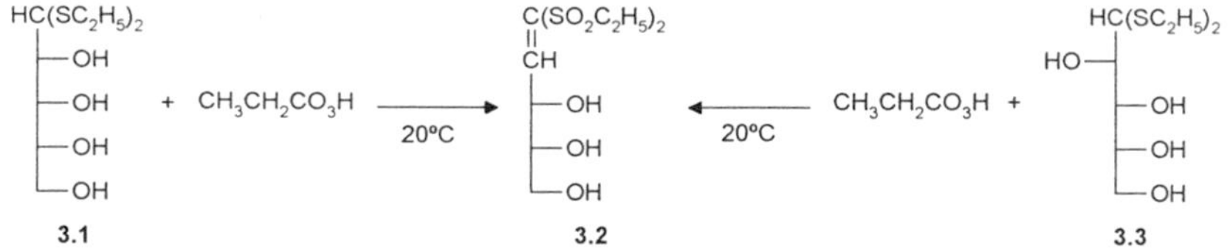

FIGURE 2.3

2 days, the pH should be kept at 9–10, and the color of the solution is darkening. The yield of the syrupy D-threose is 85–90%, $[\alpha]_D^{20}$ −10 to −12 (in water).

A combination of the descending synthesis methods discussed above serves for the preparation[19,20] of *5-deoxy-L-arabinose* from the natural sugar, L-rhamnose, as shown in Figure 2.4.

In some cases the descending procedure can be accomplished without the separation of the saturated and unsaturated disulfones obtained on oxidation. Such a methodology is illustrated by an example of the *degradation of D-arabinose and L-fucose.*

> *Preparation of D-erythrose from D-arabinose*[21] To an ice-cold solution of D-arabinose diethyl dithioacetal (80 g) in 1,4-dioxane (480 ml), 4.4 mol of peroxypropionic acid is added over a 10-min period. After stirring for 5 min, the mixture is allowed to remain overnight, and the solution containing crystals is gradually diluted with ether (a total of 3 liters) and then kept at −10°C for 1 day. The product (91.3 g), containing two components according to paper chromatography in 4:1:5 *n*-butanol–acetic acid–water, is filtered off, washed with water and dried over P_2O_5. The preceding sulfone mixture (90 g) is mixed with water (50 ml), 4 ml of concentrated ammonium hydroxide is added, and the mixture is kept at room temperature for 2 days. During this time the initial pH (9.5) value of the solution decreases, and the pH is continuously adjusted back to 9.5 by the addition of ammonium hydroxide. The separated bis(ethylsulfonyl)-methane (41.7 g) is filtered off, and the filtrate is extracted with chloroform (3 × 100 ml) to remove the by-products. Evaporation of the chloroform layer gives and additional 9.9 g crop of crude bis(ethylsulfonyl)-methane, which is recrystallized together with the first crop from dry ethanol to obtain 49.2 g (80%) of pure bis(ethylsulfonyl)methane. The aqueous layer is passed through two 3.2 × 20 cm columns packed, separately, with Amberlite IR-100 (H⁺) and IR-4B. The combined eluate–washing is decolorized with charcoal; Willstätter-Schudel determination indicated a 58% yield–calculated for the dithioacetal. Following evaporation at 45°C, the resulting thick, yellow syrup contains negligible quantities of two by-products besides D-erythrose. The crude product can be directly transformed into the crystalline 2,3-di-*O*-acetyl-4-*O*-(triphenylmethyl)-D-erythrose diethyl dithioacetal.

The preparation of *5-deoxy-L-lyxofuranose* (**5.4**) is described in detail in the following sequence of pocedures[12] (see Fig. 2.5).

> *L-Fucose diethyl dithioacetal (5.1)*[12] L-Fucose (15 g) is dissolved in 110 ml of dry 1,4-dioxane containing 10% (g/g) of dry hydrochloric acid, ethylmercaptane (15 ml) is added, and the mixture is shaken for 3 days. The separated crystals are filtered off, and the filtrate is concentrated to obtain (in two crops) 19.8 g (80%) of a crude product with m.p. 163–169°C. Recrystallization from water containing a small volume of methanol gives 15.41 g of the pure dithioacetal, m.p. 173°C.

> *Oxidation of the dithioacetal 5.1 to 1,1-bis(ethylsulfonyl)-1-fuco-2,3,4,5-tetrahydroxyhexane (5.2)* To a vigorously stirred suspension of the dithioacetal **5.1** (14 g) in purified 1,4-dioxane (100 ml), 5.3 M aqueous peroxypropionic acid (44 ml) is added over a period of 30 min, keeping the temperature at 17–20°C (!). After 2 h, the resulting solution is concentrated (bath temperature 25–30°C). The crystalline crude product, obtained in two crops, is washed with 1,4-dioxane and ether and then triturated with ether to furnish 13.0 g (75%) of a colorless crystalline mass

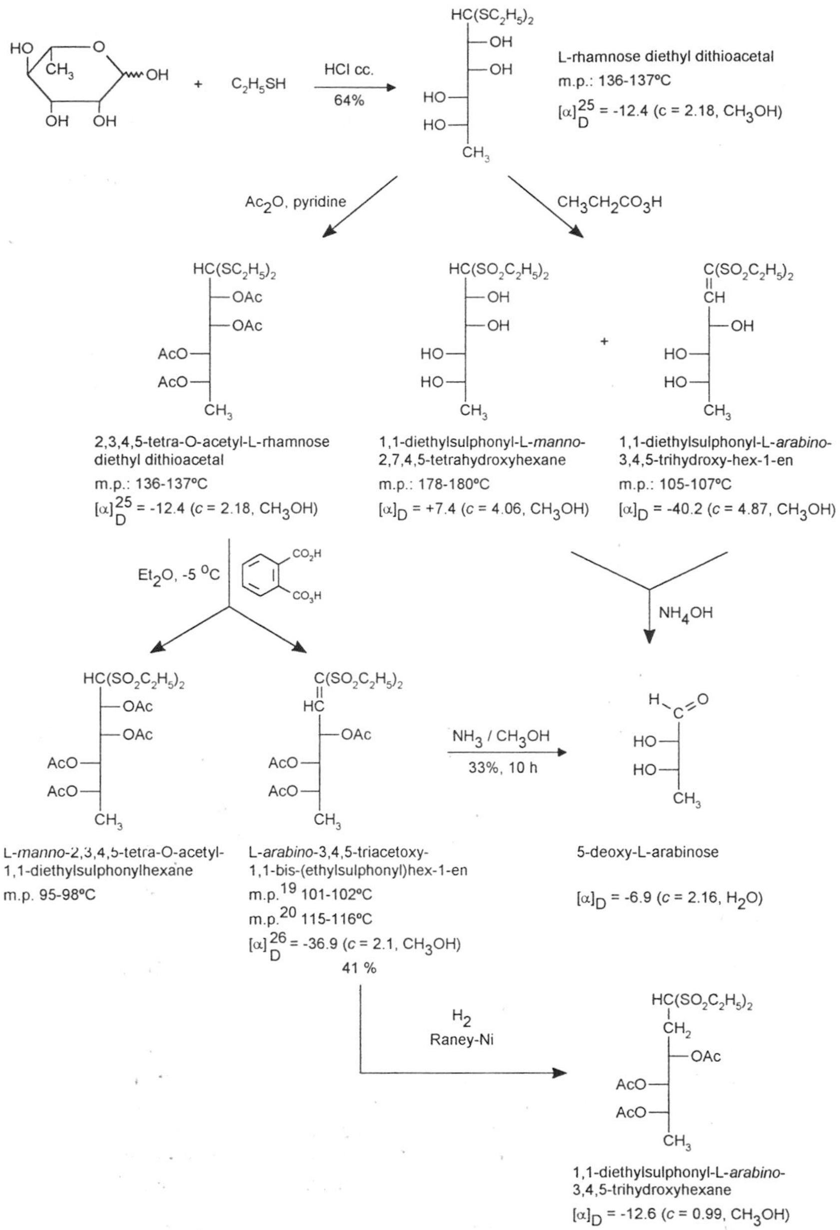

HC(SC$_2$H$_5$)$_2$

+ C$_2$H$_5$SH

$\xrightarrow[64\%]{\text{HCl cc.}}$

HC(SC$_2$H$_5$)$_2$
—OH
—OH
HO—
HO—
CH$_3$

L-rhamnose diethyl dithioacetal
m.p.: 136-137°C

$[\alpha]_D^{25} = -12.4$ (c = 2.18, CH$_3$OH)

Ac$_2$O, pyridine

CH$_3$CH$_2$CO$_3$H

HC(SC$_2$H$_5$)$_2$
—OAc
—OAc
AcO—
AcO—
CH$_3$

2,3,4,5-tetra-O-acetyl-L-rhamnose
diethyl dithioacetal
m.p.: 136-137°C
$[\alpha]_D^{25} = -12.4$ (c = 2.18, CH$_3$OH)

HC(SO$_2$C$_2$H$_5$)$_2$
—OH
—OH
HO—
HO—
CH$_3$

1,1-diethylsulphonyl-L-*manno*-
2,7,4,5-tetrahydroxyhexane
m.p.: 178-180°C
$[\alpha]_D = +7.4$ (c = 4.06, CH$_3$OH)

+

C(SO$_2$C$_2$H$_5$)$_2$
‖
CH
—OH
HO—
HO—
CH$_3$

1,1-diethylsulphonyl-L-*arabino*-
3,4,5-trihydroxy-hex-1-en
m.p.: 105-107°C
$[\alpha]_D = -40.2$ (c = 4.87, CH$_3$OH)

Et$_2$O, -5 °C

CO$_2$H
CO$_2$H

NH$_4$OH

HC(SO$_2$C$_2$H$_5$)$_2$
—OAc
—OAc
AcO—
AcO—
CH$_3$

L-*manno*-2,3,4,5-tetra-O-acetyl-
1,1-diethylsulphonylhexane
m.p. 95-98°C

C(SO$_2$C$_2$H$_5$)$_2$
‖
HC
—OAc
AcO—
AcO—
CH$_3$

L-*arabino*-3,4,5-triacetoxy-
1,1-bis-(ethylsulphonyl)hex-1-en
m.p.^{19} 101-102°C
m.p.^{20} 115-116°C
$[\alpha]_D^{26} = -36.9$ (c = 2.1, CH$_3$OH)
41 %

$\xrightarrow[33\%, 10 \text{ h}]{\text{NH}_3 / \text{CH}_3\text{OH}}$

H
C=O
HO—
HO—
CH$_3$

5-deoxy-L-arabinose
$[\alpha]_D = -6.9$ (c = 2.16, H$_2$O)

H$_2$
Raney-Ni

HC(SO$_2$C$_2$H$_5$)$_2$
CH$_2$
—OAc
AcO—
AcO—
CH$_3$

1,1-diethylsulphonyl-L-*arabino*-
3,4,5-trihydroxyhexane
$[\alpha]_D = -12.6$ (c = 0.99, CH$_3$OH)

FIGURE 2.4

(m.p. 150–151°C) consisting mainly of the unsaturated disulfone **5.3.** Three recrystallizations from methanol give pure **5.2,** m.p. 159–162°C, $[\alpha]_D^{22}$ +29 (14 min) → +16 (2 days) (end value; c = 0.5 in water). Addition of ether and petroleum ether to the mother liquor of the first recrystallization affords a further 3.06 g of the product,

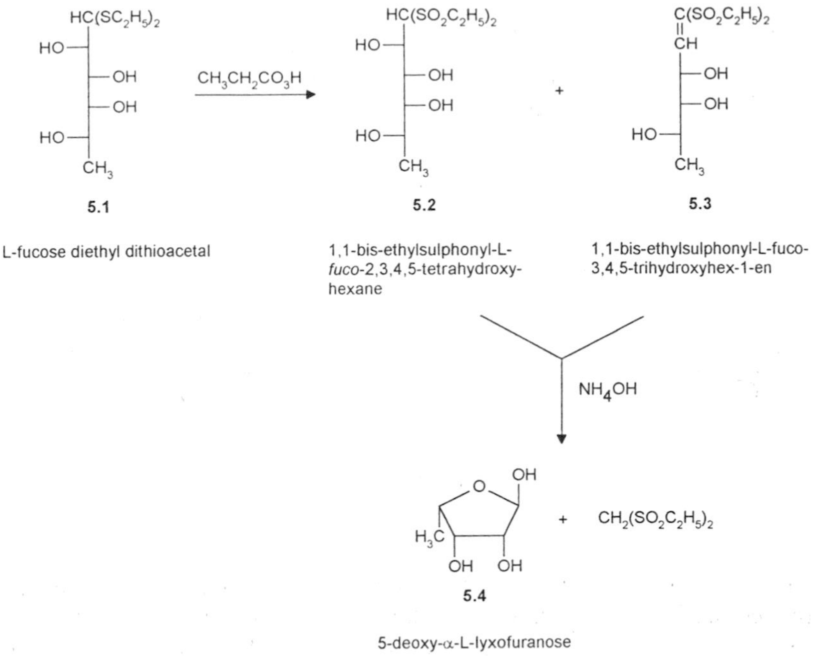

$$HC(SC_2H_5)_2$$

HO—

—OH

—OH

HO—

$$CH_3$$

5.1

L-fucose diethyl dithioacetal

$$HC(SO_2C_2H_5)_2$$

HO—

—OH

—OH

HO—

$$CH_3$$

5.2

1,1-bis-ethylsulphonyl-L-
fuco-2,3,4,5-tetrahydroxy-
hexane

$$C(SO_2C_2H_5)_2$$
$$\overset{\parallel}{C}H$$

—OH

—OH

HO—

$$CH_3$$

5.3

1,1-bis-ethylsulphonyl-L-fuco-
3,4,5-trihydroxyhex-1-en

$$CH_3CH_2CO_3H$$ →

+

$$NH_4OH$$

+ $$CH_2(SO_2C_2H_5)_2$$

5.4

5-deoxy-α-L-lyxofuranose

FIGURE 2.5

in three fractions, with m.p. 140–145°C, raising the overall yield of the sulfones as high as 92%. Recrystallization of this latter crystalline fraction from ethanol yields 0.67 g of the unsaturated **5.3**, m.p. 143–144°C, $[\alpha]_D^{22}$ −45 (c = 1.08 in water).

5-Deoxy-D-lyxofuranose (5.4)[12]   The pH of a solution of the disulfones **5.2** and **5.3** (14.03 g) in water (250 ml) is adjusted to 9.0–9.5 by the addition of a few drops of 2 N ammonium hydroxide. After 24 h, the precipitated diethyldisulfonylmethane is filtered off and the filtrate is washed six times with chloroform. The combined organic solution is extracted once with water, and the aqueous phase is combined with the main aqueous solution. It is then concentrated and passed through a column filled with Amberlite IR-120 (H⁺) resin, the column is washed with water and the slightly acidic eluate is neutralized with Amberlite IR-45 (OH⁻) resin. Following decolorization with charcoal and concentration, the colorless syrupy residue has $[\alpha]_D^{22}$ −24 (c = 1.97 in water), which spontaneously crystallizes after removal of the traces of water by codistillation with abs. ethanol and drying in a vacuum desiccator over phosphorous pentoxide. The crystals are finely powdered under a layer of abs. ethanol (3 ml) and abs. ether (18 ml), filtered cautiously to obtain the extremely hygroscopic product **5.4** (4.07 g, 70%), m.p. 68–69°C (in a sealed tube, shrinking at 58°C), $[\alpha]_D^{24}$ −38 (3 min) → −31.5 (8 min, end value, c = 3.17 in water). The crystals are readily soluble in abs. ethanol. Addition of ether–hexane produces agglomerates of large prisms which show greater specific optical rotation: $[\alpha]_D^{24}$ −43 (+ min) → −34.5 (10 min, end value, c = 1.17 in water).

Studies on oxidation products have shown that 1,1-(dialkylsulfonyl)-polyhydroxy-1-alkenes (**6.2**) are not always the stable end products of the transformation of dithioacetals (**6.1**) since, by the intramolecular attack of

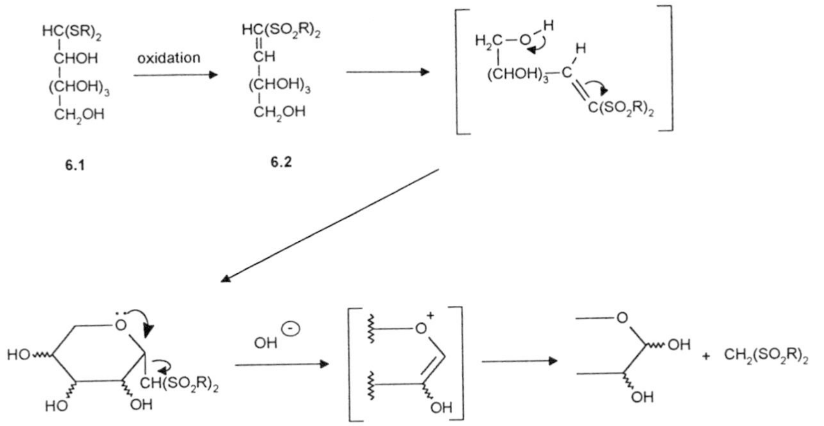

FIGURE 2.6

the terminal hydroxyl group, anhydroaldopyranosyl-1,1-(dialkylsulfonyl)-methanes (**6.3**) may be produced. Then degradation of these latter substances esaily proceeds with the formation of an aldose (**6.4**) shortened by one carbon atom (Fig. 2.6).

The next example illustrates a related degradation[22] of D-galactose diethyl dithioacetal (**7.1**) to D-lyxose (**7.3**). The reaction sequence (see Fig. 2.7) proceeds *similarly with the other hexoses,* and from the C-2 epimeric sugars, the same chain-shortened pentose is produced.[8,14,22-26]

2,6-Anhydro-1-deoxy-1,1-bis(ethylsulfonyl)-D-talitol (**7.2**)[22] (see also Hough and Taylor[14]) D-Galactose diethyl dithioacetal (**7.1**; 2 g) is dissolved in 40 ml of hot 1,4-dioxane, the solution is brought into reflux, and an amount of 4 M + 15% of peroxypropionic acid is quickly added and overheated (105°C). After shaking for 5–10 min, separation of crystals begins and a semisolid mass is produced. After being cooled to room temperature, the product is filtered and washed five times with cold 1,4-dioxane and then with ether to obtain 2.0 g (86%) of **7.2**, as needles, m.p. 202–202.5°C, $[\alpha]_D^{22}$ +4.7 (c = 1.3 in methanol), +14.7 (c = 2.17 in water). Acetylation or benzoylation of **7.2** gives the crystalline triacetate (m.p. 188-189°C) and the crystalline tribenzoate (m.p. 201°C), respectively.

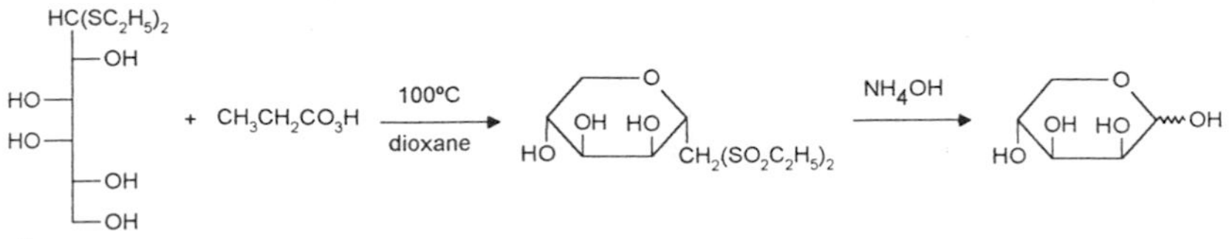

FIGURE 2.7

Preparation of D-lyxose (7.3) Compound **7.2** (0.5 g) is suspended in water (5 ml) and 1 drop of concentrated ammonium hydroxide is added. After 6 days the reaction is complete (TLC), the reaction mixture is extracted with chloroform (4 × 10 ml) to remove bis(ethylsulfonyl)methane, the aqueous layer is concentrated and dried *in vacuo* at 40°C overnight, and the dry residue is recrystallized from methanol to give 0.19 g (85%) of D-lyxose (**7.3**), $[\alpha]_D^{22}$ −13 (equilibrium value, c = 2.0 in water).

Figure 2.8 shows that oxidation of the diethyl dithioacetal of D-allose and D-altrose (**8.1** and **8.2,** respectively) with peroxypropionic acid in aqueous 1,4-dioxane gives rise to the same product: 2,6-anhydro-1,1-bis(ethylsulfonyl)-D-altritol (**8.3**), whose treatment with ammonia, as discussed above, leads[25] to D-*ribose*.

Steric effects may influence the descending syntheses of 2,6-anhydro-1-deoxy-1,1-(dialkylsulfonyl)alditols. Thus, detailed studies have revealed that 2,6-anhydro-1-deoxy-1,1-bis(ethylsulfonyl)-2,3-*O*-isopropylidene-D-talitol does not give 2,3-*O*-isopropylidene-D-lyxose with aqueous ammonia. Since the oxonium ion intermediate (see Fig. 2.6) is not produced readily in this case, the degradation can be effected only with 3 N NaOH or with concentrated ammonium hydroxide. On the contrary, quick degradation of 2,6-anhydro-1-deoxy-1,1-bis(ethylsulfonyl)-3,4-*O*-isopropylidene-D-mannitol into 3,4-*O*-isopropylidene-D-arabinose was observed with dilute aqueous ammonia, and this was explained by the fact that the molecule easily adopted the conformation favored for the degradation.[24]

Anhydro ring formation has also been observed with pentoses, and, depending on the reaction conditions can be obtained[26]; from D-arabinose

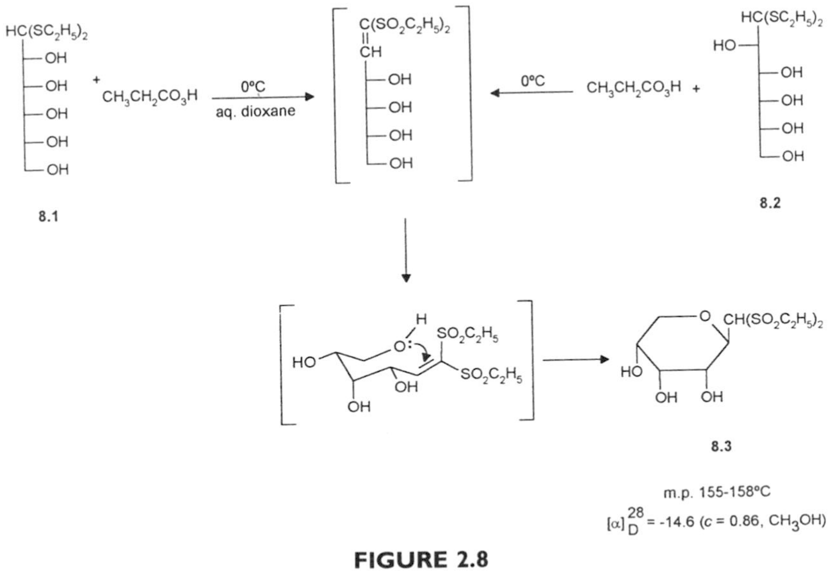

m.p. 155-158°C

$[\alpha]_D^{28}$ = -14.6 (c = 0.86, CH$_3$OH)

FIGURE 2.8

diethyl dithioacetal (**9.1**) D-arabinose-diethylsulfone [**9.2**, 1-deoxy-1,1-bis (ethylsulfonyl)-D-arabinitol] or 2,5-anhydro-1-deoxy-1,1-bis(ethylsulfonyl)- D-ribitol (**9.3**) (see Figure 2.9).

This disulfone procedure has been found very useful *for descending synthesis of aminodeoxy sugars,* as well; the disulfone derived from the diethyl dithioacetal of D-glucosamine gave the same product (D-arabinose) as that obtained from D-glucose diethyl dithioacetal. However, when 2-acetamido-2-deoxysugars were subjected to an analogous descending process, different products were isolated—depending, again, on the reaction conditions. Thus, from *paromose* (2,6-diamino-2,6-dideoxy-L-idose), 5-acetamido-5-deoxy-L-xylose (**10.4**) was obtained[27] via the dibenzyl dithioacetal **10.1** as shown in Figure 2.10.

2,6-Diacetamido-1,1-bis(benzylsulfonyl)-1,2,6-trideoxy-L-iditol (**10.2**)[27] To a cold (−10°C), stirred solution of 2,6-diacetamido-2,6-dideoxy-L-idose dibenzyl dithioacetal (**10.1**, 1.02 g) in methanol (10 ml), peroxypropionic acid (3.7 M, 4.3 ml) is added dropwise, and after remaining at this temperature for 1 h, it is allowed to warm to room temperature and stirred for further 2 h. The mixture is then concentrated to a syrup (bath temperature 37°C) and codistilled several times with methanol, and trituration of the glassy residue with ether gives a white solid (1.19 g) that liberates iodine from potassium iodide (due to traces of the oxidizing agent), but

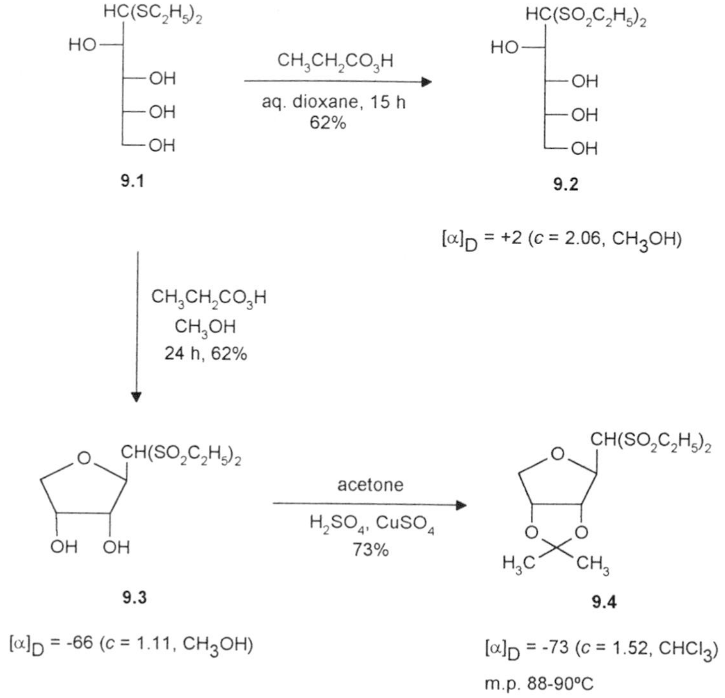

FIGURE 2.9

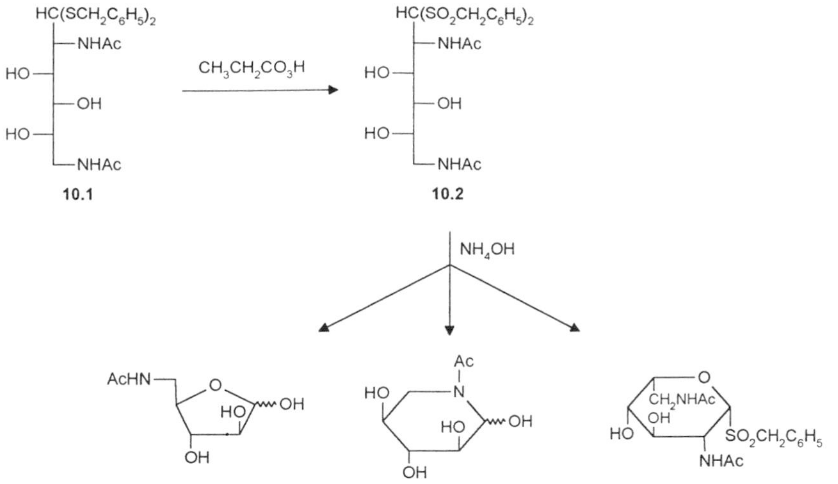

HC(SCH₂C₆H₅)₂ → written as $HC(SCH_2C_6H_5)_2$

$HC(SCH_2C_6H_5)_2$
—NHAc
HO—
—OH
HO—
—NHAc

10.1

$CH_3CH_2CO_3H$ →

$HC(SO_2CH_2C_6H_5)_2$
—NHAc
HO—
—OH
HO—
—NHAc

10.2

NH_4OH

AcHN— O
HO— —OH
—OH

10.3

5-acetamido-5-deoxy-
L-xylofuranose

syrup

Ac
|
N
HO— —OH
HO—
—OH

10.4

5-acetamido-5-deoxy-
L-xylopyranose

m.p. 160-162°C

O
CH₂NHAc
OH
HO— SO₂CH₂C₆H₅
NHAc

10.5

2,6-diacetamido-2,6-dideoxy-
L-idopyranosyl-β-benzylsulphone

m.p. 177-178°C

FIGURE 2.10

does not give precipitate with BaCl₂. For purification, this material is codistilled several times with methanol and precipitated with ether to furnish 0.82 g of pure **10.2**, m.p. 125°C (softening from 108°C), $[\alpha]_D^{23}$ −31.4 (c = 1.05 in methanol).

Degradation of the iditol derivative **10.2** with ammonia gave rise to the three products **10.3–10.5**, shown in Figure 2.10.

Careful oxidation of 3-acetamido-3-deoxy-D-altrose diethyl dithioacetal with peroxypropionic acid does not give an isolable open-chain diethylsulfone; the products are 3-acetamido-2,6-anhydro-1,2-dideoxy-1-(diethylsulfonyl)-D-ribose, and a smaller quantity of 2-acetamido-2-deoxy-D-ribopyranose, arising from C-1—C-2 splitting.[27] The same mixture is produced[28] on the oxidation of 3-acetamido-3-deoxy-D-altrose diethyl dithioacetal, and descending synthesis[29] of 5-acetamido-5-deoxy-L-arabinose via 5-acetamido-1,1-bis(ethylsulfonyl)-1,5-dideoxy-L-arabinitol gave only 18–20% of 4-acetamido-4-deoxy-L-erythrofuranose.

It is to be noted that in the case of 2-amino-1,1-dialkylsulfonyl derivatives, epimerization may occur, and that the primary degradation product, 2-acetamido-2-deoxy-D-ribose, is transformed[25] into the D-arabinose derivative, due to the inductive effect of the acetamido group.

Oxidation of 2,3,5,6,2′,3′,4′,6′-octa-O-methylmaltose diethyl dithioacetal (**11.2**), obtained from N-methyl-hepta-O-methyl-N-(p-nitrophenyl)-β-maltosylamine (**11.1**) into the corresponding disulfone [1-deoxy-1,1-bis(ethylsulfonyl)-2,3,5,6,2′,3′,4′,6′-octa-O-methylmaltitol, **11.3**] was investigated by Lehmann.[30] Fragmentation of this latter compound by ammonium hydroxide provided, among other things, 2,3,4,6-tetra-*O*-methyl-D-glucose (**11.4**), showing that this degradation procedure has a *potential for sequencing* branched oligosaccharides (see Fig. 2.11).

*1-Deoxy-1,1-bis(ethylsulfonyl)-2,3,5,2′,3′,4′,6′-octa-O-methylmaltitol (**11.3**)* A solution of 3-chloroperoxybenzoic acid (17.3 g, 100 mmol) in dichloromethane (150 ml) is added dropwise to a stirred solution of the diethyl dithioacetal **11.2** (10 g, 17.9 mmol) in dichloromethane (30 ml). After 4 h, the mixture is neutralized with saturated aqueous $NaHCO_3$ (3 × 100 ml), washed with water (100 ml), dried over $CaSO_4$, and concentrated. Column chromatography (eluant: 1 : 1 ethyl acetate–cyclohexane) of the residue and recrystallization from ethyl acetate–petroluem ether gives the sulfone **11.3** (8.0 g, 72%), m.p. 74°C, $[\alpha]_D^{22}$ +93 (c = 0.75 in chloroform).

*1,2-Dideoxy-1,1-bis(ethylsulfonyl)-hepta-O-methylmalt-1-enitol (**11.5**)* A solution of the sulfone **11.3** (1.5 g, 2.4 mmol) in 4 : 1 tetrahydrofuran–water (25 ml) is stored at room temperature for 10 h, then diluted with water (200 ml) and extracted with chloroform (3 × 50 ml). The combined extract is dried ($CaSO_4$), concentrated, and the residue is purified by column chromatography (eluant: 3 : 1 ethyl acetate–cyclohexane) to give syrupy **11.5** (1.4 g, 98%), $[\alpha]_D^{23}$ +69 (c = 1.1 in chloroform).

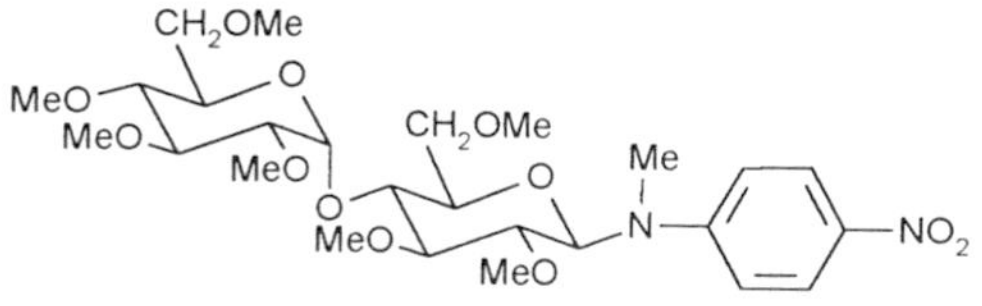

11.1

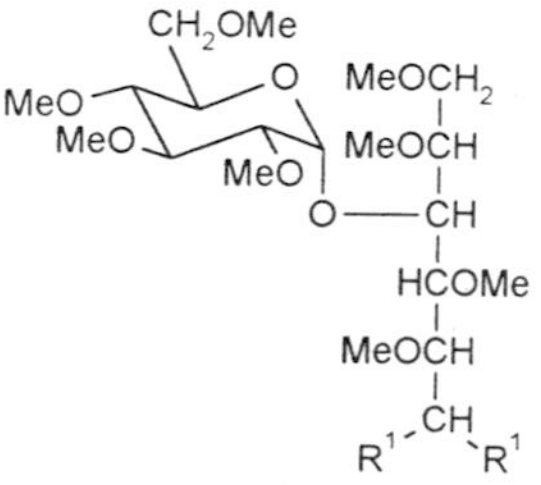

11.2 R^1 = SEt
11.3 R^1 = SO_2Et

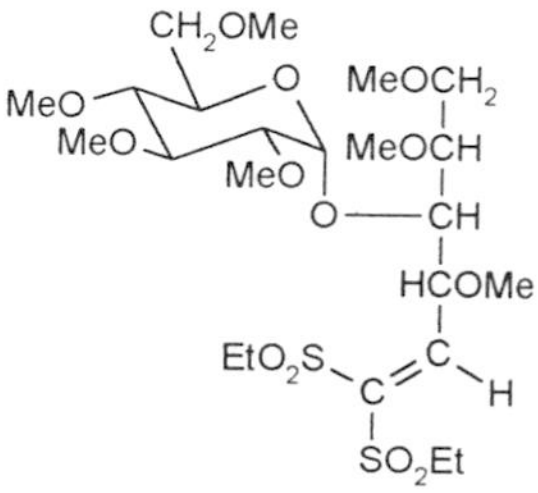

11.5

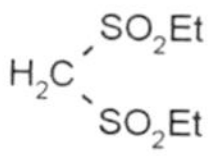

11.6 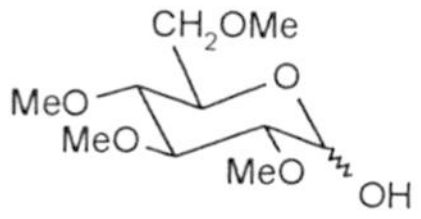   11.4 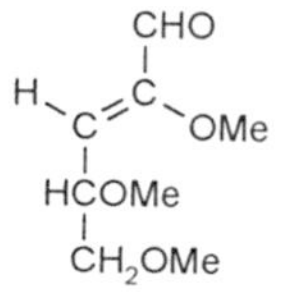   11.7

FIGURE 2.11

Fragmentation of 11.5 A solution of **11.5** (1.05 g, 1.69 mmol) in tetrahydrofuran (20 ml) is added to aqueous ammonia (30 ml, 2.5%), and the mixture is kept at room temperature for 2 h, when TLC shows that all of the starting material has reacted and three new compounds are detected. The reaction mixture is diluted with water (200 ml) and extracted with dichloromethane (3 × 100 ml), the combined extract is dried over CaSO$_4$ and concentrated, and the residue is subjected to column chromatography [column: 3 × 50 cm, eluant: 3:1 ethyl acetate–cyclohexane for tetra-O-methyl-D-glucose (**11.4**, R_f = 0.18) and column: 3 × 15 cm, eluant: 5:6 ethyl acetate–cyclohexane for **11.6** and **11.7**]. Compound **11.6** (strong staining with iodine in TLC) is identical to authentic bis(ethylsulfonyl)methane, R_f = 0.54 (in 3:1 ethyl acetate–cyclohexane). Compound **11.7** (250 mg, 85%) is shown to be 3-deoxy-2,4,5-tri-*O*-methyl-D-*glycero*-pent-2-enose [strong UV absorbance in TLC, R_f = 0.50 (in 3:1 ethyl acetate–cyclohexane)].

As shown by Kuhn *et al.*,[13] the disulfoxides of sugar–dithioacetals (dialkyldithioacetals), produced in the form of four stereoisomers, can be quantitatively degraded with dilute aqueous ammonia (1 day at room temperature) into the sugar *one carbon atom shorter* in the chain. The simultaneous electron-withdrawing effect of the two sulfoxide functions and the "attracting" effect of the electron pair of the C-2 hydroxyl function induce rupture of the bond between C-1 and C-2 (Fig. 2.12) similar to that observed for the sulfones.

Because of differences in the stereochemistry, extremely varying physical data have been reported[1,9,13] for the prepared disulfoxides.

D-Galactose dibenzyl dithioacetal bis(S-oxide)[13] Method A D-Galactose dibenzyl dithioacetal (2.05 g) is dissolved in warm glacial acetic acid (15 ml), and the solution is quickly cooled to 30°C, followed by a qiuck addition of 30% hydrogen peroxide (5 ml). The mixture is kept at 20°C for 2 h, and ether (~75 ml) is added to result in the separation of the crystalline product, which is recrystallized from 2-propanol by the addition of a small volume of abs. ethanol to yield 520 mg (24%), m.p. 180–184°C, $[\alpha]_D^{25}$ −86 (c = 1.50 in pyridine), $[\alpha]_D^{25}$ −61 (c = 0.75 in DMF). After a further recrystallization, m.p. 181–186°C (dec.), $[\alpha]_D^{24}$ −82 (c = 1.0 in pyridine).

Method B By repeating the reaction as described in method A, two crystalline fractions are obtained (250–250 mg) with m.p. ~185°C, $[\alpha]_D^{21}$ −42 (c = 1.5 in pyridine) and $[\alpha]_D^{21}$ −50 (c = 1.1 in pyridine), respectively. These two fractions are combined and recrystallized from 2-propanol to give 240 mg of the bis-*S*-oxide with m.p. 183–187°C and $[\alpha]_D^{21}$ −29 (c = 1.0 in pyridine).

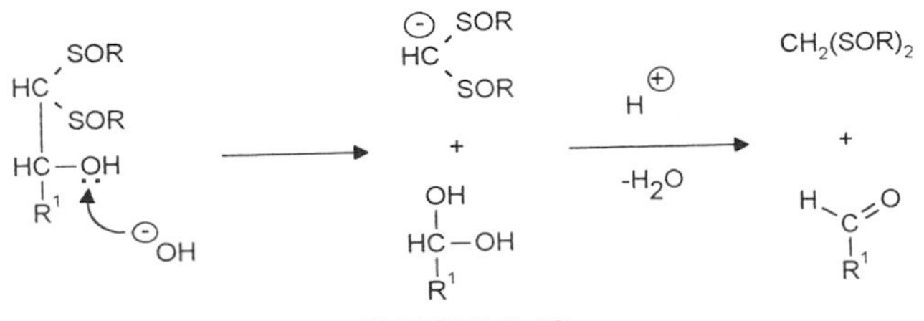

FIGURE 2.12

Method C When the reaction described in method A is carried out in a double volume of glacial acetic acid and 10 ml of hydrogen peroxide, and precipitation of the product is executed after 12 h, 180 mg (8%) of crystalline bis-S-oxide is obtained with m.p. 189–195°C and $[\alpha]_D^{19}$ +37 (c = 0.5 in pyridine).

Alkaline degradation of D-galactose dibenzyl dithioacetal-S-oxides[13] Method A First, 440 mg of the disulfoxide with $[\alpha]_D^{25}$ −82 (pyridine) is dissolved in hot water (150 ml) and cooled to ambient temperature, and the pH of the solution is adjusted to 9.7 by the addition of 2 drops of concentrated ammonium hydroxide. Separation of sparkling crystals starts in about 10 min, which are filtered off after 21 h, to yield 222 mg (76%) of methylene-bis(benzyl)-sulfoxide, m.p. 212–214°C (dec.). A second crop [43 mg, 13%, m.p. 202–205°C (dec.)] of this material is obtained on concentration of the mother liquor. After recrystallization from methanol–ethanol or acetic acid, the substance (sparkling platelets) had an m.p. 220°C (dec.) and $[\alpha]_D$ ±0. The syrup obtained from the mother liquor is dissolved in 6 ml of 96% ethanol, and after the addition of 4-bromophenylhydrazine (206 mg), the mixture is boiled under reflux for 15 min. After refrigeration of the solution, 92 mg of D-lyxose 4-bromophenylhydrazone (m.p. 156–157°C) is obtained and further crops (33 mg; overall yield 40%) can be isolated from the mother liquors.

Method B Treatment of the disulfoxide with $[\alpha]_D^{19}$ +37 (pyridine) (120 mg) is carried out as described in method A. In this case the starting material does not dissolve readily in cold water, and partly precipitates. Degradation of the mixture at pH 9.5 is complete in ~2 days to allow to isolate 26 mg (33%) of methylene-bis(benzyl)sulfoxide, m.p. 216–217°C (dec.).

Treatment of the monosulfoxides of sugar–dithioacetals with acids results in the conversion[13] into the starting material (see Fig. 2.13). Thus, when the monosulfoxide **13.2**, derived from 2,3,4,5,6-penta-O-acetyl-D-

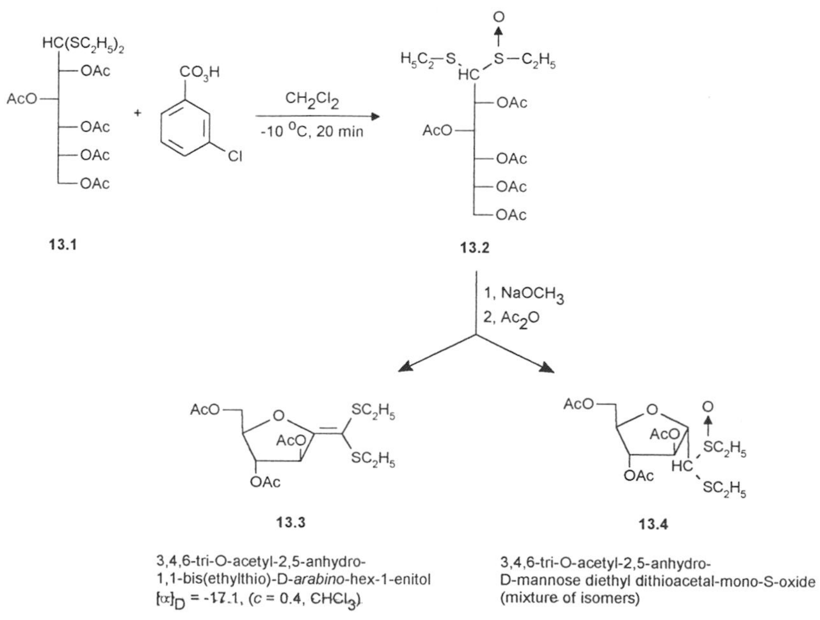

13.1   **13.2**

1, NaOCH₃
2, Ac₂O

13.3   **13.4**

3,4,6-tri-O-acetyl-2,5-anhydro-
1,1-bis(ethylthio)-D-*arabino*-hex-1-enitol
$[\alpha]_D$ = -17.1, (c = 0.4, CHCl₃)

3,4,6-tri-O-acetyl-2,5-anhydro-
D-mannose diethyl dithioacetal-mono-S-oxide
(mixture of isomers)

FIGURE 2.13

glucose diethyl dithioacetal (**13.1**), is successively treated with sodium methoxide and acetic anhydride, two compounds (**13.3** and **13.4**) of synthesis-related interest are produced.[31]

REFERENCES TO SECTION 2.I

1. E. Rothstein, *J. Chem. Soc.,* p. 684 (1934), p. 1560 (1940).
2. E. Fischer, *Ber. Dtsch. Chem. Ges.* **27,** 673 (1894).
3. D. L. MacDonald and H. O. L. Fischer, *J. Am. Chem. Soc.* **74,** 2087 (1952); *Biochim. Biophys. Acta* **12,** 203 (1953).
4. D. L. MacDonald, *Methods Carbohydr. Chem.* **1,** 73 (1962).
5. E. J. Bourne and R. Stephens, *J. Chem. Soc.,* p. 4009 (1954).
6. D. L. MacDonald and H. O. L. Fischer, *J. Am. Chem. Soc.* **77,** 4348 (1955).
7. H. Böhme, *Org. Synth.* **20,** 70 (1940).
8. L. D. Hall, L. Hough, S. H. Shute, and T. J. Taylor, *J. Chem. Soc.,* p. 1154 (1965).
9. H. Zinner and K.-H. Falk, *Chem. Ber.* **88,** 566 (1955).
10. H. Zinner and K.-H. Falk, *Chem. Ber.* **89,** 2451 (1956).
11. B. Gauthier and C. Vaniscotte, *Bull. Soc. Chim. Fr.,* p. 30 (1956).
12. R. Kuhn, W. Bister, and D. Dafeldecker, *Justus Liebigs Ann. Chem.* **628,** 186 (1959).
13. R. Kuhn, W. Baschang-Bister, and W. Dafeldecker, *Justus Liebigs Ann. Chem.* **641,** 160 (1961).
14. L. Hough and T. J. Taylor, *J. Chem. Soc.,* p. 970 (1956).
15. R. Barker and D. L. MacDonald, *J. Am. Chem. Soc.* **82,** 2297 (1960).
16. J. D. Wander and D. Horton, *Adv. Carbohydr. Chem. Biochem.* **32,** 15 (1976).
17. L. Hough and T. J. Taylor, *J. Chem. Soc.,* p. 1212 (1955).
18. R. Kuhn and G. Baschang, *Justus Liebigs Ann. Chem.* **628,** 193 (1959).
19. E. L. Patterson, R. Milstery, and E. L. R. Stokstad, *J. Am. Chem. Soc.* **78,** 5868 (1956).
20. L. Hough and T. J. Taylor, *J. Chem. Soc.,* p. 3544 (1955); E. C. Taylor and P. A. Jacobi, *J. Am. Chem. Soc.* **96,** 6781 (1974); W. L. F. Armarego, P. Waring, and B. Paal, *Aust. J. Chem.* **35,** 785 (1982).
21. C. E. Ballou, H. O. L. Fischer, and D. L. MacDonald, *J. Am. Chem. Soc.* **77,** 5967 (1955).
22. R. Barker and D. L. MacDonald, *J. Am. Chem. Soc.* **82,** 2297 (1960).
23. L. Hough and T. J. Taylor, *J. Chem. Soc.,* p. 970 (1956); L. Hough, and M. I. Taha, *J. Chem. Soc.,* p. 3564 (1957).
24. L. Hough and A. C. Richardson, *J. Chem. Soc.,* pp. 1019, 1024 (1962).
25. B. Coxon and L. Hough, *Carbohydr. Res.* **8,** 379 (1968).
26. A. Farrington and L. Hough, *Carbohydr. Res.* **16,** 59 (1971).
27. T. H. Haskell and S. Hanessian, *J. Org. Chem.* **28,** 2598 (1963).
28. B. Coxon and L. Hough, *J. Chem. Soc.,* pp. 1463, 1643 (1961).
29. S. Hanessian and T. H. Haskell, *J. Heterocycl. Chem.* **1,** 57 (1964).
30. B. Jäger, H. Lay, J. Lehmann, and L. Ziser, *Carbohydr. Res.* **217,** 99 (1991).
31. J. A. López Sastre, J. Molina Molina, D. Portal Olea, and C. Romero Avila, *Can. J. Chem.* **66,** 2975 (1988).

2.2. DEGRADATION OF CALCIUM SALTS OF ALDONIC ACIDS WITH HYDROGEN PEROXIDE

Hydrogen peroxide is known to effect different types of degradation of carbohydrates, giving rise to various products, as a result of the random oxidation. Combination of this oxidizing agent with Fe^{2+} and Fe^{3+} ions (the so-called Fenton reagent[1]) for the degradation of hydroxycarboxylic acids has long been applied, but no practical utilization has been found in the field of sugar chemistry.[2–4] However, when the alkaline-earth metal salts of aldonic acids are reacted with hydrogen peroxide in the presence of Fe^{3+} (or Cu^{2+}) salts, an *aldose shortened by one carbon atom* is obtained,[5] generally with a moderate yield. Studies on the reaction mechanism have revealed that chain shortening proceeds[6] via the loss of a hydrogen atom at the β-carbon, as shown in Figure 2.14. This mechanism could be unambiguously substantiated[7] by *deuterium-labeling*: calcium D-gluconate-2-d afforded D-arabinose-1-d. The descending procedure was studied[8–10] in detail on D-gluconic acid, in an application of an ion-exchange technique for workup, the yield could be improved[11] to 44%.

> *Preparation of D-arabinose from calcium D-gluconate*[12]   A mixture of calcium D-gluconate monohydrate (192.3 g), barium acetate monohydrate (20.86 g), and ferric(III) sulfate (10.2 g) in water (2 liters) is brought to boil with stirring, filtered through a pad of Celite, washed with 50 ml of water, and cooled to 40°C, and 30% hydrogen peroxide (120 ml) is added. When the temperature lowers to 40°C a further 120 ml of hydrogen peroxide is added. After completion of the reaction (indicated by a change in color to deep-violet), the mixture is filtered through a pad of charcoal and passed through a 5.5 × 103-cm Amberlite IR-120 column and then a 5.5 × 97-cm Duolite A-4 column. The columns are washed with distilled water until a negative Fehling probe is obtained, and the combined eluates and washings (~8 liters) are concentrated to a thick syrup at 60°C bath temperature. The residue is treated with methanol (100 ml) at 5°C for 5 days to furnish 57.5 g (44.4%) of D-arabinose, $[\alpha]_D^{20}$ −103.3 (equilibrium value, $c = 0.92$ in water). Recrystallization from 0.7 part of water or aqueous methanol the constant specific rotation value is −104.4.

Calcium D-galactonate was degraded[12,13] into D-*lyxose* in an essentially similar way, and further prescriptions can be found in the papers of Fletcher[14] and Whistler and BeMiller.[15] D-Erythrose could be prepared according to the original procedure with rather low yield.[16,17] Ruff obtained[18] 5-deoxy-L-arabinose from calcium L-rhamnonate (**15.1**) and characterized in the form of the benzylphenylhydrazone **15.2** (Fig. 2.15).

> *5-Deoxy-L-arabinose benzylphenylhydrazone (**15.2**)*[18]   Calcium L-rhamnonate (**15.1**, 280 g) is dissolved in water (1 liter), and ferric(III) acetate (50 g) and hydrogen

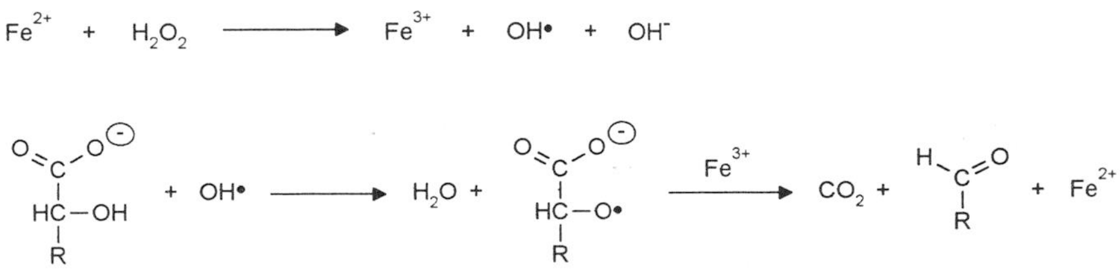

FIGURE 2.14

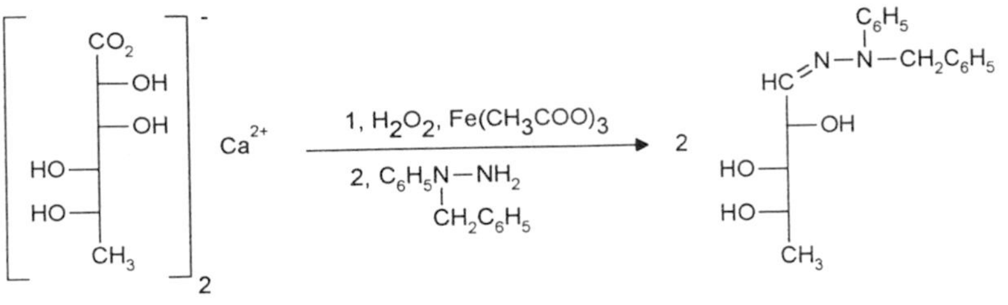

FIGURE 2.15

peroxide (1.5 molar eq) are added. After 15 min at room temperature, vigorous evolution of carbon dioxide begins and the mixture smells like dough. The mixture is concentrated under diminished pressure (bath temperature $\leq 50°C$) to obtain a dark syrup, from which the title product is extracted by triturating with ethanol. The combined ethanolic extract is concentrated to a syrup, the residue is boiled with 50 ml of abs. ethanol, and the solution is decanted from the fleecy residue on the bottom of the flask. Titration of the solution with a Fehling solution indicates a reducing power correspondent to ~16% yield. This ethanolic solution is boiled with an ethanolic solution of a calculated amount of benzylphenylhydrazine and cooled, and water (a triple volume) is added. The separated syrup crystallizes in the form of radially arranged needles in 1.5 days. The solvent is decanted, and the product is washed with benzene and hexane to obtain the pure hydrazone **15.2**. The mother liquor is titrated, and treated (if necessary) with a calculated amount of benzylphenylhydrazine to yield a second crop. Overall yield: 27 g (31%) of the pure hydrazone, m.p. 96–97°C (from benzene) from the sugar titrated as an amount of 35 g.

D-*Threose* can be obtained from the crystalline strontium D-xylonate, and identification of the product is carried out in form of 1,2,3-tri-*O*-acetyl-D-threofuranose[19].

Degradation of D-xylonic acid into D-threose[19]   A solution of barium acetate (1 M, 75 ml) and that of ferric(III) sulfate (0.5 M, 50.2 ml) are mixed in 2 liters of water, strontium D-xylonate (200 g) is added, and the mixture is brought into boiling. After cooling it is filtered through a pad of Celite, and 30% hydrogen peroxide (120 ml) is added at 35°C. After the vigorous carbon dioxide evolution has finished (~10 min), the solution is cooled to 35°C and an additional 120 ml of hydrogen peroxide is added. The solution is filtered, again, through a pad of Celite, then concentrated *in vacuo* to 250 ml, and the residue is taken up with methanol (1.5 liters) and filtered. The precipitated salts are treated with 300 ml of methanol (or acetone), the fleecy precipitate is filtered off, and the filtrate is concentrated to a thick syrup. This is dissolved in methanol, the solution is evaporated, and for complete removal of methanol, the residue is codistilled with ethyl acetate. Then sodium acetate (melted, 10 g) and acetic anhydride (100 ml) are added to the residue and the mixture is stirred in a 100°C bath. After completion of the acetylation, the mixture is poured into ice water, neutralized with $NaHCO_3$, and extracted several times with chloroform, and the organic layer is dried (Na_2SO_4). After evaporation, the residual syrup is dissolved in hot methanol to induce crystallization of the title product on cooling; yield 12 g (two-thirds of the crude product), m.p.

117–118°C, $[\alpha]_D$ +35.6 (c = 3.4 in chloroform). No crystalline product could be obtained from the mother liquor.

This descending procedure *permits the synthesis,* although in moderate yield, *of an important 2-deoxysugar:* 2-deoxy-D-*erythro*-pentose (2-deoxy-D-ribose), as well, by means of treating[20–26] a mixture of calcium 3-deoxy-D-*ribo*- and -*arabino*-hexonates with hydrogen peroxide. In addition, *2-deoxy-*D-glycero-*tetrose* (2-deoxy-D-tetrose) and its enantiomer are also available[27] with this procedure.

> *2-Deoxy-*D-glycero-*tetrose*[27] To an aqueous solution of D-arabinose (or D-xylose; 60 g in 160 ml of water), a solution of NaOH (170 g) in water (280 ml) is added under nitrogen atmosphere and the mixture is stirred rapidly at 100°C for 10 h. After cooling to −10°C, it is neutralized with concentrated HCl (*the temperature must not rise higher than* −*5°C*): during neutralization the deep-brown color changes to light yellow (the thymol blue indicator shows a color change from blue to yellow). *No excess of hydrochloric acid should be added!* The solution is decolorized with charcoal and then filtered, the filtrate is concentrated to its half volume, NaCl precipitated is filtered off, and the filtrate is concentrated at 40°C bath temperature. This operation is repeated three times, and the residual syrup-like filtrate is diluted with a sixfold volume of water. The solution is quickly warmed to 80°C (by avoiding local overheating) and alkalized with CaO until a definite alkaline pH. Then it is quickly cooled to room temperature and neutralized with dry ice, and the precipitated $CaCO_3$ is filtered off following a quick warmup of the suspension to 80°C. The filtrate is treated with hydrogen peroxide in the presence of ferric(III) acetate according to the Ruff degradation procedure,[27] and the reaction mixture is deionized by passsing through cation- and anion-exchange resins. The eluate is concentrated to a syrup (bath temperature ≤40°C), dried over phosphorous pentoxide, and dissolved in an equivalent volume of methanol, and a fivefold excess of acetone or ether is added. On stirring or shaking, the initial precipitate aggregates to a colorless mass of fleecy crystals that is filtered off as soon as possible and dried in a vacuum desiccator over P_2O_5. Further crops of the product may be obtained by repeated concentration and treatment with methanol or acetone. The yield of 2-deoxy-D-glycero-tetrose is 4.58 g (11%) and 4.4 g (10.6%) from D-arabinose and D-xylose, respectively, m.p. 67–69°C, and the specific rotation values for the products obtained form these sugars are, respectively, $[\alpha]_D^{24}$ −2.3 (10 min), −4.0 (24 h, c = 2.62 in water) and $[\alpha]_D^{24}$ −2.1 (10 min), −3.8 (24 h, c = 4.36 in water).

According to this principle, *mucic amide* was degraded to D,L-lyxuronic acid,[28] but the structures of the intermediates were not unequivocally determined. In the field of disaccharides, *lactose* was degraded into β-D-galactopyranosyl-(1→4)-D-arabinose,[13] and β-D-glucopyranosyl-(1→5)-D-arabinose was obtained[29] from *gentiobiose.*

REFERENCES TO SECTION 2.2

1. H. J. H. Fenton, *J. Chem. Soc.* **65**, 899 (1894); **67**, 774 (1895); **69**, 546 (1896).
2. G. J. Moody, *Adv. Carbohydr. Chem.* **19**, 149 (1964).
3. B. Larsen and O. Smidsrod, *Acta Chem. Scand.* **21**, 552 (1967).
4. H. S. Isbell, H. L. Frush, and E. W. Parks, *Carbohydr. Res.* **51**, C5 (1976).

5. V. Bilik, Slovak Academy of Sciences, Czech. Pat. 232,647 (1986/1983); *Chem. Abstr.* **108,** 38310n (1988).
6. K. J. Buchanan, A. Goosen, and J. D. Lovelock, *South Afr. J. Chem.* **30,** 191 (1977); H. S. Isbell and P. Czubarow, *Carbohydr. Res.* **203,** 287 (1990).
7. H. S. Isbell and M. A. Salam, *Carbohydr. Res.* **90,** 123 (1981).
8. O. Ruff, *Ber. Dtsch. Chem. Ges.* **31,** 1573 (1898); *ibid.* **32,** 550 (1899).
9. R. C. Hockett and C. S. Hudson, *J. Am. Chem. Soc.* **56,** 1632 (1934).
10. F. J. Bates, *Polarimetry, Saccharimetry and the Sugars,* p. 469. U. S. Govt. Printing Office, Washington, DC, 1942,.
11. H. S. Isbell, N. B. Holt, and H. L. Frush, *J. Res. Natl. Bur. Stand.* **57,** 95 (1956).
12. H. G. Fletcher, Jr., H. W. Diehl, and C. S. Hudson, *J. Am. Chem. Soc.* **72,** 4546 (1950).
13. O. Ruff and G. Ollendorff, *Ber. Dtsch. Chem. Ges.* **33,** 1798 (1900).
14. H. G. Fletcher, Jr., *Methods Carbohydr. Chem.* **1,** 77 (1962).
15. R. L. Whistler and J. N. BeMiller, *Methods Carbohydr. Chem.* **1,** 79 (1962).
16. O. Ruff, *Ber. Dtsch. Chem. Ges.* **32,** 3672 (1899).
17. W. G. Overend, M. Stacey, and L. F. Wiggins, *J. Chem. Soc.,* p 1358 (1949).
18. O. Ruff, H. Kohn, A. Meusser, and A. Franz, *Ber. Dtsch. Chem. Ges.* **35,** 2360 (1902).
19. R. C. Hockett, *J. Am. Chem. Soc.* **57,** 2260, 2266 (1935).
20. J. C. Sowden, *J. Am. Chem. Soc.* **76,** 3541 (1954).
21. J. C. Sowden, *Biochem. Prep.* **5,** 75 (1957).
22. G. N. Richards, *J. Chem. Soc.,* p. 3639 (1954).
23. G. N. Richards, *Chem. Ind. (London),* p. 1035 (1953).
24. H. W. Diehl and H. G. Fletcher, Jr., *Chem. Ind. (London),* p. 1087 (1958); *Arch. Biochem. Biophys.* **78,** 386 (1958).
25. H. W. Diehl and H. G. Fletcher, Jr., *Biochem. Prep.* **8,** 49 (1961).
26. G. N. Richards, *Methods Carbohydr. Chem.* **1,** 18 (1962).
27. H. Venner, *Chem. Ber.* **90,** 121 (1957).
28. M. Bergmann, *Ber. Dtsch. Chem. Ges.* **54,** 1362 (1921).
29. R. Schaffer and H. S. Isbell, *J. Res. Natl. Bur. Stand.* **57,** 33 (1956).

2.3. DESCENDING SYNTHESES OF ACYLATED ALDONONITRILES

Degradation of sugar oximes or aldononitriles (derived from the former oximes) represents a valuable method for the descending procedures leading through open-chain saccharides. The very first successful experiments in this field were carried out by Wohl,[1,2] and a significant improvement was reported by Zemplén,[3]—thus this methodology is generally referred as the "Wohl–Zemplén degradation."

The Wohl–Zemplén degradation involves treatment of the readily available[4] acylated aldononitriles (**16.1**) with silver hydroxide and ammonia (Fig. 2.16) to result in the diacylamide of the *one-carbon-shortened aldose* (**16.2**) and silver cyanide. To isolate the aldose **16.3,** the usually weakly soluble 1-deoxy-1,1-diacylamidoalditol (**16.2**) is subjected to acid hydrolysis.

1-Deoxy-1,1-diacylaminoalditols are produced from the intermediary *aldehydo*-sugars (formed from the nitrile by fission of hydrogen cyanide), followed by acyl migration and formation of an orthoester intermediate[5,6]

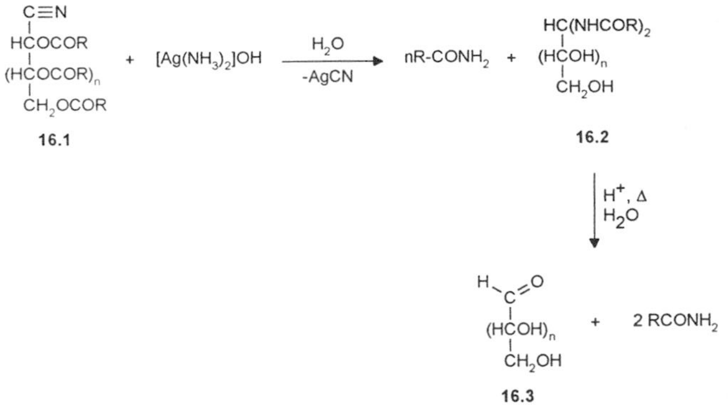

FIGURE 2.16

(Fig. 2.17). Thus, this degradation represents the *reverse process* of the cyanohydrin synthesis (see Section 1.2.1).

The potential of the Wohl–Zemplén methodology is illustrated by the following practical one-pot procedure, in which the starting acylated aldononitrile is obtained directly from the aldose.

2,3,4,5,6-Penta-O-acetyl-D-galactononitrile[7]   In this procedure 50 g of D-galactose is dissolved in pyridine (140 ml) and mixed, in a 1-liter round-bottomed flask, with a solution of hydroxylamine hydrochloride (27.5 g) in pyridine (140 ml). Then acetic anhydride (370 ml) is added in portions, when the mixture warms up severely. For completion of the reaction, the mixture is stirred in a nitrogen atmosphere at 100°C for 3 h, and after cooling, the dark solution is poured onto ice. The separated dark precipitate is filtered off and washed with water to yield 96.1 g, m.p. 138–142°C. By repeated recrystallizations from ethanol and workup of the mother liquor the overall yield is 71.6 g, m.p. 139–139.5°C, $[\alpha]_D^{22}$ +41 (c = 5.0 in chloroform).

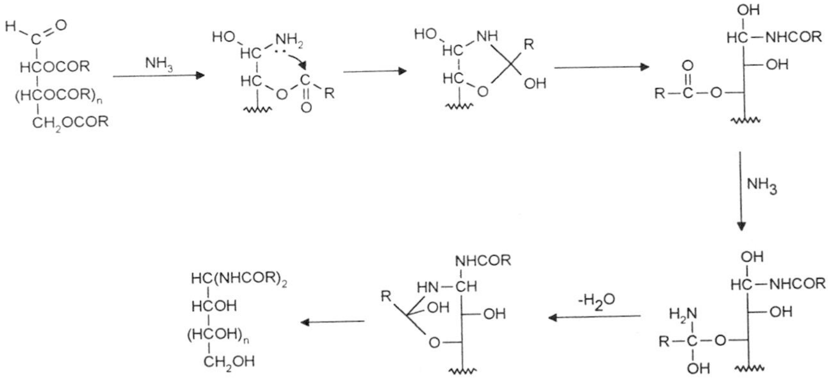

FIGURE 2.17

Of the known mono- and disaccharides, lyxose, cymarose, digitoxose, and lactose did not give crystalline nitrile with this procedure.[7]

The Wohl degradation procedure is shown by the example of hexa-*O*-benzoyl-D-*glycero*-D-*galacto*-heptononitrile (**18.1**), which gives rise[8] to a two-component product mixture. By fractional crystallization, this is separated to 1,1-bis(benzamido)-1-deoxy-D-mannitol (**18.2**) and the so-called D-mannose–benzamide (Fig. 2.18).

> *Degradation of hexa-O-benzoyl-D-glycero-D-galacto-heptononitrile (18.1)*[8] In methanol (250 ml) saturated with ammonia, silver nitrate (2 g) and the title compound (8 g) are dissolved. After 2 days the mixture is concentrated *in vacuo*, the residue is taken up with water and the insolubles are extracted with hot ethyl acetate to remove benzamide. A further treatment with hot alcohol leaves silver cyanide insoluble, and from the ethanolic solution 1,1-bis(benzamido)-1-deoxy-D-mannitol (**18.2**) crystallizes as long needles. After three recrystallizations from ethanol, the yield is 1.5 g, m.p. 226°C (dec.), $[\alpha]_D^{24}$ +3.6 (c = 2.5 in pyridine). The silver ions are precipitated in the form of AgCl with hydrochloric acid, the aqueous layer is extracted with benzene or ethyl acetate to furnish a substance, with very low yield, that can be crystallized from water. This substance is the so-called D-mannose-monobenzamide: long needles that start to melt at 230°C (complete melting at 254°C).

Although the major product of the degradation of aldononitriles with silver hydroxide–ammonia is the corresponding 1-deoxy-1,1-bis(acylamino)-alditol,[4] a cyclic glycosylamine (such as D-mannose-monobenzamide) is also produced as the by-product. In some cases this substance may be even the main product; this is the case with the degradation of hexa-*O*-acetyl-D-*glycero*-D-*gulo*-heptononitrile.[9,10]

For preparation of the free sugar, the 1,1-diacetamido derivative should be selected, whose acid hydrolysis leads to the target sugar. Figure 2.19 illustrates the degradation of tetra-*O*-acetyl-D-xylononitrile (**19.1**) into D-threose (**19.2**).[11]

It has been found that 1-deoxy-1,1-bis(acylamino)-alditols are also produced[8] on treatment of aldononitriles with methanolic ammonia. For example, 2,3,4,5,6,7-hexa-*O*-acetyl-D-*glycero*-D-*ido*-heptononitrile (**20.1**) gives[12] *N*-acetyl-D-glucofuranosylamine (**20.2**; see Fig. 2.20), and degradation[13] of

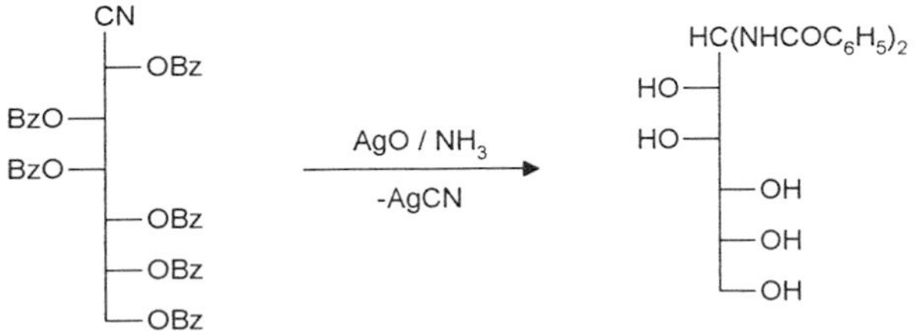

FIGURE 2.18

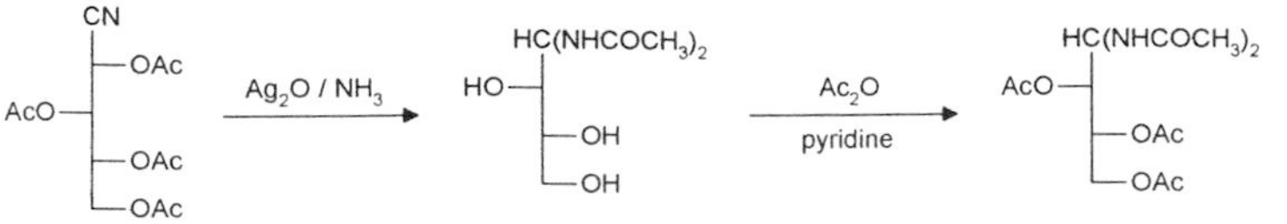

tetra-O-acetyl-D-xylononitrile

m.p. 81-82°C
$[\alpha]_D$ = +50.3 (c = 0.76, CHCl₃)

1-deoxy-1,1-bis(acetamido)-D-threitol

m.p. 165-167°C
$[\alpha]_D$ = -10.8 (c = 0.60, H₂O)

2,3,4-tri-O-acetyl-1-deoxy-1,1-bis(acetamido)-D-threitol

m.p. 179-180°C
$[\alpha]_D$ = +74.2 (c = 0.34, CHCl₃)

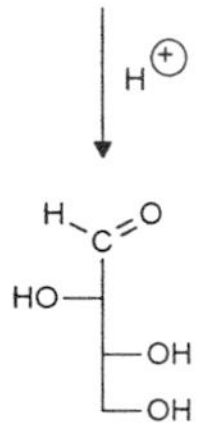

19.2

D-threose
$[\alpha]_D^{20}$ = -12 .5
(equilibrium value, H₂O)

FIGURE 2.19

the heptononitrile with D-*glycero*-D-*gulo*-configuration also produces **20.2**, with the same yield. No exact explanation about the elimination of the nitrile group has been reported.

N-*Acetyl*-D-*glucofuranosylamine (20.2)*[12]* The nitrile **20.1** (5 g) is dissolved in methanolic ammonia (150 ml); a clear solution is produced quite quickly. After 1 day it is concentrated, and the syrupy residue is dried thoroughly, extracted with ethyl acetate, and warmed cautiously with 30 ml of abs. ethanol. Crystallization starts at 0°C in about 2 h, and the crystals are filtered and washed with a small volume of abs. ethanol to give 690 mg, m.p. 200–201°C. A second crop of the substance is obtained from the mother liquor. Overall yield: 840 mg (34.9%). Recrys-

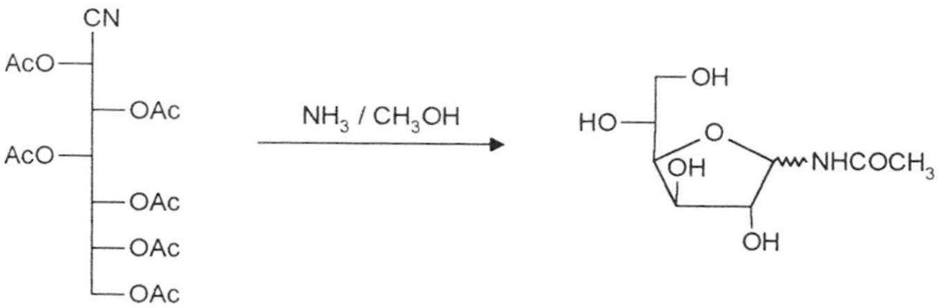

20.1   **20.2**

FIGURE 2.20

tallization from 80% ethanol gives the pure glycosylamine **20.2**, m.p. 201–202°C, $[\alpha]_D^{20}$ +86.2 (in water).

The following *aldononitriles* were degraded into the corresponding 1-deoxy-1,1-(diacylamino)-alditols: 2,3,4,5-tetra-*O*-acetyl-D-arabinonitrile,[14] 2,3,4,5,6-penta-*O*-acetyl-D-gluconitrile and -D-mannononitrile,[15] and the respective *O*-propionates[16] and 2,3,4,5,6,7-hexa-*O*-acetyl-D-*glycero*-L-*manno*-heptononitrile. The Wohl procedure has also been *extended* for a few *disaccharide* representatives. Figure 2.21 shows the degradation products (**21.2–21.4**) of octa-*O*-acetylcellobiononitrile (**21.1**), as described by Deferrari *et al.*[18]

Analogous degradations carried out with octa-*O*-acetyllactononitrile[19] and octa-*O*-acetylmelibiononitrile[20] proceeded with very low yields. Degradation of octa-*O*-benzoylmelibiononitrile with ammonia in methanol[21] gave rise to the products shown in Figure 2.22, which were separated by column chromatography.

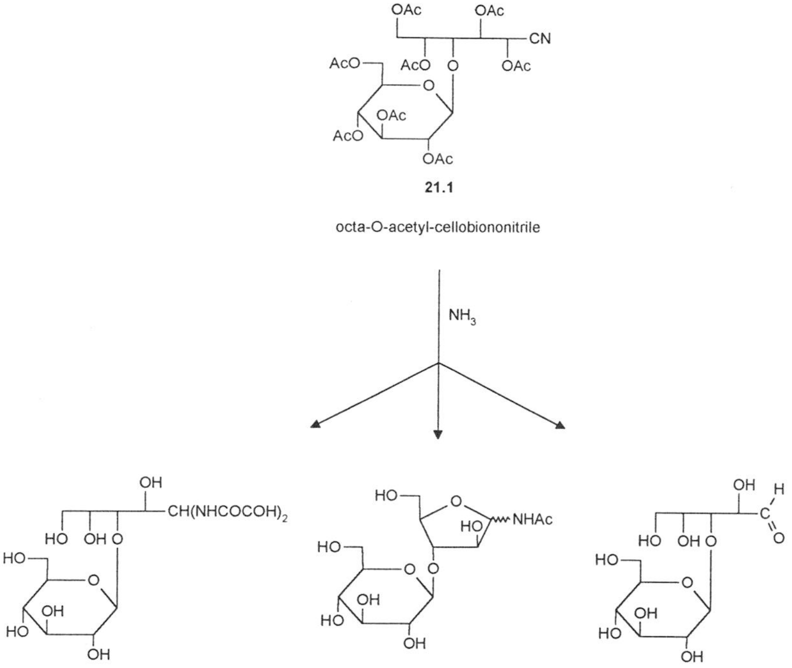

21.1

octa-O-acetyl-cellobiononitrile

NH₃

21.2

3-O-β-D-glucopyranosyl-1,1-
bis(acetamido)-1-deoxy-D-arabinitol
m.p. 214-215°C
$[\alpha]_D^{20}$ = +25.2, (c = 0.99, H₂O)
24%

21.3

3-O-β-D-glucopyranosyl-N-acetyl-
D-arabinofuranosylamine
m.p. 130-131°C
$[\alpha]_D^{23}$ = +72.7, (c = 0.50, H₂O)
3.3%

21.4

3-O-β-D-glucopyranosyl-
D-arabinose
m.p. 143-145°C
$[\alpha]_D^{20}$ = +37.4, (c = 0.55, H₂O)
0.4%

FIGURE 2.21

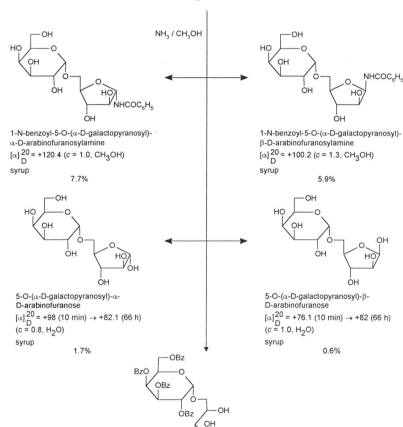

octa-O-benzyl-melibiononitrile

NH$_3$ / CH$_3$OH

1-N-benzoyl-5-O-(α-D-galactopyranosyl)-
α-D-arabinofuranosylamine
$[\alpha]_D^{20}$ = +120.4 (c = 1.0, CH$_3$OH)
syrup
7.7%

1-N-benzoyl-5-O-(α-D-galactopyranosyl)-
β-D-arabinofuranosylamine
$[\alpha]_D^{20}$ = +100.2 (c = 1.3, CH$_3$OH)
syrup
5.9%

5-O-(α-D-galactopyranosyl)-α-
D-arabinofuranose
$[\alpha]_D^{20}$ = +98 (10 min) → +82.1 (66 h)
(c = 0.8, H$_2$O)
syrup
1.7%

5-O-(α-D-galactopyranosyl)-β-
D-arabinofuranose
$[\alpha]_D^{20}$ = +76.1 (10 min) → +82 (66 h)
(c = 1.0, H$_2$O)
syrup
0.6%

1,1-bis(benzamido)-1-deoxy-5-O-
(α-D-galactopyranosyl)-D-arabinitol
m.p.: 231-232°C (benzene)
$[\alpha]_D^{20}$ = +78.5 (c = 0.7, pyridine)
33.7%

FIGURE 2.22

Zemplén has shown that splitting of the nitrile function proceeds easily with sodium methoxide to give, with good yield, the respective one-carbon-atom-shortened aldose,[3] and further studies have revealed that this procedure *works in practice extremely well* for di- and oligosaccharides.

Several reports[4,22,23] have appeared on the degradation of penta-*O*-acetyl-D-glucononitrile. The following experimental procedure[24] describes the preparation of 5-deoxy-L-arabinose (**23.2**), as shown in Figure 2.23.

> *Preparation of 5-deoxy-L-arabinose (23.2)*[24]   A solution of 2,3,4,5-tetra-*O*-acetyl-L-rhamnononitrile (**23.1**, 13 g) in abs. methanol (90 ml) is cooled to −20°C, and a methanolic solution of sodium methoxide (prepared from 2 g of Na and 90 ml of abs. methanol) is added. After the solution has remained for 15 min at room temperature, 100 ml of 1 N acetic acid is added and the mixture is evaporated immediately at ≤45°C bath temperature. The residue is codistilled several times with methanol to remove HCN, and the residual yellow syrup is taken up with water (100 ml), filtered, and passed through an Amberlite IR-120 (H⁺) column (3 × 26 cm, flow rate: ~120 ml/h) and the column is washed with water. The Fehling-positive fractions are concentrated, codistilled with methanol and dried over phosphorous pentoxide–potassium hydroxide. The yield of the pale syrupy product **23.2** is 91–100%, $[\alpha]_D^{21}$ −8 (15 min) → +3 (14 h, $c = 4.5$ in water). This product contains traces of L-rhamnose and an unidentified product, which could not be removed by further purification of the syrupy substance with chromatography.

Zemplén-degradation of acylated biononitriles has also been reported.[25–30]

A saccharide-degradation procedure, very closely related to the Wohl–Zemplén method, is based on the treatment of *sugar–oximes* with 1-fluoro-2,4-dinitrobenzene at 20–70°C in aqueous sodium hydrogencarbonate, by passing carbon dioxide through the mixture. The reaction products are 2,4-dinitrophenol, hydrogen cyanide, and the aldose shortened with one carbon atom. Unidentified yellow and red by-products are also formed, and the HCN produced is delivered into a silver nitrate solution with the CO_2 carrier gas, and in this way the degradation can be monitored quantitatively. An example of this type of saccharide chain shortening, described by Weygand,[31] is shown in Figure 2.24.

Using this methodology, D-*xylose* was obtained[31] with a 23% yield from the oxime of D-galactose, and from 6-methylthio-D-glucose oxime, 29%

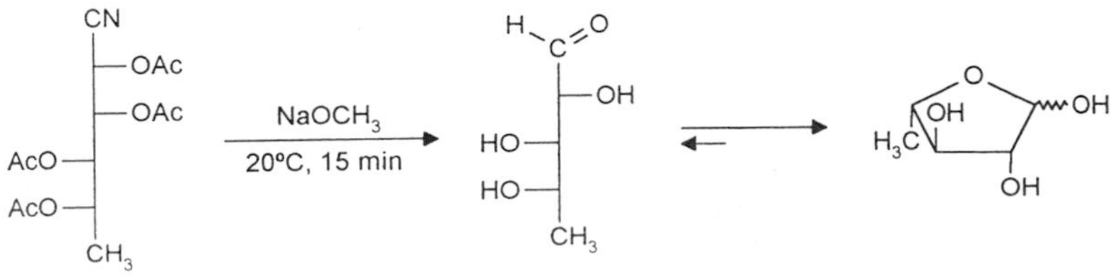

FIGURE 2.23

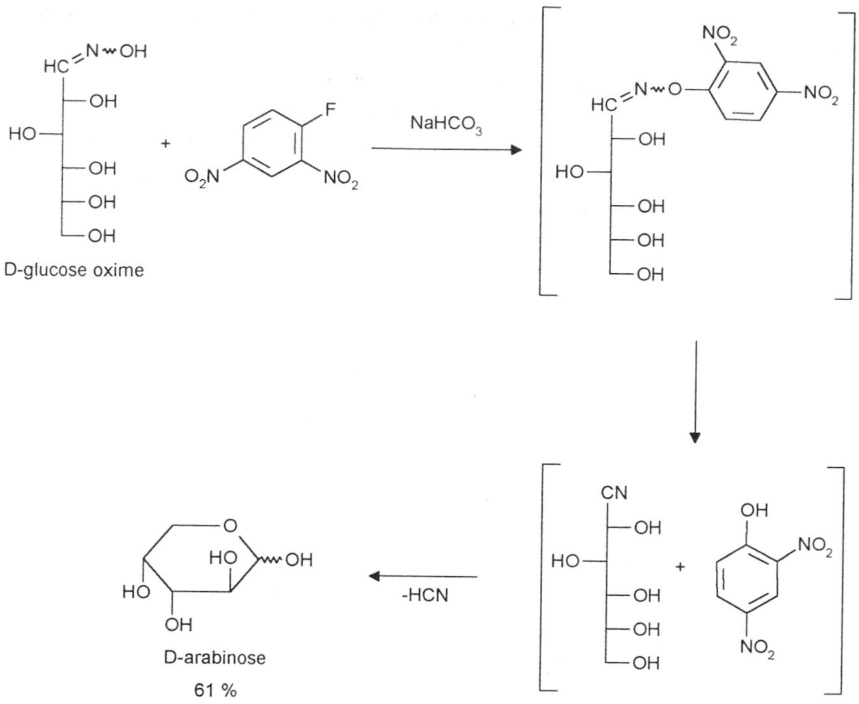

FIGURE 2.24

of 5-methylthio-D-arabinose was prepared.[32] *2-Deoxy-D-threo-pentose* was synthesized[33] from 3-deoxy-D-*xylo*-hexose oxime by applying analogous reaction conditions.

> *Preparation of 2-deoxy-D-threo-pentose*[33] To a solution of 3-deoxy-D-*xylo*-hexose oxime (4.0 g) in water (20 ml) and methanol (5 ml), NaHCO₃ (4 g) in 90 ml of water is added. The solution is warmed to 65°C in a vigorous stream of CO_2. From a solution of 1-fluoro-2,4-dinitrobenzene (9 g) in *n*-propanol (40 ml) 30 ml is added to the mixture, and a 3-ml volume of the reaction mixture is taken and refluxed for 1 min. Then this sample is added to the mixture; after 2 min, vigorous evolution of HCN starts, indicated by precipitation of silver cyanide from the acidified silver nitrate solution into which the carrier gas is delivered. After 45 min and 60 min reaction times, 5–5 ml each of the remaining 10 ml reagent–solution is added to the mixture. The sample is then kept at 65°C for 2 h and allowed to cool down to ambient temperature in a continuous CO_2 stream. The yield of AgCN is 1.29 g (42.9%), which corresponds to 1.29 g of 2-deoxy-D-*threo*-pentose. Following filtration of 2,4-dinitrophenol, the filtrate is extracted with 30 ml of ether, three times with *n*-butanol (30, 20, and 20 ml) and then with 2 × 20 ml of ether. The organic extracts are combined and washed with water (3 × 25 ml) (since the product dissolves slightly in *n*-butanol), and then the aqueous phase is reextracted with *n*-butanol. The combined organic extract is washed with aqueous NaHCO₃ until neutral, decolorized with charcoal, and concentrated to a syrup *in vacuo*. The sugar thus produced is extracted with hot abs. ethanol, and after evaporation, this operation is repeated. Following the two evaporations, 2.19 g of a syrupy residue

is obtained that contains, according to chromatographic analysis in *n*-butanol–water, the title sugar, 3-deoxy-D-*xylo*-hexose, 3-deoxy-D-*xylo*-hexose oxime, and traces of D-glucose and D-arabinose. 2-Deoxy-D-*threo*-pentose can be converted into the crystalline anilide (m.p. 132–134°C) and the benzylphenylhydrazone (m.p. 114–115°C).

REFERENCES TO SECTION 2. 3

1. A. Wohl, *Ber. Dtsch. Chem. Ges.* **26**, 730 (1893); **32**, 3666 (1899).
2. F. Micheel, *Chemie der Zucker und Polysaccharide*, p. 179. Akademische Verlagsgesellschaft Geest & Portig, Leipzig, 1956.
3. G. Zemplén, *Ber. Dtsch. Chem. Ges.* **59**, 1254, 2402.
4. V. Deulofeu, *Adv. Carbohydr. Chem.* **4**, 119 (1949).
5. H. S. Isbell and H. L. Frush, *J. Am. Chem. Soc.* **71**, 1579 (1949).
6. R. Allerton and W. G. Overend, *J. Chem. Soc.*, p. 35 (1952).
7. C. H. Trabert, *Arch. Pharm. (Weinheim, Ger.)* **291**, 246 (1961).
8. P. Brigl, H. Mühlschlegel, and R. Schinle, *Ber. Dtsch. Chem. Ges.* **64**, 2921 (1931).
9. R. C. Hockett and L. R. Chandler, *J. Am. Chem. Soc.* **66**, 957 (1944).
10. R. C. Hockett, M. H. Nickerson, and W. H. Ruder, *J. Am. Chem. Soc.* **66**, 472 (1944).
11. V. Deulofeu, *J. Chem. Soc.*, p. 2458 (1929); R. C. Hockett, *J. Am. Chem. Soc.* **57**, 2260 (1935); K. Iwadare, S. Fukunaga, and B. Kubota, *Bull. Chem. Soc. Jpn.* **12**, 116 (1937).
12. V. Deulofeu and J. O. Deferrari, *J. Org. Chem.* **17**, 1087 (1952).
13. V. Deulofeu and J. O. Deferrari, *An. Asoc. Quim. Argent.* **38**, 241 (1950).
14. R. C. Hockett, *J. Am. Chem. Soc.* **57**, 2265 (1935); R. C. Hockett and C. W. Maynard, Jr., *ibid.* **61**, 2111 (1939).
15. R. C. Hockett, V. Deulofeu, A. L. Secloff, and J. R. Mendive, *J. Am. Chem. Soc.* **60**, 278 (1938).
16. V. Deulofeu and F. Giménez, *J. Org. Chem.* **15**, 460 (1950).
17. J. O. Deferrari and V. Deulofeu, *J. Org. Chem.* **17**, 1097 (1952).
18. J. O. Deferrari, M. E. Gelpi, and R. A. Cadenas, *J. Org. Chem.* **30**, 2328 (1965).
19. M. E. Gelpi, J. O. Deferrari, and R. A. Cadenas, *J. Org. Chem.* **30**, 4064 (1965).
20. J. O. Deferrari, B. N. Zuazo, and M. E. Gelpi, *Carbohydr. Res.* **30**, 313 (1973).
21. B. N. Zuazo and I. M. E. Thiel, *Carbohydr. Res.* **172**, 156 (1988).
22. G. Zemplén and D. Kiss, *Ber. Dtsch. Chem. Ges.* **60**, 165 (1927).
23. H. T. Clarke and S. M. Nagy, *Org. Synth.* **20**, 14 (1940).
24. R. Kuhn, W. Bister, and W. Dafeldecker, *Justus Liebigs Ann. Chem.* **617**, 115 (1958).
25. N. B. D'Accorso and I. M. E. Thiel, *J. Carbohydr. Chem.* **8**, 743 (1989).
26. M. E. Gelpi and R. A. Cadenas, *Carbohydr. Res.* **88**, 277 (1981).
27. G. Zemplén, *Ber. Dtsch. Chem. Ges.* **60**, 1555 (1927).
28. G. Zemplén, *Ber. Dtsch. Chem. Ges.* **60**, 923 (1927).
29. M. E. Gelpi, B. N. Zuazo, and J. O. Deferrari, *An. Asoc. Quim. Argent.* **62**, 35 (1974).
30. N. S. MacDonald and W. L. Evans, *J. Am. Chem. Soc.* **64**, 2731 (1942).
31. F. Weygand and R. Löwenfeld, *Ber. Dtsch. Chem. Ges.* **83**, 559 (1950).
32. F. Weygand, O. Trauth, and R. Löwenfeld, *Ber. Dtsch. Chem. Ges.* **83**, 563 (1950).
33. F. Weygand and H. Wolz, *Ber. Dtsch. Chem. Ges.* **85**, 256 (1952).

2.4. DEGRADATION OF SACCHARIDES WITH OXIDATIVE METHODS

Of the oxidative methods employed in carbohydrate chemistry, this section discusses only those that are associated with shortening of the carbon chain and have been demonstrated as reproducibly useful for preparative purposes.

2.4.1. Degradation by Cleavage with Periodates

The carbon chain of vicinal diols,[1] 1,2-aminoalcohols,[2] 1,2-diketones, α-hydroxy-ketones, and 1,3-diketones are readily split with periodic acid or alkali periodates in polar solvents (water, methanol, dioxan, acetic acid). In this way, carbonyl compounds (**25.2**) are obtained from vicinal diols (**25.1**), as shown in Figure 2.25.

The reaction is fastest at pH 3–5, and in the case of *cis*-diols, the cleavege proceeds more quickly than with *trans*-glycols.[3] If the molecule contains more vicinal hydroxyl groups, splitting of the chain occurs in each place to give formaldehyde or formic acid, respectively, from the primary or secondary hydroxyl functions, and both of these oxidation products can be exactly determined[3] by quantitative methods. This clean, and *easily reproducible* procedure is generally used for the preparation of trioses and tetroses from suitably protected starting materials, which are—most of all—readily available pentose and hexose derivatives. Thus, one of the key intermediates to enantiomerically pure substances—2,3-*O*-isopropylidene-D-glyceraldehyde (**25.4**)—is readily obtained[4] (Fig. 2.25) from 1,2:5,6-di-*O*-isopropylidene-D-mannitol (**25.3**). A convenient method for the preparation of this compound is described later in this section.

This section includes *three examples* of the synthesis of this extremely *versatile chiral compound* (**25.4**), which is employed, in many cases, as a building block for a plethora of organic compounds. The *first* procedure[5] discussed here applies an aqueous reaction medium, the *second* employs[6] a mixture of dichloromethane and water, and the *third* could be reliably

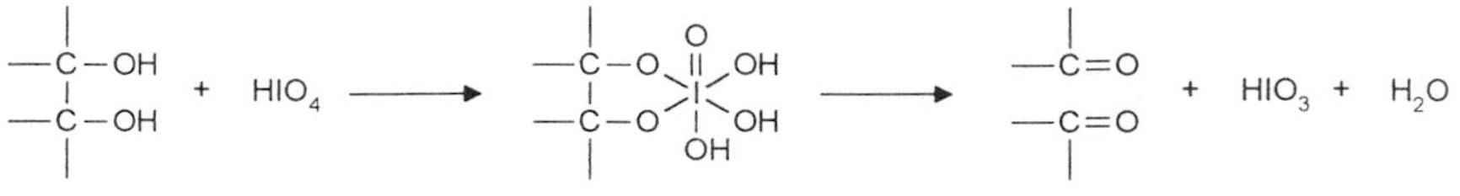

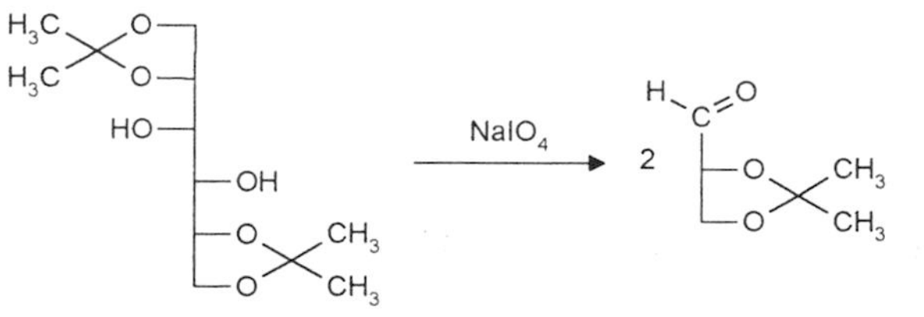

FIGURE 2.25

executed[7] on large scale, and with large volumes (e.g., 7500 liters) of the solvent.

2,3-O-Isopropylidene-D-glyceraldehyde (25.4)[5]   To an aqueous solution of NaHCO$_3$ (25.2 g, 0.3 M, 1.5 liters), 1,2:5,6-di-*O*-isopropylidene-D-mannitol (**25.3**; 78 g, 0.3 M) is added with stirring, and the solution is cooled to 5–8°C. Then a solution of sodium metaperiodate (68.0 g, 0.31 M) in water (250 ml) is slowly added, when the temperature rises to ~10°C. After 30 min, the cooling bath is removed, and stirring is continued at room temperature for 3 h. The product is then obtained from the filtered solution by continous extraction with ether (12 h), and the organic solution is dried (Na$_2$SO$_4$) and concentrated to give an intensely smelling oil (60 g, 78%), R_f = 0.25 (1 : 1 ethyl acetate–cyclohexane).

2,3-O-Isopropylidene-D-glyceraldehyde (25.4)[6]   In this procedure 50 g (0.19 M) of 1,2:5,6-di-*O*-isopropylidene-D-mannitol (**25.3**) is dissolved in dichloromethane (0.5 liter) and palced in a 25°C water bath. Then, sodium metaperiodate (81 g, 0.38 M) is added under rapid stirring, followed by the addition of 20 ml of water. The temperature of the mixture rises to 32°C and stirring is continued for an additional 1 h, until the reaction is complete [TLC in 3:17 acetone–dichloromethane; the chromatogram is sprayed with cold phosphomolybdic acid, and heating with a hot stream of air should be effected on the *face* (and not on the back) of the plate to avoid volatilization of the substance]. The reaction mixture is filtered, and the filter cake is washed with 2 × 100 ml of dichloromethane. The solvent is distilled off by using a Vigreux column up to a 40°C head temperature. The major fraction is distilled at 2.67 kPa (b.p. 60–62°C). Yield of the product **25.4** is 45 g (91%), [α]$_D$ +63.3 (c = 1.25 in benzene).

The physical data for 2,3-*O*-isopropylidene-D-glyceraldehyde prepared by the Eli Lilly researchers[7] somewhat differ from those reported earlier, but a considerable benefit of this procedure is its potential *use for large-scale preparations.*

1,2:5,6-Di-O-isopropylidene-D-mannitol (25.3)[7]   To a vessel equipped with a mechanical stirrer and a reflux condenser is added D-mannitol (75 g, 0.41 mol), freshly distilled diglyme (180 ml), and 2,2-dimethoxypropane (120 ml, 0.98 mol). To this stirred mixture is added SnCl$_2$ (75 mg, 0.4 mmol), and the mixture is heated to reflux until a clear solution is obtained (~1 h). The mixture is held at this temperature for 30 min, then cooled to ambient temperature, and pyridine (0.09 ml, 1.14 mmol) is added. The solvents are distilled off at 6–10 mmHg pressure (inside temperature ~80–90°C), and the crude residue is mixed with dichloromethane (540 ml). The mixture is stirred at ambient temperature for 1 h and filtered, the filtrate (containing ~58 g; 54% of **25.3**, as determined by capillary GC analysis) is concentrated, and the residue is recrystallized form *n*-butyl ether to give pure **25.3**, m.p. 121.8–123.4°C, [α]$_D$ +1.9 (c = 1.74 in methanol).

2,3-O-(Isopropylidene)-D-glyceraldehyde (25.4)[7]   <u>Method A</u>   In a vessel equipped with a mechanical stirrer and a thermometer is placed the mannitol **25.3** (33 g, 0.13 mol) and dichloromethane (300–350 ml), and then saturated aqueous NaHCO$_3$ (11.9 ml) added while maintaining the temperature below 25°C. Solid sodium metaperiodate (52.8 g, 0.25 mol) is then added over a period of 25 min with vigorous stirring, and the reaction is allowed to proceed for 2 h at <30°C. The solids are filtered off and the filtrate is concentrated at atmospheric pressure to a temperature of 55°C. The residual syrup is distilled at 30 mmHg, to obtain 22 g (67%) of **25.4**, b.p. 72–74°C (30 Hgmm), $[\alpha]_D$ +80.1 (c = 1.534 in benzene).

Method B In an apparatus described in method A, the diacetonide **25.3** (16.5 g, 60 mmol) is dissolved in dichloromethane (150–175 ml), and saturated aqueous NaHCO$_3$ (6 ml) is added. Then sodium metaperiodate (18.9 g, 84 mmol, 1.4 eq) that has been sifted through a 140-mesh screen is added in five portions over 20 min, with vigorous stirring and maintaining the temperature below 25°C. After stirring for 2 h, the solution is decanted into a second vessel, and the remaining solids are stirred with additional dichloromethane (53 ml) for 5 min. This solution is then combined with the dichloromethane solution, and the solvents are removed by distillation at atmospheric pressure (still-pot temperature ≤55°C). The residual syrup is then submitted to fractional distillation (still-pot temperature ≤135°C) through a Vigreux column to afford pure **25.4** (12 g, 72%), b.p. 72–74°C (30 mmHg), $[\alpha]_D$ +73.1 (c = 1.34 in benzene).

In many cases, chiral syntheses necessitate the optical antipode (L-glyceraldehyde) of **25.4,** which cannot be obtained with the preceding procedure as L-mannitol is not a readily available natural compound. One of the *possibilities for synthesizing*[8] 2,3-O-isopropylidene-L-glyceraldehyde **(26.3)** is depicted in Figure 2.26, when L-galactono-1,4-lactone **(26.1)** is transformed into the 5,6-O-isopropylidene derivative **26.2,** whose periodate degradation gives **26.3**. Then hydrolysis of this latter allows the isolation of L-glyceraldehyde **(26.4)**.

A significantly less expensive starting material for obtaining[9] the protected L-glyceraldehyde **26.3** is 5,6-*O*-isopropylidene-L-*gulono*-1,4-lactone **(26.5)**, whose oxidative splitting with NaIO$_4$ also readily gives the target chain-shortened sugar with a 69% overall yield (Fig. 2.26).

2,3-O-Isopropylidene-L-glyceraldehyde (26.3)[9] To a suspension of the lactone **26.5** (43.6 g, 0.2 mol) in water (200 ml), sodium metaperiodate (85.5 g, 0.4 mol) is added gradually at 0°C and at pH 5.5 (continuously kept by adddition of 2 N NaOH). The suspension is stirred for 2 h at ambient temperature, saturated with

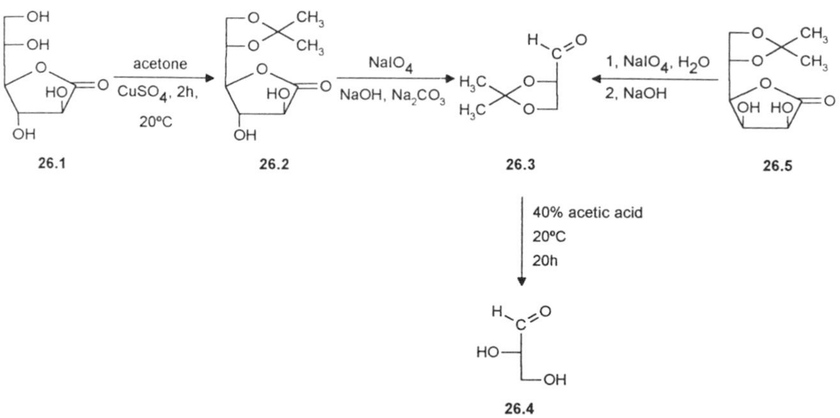

FIGURE 2.26

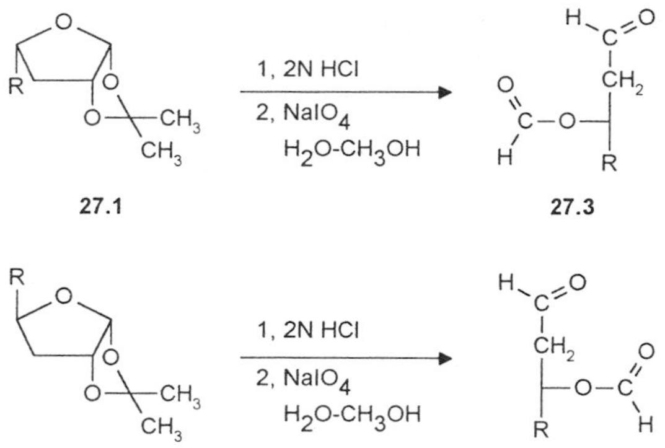

27.1 27.3

27.2 27.4

FIGURE 2.27

NaCl, and filtered, and the pH is adjusted to 6.5–7.0. GLC analysis of the filtrate indicates that the concentration of the product is 70.6 g/liter (corresponding to 95% in the 350-ml solution). This filtrate is extracted with dichloromethane (5 × 200 ml) and ethyl acetate (4 × 200 ml), and the combined extract is dried ($MgSO_4$) and concentrated. Distillation of the residue gives 18 g (69%) of pure **26.3,** b.p. 64–66°C/4.67 kPa, $[\alpha]_D^{20}$ −63.5 (*c* = 8.0 in benzene).

The (3*S*) and (3*R*)-hydroxyaldehydes containing one chiral center can be also readily obtained[10] in the form of their respective O-formates (**27.3** and **27.4**) by the periodate splitting of the 3-deoxyhexoses **27.1** and **27.2,** as shown in Figure 2.27.

Derivatives of D*-eythrose* (including erythrofuranoses) are available[11–18] with the periodate cleavage as well (Fig. 2.28). Thus, oxidation of 4,6-*O*-ethylidene-D-glucopyranose (**28.1**) leads to the dimer (**28.2**), from which

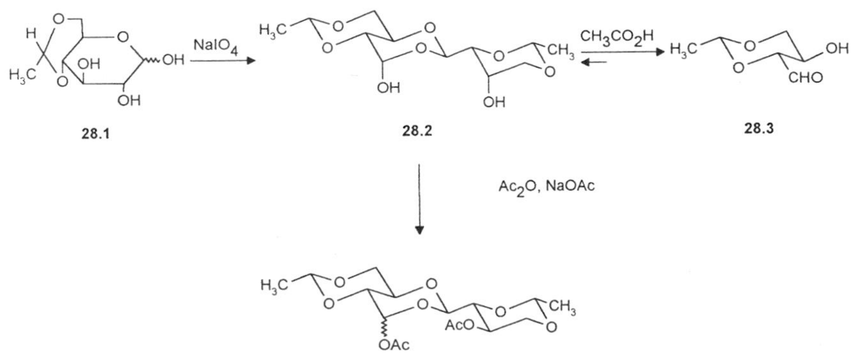

28.1 28.2 28.3

28.4

FIGURE 2.28

the free sugar 2,4-*O*-ethylidene-D-erythrose (**28.3**) can be obtained by hydrolysis with acetic acid.[15]

> 2,4-O-*Ethylidene-*D-*erythrose (28.3)*[13]   (see van Cleve[19]) 4,6-*O*-Ethylidene-D-
> glucose (**28.1**, 103 g, 0.5 mol) is dissolved in water (250 ml), and to the vigor-
> ously stirred solution 216 g (1.01 mol), sodium metaperiodate in water (2 liters) is
> added over 30 min. The pH is kept at ~4 by the addition of 0.5 M aqueous NaOH
> (60 ml) with cooling (10°C). At this point the periodate test of the reaction mixture
> is slightly positive (wet filter paper moisturized with a 0.5% solution of benzidine
> in 4 : 1 acetic acid–ethanol). The pH is adjusted to 8 (with 8 N NaOH, ~60 ml)
> to induce quick hydrolysis of the formyl group, the mixture is concentrated at
> 40–45°C (bath temperature), and the residue is dried *in vacuo* (13.3 Pa) overnight.
> It is then extracted with 3 × 200 ml of hot ethyl acetate, and the combined extract
> is dried (Na$_2$SO$_4$) and evaporated to a yellow mass (65–72 g, 89–99%). This glassy
> product is homogeneous on TLC and of 95–100% purity (as determined by hypoio-
> dite titration), $[\alpha]_D^{20}$ −36.8 (equilibrium value; c = 8.25 in water). The product (**28.3**)
> can be identified[14,20–22] in the form of the crystalline bis(cyclic acetal) **28.4**, m.p.
> 176–176.5°C, $[\alpha]_D^{25}$ −47.4 (c = 0.8 in chloroform).

An alternative route to D-erythrose derivatives involves[23] periodate oxidation of 3,4-*O*-isopropylidene-D-arabinose (**29.1**) and proceeds via 3,4-*O*-isopropylidene-D-arabinitol (**29.2**) to furnish **29.3**, as shown in Figure 2.29. This chain-shortened product can also be obtained from 4,6-*O*-isopropylidene-D-glucopyranose[24] in a similar fashion.

D-Erythrono-1,4-lactone can be synthesized[25] by an analogous procedure starting from 2,3-*O*-isopropylidene-D-ribonic acid.

For the preparation of *L-erythrose derivatives,* the descending synthesis of 4,6-*O*-ethylidene-D-glucose[26] and 2,3-*O*-isopropylidene-L-rhamnitol[27] has been reported. Still other procedures,[28,29] allowing the *convenient synthesis* of 2,3-*O*-isopropylidene-L-erythrofuranose (**30.5**), employ 2,3-*O*-isopropylidene-D-gulono-1,4-lactone[28] (**30.1**) and 2,3-*O*-isopropylidene-D-ribono-1,4-lactone[29] (**30.3**), or the 2,3-*O*-cyclohexylidene analog[30] of **30.3** (see Fig. 2.30).

> 2,3-O-*Isopropylidene-*D-*gulono-1,4-lactone   (30.1)*[28]   2,3:5,6-Di-*O*-isopropyli-
> dene-D-gulono-1,4-lactone (14 g) is dissolved in a mixture of acetic acid (224 ml)
> and water (67.2 ml), and this mixture is left, in a crystallizing dish, to evaporate
> (3–4 days). The residual solid (1.6 g) is suspended in a large volume of ethyl acetate
> and heated under reflux. A small amount of the undissolved starting material is
> filtered off {m.p. 180–182°C, $[\alpha]_D^{24}$ −56.8 (c = 4.03 in water} and the filtrate is

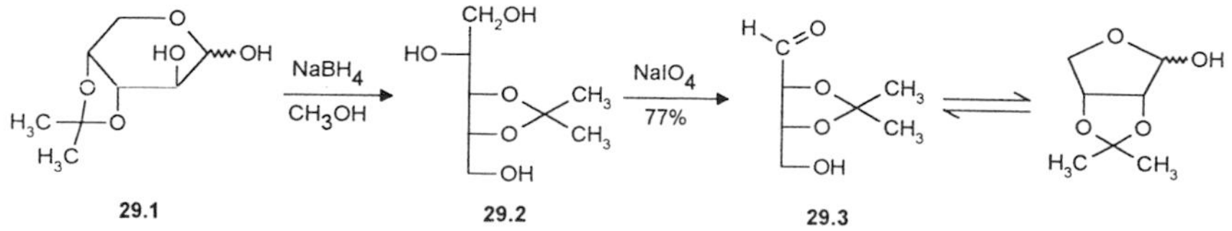

FIGURE 2.29

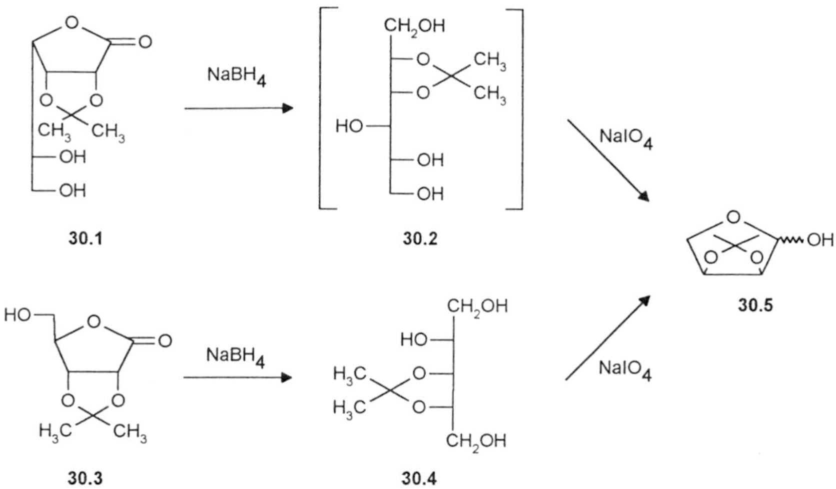

FIGURE 2.30

concentrated to give the desired product **30.1** (9.8 g, 89%), m.p. 142–143.5°C, $[\alpha]_D^{24}$ −74.5 (c = 2.75 in acetone).

2,3-O-Isopropylidene-β-L-erythrofuranose (30.5)[28]   Compound **30.1** (9.8 g) is dissolved in water (400 ml), and this solution is added dropwise to a mixture of sodium borohydride (4 g) in water (200 ml), chilled with an ice bath. The mixture is kept for 4 h at room temperature, and the pH is adjusted to 6.0–6.2 with acetic acid and then cooled again in an ice bath, and sodium metaperiodate (10.8 g) is added in small portions over a 15-min period. The solution is kept in the dark for 3 h at ambient temperature and concentrated to a volume of ~75–100 ml after addition of 5–10 drops of nonyl alcohol. The white precipitate is filtered off and washed with ethyl acetate, and the aqueous layer of the filtrate is extracted with ethyl acetate (2 × 100 ml). The combined organic solution is washed with water (2 × 50 ml), dried over $MgSO_4$, and concentrated to a syrup (3.63 g), which is submitted to distillation *in vacuo* to afford 2.44 g of pure syrupy **30.5**, b.p. 67–74°C (0.45 mmHg), $[\alpha]_D^{23}$ +83.2 (c = 4.36 in ethyl acetate).

2,3-O-Isopropylidene-L-erythrofuranose (30.5)[29] *from 30.3*   The ribonolactone **30.3** (9.4 g, 50 mmol) is dissolved in a mixture of water (550 ml) and ethanol (100 ml), and after cooling in an ice bath, a cold solution of sodium borohydride (4.46 g, 118 mmol) in water (220 ml) is added dropwise. After stirring for 15 h at room temperature, the pH is adjusted to 5–6 with 1.7 N acetic acid, the mixture is placed in an ice bath and sodium metaperiodate (11.76 g, 5 mmol) is added in five portions. The reaction mixture is stirred at ambient temperature for 3 h, concentrated to ~75 ml, and the solids precipitated are filtered off and washed with ethyl acetate (200 ml). The aqueous layer of the filtrate is extracted with ethyl acetate, and the combined organic layer is washed with water (2 × 50 ml), dried over Na_2SO_4 and concentrated to a pale yellow syrup (6.45 g, 80%). This crude product is purified by distillation at 0.7 kPa (bath temperature 130–135°C) to obtain 4.58 g (57.3%) of the pure sugar **30.5**, $[\alpha]_D^{23}$ +73.8 (c = 0.48 in methanol), $[\alpha]_D^{23}$ +81.7 (c = 0.46 in ethyl acetate).

The periodate cleavage *permits the preparation* of various D-threose derivatives, such as 2-*O*-methyl-D-threose and 2,4-*O*-isopropylidene-D-threose,[31] as well as 1,2-*O*-isopropylidene-3-*O*-(methanesulfonyl)-D-*xylo*-hexos-1,4-ulose,[32] 3-*O*-benzyl-1,2-*O*-isopropylidene-D-*xylo*-hexos-1,4-ulose,[33] and certain *O*-methyl derivatives of D- and L-xylose.[34,35] An analogous chain shortening of 1,2:3,4-di-*O*-isopropylidene-D-mannitol, involving periodate-cleavage and reduction with NaBH$_4$, has opened a *convenient route* to the otherwise tediously available 1,2:3,4-di-*O*-isopropylidene-L-arabinitol[36].

1,2:3,4-Di-O-isopropylidene-D-mannitol[36] To a stirred solution of 1,2:3,4:5,6-tri-*O*-isopropylidene-D-mannitol (66 g, 218 mmol) in methanol (300 ml) are added water (13.5 ml) and trifluoroacetic acid (5.3 ml) and the reaction is monitored on TLC. After 2.5 h, the hydrolysis is quenched by the addition of a concentrated solution of ammonium hydroxide (6.8 ml), the solvents are evaporated *in vacuo,* and the residue is dissolved in water. This solution is extracted three times with ether (to remove the unreacted starting material) and then three times with ethyl acetate. The combined ethyl acetate extract is dried (MgSO$_4$), and evaporated to yield the title compound as a pale-yellow syrup (20.4 g, 35.7%), $[\alpha]_D^{20}$ +5.5 (c = 1.7 in chloroform).

1,2:3,4-Di-O-isopropylidene-L-arabinitol[36] To a solution of 1,2:3,4-di-*O*-isopropylidene-D-mannitol (18 g, 85.5 mmol) in water (180 ml) is added at 0°C a solution of NaIO$_4$ (12.8 g) in water (100 ml). The reaction is complete in about 1 h; the mixture is concentrated under diminished pressure, and the residue is extracted three times with ethyl acetate. The combined extract is washed with saturated aqueous NaHCO$_3$ and brine, dried (MgSO$_4$), and concentrated to furnish 13 g (55 mmol) of 1,2:3,4-di-*O*-isopropylidene-L-arabinose, which is used for the next step without further purification. This crude product is dissolved in methanol, the solution is cooled, and then sodium borohydride (2.2 g, 57 mmol) is added in small portions. The mixture is stirred at room temperature for 1 h, the reaction is stopped by the addition of water (30 ml), and the solvents are removed *in vacuo.* The crude product is dissolved in ether, the solution is washed with water and brine, the organic layer is dried and concentrated, and the residue is submitted to purification by means of column chromatography (eluant: 1 : 1 ethyl acetate–hexane) to afford the pure title arabinitol as a colorless oil (10.2 g, 75%), $[\alpha]_D^{20}$ +0.3 (c = 1.2 in chloroform).

Characterization of 1,2-*O*-isopropylidene-α-D-*xylo*-hexos-1,4-ulose in form of the corresponding oxime has shown that both of the (*E*)- and (*Z*)-oximes are available[37] from the ulose obtained by periodate fission.

The key step of a practically very *useful synthesis*[38] of D-ribose (**31.5**) is, again, a chain-descending synthesis by periodate cleavage, as shown in Figure 2.31. Thus, 1,2:5,6-di-*O*-isopropylidene-D-glucofuranose (**31.1**) is first converted into the 3-*O*-mesylate **31.2**, then following acid hydrolysis, the product **31.3** is treated with sodium periodate to lead to the target sugar **31.5** via the tosylhydrazone **31.4**.

1,2:5,6-Di-O-isopropylidene-3-O-(methanesulfonyl)-D-glucofuranose (*31.2*)[39]
To a stirred solution of the glucofuranose **31.1** (170 g) in pyridine (460 ml) methanesulfonyl chloride (73 ml) is added dropwise at −10°C. Stirring is continued at this

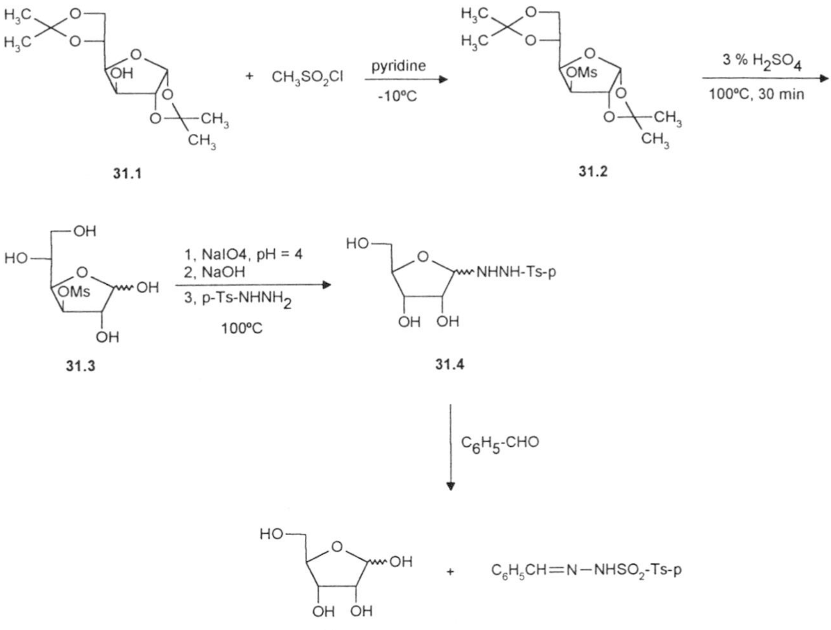

FIGURE 2.31

temperature for 4 h, the deep-red solution is poured into 1 liter of water, and this mixture is diluted with 6 liters of water. The precipitating oil, which solidifies to a solid mass, is filtered off, washed with water and recrystallized from 70% aqueous methanol. Yield of **31.2** is 196 g (88%), m.p. 83–84°C.

3-O-(Methanesulfonyl)-D-glucose (31.3)[39]   To a hot, 3% aqueous solution of sulfuric acid (2 liters) is added **31.2** (151 g), and the mixture is boiled for 30 min. Then it is neutralized with CaCO$_3$, CaSO$_4$ is filtered off, the filtrate is decolorized, and the solvent is distilled off under diminished pressure. The residual syrup is dissolved in methanol, the solution is filtered, and the solvent is evaporated. The crude residual product (151 g, 90%), m.p. 123–128°C is sufficiently pure for the next step. The pure sugar **31.3** (fine needles) can be obtained by dissolving the crude syrup in a minimum volume of methanol and treated with an eightfold excess of benzene. Yield: 135 g (80%), m.p. 133–134°C.

D-Ribose-(p-tolylsulfonyl)hydrazone (31.4)[39]   First, 151 g of the crude 3-O-mesylate **31.3** is dissolved in 1.2 liters of water (previously acidified to pH 4 with 3 N sulfuric acid). Then sodium metaperiodate (248 g) is added in portions at 15°C with vigorous stirring over 40 min, and the mixture is stirred at this temperature for 4 h. To the yellowish green suspension, barium chloride is added until precipitation of barium iodate and barium periodate is complete. Following neutralization with NaHCO$_3$, the mixture is filtered and the filtrate is warmed to 60°C. Under N$_2$ atmosphere, 1 N NaOH solution (~1050–1200 ml) is added dropwise to adjust the pH to 9, followed by neutralization with dilute sulfuric acid, decolorization with charcoal and evaporation to dryness. The residue is extracted three times with ethanol, the alcoholic extracts are combined and concentrated, and the iorganic salts are filtered off from the cooled mixture. Ethanol is distilled off from the filtrate, the residue is taken up with methanol (750 ml), and to the filtered and stirred solution p-toluenesulfonylhydrazine (55–60 g, corresponding to the D-ribose content) is added and the reaction mixture is stirred for 40 min. Then, after remaining for 1 day, the precipitated hydrazone is filtered off, the filtrate is evaporated to its half-volume, and 75 ml of water is added. The crystallized material is filtered off, water is added, and this operation is repeated until no separation of crystals is observed. The combined hydrazone fraction is recrystallized from a 5 : 2 mixture of methanol–water to obtain 108 g (60%) of pure **31.4**, m.p. 164°C.

D-*Ribose (31.5)*[39] D-Ribose-(p-tolylsulfonyl)hydrazone (**31.4**, 108 g) is suspended in a mixture of water (3.5 liters) and benzene (3.5 liters) and heated at 70°C with stirring in an inert-gas atmosphere. Then concentrated H_2SO_4 (12.5 ml) and benzaldehyde (125 ml) are added, and stirring is continued at this temperature until the hydrazone completely dissolves. The two phases are separated, the aqueous layer is washed twice with benzene and twice with ether, the aqueous layer is neutralized with calcium carbonate, and the filtered solution is concentrated under reduced pressure under nitrogen. The residue is taken up with ethanol, the mixture is filtered, and the filtrate is seeded with D-ribose. After storage for 3 weeks, the precipitate containing crystals is dissolved in a small volume of cold ethanol, the insolubles (mainly D-arabinose) are filtered off, and the filtrate is refrigerated for 3–4 days. D-Ribose (**31.5**) is filtered off, and the filtrate is concentrated and stored to obtain a novel crop of the product. D-Ribose is washed with ether and then dried *in vacuo*, m.p. 93–95°C, $[\alpha]_D^{20}$ −22 (c = 1 in water). Yield: 36 g (70%; for the consumed D-glucose: 24%).

Several additional examples are known to *cleave the C-1—C-2 bond of aldohexoses* in the absence of a free hydroxyl function at C-3. In such cases the products are the 4-*O*-formate esters of pentoses (see Fig. 2.27), which are sufficiently stable (up to pH 3.5) to avoid further oxidative cleavage.[40–42] According to this principle, 3,5,6-tri-*O*-benzoyl-D-glucose (**32.1**) can be degraded into 2,4,5-tri-*O*-benzoyl-D-arabinose (**32.2**), which is readily characterized in the form of semicarbazone **32.3** (Fig. 2.32).

2,4,5-*Tri-O-benzoyl-D-arabinose (32.2)*[43] To a cold (10°C) solution of 3,5,6-tri-*O*-benzoyl-D-glucose (**32.1**; 4.5 g) in ethanol (200 ml), a cold 0.2 M solution of $NaIO_4$ (50 ml) is added. The inorganic salts are filtered off, and the filtrate is kept at ambient temperature for 1 h (TLC: 4 : 1 benzene–methanol). The excess of the periodate and iodate is precipitated by the addition of barium carbonate (1.89 g), the precipitate is filtered off, the filtrate is concentrated and extracted with chloro-

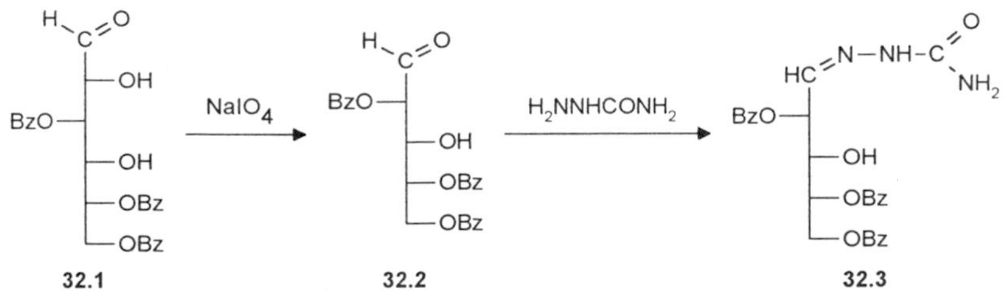

FIGURE 2.32

form, and the organic layer is dried (Na$_2$SO$_4$). Evaporation of the solvent gives a syrup, to be converted into D-arabinose (by means of Zemplén transesterification) or into the semicarbazone **32.3**, m.p. 178–180°C, $[\alpha]_D^{24}$ +10.4 (c = 0.8 in methanol).

An interesting utilization of the protected sugars in descending syntheses is the *oxidative cleavage* of 1,6-anhydrohexopyranoses. Because of the presence of the anhydro-ring, these compounds contain only two vicinal-glycol functions, and protection of one of these leaves a single oxidizable glycol unit. Cleavage of this function by periodate gives rise to an (oxydimethylene)-bridged dialdehyde, whose further transformations have been successfully utilized for the synthesis[44–49] of nucleosides carrying a dioxolane moiety instead of the furanoid sugar portion. Figure 2.33 illustrates a related conversion of 1,6-anhydro-D-mannopyranose (**33.1**) into the dioxolane **33.2** [useful for the preparation of *anti-HIV (human immunodeficiency virus) nucleosides*], as well as the transformation of L-gulose (**33.3**) into the *optical antipode* (**33.4**) of **33.2**.

Oxidative cleavage of 2-*O*-benzoyl-1,6-anhydro-D-galactopyranose (**34.1**) into the dioxolane **34.2**, an epimer of compounds **33.2** and **33.4**, was reported by Chu *et al.*[49] (Fig. 2.34).

> *(1'R,2R,4S)-2-(2-O-Benzoyl-1-hydroxyethyl)-4-(hydroxymethyl)-1,3-dioxolane (34.2)*[49] To a solution of NaIO$_4$ (11.7 g, 0.55 mol) in water (400 ml) is added a solution of the anhydro sugar **34.1** (13 g, 0.048 mol) in 95% ethanol (400 ml), and the mixture is stirred at room temperature for 1 h. The reaction mixture is then concentrated to its half–volume, cooled to 5°C, NaBH$_4$ (7.94 g, 0.209 mol) is added portionwise over 5 min, and the mixture is stirred for another 10 min. It is neutralized with glacial acetic acid and concentrated to dryness to obtain crude **34.2** as a syrup, which is subjected to column chromatography on silicagel (eluant: 10:0.3 chloroform–methanol) to give 9 g (77%) of the pure product, $[\alpha]_D^{25}$ +24.5 (c = 0.57 in chloroform).

Descent by the periodate cleavage is utilized also for the synthesis of *dipeptide-aldehydes* when L-serinal is the required aminoaldehyde. Figure 2.35 shows the work of Giannis *et al.*,[50] who acylated D-glucosamine at the C-2 amino group with protected amino acids (**35.1**), then reduced the hemiacetal function, and oxidized the resulting *N*-acyl-2-deoxy-D-glucitol derivative with periodate to obtain compounds **35.2**.

The benzylidene-acetal function is also compatible with the conditions of the periodate cleavage reaction. Thus, the free glycol moiety of the easily available 2,4-*O*-benzylidene-D-glucitol (**36.1**) can be split with periodate, and subsequent hydrolysis of the benzylidene acetal unit gives[51–53] L-xylose (**36.3**) as shown in Figure 2.36. The intermediate (2,4-*O*-benzylidene-L-xylose) of this reaction sequence could not be unequivocally detected because of its reaction with the formaldehyde produced, into methylene–acetals, branched-chain products, and dimeric compounds.[54] However, since hydrolysis of these latter compounds also results in L-xylose (**36.3**), the present method is *easily reproducible and quite useful* for obtaining the

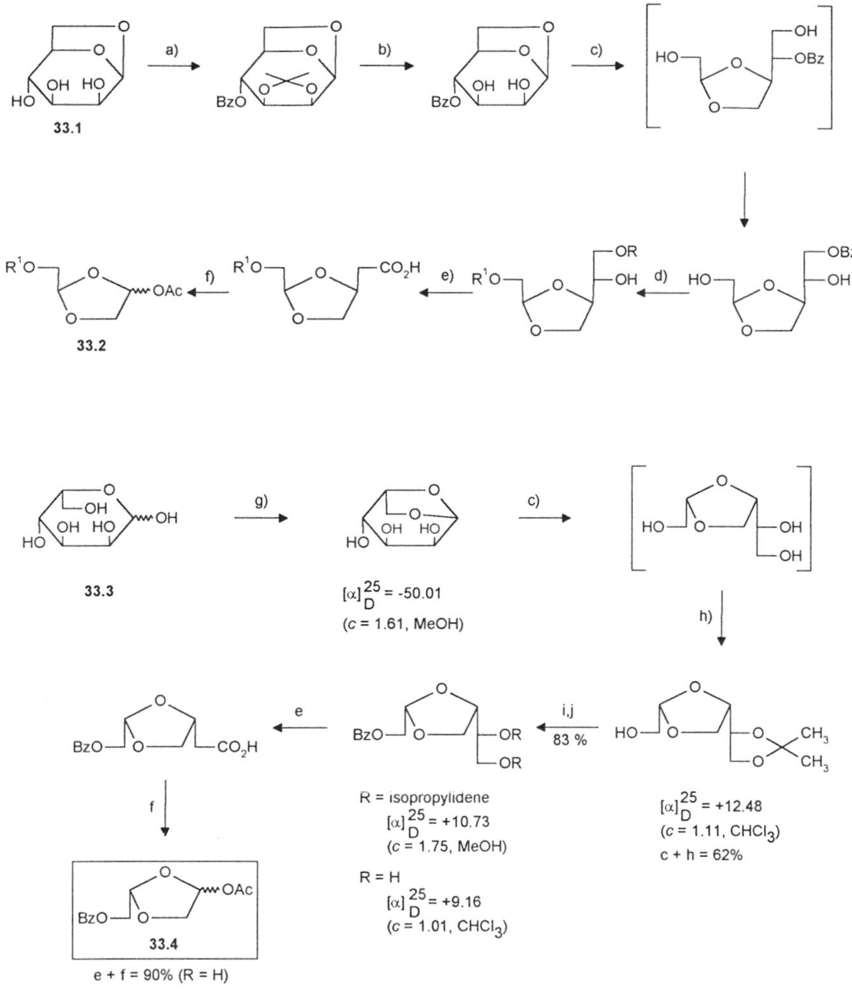

Reagents: a) acetone dimethyl acetal, H^+ / BzCl; b) H^+; c) $NaIO_4$, MeOH, H_2O, 0°C / $NaBH_4$;

d) TBDPS-Cl / NaOMe; e) $NaIO_4$, RuO_2, $CH_3CN:CCl_4:H_2O$ (2:2:3), RT; f) $Pb(OAc)_4$, THF, RT;

g) 0.5 N HCl, 100°C; h) p-TsOH, acetone, RT; i) BzCl, pyridine, CH_2Cl_2; j) p-TsOH, MeOH, RT;

FIGURE 2.33

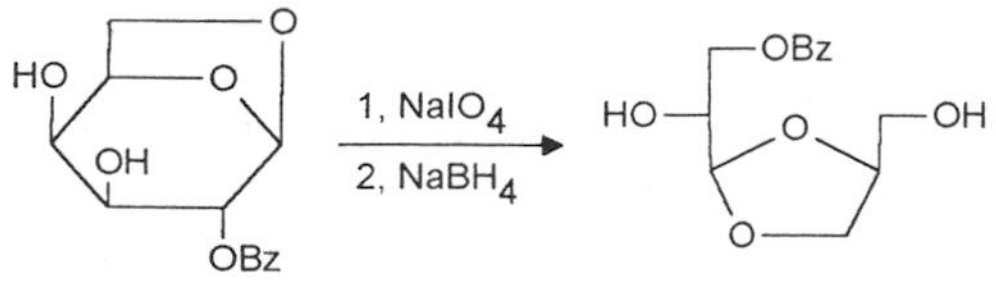

FIGURE 2.34

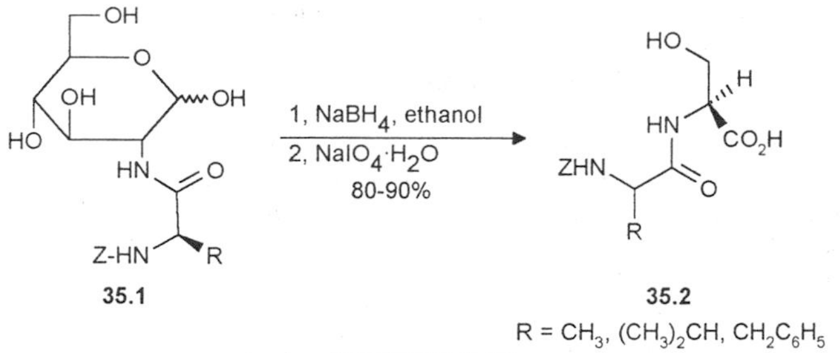

FIGURE 2.35

target pentose. Similar oxidation[55] of 3,5-O-benzylidene-D-arabinitol gives 85% of 2,4-O-benzylidene-D-erythritol.

It is to be noted that cyclohexylidene acetals have also been employed in descending syntheses based on the periodate-cleavage technique. Thus, a related reaction of 2,3-O-cyclohexylidene-D-gulono-1,4-lactone has been reported,[56] and this acetal protecting group is most useful for the synthesis[57,58] of *both enantiomers* of 2,3-O-cyclohexylidene-D-glyceraldehyde. The following procedures represent easily reproducible prescriptions for the preparation of 1,2:5,6-di-O-cyclohexylidene-D-mannitol,[59] 2,3-O-cyclohexylidene-D-glyceraldehyde,[60] and the oxime[59] of this latter sugar.

1,2:5,6-Di-O-cyclohexylidene-D-mannitol[59] A mixture of D-mannitol (9 g, 49.5 mmol), cyclohexanone (15.5 ml, 150 mmol), triethyl orthoformate (8.31 ml, 50 mmol), and boron trifluoride etherate (0.5 ml, 4.06 mmol) in dry Me_2SO (20 ml) is stirred for 10 h at ambient temperature. The mixture is poured into 50 ml of 10% ice-cold $NaHCO_3$ solution, extracted with ether, and after the usual workup the solvents are removed *in vacuo*. The residue is treated with hexane to result in the crystallization of the product as a white solid, which is filtered, washed with hexane, and dried *in vacuo*. This product (5.01 g, 56%) is useful for further reactions without any purification, m.p. 104–105°C.

(R)-(+)-*2,3-O-Cyclohexylideneglyceraldehyde*[60] To a stirred solution of 1,2:5,6-di-O-cyclohexylidene-D-mannitol (68.4 g, 0.2 mol) in 60% aqueous acetonitrile (300 ml), $NaIO_4$ (85.6 g, 0.4 mol) is added in small portions under nitrogen atmosphere over 40 min. The mixture is stirred for 1 h more and filtered, and the filtrate is mixed with water and extracted with chloroform. The organic layer is washed with water and brine and dried, and the solvent is evaporated under reduced

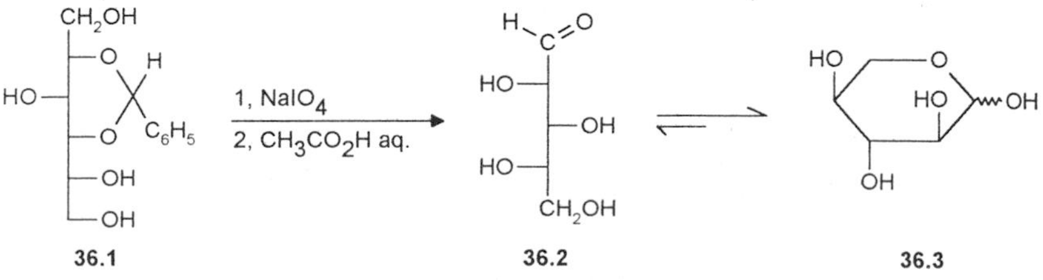

FIGURE 2.36

pressure to afford the title compound in almost quantitative yield. This is sufficiently pure for further reactions. An analytic sample is obtained by vacuum distillation, b.p. 96–98°C (at 10 mmHg), $[\alpha]_D^{23}$ +60.5 (c = 3.5 in benzene).

(2S)-2,3-O-Cyclohexylidene-D-glyceraldoxime[59] To a solution of 1,2:5,6-di-*O*-cyclohexylidene-D-mannitol (5.04 g, 14.74 mmol) in ether (50 ml) is added a solution of NaIO$_4$ (3.64 g, 17 mmol) and Bu$_4$NF (7 mg, 0.27 mmol) in water (30 ml). The reaction mixture is stirred at room temperature for 4 h, then poured into a solution of hydroxylamine hydrochloride (2.35 g, 33.81 mmol) in water (50 ml) and stirred for 4 h. Following extraction with dichloromethane (3 × 50 ml), the organic layer is washed with water, dried, and concentrated. The crude syrupy glyceraldoxime (4.6 g, 89%) is a mixture of the *cis*- and *trans*-isomers, which is sufficiently pure for further transformations.

As the *glyceraldehyde synthons* are important and widely used *key intermediates* in the syntheses of chiral compounds, the Lilly researchers[61] have developed a procedure for the preparation of 2,3-*O*-(3-pentylidene)-D-glyceraldehyde, which can be more easily extracted from the reaction mixture, and ketalization of the starting D-mannitol can be more efficiently carried out with 3,3-dimethoxypentane. As an alternative oxidizing agent, KIO$_4$ was introduced,[61] wihich is more soluble than the sodium salt, and in the presence of KHCO$_3$ it is a rather powerful oxidizing agent to carry out the glycol-cleavage reaction.

The Lilly people[61] have also synthesized the enantiomeric 2,3-*O*-(3-pentylidene)-L-glyceraldehyde (**37.3**) by the oxidation of the readily available 5,6-*O*-(3-pentylidene)-L-*gulono*-1,4-lactone (**37.2**), as shown in Figure 2.37.

5,6-O-(3-Pentylidene-L-gulono-1,4-lactone (37.2)[61] To a stirred suspension of L-gulono-1,4-lactone (**37.1**, 25 g, 140 mmol) in DMF (125 ml) containing 0.5 g of camphorsulfonic acid (CSA) is added 3,3-dimethoxypentane (33.3 g, 253 mmol) in one portion at 23°C. The reaction mixture is stirred for 24–48 h, until becoming homogeneous (at this time ^{1}H-NMR examination of an aliquot shows the reaction to be ≥95% complete). Triethylamine (1 ml) is added, and the mixture is transferred to a larger vessel and concentrated (bath temperature 60°C) *in vacuo* to afford a syrup. A large magnetic stirring bar is added to the hot syrup, and toluene (375 ml) is rapidly added while vigorous stirring is applied. A precipitate begins to form almost immediately, the mixture is stirred and cooled to 5°C, and filtered by suction, and the filter cake is rinsed with cold toluene. The material is further dried on the vacuum filter, then *in vacuo* at 60°C for 1–3 h, to furnish 25.93 g (75%) of **37.2** as a white solid containing 1–2% of residual starting material and less than 1% of solvent, m.p. 148.5–149.5°C. This material is sufficiently pure for the next

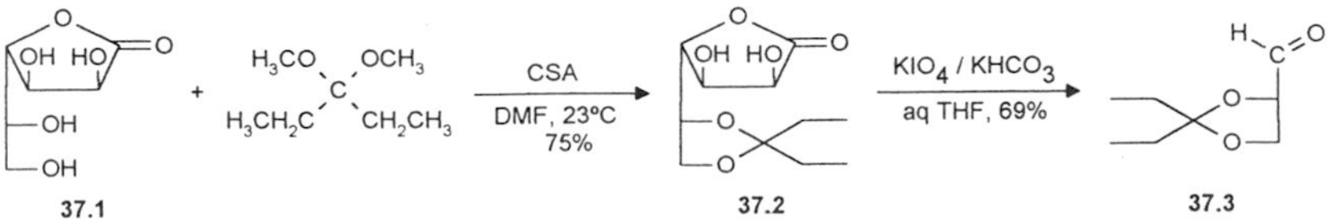

FIGURE 2.37

step. An analytic sample is obtained by recrystallization from acetone, m.p. 149.7–150.8°C, $[\alpha]_D$ +34.4 (c = 0.978 in methanol).

2,3-O-(3-Pentylidene)-L-glyceraldehyde (37.3)[61]   To a slurry of KIO_4 (19.65 g, 85.2 mmol) and $KHCO_3$ (8.54 g, 85.4 mmol) in water (50 ml) at 23°C (water bath cooling) is added a solution of the acetal **37.2** (10 g, 40.4 mmol) in THF (50 ml) over 10 min, while maintaining the temperature between 23–27°C. After 3 h, the reaction is chilled to 5°C and filtered, and ethyl acetate (25 ml) is added to the filtrate. The two-phase mixture is warmed to room temperature, saturated by addition of solid NaCl, and filtered again. The layers are separated, and the aqueous layer is extracted with an additional 25 ml of ethyl acetate. The combined organic layer is dried and concentrated, and the residual syrup is transferred to a distillation apparatus and placed under oil pump vacuum (0.3 mmHg) while gentle heating is applied. When the material begins to distill, chilled fluid (5°C) is circulated through the condenser, and the receiving flask is immersed in an ice-water bath. Distillation affords 4.42 g (69%) of pure **37.3**, b.p. 43–44°C (0.3 mmHg), $[\alpha]_D$ −79.4 (c = 1.18 in toluene).

The benzyl–ether protecting group is also compatible with the conditions of the periodate cleavage, as demonstrated[62] by the *preparation of 2-O-benzyl-D-ribose* (**38.3**) from 3-*O*-benzyl-D-allose (**38.1**) (Fig. 2.38).

2-O-Benzyl-D-ribose (38.3)[62]   In this procedure 2.5 g of $NaIO_4$ (11.6 mmol) is dissolved in hot water (10 ml), and this is added to a solution of 3-*O*-benzyl-D-allose (**38.1**; 3.0 g, 11.1 mmol) in water (15 ml). After storing at room temperature for 30 min, methanol (100 ml) is added, the precipitate is filtered off, the filtrate is concentrated, and the residual syrup is filtered through a short silicagel column with 7:3 benzene–acetone. The intermediary 2-*O*-benzyl-4-*O*-formyl-D-ribose (**38.2**) is stirred with 116 ml of 0.1 N aqueous NaOH at room temperature for 20 min, the mixture is neutralized with Amberlite IR-120 (H⁺), and the crude product (**38.3**) is purified by means of column chromatography (eluant: 1:1 benzene–acetone) to afford a syrup that crystallizes, m.p. 90°C, yield: 1.1 g (43%).

This descending procedure has been employed for chain shortening of *methyl 3-acetamido-3-deoxy-heptopyranosides* by oxidizing the C-6–C-7 glycol function with 1 M $NaIO_4$ to obtain the corresponding hexose, as demonstrated by the example (Fig. 2.39) of the preparation of methyl 3-acetamido-3-deoxy-α-D-gulopyranoside (**39.2**).

Methyl 3-acetamido-3-deoxy-α-D-gulopyranoside (39.2)[63]   To a solution of methyl 3-acetamido-3-deoxy-D-*glycero*-D-*gluco*-heptopyranoside (**39.1**, 3 g) in water (25 ml), 2.45 g of $NaIO_4$ is added and the mixture is kept in the dark for 2.4 h. The reaction mixture is concentrated, codistilled with methanol and abs. ethanol;

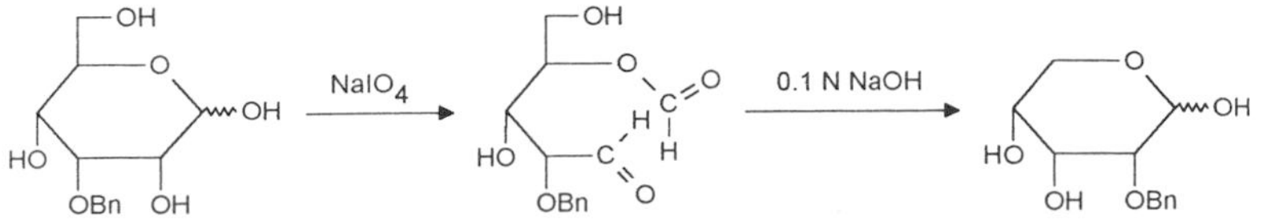

FIGURE 2.38

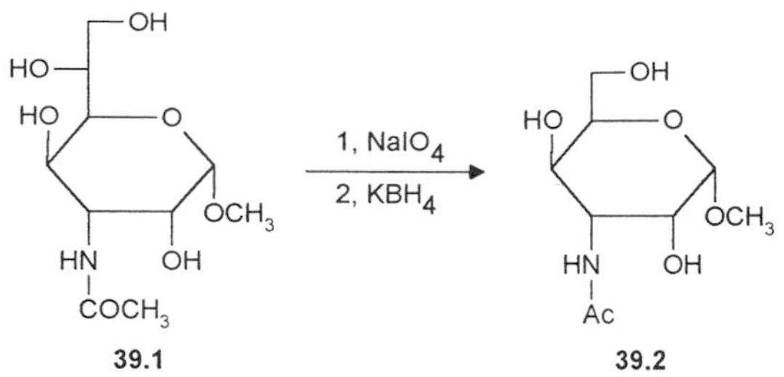

FIGURE 2.39

the residue is dissolved in abs. ethanol, NaIO$_3$, precipitated is filtered off, and the filter cake is washed with ethanol. Following evaporation of the solvent, the residue is dissolved in methanol and KBH$_4$ (0.93 g) is added. The mixture is kept at ambient temperature until completion of the reduction (~3 h), then poured onto the top of a column packed with cation-exchange resin, and the pH of the eluate is adjusted to 4.5. After evaporation, the residue is codistilled with methanol (to remove boric acid), and the resulting syrup (2.2 g, 83%) is crystallized from 2-propanol–ethyl acetate to obtain pure **39.2**, m.p. 169–170°C, $[\alpha]_D^{23}$ +91.6 (c = 1.31 in water).

The recognition of Wu and Wu[64] that the terminal isopropylidene acetal function can be *selectively removed* in the presence of other acid-labile groups with periodic acid in ether may be of interest in synthetic practice. Ethereal periodic acid cleaves the vicinal-glycol system or epoxide smoothly, and this is rather significant in the case of water-insoluble compounds, or where the cleavage product is sensitive to aqueous acid. This simple procedure appears to be *quite efficient for selective hydrolytic cleavage* of terminal acetals (Fig. 2.40), followed by a glycol cleavage in one pot. It is to be noted that the methoxymethyl- (MOM) protecting group, as well as acyl groups, are compatible with the applied conditions, but the tetrahydropyranyl- (THP) function is not. A general procedure for the application of the reagent is as follows.

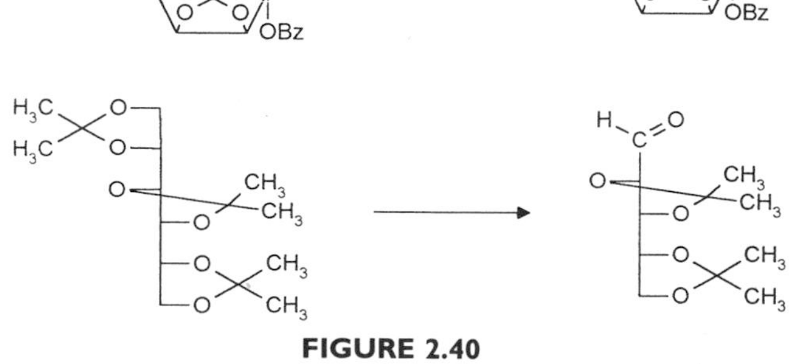

FIGURE 2.40

General procedure for the reaction of acetals with periodic acid in ether[64]   *(see also Fig. 2.40)* The acetal compound (1 mmol) is added at room temperature under nitrogen atmosphere to a well-stirred slurry of periodic acid (1.5–3.0 mmol) in dry ether. Stirring is continued for 4–10 h, and the reaction mixture is worked up by filtering and evaporating the solution. Purification of the product is carried out, if necessary, by recrystallization or column chromatography.

REFERENCES TO SECTION 2.4.1

1. L. Malaprade, *Bull. Soc. Chim. Fr.* **39,** 325 (1926); **43,** 683 (1928); P. Fleury, and J. Lange, *C. R. Hebd. Seances Acad. Sci.* **195,** 1395 (1932).
2. M. Cantley and L. Hough, *J. Chem. Soc.,* p. 2711 (1963).
3. J. M. Bobbitt, *Adv. Carbohydr. Chem.* **11,** 1 (1956); G. J. Buist, C. A. Bunton, and W. C. Hipperson, *J. Chem. Soc. B,* p. 2128 (1971).
4. J. C. Sowden, *J. Am. Chem. Soc.* **72,** 808 (1949); J. LeCocq and C. E. Ballou, *Biochemistry* **3,** 976 (1964); B. T. Golding and P. V. Ioannou, *Synthesis,* p. 423 (1977); J. J. Baldwin, A. W. Raab, K. Mensler, B. H. Arison, and D. E. McClure, *J. Org. Chem.* **43,** 4876 (1978); H. Eibl, *Chem. Phys. Lipids* **28,** 1 (1978); S. Takano, E. Goto, M. Hirama, and K. Ogasawara, *Heterocycles* **16,** 381 (1981); G. Hirth, and W. Walther, *Helv. Chim. Acta* **68,** 1863 (1985); S. Takano, A. Kurotaki, M. Takahashi, and K. Ogasawara, *Synthesis,* p. 403 (1986); *J. Chem. Soc., Perkin Trans. 1,* p. 91 (1987); G. J. F. Chittenden, *Recl. Trav. Chim. Pays-Bas* **107,** 455 (1988).
5. E. Diekman, K. Friderich, and J. Lehmann, *Justus Liebigs Ann. Chem.,* p. 1247 (1989).
6. D. Y. Jackson, *Synth. Commun.* **18,** 337 (1988).
7. C. R. Schmid, J. D. Bryant, M. Dowlatzedah, J. L. Phillips, D. E. Prather, R. D. Schantz, N. L. Sear, and C. S. Vianco, *J. Org. Chem.* **56,** 4056 (1991).
8. S. Morgenlie, *Carbohydr. Res.* **107,** 137 (1982).
9. C. Hubschwerlen, *Synthesis,* p. 962 (1986).
10. S.-K. Kang and H.-S. Cho, *Tetrahedron Lett.* **32,** 367 (1991).
11. H. L. Frush and H. S. Isbell, *J. Res. Natl. Bur. Stand.* **51,** 307 (1953).
12. C. E. Ballou, H. O. L. Fischer, and D. L. MacDonald, *J. Am. Chem. Soc.* **77,** 5967 (1955).
13. R. Barker and D. L. MacDonald, *J. Am. Chem. Soc.* **82,** 2301 (1960).
14. D. K. Carlson, C. R. Smith, Jr., and I. A. Wolf, *Carbohydr. Res.* **13,** 391 (1970).
15. J. R. Hauske and H. Rapoport, *J. Org. Chem.* **44,** 2472 (1979).
16. S. R. Barker, D. W. Clissold, and A. C. McKillop, *Tetrahedron Lett.* **29,** 991 (1988).
17. K. Tadano, M. Minami, and S. Ogawa, *J. Org. Chem.* **55,** 2108 (1990).
18. M. Dolder, X. Shao, and C. Tamm, *Helv. Chim. Acta* **73,** 63 (1990).
19. J. W. Van Cleve, *Carbohydr. Res.* **106,** 239 (1982).
20. R. Schaffer, *J. Am. Chem. Soc.* **81,** 2838 (1959).
21. N. Baggett, K. W. Buck, A. B. Foster, B. H. Rees, and J. M. Webber, *J. Chem. Soc. C,* p. 212 (1966).
22. L. W. Hertel, C. S. Grossman, and J. S. Kroin, *Synth. Commun.* **21,** 151 (1991).
23. C. E. Ballou, *J. Am. Chem. Soc.* **79,** 165 (1957).
24. N. Cohen, B. L. Banner, R. J. Lopresti, F. Wong, M. Rosenberger, Y. Y. Liu, E. Thom, and A. A. Liebman, *J. Am. Chem. Soc.* **105,** 3661 (1983).
25. D. L. Mitchell, *Can. J. Chem.* **41,** 214 (1963).
26. D. A. Rappoport and W. Z. Hassid, *J. Am. Chem. Soc.* **73,** 5524 (1951).
27. J. N. Baxter and A. S. Perlin, *Can. J. Chem.* **38,** 2217 (1960).
28. L. M. Lerner, *Carbohydr. Res.* **9,** 1 (1969).
29. R. H. Shah, *Carbohydr. Res.* **155,** 212 (1986).

30. A.-M. Sepulchre, A. Gateau, and S. D. Gero, *C. R. Hebd. Seances Acad. Sci., Ser. C* **269**, 1312 (1969).
31. M. Kiso, A. Nakamura, Y. Tomita, and A. Hasegawa, *Carbohydr. Res.* **158**, 101 (1986).
32. K. M. Sun and B. Fraser-Reid, *Synthesis*, p. 28 (1982).
33. J.-P. Gesson, J.-C. Jacquesy, and M. Mondon, *Tetrahedron* **45**, 2627 (1989).
34. G. W. Huffmann, B. A. Lewis, F. Smith, and D. R. Spriesterbach, *J. Am. Chem. Soc.* **77**, 4346 (1955).
35. A. Lipták, *Carbohydr. Res.* **107**, 296 (1982).
36. J. Mulzer, S. Greifenberg, A. Becksett, and M. Gottwald, *Justus Liebigs Ann. Chem.*, p. 1131 (1992).
37. M. Lamchen and R. L. Whistler, *Carbohydr. Res.* **16**, 309 (1971).
38. D. C. C. Smith, *Chem. Ind. (London)*, p. 92 (1955).
39. H.-H. Stroh, D. Dargel, and R. Häussler, *J. Prakt. Chem.* **23**, 309 (1964).
40. J. C. P. Schwarz and M. McDougall, *J. Chem. Soc.*, p. 3065 (1956).
41. H. H. Baer and H. O. L. Fischer, *J. Am. Chem. Soc.* **82**, 3709 (1960).
42. G. Rembarz, *Chem. Ber.* **95**, 1565 (1962).
43. M. A. E. Sallam, S. Singuram, and U. Hornemann, *Carbohydr. Res.* **72**, 320 (1979).
44. C. K. Chu, S. K. Ahn, H. O. Kim, J. W. Beach, A. J. Alves, L. S. Jeong, Q. Islam, P. Van Roey, and R. F. Schinazi, *Tetrahedron Lett.* **32**, 3791 (1991).
45. H. O. Kim, S. K. Ahn, A. J. Alves, J. W. Beach, L. S. Jeong, B. G. Choi, P. Van Roey, R. F. Schinazi, and C. K. Chu, *J. Med. Chem.* **35**, 1987 (1992).
46. H. O. Kim, K. Shanmuganathan, A. J. Alves, L. S. Jeong, J. W. Beach, R. F. Schinazi, C.-N. Chang, Y.-C. Cheng, and C. K. Chu, *Tetrahedron Lett.* **33**, 6899 (1992).
47. L. S. Jeong, R. F. Schinazi, J. W. Beach, H. O. Kim, S. Nampalli, K. Shanmuganathan, A. J. Alves, A. McMillan, C. K. Chu, and R. Mathis, *J. Med. Chem.* **36**, 181 (1993).
48. L. S. Jeong, R. F. Schinazi, J. W. Beach, H. O. Kim, K. Shanmuganathan, S. Nampalli, M. W. Chun, W.-K. Chung, B. G. Choi, and C. K. Chu, *J. Med. Chem.* **36**, 2627 (1993).
49. C. Liang, D. W. Lee, M. G. Newton, and C. K. Chu, *J. Org. Chem.* **60**, 1546 (1995).
50. T. Kolter, A. Klein, and A. Giannis, *Angew. Chem.* **104**, 1394 (1992); *Angew. Chem., Int. Ed. Engl.* **31**, 1 (1992).
51. E. Dimant and M. Banay, *J. Org. Chem.* **25**, 475 (1950).
52. J. E. Courtois and P. LeDizet, *Bull. Soc. Chim. Biol.* **37**, 387 (1955).
53. R. K. Ness, *Methods Carbohydr. Chem.* **1**, 90 (1962).
54. S. J. Angyal and K. James, *Carbohydr. Res.* **15**, 91 (1970).
55. H. Zinner, H. Voigt, and J. Voigt, *Carbohydr. Res.* **7**, 38 (1968).
56. M. S. Wolfe, B. L. Anderson, D. R. Borcherding, and R. T. Borchardt, *J. Org. Chem.* **55**, 4712 (1990); H. Sano and S. Sugai, *Tetrahedron: Asymmetry* **6**, 1143 (1995).
57. T. Sugiyama, H. Sugawara, M. Watanabe, and K. Yamashita, *Agric. Biol. Chem.* **48**, 1841 (1984).
58. M. Grauert and U. Schöllkopf, *Justus Liebigs Ann. Chem.*, p. 1817 (1985).
59. H. Yiu, R. W. Franck, S.-L. Chen, G. J. Quiegly, and L. Todaro, *J. Org. Chem.* **57**, 644 (1992).
60. A. Chattopadhyay and V. R. Mamdapur, *J. Org. Chem.* **60**, 585 (1995).
61. C. R. Schmid and D. A. Bradley, *Synthesis*, p. 587 (1992).
62. R. R. Schmidt and A. Gohl, *Chem. Ber.* **112**, 1689 (1979).
63. R. Kuhn and G. Baschang, *Justus Liebigs Ann. Chem.* **636**, 164 (1960).
64. W.-L. Wu and Y.-L. Wu, *J. Org. Chem.* **58**, 3586 (1993).

2.4.2. Degradation by Means of Cleavage with Lead Tetraacetate

Oxidative cleavage of the vicinal-glycol system can also be accomplished with lead tetraacetate, and 1,2-diols, ketols, 1,2-oxyamines, α-hydroxy- and

α-amino acids, and 1,2-diamines are rather susceptible to this kind of oxidative degradation.[1,2] The reaction proceeds under very mild conditions in dilute acteic acid or in benzene at room temperature (Fig. 2.41).

It is supposed that the intermediate of the process is the lead–glycolate **41.1,** which is transformed into the final products **41.2** by a simple electron transfer.[3] This method for oxidation is suitable to distinguish[2,4] between glycols of different order and with different stereochemistry; the *cis*-glycol system is split faster than the *trans*-isomer, and the cleavage of five-membered rings is quicker than that of the six-membered compounds. As free sugars exist in the cyclic form, and oxidation proceeds with the species present in the equilibrium state, various chain-shortened sugars are produced. In the case of hexoses, 2 molar eq of lead tetraacetate is rapidly consumed, and it is supposed that the 1,2-diol system adjacent to the anomeric center and complexed by the lead atom is split, and that one of the hydroxyl groups is esterified with the formic acid produced in the reaction. (On the contrary, similar oxidation of glycosides and polyols proceeds much more slowly.) The place of esterification cannot be determined unequivocally—because of migration—but, in any case, hydrolytic removal of the formate group provides the chain-shortened aldose.[5–12]

With D-*glucose,* oxidation with lead tetraacetate gives 2,3-di-O-formyl-D-erythrose, to be hydrolized into D-erythrose. From the enantiomeric sorboses, L- or D-glyceraldehyde is produced with high yield,[11] but descending synthesis of D-mannose and D-galactose into D-arabinose and D-lyxose, respectively, does not proceed as efficiently. Analogous oxidation of L-*rhamnose* afforded[12] 5-deoxy-L-arabinose, which was isolated by chromatographic purification.

By employing *deuterium-labeled* sugars, detailed studies have suggested[10] that the reacting species in these oxidations are the furanose forms of the aldoses.

For preparation of 2,3-O-isopropylidene- or 2,3-O-cyclohexylidene-glyceraldehyde, partially protected carbohydrates carrying a vicinal-glycol function are employed. [The former two compounds are also called as (4R)- or (4S)-2,2-dimethyl-1,3-dioxolane-4-carbaldehyde or (2R)- or (2S)-1,4-dioxaspiro[4.5]decan-2-carbaldehyde.] As discussed in the previous sec-

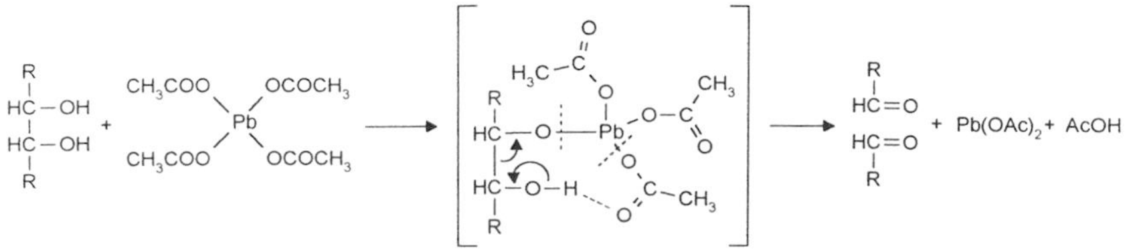

FIGURE 2.41

tions, these substances are relatively unstable and are often prepared *in situ*, to be converted into the desired compounds without characterization.[10,13–19]

> *2,3-O-Isopropylidene-D-glyceraldehyde*[20]   To a cold (0°C) solution of 1,2:5,6-di-*O*-isopropylidene-D-mannitol (13.7 g, 52.3 mmol) in dichloromethane (200 ml) are added first sodium hydrogencarbonate (55.4 g, 0.523 mol) and then lead tetraacetate (24.3 g, 54.9 mmol). After 10-min reaction time no oxidizing agent can be detected (KI–starch paper probe). The solution is filtered through Celite–Na₂SO₄, and is washed three times with dichloromethane, and the solvent is distilled off. The crude residue is subjected to vacuum distillation to afford 11.0 g of the product as a viscous liquid, b.p. 39°C (2.0 kPa).

Neutralization of the acid formed during the oxidation reaction may also be carried out with potassium carbonate to furnish[19] 72–76% of an acid-free product (b.p. 51°C at 2.13 kPa).

Similar descending procedures with lead tetraacetate allowed the preparation of 2,3-di-*O*-acetyl-, 2,3-*O*-diisopropylmethylene- and 2,3-di-*O*-(*tert*-butyldimethylsilyl)-D-glyceraldehyde,[21] and for the *synthesis of D,L-glyceraldehyde* degradation of 1,2:5,6-di-*O*-isopropylidene-D,L-sorbitol (glucitol) was selected.[22]

> *2,3-O-Isopropylidene-D,L-glyceraldehyde*[22]   A mixture of sorbitol (85 g, 467 mmol), zinc chloride (135 g, 991 mmol), and dry acetone (675 ml) is stirred for 4 h, and then the mixture is poured into a rapidly stirred solution of K₂CO₃ (170 g) in water (170 ml) layered with ether (675 ml). The reaction mixture is stirred for 20 min, filtered, the salts are washed with a 1 : 1 mixture of acetone and ether (400 ml), and the combined filtrate is dried (K₂CO₃) and concentrated. The crude residue is refluxed with heptane (800 ml) for 3 h, the mixture is cooled, the supernant is decanted, and the solvent is removed *in vacuo* to give 56.5 g of a syrup that solidifies in high vacuum overnight. This is recrystallized from hot di-*n*-butyl ether to give 6.64 g of 1,2:5,6-di-*O*-isopropylidene-D,L-sorbitol, m.p. 95–95.5°C. To a solution of the preceding acetonide (1.5 g, 5.7 mmol) in dry benzene (20 ml) is added lead tetraacetate (2.53 g, 5.7 mmol), the mixture is filtered through a pad of Celite, and the solvent is removed *in vacuo* at 10°C. To the residue is added 50 ml of carbon tetrachloride, the mixture is evaporated, and the crude material is distilled by Kugelrohr (≤40°C, 1.5 torr) to give 1.0 g (67%) of the racemic title compound.

> *2,3-O-Cyclohexylidene-D-glyceraldehyde*[23]   To a solution of 1,2:5,6-di-*O*-cyclohexylidene-D-mannitol (28.0 g, 81.7 mmol) in dichloromethane (300 ml) are added potassium carbonate (112.9 g, 0.817 mol) and lead tetraacetate (37.9 g, 85.5 mmol), and the reaction mixture is stirred for 15 min. At this point no oxidizing agent can be detected by the KI–starch paper probe. The mixture is filtered, the filter cake is washed three times with dichloromethane, the filtrate is concentrated, and the residue is submitted to vacuum distillation to obtain the title acetal (22.3 g, 80.3%) as a viscous oil, b.p. 68–70°C/60 Pa. $[\alpha]_D^{20}$ +60.7 (c = 3.4 in benzene).

Both D- *and* L-*threose are obtained* from the enantiomeric 1,3-*O*-benzylidene-arabinitols and characterized[24] in the form of the respective 1,2-*O*-isopropylidene-threofuranose derivative (Fig. 2.42).

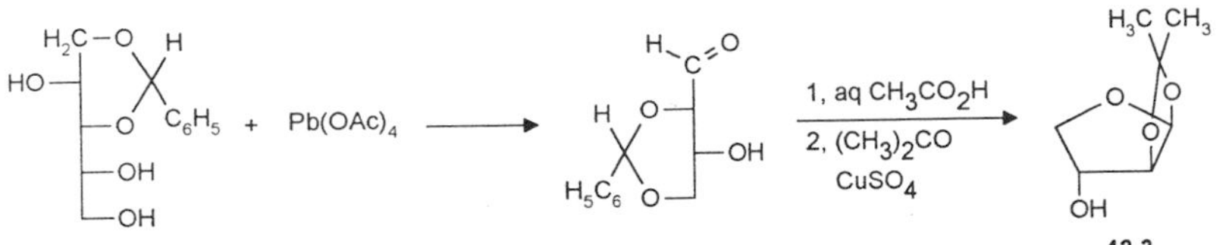

FIGURE 2.42

*1,2-O-Isopropylidene-*D*-threofuranose (42.3)*[24] To a suspension of 1,3-*O*-benzylidene-D-arabinitol (**42.1**, 11 g) in glacial acetic acid (110 ml), lead tetraacetate (24.5 g) is added, and the mixture is shaken for 1.5 h. At the first stage of the reaction the mixture warms, and no crystalline Pb(OAc)$_4$ is present when the reaction is completed. The syrup obtained on evaporation is taken up with 50 ml of ice water, ethyl acetate (150 ml) is added and the aqueous layer is extracted twice with this solvent (80–80 ml). The combined organic solution is washed with a small volume of ice-cold water and aqueous sodium carbonate until neutral, and then washed again with water. The dried (Na$_2$SO$_4$) solution is concentrated to a syrup (**42.2**, 16.5 g), which is hydrolized with 10% aqueous acetic acid (200 ml) in a 100°C water bath and then evaporated *in vacuo*. The residue is dissolved in water (30 ml) and extracted two times with ether. The aqueous layer is filtered through a pad of charcoal and transferred into a preweighed 0.5-liter flask together with 20 g of glass pearls. Evaporation of the solution in high vacuum (bath temperature 40°C) gives a syrupy sugar sticking on the glass pearls (yield of the crude product is 95%). Then anhydrous CuSO$_4$ (25 g), acetone (240 ml), and concentrated sulfuric acid (0.4 ml) are added to the flask, and the content is shaken for 2 days. Following filtration, 5 g of powdered K$_2$CO$_3$ is added, and shaking is continued for 2 h more. To the filtered solution 0.2 g of K$_2$CO$_3$ is added, the solvent is distilled off, the residue is taken up with ether, the organic solution is washed twice with 30% aqueous K$_2$CO$_3$, dried over K$_2$CO$_3$, the solvent is removed by distillation under diminished pressure, and the solidifying residue is submitted to high-vacuum distillation at 0.1 kPa/95°C to give 5.2 g of the crude title sugar, which is crystallized from ether (the residue from the mother liquor is crystallized from ether–pentane) to afford 3.0 g of colorless needles of **42.3**, m.p. 84°C, $[\alpha]_D^{22}$ −15.3 (*c* = 3.0 in acetone).

For descending synthesis of 1,2-*O*-isopropylidene-D-glucofuranose (**43.1**) with lead tetraacetate, two *easily reproducible procedures*[25,26] are available to obtain the dimeric 1,2-*O*-isopropylidene-α-D-*xylo*-pentodialdo-1,4-furanose (**43.2**) and the mixed-aldol product: 1,2-*O*-isopropylidene-3,5-methylene-5-hydroxy-α-D-xylofuranose (**43.3**) (Fig. 2.43).

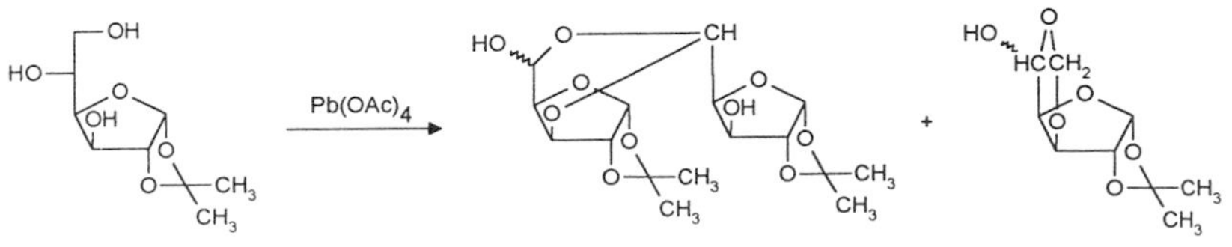

FIGURE 2.43

Oxidation of 1,2-O-isopropylidene-α-D-glucofuranose (43.1) with lead tetraacetate[25]   To a suspension of the sugar **43.1** (20 g) in benzene (1 liter) a solution of lead tetraacetate (50 g) in benzene (250 ml) is added, and the reaction mixture is boiled under reflux for 30 min. The cooled mixture is filtered by suction, and the filtrate is neutralized with sodium hydrogencarbonate. After filtration, the filtrate is concentrated, the residue is washed with ethanol, and the extract is evaporated. The residue is thoroughly washed with ether, the ethereal solution is evaporated, and the residue is submitted to column chromatography on silicagel to obtain 10 g (50%) of the 3,5-methyleneacetal **43.3**, $[\alpha]_D$ +47 (c = 2.4 in chloroform) and 2.0 g of the dimer **43.2**, m.p. 182°C, $[\alpha]_D$ ±0 (10 min) → +26 (equilibrium value; c = 1.7 in water).

Oxidation of 1,2-O-isopropylidene-α-D-glucofuranose (43.1) with minium in acetic acid[26]   To a suspension of the sugar **43.1** (22 g, 0.1 mol) in glacial acetic acid (200 ml) 100 g of finely powdered *minium* is added at 50–60°C over a period of 40 min. When warming is finished, the mixture is stirred for 10 min to allow it to cool, benzene (200 ml) is added, and stirring is continued for an additional 1 h. The mixture is decolorized with charcoal and concentrated (bath temperature 40–50°C), the residue is taken up in benzene (500 ml), and the decanted supernatant is concentrated. Both fractions are extracted with ethyl acetate (4 × 200 ml), the extracts are removed from the insoluble lead salts [the lead(II) acetate obtained can be transformed into lead(IV) acetate] and the solution is washed with aqueous NaHCO₃, dried over Na₂SO₄, and concentrated. The residual white, amorphous powder (10–20 g) consists of (TLC in 7:3 acetone–petroleum ether) the dimeric product **43.2**, and the methylene acetal **43.3**, and no starting material is present. The ratio of these two compounds varies, but usually twice as much of the methylene acetal as the dimer can be isolated. Purification of this mixture is accomplished by column chromatography on a 20-fold excess of silicagel (eluant: 1:9 → 4:1 ether–benzene) to furnish 3.7 g of **43.3** and 1.2 g of the dimer **43.2**. Compound **43.3**: white foam (dried *in vacuo* at 40°C), $[\alpha]_D^{25}$ +52.2 (c = 0.69 in chloroform). Upon storage for several weeks or high-vacuum distillation, the liberation of formaldehyde and formation of a dimeric substance is observed. Compound **43.2**: m.p. 181–182°C (from ethyl acetate–hexane), $[\alpha]_D^{25}$ +27.8 → +30.1 (30 h, c = 0.33 in chloroform).

In a few cases *sulfur-containing sugars* were subjected to oxidative chain shortening with lead tetraacetate; by performing the reaction rapidly, no oxidation of the sulfur atom is observed. Related oxidation of glyceraldehyde–diethyl dithioacetal[27] gives rise to glyoxalmono(diethyl dithioacetal). Among the cleavage products of aldose–diethyl dithioacetals, diethyl trithioorthoglyoxylate (isolated in form of its semicarbazone) is also present,[28] which is formed by acyloin condensation of the oxidation products. By oxidation of 4,5-O-isopropylidene-D-fucose dibenzyl dithioacetal (**44.1**) only glyoxal mono(dibenzyl dithioacetal) (**44.2**) could be isolated[29] (Fig. 2.44).

Glyoxal mono(dibenzyl dithioacetal) (44.2)[29]   To a solution of lead tetraacetate (86%, 4.8 g) in benzene (~100 ml) is added a solution of the sugar **44.1** (4 g) in benzene (~50 ml) and the mixture is completed to a volume of 250 ml with the same solvent. It is mixed well, and lead(II) acetate, precipitated in 30 min, is filtered off. The filtrate is dried over anhydrous Na₂CO₃ for 1 h, filtered, and evaporated to obtain an almost colorless, pungent syrup, which is dissolved in ether. After

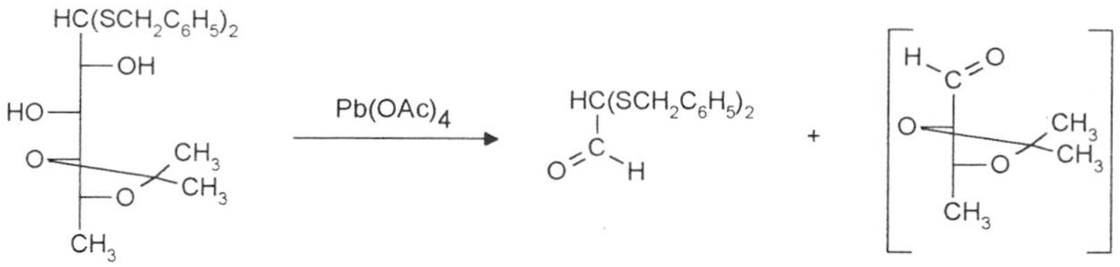

FIGURE 2.44

addition of a seeding crystal, ether is allowed to evaporate, when the syrup crystal-lizes. This is taken up with ether, filtered, and washed several times with ether to give 0.7 g of prisms with m.p. 170°C. This crude material is recrystallized from a large volume of acetone to obtain pure **44.2**, m.p. 174°C.

Several invaluable chiral building blocks for various natural pro-ducts[30-32] have been synthesized by the oxidation of suitably protected sugar dithioacetals with lead tetraacetate. Zinner and Kristen[30] prepared 2,3-O-isopropylidene-D-*threo*-tetrodialdose dimethyl dithioacetal by oxidiz-ing 2,3:4,5-di-O-isopropylidene-D-arabinose dimethyl dithioacetal, and the respective diethyl dithioacetal (**45.2**) was obtained by Herczegh et al.,[31] as shown in Figure 2.45.

> *2,3-O-Isopropylidene-D-*threo-*tetrodialdose diethyl dithioacetal (45.2)*[31]   To a vigorously stirred solution of 2,3-O-isopropylidene-D-arabinose diethyl dithioacetal (**45.1**, 10.53 g, 35.5 mmol) is added lead tetraacetate (17.3 g, 39 mmol). After 10 min, the reaction mixture is filtered through a pad of Celite, the filter cake is washed with 2 × 100 ml of benzene, the combined filtrate is washed with saturated aqueous NaHCO$_3$ solution, and the combined aqueous solution is reextracted with benzene (50 ml). After drying, the benzene solution is concentrated to a syrup (9.3 g, 99%) and the crude product (**45.2**) is characterized in form of the p-nitrophenylhydrazone, m.p. 110–111°C, [α]$_D$ −8.3 (c = 1.32 in chloroform).

The lead tetraacetate oxidation procedure has been carried out *with uronic acids* as well (e.g., with D-glucuronic acid, D-galacturonic acid, po-tassium D-galacturonate), and the D-*arabino*-penturonic acid, D-*threo*-tetruronic acid, and D-*erythro*-tetruronic acid produced thereby were char-acterized[33] after hydrolysis of the formate esters. Descending synthesis of the *lactams* of D-lyxonic acid and D-ribonic acid with the present procedure has also been investigated.[34]

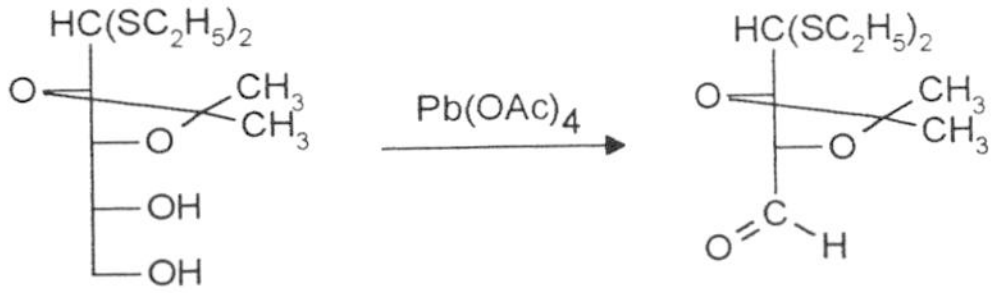

FIGURE 2.45

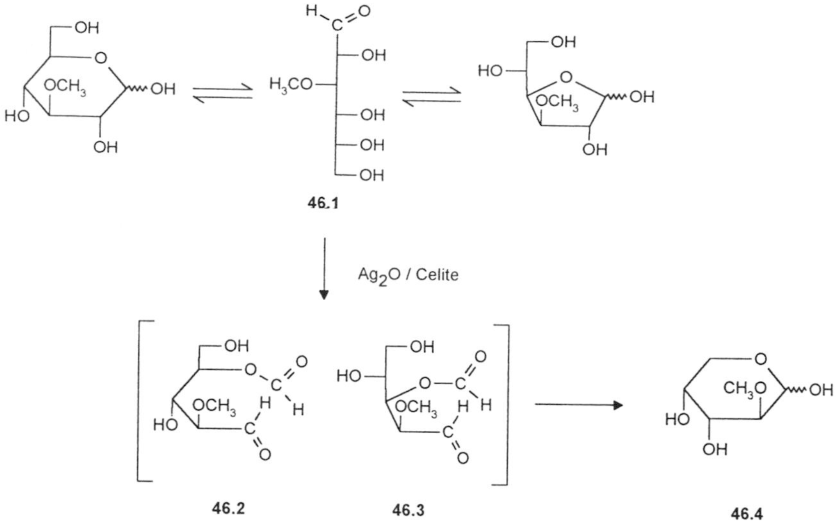

FIGURE 2.46

Silver carbonate precipitated onto Celite, a simple oxidizing agent[35] for carbohydrates (Fetizon reagent), induces an oxidative cleavage similar to those of the lead tetraacetate oxidations (Fig. 2.46). Thus, cleavage[36] of 3-*O*-methyl-D-glucose (**46.1**) with this reagent results in 2-*O*-methyl-D-arabinose (**46.4**) via the intermediary formate esters **46.2** and **46.3**.

Depending on the conditions, *oxidative degradation of D-fructose* with silver carbonate on Celite gives rise to either D-erythrose (or its glycolic ester) or D-glyceraldehyde,[37] and L-threose is obtained[38] from L-sorbose with 39% yield in the form of 1,2-*O*-isopropylidene derivative (see Section 1.3.4.1). This sugar could also be prepared by the oxidation[39] of L-arabinose.

REFERENCES TO SECTION 2.4.2

1. R. Criegee, *Angew. Chem.* **53**, 324 (1940); **70**, 173 (1958); *Neuere Methoden der präparativen organischen Chemie,* 3rd ed., p. 21. Verlag Chemie, Weinheim, 1949.
2. A. S. Perlin, *Methods Carbohydr. Chem.* **1**, 427 (1962).
3. R. Criegee, E. Högher, G. Huber, P. Kruck, F. Marktscheffel, and H. Schellenberger, *Justus Liebigs Ann. Chem.* **599**, 81 (1956).
4. A. S. Perlin, *Adv. Carbohydr. Chem.* **14**, 9 (1959).
5. R. Criegee, *Ber. Dtsch. Chem. Ges.* **64**, 260 (1931).
6. R. Criegee, *Justus Liebigs Ann. Chem.* **495**, 211 (1932).
7. R. C. Hockett and M. Zief, *J. Am. Chem. Soc.* **72**, 2130 (1950).

8. A. S. Perlin and C. Brice, *Can. J. Chem.* **34**, 85 (1956).
9. A. S. Perlin and C. Brice, *Can. J. Chem.* **34**, 541 (1956).
10. A. S. Perlin, *Can. J. Chem.* **42**, 2365 (1964).
11. A. S. Perlin, *Methods Carbohydr. Chem.* **1**, 61, 64, 68 (1962); A. B. Smith, III, G. A. Sulikowski, M. M. Sulikowski, and K. Fujimoto, *J. Am. Chem. Soc.* **114**, 2567 (1992).
12. L. Stankovic, V. Bilik, and K. Linek, Czech. Pat. CS 183,876 (1980), *Chem. Abstr.* **94**, 175441m (1981).
13. J. Jurczak, S. Pikul, and T. Bauer, *Tetrahedron* **42**, 447 (1986).
14. K. Ichimura, *Bull. Chem. Soc. Jpn.* **43**, 2501 (1970).
15. J. Leonard, S. Mohialdin, and P. A. Swain, *Synth. Commun.* **19**, 3529 (1989).
16. E. B. Rodriguez, G. D. Scally, and R. V. Stick, *Aust. J. Chem.* **43**, 1391 (1990).
17. R. W. Kirstead, A. Faraone, F. Menonna, J. Mullin, R. W. Guthrie, H. Crowley, B. Simko, and L. C. Blaber, *J. Med. Chem.* **26**, 1561 (1983).
18. M. E. Jung and T. J. Shaw, *J. Am. Chem. Soc.* **102**, 6304 (1980).
19. B. Häfele and V. Jäger, *Justus Liebigs Ann. Chem.*, p. 85 (1987).
20. R. Dumont and H. Pfander, *Helv. Chim. Acta* **66**, 814 (1983).
21. J. Jurczak, T. Bauer, and M. Chmielewski, *Carbohydr. Res.* **164**, 493 (1987).
22. C. H. Heathcock, M. C. Pirrung, J. Lampe, C. T. Buse, and S. D. Young, *J. Org. Chem.* **46**, 2290 (1981).
23. E. Schrötter, T. T. Luong, and H. Schick, *J. Prakt. Chem.* **332**, 191 (1990).
24. M. Steiger and T. Reichstein, *Helv. Chim. Acta* **19**, 1016 (1936).
25. T. D. Inch, *Carbohydr. Res.* **5**, 53 (1967).
26. J. Kiss, R. D'Souza, and P. Taschner, *Helv. Chim. Acta* **58**, 31 (1975).
27. H. O. L. Fischer and E. Baer, *Helv. Chim. Acta* **18**, 514 (1935).
28. M. L. Wolfrom and E. Usdin, *J. Am. Chem. Soc.* **75**, 4619 (1953).
29. O. T. Schmidt and E. Wernicke, *Justus Liebigs Ann. Chem.* **556**, 179 (1944).
30. H. Zinner and H. Kristen, *Chem. Ber.* **97**, 1654 (1964).
31. P. Herczegh, I. Kovács, and F. J. Sztaricskai, *Tetrahedron* **47**, 1541 (1991).
32. P. Herczegh, M. Zsély, I. Kovács, Gy. Batta, and F. J. Sztaricskai, *Tetrahedron Lett.* **31**, 1195 (1990).
33. P. A. J. Gorin and A. S. Perlin, *Can. J. Chem.* **34**, 693 (1956).
34. S. A. Miller and A. R. Chamberlin, *J. Am. Chem. Soc.* **112**, 8100 (1990).
35. V. Balogh, M. Fetizon, and M. Golfier, *Angew. Chem.* **81**, 423 (1969); *Angew. Chem., Int. Ed. Engl.* **8**, 444 (1969).
36. S. Morgenlie, *Acta Chem. Scand.* **25**, 2773 (1971).
37. S. Morgenlie, *Acta Chem. Scand.* **27**, 1557 (1973).
38. S. Morgenlie, *Acta Chem. Scand.* **26**, 2146 (1972).
39. S. Morgenlie, *Acta Chem. Scand.* **26**, 1709 (1972).

2.4.3. Descending Syntheses of Onic Acid and Uronic Acid Derivatives

The acid derivatives of sugars with various degrees of oxidation are suitable candidates for descending syntheses. The present section intends to summarize the most frequently employed methods published in this field.

2.4.3.1. Descending Syntheses of Onic and Uronic Azides

It is generally known that the thermal rearrangement of various acyl azides leads to isocyanates, whose solvolysis gives rise to urethanes with the liberation of carbon dioxide, and this reaction is known as the *Curtius*

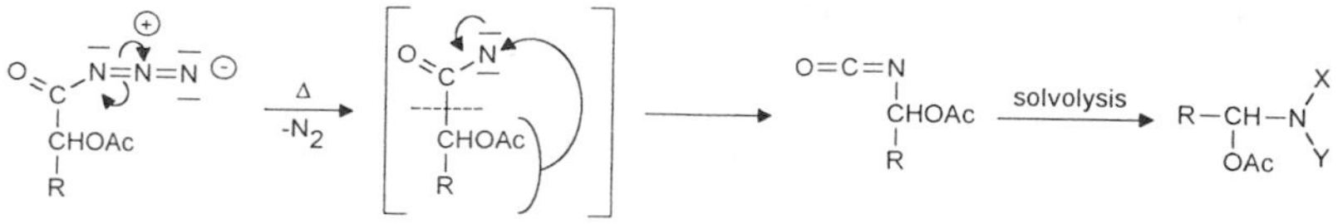

FIGURE 2.47

degradation[1]. In the field of carbohydrates, the isocyanates obtained in these reactions are also transformed into urethanes or diacylimides, which are subjected to further transformations into the aldose shortened[2-4] *with one carbon atom* in the chain. Experiences have shown that this procedure (Fig. 2.47) is more adavantageous—from a preparative point of view—than the Wohl degradation.

For example, the degradation of penta-*O*-acetyl-D-gluconyl azide (**48.3**; Fig. 2.48) is described in the following procedure as reported by Bognár and Farkas,[2] who characterized the reaction-produced D-arabinose in form of its osazone (**48.4**).

> *2,3,4,5,6-Penta-O-acetyl-D-gluconyl chloride (48.2)*[5] A mixture of penta-*O*-acetyl-D-gluconic acid (**48.1**, 1 g) and asymmetric dichlorodimethyl ether (1 ml) is heated on a 100°C steam bath for 1 h, under a well-ventilated hood. The clear solution is then concentrated, and the syrupy residue is crystallized from ether–hexane to obtain the title compound (**48.2**) in almost quantitative yield, m.p. 71–72.5°C, $[\alpha]_D$ +1.9 (c = 6.0 in chloroform).

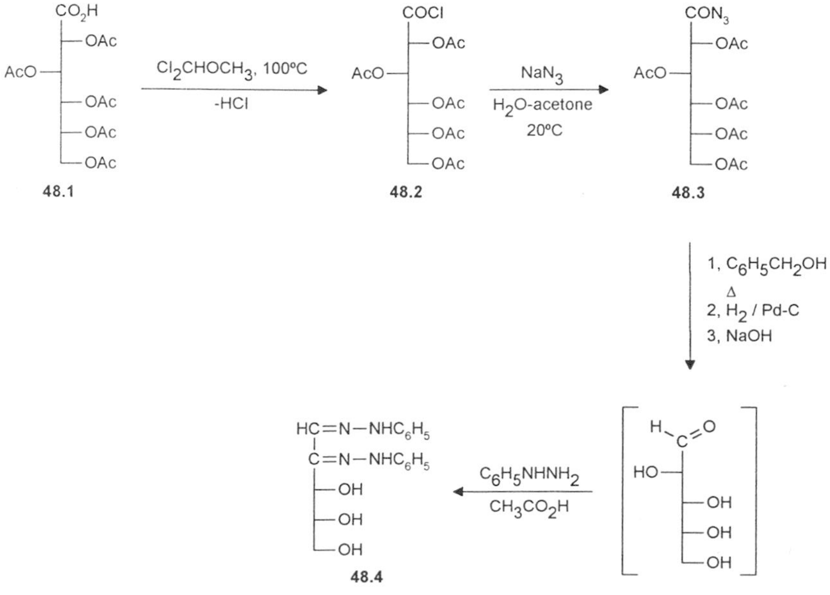

FIGURE 2.48

*2,3,4,5,6-Penta-O-acetyl-D-gluconyl azide (**48.3**)*[2] To a solution of the chloride **48.2** (1 g) in ice-cold acetone (10 ml), a slight excess of sodium azide (0.3–0.4 g in 10 ml of water) is added. The reaction mixture is kept at 0°C for 30 min, then water is added when the product is precipitated. The crude product can be recrystallized from acetone–water to obtain the pure azide **48.3** (72.7%), $[\alpha]_D$ +17 (c = 1.71 in chloroform). The substance can be stored in a desiccator over KOH for several days without decomposition.

*Degradation of 2,3,4,5,6-penta-O-acetyl-D-gluconyl azide (**48.3**) into D-arabinose*[2] First, 3 g of the azide **48.3** is dissolved in dry benzene (18 ml), benzyl alcohol is added, and the mixture is heated under reflux and then concentrated in high vacuum. The residue is dissolved in ether, concentrated again, and the syrupy residue is dissolved in ethanol (25 ml), and after the addition of Pd/C (10%, 0.4 g), the mixture is hydrogenated at atmospheric pressure for 5–7 h. The catalyst is filtered off, the filtrate is evaporated, and the syrupy residue is stirred with 20 ml of aqueous NaOH (10%) at 40°C. After 2 h, evolution of ammonia is finished to leave an almost homogeneous solution to which a few drops of ethanol are added. To the clear solution 1 drop of acetic acid and then a solution of phenylhydrazine (2 ml) in a mixture of acetic acid (2 ml) and water (10 ml) are added. The precipitated D-arabinose–phenylosazone (**48.4**) is filtered the next day and recrystallized twice from 40% aqueous ethanol to obtain 0.34 (15%) of the pure osazone with m.p. 154–156°C.

The *degradation* of 2,3,4,5,6-penta-*O*-acetyl-D-galactonyl azide into D-lyxose, and that of 2,3,4,5-tetra-*O*-acetyl-D-arabonyl azide into D-erythrose, was accomplished with another version of the Curtius degradation, which is based on the reaction of acyl azides with anhydrides. Namely, the reaction of the isocyanic ester (produced on thermal treatment) with anhydrides gives an *N*-acylated amine, and from α-hydroxy acids a geminal hydroxyamine is formed under the same conditions. After removal of the acyl protecting groups, this "aldehyde-ammonia"-type compound is converted into the aldehyde, which is *shorter by one carbon* atom. This reaction sequence is *illustrated* by the example of the degradation of the arabonic acid **49.1** (Fig. 2.49).

*2,3,4,5-Tetra-O-acetyl-D-arabonic acid (**49.1**)*[3] A suspension of the powdered potassium salt of D-arabonic acid (7.26 g)[6] in 36 ml of acetic anhydride is saturated with hydrochloric acid gas with external cooling in an ice bath. The mixture is kept at this temperature for 1 h, and then 1 h each at 60°C and 100°C. After 16 h, the inhomogeneous mixture is concentrated under diminished pressure (bath temperature 20°C), and the residue is scrubbed with 100 g of ice. The crystalline precipitate is filtered, washed with ice water and dried on air. Following recrystallization from toluene (10 ml), 3.7 g of pure **49.1** is obtained. The aqueous mother liquor is

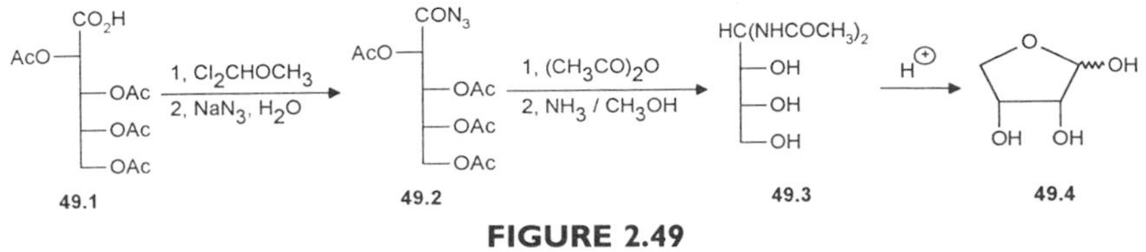

FIGURE 2.49

extracted with chloroform, the combined organic layer is dried over Na_2SO_4, and concentrated, and the residue is recrystallized from toluene to yield a further crop (1.6 g) of the title acid. The overall yield is 5.3 g (87.2%), m.p. 135°C, $[\alpha]_D$ +31.7 (c = 1.94 in chloroform).

2,3,4,5-Tetra-O-acetyl-D-arabonyl chloride[3]   A mixture of the acid **49.1** (0.5 g) and asymmetric dichloro-dimethyl ether (0.8 ml) is warmed at 70°C for 30 min under a well-ventilated hood. The homogeneous solution, formed in ~5–10 min by evolution of HCl, is concentrated *in vacuo*, the residue is taken up with ether (10 ml), and the solution is decolorized with charcoal without warming, and then is filtered and concentrated to 3 ml. Addition of hexane until turbulence produces an amorphous precipitate, which crystallizes on refrigeration for 1 day. The yield of the pure chloride (small needles) is 0.33 g (62.5%), m.p. 60–61°C, $[\alpha]_D$ +32.8 (c = 2.49 in chloroform).

2,3,4,5-Tetra-O-acetyl-D-arabonyl azide (49.2)[3]   The chloride, obtained in the preceding procedure from 2 g of the acid **49.1,** is dried over KOH for 16 h *in vacuo* and dissolved in acetone (20 ml), and under ice cooling, a solution of sodium azide (0.8 g in 4 ml of water) is added, and the mixture stirred in an ice bath for 20 min, and then diluted with water. The precipitated azide is filtered off, washed with ice water, and recrystallized from acetone–water to give 1.71 g (70%) of the pure azide **49.2,** as prisms, m.p. 105–106°C (dec.), $[\alpha]_D$ −38.8 (c = 2.61 in chloroform).

1,1-Diacetamido-D-erythrose (49.3)[3]   A solution of the azide **49.2** (1.7 g) in acetic anhydride (16 ml) is stirred at 100°C for 1 h. After 5–10 min a vigorous gas evolution is observed. The reaction mixture is poured into ice water and extracted with chloroform (5 × 20 ml). The combined extract is dried over Na_2SO_4, decolorized with charcoal, and the filtrate is evaporated *in vacuo*. The residue is taken up with ammonia in methanol (15 ml), left at room temperature for 12 h, and concentrated under diminished pressure, and the residue is scrubbed with 10 ml of ethyl acetate. The solid material is filtered off, washed with ethyl acetate, and crystallized from ethanol (15 ml) to obtain 0.26 g (25%) of **49.3,** as fine needles, m.p. 209°C, $[\alpha]_D$ +7.2 (c = 1.96 in 1 N sulfuric acid).

Preparation of D-erythrose (49.4) from 49.3   Hydrolysis of **49.3** with 2.5% aqueous sulfuric acid at 100°C for 40 min gives rise to D-erythrose (**49.4**), which can be identified by TLC.

When a mixture of octa-*O*-acetyl-cellobionyl azide (**50.1**) and acetic anhydride is heated, the expected geminal oxyamino compound; *N*-[D-*gluco*-1,2,3,5-tetraacetoxy)-4-(2,3,4,6-tetra-*O*-acetyl-β-D-glucopyranosyl)-pentyl]-acetamide (**50.2**), is obtained (81%). The structure of this compound is proved by the degradation (Fig. 2.50) into 3-β-D-gluco-pyranosyl-1,1-bis(acetamido)-D-arabinitol (**50.3**). Also, when compound **50.2** is treated with sodium methoxide, followed by acid hydrolysis, only D-glucose and D-arabinose can be detected[4] in the mixture.

N-[D-Gluco-1,2,3,5-tetraacetoxy-4-(2,3,4,6-tetra-O-acetyl-β-D-glucopyranosyl)-pentyl]-aceamide (50.2)[4]   A mixture of octa-*O*-acetyl-cellobionyl azide (**50.1,** 1.64 g) and acetic anhydride (11 ml) is kept at 100°C for 1 h. The clear solution is then poured into ice water, neutralized with $KHCO_3$, and extracted with chloroform. The organic layer is washed with aqueous $KHCO_3$, dried over Na_2SO_4, and concen-

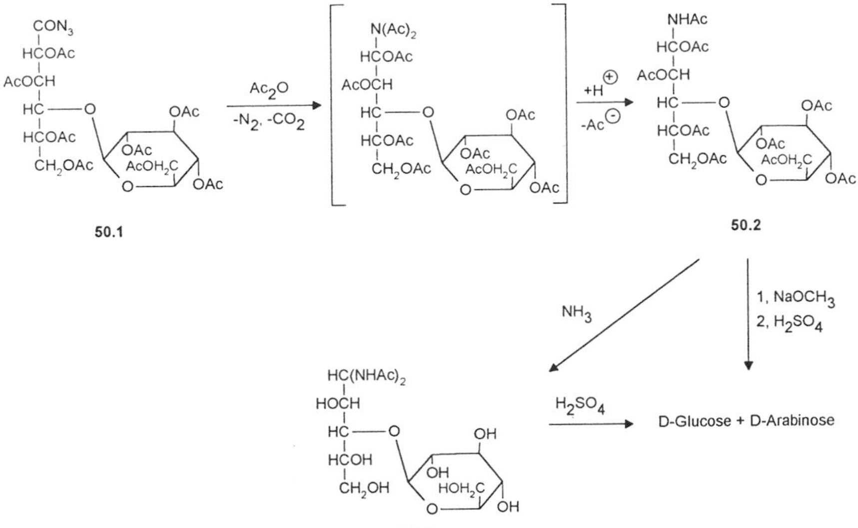

FIGURE 2.50

trated. By treatment with ether, the syrupy residue transforms into a colorless, amorphous powder, that is filtered off after standing for a few hours, washed with ether, and dried over P_2O_5 to afford 1.3 g of the title product **50.2**, m.p. 80°C (softening) and melts at ~85°C, $[\alpha]_D$ +17.5 (c = 0.97 in chloroform).

3-β-D-Glucopyranosyl-1,1-bis(acetamido)-D-arabinitol (50.3)[4]   First, 2.3 g of the azide **50.1** is heated in 15 ml of acetic anhydride at 100°C. After workup as described in the previous procedure, the syrupy residue is treated with 25 ml of concentrated NH_4OH at 50°C until complete dissolution. After standing for 4 h, the mixture is evaporated and codistilled with 2 × 5 ml of ethanol to remove traces of water, and from the solid residue the product is extracted with warm ethyl acetate (2 × 10 ml). Recrystallization from hot ethanol gives 0.68 g (51%) of the title compound (**50.3**), m.p. 217–218°C (dec.), $[\alpha]_D$ +24.2 (c = 1.15 in water).

A novel method,[7] employing milder and neutral conditions,[7,8] is based on a modified Curtius degradation, which allows *selective cutting* of β-D-glucuronic acid derivatives from *O*-permethylated oligosaccharides. Thus, treatment of methylated uronic acids (**51.1**) with diphenylphosphoroazidate and triethyl amine in *tert*-butanol or benzyl alcohol (Fig. 2.51), results in 5-(*tert*-butoxycarbonyl/benzyloxycarbonyl)-aminopentopyranosides (**51.2**), whose hydrolysis/hydrogenolysis leads (with retention of the configuration) to pentodialdoses. Characterization of these sugars is usually done by conversion into the corresponding alditols.

General procedure for the preparation of tert-*butylurethanes (benzylurethanes) from* O-*methylated uronic glycosides*[7]   A mixture of an equimolar amount of the uronic glycoside (**51.1**), diphenylphosphoroazidate, and triethylamine (0.5–1.0 mmol each) in anhydrous *tert*-butanol (or in a mixture of 1.2 eq of benzyl alcohol

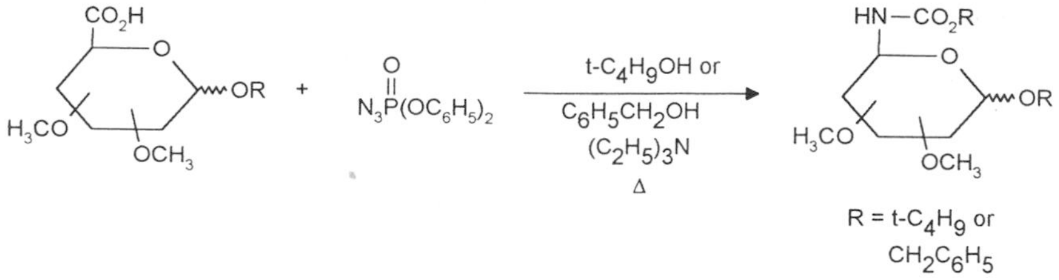

51.1 **51.2**

FIGURE 2.51

and 15 ml of benzene) is boiled under reflux for 20 h. Following evaporation, the residue is taken up with benzene, and the organic solution is successively washed with 5% aqueous citric acid, water, and aqueous $NaHCO_3$, and is then dried and evaporated. The product (**51.2**) is isolated by means of column chromatography (eluant: 4 : 1 ether–hexane) and recrystallized from a mixture of ether and hexane.

Application of this procedure for two substrates—methyl 2,3,4-tri-*O*-methyl-β-glucuronic acid (**52.1**) and the corresponding gentiobiose derivative (**52.2**)—is shown in Figure 2.52.

Descending synthesis[7] of uronic amides into *tert*-butylurethanes (or benzylurethanes) can also be accomplished by means of another variant of the Curtius degradation.[8,9] Figure 2.53 shows *three examples* for this methodology, according to the work of Aspinall *et al.*[7]

> *Degradation of O-methylated uronic glycosides with lead tetraacetate*[7] A mixture of the permethylated uronic glycoside (1 mmol), pyridine (1 mmol), lead tetraacetate (4.5 mmol), and 15 ml of *tert*-butanol (or a mixture of 15 ml of benzene and 1.2 mmol of benzyl alcohol) is boiled under reflux for 4.5 h. Then an additional amount (4.5 mmol) of lead tetraacetate is added, and the reaction mixture is boiled for another 20 h. It is then concentrated, the residue is extracted with ether or ethyl acetate, and the extracts are washed with water and concentrated. Purification of the products is done by column chromatography (eluant: 4 : 1 ether–hexane).

2.4.3.2. Degradation of Onic and Uronic Amides with Hypochlorite

Descending synthesis of the amide derivatives of onic and uronic acids can also be effected by the well-known *Hofmann degradation* with hypohalogenite ion. Shortening of the sugar chain is a result of a reaction sequence involving transformation into *N*-halogenoamide and isocyanate. The glycosides of the uronic amides (**54.1**) were also subjected to these conditions (Fig. 2.54), but the primary products of the transformations could be detected only by mass spectrometry in the form of *O*-glycosides or *O*-acetyl derivatives. The products can also be identified by gas chromatography after conversion (with $NaBH_4$ reduction) into the corresponding alditol derivatives.[10]

A similar conversion of *O*-methylated aldonic amides with sodium hypochlorite (Weerman degradation) also gives rise to the isocyanate,

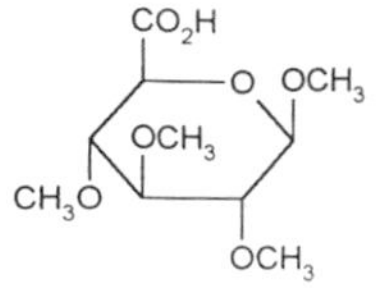

52.1

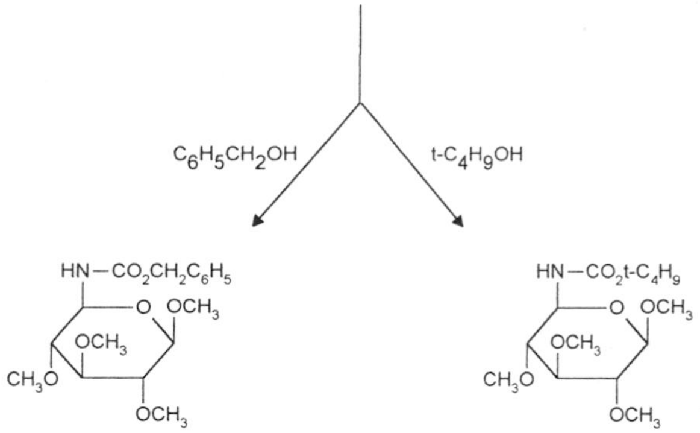

$C_6H_5CH_2OH$ $t-C_4H_9OH$

Methyl (5S)-5-benzyloxycarbonylamino-
2,3,4-tri-O-methyl-β-D-xylopyranoside
m.p. 137°C
$[\alpha]_D$ = -14.2 (CHCl$_3$)^7
87%

Methyl (5S)-5-tert-butyloxycarbonylamino-
2,3,4-tri-O-methyl-β-D-xylopyranoside
m.p. 123.5-124.5°C
$[\alpha]_D$ = -12.4 (CHCl$_3$)^7
87%

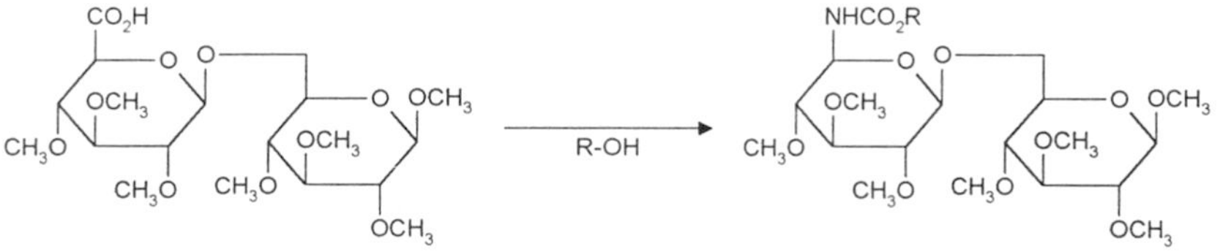

52.2   R-OH →

R = tert-butyl: Methyl 2,3,4-tri-O-methyl-6-O-[(5S)-5-
tert-butyloxycarbonylamino-2,3,4-tri-O-
methyl-β-D-xylopyranosyl)-β-D-glucopyranoside
m.p. 128-130°C
$[\alpha]_D$ = -3 (CHCl$_3$)^7
86%

R = benzyl: Methyl 2,3,4-tri-O-methyl-6-O-[(5S)-5-
benzyloxycarbonylamino-2,3,4-tri-O-methyl-
β-D-xylopyranosyl)-β-D-glucopyranoside
m.p.: 177-179°C
$[\alpha]_D$ = -3 (CHCl3)^7
92 %

FIGURE 2.52

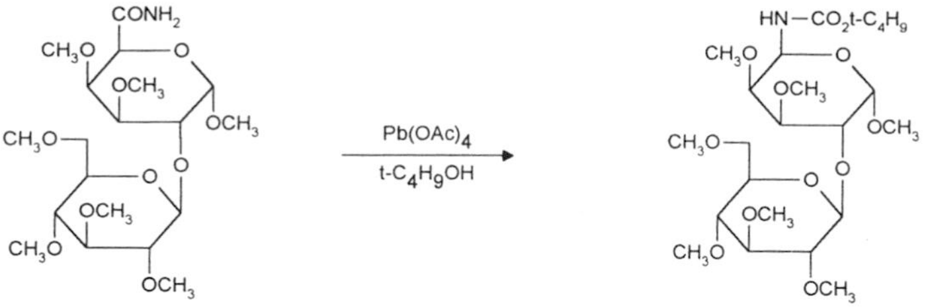

$Pb(OAc)_4$
$t\text{-}C_4H_9OH$

Methyl 3,4-di-O-methyl-2-O-(2,3,4,6-tetra-O-methyl-β-D-glucopyranosyl)-5-(5S)-tert-butyloxycarbonylamino-β-L-arabinopyranoside
m.p. 107°C
$[\alpha]_D$ = +77 (c = 1, $CHCl_3$)

86%

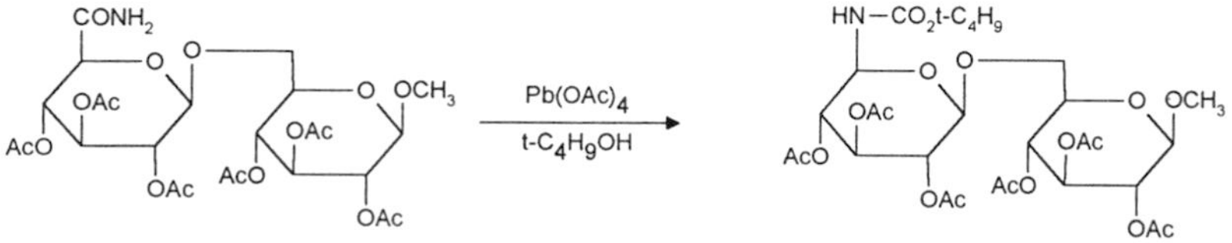

$Pb(OAc)_4$
$t\text{-}C_4H_9OH$

Methyl 2,3,4-tri-O-acetyl-6-O-[(5S)-tert-butyloxycarbonylamino-2,3,4-tri-O-acetyl-β-O-xylopyranosyl]-β-D-glucopyranoside
m.p. 132-133°C
$[\alpha]_D$ = -12 (c = 0.3, $CHCl_3$)

81%

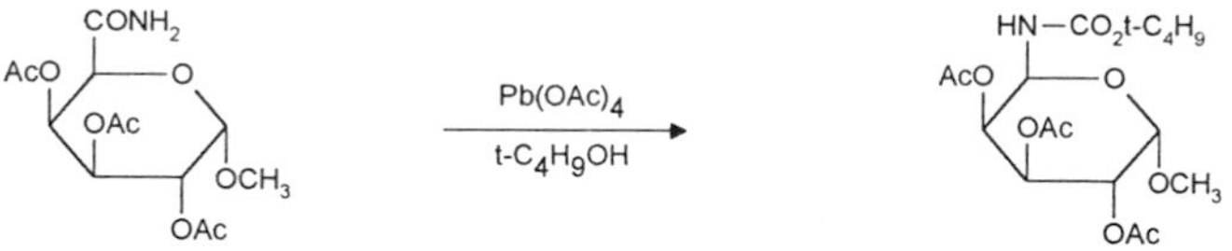

$Pb(OAc)_4$
$t\text{-}C_4H_9OH$

Methyl 2,3,4-tri-O-acetyl-(5S)-5-tert-butyloxycarbonylamino-β-L-arabinopyranoside
m.p. 184-185°C
$[\alpha]_D$ = +139 (c = 0.17, $CHCl_3$)

83%

FIGURE 2.53

which is transformed, again (without isolation) into either the stable urethane or the one-carbon-atom-shortened aldose by treatment with a base to induce split off of the isocyano function in form of NaOCN. The degradation also proceeds when all of the hydroxyl groups are methylated, and the products are the descended aldose, carbon dioxide, ammonia, and methanol.[11]

The preceding methodology (first used as an analytic degradation procedure[12] exclusively) is quite suitable for the *specific chain shortening* of methylated aldonic amides. For example, Figure 2.55 shows the sodium hypochlorite–induced descending synthesis[11] of 2,3,4,5,6-penta-O-methyl-D-gluconyl amide (**55.1**).

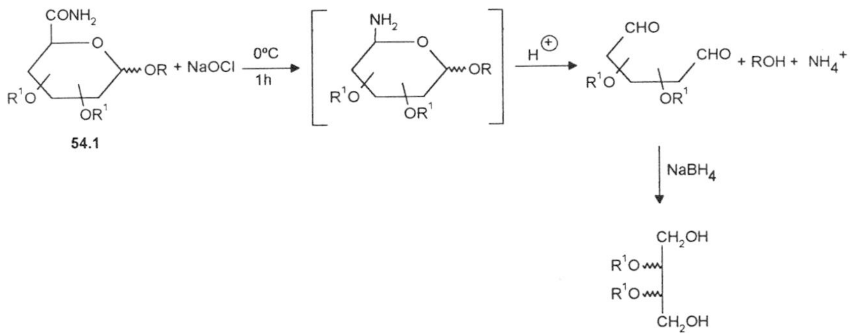

FIGURE 2.54

*2,3,4,5-Tetra-O-methyl-*aldehydo-*D-arabinose (55.2)*[11]   A solution of 2,3,4,5,6-penta-*O*-methyl-D-gluconyl amide (**55.1**, 1.0 g) in water (12 ml) is treated at 0°C with a standardized NaOCl solution[13] (4.9 ml). After 2 days, the mixture is acidified with HCl, neutralized with BaCO$_3$, and evaporated to dryness. The residue (0.7 g) is completely soluble in water. The product is subjected to vacuum distillation at 1.33 Pa (bath temperature 85°C) to give pure **55.2**, n_D^{17} 1.4340, $[\alpha]_D^{17.5}$ +16.6 (c = 2.89 in water, no mutarotation is observed).

This above descending procedure permits the isolation of the cyclic urethanes of the corresponding methoxyaminals from partially protected D-glyconic amides. Three of these products (**56.2, 56.4,** and **56.6**), derived from the sugars **56.1, 56.3,** and **56.5,** are shown in Figure 2.56.[11,14,15]

2.4.3.3. Descending Synthesis by Decarboxylation of Mercuric and Silver Salts of Uronic Acids

The long-known degradation of the mercuric and silver salts of simple carboxylic acids with iodine or bromine (Borodin–Hunsdiecker reaction) into the one-carbon-shorter alkyl or aralkyl halides[16–19] can be employed for descending synthesis of carbohydrate derivatives as well. In this radical-type process carbon dioxide is liberated, and the first step of the transformation is heterogeneous, resulting in the cleavage of only a portion of the halogen (in the form of metal halides), which is of positive character in solution, similar to that present in the hypohalides. It is supposed that the

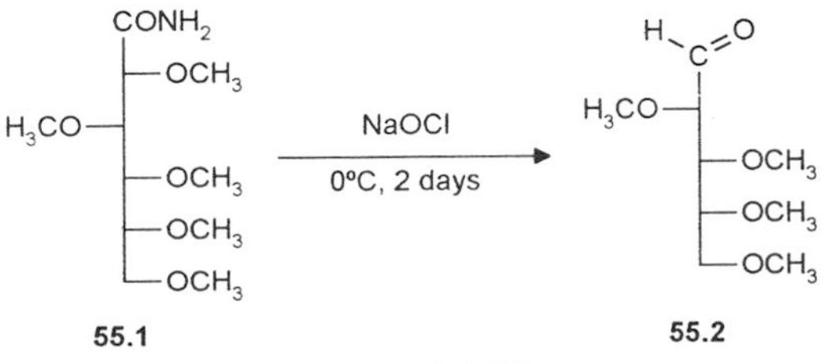

FIGURE 2.55

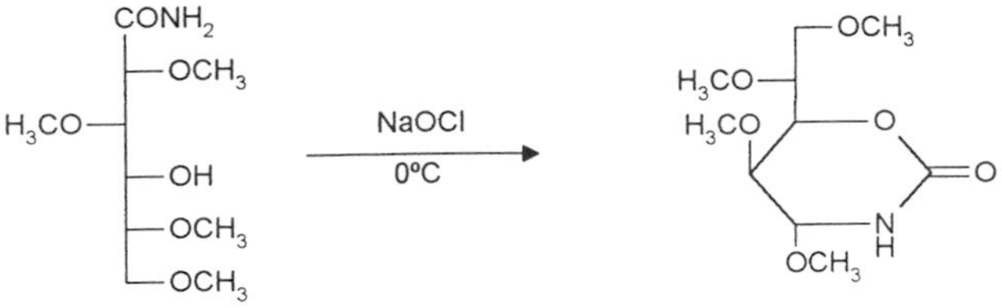

56.1   NaOCl / 0°C   56.2

m.p. 110°C
$[\alpha]_D^{18} = +99.3$ (c = 0.56, H_2O)

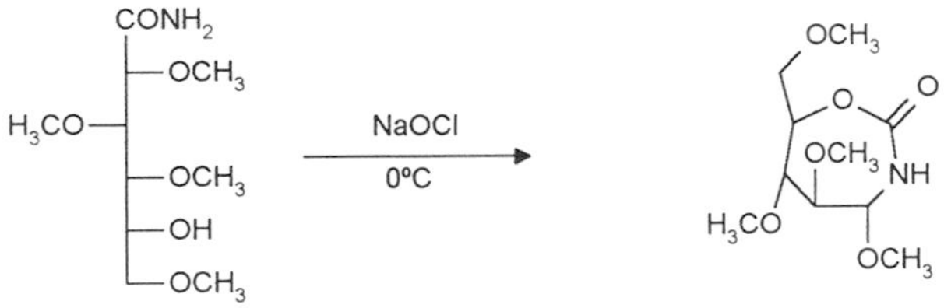

56.3   NaOCl / 0°C   56.4

m.p. 167-168°C
$[\alpha]_D^{18} = +167.8$ (c = 1.49, H_2O)
b.p. 170°C / 1.33 kPa

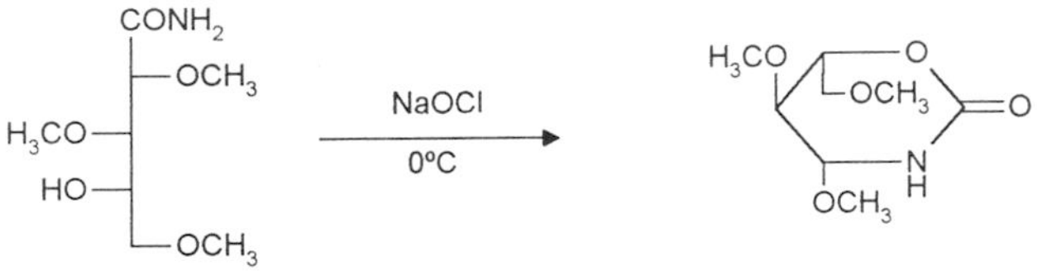

56.5   NaOCl / 0°C   56.6

m.p. 75°C

FIGURE 2.56

reaction mixture contains an acylhalogenite of the type RC(O)OHal, and the reaction proceeds with a radical mechanism, as shown in Figure 2.57.

By treatment of 2,3,4,5,6-penta-O-acetyl-D-gluconic acid and the corresponding acid chloride with bromine, 1-acetoxy-1-bromo-2,3,4,5-tetra-O-acetyl-D-arabinitol was obtained, which was identified in form of 1,1,2,3,4,5-hexa-O-acetyl-D-arabinitol (m.p. 89–90°C, $[\alpha]_D^{21}$ +30 (c = 2.0 in chloroform).[20,21] The following procedure[22] gives an experimental prescription for the execution of the *Borodin–Hunsdiecker reaction* (see Fig. 2.58).

2,6-Anhydro-1-bromo-1-deoxy-3,4,5,7-tetra-O-acetyl-D-gluco-heptitol (**58.2**)[22]
In a dark flask, to a solution of 2-(tetra-O-acetyl-β-D-glucopyranosyl)acetic acid

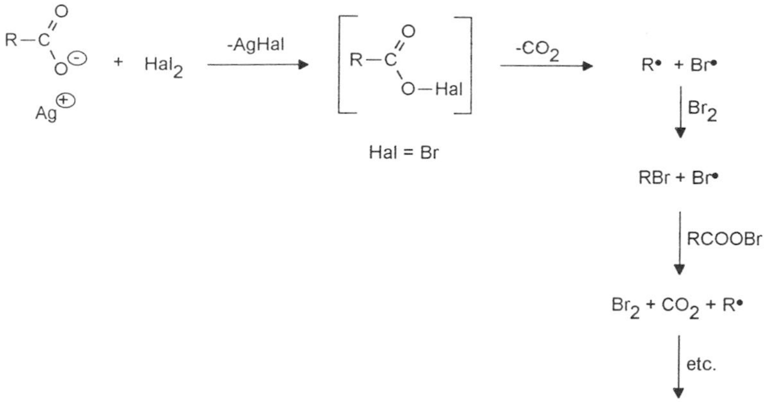

FIGURE 2.57

(**58.1**, 54 mg, 0.14 mmol) in carbon tetrachloride (1 ml), yellow mercuric oxide (30 mg) and a solution of bromine (40 mg) in 1 ml of carbon tetrachloride are added, and the mixture is boiled under reflux for 3 h. The resulting suspension is placed on top of a silicagel column (2 × 20 cm), and eluted with chloroform, and the eluate is concentrated to give a crystalline residue. This is scrubbed with ethanol, and the crystals are filtered off to give 51 mg (87%) of crude **58.2**. Twice recrystallizations from ethanol gives the pure target compound with m.p. 119.5–120°C, $[\alpha]_D^{25}$ −12.4 (c = 1.1 in chloroform).

Generation of the radical in the Borodin–Hunsdiecker degradation may be effected by the application of the N-hydroxypyridin-2-thione esters **59.1** by heating in bromotrichloromethane to induce "decarboxylative halogenation" as shown in Figure 2.59.[23–25]

The Fleet group[26] successfully employed this strategy in the carbohydrate field for preparation of the four-membered ring oxetane derivatives (oxetanosides) of carbohydrates. Fleet et al.[26] used this strategy to synthesize the anomeric 2-azido-4-O-(tert-butyldimethylsilyl)-2-deoxy-D-erythro-oxetanosyl chlorides (**60.2**) from the carboxylic acids **60.1** (Fig. 2.60).

An analogous degradation of a 1:1 mixture of the sodium salts of 3,5-anhydro-1,2-O-isopropylidene-D-glucuronic- and L-iduronic acid (**61.1**) proceeds[27] with only a 27% overall yield via the N-hydroxypyridin-2-thionoester (Fig. 2.61) to give[28] the xylofuranose **61.2**.

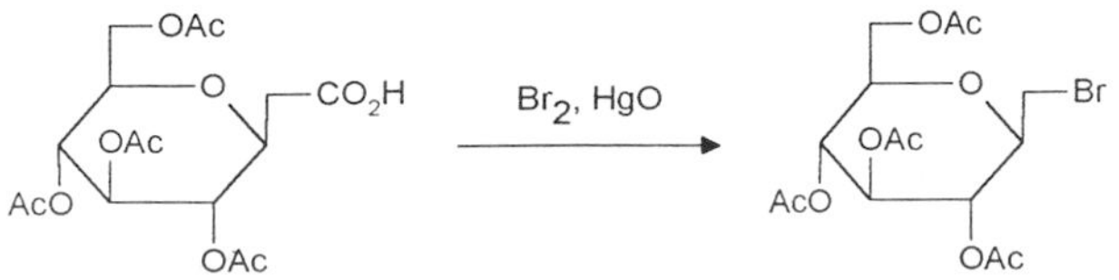

FIGURE 2.58

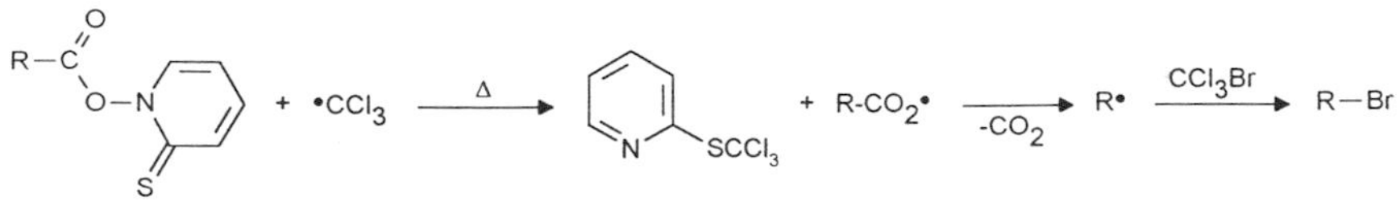

FIGURE 2.59

Chain shortening of the mixture of the 2,4-anhydro-D-arabonic and ribonic lactones **62.1**, available from 3,5-di-O-benzyl-D-*ribono*-1,4-lactone, also gives a separable mixture of the chain-shortened products **62.2** and **62.3**, as shown in Figure 2.62.

There are also reports in the literature for the preparation of 2,3,4,5-tetra-O-acetyl-D-arabonic acid derivatives from the corresponding D-gluconic acid by means of a similar procedure.[29,30]

2.4.3.4. Decarboxylation of Uronic Acids with Lead Tetraacetate

Contrary to the generally observed outcome[31–33] of the oxidation of hydroxycarboxylic acids with lead tetraacetate, degradation of protected uronic acids (**63.1**) leads to a mixture of (5R)- and (5S)-acetoxy-aldopyranoses (**63.2**) by replacement[34] of the carboxyl group with an acetoxy substituent (Fig. 2.63).

Figure 2.64 summarizes the degradation products (**64.2–64.5**) obtained[35] by the lead tetraacetate oxidation of methyl 2,3,4-tri-O-methyl-β-D-glucuronate (**64.1**).

The outcome of this process is obviously dependent on the configuration of the anomeric center; from the corresponding α anomer no dimers except the two 5-C-acetoxylated sugars are produced. An analogous descending synthesis of methyl 2,3,4-tri-O-methyl-β-D-galactopyranuronic acid (**65.1**) and the corresponding α anomer (**65.3**) gives rise[35] exclusively to the 5-C-acetoxy sugars (**65.2** and **65.4**, respectively) as shown in Figure 2.65.

Sometimes the C-5 epimeric products cannot be separated, as in the case[36] of the mixture (**66.2**, Fig. 2.66) obtained from benzyl 2-acetamido-2-deoxy-3,4-di-O-benzyl-α-D-glucopyranuronic acid (**66.1**).

*(R,S)-Benzyl 2-acetamido-5-C-(acetoxy)-3,4-di-O-benzyl-α-D-xylopyranoside (**66.2**)[36]* To a solution of the uronic acid **66.1** (8.0 g, 0.02 mol) in dry benzene (150 ml), lead tetraacetate (23 g, 0.05 mol) is added, and the mixture is boiled under reflux for 2 h. After cooling, it is diluted with ethyl acetate and extracted with water to remove inorganic salts. The organic layer is dried (MgSO₄) and concentrated to a syrup. The anomeric mixture **66.2** (5.9 g, 72%) is obtained after scrubbing with hexane.

Similar oxidation of methyl 2,3,4-tri-O-benzyl-α-D-mannopyranuronate led[37] to the C-5 epimeric methyl 5-(acetoxy)-2,3,4-tri-O-benzyl-lyxopyranosides [24% (R) and 55% (S)]. This procedure has been successfully employed

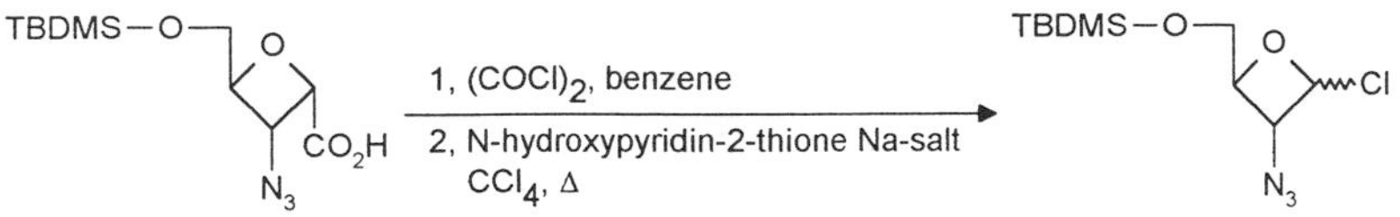

60.1 60.2

FIGURE 2.60

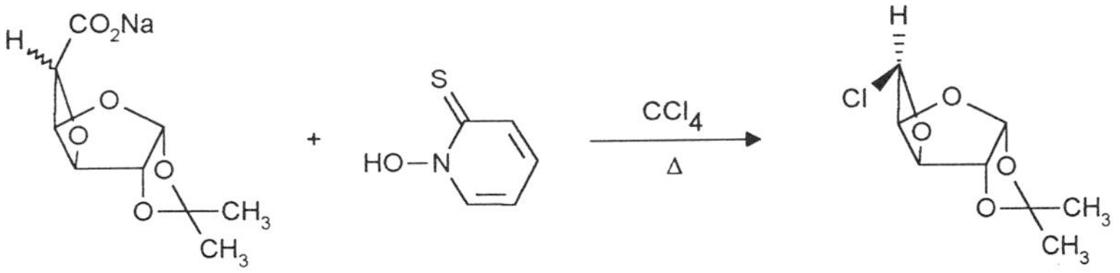

61.1 61.2

3,5-anhydro-5*R*-chloro-1,2-O-isopropylidene-D-xylofuranose
m.p. 62-63°C
$[\alpha]_D^{20}$ = +92, (*c* = 1.14, $CHCl_3$)

FIGURE 2.61

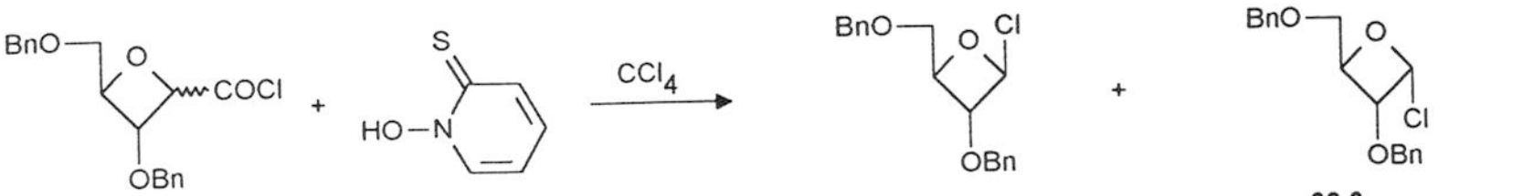

62.1 62.2 62.3

2,4-di-O-benzyl-β-D-*erythro*-octanoyl chloride
$[\alpha]_D^{20}$ = -32
(*c* =1.4, $CHCl_3$)

2,4-di-O-benzyl-α-D-*erythro*-octanoyl chloride
$[\alpha]_D^{20}$ = +130.2
(*c* = 0.9, $CHCl_3$)

FIGURE 2.62

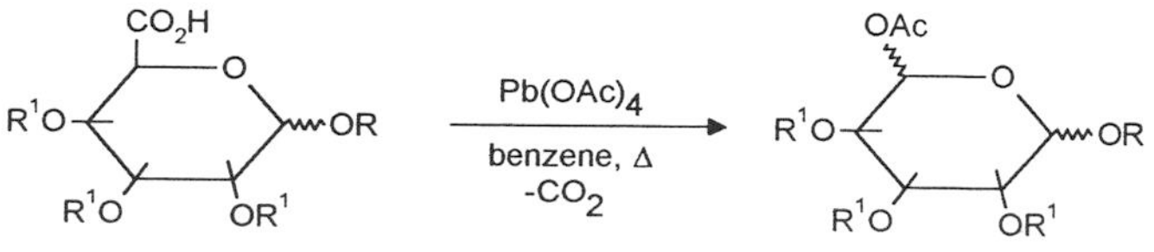

63.1 63.2

FIGURE 2.63

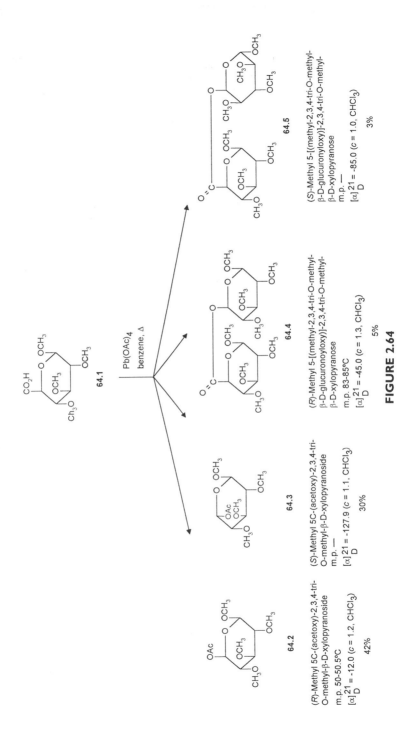

FIGURE 2.64

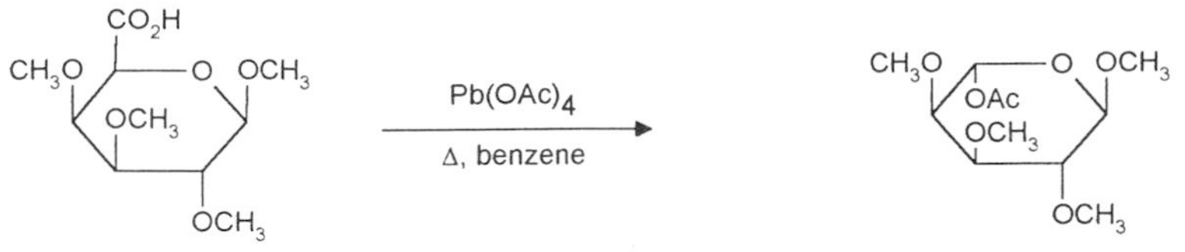

65.1 → **65.2**

Pb(OAc)$_4$
Δ, benzene

(S)-Methyl 5C-(acetoxy)-2,3,4-tri-O-methyl-
β-L-arabinopyranoside
$[\alpha]_D^{21}$ = -85.0 (c = 1.2, CHCl$_3$)
73%

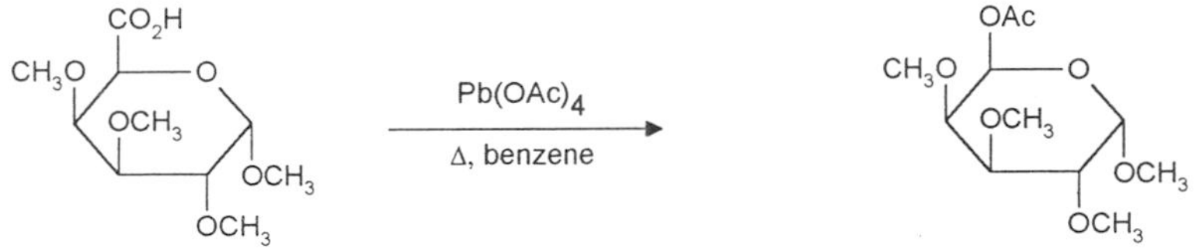

65.3 → **65.4**

Pb(OAc)$_4$
Δ, benzene

(R)-Methyl 5C-(acetoxy)-2,3,4-tri-O-methyl-
α-L-arabinopyranoside
$[\alpha]_D^{19}$ = +123.7 (c = 1.2, CHCl$_3$)
7% (82% of the starting material
remains unchanged)

FIGURE 2.65

for *disaccharide–uronates,*[38] complex *glucuronide–saponines,*[39] and other *polysaccharides.*[38]

In terms of synthesis, a clear advantage of the oxidative decarboxylations is that the produced 5-C-acetoxy sugars—as masked dialdehydes—can be employed for *nitromethane condensations* to afford nitrocyclitols (see Section 1.2.3). On the basis of this synthetic potential, the *formal synthesis of aminocyclitol antibiotics,* such as *kanamycin C,* has been elaborated, in which the key step (Fig. 2.67) is the oxidative descending synthesis[40] of the disaccharide **67.1** into **67.2**.

66.1 → **66.2**

Pb(OAc)$_4$

FIGURE 2.66

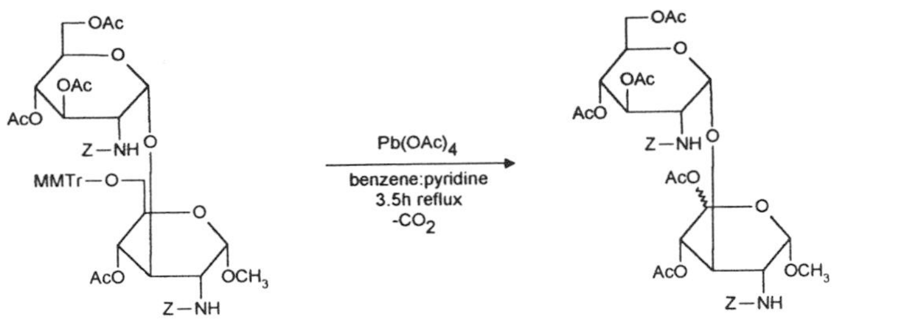

Methyl 3-O-acetyl-2-deoxy-3-O-(2-deoxy-2-benzyloxy-
carbonylamino)-α-D-(glucopyranosyl)-2-
[/(benzyloxycarbonyl)amino/-6-(monomethoxytrityl)]-
α-D-glucopyranoside

1,2-di-O-acetyl-4-deoxy-5C-methoxy-4-
[/(benzyloxycarbonyl)amino/-α-D-xylopyranosyl-
3-O-(3,4,6-tri-O-acetyl-2-deoxy-
2-(benzyloxycarbonyl)amino]-α-D-glucopyranoside
71%

FIGURE 2.67

The preceding chain shortening strategy has also been successfully used in the synthesis[41] of *ribostamycin* from the trisaccharide shown in Figure 2.68.

Recent studies have shown[42,43] that the descending reaction of uronic acids also proceeds at room temperature under very mild conditions. Oxidation of 1,2-O-isopropylidene-3-O-benzyl-α-D-ribofuranuronic acid (**69.1**) is complete in 2.5 h at 20°C (Fig. 2.69) and gives the chain-shortened sugar **69.2**.

Instead of lead tetraacetate, 3-chloroperoxybenzoic acid has also been used for related oxidative degradations. For example, Figure 2.70 shows the conversion of 2,6-anhydro-3,4,5-tri-O-benzyl-7-O-(trimethylacetyl)-L-*glycero*-L-*gulo*-heptonic acid (**70.1**) into the L-glucopyranose **70.2**, representing *an interesting entry* to the rare L-sugar series.[43] Shiozaki *et al.*[43] have reported the preparation of additional L-sugars with this methodology.

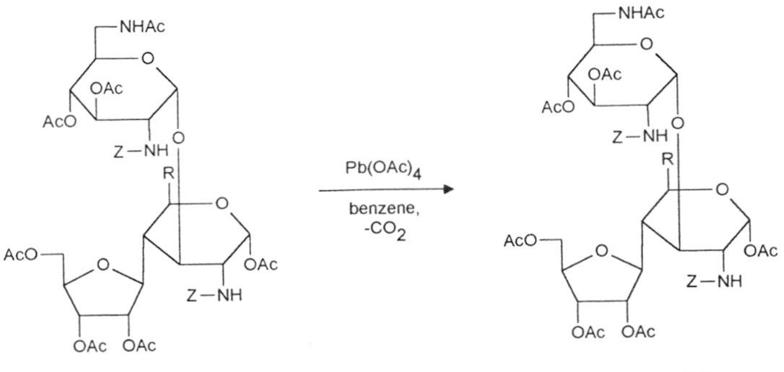

FIGURE 2.68

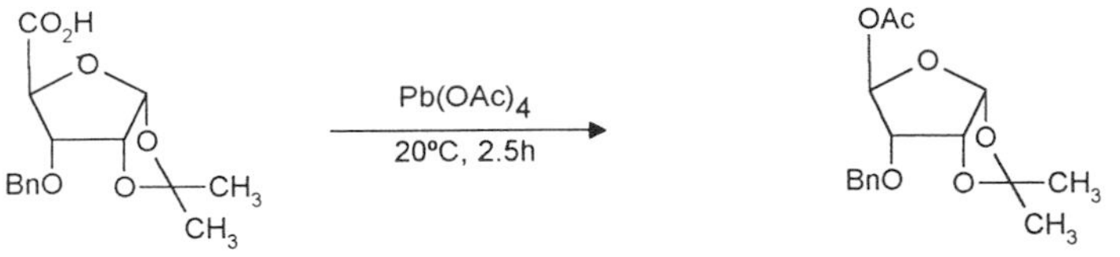

69.1   **69.2**

[3aR(3aα,5β,6α,6aα)]-tetrahydro-2,2-dimethyl-
5-acetoxy-6-(phenylmethoxy)furo-[2,3-d]-1,3-dioxol
m.p. 72-73°C
$[\alpha]_D^{25}$ = +82.3 (c = 1.03, CH_3OH)
· 83%

FIGURE 2.69

The effect of $WOCl_4$, and that of $WOCl_4$ and a "proton sponge" have also been investigated[44] to produce enol derivatives. However, no related studies on sugars have been reported as yet.

2.4.3.5. Electrochemical Oxidation of Uronic Acids

It has long been recognized that the electrolysis of D-gluconic acid leads[45] to oxidative decarboxylation instead of Kolbe-type chain extension. The voltage-controlled electrolysis of methyl 2,3,4-tri-O-methyl-β-D-glucopyranuronic acid in the presence of methanol gave (R)- and (S)-5-C-methoxy-2,3,4-tri-O-methyl-β-D-xylopyranoside. When acetic acid was present, the corresponding 5-acetoxy derivatives were produced, and these latter compounds were identical to the products of the lead tetraacetate oxidations (see Section 2.4.3.4).

Voltage-controlled electrolysis of sodium methyl 2,3,4-tri-O-methyl-β-D-gluco-pyranuronate[46]   To a solution of the title sodium salt (0.15 g) in methanol (50 ml), $NaClO_4$ (0.5 g) is added, and this is subjected to voltage-controlled electrolysis in an open beaker at 1.72 V (saturated kalomel-electrode, potentiostat–galvanostat equipment, Hokutu Denko Co. Model HA-105). Then the solvent is distilled off,

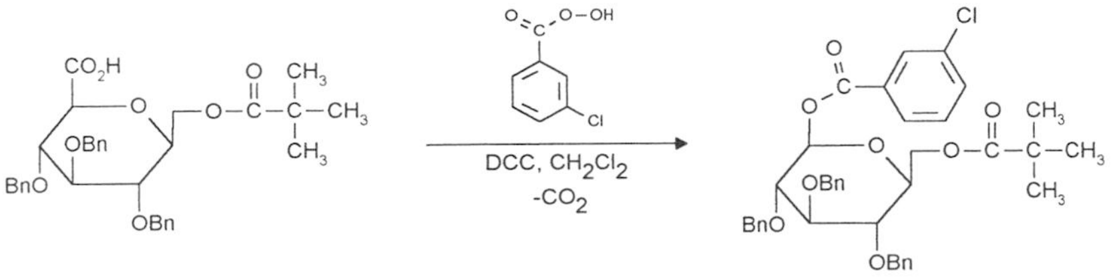

70.1   **70.2**

$[\alpha]_D^{25}$ = +32 (c = 0.9, $CHCl_3$)
34%

FIGURE 2.70

water is added to the residue, and the product is extracted with ethyl acetate. The organic phase is dried over MgSO$_4$ and evapoated to a syrup, which is purified by means of preparative layer chromatography (running system: 1:1 hexane–ethyl acetate) to obtain 91 mg (63%) of (5S)-methyl-5-C-methoxy-2,3,4-tri-O-methyl-β-D-xylopyranoside, $[\alpha]_D^{23}$ −109.7 (c = 10.2 in chloroform), and 47 mg (33%) of the (5R)-epimer, $[\alpha]_D^{28}$ ±0 (c = 5.0 in chloroform).

The obvious *advantage* of the electrolytic oxidation is that descending synthesis can be effected *without introduction of protecting groups,* so that the methyl glycoside of the dialdehyde is suitable for a direct, further derivatization. From D-glucuronic acid (**71.1**), an unstable product (**71.2**) is formed, which can be isolated and characterized on subsequent acetylation in the form of the furanoside mixture **71.3** (Fig. 2.71).[47]

The electrolytic decarboxylation of *complex glycosides* into the respective C-5-acetoxylated sugars, and subsequent condensation with nitromethane into nitrocyclitols, have been carried out. The products were then hydrogenated and acetylated into protected *aminocyclitol glycosides,* and the by-products are the aglycons produced on cleavage of the glycosidic bond. Such a multistep synthesis is illustrated by the degradation of *sakuraso-saponin* (**72.1**, Fig. 2.72); the aglycons, *protoprimulagenin A* (**72.2**) and *aegicerin* (**72.3**), can be isolated after the degradation step (1), and the resulting C-5-acetoxy-bis(glycosylated dialdose) can be converted into the nitrocyclitol **72.4**, a target for transformation into the amino compounds **72.5**.

2.4.3.6. Degradation of Ascorbic Acid Derivatives

When investigating the reactions of ascorbic acid (**73.1**) with diazonium salts a degradation process characteristic of the endiol structure, was observed[48] (Fig. 2.73). First, an arylazo compound (**73.2**) is formed, which is then converted into the 2-(4-methylphenyl)hydrazide of (3R,4S)-mono(tetrahydro-4-hydroxy-2-oxo-3-furanyl) oxalate (**73.3**). In hot water the hydrazide **73.3** can be split into L-threonic acid (**73.4**), easily isolable in form of its derivatives.[48] The epimeric isoascorbic acid (D-*arabino*-ascorbic

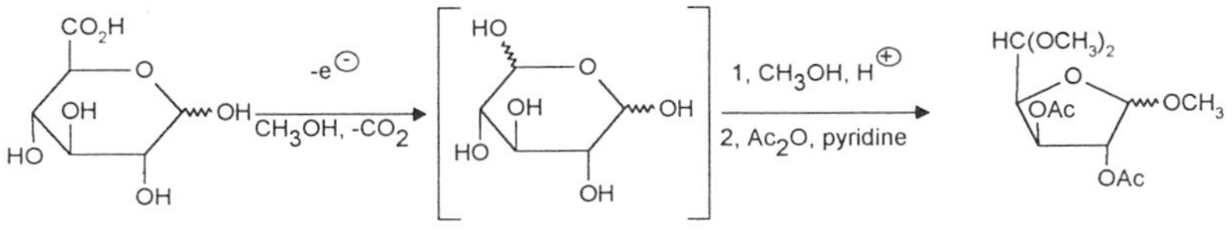

Methyl α- and β-D-*xylo*-pentodialdo-
(1,4)-furanoside dimethylacetal
$[\alpha]_D$ = 0 (CHCl$_3$)
(in case of both anomers)[47]

FIGURE 2.71

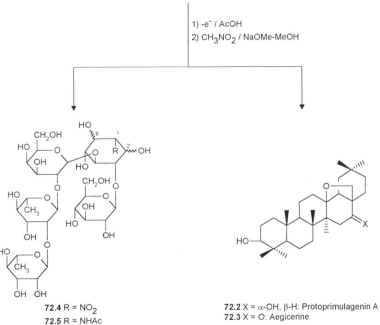

72.1 (sakuraso-saponin)

1) -e⁻ / AcOH
2) CH_3NO_2 / NaOMe-MeOH

72.4 R = NO_2
72.5 R = NHAc

72.2 X = α-OH, β-H: Protoprimulagenin A
72.3 X = O: Aegicerine

FIGURE 2.72

acid) can be degraded[48] into D-erythronic acid with this method. The following procedure[49] gives reproducible experimental details for the execution of this latter degradation.

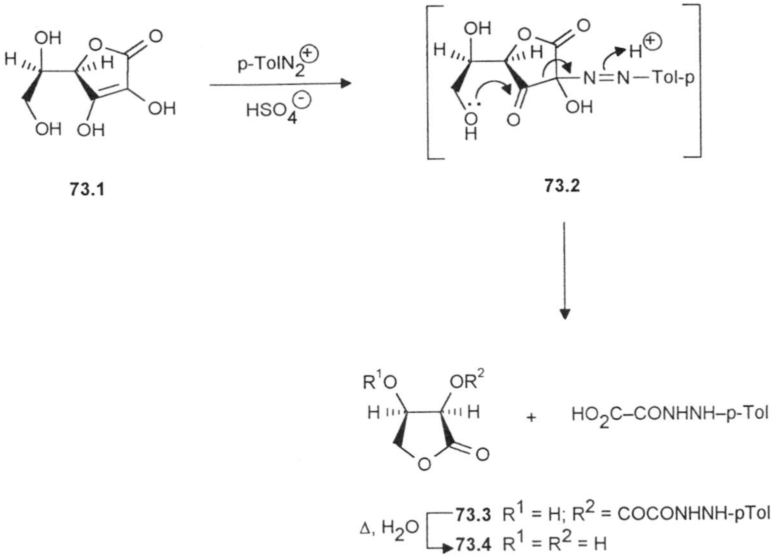

FIGURE 2.73

(−)-(3R-cis)-Mono(tetrahydro-4-hydroxy-2-oxo-3-furanyl) ester 2-(4-methylphe-nyl)hydrazide of ethanedioic acid (73.3)[49] In a 3 liter, three-necked, round-bottomed flask equipped with an air-driven Teflon paddle stirrer, thermometer, and dropping funnel is placed 500 ml of deionized water. With stirring, 53.3 ml (98.44 g, 0.96 mol) of concentrated sulfuric acid is added, when the temperature rises to ~40°C. *Para*-toluidine (53.3 g, 0.5 mol) is added with vigorous stirring at this temperature, and within a few minutes a dark-yellow solution is formed. This is cooled in an ice bath when the sulfate precipitates. To the intensely stirred, dense slurry, at 3°C is added dropwise a solution of 35 g (0.507 mol) of sodium nitrite in 63 ml of deionized water over 25 min, while the internal temperature is kept at 3–8°C. The resulting diazonium salt solution is stirred at 2–5°C for 30 min, whereupon a solution of 75.5 g (0.429 mol) of D-(−)*arabino*-ascorbic acid (73.1) in water (500 ml) is added dropwise over a period of 30 min, at ~4–5°C with rapid stirring. An orange color forms along with gummy brown material that may impede stirring somewhat. When the addition is complete, the mixture is slowly warmed to room temperature with a water bath and then stirred for 3 h at room temperature, during which time a yellow solid forms. This is filtered with suction and washed with 700 ml of water in small portions. The solid is then washed with 200 ml of ice-cold 96% ethanol in small portions. The filter cake is refluxed with 1 liter of 96% ethanol in a 3-liter round-bottomed flask for 15 min. The slurry is allowed to cool to room temperature and kept at this temperature overnight. The slurry is filtered with suction and the solid is washed with 250 ml of ice-cold 96% ethanol in small portions. After drying at 45°C using water aspirator pressure and then high vacuum, 70 g (55.5%) of the hydrazide lactone is obtained as a white solid, m.p. 182–184°C (dec.), $[\alpha]_D^{25}$ −59.3 (c = 0.5 in ethanol).

(−)-(3R-cis)-Dihydro-3,4-dihydroxy-2(3H)-furanone   (D-erythronolactone) (73.4)[49] In a 2-liter one-necked, round-bottomed flask, equipped with a reflux condenser, magnetic stirring bar, and heating mantle, a slurry of 69.9 g (0.238 mol)

of the preceding hydrazide (**73.3**) in 700 ml of deionized water is heated to reflux under argon with stirring, and reflux is continued for 50 min. Then, the resulting yellow solution is cooled in an ice bath with stirring to produce a dense precipitate. At ~5°C, the solid (oxalic acid tolylhydrazide) is filtered off and washed with small portions of 250 ml of water. The washings–filtrate combination is extracted with 3 × 200 ml of ethyl acetate. The organic phase is discarded, and the aqueous phase is concentrated under diminished pressure at 50°C, and the resulting syrup is dried in high vacuum at 40°C. The residue (which is crystallizes on seeding) is taken up in 500 ml of ethyl acetate at reflux and filtered hot through a pad of Celite. The filter cake is washed with ~25 ml of ethyl acetate, and the filtrate is allowed to cool to room temperature and refrigerated overnight at ~5°C. The crystals are filtered by suction, washed with 75 ml of cold ethyl acetate in small portions, and dried under high vacuum at room temperature to furnish the desired title lactone (20.7 g, 73.7%), as colorless needles, m.p. 97.5–99°C, $[\alpha]_D^{25}$ −72.07 (c = 0.487 in water).

L-Ascorbic acid (**74.1**) can be *directly degraded* into L-threonic acid (**74.4**) in a radical process by treatment with hydrogen peroxide (Fig. 2.74). The chain shortening proceeds[50–52] via dehydroascorbic acid (**74.2**) and a peroxide (**74.3**) to result in the acid **74.4,** isolated as the calcium or lithium salt. The same descending procedure with the 5,6-O-benzyloxyethylidene acetal of L-ascrobic acid has also been reported.[53]

Preparation of calcium L-threonate (Ca salt of **74.4**)[50] Calcium carbonate (2 g) is added to a solution of L-ascorbic acid (**74.1**; 1.36 g, 10 mmol) in water

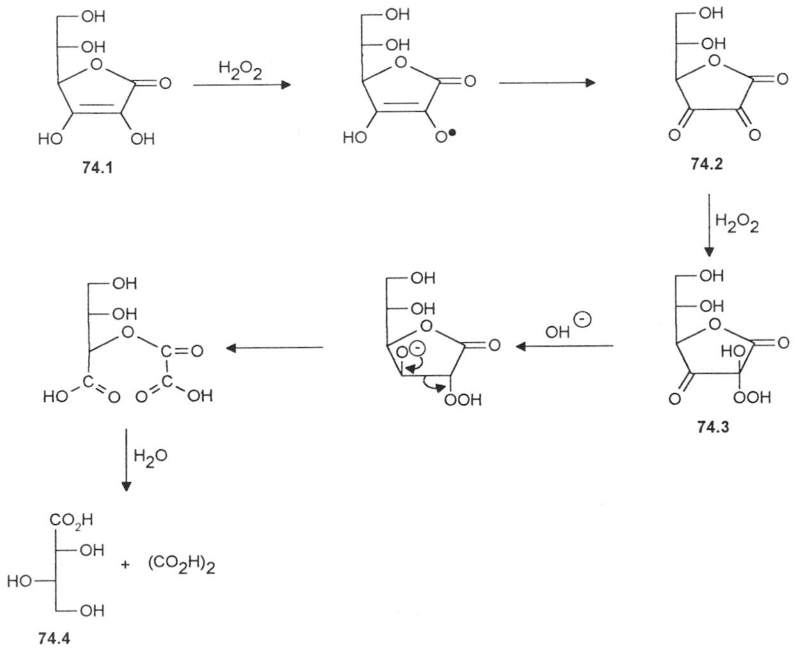

FIGURE 2.74

(25 ml), and the mixture is cooled in an ice bath and shaken gently during the addition of 30% hydrogen peroxide (4 ml) in small portions. The mixture is kept at 30–40°C for 30 min, and then treated with 0.4 g of activated carbon (Norit), and heated on a steam bath to decompose the excess of hydrogen peroxide. When evolution of oxygen has ceased, the hot mixture is filtered, and the filtrate is concentrated under diminished pressure (bath temperature ≤40°C) to ~10 ml. Methanol is added until turbidity, and the microscopic prisms that formed within several hours are filtered, washed with 80% aqueous methanol and air-dried to obtain 1.46 g of the product **74.4**, which is recrystallized from water, $[\alpha]_D^{25}$ +13.8 (c = 1.0 in water).

Preparation of lithium L-threonate (Li salt of 74.4)   A solution of calcium L-threonate, prepared from L-ascorbic acid (**74.1**, 10 mmol) by the procedure described above, is passed through Amberlite IR-120 (H⁺) cation-exchange resin (20 ml), and the resulting solution is neutralized with aqueous 1.0 M lithium hydroxide. Concentration of the solution *in vacuo* produced prisms (1.3 g, 92%), which are recrystallized from water to give the pure title salt, $[\alpha]_D^{25}$ +17 (c = 4.0 in water).

The epimeric D-erythrono-1,4-lactone can be prepared[49] from D-*ara-bino*-ascorbic acid in an analogous manner.

The decarboxylative degradation of ascorbic acid (**75.1**) under acidic conditions leads to other products, but—as shown by Sakurai and Feather[51,52]—dehydroascorbic acid (**75.2**) is an intermediate of this process as well. Under various acidic conditions (at pH 2–8) the degradation products [i.e., 3-deoxy-L-*glycero*-pentos-2-ulose (**75.3**), L-*threo*-pentos-2-ulose (**75.4**), and L-threose] shown in Figure 2.75 can be detected.

Several acetals and ketals of the ascorbic acid have also been degraded[54] by a *ruthenium-catalyzed* oxidation (Fig. 2.76) to furnish optically active glyceric acids. These results have shown that L-glyceric acid derivatives (**76.2**) are obtained from L-ascorbic acid (**76.1**), whereas the degradation of D-isoascorbic acid (**76.3**) leads to the corresponding D-series substances (**76.4**). To accomplish this Ru-catalyzed procedure, water was used without addition of organic cosolvents, and sodium hypochlorite was employed as a stoichiometric oxidant. In order to reduce acid- or base-catalyzed epimerization of the glyceric acid products, the pH was kept close to neutral during these reactions.

The experimental details of the Ru-catalyzed oxidation of *ascorbic acid acetals* and ketals are as follows.

Ruthenium-catalyzed oxidation of acetals and ketals of ascorbic acid (76.1) and isoascorbic acid (76.3)[54]*:general procedure*   To a solution containing 10 mmol of **76.1** or **76.3** in water (25 ml) is added 15 mg of RuO₂-hydrate, (~1 mol%), and the pH is adjusted to 8 with 2 M NaOH. To the stirred solution is then slowly added ~85 ml (0.11 mol) of 10% (~1.2 M) aqueous solution of sodium hypochlorite. The temperature increased to 55–60°C and is kept there by regulating the addition rate and, when necessary, by means of an ice bath. During the reaction the pH is monitored and maintained constant at 8.0 by addition of 2 M NaOH. Usually, the reactions ceased after 40–60 min, as indicated by the appearance of a clear green–yellow color. At the same time pH became constant. The reaction mixture is then cooled to room temperature and the Ru–catalyst extracted with five

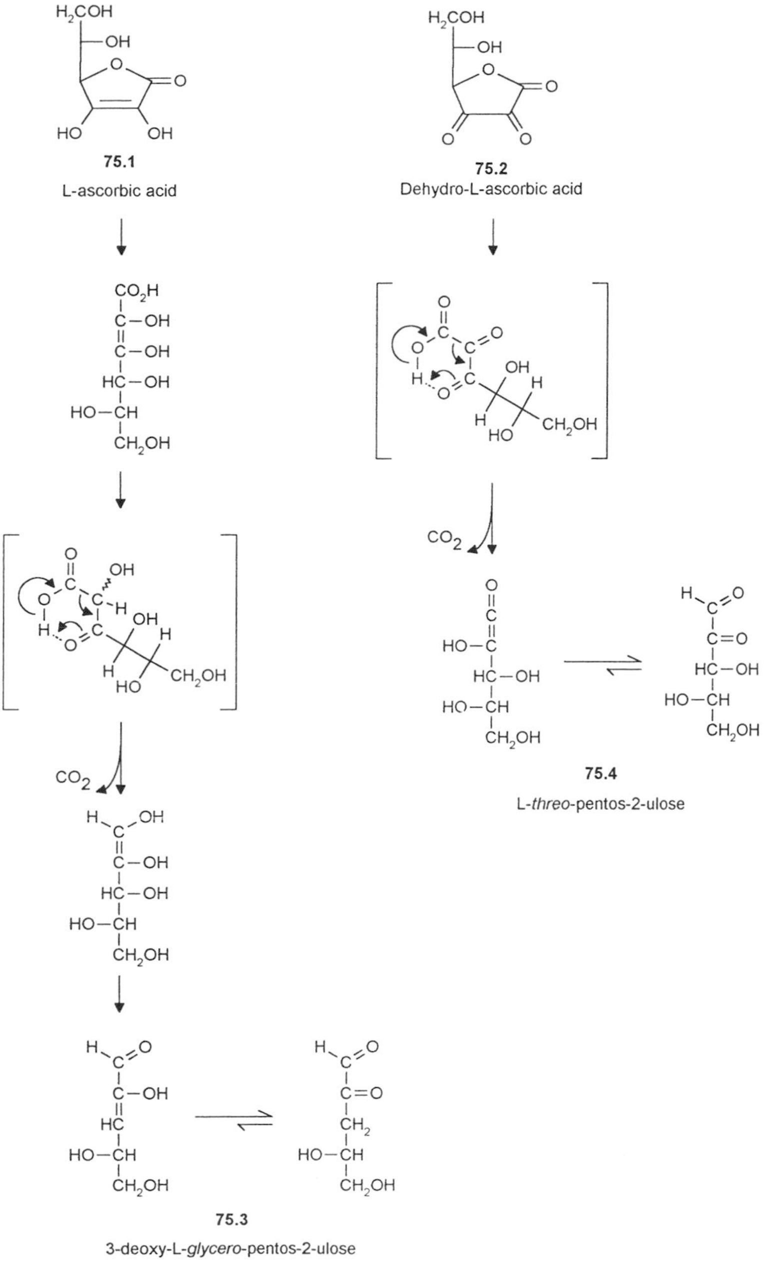

FIGURE 2.75

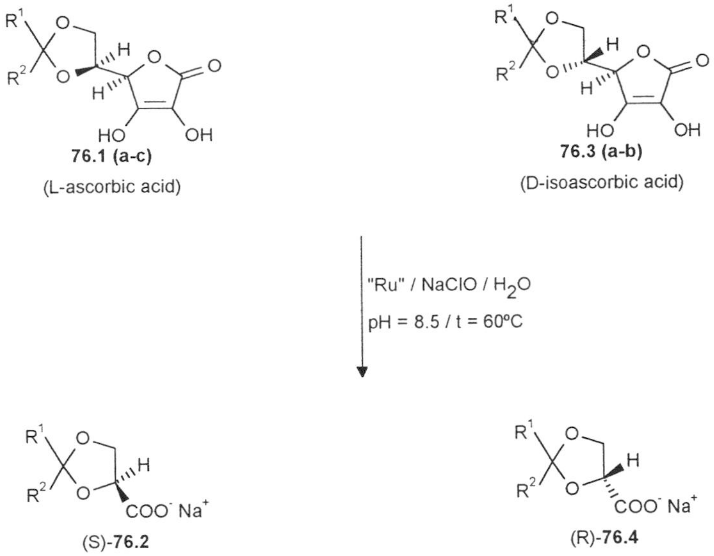

a: $R^1 = R^2 = CH^3$

b: $R^1 = R^2$ = cyclohexyl

c: $R^1 = H, R^2 = Ph$

FIGURE 2.76

5 ml-portions of CCl_4. The aqueous phase is concentrated under reduced pressure and then extracted with 50 ml of refluxing methanol. Inorganic salts are removed by filtration, and on cooling the desired crystalline products precipitate.

(S)-Sodium 2,2-dimethyl-1,3-dioxolane-4-carboxylate: (S)-**76.2a.** By oxidation of 5,6-O-isopropylidene-L-ascorbic acid (**76.1a**). Yield: 87%, $[\alpha]_D^{25}$ −23.4 ($c = 2.0$ in water).

(S)-Sodium spiro[cyclohexane-1,2'-(1,3-dioxolane)]-4'-carboxylate: (S)-**76.2b.** This product was prepared from the L-ascorbic acid ketal **76.1b.** Yield: 87%, $[\alpha]_D^{25}$ −24.3 ($c = 3.0$ in water).

(S)-Sodium 2-phenyl-1,3-dioxolane-4-carboxylate: (S)-**76.2c.** This compound was obtained from the L-ascorbic acid ketal **76.1c.** Yield: 71%.

(R)-Sodium 2,2-dimethyl-1,3-dioxolane-4-carboxylate: (R)-**76.4a,** obtained from the D-isoascorbic acid ketal **76.3a.** Yield: 91%, $[\alpha]_D^{25}$ +22.9 ($c = 2.0$ in water), corresponding to an enantiomeric excess (ee) of >98%.

(R)-Sodium spiro[cyclohexane-1,2'-(1,3-dioxolane)]-4'-carboxylate: (R)-**76.4b,** prepared from the D-isoascorbic acid ketal **76.3b.** Yield: 86%, $[\alpha]_D^{25}$ +25.6 ($c = 3.0$ in water).

REFERENCES TO SECTION 2.4.3

1. *Houben-Weyl, Methoden der Organischen Chemie*, Vol. 11/1, p. 868 (1964); S. Patai, *The Chemistry of the Azido Group*, pp. 397–405. Wiley (Interscience), New York, 1971.

2. R. Bognár, I. Farkas, I. F. Szabó, and D. G. Szabó, *Chem. Ber.* **96,** 689 (1963).
3. R. Bognár, I. Farkas, and I. F. Szabó, *Justus Liebigs Ann. Chem.* **680,** 118 (1964).
4. I. Farkas, I. F. Szabó, and R. Bognár, *Acta Chim. Acad. Sci. Hung.* **59,** 419 (1969).
5. H. Gross and I. Farkas, *Chem. Ber.* **93,** 95 (1960).
6. K. Maurer, *Ber. Dtsch. Chem. Ges.* **62,** 332 (1929).
7. G. O. Aspinall, H. K. Fanous, N. S. Kumar, and V. Puvanesarajah, *Can. J. Chem.* **61,** 1858 (1983); G. O. Aspinall and M. C. Knebl, *Carbohydr. Res.* **157,** 261 (1986).
8. K. Ninomya, T. Shiori, and S. Yamada, *Chem. Pharm. Bull.* **22,** 1398 (1974).
9. K. Ninomya, T. Shioiri, and S. Yamada, *Tetrahedron* **30,** 2151 (1974).
10. N. K. Kochetkov, O. S. Chizov, and A. F. Sviridov, *Izv. Akad. Nauk SSSR, Otd. Khim. Nauk,* p. 2316 (1967); 1920 (1969); *Carbohydr. Res.* **14,** 277 (1970).
11. W. N. Haworth, S. Peat, and J. Whetstone, *J. Chem. Soc.,* p. 1975 (1938).
12. R. A. Weerman, *Recl. Trav. Chim. Pays-Bas* **36,** 16 (1917); **37,** 16 (1938).
13. R. A. Weerman, *Justus Liebigs Ann. Chem.* **401,** 1 (1913).
14. J. C. Irwine and J. Pryde, *J. Chem. Soc.* **125,** 1045 (1924).
15. R. W. Humphreys, J. Pryde, and E. T. Waters, *J. Chem. Soc.,* p. 1298 (1931).
16. A. Borodin, *Justus Liebigs Ann. Chem.* **119,** 121 (1861).
17. H. Hunsdiecker and C. Hunsdiecker, *Ber. Dtsch. Chem. Ges.* **75,** 291 (1942).
18. J. Kleinberg, *Chem. Rev.* **40,** 381 (1947).
19. R. G. Johnson and R. K. Ingham, *Chem. Rev.* **56,** 219 (1956).
20. F. A. H. Rice and A. H. Johnson, *J. Am. Chem. Soc.* **78,** 428 (1956).
21. F. A. H. Rice, *J. Am. Chem. Soc.* **78,** 3173 (1956).
22. S. Hanessian and A. G. Pernet, *Can. J. Chem.* **52,** 1266 (1974).
23. D. H. R. Barton, D. Crich, and W. B. Motherwell, *Tetrahedron* **41,** 3901 (1985).
24. D. H. R. Barton, D. Crich, and G. Kretzschmar, *J. Chem. Soc., Perkin Trans 1,* p. 39 (1986).
25. D. H. R. Barton, D. Bridon, I. Fernandez-Picot, and S. Z. Zard, *Tetrahedron* **43,** 2733 (1987).
26. Y. Wang, G. W. J. Fleet, F. X. Wilson, R. Storer, P. L. Myers, C. J. Wallis, O. Doherty, D. J. Watkin, K. Vogt, D. R. Witty, and J. M. Peach, *Tetrahedron Lett.* **32,** 1675 (1991).
27. G. W. J. Fleet, J. C. Son, J. M. Peach, and T. A. Hamor, *Tetrahedron Lett.* **29,** 1449 (1988).
28. F. X. Wilson, G. W. J. Fleet, D. R. Witty, K. Vogt, Y. Wang, R. Storer, P. L. Myers, and J. C. Wallis, *Tetrahedron: Asymmetry* **1,** 525 (1990); Y. Wang, G. W. J. Fleet, R. Sorer, P. L. Myers, J. C. Allis, O. Doherty, D. J. Watkin, K. Vogt, D. R. Witty, F. X. Wilson, and J. M. Peach, *ibid.* **1,** 527 (1990).
29. B. Giese, B. Carboni, T. Göbel, R. Muhn, and F. Wetterich, *Tetrahedron Lett.* **33,** 2673 (1992).
30. D. H. R. Barton, C. Y. Chern, J. Cs. Jászberényi, and T. Shinada, *Tetrahedron Lett.* **34,** 6505 (1993).
31. R. A. Sheldon and J. K. Kochi, *Org. React. (N.Y.)* **19,** 279 (1972).
32. J. B. Aylward, *Quart. Rev. Chem. Soc.* **25,** 407 (1971).
33. Y. Pocker and B. C. Davis, *J. Am. Chem. Soc.* **95,** 6216 (1973).
34. I. Kitagawa and M. Yosikawa, *Heterocycles* **8,** 783 (1977).
35. I. Kitagawa, A. Yoshikawa, and A. Kadota, *Chem. Pharm. Bull.* **26,** 484 (1978).
36. I. Kitagawa, A. Kadota, and M. Yoshikawa, *Chem. Pharm. Bull.* **26,** 3825 (1978).
37. M. Yoshikawa, Y. Ikeda, H. Kayakiri, and I. Kitagawa, *Heterocycles* **17,** 209 (1982).
38. G. O. Aspinall, H. K. Fanous, N. S. Kumar, and V. Puvanesarayah, *Can. J. Chem.* **59,** 935 (1981).
39. I. Kitagawa, M. Yoshikawa, K. S. Im, and Y. Ikenishi, *Chem. Pharm. Bull.* **25,** 657 (1977).
40. M. Yoshikawa, Y. Ikeda, H. Kayakiri, K. Takenaki, and I. Kitagawa, *Tetrahedron Lett.* **23,** 4717 (1982).
41. M. Yoshikawa, Y. Ikeda, K. Takenaka, M. Torihara, and I. Kitagawa, *Chem. Lett.,* p. 2097 (1984).
42. D. D. Dhavale, E. Tagliavini, C. Trombini, and A. Umani-Ronchi, *J. Org. Chem.* **54,** 4100, (1989); K. Wallimann and A. Vasella, *Helv. Chim. Acta* **73,** 1359 (1990); A. Vasella, and

R. Wyler, *ibid.* **74,** 451 (1991); J. J. Potter and M. von Itzstein, *Carbohydr. Res.* **282,** 181 (1996).

43. M. Shiozaki, *J. Org. Chem.* **56,** 528 (1991).
44. H. K. B. Yu and J. Schwartz, *Tetrahedron Lett.* **33,** 6787, 6791 (1992).
45. C. Neuberg, *Biochem. Z.* **7,** 527 (1907); C. Neuberg and E. Hirschberg, *ibid.* **37,** 327 (1910); V. Jiricny and V. Stanek, *Collect. Czech. Chem. Commun.* **60,** 863 (1995).
46. I. Kitagawa, T. Kamigauchi, H. Ohmori, and M. Yoshikawa, *Chem. Pharm. Bull.* **28,** 3078 (1980).
47. I. Kitagawa, M. Yoshikawa, T. Kamigauchi, K. Shirakawa, and Y. Ikeda, *Chem. Pharm. Bull.* **29,** 2571 (1981).
48. R. Weidenhagen, H. Wegner, K. H. Lung, and L. Nordström, *Ber. Dtsch. Chem. Ges.* **72,** 2010 (1939).
49. N. Cohen, B. L. Baumer, R. J. Lopresti, F. Wong, M. Rosenberger, Y.-Y. Liu, E. Thom, and A. A. Liebman, *J. Am. Chem. Soc.* **105,** 3661 (1983).
50. H. S. Isbell and H. L. Frush, *Carbohydr. Res.* **72,** 301 (1979).
51. T. Kurata and Y. Sakurai, *Agric. Biol. Chem.* **31,** 170 and 177 (1967).
52. M. A. Madson and M. S. Feather, *Carbohydr. Res.* **94,** 183 (1981); D. B. Shin and M. S. Feather, *ibid.* **208,** 246 (1990); R. E. Ireland and D. M. Obrecht, *Helv. Chim. Acta* **69,** 1273 (1986); A. B. Smith, III., G. A. Sulikowski, M. M. Sulikowski, and K. Fujimoto, *J. Am. Chem. Soc.* **114,** 2567 (1992).
53. B. R. Beleau, C. A. Evans, H. L. Allan Tse, H. Jin, D. M. Dixit, and T. S. Mansour, *Tetrahedron Lett.* **33,** 6949 (1992).
54. P. H. J. Carlsen, K. Misund, and J. Roe, *Acta Chem. Scand.* **49,** 297 (1995).

2.4.4. Oxidative Degradation of Aldoses to Aldonic Acids with Chain Shortening

In cold, slightly alkaline solutions, reducing sugars undergo an intramolecular oxido-reduction process (the so-called Lobry de Bruyn–Alberda van Ekenstein rearrangement) permitting the preparation[1-3] of the epimeric sugars. If oxygen is also involved in this rather complicated process, the degradation products of the saccharide employed are obtained,[4] such as when an alkaline cellulose solution is exposed to air ("aging of cellulose").

The main role in this process is attributed to the chain-shortened aldonic acids, and the degradation, proceeding—in principle—via enolate ions (and non-isolated peroxides), leads to the products shown[5] by the integrated reaction scheme illustrated in Figure 2.77.

The schematic pattern of degradation, shown in Figure 2.77 has been experimentally substantiated, which helped elaborate optimum conditions for isolation of the degradation products even on preparative scales.[6-8]

Reducing sugars can be converted into the chain-shortened aldonic acids by elimination of one carbon atom in the form of formic acid. Thus, exposure of the alkalized (KOH) solutions of D-ribose, L-arabinose, or L-xylose to oxygen atmosphere gives the potassium salt of D- and L-erythronic acid or D-threonic acid, respectively. The free acids liberated from the salts can then be converted into the crystalline lactones on high-vacuum distillation. The lactone of L-threonic acid can be conveniently obtained[9] from L-ascorbic acid.

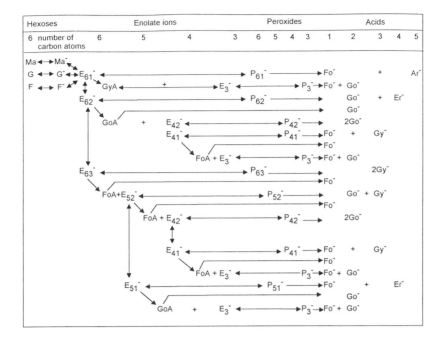

An integral reaction model. E_{ij}^- enolate ion, where i is the number of carbon atoms and j is the position of the double bond between carbon atoms j and j+1; Ma : D-mannose; G : D-glucose: F : D-fructose; GyA : D-glyceraldehyde; FoA: formaldehyde; GoA : glycolaldehyde

FIGURE 2.77

D-Erythronic acid-1,4-lactone[9]   D-Ribose (4.5 g, 30 mmol) and KOH (4.5 g) are dissolved in 100 ml of water each, and both solutions are cooled to 0°C and combined in a hydrogenating vessel, which is shaken in an oxygen atmosphere. After shaking for 120 h at room temperature, the oxygen consumption was (in a particular run) 735 ml (theoretical volume: 720 ml). The pale-yellow solution is filtered through Wofatit KS ion-exchange resin and evaporated *in vacuo* (bath temperature 100°C). The residue is taken up in methanol and subjected, in 1-g portions, to Kugelrohr distillation at 140–160°C. The distillates weigh 0.6 to 0.7 g and crystallize within a few hours. Recrystallization from ethyl acetate, followed by further purification by sublimation at 90°C, gives the pure title lactone with m.p. 101–102°C, $[\alpha]_D$ −71 (c = 0.8 in water).

Further examples for the oxidative degradation of saccharides with the present methodology are shown in Table 2.1.[10–18]

In the case of hexoses, a prolonged reaction time leads to higher yields; when the oxidation proceeds for 3 days, 68% and 64%, respectively, of the potassium salt of D-lyxonic acid and L-erythronic acid are obtained. Oxidation of D-glucose is carried out as described in the following experiment.[19]

TABLE 2.1 Oxidative Degradation of Ketoses and Aldoses in Basic Solution

Starting saccharide	Isolated product	Yield (%)	Ref(s).
L-Fucose	5-Deoxy-L-lyxonic acid	—	10
L-Rhamnose	5-Deoxy-L-arabinoic acid	—	11
D-Fructose-6-phosphate	D-Arabinoic acid 5-phosphate	—	12
D-Galactose	D-Lyxonic acid-1,4-lactone	—	13–15
L-*gluco*-Heptose	Potassium-L-arabinonate L-gluconic acid, and	31	16
	L-erythronic acid brucine salt	14	
Perseulose (L-*galacto*-heptulose)	Potassium-L-galactonate	45	17
Sedoheptulose (D-*altro*-heptulose)	Calcium-L-altronate	—	18

Preparation of the potassium salt of D-arabonic acid from D-glucose[19]   Oxygen gas is passed through a rapidly stirred mixture of water (1.44 liters), methanol (6 liters) and KOH (672 g) with the aid of two glass filters, while a solution of D-glucose (0.72 kg, 4 mol) in water (1.44 liters) is added dropwise over a 7.75 h period. The temperature of the reaction mixture is kept at ~30–35°C. Crystallization of the product begins in ~3 h; after addition of the entire volume of the glucose solution, the mixture is stirred for an additional 30 min, and then the oxygen stream is maintained for 2 days and methanol is added to supplement the volume evaporated. Filtration of the mixture gives 0.62 kg (66%) of potassium D-arabonate.

The yield of the aldonic acids cannot be raised because of parallel, competitive processes[20] such as β-elimination, formose reaction with the produced formaldehyde (see Section 1.1.1) and benzylic acid-rearrangement into saccharinic acid, metasaccharinic acid, and isosaccharinic acid. Detailed studies of the oxidative degradation of D-glucose have shown[21] the presence of a series of by-products formed in the very complex reaction; 2-deoxy-D-*erythro*-pentonic acid, 3,4-dihydroxybutyric acid, β-*gluco*-metasaccharinic acid, 3-deoxy-D-*erythro*-pentonic acid, D-ribonic acid, and D-gluconic acid, as well as D-arabonic acid, D-erythronic acid, glyceric acid, lactic acid, glycolic acid, and formic acid were isolated or detected by ion-exchange chromatography. The degradation of *cellobiose* was also thoroughly monitored,[21] and investigation of the process in dimethylsulfoxide permitted the detection[22] of semidione-type radicals in the reaction mixture.

It has been shown[23] that oxidation of methyl aldopentopyranosides with chromium trioxide is *accompanied by a descending process.* Thus, methyl α,β-D-erythruronic acid is produced from methyl 2,3-*O*-isopropylidene-α,β-D-ribofuranoside. For descending synthesis of 3-deoxy-D-*arabino*-hexone-1,4-lactone, ceric sulfate is employed as the oxidant to allow the isolation[24] of 2-deoxy-D-*erythro*-pentose with 40% yield.

Of the *disaccharides,* the oxidative degradation of *lactose* (the so-called Spengler–Pfannenstiel-reaction) is to be mentioned here, where, under alkaline conditions, potassium O-β-D-galactopyranosyl-$(1 \rightarrow 3)$-D-arabonate is isolated with 75–80% yield as the final product. The rather long reaction time (50 h) could be shortened by the addition of a catalytic amount of anthraquinone-2-sulfonate and hydrogen peroxide. This led, however, to a drastically improved selectivity for the potassium salt. Compared with the alkali-catalyzed oxidative degradation of lactose, an increase of the reaction temperature of the alkaline anthraquinone-2-sulfonate (AMS)-H_2O_2-catalyzed oxidation of lactose did not result in a decrease of selectivity for the potassium salt, the batch time of the process could be decreased from 50 to 1.5 h. Similar results were obtained for the alkaline AMS-H_2O_2-catalyzed oxidative degradation[25] of D-glucose to D-arabonate (see Fig. 2.78 for the AMS-H_2O_2-catalyzed oxidative degradation of carbohydrate endiol anions). The endiol anion is selectively oxidized with AMS to an aldulose. The hydroquinone anion (AMSH$^-$), formed, is reoxidized by oxygen to AMS, which can oxidize a new 1,2-endiol molecule. In the reoxidation of AMSH$^-$, oxygen is reduced to a H_2O_2 anion, and the aldulose, produced in the oxidation of the 1,2-endiol anion with AMS, reacts selectively with the H_2O_2 anion. This gives rise to the corresponding peroxy compounds (see Section 2.4.5.), which can undergo hydroxylation to result in the cleavage of the C-1—C-2 bond.

Whistler *et al.*[26] have described the *preparation of D-arabinose from D-glucose* by a two-stage but single-batch hypochlorite oxidation. Using this convenient procedure, β-*maltose* is converted into 3-O-α-D-glucopyranosyl-α-D-arabinose in 33% yield, and *lactose* (both as monohydrates) is transformed[26] to 3-O-α-D-galactopyranosyl-α-D-arabinose in 38% yield. This convenient procedure is apparently well suited to the degradation of other oligosaccharides, as well.

Oxidative degradation of lactose[26] β-D-Maltose monohydrate (10 g) is dissolved in 200 ml of water, the pH is adjusted to 11 with aqueous NaOH, and to this solution is added 500 ml of 0.334 N sodium hypochlorite (3 mol of oxidant per mole of maltose), which is adjusted to pH 11 with aqueous NaOH and Na_2CO_3. The mixture is kept in the dark at 25°C, and the pH is frequently checked and corrected by adding aqueous NaOH. In 22 h, when ~2.4 mol of NaOCl per mole of maltose is consumed, the solution is brought to pH 5.0 by the addition of aqueous HCl. To this is added 300 ml of 0.266 N NaOCl: 1.4 mol of the original maltose. The mixture is kept in the dark, and the pH is maintained at 4.5–5.0 with aqueous NaOH. After 12 h, when the oxidant is consumed, the solution is neutralized and concentrated under diminished pressure until large amounts of NaCl crystallize. After addition of 3 volumes of methanol, the salt is filtered off and the filtrate is passed through Amberlite IR-120 (H^+) and IR-45 (OH^-) resins. The eluate is filtered through a thin layer of charcoal and concentrated to a syrup *in vacuo.* This crude product is chromatographed on a carbon–Celite column (3 × 170 cm) by eluting with 5% aqueous ethanol, and the eluate is concentrated under reduced pressure to a syrup,

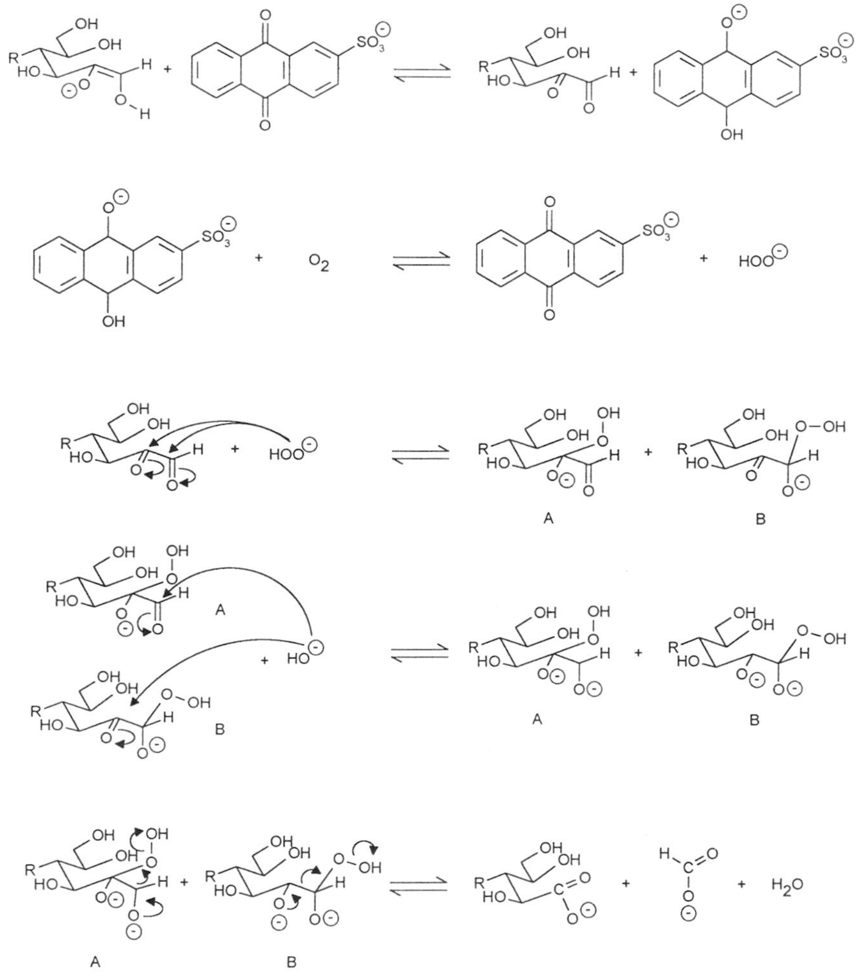

FIGURE 2.78

which is triturated with abs. ethanol to give 2.83 g (32.6%) of an amorphous disaccharide.

Isolation and degradation of 3-O-β-D-galactopyranosyl-α-D-arabinose[26]   A 0.6 g sample of the amorphous disaccharide, obtained as described above, is dissolved in 3 ml of methanol and filtered, and the filtrate is seeded with an authentic sample. On standing at room temperature crystallization proceeds gradually for 2 weeks, at which time the crystals are filtered off, washed with methanol, and dried; m.p. 160–163°C, yield 0.25 g. Recrystallization of the crude product is carried out from a few drops of water by the addition of 20 ml of methanol, filtering the resulting solution, concentrating the filtrate to ~3 ml under reduced pressure, and allowing the solution to stand at room temperature for a week, m. p. 166–168°C, $[\alpha]_D^{25}$ −50.2 → −63.0 (constant after 15 h, $c = 1.0$ in water).

For further identification, the crystalline aniline derivative of the disaccharide is prepared according to Kuhn and Kirschenlohr as follows. The mother liquor separated from the crude crystals of the disaccharide is evaporated to dryness, the residue (0.30 g) is dissolved in methanol (2 ml), 0.10 g of aniline is added, and the mixture is heated under reflux for 1.5 h. After cooling, 0.31 g of N-phenyl-(3-O-β-D-galactopyranosyl)-D-arabinosylamine monohydrate is obtained, m.p. 169–170°C. Recrystallization from 80% aqueous ethanol gives the pure substance with m.p. 170–171°C and $[\alpha]_D$ +34 (c = 0.5 in pyridine); $[\alpha]_D^{25}$ +2.6 → 10.5 (after 1 h) → −44.3 (constant after 10 h, c = 0.42 in water).

In the case of D-*ribo*-hex-3-ulose (**79.1**), the degradation readily proceeds[27] without added reagents in warm water and the fragmentation products shown in Figure 2.79 are produced, and it is interesting that both of the possible products of the two-way process can be obtained. A mechanism that explains the sequence of this degradation reaction starts with the deprotonation of the hydrated acyclic forms of **79.1**, followed by cleavage of the C−C bond. Formic acid formed during the degradation of **79.1** and **79.2** was detected on HPLC analysis of the reaction mixture using the "organic acids column." Glycolaldehyde, expected to form together with D-erythronic acid (**79.3**), has not been observed under the reaction conditions applied.

Preparation of D-ribulose (79.2)[27]   1,2:5,6-Di-O-isopropylidene-α-D-*ribo*-hexo-furanos-3-ulose (2.0 g, 7.2 mmol) in water (25 ml) 5.0 g Dowex 50 W-X8 (100 mesh,

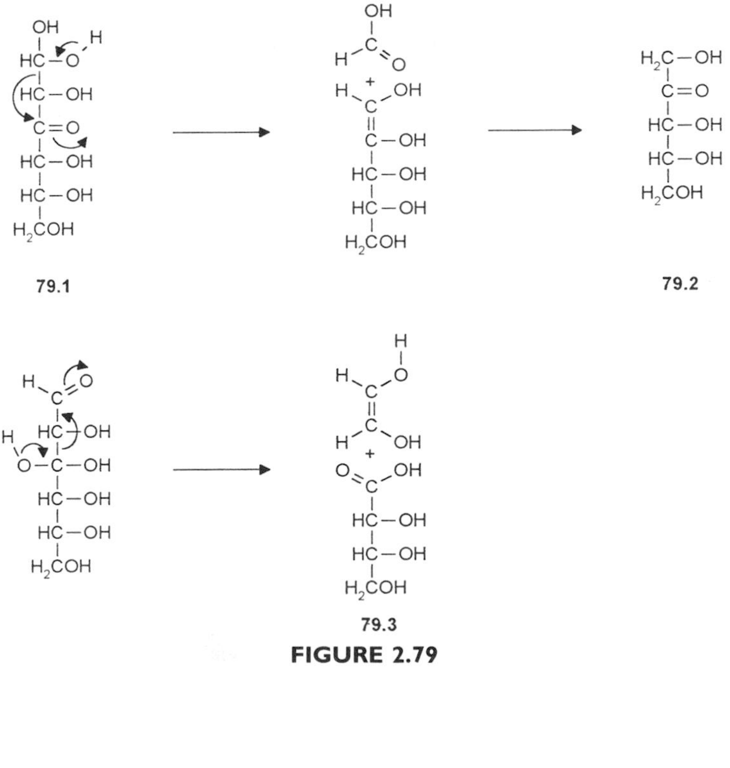

FIGURE 2.79

H$^+$) cation-exchange resin is added, the mixture is stirred, and when deprotection is complete (HPLC), the resin is filtered off and washed with 25 ml of water. HPLC analysis [HPLC conditions: a Bio-Rad 7.8 × 300 mm, HPX87H (organic acids) column with water (0.01 M trifluoroacetic acid as the mobil phase; Bio-Rad 7.8 × 300 mm HPX87C (calcium) or HPX87P (lead) column with water as the mobil phase. The flow rate is 0.6 ml/min in each case, the columns are kept at 60°C in a Spark Holland SpH 99 column oven] shows only one peak for **79.1.** The pH is adjusted to 7, and the subsequent reaction is followed by HPLC. The amount of **79.1** decreases and formic acid and an unknown compound appears (organic acids column). This latter substance co-elutes with D-ribulose on the calcium and lead columns (retention times 24.3 and 37.8 min, respectively). A small amount of D-erythronic acid (**79.3**) is also found (calcium column, retention time 16.8 min). Raising the temperature to 60°C resulted in faster decomposition of **79.1** to D-ribulose and D-erythronic acid. When the amount of D-ribulose does not increase further, the reaction mixture is cooled to room temperature, and the product is isolated by column chromatography on Dowex 50 W-X8 200 resin.

Preparation of D-erythronic acid (79.3)[27] This compound is isolated from the same reaction mixture as for **79.2**, also by column chromatography with Dowex 50 W-X8 (200 mesh), loaded with Ca^{2+}, eluant: water, with a flow rate of 1.0 ml/min. After lyophilization of the fractions with D-erythronic acid, a white powder is obtained and characterized by ^{13}C-NMR. The signals are identical to those of a sample of D-erythronic acid prepared by the hydrolysis of D-erythronolactone at pH 12 for 8 h.

REFERENCES TO SECTION 2.4.4

1. C. A. Lobry de Bruyn and W. Alberda van Ekenstein, *Recl. Trav. Chim. Pays-Bas* **14**, 150, 156, 203 (1896); **16**, 257, 262, 274, 282 (1896); **18**, 147 (1899).
2. W. L. Evans, *Chem. Rev.* **31**, 544 (1942).
3. J. C. Speck, *Adv. Carbohydr. Chem.* **13**, 63 (1958).
4. J. U. Nef, *Justus Liebigs Ann. Chem.* **357**, 296 (1907).
5. H. G. J. De Wilt and B. F. M. Kuster, *Carbohydr. Res.* **19**, 5 (1971).
6. O. Spengler and A. Pfannenstiel, *Z. Wirtschaftsgruppe Zuckerind.* **85**, 546 (1935).
7. J. U. Nef, O. F. Hedenburg, and J. W. E. Glattfeld, *J. Am. Chem. Soc.* **39**, 1638 (1917).
8. J. U. Nef, *Justus Liebigs Ann. Chem.* **357**, 214 (1907); **403**, 204 (1919).
9. E. Hardegger, K. Kreis, and H. ElKhadem, *Helv. Chim. Acta* **34**, 2343 (1951).
10. E. P. Clark, *J. Biol. Chem.* **54**, 70 (1922).
11. C. S. Hudson and I. Chernoff, *J. Am. Chem. Soc.* **40**, 1005 (1918).
12. C. Neuberg and H. Collatz, *Cellul.-Chem.* **17**, 125 (1936).
13. J. U. Nef, *Justus Liebigs Ann. Chem.* **403**, 220, 246 (1914).
14. H. S. Isbell, *J. Res. Natl. Bur. Stand.* **29**, 227 (1942).
15. A. Thompson and M. L. Wolfrom, *J. Am. Chem. Soc.* **68**, 1509 (1946).
16. N. K. Richtmyer and C. S. Hudson, *J. Am. Chem. Soc.* **64**, 1609 (1942).
17. N. K. Richtmyer, R. M. Hann, and C. S. Hudson, *J. Am. Chem. Soc.* **61**, 340 (1939).
18. N. K. Richtmyer, R. M. Hann, and C. S. Hudson, *J. Am. Chem. Soc.* **61**, 343 (1939).
19. W. J. Humphlett, *Carbohydr. Res.* **4**, 157 (1967).
20. J. M. Brijn, A. P. G. Kieboom, H. van Bekkum, and W. P. van der Poel, *Sugar Technol. Rev.* **13**, 21 (1986).
21. O. Samuelsson and L. Thede, *Acta Chem. Scand.* **22**, 1913 (1986).
22. P. Calle, A. Sanchez, and C. Sieiro, *J. Chem. Soc., Perkin Trans 2,* p. 1181 (1990).

23. S. M. Ali, K. Ramesh, and R. T. Borchardt, *Tetrahedron Lett.* **31,** 1509 (1990).
24. R. M. de Lederkremer and L. F. Sala, *Carbohydr. Res.* **40,** 385 (1975).
25. H. E. J. Hendriks, B. F. M. Kuster, and G. B. Marin, *Carbohydr. Res.* **214,** 71 (1991).
26. R. L. Whistler and R. Schweiger, *J. Am. Chem. Soc.* **81,** 5190 (1959); R. L. Whistler and K. Yagi, *J. Org. Chem.* **26,** 1050 (1961).
27. D. de Wit, F. van Rantwijk, L. Maat, and A. P. G. Kieboom, *Recl. Trav. Chim. Pays-Bas* **110,** 271 (1991).

2.4.5. Degradation of Peroxide Derivatives of Saccharides

2.4.5.1. Descending Synthesis of Sugar-Derived 1-Phenylazohydroperoxides

Simple hydrazones carrying hydrogens at the nitrogen atom can be transformed by oxygen into substituted alkylhydroperoxides.[1,2] The sugar-derived analogs of these peroxides suffer fragmentation: attempted *O*-deacetylation with sodium methoxide gives rise to an aldose, *shortened by one carbon* atom, and additional products as shown in Figure 2.80.

A similar degradation of L-*manno*-1-phenylazo-2,3,4,5-tetrahydroxy-hexylhydroperoxide readily gave[3] 5-deoxy-L-arabinose. A slight modification of the reaction conditions involves[4] treatment of unprotected aldose arylhydrazones with hydrogen peroxide in the presence of molybdate ions in a single step. This descending process *works only with acyclic hydrazones;* splitting products are formed exclusively from the cyclic 1-glycosyl-2-arylhydrazones. D-Galactose-(2,5-dichlorophenylhydrazone) was employed for the preparation of D-lyxose, and according to this principle, D-(U-^{14}C)-arabinose was obtained[5] from D-(U-^{14}C)-glucose. Descending synthesis of the 4-nitrophenylhydrazones of maltose, cellobiose, and lactose with the

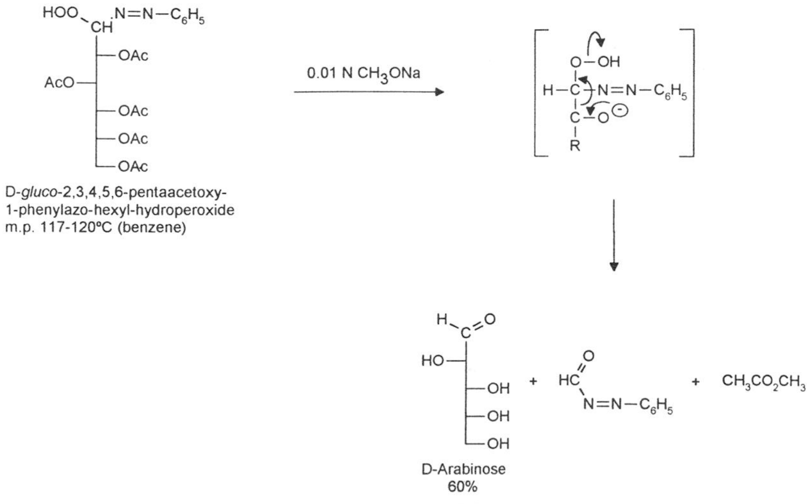

D-*gluco*-2,3,4,5,6-pentaacetoxy-
1-phenylazo-hexyl-hydroperoxide
m.p. 117-120°C (benzene)

D-Arabinose
60%

FIGURE 2.80

preceding methodology gave rise[6] to 3-*O*-α-D-glucopyranosyl-D-arabinose, 3-*O*-β-D-glucopyranosyl-D-arabinose, and 3-*O*-β-D-galactopyranosyl-D-arabinose, respectively, with 15–18% yield.

2.4.5.2. Degradation of Saccharides by Fragmentation of Acylated Peroxyglycosides

Treatment of *tert*-butylperoxyglycosides (such as **81.1**)—available by the usual methods for glycosylation—with sodium methoxide readily furnishes the *one-carbon-atom-shorter* aldose, together with *tert*-butanol and methyl formate, as shown in Figure 2.81. Thus, in the case of *O*-acylated *tert*-butylperoxyglycoside, besides *O*-deacylation two cleavage reactions proceed[7]: splitting of the C-1—C-2 bond and the polar cleavage of the O—O bonding (see Fig. 2.81).

The following *experimental details* cover the preparation of *tert*-butylperoxyglycosides, as well as their degradation, according to the work of Schulz.[7]

General procedures for the synthesis of tert-*butylperoxyglycosides*[7]

A. The silver carbonate method[7] (All work carried out with peroxy compounds should be include strict safety precautions; generally required: safety glasses and a safety glass wall, etc.!) To a solution of *tert*-butylhydroperoxide (50 mmol) in abs. benzene (30 ml) is added freshly precipitated, dry silver carbonate (15 mmol) and Na₂SO₄ (2 g), followed by the acylated glycosyl halide (10 mmol). The reaction mixture is stirred at room temperature for 5–7 h, the insolubles are filtered off, and the filtrate is washed three times with water and then concentrated under reduced pressure. The residue is dissolved in a small volume of methanol, water is added until turbulence, and scrubbing of the material results in crystallization of the glycoside, which is filtered off after overnight refrigeration.

B. The silver perchlorate method[7] A solution of the acylated glycosyl halide (6 mmol) in abs. benzene (25 ml) is dried over Drierite for a few hours, and after filtration, *tert*-butylhydroperoxide (12 mmol) and a solution of silver perchlorate (7 mmol) in benzene (50 ml) are added with external ice cooling. After 2 min, 7 mmol of pyridine or *s*-collidine is added, the mixture is refrigerated for 2 h, and filtered. The organic layer is washed with water (4 × 10 ml) until no silver ions can be detected and the solution is neutral. It is then decolorized with charcoal,

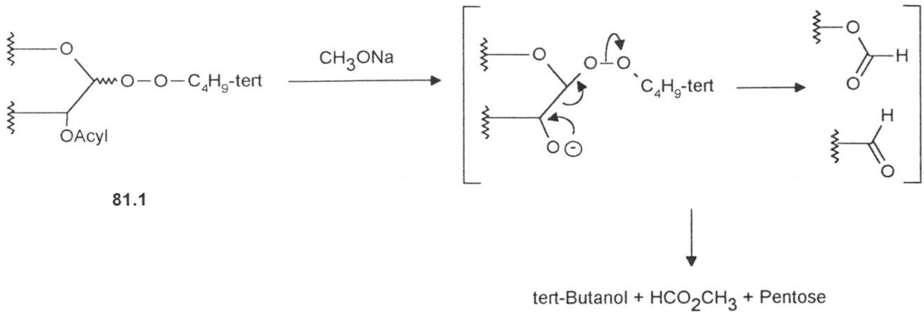

81.1

tert-Butanol + HCO₂CH₃ + Pentose

FIGURE 2.81

dried over Na_2SO_4, and the solvent is distilled off and the residue is worked up as described in method *A*.

General procedure for the degradation of acylated tert-*butylperoxyglycosides*[7]   A solution of the glycoside (4 mmol) prepared by methods A or B in 50 ml of 0.005 to 0.1 N methanolic sodium methoxide is kept at room temperature until no more starting material is detected by TLC (~1 day; in the case of hardly soluble materials, dichloromethane should be added, and maintaining the mixture at 40–50°C the reaction time may be considerably shortened). After treating the reaction mixture with a cation-exchange resin, the volatile substances (methanol, methyl acetate, methyl formate, and *tert*-butanol) are removed by evaporation under diminished pressure, to leave the chromatographically homogeneous, chain-shortened aldoses displayed in Table 2.2.

Analogous descending synthesis of ketosides has also been thoroughly investigated[8] and revealed[8] the formation of aldoses shortened *with two carbon atoms* in the chain. In this manner, D-erythrose (**82.2**) and methyl glycolate (**82.3**) are produced from *tert*-butylperoxy 1,3,4,5-tetra-*O*-acetyl-β-D-fructopyranoside (**82.1**) (Fig. 2.82).

On peroxidation of aldose phenylhydrazones by exposure of air in KOH solution (see Fig. 2.83), *N*-aryl-aldonohydrazido-1,4-lactones are ob-

TABLE 2.2   Chain-Shortened Aldoses from *tert*-butylperoxyglycosides

	Yield (%)				
Synthesized acetylated	**Method**		**M.p.**		**Yield**
tert-**butylglycoside**	**A**	**B**	**(°C)**	**Degradation product**	**(%)**
2,3,4,6-Tetra-*O*-acetyl-β-*tert*-butylperoxy-D-glucopyranoside	50	58	119–120	D-Arabinose	~100
2,3,4,6-Tetra-*O*-acetyl-β-*tert*-butylperoxy-D-galactopyranoside	24	50	120–121	D-Lyxose	98
2,3,4-Tri-*O*-acetyl-β-*tert*-butylperoxy-D-xylopyranoside	37	70	117–118	D-Threose	97
2,3,4-Tri-*O*-acetyl-β-*tert*-butylperoxy-L-arabinopyranoside	—	90	Syrup	L-Erythrose	—
2,3,4-Tri-*O*-benzoyl-α-*tert*-butylperoxy-L-arabinofuranoside	—	85	Syrup	L-Erythrose	—
2,3,4-Tri-*O*-benzoyl-α-*tert*-butylperoxy-L-arabinopyranoside	28	85	175–176	L-Erythrose	95
2,3,4,6-Tetra-*O*-acetyl-α-*tert*-butylperoxy-D-mannopyranoside	—	49	71–73	D-Arabinose	94
2,3,4-Tri-*O*-acetyl-α-*tert*-butylperoxy-L-rhamnopyranoside	—	52	75	5-Deoxy-L-arabinose	99

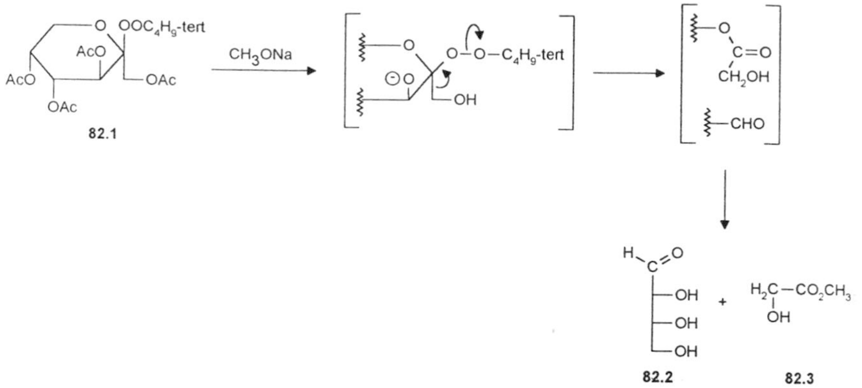

FIGURE 2.82

tained.[9-11] The lack of degradation in these cases is not convincingly explained as yet.

A further descending synthesis of sugar-derived peroxides has been reported by Lichtenthaler *et al.*[12] (Fig. 2.84). Thus, the boron trifluoride–catalyzed peracid oxidation of glycal or hydroxyglycal esters (such as **84.1**) is an *efficient one-pot conversion*, involving initial Lewis acid–induced removal of the allylic acyloxy group, subsequent seizure of the allyloxycarbon-

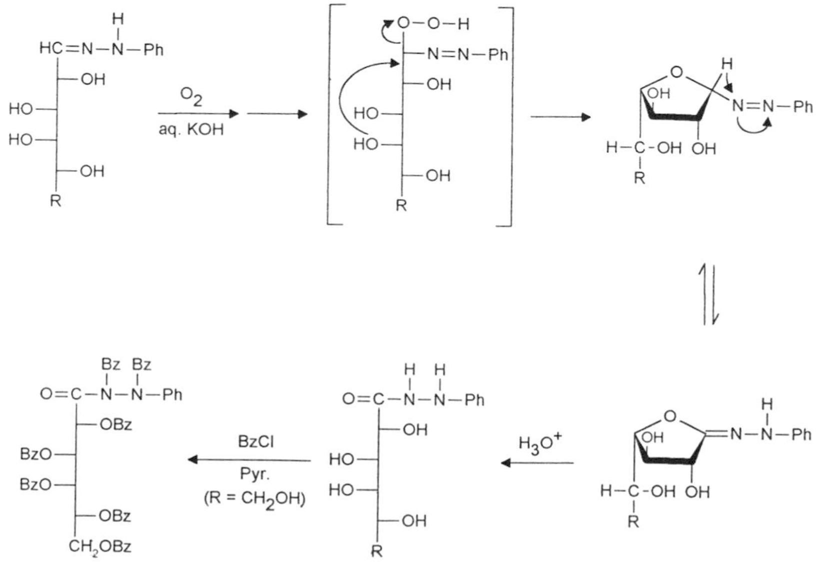

FIGURE 2.83

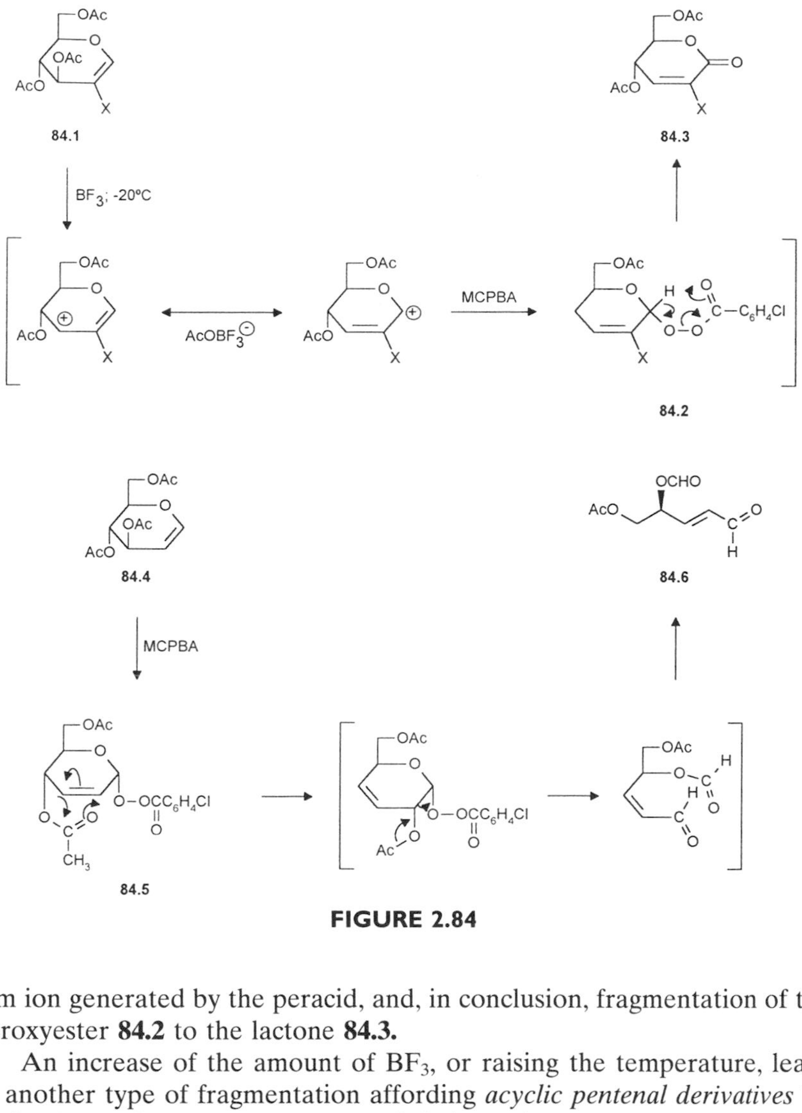

FIGURE 2.84

ium ion generated by the peracid, and, in conclusion, fragmentation of the peroxyester **84.2** to the lactone **84.3**.

An increase of the amount of BF_3, or raising the temperature, leads to another type of fragmentation affording *acyclic pentenal derivatives* by chain shortening. As an example, $(+)$-$(2E,4S)$-5-acetoxy-4-formyloxy-2-pentenal (**84.6**) is obtained[12] from 3,4,6-tri-O-acetyl-D-glucal (**84.4**). The experimental details for this reaction are as follows.

> *General procedure for the boron trifuoride–catalyzed oxidation of glycal esters*[12] A solution of 3.7 g (18 mmol) of 85% anhydrous 3-chloroperoxybenzoic acid in dry dichloromethane (50 ml) is cooled to −50°C and added to a stirred, cold (−20°C) solution of the respective glycal ester (15 mmol) in dichloromethane (50 ml). Subsequently, BF_3-Et_2O (1 ml, 7.9 mmol or less, if a violet color appears before) is added dropwise, and stirring is continued at −20°C for another 15 min. The cold reaction mixture is poured into saturated aqueous $NaHCO_3$ solution

(50 ml) containing 10 to 20 mg of $Na_2S_2O_3$, the organic phase is removed, and the aqueous layer is extracted with dichloromethane (2 × 50 ml). The organic extract is concentrated to a syrup, which occasionally crystallizes to a mixture of the product and 3-chlorobenzoic acid. The latter is removed by dissolution in chloroform (50 ml), repeated washing with 2 N $NaHCO_3$ solution (3 × 30 ml), and water (30 ml). Following drying (Na_2SO_4) and evaporation of the solvent, the residual crude product is purified by means of column chromatography or recrystallization.

Preparation of (+)-(2E,4S)-5-acetoxy-4-formyloxy-2-pentenal (84.6) from the glycal 84.4[12]   When 3,4,6-tri-*O*-acetyl-D-glucal (**84.4**, 1.0 g) is subjected to the oxidation procedure described above, and if the reaction mixture resulting after 15 min at −20°C is *not* immediately quenched by aqueous $NaHCO_3$, but is allowed to warm to room temperature, a deep-violet solution is obtained. According to ^{1}H-NMR, it contains only traces of the ene-lactone **84.3** (X = H) and the perester **84.5**, but to >90% the pentenal **84.6**, as evidenced by the low field aldehyde and formyl protons. Workup after 1 h at 25°C as described in the preceding general procedure, and purification of the crude syrupy residue by elution from a silicagel column (1.5 × 30 cm) with 2:1 CCl_4–EtOAc gives 310 mg (46%) of syrupy **84.6**, $[\alpha]_D^{20}$ +38.3 (*c* = 0.9 in chloroform).

A new field of the chain shortening of aldoses *by rupture of the C-1 — C-2 bond* with hypervalent ioidine reagents has been reported recently by Spanish[13] and Japanese[14] researchers. Thus, treatment of aldoses carrying free anomeric hydroxyl group with (diacetoxyiodo)benzene, a reagent known to facilitate β-fragmentation reactions, gives rise to a descent of the educt with one carbon atom (Fig. 2.85), and C_4 and C_5 chiral blocks are produced, respectively, from aldopentoses and aldohexoses. During oxidation, first the ring-oxygen atom is formylated (**85.1 → 85.2**), followed by hydrolysis of this ester on the action of an alcohol and acid to produce the chain-shortened glycoside **85.3** and the respective benzyl glycoside (**85.4**), as the by-product.

As expected, from the C-2 epimeric sugars (such as **85.5** and **85.6**), the same descended aldose (**85.7**) is obtained. A general procedure for the execution of this reaction is given below, according to the work of the Japanese group.[14]

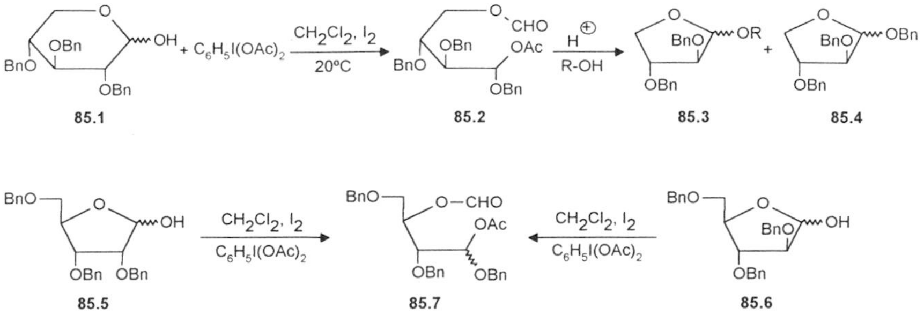

FIGURE 2.85

General procedure for the oxidative descending synthesis of aldoses with hypervalent iodine reagents[14] A mixture of the 1-OH sugar (0.1 mmol), (diacetoxyiodo)benzene (64.3 mg, 0.2 mmol), and iodine (5.4 mg, 0.02 mmol) in dichloromethane (2 ml) is stirred at room temperature for 2 h. The resulting light-reddish–purple suspension is added to an aqueous solution of $Na_2S_2O_3$, and the crude product is extracted with dichloromethane. The organic layer is washed with water and dried over $MgSO_4$, and evaporation of the solvent leaves a residue that is purified by preparative layer chromatography on silicagel.

REFERENCES TO SECTION 2.4.5

1. *Houben-Weyl, Methoden der Organischen Chemie*, Vol. E13/1, p. 565 (1985).
2. I. Dyong, *Z. Naturforsch. B: Anorg. Chem., Org. Chem., Biochem., Biophys., Biol.* **23B,** 750 (1968).
3. M. Schulz and L. Somogyi, *Angew. Chem.* **79,** 145 (1967); *Angew. Chem., Int. Ed. Engl.* **6,** 168 (1967).
4. L. Petrus, V. Bílik, K. Linek, and M. Misiková, *Chem. Zvesti* **32,** 701 (1978).
5. V. Bílik, P. Biely, and M. Matulová, *Chem. Zvesti,* **33,** 782 (1979).
6. V. Bílik, J. Alföldi, and R. Sandtnerová, *Chem. Zvesti,* **34,** 829 (1981).
7. M. Schulz, H.-F. Boeden, and P. Berlin, *Justus Liebigs Ann. Chem.* **703,** 190 (1967).
8. M. Schulz, H.-F. Boeden, and E. Gründemann, *Z. Chem.* **7,** 14 (1967).
9. H. S. El Khadem, A. Crossman, Jr., D. Bensen, and A. Allen, *J. Org. Chem.* **56,** 6946 (1991).
10. H. S. El Khadem, A. Crossman, Jr., and D. Bensen, *Carbohydr. Res.* **212,** C9 (1991).
11. H. S. El Khadem and A. Crossman, Jr., *Carbohydr. Res.* **228,** 451 (1992).
12. F. W. Lichtenthaler, S. Rönninger, and P. Jarglis, *Justus Liebigs Ann. Chem.,* p. 1153 (1989).
13. P. de Armas, C. G. Francisco, and E. Suárez, *Angew. Chem.* **104,** 746 (1992); *Angew. Chem., Int. Ed. Engl.* **31,** 772 (1992); *J. Am. Chem. Soc.* **115,** 8865 (1993); C. G. Francisco, C. C. González, and E. Suárez, *Tetrahedron Lett.* **37,** 1687 (1996).
14. J. Inanaga, Y. Sugimoto, Y. Yokoyama, and T. Hanamoto, *Tetrahedron Lett.* **33,** 8108 (1992).

2.4.6. Chain Shortening of Saccharides by Means of Photochemical Methods

The preparative procedures reported and successfully used for photochemical degradation of sugars are divided into two groups in this section: light-exposure-induced and metal-ion-catalyzed reactions.

2.4.6.1. Light-Induced Degradation of Saccharides

On exposure to light, cyclic aldose oximes (such as **86.1**) undergo photochemical degradation, and, through the nonisolated iminolactone (**86.2**), the aldose (**86.3**) *shortened by one carbon atom* is produced[1] (Fig. 2.86). Since the loss of hydrogen cyanide does not occur in each case, the iminolactone (**86.2**) may be converted into the acetylated aldononitrile (such as **86.4**) without chain shortening by means of acetylation and subsequent dehydration. On storage for a longer time the iminolactone may also loose HCN to allow isolation of the degraded aldose.

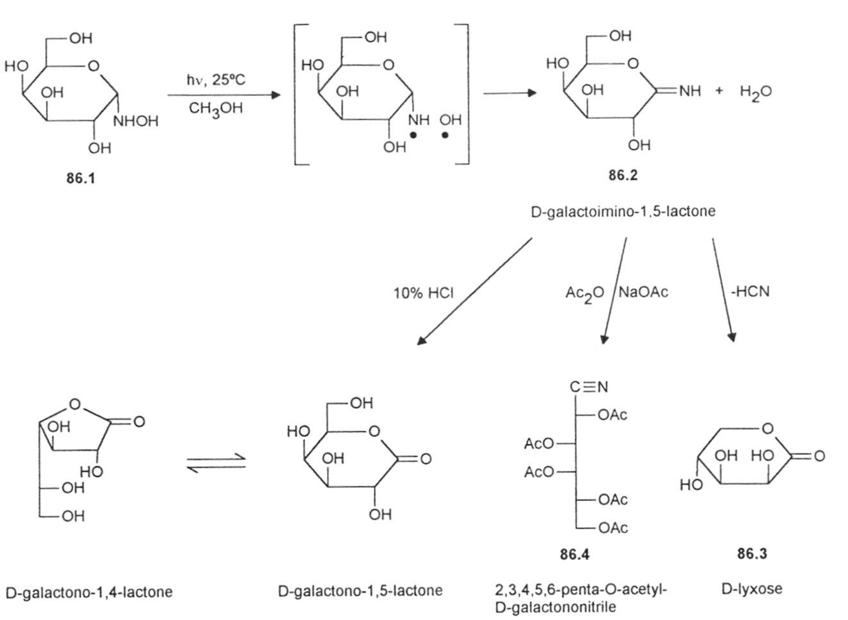

FIGURE 2.86

The degradation products formed by irradiation of D-galactose-oxime (**86.1**) are shown in Figure 2.86. D-Glucose-oxime and the pentose–oximes are much less susceptible to an analogous descending synthesis, and the yield of the iminolactones are in the range of 0–23%.

Horton has observed[2] that sodium 2-deoxy-2-(2,4-dinitroanilino)-D-gluconate (**87.1**) is degraded to D-arabinose (**87.2**) on exposure to light (Fig. 2.87), but the corresponding aminoalditol (**87.3**) does not change and can be recovered from the reaction mixture. This difference in the behavior of the two substances *allows diagnostic differentiation* between alditols and aldoses.

*Preparation and photochemical degradation of sodium 2-deoxy-2-(2,4-dinitroanil-ino)-D-gluconate (**87.1**)*[2] To a solution of 2-amino-2-deoxy-D-gluconic acid (2.6 g) and NaHCO$_3$ (4.66 g) in water (60 ml), is added a solution of 1-fluoro-2,4-dinitrobenzene (4.96 g) in ethanol (60 ml), and the mixture is stirred at room temperature for 3 h. It is then conecntrated *in vacuo* to remove ethanol, and the aqueous solution is washed three times with ether to remove excess of 1-fluoro-2,4-dinitrobenzene. The pH of the aqueous solution is adjusted to 7 by adding 1 M HCl, and then evaporated below 35°C, and the residue is dried in a vacuum desiccator. It is then extracted with methanol (50 ml), and the extract is filtered from the insoluble salts. The extract is concentrated, the residue is dried, reextracted with methanol and filtered, again, from the insolubles. Evaporation of the filtrate gives the crude, syrupy gluconate **87.1** in quantitative yield. TLC of this substance (3:2 chloroform–methanol) shows the presence of the yellow, major component ($R_f = 0.2$) and minor, yellow components with $R_f = 0.6$ and 0.8. The major compo-

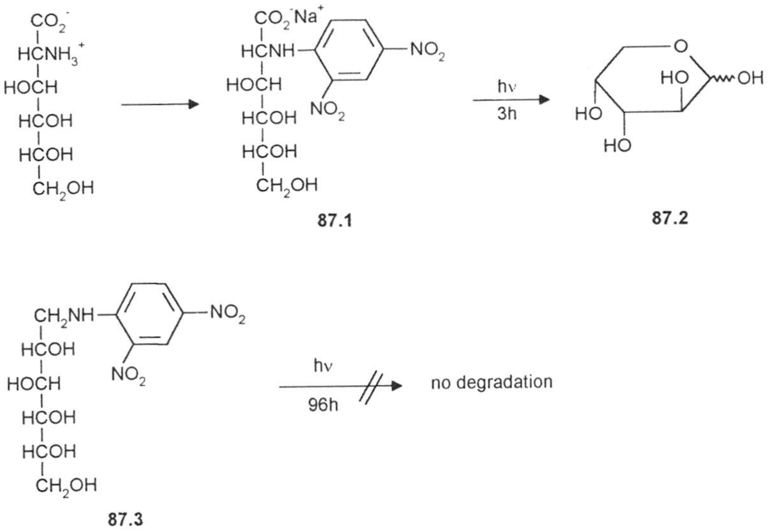

FIGURE 2.87

nent (320 mg) is isolated by preparative TLC to give 219 mg (68%) of the pure product with $[\alpha]_D^{21}$ -44 ± 2 ($c = 0.8$ in water).

Isolation of D-arabinose (87.2)[2]   A solution of the gluconate **87.1** (315 mg) in water (150 ml) is photolyzed for 6 h at room temperature under nitrogen. The solution is extracted with ethyl acetate to remove a yellow material (79 mg), and the colorless aqueous phase is concentrated to ~20 ml. The solution is passed through a column of Amberlite MB-3 mixed-bed resin (15 ml), and the column is washed with 200 ml of water. Evaporation of the combined filtrate gives pure D-arabinose (**87.2**), yield: 65 mg (52%). Crystallization from aqueous methanol affords the β anomer with m.p. 158–159°C, $[\alpha]_D^{21}$ -103 (equilibrium; $c = 1.0$ in water).

Glycosyl azides suffer an analogous light-induced degradation. From 1,2-trans-1-azidoaldoses, previously investigated,[3] the one-carbon-shorter aldoses are produced[4,5] via the non-isolated iminolactone and loss of HCN. On the contrary, ω-azidosaccharides (**88.1**) are transformed[6] into the aldehydes **88.2** on irradiation (see Fig. 2.88). A general procedure[5] for the photochemical descending of glycosyl azides is as follows.

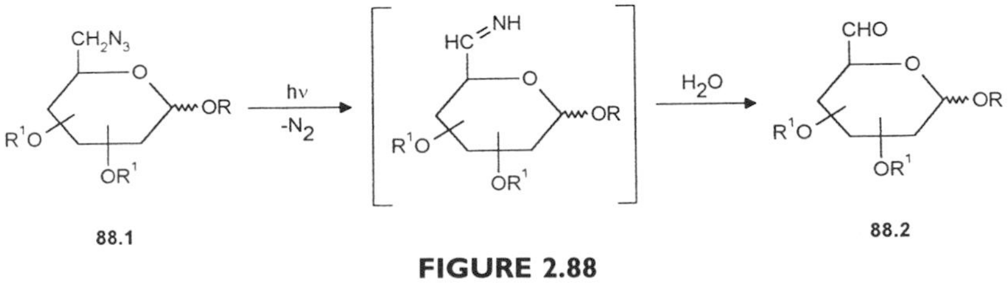

FIGURE 2.88

General procedure for the irradiation of glycosyl azides; preparation of L-arabinose from β-D-glucopyranosyl azide[5]   β-D-Glucopyranosyl azide (1.5 g, 0.73 mmol) is dissolved in dry methanol (65 ml), and the solution is irradiated for 4 h under nitrogen in a borosilicate glass reaction vessel in which is mounted a 450-W Hanovia medium-pressure mercury-arc lamp (Catalog No. 679A-36) contained in a water-cooled immersion well, fitted with a Vycor 7010 filter sleeve. After 4 h, TLC (3:1 ethanol–benzene) shows that all the starting material has been consumed and the presence of a slower-moving component and a nonmigrating component; the mixture is concentrated and the former component isolated by column chromatography to furnish crude L-arabinose (0.51 g, 47%). After recrystallization form ethanol the pure product has m.p. 154–156°C, $[\alpha]_D$ −105 (c = 1.0 in water). A commercial sample of L-arabinose has m.p. 156-160°C, $[\alpha]_D$ +105.1 ± 0.3 (c = 3.0 in water).

Further Photochemical Degradation Reactions

Educt	Product	Yield (%)
β-D-Galactopyranosyl azide	D-Lyxose	65
α-D-Mannopyranosyl azide	D-Arabinose	60
β-Cellobiosyl azide	β-D-Glucopyranosyl-(1 → 3)-D-arabinose	53
β-Lactosyl azide	β-D-Galactopyranosyl-(1 → 3)-D-arabinose	51

It is interesting to note that neither α-L-arabinopyranosyl azide, β-D-ribofuranosyl azide, β-maltosyl azide, 2-deoxy-β-D-*arabino*-hexopyranosyl azide, nor 2-*O*-methyl-β-D-glucopyranosyl azide could be degraded by an analogous irradiation procedure.[5]

2.4.6.2. Metal-Ion-Catalyzed Photochemical Descending Syntheses of Aldoses

When an oxygen-purged pyridine solution of an aldose (**89.1**) is irradiated in the presence of ferric(III) salts, a *fragmentation reaction* occurs (Fig. 2.89), resulting in the formate ester (**89.2**) of the one-carbon-descended aldose, and the process is formally similar to that of the lead tetraacetate oxidation of free, reducing saccharides (see Section 2.4.2). As the by-products, the two-carbon-descended aldose-3-*O*-formates are also present[7–10] in the reaction mixtures.

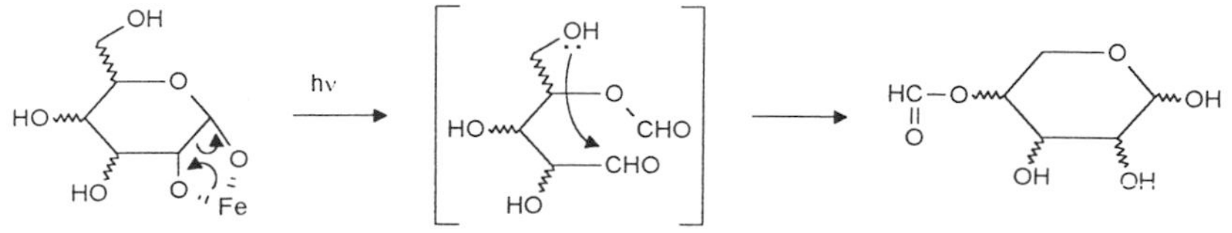

89.1   **89.2**

FIGURE 2.89

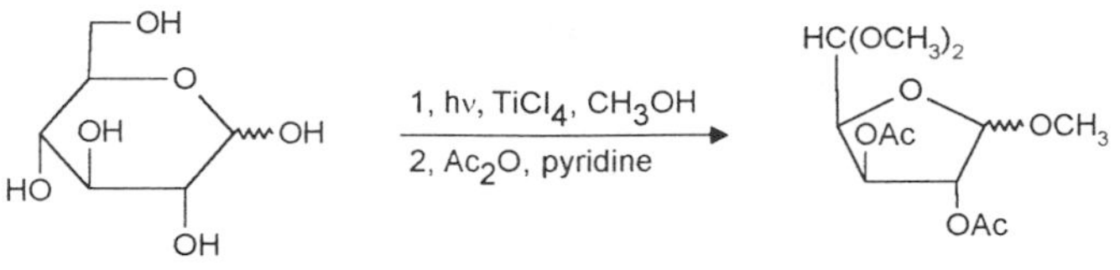

FIGURE 2.90

Degradation of D-mannose to 1,2,3-tri-O-acetyl-D-arabinopyranose[10]   In a Pyrex vessel a mixture of D-mannose (9 g, 50 mmol), pyridine (900 ml), and ferric(III)-trifluoromethanesulfonate (0.25 g, 0.5 mmol) is irradiated with a water-current-cooled high-pressure mercury lamp (2 kW, type Sen SL-2000) for 8 h, by passing oxygen through the reaction mixture. Then acetic anhydride (70 ml) is added, and the mixture is stirred for 14 h. Following evaporation (bath temperature ≤35°C), the residue is partitioned between ether and saturated aqueous NaHCO₃ (100–100 ml). The separated aqueous layer is extracted with ether (2 × 100 ml), and the combined organic phase is dried over MgSO₄. The solvent is distilled off under diminished pressure, and the residue is treated with a solution of AlCl₃ (0.41 g) and water (25 ml) in methanol (500 ml). After stirring for 36 h, the mixture is evaporated *in vacuo,* and taken up with 50 ml of water. The resulting mixture is extracted with dichloromethane, the organic phase is dried over MgSO₄, and the solvent is removed by evaporation. Chromatographic purification of the residue (eluant: ether) gives 3.26 g (24%) of 1,2,3-tri-*O*-acetyl-D-arabinose, as an anomeric mixture, b.p. 148–150°C (38.2 Pa).

During the analogous transformation of D-fructose, *reaction-kinetic studies* have also been carried out[8] to investigate the process in detail. Formation of the product of this reaction, D-erythrose (formed in 80% yield), on the irradiation of D-glucose and D-mannose in pyridine has also been obsereved. The maximum yield was found[8] at 300–350-nm wavelength.

Photooxidation of aldoses in the presence of *titanium tetrachloride* leads[11] to pentodialdoses by cleavage of the C-5 — C-6 bond. In this descending process the role of the added reagent is associated with an electron transfer and, for example, from D-glucose (**90.1**) an anomeric mixture of D-xylos(1,4)ulose dimethylacetal (**90.2**) is produced with 85% yield (Fig. 2.90). With D-mannose and D-galactose the analogous chain shortening can be executed with 50% and 30% yield, respectively.

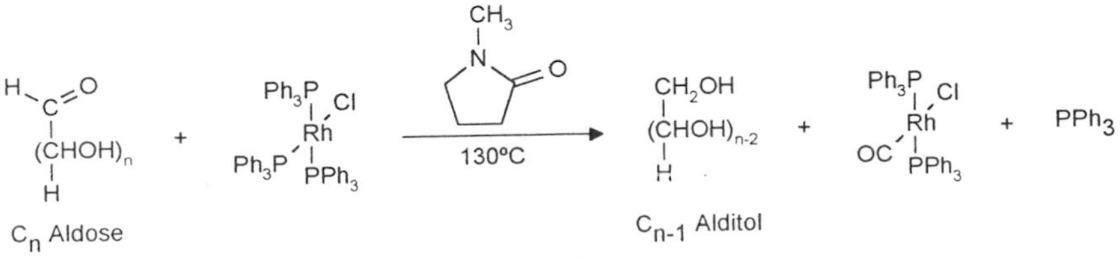

FIGURE 2.91

TABLE 2.3 **Decarbonylation of C_n Aldoses to C_{n-1} Alditols by Chlorotris(triphenylphosphine)rhodium(I)**

Aldose	n	Time (h)	Alditol	Yields (%)
A. Simple Aldoses				
Glucoheptose	7	<3.5	Glucitol	88
Glucose	6	8	Arabitol	88
Allose	6	<4.5	Ribitol	68 (50)
Arabinose	5	3	Erythritol	86 (87)
Xylose	5	<7	Threitol	81 (76)
Erythrose	4	2.5	Glycerol	95
Glyceraldehyde	3	0.5	Ethyleneglycol	95
Glycolaldehyde	2	0.3	Methanol	85
B. Deoxyaldoses				
2-Deoxyglucose	6	2	1-Deoxyarabitol	91 (83)
6-Deoxygalactose	6	6	1-Deoxyarabitol	79
2-Deoxygalactose	6	2	5-Deoxyarabitol	89 (69)
6-Deoxyglucose	6	7	5-Deoxyarabitol	76
6-Deoxymannose	6	4	5-Deoxyarabitol	81
2-Deoxyallose	6	<1.5	1-Deoxyribitol	91 (81)
2-Deoxyribose	5	0.3	1-Deoxyerythritol	99 (70)
C. Functionalized Aldoses				
N-Acetyl-glucosamine	6	12	1-(Acetylamino)-1-deoxyarabitol	56
N-Acetyl-mannosamine	6	15	1-(Acetylamino)-1-deoxyarabitol	47 (37)
N-Acetyl-galactosamine	6	5	5-(Acetylamino)-5-deoxyarabitol	56
2-Deoxy-2-fluoroglucose	6	49	1-Deoxy-1-fluoroarabinitol	~40
D. Disaccharides				
Melibiose	12	24	5-*O*-α-Galactopyranosylarabitol	91 (72)
Gentiobiose	12	18	5-*O*-β-Glucopyranosylarabitol	82 (50)
Lactose	12	24	3-*O*-β-Galactopyranosylarabitol	56 (47)
Maltose	12	13	3-*O*-α-Glucopyranosylarabitol	64
Cellobiose	12	18	3-*O*-β-Glucopyranosylarabitol	61
3-*O*-β-galactopyranosyl-arabinose	11	22	2-*O*-β-Galactopyranosylerythritol	40

Decarbonylation of saccharides can also be effected in the free aldehydo form, or as the hemiacetal. When the four stereoisomeric 2,3,5-tri-*O*-benzyl-*aldehydo*-D-pentoses are heated in acetonitrile solution with chlorotris(triphenylphosphine)rhodium(I), the corresponding 1,2,4-tri-*O*-benzyl-3-*O*-benzoyl-tetritols are obtained[12] in 40–60% yield. In an analogous decarbonylation that can also be effected with free sugars, the saccharide

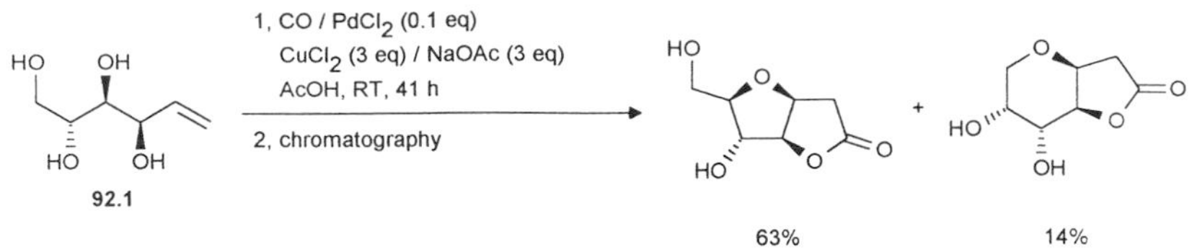

FIGURE 2.92

is heated with the rhodium reagent in *N*-methyl-2-pyrrolidone at 130°C for 1–24 h, and the major products are the chain-shortened alditols, as shown in Figure 2.91.[13]

The decarbonylation of aldoses reported previously is summarized in Table 2.3.

When discussing the descending procedure described in the preceding paragraphs, the *reverse* process, introduced by Jäger *et al.*,[14] and involving the palladium(II)-catalyzed, regioselective oxycarbonylation of five- and six-carbon enitols, should also be mentioned. For details on this methodology, see the original paper.[14] Figure 2.92 shows the inclusion of carbon monoxide into the educt **92.1.** Oxycarbonylation of the substrates is generally carried out with palladium(II) chloride (0.1 eq), sodium acetate (3 eq) and copper(II) chloride oxidant (3 eq) in acetic acid under atmospheric CO pressure and at room temperature. This system has been shown to be advantageous for numerous intramolecular carbonylations.

REFERENCES TO SECTION 2.4.6

1. R. W. Binkley and W. W. Binkley, *Carbohydr. Res.* **23,** 283 (1972).
2. A. E. El Ashmawy, D. Horton, and K. D. Philips, *Carbohydr. Res.* **9,** 350 (1969).
3. Z. Györgydeák, L. Szilágyi, and H. Paulsen, *J. Carbohydr. Chem.* **12,** 139 (1993).
4. J. Plenkiewicz, G. W. Hay, and W. A. Szarek, *Can. J. Chem.* **52,** 183 (1974).
5. W. A. Szarek, O. Achmatowicz, Jr., J. Plenkiewicz, and B. Radatus, *Tetrahedron* **34,** 1427 (1978).
6. R. W. Binkley, *Adv. Carbohydr. Chem. Biochem.* **38,** 105 (1981); S. Singh, S. Nambiar, R. A. Porter, T. L. Sander, K. G. Taylor, and R. J. Doyle, *J. Org. Chem.* **54,** 2300 (1989); M. Petrusová, M. Matulová, M. Fedoronko, and L. Petrus, *Synthesis,* p. 209 (1991).
7. K. Araki, M. Sakuma, and S. Shiraishi, *Bull. Chem. Soc. Jpn.* **57,** 997 (1984).
8. K. Araki and S. Shiraishi, *Bull. Chem. Soc. Jpn.* **59,** 229 (1986).
9. S. Ichikawa, I. Tomita, A. Hosaka, and T. Sato, *Bull. Chem. Soc. Jpn.* **61,** 513 (1988).
10. A. Hosaka, S. Ichikawa, H. Shindo, and T. Sato, *Bull. Chem. Soc. Jpn.* **62,** 797 (1989).
11. S. Ichikawa, K. Takahashi, M. Tanaka, and T. Sato, *Bull. Chem. Soc. Jpn.* **61,** 505 (1988).
12. M. MacCoss, A. Chen, and R. L. Tolman, *Tetrahedron Lett.* **26,** 4287 (1985).
13. M. A. Andrews, G. L. Gould, and S. A. Klaeren, *J. Org. Chem.* **54,** 5257 (1989).
14. T. Gracza, T. Hasenörl, U. Stahl, and V. Jäger, *Synthesis,* p. 1108 (1991).

3

PREPARATION OF SUGARS
WITH ISOMERIZATION

3.1. EPIMERIZATION OF SACCHARIDES IN ALKALINE MEDIA

Investigation of the principal properties of saccharides has shown that in the presence of bases, four types of transformation should be considered: (1) anomerization, (2) aldose–ketose isomerization (Lobry de Bruyn–Alberda van Ekenstein reaction), (3) reversible aldol reaction, and (4) β-elimination or benzylic acid rearrangement (formation of saccharinic acid) after the aldol reaction.

The isomerization,[1-4] and related reactions[5] of aldoses depend strongly on the pH; anomerization, and isomerization proceed under very slightly alkaline conditions, whereas the aldol reaction, and benzylic acid rearrangement require a much stronger alkaline milieu.

The isomerization of aldoses is *frequently employed in practice,* sometimes offering the exclusive route to the otherwise hardly available, unnatural saccharides. Treatment of reducing sugars with bases[4-21] leads mutarotation through a pseudo-acyclic form.[22,23] From the individual anomers, endiols are formed, which are transformed into the two C-2 epimeric aldoses and the structural isomeric ketose, as shown in Figure 3.1.

Because of this rather complicated process, conversion of an aldose with a base results in a mixture of products even under very mild conditions.

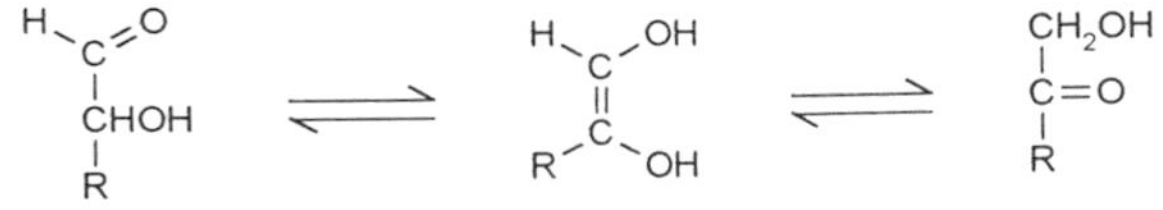

FIGURE 3.1

The complex reaction has been thoroughly studied[17,24,25] by kinetic analysis; for instance, formation of the products of the probably best known triple equilibrium between D-glucose, D-fructose, and D-mannose is explained[15,20] by a symmetric "3,4-endiol" intermediate.

The alkaline epimerization of a mixture of the two epimeric aldoses and the respective ketose never reaches the same quilibrium state, even after treatment for a longer time. The degree of isomerization of aldoses at 25°C and at pH 11.5 can be found in the paper of El Khadem et al.[21]

For the alkaline isomerization of saccharides on the preparative scale, potassium or calcium hydroxide, triethylamine, pyridine, or 1,3-dicyclohexylcarbodiimide (in melt) are usually employed.

Epimerization of L-rhamnose in pyridine, and monitoring the progress of the reaction by paper chromatography, showed[26] the formation of 6-deoxy-L-*arabino*-hexulose (6-deoxy-L-fructose), 6-deoxy-L-*ribo*-hexulose, 6-deoxy-L-glucose and 5-deoxy-L-*xylo*-hexulose, which were identified by conversion into the respective 2-(nitrophenyl)-hydrazones.

The following experimental procedure describes the preparation[27] of 6-deoxy-L-fructose (**2.2**), which is the major product of the epimerization of L-rhamnose (**2.1**) (Fig. 3.2).

*Preparation of 6-deoxy-L-*arabino-*hexulose (2.2)*[27] A solution of L-rhamnose monohydrate (4.5 g) in dry pyridine (30 ml) is boiled under reflux for 5 h. The solvent is removed by concentration, and coevaporation (twice) with ethanol. (Complete removal is not necessary for crystallization of the unchanged rhamnose.) The residue is triturated with acetone and seeded with crystals of L-rhamnose. After 1–2 h, more acetone (5 ml) is added, and the mixture is kept at 0°C overnight. The crystals of L-rhamnose (2.6 g) are collected by filtration and washed with acetone (10 ml). The filtrate and the washings are concentrated, and a solution of the residue (1.9 g) in water (15 ml) is stirred with an excess of barium carbonate. Bromine

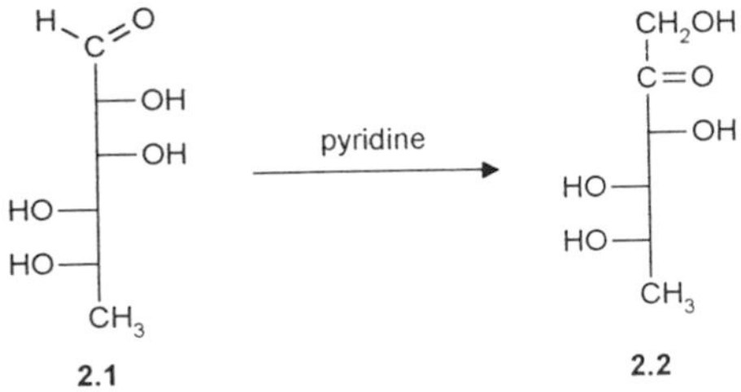

FIGURE 3.2

(~0.5 ml) is added dropwise over 1–2 h, until a faint yellow color persists. The solution is kept overnight in the dark, and then aerated to remove excess bromine, filtered, and passed through, successively, columns filled with Amberlite IRA-400 and Rexyn I-300 (mixed H^+–OH^-) resins. Following evaporation, 1.2 g (95–97%) of pure, syrupy **2.2** is obtained (63%, based on the L-rhamnose consumed).

6-Deoxy-D-arabino-hexulose 2-(nitrophenyl)hydrazone[27]   A solution of **2.2** (100 mg) in water (1 ml) is treated with a solution of 2-(nitrophenyl)hydrazine (100 mg) in hot ethanol (2 ml), and the mixture is refluxed for 10 min. After seeding, the hydrazone separates as orange–yellow crystals, m.p. 132–134°C. Recrystallization from a mixture of abs. ethanol–ether gives yellow needles, m.p. 135–137°C, $[\alpha]_D^{20}$ −39 (c = 1.0 in water).

The hardly available D-*psicose* (**3.2**) can be readily prepared by the isomerization (Fig. 3.3) of the cheap D-fructose (**3.1**) as described in the following procedure.[28]

Preparation of D-psicose (3.2)[28]   A mixture of D-fructose (**3.1**, 125 g), ethanol (750 ml) and triethylamine (25 ml) is boiled under reflux for 15 h. The solution is evaporated to a syrup, which is dissolved in water (500 ml) and the solution is washed with chloroform (500 ml) and ether (400 ml), stirred with charcoal for 1 h, and filtered, and the filtrate is deionized by stirring with Dowex 50 (H^+) resin (100 ml) for 1 h. The suspension is filtered; the filtrate is evaporated to a syrup, which is dissolved in a 3 : 7 mixture (150 ml) of methanol and water; and the solution is chromatographed in three portions (50 ml each) on a column (4.5 × 40 cm) of Dowex AG-5 W X-2 (Ca^{2+}) resin (200–400 mesh) (eluant: 3 : 7 methanol–water), and 50 ml fractions are collected. The fractionation is monitored by TLC on plastic sheets precoated with PE1-Cellulose F, with a 8 : 6 : 3 : 3 *tert*-butanol–butanone–88% formic acid–water eluant, and the plates are sprayed with 1% *p*-anisidine hydrochloride in ethanol, and developed in an oven for 10 min at 95°C. The fractions containing mainly D-psicose are combined and evaporated to a syrup, which is dissolved in water (35 ml), and the solution is chromatographed on the aforementioned column with water, as the eluant. Before fractionation the column is thoroughly eluted with water (~7 liters). The appropriate fractions are collected, evaporated *in vacuo*, and freeze-dried for 24 h to obtain 10.0 g (8%) of D-psicose (**3.2**). The equilibrium composition of D-psicose in solution contains four cyclic forms (anomers of the pyranose and furanose) in substantial portions, and these vary with temperature: $[\alpha]_D^{22}$ +2.9 (c = 1.0 in water).

Epimerization of *uronic acids* in a warm solution proceeds[29,30] even at pH 7, and more easily than that of the corresponding aldoses. The

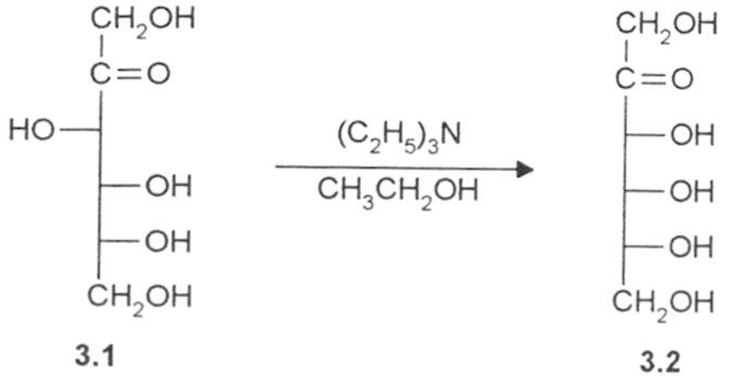

FIGURE 3.3

isomerization of D-glucuronic acid was investigated in detail[30] (pH 7, 3 h, 100°C) to reveal the presence of the products shown in Figure 3.4.

The *other uronic acids* can be isomerized by an analogous procedure. Treatment of calcium D-arabonate in hot pyridine for 2 days gives rise[31] to the formation of calcium D-ribonate, a target for conversion into D-ribono-1,4-lactone. Kinetic studies on this epimerization reaction were carried out[32] with the deuterium-labeling technique.

Instead of simple bases, other substances have also been investigated for inducing epimerization of saccharides. Alkaline borate solutions were applied for the conversion[33] of D-xylose into D-xylulose (20% yield) and lactose into lactulose; without adding borate, the conversion is much slower in a given period of time. Arylboric acids,[34] poly(4-vinyl-phenylboric acid)resins,[35] and aluminate resins[36] also have an accelerating effect on the base-induced epimerization of saccharides.

As shown above, the base-induced isomerization of free sugars and onic acids leads to mixtures of aldoses and ketoses. However, when the hydroxyl group(s) adjacent to the aldehyde function is (are) blocked with a protecting group, no 1,2-endiol intermediate is produced, and thus epimerization at C-2 can occur[37] only on the action of a base. By application of isopropylidene protection, isomerization of the 2,3-*erythro*-aldoses (**5.1**) into the corresponding *threo*-isomers (**5.2**) was observed[38], and the driving force of this conversion is that the stereoisomer with *trans*-substituents is obviously more stable (Fig. 3.5).

Saccharide O-methyl ethers are epimerized to a certain equilibrium state; treatement of an aquoeus solution of 2,4,6-tri-O-methyl-D-glucose

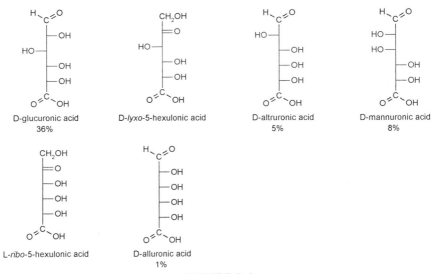

FIGURE 3.4

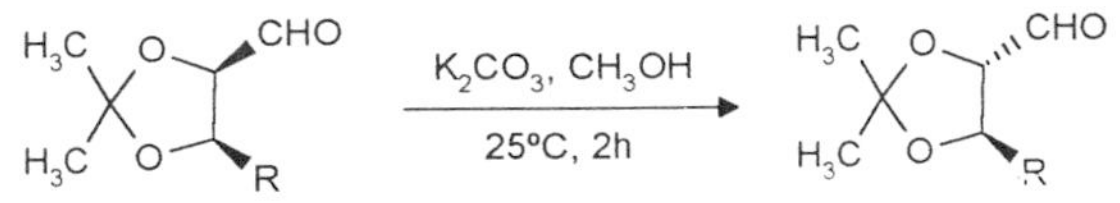

5.1   **5.2**

FIGURE 3.5

with barium hydroxide (35°C, 8 days) leads[39] to a 1:1 mixture of 2,4,6-tri-
O-methyl-D-mannose and the starting educt. On the action of potassium
carbonate on benzylated hexoses [such as 2,3,4,6-tetra-O-benzyl-D-mannose
(**6.1**) or -D-glucose (**6.2**)], benzyl alcohol is split and the products **6.3** and
6.4 are formed,[40–46] as shown in Figure 3.6.

L-Iduronic acid derivatives can be *conveniently synthesized on preparative scales* by the C-5 isomerization[47–50] of the readily available D-glucuronic
acids (Fig. 3.7).

*Preparation of methyl 3,5-O-benzylidene-1,2-O-isopropylidene-β-L-idofuranuro-
nate (7.2)*[50]   A solution of sodium methoxide [prepared from 20.5 mg (0.89 mmol)
of sodium in a small volume of methanol] is added to a solution of methyl 3,5-O-
benzylidene-1,2-O-isopropylidene-α-D-glucofuranuronate (**7.1**, 3.0 g, 8.9 mmol) in
abs. methanol (70 ml). Then a few seeding crystals of the product are added, the
mixture is refrigerated overnight, and the same amount of sodium methoxide is

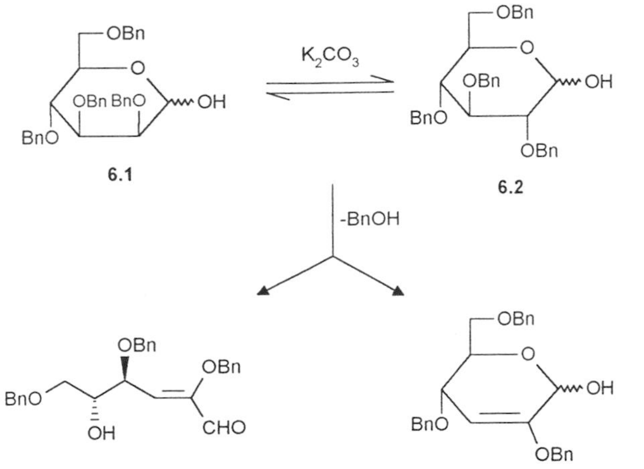

6.1   **6.2**

-BnOH

6.3   **6.4**

(2Z,4S,5R)-2,4,6-tris(benzyloxy)-   2,4,6-tri-O-benzyl-3-deoxy-
5-hydroxy-hex-2-enal   D-*erythro*-hex-2-enopyranose
$[\alpha]_D^{20} = -20.8$ (c = 1, CHCl$_3$)   m.p. 116-119°C
                                            $[\alpha]_D^{25} = +38$ (c = 1, CHCl$_3$)

FIGURE 3.6

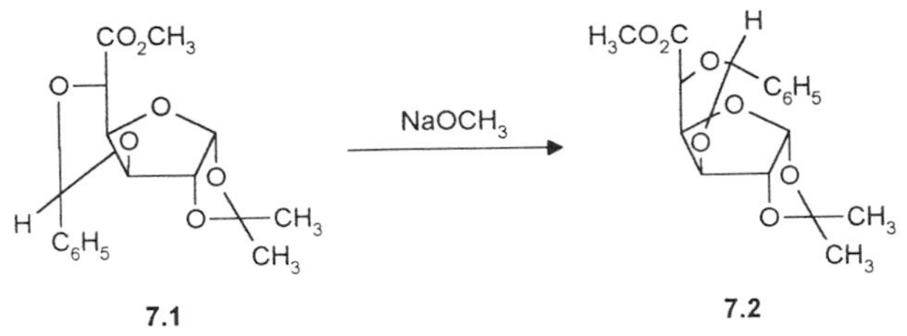

FIGURE 3.7

added. The next day the precipitated crystals are collected by filtration, and the crude product (1.6 g) is recrystallized from methanol to furnish 689 mg (23%) of **7.2**. The residue, obtained on evaporation of the mother liquor, is subjected to column chromatographic purification, to afford 981 mg (32.7%) of the starting sugar (**7.1**) and a further crop of the pure product **7.2** (311 mg, 10.3 %), m.p. 188–189°C, $[\alpha]_D^{23}$ +13.7 (c = 0.75 in chloroform).

2-Acetamido-2-deoxyaldoses (**8.1**) are also epimerized via the acyclic enolate ion **8.2** with dilute bases, and—because of the presence of the acetamido group—no formation of ketoses is observed (Fig. 3.8). The epimeric mixtures (**8.3**) produced in the reaction can be readily separated by conventional chromatographic methods.[51–56] This way, N-acetyl-D-mannosamine (**8.5**; a popular starting material in organic synthesis) can be prepared[56] with 14–16% yield from the cheap D-glucosamine by epimerization with dilute aqueous ammonia.

Preparation of N-acetyl-D-mannosamine (8.5) from N-acetyl-D-glucosamine (8.4)[56]   To a solution of N-acetyl-D-glucosamine (**8.4**, 1 kg) in water (3 liters) is added 30 ml of concentrated aqueous ammonium hydroxide, and the solution is kept under a stream of nitrogen for 4 days. Following decolorization with charcoal and subsequent filtration, the filtrate is evapoarted twice to its half-volume (to remove ammonia). N-Acetyl-D-glucosamine, precipitated, is separated by filtration, the filter cake is washed with ethanol, and the combined filtrate–washing combina-

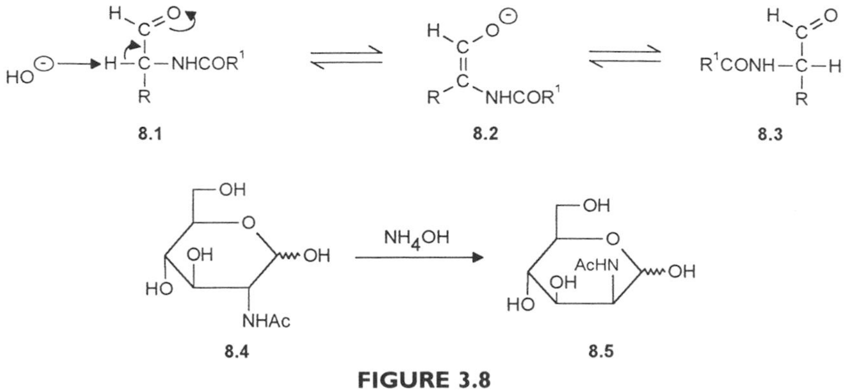

FIGURE 3.8

tion is concentrated until separation of crystals. This second crystalline precipitate is filtered, washed with *n*-propanol, boiled under reflux with *n*-propanol for 20 min, and then allowed to remain until the next day. This workup procedure is repeated three times with the insoluble material when no *N*-acetyl-D-mannosamine can be detected by chromatography. The combined *n*-propanol extract is concentrated to a thick syrup, a small volume of water is added, and the product (**8.5**, 175 g, with ~90% purity) is filtered off. Recrystallization may be carried out from hot water by adding acetone until turbidity, when the pure sugar is obtained with 14–16% yield, m.p. 113–115°C, $[\alpha]_D^{20}$ −11.6 (3 min) → +10 (final value, in water).

REFERENCES TO SECTION 3.1

1. J. C. Speck, Jr., *Adv. Carbohydr. Chem.* **13**, 63 (1958).
2. H. S. Isbell, *Adv. Chem. Ser.* **117**, 70 (1973).
3. L. Hough and A. C. Richardson, *Rodd's Chemistry of Carbon Compounds* (S. Coffey ed.),Vol. **1F**, p. 251. Elsevier, Amsterdam, 1967; P. Collins and R. Ferrier, *Monosaccharides—Their Chemistry and Their Roles in Natural Products,* p. 139. Wiley, Chichester and New York, 1995.
4. C. A. Lobry de Bruyn and W. Alberda van Ekenstein, *Recl. Trav. Chim. Pays-Bas* **15**, 92 (1897); **14**, 156, 203 (1895); **16**, 241, 257, 262, 274, 282 (1897); **18**, 147 (1899); **19**, 1 (1900).
5. J. U. Nef, *Justus Liebigs Ann. Chem.* **357**, 214 (1907); **376**, 1 (1910).
6. M. L. Wolfrom and W. L. Lewis, *J. Am. Chem. Soc.* **50**, 837 (1928).
7. M. L. Wolfrom and J. N. Schumacher, *J. Am. Chem. Soc.* **77**, 3318 (1955).
8. M. G. Blair and J. C. Showden, *J. Am. Chem. Soc.* **77**, 3323 (1955).
9. J. C. Showden and R. R. Thompson, *J. Am. Chem. Soc.* **80**, 1435 (1958).
10. C. D. Gutsche, D. Redmore, R. S. Burkis, K. Nowotny, H. Grassner, and C. W. Armbruster, *J. Am. Chem. Soc.* **89**, 1235 (1967).
11. C. Degani and M. Halmann, *J. Am. Chem. Soc.* **90**, 1313 (1968).
12. H. S. Isbell, K. Línek, and K. E. Hepner, Jr., *Carbohydr. Res.* **19**, 319 (1971).
13. L. F. Fieser and M. Fieser, *Organic Chemistry,* p. 360. Reinhold, New York, 1956.
14. W. B. Gleason and R. Barker, *Can. J. Chem.* **49**, 1425, 1433 (1971).
15. M. J. King-Morris and A. S. Serianni, *Carbohydr. Res.* **154**, 29 (1986).
16. R. Barker and A. S. Serianni, *Acc. Chem. Res.* **19**, 307 (1986).
17. T. Vourinen and E. Sjöström, *Carbohydr. Res.* **108**, 23 (1982).
18. G. de Wit, A. P. G. Kieboom, and H. van Bekkum, *Carbohydr. Res.* **74**, 157 (1979).
19. J. M. de Bruijn, A. P. G. Kieboom, and H. van Bekkum, *Recl. Trav. Chim. Pays-Bas* **105**, 176 (1986).
20. H. S. El Khadem, S. Ennifar, and H. S. Isbell, *Carbohydr. Res.* **169**, 13 (1987).
21. H. S. El Khadem, S. Ennifar, and H. S. Isbell, *Carbohydr. Res.* **185**, 51 (1989).
22. D. J. MacLaurin and J. W. Green, *Can. J. Chem.* **47**, 3947 (1969).
23. H. S. Isbell, H. L. Frush, C. W. R, Wade, and C. E. Hunter, *Carbohydr. Res.* **9**, 163 (1969).
24. E. R. Garrett and J. F. Young, *J. Org. Chem.* **35**, 3502 (1970).
25. H. G. J. de Wit and B. F. M. Kuster, *Carbohydr. Res.* **19**, 5 (1971).
26. S. Kucár, J. Zámocky, and J. Zemek, *Collect. Czech. Chem. Commun.* **44**, 3119 (1979).
27. S. Ennifar and H. S. El Khadem, *Carbohydr. Res.* **193**, 303 (1989).
28. R. J. Beveridge, M. Davis, J. L. Morris, and N. J. Hoogenraad, *Carbohydr. Res.* **101**, 348 (1982); L. W. Doner, *ibid.* **70**, 209 (1979); S. J. Angyal, G. S. Bethell, and R. J. Beveridge, *ibid.* **73**, 9 (1979); V. Bílik and K. Tihlárik, *Chem. Zvesti* **28**, 106 (1974).
29. F. G. Fischer and H. Schmidt, *Chem. Ber.* **92**, 2184 (1959).
30. B. Carlsson, O. Samuelson, T. Popoff, and O. Theander, *Acta Chem. Scand.* **23**, 261 (1969).

31. M. Steiger, *Helv. Chim. Acta* **19**, 189 (1936).
32. M. Kalman, J. Sokolowski, J. Safranek, and H. Lönnberg, *J. Carbohydr. Chem.* **6**, 587 (1987).
33. J. F. Mendicino, *J. Am. Chem. Soc.* **82**, 4975 (1960).
34. S. A. Barker, B. W. Hatt, and P. J. Somers, *Carbohydr. Res.* **26**, 41 (1973).
35. S. A. Barker, B. W. Hatt, and R. R. Woodbury, *Carbohydr. Res.* **26**, 55 (1973).
36. J. A. Rendleman, Jr. and J. E. Hodge, *Carbohydr. Res.* **75**, 83 (1979).
37. J. F. Kennedy, *Carbohydrate Chemistry,* p. 382. Clarendon Press, Oxford, 1988.
38. A. V. M. Lee, V. S. Martin, S. Masamune, K. B. Sharpless, and F. J. Walker, *J. Am. Chem. Soc.* **104**, 3515 (1982).
39. N. Prentice, L. S. Cuendet, and F. Smith, *J. Am. Chem. Soc.* **78**, 4439 (1956).
40. V. S. Rao and A. S. Perlin, *Can. J. Chem.* **59**, 333 (1981).
41. V. S. Rao and A. S. Perlin, *J. Org. Chem.* **47**, 3265 (1982).
42. P. Allevi, P. Ciuffreda, D. Colombo, D. Monti, G. Speranza, and P. Manitto, *J. Chem. Soc., Perkin Trans. 1,* p. 1281 (1989).
43. D. Monti, P. Gramatica, G. Speranza, and P. Manitto, *Tetrahedron Lett.* **28**, 5047 (1987).
44. A. Calvo-Mateo, M. J. Camarasa, A. Diaz-Ortíz, F. G. de las Heras, and A. Alemany, *J. Chem. Soc., Perkin Trans. 1,* p. 2861 (1988).
45. A. B. Reitz, A. D. Jordan, Jr., and B. E. Maryanoff, *J. Org. Chem.* **52**, 4800 (1987).
46. M. Anastasia, P. Allevi, P. Ciuffreda, A. Fiecchi, and A. Scala, *J. Org. Chem.* **56**, 3054 (1991).
47. W. N. Haworth, W. G. M. Jones, M. Stacey, and L. F. Wiggins, *J. Chem. Soc.,* p. 61 (1944).
48. D. Horton and F. O. Swanson, *Carbohydr. Res.* **14**, 159 (1970).
49. M. H. Johansson and O. Samuelson, *Carbohydr. Res.* **54**, 295 (1977).
50. N. Baggett and A. Smithson, *Carbohydr. Res.* **108**, 59 (1982).
51. D. G. Comb and S. Roseman, *J. Am. Chem. Soc.* **80**, 3166 (1958).
52. R. Kuhn and R. Brossmer, *Justus Liebigs Ann. Chem.* **616**, 221 (1958).
53. C. T. Spivak and S. Roseman, *J. Am. Chem. Soc.* **81**, 2403 (1959).
54. B. Coxon and L. Hough, *J. Chem. Soc.,* p. 1577 (1961).
55. A. Giannis and T. Henk, *Justus Liebigs Ann. Chem.,* p. 789 (1991).
56. R. Kuhn and G. Baschang, *Justus Liebigs Ann. Chem.* **659**, 156 (1962).

3.2. EPIMERIZATION OF SUGARS WITH MOLYBDATE IONS

Because of their polyhydroxyaldehyde character, sugars form complexes with molybdate ions with various types of coordination, depending on the pH of the solution and the ring-member positions and steric arrangement of the hydroxyl groups of the saccharide. As the solutions of many of these molybdate complexes are heated, C-2 epimerization of the sugar occurs, and an equilibrium mixture of the two C-2 epimeric aldoses can be obtained.[1-7] It is believed that the driving force for the C-2 epimerization is not simply the oxo complexation of a monosaccharide molecule by molybdate ions, but also a d–π interaction between the central Mo(VI) atom of the heptamolybdate ion and the acyclic form of the saccharide. Such an interaction could enable a *H*-shift between C-1 and C-2, or nucleophilic attack of C-3 on C-1 via a transitory tricentric bond, through an oxaallylic cation-like transition state (Fig. 3.9).[8-14]

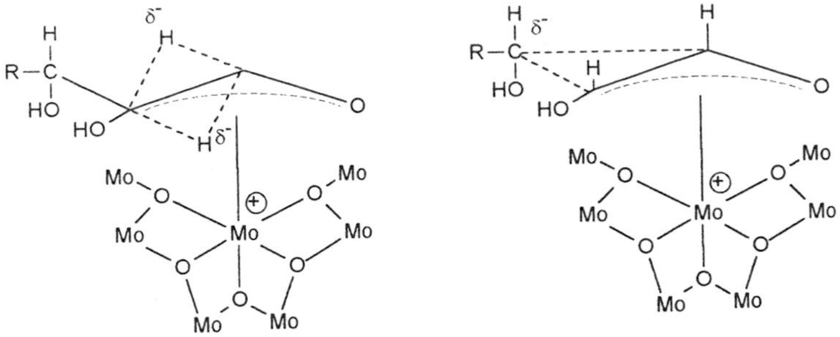

FIGURE 3.9

Formation of the molybdate complex influences the development of the thermodynamic equilibrium, and the data for a few pairs of aldoses[11] are listed in the following table.

A ⇌ B equilibrium	A / B ratio	
	Found	Calculated
Glucose → mannose	2.3	2.5
Galactose → talose	6.1	4.0
Allose → altrose	1.9	1.5

The equilibrium indicated in this table can be reached in very different periods of time when the equilibrium state is to be determined experimentally with the individual, pure epimers. The most advantageous pH range[15] for the epimerization is 2.5–3.5. The epimerization can be executed only with aldoses; the presence of hydroxyl groups at C-2 and C-3 is required, and literature data indicate that the C-4 OH group also contributes to the successful conversion. In the case of aldopentoses, each of the four pentoses is present in equilibrium state, and the ratio of these sugars[10,16,17] is arabinose : ribose : lyxose : xylose = 29 : 12 : 35 : 24. Further isomerization (i.e., to the corresponding ketose[14]), which occurs in aldose solutions heated over 100°C under pressure, can be prevented by adding dioxo-bis(2,4-pentanedionato-O,O')molybdenum(VI) catalyst.[9,18] Disaccharides, such as *epi*-lactose and *epi*-maltose are not isomerized, and no transformation has been observed with the tungsten-complexes.[19]

Several ion-exchange resins with bonded heptamolybdate (paramolybdate) ions have also been prepared to avoid undesirable side-reactions,[20] and these resins are also suitable for the preparation[21-26] of *2-¹³C-labeled hexoses* that are separated[27] by means of a Ca^{2+} ion-exchange resin. It has been shown that the epimerization effect of the molybdate ions can be quenched[28-30] by oxalic acid or citric acid.

The aldoses obtained by the molybdate ion–catalyzed epimerization are isolated and characterized with different methods as shown by the following experimental procedures.

> *Preparative epimerization of* D-galactose[31]   A solution of D-galactose (40 g) and molybdic acid (0.4 g) in water (200 ml) is kept at 95°C for 2 h. It is then filtered and deionized by passing through a column (4 × 70 cm) packed with Dowex 3 (OH⁻) resin. The eluate is evaporated to dryness, the residue is dissolved in water (40 ml), and ethanol (40 ml) is added. On storing at room temperature for 20 h, 23.8 g of D-galactose is separated and is filtered off. The filtrate is concentrated to a syrup, which is fractionated on a Dowex 50 WX-8 (3.5 × 120 cm, 100–200 mesh, Ba^{2+} form) column to eluate the following fractions (eluant: water).

Fraction	Volume (ml)	Weight (g) of sugar produced	Sugar
0	600	—	—
1	375	6.4	Galactose, idose[a]
2	535	1.7	gulose, idose[a]
3	530	Disaccharides in traces	
4	925	6.5	Talose

[a]Contains traces of disaccharides

By evaporating *fraction 1*, crystalline D-galactose (3.6 g) is obtained. Chromatography of the mother liquor is carried out on a cellulose column (3 × 130 cm, Whatman CF-12, eluant: 5:1:4 *n*-butanol–ethanol–water). *Fraction 2* is worked up in an essentially similar manner, and the following sugars are isolated:

Fraction	Volume (ml)	Weight (g) of isolated saccharide	Saccharide
1/0	2920	—	—
1/1	345	0.55	Gulose
1/2	730	1.75	Galactose
1/3	840	traces	Disaccharides
2/0	2890	—	—
2/1	330	0.8	Idose, gulose
2/2	625	0.4	Gulose
2/3	1000	traces	Disaccharides

The specific optical rotation values for the isolated sugars ($c = 2.0$ in water): D-talose: $[\alpha]_D^{24}$ +19.5; D-gulose: $[\alpha]_D^{24}$ −18.7; D-idose: $[\alpha]_D^{24}$ +14.

Separation of D-talose by the enzymatic digestion of the excess of D-galactose   A mixture of D-galactose (100 g), molybdic acid (1 g) and water (0.5 liter) is kept at 95°C for 10–12 h. The mixture is filtered, the filtrate is concentrated to ~150 ml under diminished pressure, and methanol (150 ml) and ethanol (150 ml) are added. After 20 h, the precipitated crystalline D-galactose (60–63 g) is filtered off, the filtrate is concentrated *in vacuo* (bath temperature 40°C), and an aqueous solution of the residue is deionized by passing through a Dowex 3 column. The eluate is evaporated, and the syrupy residue is dissolved in 1 liter of tap-water. Then 20 g of baker's yeast is added, and the suspension is left until digestion is complete (5–7 days). Then the mixture is filtered and evaporated to dryness *in vacuo,* and the residue is refluxed for 30 min with 0.5 liter of methanol. The solution is decolorized with charcoal and concentrated to a syrup, which is dissolved in methanol (30 ml) and left at room temperature to result in the crystallization of 4.5–5.5 g of D-talose. By chromatography of the mother liquor (see the following procedures), a second crop (6–7 g) of D-talose is obtained with an overall yield of 12–13%. Following recrystallization from 50% aqueous methanol, the pure sugar with m.p. 128–132°C and $[\alpha]_D^{23}$ +19.5 ($c = 2.0$ in methanol), is obtained.

Preparation of L-ribose from L-arabinose[18]   A mixture of L-arabinose (36 g, 240 mmol) and molybdenum(VI)oxide bis-2,4-pentanedionate (4 g, 12 mmol) is dissolved in dry DMF (400 ml) by stirring on a water bath (50°C), and kept at this temperature for a further 24 h. The reaction mixture is then diluted with ice water and extracted with dichloromethane (2 × 100 ml). The aqueous layer is evaporated to ~50 ml, deionized with Amberlyst A-26 (HCO₃⁻ form) anion-exchange resin, and evaporated to a yellow syrup. TLC analysis (in 92:8 dichloromethane–methanol) showed an epimeric mixture of L-arabinose ($R_f = 0.17$) and L-ribose ($R_f = 0.34$) in a ratio of ~3:2 and an unidentified higher-running ($R_f = 0.75$) UV-positive product (~10%). The syrup is dissolved in methanol and kept at 0–5°C for 1 day. After filtration of the partially crystallized L-arabinose (14 g, 38.8%), the filtrate is evaporated and the resulting syrup is purified using one of the following procedures.

Purification of L-ribose
A. By short-column chromatography[18]   The crude reaction mixture containing L-arabinose and L-ribose (22 g) is dissolved in a 3:7 (v/v) mixture of methanol and chloroform (20 ml) and applied to a column of silicagel (230–400 mesh, 250 g) suspended in a 1.5:8.5 methanol–chloroform mixture. Elution with the same solvent mixture affords L-ribose as a yellow syrup (9.7 g, 27%), $[\alpha]_D^{20}$ +14.7 ($c = 1.0$ in pyridine).

B. By preparative liquid chromatography[18]   The optimum separation conditions are first determined by analytic HPLC [refractive index detector, Particil 5, eluting mixture: 8.5:1.5 (v/v) chloroform–methanol]. Then preparative separation is carried out using a preparative liquid chromatograph [Jobin-Yvon; i.d. 40 mm; 150 g of Merck Lichroprep. Si60 (15 μm); sample load 5 g dissolved in 5 ml of methanol; flow rate 16 ml/min]. The appropriate fractions, after collecting a void volume of 450 ml, are combined and evaporated under reduced pressure to give syrupy L-ribose (yield: 28%).

Table 3.1 lists the literature[32–47] on the epimerization of aldoses.

TABLE 3.1   **Synthesis of Aldoses via Molybdenate-Catalyzed Epimerization**

Aldoses participating in equilibrium	Ref(s).
Allose, altrose, and glucose	32
Arabinose and ribose	9, 17, 33–35
Quinovose and rhamnose	36
3-Deoxy-D-*arabino*-hexose and 3-deoxy-D-*ribo*-hexose	37
Deoxypentoses, -hexoses, and -heptoses	24, 38
Epimelibiose, melibiose	39
Erythrose, threose	40, 41
Glucose, mannose	9, 42–44
Heptoses	45–47
Lyxose, ribose	34
5-Methylpentoses	24

REFERENCES TO SECTION 3.2

1. E. J. Bourne, D. H. Hutson, and H. Weigel, *J. Chem. Soc.*, p. 4252 (1960).
2. H. Weigel, *Angew. Chem.* **73**, 766 (1961).
3. H. J. F. Angus, E. J. Bourne, F. Searle, and H. Weigel, *Tetrahedron Lett.* **5**, 55 (1964).
4. J. T. Spence and S.-Ch. Kiang, *J. Org. Chem.* **28**, 244 (1963).
5. E. Bayer and W. Voelter, *Justus Liebigs Ann. Chem.* **696**, 194 (1966).
6. W. Voelter, E. Bayer, R. Records, E. Bunnenberg, and C. Djerassi, *Justus Liebigs Ann. Chem.* **718**, 238 (1968).
7. W. Voelter, G. Kuhfittig, G. Schneider, and E. Bayer, *Justus Liebigs Ann. Chem.* **734**, 126 (1970).
8. V. Bílik, L. Petruš, and V. Farkas, *Chem. Zvesti* **26**, 372 (1972).
9. Y. Abe, T. Takizawa, and T. Kunieda, *Chem. Pharm. Bull.* **28**, 1324 (1980).
10. G. E. Taylor and J. M. Waters, *Tetrahedron Lett.* **22**, 1277 (1981).
11. M. L. Hayes, N. J. Pennings, A. S. Serianni, and R. Barker, *J. Am. Chem. Soc.* **104**, 6764 (1982).
12. B. Klaic, Z. Raza, M. Sankovic, and V. Sunjic, *Helv. Chim. Acta* **70**, 59 (1987); G. Snatzke, J. Guo, Z. Raza, and V. Sunjic, *Croat. Chem. Acta* **64**, 501 (1991).
13. M. Sankovic, S. Emini, S. Rusman, and V. Sunjic, *J. Mol. Catal.* **61**, 247 (1990).
14. V. Bílik and M. Matulová, *Chem. Pap.* **44**, 257 (1990); M. Matulová and V. Bílik, *ibid.* **46**, 253 (1992); J. Königstein and V. Bílik, *ibid.* **46**, 257 (1992).
15. V. Bílik, L. Petrus, and J. Zemek, *Chem. Zvesti* **32**, 242 (1978).
16. V. Bílik, *Chem. Zvesti* **26**, 372 (1972).
17. V. Bílik, L. Petrus, and V. Farkas, *Collect. Czech. Chem. Commun.* **43**, 1163 (1978).
18. G. M. Visser, J. van Westrenen, C. A. A. van Boeckel, and J. H. van Boom, *Recl. Trav. Chim. Pays-Bas* **105**, 528 (1986).
19. S. Chapelle and J.-F. Verchere, *Carbohydr. Res.* **277**, 39 (1995).
20. V. Bílik, E. Jurcová, and V. Sutoris, *Chem. Zvesti* **32**, 252 (1978).
21. E. L. Clark, Jr., M. L. Hayes, and R. Baker, *Carbohydr. Res.* **153**, 263 (1986).
22. E. L. Clark, Jr., and R. Barker, *Carbohydr. Res.* **153**, 253 (1986).

23. A. S. Serianni, H. A. Nunez, M. L. Hayes, and R. Barker, in *Methods in Enzymology* (W. A. Wood, ed.), Vol. 89, Part D, p. 64. Academic Press, New York, 1982.
24. J. R. Snyder and A. S. Serianni, *Carbohyr. Res.* **163**, 169 (1987).
25. M. J. King-Moris, P. B. Bondo, R. A. Mrowca, and A. S. Serianni, *Carbohydr. Res.* **175**, 49 (1988).
26. B. J. Arena, R. J. Swedo, and B. E. Firth, Allied Signal, Inc., PCT. Int. Appl. WO 8,907,602 (1989); *Chem. Abstr.* **112**, 99132k (1989).
27. S. J. Angyal, G. S. Bethell, and R. J. Beveridge, *Carbohydr. Res.* **73**, 9 (1979).
28. V. Bílik and I. Knezek, *Chem. Pap.* **44**, 89 (1990).
29. V. Bílik and I. Knezek, Czech. Pat. CS 260,395 (1989); *Chem. Abstr.* **112**, 21250c (1989).
30. V. Bílik and I. Knezek, Czech. Pat. CS 260,390 (1987); *Chem. Abstr.* **112**, 56566n (1989).
31. V. Bílik, W. Voelter, and E. Bayer, *Justus Liebigs Ann. Chem.*, p. 1162 (1974).
32. V. Bílik, I. Knezek, and K. Bíliková, *Chem. Pap.* **42**, 401 (1988).
33. W. Dobler, H. Ernst, and J. Paust, BASF AG., Ger. Offen. DE 3,622,643 (1986); *Chem. Abstr.* **109**, 38179x (1988).
34. V. Bílik and J. Caplovic, *Chem. Zvesti* **27**, 547 (1973).
35. Czech. Pat. CS 275,890 (1992); *Chem. Abstr.* **122**, 56398r (1995).
36. V. Bílik, W. Voelter, and E. Bayer, *Justus Liebigs Ann. Chem.* **759**, 189 (1972).
37. V. Bílik and L. Petrus, *Collect. Czech. Chem. Commun.* **43**, 1159 (1978).
38. V. Bílik, L. Petrus, L. Stankovic, and K. Linek, *Chem. Zvesti* **32**, 372 (1978).
39. V. Bílik, J. Alföldi, and E. Soókyová, *Chem. Zvesti* **38**, 499 (1984).
40. V. Bílik and N. Stankovic, *Chem. Zvesti* **27**, 544 (1973).
41. A. S. Serianni, J. Pierce, and R. Barker, *Biochemistry* **18**, 1192 (1979).
42. V. Bílik, *Chem. Zvesti* **26**, 183 (1972).
43. V. Bílik, *Chem. Zvesti* **26**, 187 (1972).
44. V. Bílik and I. Knezek, *Chem. Pap.* **42**, 39 (1988).
45. V. Bílik and L. Petrus, *Chem. Zvesti* **30**, 359 (1976).
46. V. Bílik, L. Petrus, and J. Zemek, *Chem. Zvesti* **30**, 693 (1976).
47. L. Petrus, V. Bílik, D. Anderle, and F. Janecek, *Chem. Zvesti* **33**, 636 (1979).

3.3. EPIMERIZATION OF SACCHARIDES WITH AMINE COMPLEXES OF TRANSITION AND ALKALINE EARTH METALS

On the action of the Ca^{2+}, Ni^{2+}, Co^{2+}, and Sr^{2+} complexes of various diamines, aldoses undergo quick epimerization[1] under mild conditions[2-5] (60°C, 3–5 min), and these reactions proceed with a skeleton transformation similar to that discussed in Section 3.2 for the molybdate-catalyzed epimerizations[6]. Figure 3.10 illustrates the results reported thus far, from epimerization[7] of D-glucose with Ni^{2+} ions, during which the ammonium–carbinol adduct **10.1** (and not an *N*-glycoside) acts as the reactive complex. The final product, D-mannose, of the epimerization then forms from the intermediate **10.2**.

The effect of the trasition-metal complexes on the epimerization depends closely[8] on their structure; the highest rate of the D-glucose → D-mannose transformation can be achieved with the green nickel(II) tetramethyl–ethylenediamine complex. The patent literature[9-12] describes numerous additional transition metal–polyamine ligand combinations, whose effects on *mannose–glucose interconversion* have been investigated.

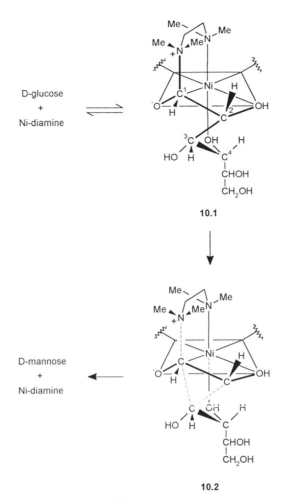

FIGURE 3.10

Osanai and Yoshikawa[13,14] suggest the following general procedure for related epimerizations.

> *General epimerization reaction*[13,14]   The selected aldose (1 eq) is added to a methanolic solution of $NiCl_2 \times 6H_2O$ (1 eq) and *tetmen* (2 eq). This solution is incubated for 5 min at 65°C with stirring. It is then kept at pH 6.5 with 1 M HCl for 0.5 h at room temperature. Samples of the mixture are rendered neutral and deionized by successive use of a cation-exchange resin (Dowex 5 WX8, H^+ form) and an anion-exchange resin (Dowex 2X8, HCO_3^- form). After elution with 500 ml of water, the aqueous solution is concentrated to exactly 250 ml. Analytic results for the epimerization are shown in Table 3.2.

The Ni(II)-*N*-substituted ethylenediamines readily catalyze the epimerization of the 1→6-linked disaccharides as well. Thus, epimerization of

TABLE 3.2   Analytic Results for Epimerization Using the Ni(II) Complex

Run	Substrate	Composition of products (%)			Recovery (%)	Color of solution
		Glc	*Man*	*Fru*		
1-1	D-Glucose	54 :	40 :	6	92	Green
1-2	D-Mannose	52 :	42 :	6	91	Green
		Gal	*Tal*	*Tag*		
1-3	D-Galactose	29 :	51 :	20	90	Green
1-4	D-Talose	27 :	55 :	18	93	Green
		Qui	*Rha*	*Ketose*		
1-5	D-Quinovose	66 :	33 :	1	90	Green
1-6	L-Rhamnose	65 :	34 :	1	88	Green
		Ara	*Rib*	*Ribu*[a]		
1-7	D-Arabinose	38 :	61 :	1	94	Green → blue-green
1-8	D-Ribose	39 :	60 :	1	100	Green → blue-green
1-9	L-Arabinose	63 :	36 :	1	100	Green → blue-green
		Xyl	*Lyx*	*Xylu*[b]		
1-10	D-Xylose	41 :	58 :	1	85	Green[c]
1-11	D-Lyxose	43 :	56 :	1	86	Green[c]
1-12	L-Xylose	43 :	56 :	1	90	Green[c]
1-13	L-Lyxose	43 :	56 :	1	89	Green[c]

[a] D-*erythro*-Pentulose.
[b] D-*threo*-Pentulose.
[c] A white precipitate was noted a few minutes later.

melibiose with [Ni(H$_2$O)N,N,N'-trimethylethylenediamine]Cl$_2$ gives rise to an epimeric mixture consisting of 46 parts of the starting sugar and 54 parts of α-D-galactopyranosyl-(1→6)-D-mannopyranose, and thus *melibiose* can be converted[15] into *epi*-melibiose more efficiently by this procedure than by the application of molybdate catalysis (see Section 3.2).

A molecular recognition ability could be detected for the Ni(II)-complexes; the complex composed of nickel(II) and the optically active N,N'-diethylcyclohexane-1,2-diamine (chxn) showed the ability to recognize the shape of the molecules in terms of the configuration of the various hydroxyl groups in aldoses during the epimerization[16] of D-glucose to D-mannose. The progress of the epimerization of glucose and mannose showed that the final solution compositions were almost identical (equilibrium) when either glucose or mannose was employed as the starting sugar. The data in Table 3.3 demonstrate that the equilibrium of the reaction system shifted in accordance with the chirality of the diamine ligand selected. This is the *first example* of observation of the molecular recognition ability of a complex that depends on the effect of the chirality of the ligand on the epimerization of aldoses.

It has also been found that Ni(II) complexes coordinated with long-chain N-alkylated ethylenediamine ligands, possess a marked C-2 epimeri-

TABLE 3.3 Epimerization of Glucose and Mannose at Various Temperatures Using Racemic and Optically Active N,N'-Diethyl-cyclohexane-1,2-diamine Ligands

Chirality of ligands	T (°C)	t (min)	Glc[a] to		Man[a] to	
			Glc	Man[b]	Glc	Man[b]
R,R	65	5	55.3	44.7	52.5	47.5
Racemate	65	5	54.2	45.8	57.5	42.5
S,S	65	5	53.3	46.7	51.7	48.3
R,R	30	5	52.6	47.4	46.8	53.2
Racemate	30	5	54.3	45.7	49.1	50.9
S,S	30	5	58.4	41.6	53.3	46.7
R,R	0	300	37.5	62.5	36.0	64.0
Racemate	0	90	45.4	54.6	44.7	55.3
S,S	0	60	60.4	39.6	60.0	40.0

[a]Glucose and mannose were epimerized as starting substrates.
[b]Composition of product (%). The corresponding ketose, fructose, was not observed in any experiments.

TABLE 3.4 Analytic Results for Epimerization Using the Ni(II) Complex

Substrate	Composition of products (%)			Recovery (%)
	Glc	Man	Fru	
D-Glucose	62 :	22 :	16	98
D-Mannose	5 :	94 :	1	100
D-Fructose	0 :	0 :	100	100
	Gal	Tal	Tag	
D-Galactose	52 :	0 :	48 :	100
D-Talose	0 :	90 :	10 :	97
	Qui	Rha	Ketose	
D-Quinovose	77 :	21 :	2	92
L-Rhamnose	3 :	96 :	1	100
	Ara	Rib	Ribu[a]	
D-Arabinose	87 :	2 :	11 :	76
D-Ribose	3 :	96 :	1	100
	Xyl	Lyx	Xylu[b]	
D-Xylose	63 :	35 :	2	80
D-Lyxose	3 :	96 :	1	92

[a]D-*erythro*-Pentulose.
[b]D-*threo*-Pentulose.

zation activity for aldoses in aqueous media. The agreement between the formation of micelles and the enhancement of epimerization was clearly recognized.[17] The analytic results and the yields of the epimers are summarized in Table 3.4. During the epimerization of aldoses, fructose was produced as a sole by-product. For the aldopentoses, the product contained the corresponding ketose, other complicated sugars, and decomposition products.

Using the present isomerization method, Osanai et al.[18,19] showed that, in the course of the epimerization, the anomeric carbon of the reacting aldose is converted into the C-2 carbon of the corresponding epimerized aldose, whereas the C-2 carbon of the reactant sugar is changed into the anomeric carbon of the product, and vice versa. These observations led to the theory that the 2-C-hydroxymethylated aldopentose could be obtained in a similar manner, if a ketohexose could be regarded as being an aldopentose carrying a hydroxymethyl group at the $C=O$ carbon atom. Four different 2-C-branched aldopentoses [2-C-hydroxymethylated D-arabinose, D-ribose (hamamelose), L-lyxose, and D-xylose] were prepared[20] from the corresponding ketoses (D-psicose, D-fructose, L-sorbose, and D-tagatose, respectively). A general procedure for these transformations is as follows.

Preparation of 2-C-hydroxymethyl aldopentoses[20] In a typical experiment, 1 mmol of $NiCl_2 \times 6H_2O$ and 2 mmol of the diamine derivative are dissolved in 15 ml of methanol. After the addition of 1 mmol of the ketose, the reaction mixture is stirred at 30°C for 20 min (the reaction time varies depending on the reaction conditions, and the resulting ternary complex is easily decomposed to its constituents by neutralization of the product solution with 1 M HCl). The product solution is treated with Dowex 50 WX2 (H^+) and Dowex 2X8 (HCO_3^-) ion-exchange resins, the eluates are worked up in the usual manner, and for qualitative and quantitative

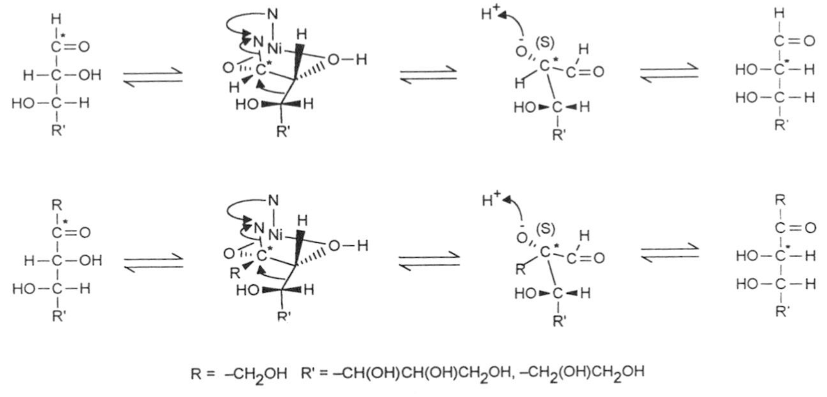

R = $-CH_2OH$ R' = $-CH(OH)CH(OH)CH_2OH$, $-CH_2(OH)CH_2OH$

Reaction mechanism of the epimerization of aldose (upper half) and the formation of 2-C hydroxymethylated aldose (bottom half).

FIGURE 3.11

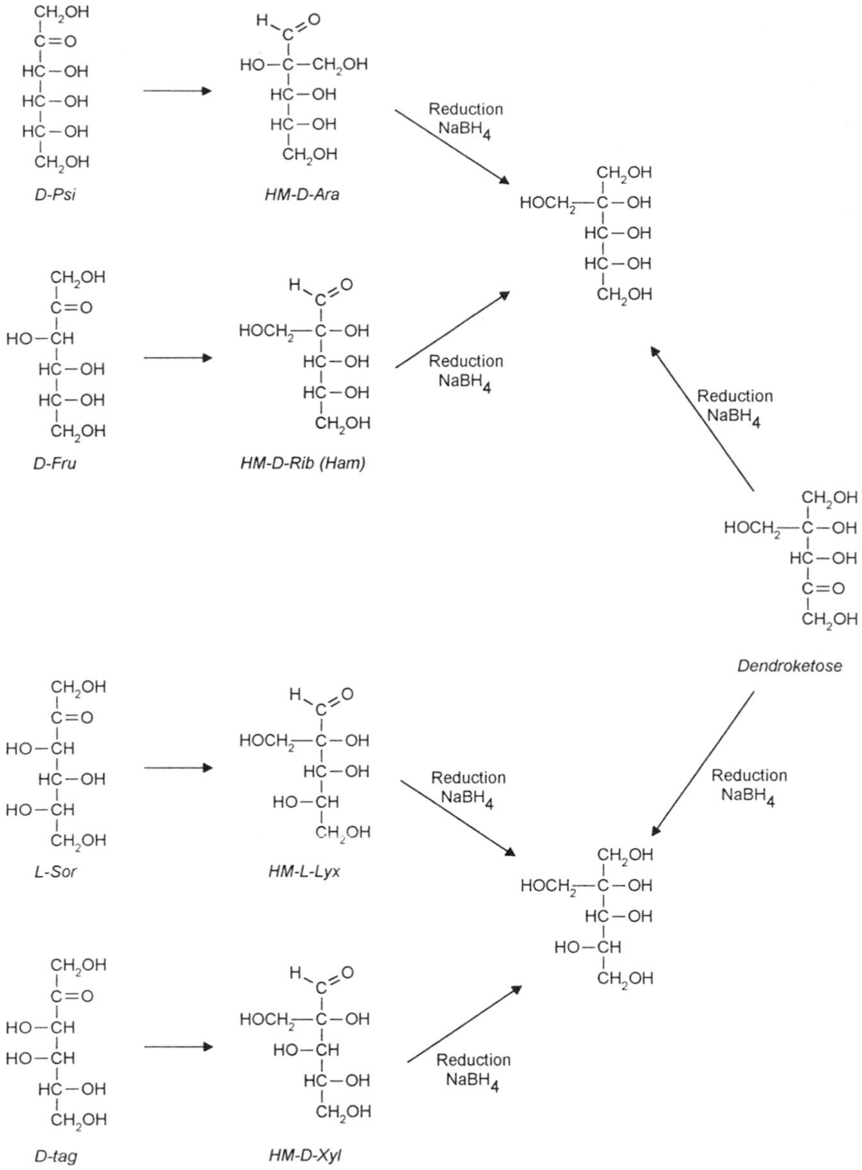

HM: Hydroxymethyl

Preparation of 2-C hydroxymethylated aldoses from the corresponding ketoses.

FIGURE 3.12

analyses, trimethylsilyl derivatives are prepared with the Sweeley reagent (hexamethyldisilazane–chlorotrimethylsilane). The TMS derivatives are extracted with chloroform, washed with water, and concentrated *in vacuo* (bath temperature ≤40°C).

The isomerization of *L-sorbose* in the presence of various alkylated diamines, the possible mechanism of the reactions, and the major products are shown in Figures 3.11 and 3.12, according to data from the work of Japanese authors.[19]

The epimerizations catalyzed with Ca^{2+}-amine complexes proceed via a different mechanism,[21] and the results obtained with various aldoses and $Ca(II)$-N,N,N',N'-tetramethylethylenediamine in methanol are summarized in Table 3.5. It is clearly shown that the "mannose-type" aldoses are not isomerized in this system,[13] but high concentrations of Ca^{2+} ions, alone,[22] in methanol leads to epimerization without formation of the ketose. According to Angyal,[20] these results can be explained by the stability of the various complexes formed between monosaccharides and Ca^{2+} ions. The data in Table 3.6, obtained by investigating the reaction of $[1\text{-}^{13}C]$-D-glucose with various metal hydroxides in water, obviously demonstrate that isomeriza-

TABLE 3.5 Epimerization Products from Glucose, Mannose, Xylose, and Lyxose

Ligands[a]	Substrate	Glc	Man	Fru	Substrate	Xyl	Lyx	Xylu[b]	Others
1,1,1′-en	Glucose	95	2	3	—	—	—	—	—
	Mannose	3	90	7	—	—	—	—	—
1,1,2′-en	Glucose	97	2	1	Xylose	84	7	5	4
	Mannose	2	95	3	Lyxose	5	75	10	10
1,1,6′-en	Glucose	97	2	1	Xylose	82	9	6	3
	Mannose	2	95	3	Lyxose	7	76	12	5
1,1,8′-en	Glucose	97	2	1	Xylose	75	11	6	8
	Mannose	3	95	2	Lyxose	10	75	9	6
1,1,9′-en	Glucose	87	11	2	Xylose	58	29	6	7
	Mannose	27	69	4	Lyxose	42	45	8	5
1,1,10′-en	Glucose	87	13	0	Xylose	55	33	5	7
	Mannose	34	63	3	Lyxose	53	37	3	7
1,1,12′-en	Glucose	80	20	0	Xylose	56	33	5	6
	Mannose	45	55	0	Lyxose	54	33	7	6
1,1,14′-en	Glucose	75	25	0	—	—	—	—	—
	Mannose	61	37	2	—	—	—	—	—
1,1,16′-en	Glucose	69	29	2	Xylose	56	33	5	6
	Mannose	67	32	1	Lyxose	57	35	4	4
1,1,18′-en	Glucose	71	29	0	—	—	—	—	—
	Mannose	69	29	2	—	—	—	—	—

[a]1,1 refers to N,N-dimethyl; en′ refers to carbon number of the N'-alkyl chain.
[b]Xylulose.

TABLE 3.6   **Reaction of [1-^{13}C]-D-Glucose with Various Metal Hydroxides in H$_2$O^a**

Base	pH	Composition of products (%)			^{13}C Position of Man^b	
		Glc	Man	Fru	C$_1$	C$_2$
LiOH	12.4	79	2	19	○	—
NaOH	12.8	74	3	23	○	—
KOH	12.8	71	3	26	○	—
Mg(OH)$_2$	9.1	99	0	1	—	—
Ca(OH)$_2$	12.4	75	17	8	□	○
Sr(OH)$_2$	12.9	79	4	17	○	□
Ba(OH)$_2$	13.0	65	5	30	○	—
Al(OH)$_3$	7.9	99	0	1	—	—
Co(OH)$_2$	7.3	99	0	1	—	—
Ni(OH)$_2$	7.1	100	0	0	—	—
Cu(OH)$_2$	8.1	99	0	1	—	—

^{a}Concentration of [1-^{13}C]-Glc and base was 66.7 mol/m^3, and calcium chloride was not used. Reaction time was 5 min.
^{b}○, major products; □, minor products; —, not detected.

tion leading to the rearrangement of the skeleton (Fig. 3.13) proceeded only with Ca(OH)$_2$.

It is to be noted that other sugar derivatives (including glycals) can also be isomerized with metal chlorides and molybdate complexes.[23,24]

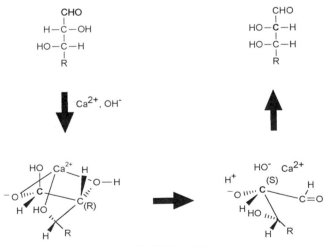

FIGURE 3.13

REFERENCES TO SECTION 3.3

1. T. Tanase, F. Shimizu, S. Yano, and S. Yoshikawa, *J. Chem. Soc., Chem. Commun.,* p. 1001 (1986).
2. S. Takizawa, H. Sugita, S. Yano, and S. Yoshikawa, *J. Am. Chem. Soc.* **102,** 7969 (1980).
3. S. Yano, S. Takizawa, H. Sugita, T. Takahashi, T. Tsubomura, H, Shioi, and S. Yoshikawa, *Carbohydr. Res.* **142,** 179 (1985).
4. T. Tanase, K. Kurihara, S. Yano, K. Kobayashi, T. Sakurai, S. Yoshikawa, and M. Hidai, *Inorg. Chem.* **26,** 3134 (1987).
5. K. Ishida, S. Nonoyama, T. Hirano, S. Yano, M. Hidai, and S. Yoshikawa, *J. Am. Chem. Soc.* **11,** 1599 (1989).
6. R. E. London, *J. Chem. Soc., Chem. Commun.,* p. 661 (1987).
7. T. Tanase, F. Shimizu, M. Kuse, S. Yano, S. Yoshikawa, and M. Hidai, *J. Chem. Soc., Chem. Commun.,* p. 659 (1987).
8. K. Fukushima, M. Takahashi, H. Nagano, S. Osnai, and S. Yoshikawa, *Nippon Kagaku Kaishi,* p. 585 (1988).
9. S. Yoshikawa, S. Yano, T. Tanase, F. Shimizu, and M. Kuse, DIC Hercules Inc., Jpn. Kokai Tokkyo Koho JP 63 22,595 (1988); *Chem. Abstr.* **110,** 154797s (1989).
10. S. Yoshikawa, S. Yano, T. Tanase, and F. Shimizu, DIC Hercules Inc., Jpn. Kokai Tokkyo Koho JP 63 22,596 (1988); *Chem. Abstr.* **110,** 154798t (1989).
11. S. Yoshikawa, S. Matsumura, S. Yano, S. Takizawa, and S. Komiyama, DIC Hercules Inc., Jpn. Tokkyo Koho JP 63 115,893 (1988); *Chem. Abstr.* **110,** 173690t (1989).
12. Y. Yoshikawa, S. Yano, T. Tanase, F. Shimizu, and M. Kuze, DIC Hercules Inc., Jpn. Kokai Tokkyo Koho JP 63 22,597 (1988); *Chem Abstr.* **11,** 154287w (1989).
13. T. Yamauchi, K. Fukushima, R. Yanagihara, S. Osanai, and S. Yoshikawa, *Carbohydr. Res.* **204,** 233 (1990).
14. S. Osanai, K. Inaba, and S. Yoshikawa, *Carbohydr. Res.* **209,** 289 (1991).
15. T. Tanase, K. Ishida, T. Watanabe, M. Komiyama, K. Kuomoto, S. Yano, M. Hidai, and S. Yoshikawa, *Chem. Lett.,* p. 327 (1988); T. Takei, S. Yano, and M. Hidai, *ibid.,* p. 1629 (1991).
16. K. Hataya, R. Yanagihara, S. Osanai, and S. Yoshikawa, *J. Chem. Soc., Chem. Commun.,* p. 1246 (1991).
17. S. Osanai, R. Yanagihara, K. Uematsu, and S. Yoshikawa, *J. Chem. Soc., Perkin Trans 2,* p. 1937 (1993).
18. R. Yanagihara, S. Osanai, and S. Yoshikawa, *Chem. Lett.,* p. 89 (1992).
19. R. Yanagihara, J. Egashira, S. Yoshikawa, and S. Osanai, *Bull. Chem. Soc. Jpn.* **68,** 237 (1995).
20. S. J. Angyal, D. Greeves, and J. A. Mills, *Aust. J. Chem.* **27,** 1447 (1974); S. J. Angyal, *Chem. Soc. Rev.* **9,** 415 (1980); S. J. Angyal, and J. S. Mills, *Aust. J. Chem.* **32,** 1993 (1979).
21. R. Yanagihara, S. Osanai, and S. Yoshikawa, *Chem. Lett.,* p. 2273 (1990).
22. R. Yanagihara, K. Soeda, S. Shiina, S. Osanai, and S. Yoshikawa, *Bull. Chem. Soc. Jpn.* **66,** 2268 (1993).
23. K. Inaba, S. Matsumura, and S. Yoshikawa, *Chem. Lett.,* p. 485 (1991).
24. B. Klaic, Z. Raza, M. Sankovic, and V. Sunjic, *Helv. Chim. Acta* **70,** 59 (1987).

NOTES ADDED IN PROOF

Since the manuscript of this volume was closed for further additions, a number of papers dealing with the buildup, degradation, and isomerization of monosaccharide sugars with chemical synthesis have appeared. It is not our intention to cite all of these communications; however, the results that appear to be most important are briefly summarized in this section. It covers the literature roughly through June 1997, and is organized according to the respective previous chapter/section numbers.

1.2.1. The Cyanohydrin Synthesis (Kiliani–Fischer Synthesis)

The Fleet group reported novel results[1,2] on the application of this methodology for the synthesis of heptono- and octonolactone derivatives. Wong *et al.*[3] prepared glycosidase inhibitors from homoaza-sugars by the reaction of imines with hydrogen cyanide. The Strecker synthesis was employed for appropriate D-glyceraldimine derivatives with the goal of obtaining 2-amino-2-deoxytetroses.[4] The reaction of nitrones has also been used[5] for synthesizing various chain-extended monosaccharides.

1.2.3.4. Chain Extension with Nitroalkane Carboxylic Acids

Nitroalkane carboxylic acids have been successfully used by Spanish[6] and Canadian[7] investigators in stereocontrolled chain extensions of monosaccharide derivatives.

1.2.4. Chain Extension with Diazoalkanes

López-Herrera et al.[8] applied this methodology for the synthesis of the aminocyclitol antibiotic *tunicamycin* by means of the chain extension of a 5-deoxy-5-diazo-D-ribofuranoside derivative as the key intermediate.

1.2.6. Chain Extension with Phosphoranes: Olefination Reactions for Synthesis of Chain-Extended Monosaccharides

As shown by the numerous reports that have appeared, the Wittig and Horner–Emmons reactions have remained extremely popular for sugar chain extension. Thus, all of the possible stereoisomers of (*E*)-4,5-dihydroxy-dec-2-enal have been prepared[9] with a related strategy, and novel oct-2(*E*)-enoates have been synthesized from 2,5-anhydroaldoses. The products of this latter reaction have been applied[11] for obtaining homoaza–disaccharides, and three additional works[12–14] reported on the chain extension of various sugar–phosphonates.

1.2.7.1.1. Extension of the Sugar Chain by the Addition of Grignard Reagents to aldehydo-*Sugars*

Novel examples have been reported[15,16] for the application of Grignard reagents; specifically, to examine the reaction of α-D-*gluco*-hexodialdo- and α-D-*xylo*-deoxyhexodialdopyranosides with trimethylsilylacetylenylmagnesium bromide. Dötz et al.[17] employed allenylmagnesium bromide for chain extensions, and in a novel procedure for the synthesis[18] of *lincosamine* the key step for the chain extension is, again, based on the Grignard methodology.

1.2.7.1.2. Extension of the Sugar Chain by Addition of Lithioorganic Compounds to aldehydo-*Sugar Derivatives*

By means of this methodology, several new *C*-glycosidic compounds have been prepared.[19–21] For example, the Kessler group[22] synthesized the *C*-glycosyl analog of *N*-glucoasparagine from a 1-lithio-D-glucosamine derivative.

1.2.7.1.3. Chain Extension of Saccharides with Organosilicon, Organotin, and Organoboron Compounds

The chain extension with allylsilane has been applied by two Japanese groups[23,24] in the monosaccharide field.

1.2.7.2. Chain Extension of *aldehydo*-Sugars with Thiazole, Furan, and Pyrrol Derivatives

Casiraghi *et al.*[25,26] reported novel results on the application of *tert*-butyldimethylsilylated heterocyclic compounds (furan, pyrrole, thiazole) for the synthesis of *muricatacin* and its analogs.

1.2.7.3. The Reformatsky Reaction for the Chain Extension of Saccharides

The indium-mediated Reformatsky procedure for sugar chain extension has been reported in two works for the preparation of *N*-acetylneuraminic acid derivatives.[27,28]

1.2.7.4. Preparation of Sugar Derivatives by Means of Chain Extension Based on Aldol Condensation

It has been shown that the aldol-type reactions are suitable for the synthesis of the stereoisomers of (+)-*hydantocidine*.[29] A related principle has been applied by Mazur *et al.*[30] and by von Itzstein *et al.*[31] to prepare 5-*C*-(hydroxymethyl)hexoses and *N*-acetylneuraminic acid, respectively.

1.2.7.5. Chain Extension of Unsaturated Sugars to Nonbranched Derivatives

In a recent paper Csuk[32] discussed the reactions between trimethylsilylated ketene acetals and glycals, and these latter unsaturated sugars have been applied by the Townsend group[33] for the preparation of pyrazine-*C*-nucleosides. Two interesting works, discussing the conversion of sugar derivatives alkylated with another monosaccharide for the preparation of *C*-glycosidic analogs have been published,[34,35] and the Sinay group[36] reported on the samarium diiodide–induced *intramolecular* coupling reaction of tethered sugars (see also the work by Johns *et al.*[37]).

1.2.7.7. Chain Extension of Aldonic Acids and Aldonolactones

Three selected papers[38–40] are recommended by the authors of this volume to study for those considering to apply protected sugar–lactones for chain extension.

1.2.7.8 Anhydroaldononitriles: The C-1 Chain-Extended Products of Cyclic Aldose Derivatives

An improved method for the preparation of α-glycopyranosylcyanides have been reported by Japanese investigators.[41]

1.2.7.9. Chain Extension of Saccharides Starting with Acetylene Derivatives

The Vasella group[42] synthesized cyclodextrine analogs from monosaccharide–dialkynes via acetylenosaccharides.

1.2.7.10. Chain Extension of Halogenide Compounds

A novel example for the transformation of ribofuranosyl fluorides into *C*-glycosyl compounds has been reported.[43] Structurally related derivatives have also been obtained[44] from bromides by means or radical reactions. Two novel studies describe the application of the Barbier–Grignard reaction in the carbohydrate field.[45,46]

1.2.7.11. Ascending Syntheses with Sulfonic Acid Esters

Coutrot *et al.*[47] employed the 1-*O*-triflate derivative of D-mannitol to prepare phosphonic acid analogs of *Kdo*.

1.2.7.12. Ascending Syntheses with Nitrogen-Containing Saccharides

In a recent work French authors[49] reported the ascending of Weinreb amides (nitrogen-containing saccharides) into 3-deoxy-D-*arabino*-heptulosonic acid.

2.4.1. Degradation by Cleavage with Periodates

The Czernecki group reported[50] the descending synthesis of acetylene sugars into the corresponding carboxylic acids by means of the application of the $NaIO_4$–$RuCl_3$ reagent.

2.4.3. Descending Syntheses of Onic Acid and Uronic Acid Derivatives

In recently available papers[51–55] numerous trials are reported on the utilization of decarboxylated onic- and uronic acid derivatives in synthetic carbohydrate chemistry. The authors of this volume strongly recommend these new studies.

3.1. EPIMERIZATION OF SACCHARIDES IN ALKALINE MEDIA

Angyal *et al.*[56] report on a recent investigation aimed at the Ca^{2+} ion-catalyzed epimerization of monosaccharides in alkaline medium with respect to the formation of metal-complex derivatives. Another two communications deal with the epimerization of *N*-acetyl-2-amino-2-deoxyhexoses, and the patent literature describes[58] the synthesis of L-ribose by means of the molybdenate-catalyzed epimerization of appropriate L-arabinose derivatives.

REFERENCES

1. C. J. Brichard, J. R. Wheatley, and G. W. J. Fleet, *Tetrahedron: Asymmetry* **5**, 431 (1994).
2. A. A. Bell, R. J. Nash, and G.W. J. Fleet, *Tetrahedron: Asymmetry* **7**, 595 (1996).
3. C. H. Wong, L. Provencher, J. A. Porco, Jr., S.-H. Jung, F. F. Wang, L. Chen, R. Wang, and D. H. Steensma, *J. Org. Chem.* **60**, 1492 (1995).
4. P. A. Wade and S. G. D'Ambrosio, *J. Carbohydr. Chem.* **14**, 1329 (1995).
5. F. L. Merchán, P. Merino, and T. Tejero, *Tetrahedron Lett.* **36**, 6949 (1995).
6. P. Borraduro, M. J. Dianez, M. D. Astrada, M. Gomez-Guillén, A. Gomez-Sanchez, A. López-Castro, and S. Perez-Garrido, *Carbohydr. Res.* **271**, 79 (1995).
7. S. Hanessian and P. V. Devasthale, *Tetrahedron Lett.* **37**, 987 (1996).
8. F. Sarabia-Garcia and F. J. López-Herrera, *Tetrahedron* **52**, 4757 (1996).
9. P. Allevi, P. Ciuffreda, G. Tarocco, and M. Anastasia, *Tetrahedron: Asymmetry* **6**, 2357 (1995).
10. J. S. Kozlowski, C. H. Marzabadi, N. P. Nath, and C. S. Spilling, *Carbohydr. Res.* **300**, 301 (1997).
11. S. Hiranuma, T. Shimizu, T. Nakat, T. Kajimoto, and C. H. Wong, *Tetrahedron Lett.* **36**, 8247 (1995).
12. L. Cipolla, B. La Ferla, F. Nicotra, and L. Panza, *Tetrahedron Lett.* **38**, 5567 (1997).
13. D. H. R. Barton, S. D. Gero, P. Holliday, and B. Quiclet-Sire, *Tetrahedron* **52**, 8233 (1996).
14. J.-B. Behr, C. M. Evina, N. Phung, and G. Guillerm, *J. Chem. Soc., Perkin Trans. 1*, p. 1597 (1997).
15. S. Czernecki, S. Horns, and J.-M. Valéry, *J. Org. Chem.* **60**, 650 (1995).
16. S. Czernecki, J.-M. Valéry, and R. Wilkens, *Bull. Chem. Soc. Jpn.* **69**, 1347 (1996).
17. R. Ehlenz, O. Neuss, M. Teckenbrock, and K. H. Dötz, *Tetrahedron* **53**, 5143 (1997).
18. F. L. van Delft, M. de Kort, G. A. van der Marel, and J. H. van Boom, *J. Org. Chem.* **61**, 1883 (1996).
19. K. Tatsuta, Y. Ikeda, and S. Miura, *J. Antibiot.* **49**, 836 (1996).
20. S. Harusawa, H. Moriyama, Y. Murai, T. Imazu, H. Ohishi, R. Yoneda, T. Kurihara, H. Hata, and Y. Sakamoto, *Chem. Pharm. Bull.* **45**, 53 (1997).
21. K. S. Gudmundsson, J. C. Drach, and L. B. Townsend, *J. Org. Chem.* **62**, 3453 (1997).
22. F. Burkhart, M. Hoffmann, and H. Kessler, *Angew. Chem., Int. Ed.* **36**, 191 (1997).
23. S. Nishiyama, T. Ohgiya, S. Yamamura, K. Kato, and T. Takita, *Nucleosides Nucleotides* **11**, 417 (1992).
24. P. Arya, S. Dion, and G. K. H. Shimizu, *Bioorg. Med. Chem. Lett.* **7**, 1537 (1997).
25. G. Rassu, L. Pinna, P. Spanu, F. Zanardi, L. Battistini, and G. Casiraghi, *J. Org. Chem.* **62**, 4513 (1997).
26. G. Rassu, F. Zanardi, L. Battistini, E. Gaetani, and G. Casiraghi, *J. Med. Chem.* **40**, 168 (1997).
27. S.-K-Choi, S. Lee, and G. M. Whitesides, *J. Org. Chem.* **61**, 8739 (1996).
28. T.-H. Chan, Z.-C. Xiu, and M. von Itzstein, *J. Org. Chem.* **62**, 3500 (1997).
29. S. Mio, M. Shiraishi, S. Sugai, H. Haruyama, and S. Sato, *Tetrahedron* **47**, 2121 (1991).
30. A. W. Mazur and G. D. Hiler, II, *J. Org. Chem.* **62**, 4471 (1997).
31. W.-Y. Wu, B. Jin, D. C. M. Kong, M. von Itzstein, *Carbohydr. Res.* **300**, 171 (1997).
32. R. Csuk, M. Schaade, and C. Krieger, *Tetrahedron* **52**, 6397 (1996).
33. J. J. Chen, J. A. Walker, II, W. Liu, D. S. Wise, and L. B. Townsend, *Tetrahedron Lett.* **36**, 8363 (1995).
34. S. Du, D. Plat, V. Belakhov, and T. Baasov, *J. Org. Chem.* **62**, 794 (1997).
35. D. Craig, J. P. Tierney, and C. Williamson, *Tetrahedron Lett.* **38**, 4153 (1997).
36. A. Chénédé, E. Perriu, E. D. Rekai, and P. Sinay, *Synlett*, p. 421 (1994).
37. B. A. Johns, Y. T. Pan, A. D. Elbein, and C. R. Johnson, *J. Am. Chem. Soc.* **119**, 4856 (1997).

38. T. H. Heightman, M. Locatelli, and A. Vasella, *Helv. Chim. Acta* **79**, 2190 (1996).
39. S. Hanessian, J. Y. Sancéau, and P. Chemla, *Tetrahedron* **51**, 6669 (1995).
40. R. Csuk, M. Kühn, and D. Röhl, *Tetrahedron* **53**, 1311 (1997).
41. Y. Igarashi, T. Shiozawa, and Y. Ichikawa, *Bioorg. Med. Chem. Lett.* **7**, 613 (1997).
42. R. Bürli and A. Vasella, *Helv. Chim. Acta* **80**, 1027 (1997).
43. M. Yokoyama, M. Nomura, H. Togo, and H. Seki, *J. Chem. Soc., Perkin Trans. 1*, p. 2145 (1996).
44. R. P. Spencer and J. Schwarz, *J. Org. Chem.* **62**, 4204 (1997).
45. D. Mazéas, T. Skrydstrup, and J.-M. Beau, *Angew. Chem.* **107**, 990 (1995); *Int. Ed. Engl.* **34**, 909 (1995).
46. C.-J. Li, *Tetrahedron* **52**, 5643 (1996).
47. P. Coutrot, C. Grison, and M. Lecouvey, *Tetrahedron Lett.* **37**, 1595 (1996).
48. W. He, H. Togo, and M. Yokoyama, *Tetrahedron Lett.* **38**, 5541 (1997).
49. G. Devianne, J.-M. Escudier, M. Baltas, and L. Gorrichon, *J. Org. Chem.* **60**, 7343 (1995).
50. S. Czernecki, S. Franco, S. Horns, and J. M. Valéry, *Tetrahedron Lett.* **37**, 4003 (1996).
51. D. H. R. Barton, S. D. Gero, B. Quiclet-Sire, and M. Samadi, *Tetrahedron: Asymmetry* **5**, 2123 (1994).
52. D. H. R. Barton and W. Liu, *Tetrahedron Lett.* **38**, 2431 (1997).
53. M. Harenbrock, A. Matzeit, and H. J. Schäfer, *Justus Liebigs Ann. Chem.*, p. 55 (1996).
54. Z. Pakulski and A. Zamojski, *Tetrahedron* **53**, 3723 (1997).
55. C. G. Francisco, C. G. González, and E. Suárez, *Tetrahedron Lett.* **38**, 4141 (1997).
56. S. J. Angyal, *Carbohydr. Res.* **300**, 279 (1997).
57. T. Sugai, A. Kobuki, S. Hiramatsu, H. Okazaji, and H. Ohta, *Bull. Chem. Soc. Jpn.* **68**, 3581 (1995).
58. J. Kubala and A. Burdatsova, Czech CS 275.890 (18 Mar. 1992); *Chem. Abstr.* **122**, 56398r (1995).

INDEX